Custom Edition for University of Minnesota

BIOLOGY

Neil A. Campbell ▪ Jane B. Reece ▪ Lisa A. Urry ▪ Michael L. Cain
Steven A. Wasserman ▪ Peter V. Minorsky ▪ Robert B. Jackson

Taken from:
Biology, Eighth Edition
by Neil A. Campbell, Jane B. Reece, Lisa A. Urry, Michael L. Cain,
Steven A. Wasserman, Peter V. Minorsky, and Robert B. Jackson

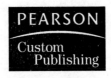

Cover Art: Courtesy of PhotoDisc/Getty Images.

Taken from:

Biology, Eighth Edition
by Neil A. Campbell, Jane B. Reece, Lisa A. Urry, Michael L. Cain, Steven A. Wasserman, Peter V. Minorsky, and Robert B. Jackson
Copyright © 2008 by Pearson Education, Inc.
Published by Benjamin Cummings
San Francisco, California 94111

This special edition published in cooperation with Pearson Custom Publishing.

Printed in the United States of America

10 9 8 7 6 5 4 3 2 1

ISBN 0-536-50766-X

2008140110

PJ

Please visit our web site at *www.pearsoncustom.com*

PEARSON CUSTOM PUBLISHING
501 Boylston Street, Suite 900, Boston, MA 02116
A Pearson Education Company

Brief Contents

About the Authors

Neil A. Campbell

Neil Campbell combined the investigative nature of a research scientist with the soul of an experienced and caring teacher. He earned his M.A. in Zoology from UCLA and his Ph.D. in Plant Biology from the University of California, Riverside, where he received the Distinguished Alumnus Award in 2001. Neil published numerous research articles on desert and coastal plants and how the sensitive plant (*Mimosa*) and other legumes move their leaves. His 30 years of teaching in diverse environments included general biology courses at Cornell University, Pomona College, and San Bernardino Valley College, where he received the college's first Outstanding Professor Award in 1986. Neil was a visiting scholar in the Department of Botany and Plant Sciences at the University of California, Riverside. In addition to his authorship of this book, he coauthored *Biology: Concepts & Connections* and *Essential Biology* with Jane Reece. Neil died shortly after the initial planning of this revision, but his legacy continues in *BIOLOGY*, Eighth Edition.

Jane B. Reece

Lead author Jane Reece, Neil Campbell's longtime collaborator, has participated in every edition of *BIOLOGY*—first as an editor and contributor, then as an author. Her education includes an A.B. in Biology from Harvard University, an M.S. in Microbiology from Rutgers University, and a Ph.D. in Bacteriology from the University of California, Berkeley. Before migrating to California from the Northeast, she taught biology at Middlesex County College and Queensborough Community College. At UC Berkeley, and later as a postdoctoral fellow in genetics at Stanford University, her research focused on genetic recombination in bacteria. Besides her work on *BIOLOGY*, she has been a coauthor on *Biology: Concepts & Connections*, *Essential Biology*, and *The World of the Cell*.

For the Eighth Edition, Jane Reece is joined by five coauthors whose contributions reflect their biological expertise as scientific researchers and their teaching sensibilities gained from years of experience as instructors.

Lisa A. Urry

Units 1–3 (Chapters 2–21) and Chapter 47
Lisa Urry is a professor at Mills College in Oakland, California, and was a major contributor to the Seventh Edition of *BIOLOGY*. After graduating from Tufts University with a double major in Biology and French, Lisa completed her Ph.D. in Molecular and Developmental Biology at MIT. Following postdoctoral appointments at Harvard Medical School, Tufts University, and UC Berkeley, she began teaching at Mills College, where she currently holds the Letts-Villard Professorship and serves as Chair of the Biology Department. She has published research articles on various topics involving gene expression during embryonic development. Her current research interest is in sea urchin development. Lisa is also deeply committed to promoting opportunities for women in science education and research.

Michael L. Cain

Units 4 and 5 (Chapters 22–34)
Michael Cain is an ecologist and evolutionary biologist currently at Bowdoin College. Michael earned a joint degree in Biology and Math from Bowdoin College, an M.Sc. from Brown University, and a Ph.D. in Ecology and Evolutionary Biology from Cornell University. After postdoctoral work in plant ecology at the University of Connecticut and molecular genetics at Washington University in St. Louis, Michael went on to teach general biology, ecology, and evolution in a diverse range of settings, including Carleton College, New Mexico State University, and Rose-Hulman Institute of Technology in Indiana. Michael is the author of dozens of scientific papers on topics that include foraging behavior in insects and plants, long-distance seed dispersal, and speciation in crickets.

Steven A. Wasserman

Unit 7 (Chapters 40–46, 48–51)
Steve Wasserman is a professor at the University of California, San Diego. He earned his A.B. in Biology from Harvard University and his Ph.D. in Biological Sciences from MIT. Since a postdoctoral sojourn at UC Berkeley, where he investigated topological transformations of DNA, he has focused on regulatory pathway mechanisms. Working with the fruit fly *Drosophila*, he has contributed to the fields of embryogenesis, reproduction, and immunity. As a faculty member at the University of Texas Southwestern Medical Center and UC San Diego, he has taught genetics, development, and physiology to undergraduate, graduate, and medical students. He has also served as the research mentor for more than a dozen doctoral students and nearly 40 aspiring scientists at the undergraduate and high school level. Steve has been the recipient of distinguished scholar awards from both the Markey Charitable Trust and the David and Lucille Packard Foundation. He recently received the 2007 Academic Senate Distinguished Teaching Award for undergraduate teaching at UC San Diego.

Peter V. Minorsky

Unit 6 (Chapters 35–39)
Peter Minorsky revised Unit 6 for the Sixth and Seventh Editions of *BIOLOGY* and is a professor at Mercy College in New York, where he teaches evolution, ecology, botany, and introductory biology. He is also the science writer for the journal *Plant Physiology*. He received his B.A. in Biology from Vassar College and his Ph.D. in Plant Physiology from Cornell University. After a postdoctoral fellowship at the University of Wisconsin at Madison, Peter taught at Kenyon College, Union College, Western Connecticut State University, and Vassar College. He is an electrophysiologist who studies plant responses to stress and is currently exploring the possible effects of geomagnetism on plant growth.

Robert B. Jackson

Unit 8 (Chapters 52–56)
Rob Jackson is a professor of biology and Nicholas Chair of Environmental Sciences at Duke University. He directed Duke's Program in Ecology for many years and is currently the Vice President of Science for the Ecological Society of America. Rob holds a B.S. in Chemical Engineering from Rice University, as well as M.S. degrees in Ecology and Statistics and a Ph.D. in Ecology from Utah State University. He was a postdoctoral scientist in Stanford University's Biology Department and an Assistant Professor at the University of Texas, Austin. Rob has received numerous awards, including being honored at the White House with a Presidential Early Career Award in Science and Engineering from the National Science Foundation. He has published a trade book about the environment, *The Earth Remains Forever*, and a children's book of poetry about biology and animals called *Animal Mischief*. His second children's book, *Not Again*, will be published in 2008.

Preface

by Jane Reece

Much has changed in the world since the completion of the previous edition of *BIOLOGY*. In the realm of the biological sciences, the sequencing of the genomes of many more species has had deep ramifications in diverse areas of research, providing new insights, for example, into the evolutionary histories of numerous species. There has been an explosion of discovery about small RNA molecules and their roles in gene regulation and, at the other end of the size spectrum, our knowledge of Earth's biodiversity has expanded to encompass hundreds of new species, including parrots, monkeys, and orchids. And during the same period, biology has become more prominent than ever in our daily lives. The news is filled with stories about the promise of personalized medicine, novel cancer treatments, the possibility of producing biofuels with the help of genetic engineering, and the use of genetic profiling in solving crimes. Other news stories report climate change and ecological disasters, new drug-resistant strains of the pathogens that cause tuberculosis and parasitic infections, and famine—crises in the world around us that are posing new challenges for biologists and their allies in the other sciences. On a personal level, many colleagues and I have missed our inspiring friend, the late Neil Campbell, even as our commitment to leadership in biological education has grown. Our changing world needs biologists and a scientifically literate citizenry as never before, and we are committed to working toward that goal.

The New Coauthors

The Seventh Edition of *BIOLOGY* has been used by more students and instructors than any previous edition, remaining the most widely used college textbook in the sciences. With the privilege of sharing biology with so many students comes the responsibility of improving the book to serve the biology community even better. For that reason, Neil would have been delighted to see that this Eighth Edition fulfills our decade-long goal of expanding the author team. As biological discoveries proliferated, Neil and I realized that it was becoming harder than ever to make judicious decisions about which biological concepts are most important to develop in depth in an introductory textbook. We needed an author team with first-hand expertise across the biological spectrum, and we wanted coauthors who had honed their teaching values in the classroom. Our new coauthors—Lisa Urry, Michael Cain, Steve Wasserman, Peter Minorsky, and Rob Jackson—represent the highest standards of scientific scholarship across a broad range of disciplines and a deep commitment to undergraduate teaching. As described on pages iv–v, their scientific expertise ranges from molecules to ecosystems, and the schools where they teach range from small liberal arts colleges to large universities. In addition, both Lisa and Peter, as major contributors to earlier editions, had prior experience working on the book. The six of us have collaborated unusually closely, starting with book-wide planning meetings and continuing with frequent exchanges of questions and advice as we worked on our chapters. For each chapter, the revising author, editors, and I together formulated a detailed plan; subsequently, my own role involved commenting on early drafts and polishing the final version. Together, we have strived to extend the book's effectiveness for today's students and instructors, while maintaining its core values.

Our Core Values

What are the core values of this book? They start with getting the science right but then focus on helping students make sense of the science. Below I highlight our longtime values and describe how they've been put into practice in the Eighth Edition. You can see examples of many of the book's features in "To the Student: How to Use This Book" (pp. xiv-xix).

Accuracy and Currency

Getting the science right goes beyond making sure that the facts are accurate and up-to-date. Equally important is ensuring that our chapters reflect how scientists in the various subdisciplines of biology, from cell biology to ecology, currently view their area. Changes in the basic paradigms in various biological fields may call for us to reorganize some chapters and even create new ones in a new edition. For example, a new Chapter 21 discusses genomes and their evolution, and neurobiology is now covered in two chapters (Chapters 48 and 49), one focused on the cellular level and one at the organ system level. On pages ix–x, you can read more about new content and organizational improvements in the Eighth Edition.

A Framework of Key Concepts

The explosion of discoveries that makes biology so exciting today also threatens to suffocate students under an avalanche of information. Our primary pedagogical goal is to help students build a framework for learning biology by organizing each chapter around a small number of "Key Concepts," typically three to six. Each chapter begins with a list of its Key Concepts, a photograph that raises an intriguing question, and an Overview section that addresses the question and introduces the chapter. In the body of the chapter, each Key Concept serves as a numbered heading for a major section, in which the prose and pictures tell a more detailed story. At the end of each concept section, Concept Check questions enable students to assess their understanding of that concept before going on to the next concept. Students encounter the Key Concepts one last time when they reach the Chapter Review at the end of the chapter; the Summary of Key Concepts restates them and offers succinct explanatory support in both words and summary diagrams—new to this edition.

Active Learning

Increasingly, instructors tell us that they want their students to take a more active role in learning biology and to think about biological questions at a higher level. In the Eighth Edition, we provide several new ways for students to engage in active learning. First, the Concept Check questions in this edition build in difficulty, and each set now ends with a new "What if?" question that challenges students to integrate what they have learned and to think analytically. There are also questions accompanying selected figures within the text; each of these questions encourages students to delve into the figure and assess their understanding of its underlying ideas. And new "Draw It" exercises in every chapter ask students to put pencil to paper and draw a structure, annotate a figure, or graph experimental data. In addition to appearing regularly in the Chapter Review, a "Draw It" question may show up in a Concept Check or figure legend. Finally, the website that accompanies the book features two especially exciting new student tools, both of which focus on biology's toughest topics: MasteringBiology tutorials and BioFlix 3-D animations and tutorials. These are described on page xx.

Evolution and Other Unifying Themes

Together with *BIOLOGY*'s emphasis on key concepts, a thematic approach has always distinguished our book from an encyclopedia of biology. In the Eighth Edition, as previously, the central theme is evolution. Evolution unifies all of biology by accounting for both the unity and diversity of life and for the remarkable adaptations of organisms to their environments. The evolutionary theme is woven into every chapter of *BIOLOGY*, and Unit Four, Mechanisms of Evolution, has undergone a major revision. In Chapter 1, the other unifying themes have been streamlined from ten to six. And throughout the book, these themes are now referenced more explicitly in Key Concepts and subheadings. The former themes of "scientific inquiry" and "science, technology, and society" continue to be highlighted throughout the book, not as biological themes but as aspects of how science is done and the role of science in our lives.

Integration of Text and Illustrations

We regard text and illustrations as equal in importance, and starting with the First Edition, have always developed them simultaneously. The Eighth Edition has a number of new and improved figures, with the increased use of a more three-dimensional art style where it can enhance understanding of biological structure. At the same time, we avoid excess detail, which can obscure the main point of the figure. We have also improved our popular "Exploring" Figures and have added more (see the list on p. xii). Each of these large figures is a learning unit that brings together a set of related illustrations and the text that describes them. The Exploring Figures enable students to access dozens of complex topics very efficiently. They are core chapter content, not to be confused with some textbooks' "boxes," which have content peripheral to the flow of a chapter. Modern biology is challenging enough without diverting students' attention from a chapter's conceptual storyline.

Telling the Story at the Right Level

Whether in pictures or prose, we are committed to explaining biology at just the right level, and we've continued to use Neil's "quantum theory of teaching biology" as a touchstone. According to this idea, there are discrete levels at which a concept can be successfully explained, and a successful explanation must avoid getting "stuck between levels." Of course, most seasoned instructors have independently recognized this issue, also known as the "too much–too little" problem. The author team has drawn upon both scientific expertise and teaching experience to tell the story of biology at an appropriate level.

The Importance of Scientific Inquiry

Another of our core values is our belief in the importance of introducing students to the scientific way of thinking. In both lecture hall and laboratory, the authors and many of our colleagues are experimenting with diverse approaches for involving students in scientific inquiry, the process by which questions about nature are posed and explored. Special features in the textbook and in inquiry-based supplements make this edition of *BIOLOGY* more effective than ever in helping instructors convey the process of science in their courses.

Modeling Inquiry by Example

Every edition of *BIOLOGY* has traced the history of many research questions and scientific debates to help students appreciate not just "what we know," but "how we know," and "what we do not yet know." In *BIOLOGY*, Seventh Edition, we strengthened this aspect of the book by introducing "Inquiry" Figures, which showcase examples of experiments and field studies in a format that is consistent throughout the book. Each of these inquiry cases begins with a research question, followed by sections describing the experiment, results, and conclusion. Complementing the Inquiry Figures are "Research Method" Figures, which walk students through the techniques and tools of modern biology.

In the Eighth Edition, we have added many more Inquiry Figures; there is now at least one in every chapter and often more (see the list of Inquiry Figures on pp. xii–xiii). Each

Inquiry Figure now ends with a "What if?" question that requires students to demonstrate their understanding of the experiment described. We have also expanded the usefulness of the Inquiry Figures in another important way: In response to feedback from many instructors, we now cite the journal article that is the source of the research, providing a gateway to the primary literature. And the full papers for nine of the Inquiry Figures are reprinted in *Inquiry in Action: Interpreting Scientific Papers*, by Ruth Buskirk and Christopher Gillen. This new supplement, which can be ordered with the book for no additional charge, provides background information on how to read scientific papers plus specific questions that guide students through the nine featured articles.

Learning Inquiry by Practice

BIOLOGY, Eighth Edition, encourages students to practice thinking as scientists by tackling the "What if?" questions in the Concept Checks and Inquiry Figures (and occasional figure legends), as well as the "Scientific Inquiry" questions in the Chapter Review. Many of those in the Chapter Reviews ask students to analyze data or to design an experiment.

The supplements for the Eighth Edition build on the textbook to provide diverse opportunities for students to practice scientific inquiry in more depth. In addition to *Inquiry in Action: Interpreting Scientific Papers*, these include new editions of several other supplements that can be made available without cost. One is *Biological Inquiry: A Workbook of Investigative Cases*, Second Edition, by Margaret Waterman and Ethel Stanley; another is *Practicing Biology: A Student Workbook*, Third Edition, by Jean Heitz and Cynthia Giffen. You can find out more about these and other student supplements, both print and electronic, on pages xx–xxiii.

The BIOLOGY Interviews: A Continuing Tradition

Scientific inquiry is a social process catalyzed by communication among people who share a curiosity about nature. One of the many joys of authoring *BIOLOGY* is the privilege of interviewing some of the world's most influential biologists. Eight new interviews, one opening each unit of the textbook, introduce students to eight of the fascinating individuals who are driving progress in biology and connecting science to society. And in this edition, each unit of the text includes an Inquiry Figure based upon the research of the unit's interviewee; for example, see Inquiry Figure 2.2, on page 31. The interviewees for this edition are listed on page xi.

A Versatile Book

Our book is intended to serve students as a textbook in their general biology course and also later as a useful tool for review and reference. *BIOLOGY's* breadth, depth, and versatile organization enable the book to meet these dual goals. Even by limiting our scope to a few Key Concepts per chapter, *BIOLOGY* spans more biological territory than most introductory

courses could or should attempt to cover. But given the great diversity of course syllabi, we have opted for a survey broad enough and deep enough to support each instructor's particular emphases. Students also seem to appreciate *BIOLOGY's* breadth and depth; in this era when students sell many of their textbooks back to the bookstore, more than 75% of students who have used *BIOLOGY* have kept it after their introductory course. In fact, we are delighted to receive mail from upper division students and graduate students, including medical students, expressing their appreciation for the long-term value of *BIOLOGY* as a general resource for their continuing education.

Just as we recognize that few courses will cover all 56 chapters of the textbook, we also understand that there is no single correct sequence of topics for a general biology course. Though a biology textbook's table of contents must be linear, biology itself is more like a web of related concepts without a fixed starting point or a prescribed path. Diverse courses can navigate this network of concepts starting with molecules and cells, or with evolution and the diversity of organisms, or with the big-picture ideas of ecology. We have built *BIOLOGY* to be versatile enough to support these different syllabi. The eight units of the book are largely self-contained, and, for most of the units, the chapters can be assigned in a different sequence without substantial loss of coherence. For example, instructors who integrate plant and animal physiology can merge chapters from Unit Six (Plant Form and Function) and Unit Seven (Animal Form and Function) to fit their courses. As another option, instructors who begin their course with ecology and continue with this top-down approach can assign Unit Eight (Ecology) right after Chapter 1, which introduces the unifying themes that provide students with a panoramic view of biology no matter what the topic order of the course syllabus.

Our Partnership with Instructors

A core value underlying all our work as authors is our belief in the importance of our partnership with instructors. Our primary way of serving instructors, of course, is providing a textbook that serves their students well. In addition, Benjamin Cummings makes available a wealth of instructor resources, in both print and electronic form (see pp. xx–xxiii). However, our relationship with instructors is not a one-way street. In our continuing efforts to improve the book and its supplements, we benefit tremendously from instructor feedback, not only in formal reviews from hundreds of scientists, but also via informal communication in person and by phone and e-mail. Neil Campbell built a vast network of colleagues throughout the world, and my new coauthors and I are fully committed to continuing that tradition.

The real test of any textbook is how well it helps instructors teach and students learn. We welcome comments from the students and professors who use *BIOLOGY*. Please address your suggestions to me:

Jane Reece, Pearson Benjamin Cummings
1301 Sansome Street, San Francisco, CA 94111
E-mail address: JaneReece@cal.berkeley.edu

New to the Eighth Edition

This section provides just a few highlights of new content and organizational improvements in *BIOLOGY*, Eighth Edition.

UNIT ONE The Chemistry of Life

New examples make basic chemistry more engaging for students, including an explanation of why steam can burn your skin in Chapter 3, the structures of the enantiomeric medications ibuprofen and albuterol in Chapter 4, and information on trans fats in Chapter 5. A new Inquiry Figure in Chapter 3 relates acidity to the emerging global problem of ocean acidification and its effects on coral reefs. The new Inquiry Figure in Chapter 5 shows Roger Kornberg's 3-D model of the RNA polymerase–DNA–RNA complex, work for which he won the 2006 Nobel Prize in Chemistry.

UNIT TWO The Cell

The judicious addition of recent research includes updated coverage of the sensory roles of primary cilia in Chapter 6, new developments regarding the membrane model in Chapter 7, and Paul Nurse's Nobel Prize–winning work on the cell cycle in Chapter 12. Chapter 11 now ends with a section on apoptosis, formerly in Chapter 21. New Inquiry Figures in this unit describe research on the role of microtubules in orienting cellulose in cell walls (Chapter 6), allosteric regulators of enzymes (Chapter 8), ATP synthase (Chapter 9), yeast cell signaling (Chapter 11), and a cell cycle regulator (Chapter 12).

UNIT THREE Genetics

Chapter 14 now includes "Tips for Genetics Problems." In Chapter 15, sex linkage is discussed directly after the discussion of the white-eye trait in Morgan's fruit flies. Chapter 16 covers replication of the bacterial chromosome and the structure of the eukaryotic chromosome (including a new Exploring Figure), formerly in Chapters 18 and 19, respectively.

We have reorganized Chapters 18–21 with the dual aims of telling a more coherent story and facilitating instructors' coverage of molecular genetics. Regulation of gene expression for both bacteria and eukaryotes is now consolidated in Chapter 18, which also includes a concept section on the crucial role of small RNAs in eukaryotes. We have streamlined material on the genetic basis of development (formerly in Chapter 21), and included it in Chapter 18, where it provides the ultimate example of gene regulation. Chapter 18 ends with a section on the molecular basis of cancer (previously in Chapter 19), to demonstrate what happens when gene regu-

lation goes awry. Material on bacterial genetics in Seventh Edition Chapter 18 has been moved to other chapters within the genetics unit and to Chapter 27 on prokaryotes.

Chapter 19 now covers only viruses (from Seventh Edition Chapter 18), giving this chapter the flexibility to be assigned at any point in the course. Chapter 20 continues to cover biotechnology, but genome sequencing and analysis have been moved to Chapter 21. Cloning and stem cell production are now in Chapter 20. Newly explained techniques include the screening of an arrayed library, BAC clones, Northern blotting, RT-PCR, and *in situ* hybridization. The explosion of discoveries about genomes and their evolution led us to develop a chapter devoted to this subject, the new Chapter 21. This chapter consolidates new material with topics from Chapters 19–21 of the Seventh Edition.

UNIT FOUR Mechanisms of Evolution

Our revision emphasizes the centrality of evolution to biology and the breadth and depth of evidence for evolution. New examples and Inquiry Figures present data from field and laboratory studies and reveal how scientists study evolution.

Chapter 22 discusses how evolution can be viewed as both a pattern and a process, and introduces three key observations about life that are explained by evolution: the match between organisms and their environments (adaptation); the shared characteristics (unity) of life; and the diversity of life. This discussion serves as a conceptual anchor throughout Units Four and Five.

Chapters 24 and 25 have been significantly reorganized. Chapter 24 is now more tightly focused on speciation, enabling better pacing of this highly conceptual material. A new concept section explores hybrid zones as natural laboratories for studying speciation. Chapter 25 focuses on macroevolution, incorporating topics formerly in Chapters 24 and 26, such as the correlations between Earth's geologic and biological history. But the primary storyline concerns what we can learn from the fossil record about the evolutionary history of life. New text and figures explore how the rise and fall of dominant groups of organisms are linked to large-scale processes such as continental drift, mass extinctions, and adaptive radiations. Coverage of evo-devo has been expanded.

Phylogenetic trees are introduced earlier, in a new section on "tree-thinking" in Chapter 22. This material supports students in interpreting diagrams before studying phylogenetics more fully in Chapter 26.

UNIT FIVE The Evolutionary History of Biological Diversity

A new Chapter 26, Phylogeny and the Tree of Life, introduces the unit. Extending material formerly in Chapter 25, it describes how evolutionary trees are constructed and underscores their role as tools for understanding relationships, rather than facts to be memorized. New sections address common misconceptions in interpreting trees and help motivate students with practical applications.

Chapter 27 has a new concept section on prokaryotic reproduction, mutation, and recombination (formerly in Chapter 18). This unifies the coverage of prokaryote biology and supports students in developing a fuller understanding of these microorganisms.

Throughout Unit Five, along with updating the phylogenies of various groups of organisms—introducing, for example, the "supergroup" hypothesis of eukaryotic phylogeny (in Chapter 28) —we have found new opportunities to use the study of phylogeny as an opportunity to illustrate the iterative nature of the scientific process. We aim to help students stay focused on the big picture of why biologists study evolutionary relationships. Each chapter also now includes an Inquiry figure that models how researchers study organisms and their relationships. At the same time, in each chapter we highlight the key roles that various organisms play in the biosphere as well as their applied importance for humans.

UNIT SIX Plant Form and Function

Revisions to this unit draw more attention to the experimental basis of our understanding of plant biology. New examples include recent progress toward identifying the flowering "hormone" (Chapter 39). Featured in new Inquiry Figures are experiments demonstrating, for example, that trichomes affect insect feeding (Chapter 35) and that informational molecules transported through the symplast affect plant development (Chapter 36).

In Chapter 36, now titled Resource Acquisition and Transport in Vascular Plants, a new first concept section explores how architectural features of plants facilitate resource acquisition, helping students relate the transport of water and nutrients to what they learned in Chapter 35 about plant structure and growth. Another new concept section, on symplastic transport, discusses recent insights into changes in plasmodesmata shape and number and the transmission of electrical and molecular signals throughout the plant.

This unit now has more examples of practical applications of plant biotechnology. For instance, Chapter 37 discusses how genetic modification has increased the resistance of some plants to aluminum toxicity and has improved the flood tolerance of rice crops. Chapter 38 elaborates on the principles of plant breeding and incorporates a new section on genetic engineering of biofuels.

UNIT SEVEN Animal Form and Function

An evolutionary perspective more strongly pervades this unit, underscoring how environment and physical laws shape adaptations across animal groups. Each chapter now includes at least one Inquiry Figure; together, these figures highlight the wide range of methodologies used to study animal physiology, including several experiments using molecular biology techniques students studied earlier in the book.

Chapter 40 has been revised and reorganized to highlight functional relationships at all levels of organization in animal bodies; thermoregulation serves as an extended example throughout the chapter. Chapter 43, The Immune System, has been extensively revised. For instance, we now contrast recognition of pathogen class in innate immunity with antigen-specific recognition in adaptive immunity, helping overcome the common misconception that recognition is absent in innate immunity.

We have divided the former nervous system chapter into two, enabling us to better pace difficult material and highlight dynamic current research by focusing first on cellular processes in Chapter 48, and then on nervous system organization and function in Chapter 49. Chapter 50 rounds out the discussion of nervous system function by examining sensory and motor mechanisms. This sequence leads naturally into Chapter 51 on animal behavior (formerly in Unit Eight), which ties together aspects of genetics, natural selection, and physiology, and provides a bridge to the ecology unit.

UNIT EIGHT Ecology

This unit, which now includes Chapters 52-56, incorporates many new examples that demonstrate a range of methods and scales of study. For example, a new figure in Chapter 52 describes a large-scale field experiment in which researchers manipulated precipitation levels in forest plots, while new Research Method figures describe determining population size using the mark-recapture method (Chapter 53), using molecular tools to measure diversity of soil microorganisms (Chapter 54), and determining primary production with satellite data (Chapter 55). By building on earlier units, we hope to demonstrate how ecology represents a fitting capstone to the book.

We provide more microbial examples and more aquatic ones, from diverse locations around the globe. For instance, Chapter 52 now discusses the importance of salinity in determining the distribution of aquatic organisms, and Chapter 54's coverage of the intermediate disturbance hypothesis includes a new figure on a quantitative test of the hypothesis in New Zealand streams. The unit highlights the great relevance of ecology to society and to students' lives. A new concept section in Chapter 54, for example, discusses how community ecology helps us understand pathogen life cycles and control disease.

Interviews

xi

Featured Figures

Exploring Figures

Inquiry Figures

*The original research paper and study questions are provided in *Inquiry in Action: Interpreting Scientific Papers.*

Research Method Figures

Focus on the Key Concepts

Each chapter is organized around a framework of 3 to 6 **Key Concepts** that will help you stay focused on the big picture and give you a context for the supporting details.

Before you begin reading the chapter, get oriented by reading the list of Key Concepts, which introduces the big ideas covered in the chapter.

25

The History of Life on Earth

KEY CONCEPTS

25.1 Conditions on early Earth made the origin of life possible

25.2 The fossil record documents the history of life

25.3 Key events in life's history include the origins of single-celled and multicelled organisms and the colonization of land

25.4 The rise and fall of dominant groups reflect continental drift, mass extinctions, and adaptive radiations

25.5 Major changes in body form can result from changes in the sequences and regulation of developmental genes

25.6 Evolution is not goal oriented

OVERVIEW

Lost Worlds

Visitors to Antarctica today encounter one of Earth's harshest, most barren environments. In this land of extreme cold where there is almost no liquid water, life is sparse and small—the largest fully terrestrial animal is a fly 5 mm long. But even as early antarctic explorers struggled to survive, some of them made an astonishing discovery: fossil evidence that life once thrived where it now barely exists. Fossils reveal that 500 million years ago, the ocean waters surrounding Antarctica were warm and teeming with tropical invertebrates. Later, the continent was covered in forests for hundreds of millions of years. At various times, a wide range of animals stalked through these forests, including 3-meter-tall predatory "terror birds" and giant dinosaurs such as the voracious *Cryolophosaurus* **(Figure 25.1)**, a 7-meter-long relative of *Tyrannosaurus rex*.

Fossils discovered in other parts of the world tell a similar, if not quite as surprising, story: Past organisms were very different from

Each Key Concept serves as the heading for a major section of the chapter.

▲ Figure 25.1 **What does fossil evidence say about where these dinosaurs lived?**

▲ *Cryolophosaurus* **skull**

those now alive. The sweeping changes in life on Earth revealed by fossils illustrate **macroevolution**, the pattern of evolution over large time scales. Specific examples of macroevolutionary change include the origin of key biochemical processes such as photosynthesis, the emergence of the first terrestrial vertebrates, and the long-term impact of a mass extinction on the diversity of life.

Taken together, such changes provide a grand view of the evolutionary history of life on Earth. We'll examine that history in this chapter, beginning with hypotheses regarding the origin of life. The origin of life is the most speculative topic of the entire unit, for no fossil evidence of that seminal episode exists. We will then turn to the fossil record and what it tells us about major events in the history of life, paying particular attention to factors that have helped to shape the rise and fall of different groups of organisms over time.

CONCEPT 25.1

Conditions on early Earth made the origin of life possible

The earliest evidence of life on Earth comes from fossils of microorganisms that are about 3.5 billion years old. But when and how did the first living cells appear? Observations and experiments in chemistry, geology, and physics have led scientists to propose one scenario that we'll examine here. They hypothesize that chemical and physical processes on early Earth, aided by the emerging force of

When you finish reading a concept section, check your understanding using the **Concept Check questions** at the end of the section. If you can answer them (see Appendix A to check your work), you're ready to move on.

Each set of Concept Check questions builds in difficulty, ending with a **"What if?" question** that asks you to apply what you've learned. Work through these questions on your own or in a study group—they're good practice for the kinds of questions you might be asked on an exam.

CONCEPT CHECK 53.1

1. One species of forest bird is highly territorial, while a second lives in flocks. Predict each species' likely pattern of dispersion, and explain.

2. **DRAW IT** Each female of a particular fish species produces millions of eggs per year. Draw and label the most likely survivorship curve for this species, and explain your choice.

3. **WHAT IF?** As noted in Figure 53.2, an important assumption of the mark-recapture method is that marked individuals have the same probability of being recaptured as unmarked individuals. Describe a situation where this assumption might not be valid, and explain how the estimate of population size would be affected.

For suggested answers, see Appendix A.

Practice thinking like a scientist

To succeed in biology, you need to do more than just memorize facts—you need to understand how scientists go about asking and investigating questions. In each chapter, you'll find one or more **Inquiry Figures** that highlight how researchers designed an experiment, interpreted their results, and drew conclusions.

Scientific Inquiry questions in the Chapter Review provide more opportunities to practice inquiry skills, including developing hypotheses, designing experiments, and analyzing real research data.

SCIENTIFIC INQUIRY

8. **DRAW IT** The nitrogen-fixing bacterium *Rhizobium* infects the roots of some plant species, forming a mutualism in which the bacterium provides the plant with nitrogen, and the plant provides the bacterium with carbohydrates. Scientists measured how well one such plant species (*Acacia irrorata*) grew when its roots were infected by six different *Rhizobium* strains.

(a) Graph the data. (b) Interpret your graph.

Rhizobium strain	Plant mass (g) after 12 weeks of growth
1	0.91
2	0.06
3	1.56
4	1.72
5	0.14
6	1.03

Source: J. J. Burdon, et al., Variation in the effectiveness of symbiotic associations between native rhizobia and temperate Australian *Acacia*: within species interactions, *Journal of Applied Ecology*, 36:398-408 (1999).

Note: In the absence of *Rhizobium*, after 12 weeks of growth, *Acacia* plants have a mass of about 0.1 g.

Some Inquiry Figures invite you to read and analyze the original research paper in its complete form. You can find the journal article, along with a worksheet guiding you through it, in the separate book *Inquiry in Action: Interpreting Scientific Papers* (ISBN 978-0-321-53659-4 | 0-321-53659-2).

After exploring the featured experiment, test your analytical skills by answering the **"What if?" question.** Suggested answers are provided in Appendix A to help you gauge your understanding.

▼ **Figure 2.2** Inquiry

What creates "devil's gardens" in the rain forest?

EXPERIMENT Working under Deborah Gordon and with Michael Greene, graduate student Megan Frederickson sought the cause of "devil's gardens," stands of a single species of tree, *Duroia hirsuta*. One hypothesis was that ants living in these trees, *Myrmelachista schumanni*, produce a poisonous chemical that kills trees of other species; another was that the *Duroia* trees themselves kill competing trees, perhaps by means of a chemical.

To test these hypotheses, Frederickson did field experiments in Peru. Two saplings of a local nonhost tree species, *Cedrela odorata*, were planted inside each of ten devil's gardens. At the base of one, a sticky insect barrier was applied; the other was unprotected. Two more *Cedrela* saplings, with and without barriers, were planted about 50 meters outside each garden.

The researchers observed ant activity on the *Cedrela* leaves and measured areas of dead leaf tissue after one day. They also chemically analyzed contents of the ants' poison glands.

RESULTS The ants made injections from the tips of their abdomens into leaves of unprotected saplings in their gardens (see photo). Within one day, these leaves developed dead areas (see graph). The protected saplings were uninjured, as were the saplings planted outside the gardens. Formic acid was the only chemical detected in the poison glands of the ants.

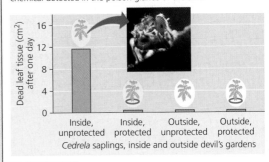

CONCLUSION Ants of the species *Myrmelachista schumanni* kill nonhost trees by injecting the leaves with formic acid, thus creating hospitable habitats (devil's gardens) for the ant colony.

SOURCE M. E. Frederickson, M. J. Greene, and D. M. Gordon, "Devil's gardens" bedevilled by ants, *Nature* 437:495–496 (2005).

Inquiry in Action Read and analyze the original paper in *Inquiry in Action: Interpreting Scientific Papers.*

WHAT IF? What would be the results if the unprotected saplings' inability to grow in the devil's gardens was caused by a chemical released by the *Duroia* trees rather than by the ants?

As you read the text, study the art and photos

◄ In selected illustrations, a **three-dimensional art style** helps you visualize biological structures.

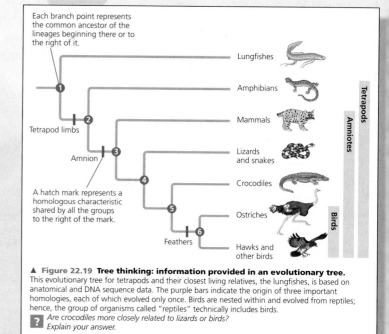

▲ **Figure 22.19 Tree thinking: information provided in an evolutionary tree.** This evolutionary tree for tetrapods and their closest living relatives, the lungfishes, is based on anatomical and DNA sequence data. The purple bars indicate the origin of three important homologies, each of which evolved only once. Birds are nested within and evolved from reptiles; hence, the group of organisms called "reptiles" technically includes birds.

? *Are crocodiles more closely related to lizards or birds? Explain your answer.*

▲ The book's **phylogenetic trees** will prepare you to analyze the evolutionary tree diagrams you may encounter in the scientific literature. This figure walks you through some of the conventions of the phylogenetic trees you will see throughout the evolution and diversity units.

"Guided Tour" figures include concise explanations that walk you through complicated diagrams. ▶

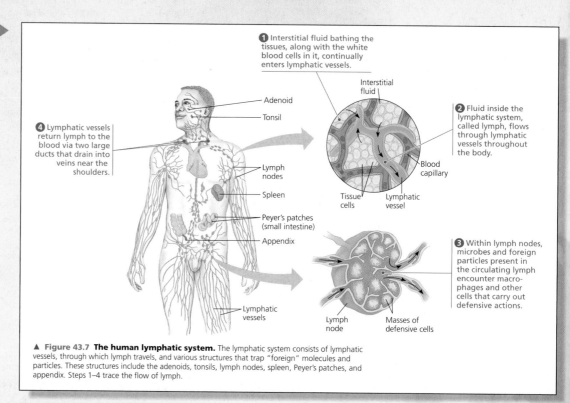

▲ **Figure 43.7 The human lymphatic system.** The lymphatic system consists of lymphatic vessels, through which lymph travels, and various structures that trap "foreign" molecules and particles. These structures include the adenoids, tonsils, lymph nodes, spleen, Peyer's patches, and appendix. Steps 1–4 trace the flow of lymph.

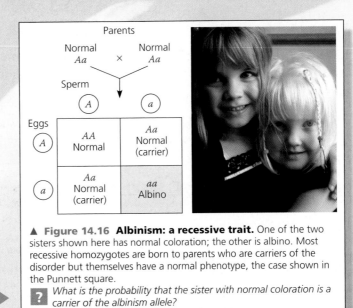

▲ **Figure 14.16 Albinism: a recessive trait.** One of the two sisters shown here has normal coloration; the other is albino. Most recessive homozygotes are born to parents who are carriers of the disorder but themselves have a normal phenotype, the case shown in the Punnett square.

? *What is the probability that the sister with normal coloration is a carrier of the albinism allele?*

Figure Legend questions prompt you to delve into a figure's content to make sure you understand it.

● By integrating text and visuals, **Exploring Figures** help you learn more efficiently.

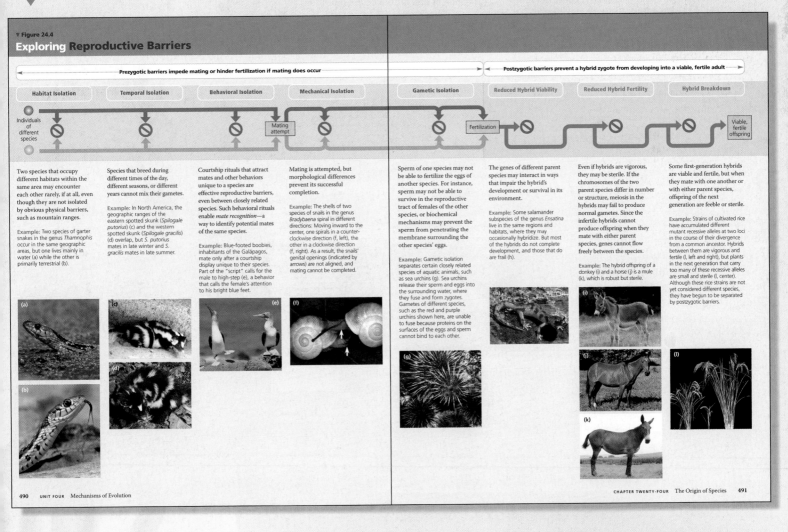

▽ **Figure 24.4**

Exploring **Reproductive Barriers**

Prezygotic barriers impede mating or hinder fertilization if mating does occur

Postzygotic barriers prevent a hybrid zygote from developing into a viable, fertile adult

| Habitat Isolation | Temporal Isolation | Behavioral Isolation | Mechanical Isolation | Gametic Isolation | Reduced Hybrid Viability | Reduced Hybrid Fertility | Hybrid Breakdown |

Individuals of different species → Mating attempt → Fertilization → Viable, fertile offspring

Two species that occupy different habitats within the same area may encounter each other rarely, if at all, even though they are not isolated by obvious physical barriers, such as mountain ranges.

Example: Two species of garter snakes in the genus *Thamnophis* occur in the same geographic areas, but one lives mainly in water (a) while the other is primarily terrestrial (b).

Species that breed during different times of the day, different seasons, or different years cannot mix their gametes.

Example: In North America, the geographic ranges of the eastern spotted skunk (*Spilogale putorius*) (c) and the western spotted skunk (*Spilogale gracilis*) (d) overlap, but *S. putorius* mates in late winter and *S. gracilis* mates in late summer.

Courtship rituals that attract mates and other behaviors unique to a species are effective reproductive barriers, even between closely related species. Such behavioral rituals enable *mate recognition*—a way to identify potential mates of the same species.

Example: Blue-footed boobies, inhabitants of the Galápagos, mate only after a courtship display unique to their species. Part of the "script" calls for the male to high-step (e), a behavior that calls the female's attention to his bright blue feet.

Mating is attempted, but morphological differences prevent its successful completion.

Example: The shells of two species of snails in the genus *Bradybaena* spiral in different directions: Moving inward to the center, one spirals in a counter-clockwise direction (f, left), the other in a clockwise direction (f, right). As a result, the snails' genital openings (indicated by arrows) are not aligned, and mating cannot be completed.

Sperm of one species may not be able to fertilize the eggs of another species. For instance, sperm may not be able to survive in the reproductive tract of females of the other species, or biochemical mechanisms may prevent the sperm from penetrating the membrane surrounding the other species' eggs.

Example: Gametic isolation separates certain closely related species of aquatic animals, such as sea urchins (g). Sea urchins release their sperm and eggs into the surrounding water, where they fuse and form zygotes. Gametes of different species, such as the red and purple urchins shown here, are unable to fuse because proteins on the surfaces of the eggs and sperm cannot bind to each other.

The genes of different parent species may interact in ways that impair the hybrid's development or survival in its environment.

Example: Some salamander subspecies of the genus *Ensatina* live in the same regions and habitats, where they may occasionally hybridize. Most of the hybrids do not complete development, and those that do are frail (h).

Even if hybrids are vigorous, they may be sterile. If the chromosomes of the two parent species differ in number or structure, meiosis in the hybrids may fail to produce normal gametes. Since the infertile hybrids cannot produce offspring when they mate with either parent species, genes cannot flow freely between the species.

Example: The hybrid offspring of a donkey (i) and a horse (j) is a mule (k), which is robust but sterile.

Some first-generation hybrids are viable and fertile, but when they mate with one another or with either parent species, offspring of the next generation are feeble or sterile.

Example: Strains of cultivated rice have accumulated different mutant recessive alleles at two loci in the course of their divergence from a common ancestor. Hybrids between them are vigorous and fertile (l, left and right), but plants in the next generation that carry too many of these recessive alleles are small and sterile (l, center). Although these rice strains are not yet considered different species, they have begun to be separated by postzygotic barriers.

Review what you've learned

At the end of the chapter, the **Chapter Review** focuses you again on the main points of the chapter, with a Summary of Key Concepts, practice questions, and references to other study tools.

Go to the **Study Area** at **www.masteringbio.com** for BioFlix 3-D animations and student tools plus MP3 Tutors, Discovery Channel Videos, Practice Tests, Activities, Investigations, an eBook, and more.

Chapter 9 Review

MEDIA Go to the Study Area at **www.masteringbio.com** for BioFlix 3-D Animations, MP3 Tutors, Videos, Practice Tests, an eBook, and more.

SUMMARY OF KEY CONCEPTS

CONCEPT 9.1
Catabolic pathways yield energy by oxidizing organic fuels (pp. 162–167)

▶ **Catabolic Pathways and Production of ATP** To keep working, a cell must regenerate the ATP it uses. The breakdown of glucose and other organic fuels is exergonic. Starting with glucose or another organic molecule and using O_2, aerobic respiration yields H_2O, CO_2, and energy in the form of ATP and heat. Cellular respiration includes both aerobic and anaerobic respiration; the latter uses another electron acceptor instead of O_2, but also yields ATP.

▶ **Redox Reactions: Oxidation and Reduction** The cell taps the energy stored in food molecules through redox reactions, in which one substance partially or totally shifts electrons to another. The substance receiving electrons is reduced; the substance losing electrons is oxidized. During cellular respiration, glucose ($C_6H_{12}O_6$) is oxidized to CO_2, and O_2 is reduced to H_2O. Electrons lose potential energy during their transfer from organic compounds to oxygen. Electrons from organic compounds are usually passed first to NAD^+, reducing it to NADH. NADH passes the electrons to an electron transport chain, which conducts them to O_2 in energy-releasing steps. The energy released is used to make ATP.

▶ **The Stages of Cellular Respiration:** *A Preview* Glycolysis and the citric acid cycle supply electrons (via NADH or $FADH_2$) to the electron transport chain, which drives oxidative phosphorylation. Oxidative phosphorylation generates ATP.

MEDIA
BioFlix 3-D Animation Cellular Respiration
Activity Build a Chemical Cycling System
Activity Overview of Cellular Respiration

CONCEPT 9.2
Glycolysis harvests chemical energy by oxidizing glucose to pyruvate (pp. 167–169)

MEDIA
MP3 Tutor Cellular Respiration Part 1—Glycolysis
Activity Glycolysis

CONCEPT 9.3
The citric acid cycle completes the energy-yielding oxidation of organic molecules (pp. 170–172)

▶ In eukaryotic cells, the import of pyruvate into the mitochondrion and its conversion to acetyl CoA links glycolysis to the citric acid cycle. (In prokaryotic cells, the citric acid cycle occurs in the cytosol.)

MEDIA
Activity The Citric Acid Cycle

Summary Figures present key information in a visual way, serving as "one-stop shopping" study tools.

MP3 Tutors explain some of the most difficult biological concepts in simple terms. A tutor that goes anywhere you go, anytime.

BioFlix animations and student tools review the most difficult biology topics with 3-D, movie-quality animations, labeled slide shows, carefully constructed student tutorials, study sheets, and quizzes that support all types of learners.

TESTING YOUR KNOWLEDGE

SELF-QUIZ

1. What is the reducing agent in the following reaction?

   Pyruvate + NADH + H^+ → Lactate + NAD^+

   a. oxygen
   b. NADH
   c. NAD^+
   d. lactate
   e. pyruvate

2. The *immediate* energy source that drives ATP synthesis by ATP synthase during oxidative phosphorylation is
   a. the oxidation of glucose and other organic compounds.
   b. the flow of electrons down the electron transport chain.
   c. the affinity of oxygen for electrons.
   d. the H^+ concentration gradient across the inner mitochondrial membrane.
   e. the transfer of phosphate to ADP.

3. Which metabolic pathway is common to both fermentation and cellular respiration of a glucose molecule?
   a. the citric acid cycle
   b. the electron transport chain
   c. glycolysis
   d. synthesis of acetyl CoA from pyruvate
   e. reduction of pyruvate to lactate

4. In mitochondria, exergonic redox reactions
   a. are the source of energy driving prokaryotic ATP synthesis.
   b. are directly coupled to substrate-level phosphorylation.
   c. provide the energy that establishes the proton gradient.
   d. reduce carbon atoms to carbon dioxide.
   e. are coupled via phosphorylated intermediates to endergonic processes.

To start preparing for a test, take the **end-of-chapter Self-Quiz.**

"Draw It" exercises ask you to put pencil to paper and draw a structure, annotate a figure, or graph experimental data. Check your work by turning to the suggested answers in Appendix A.

11. **DRAW IT** Trace the uptake of water and minerals from root hairs to the vessels in a root, following a symplastic route and an apoplastic route. Label the routes.

10. **DRAW IT** The graph here shows the pH difference across the inner mitochondrial membrane over time in an actively respiring cell. At the time indicated by the vertical arrow, a metabolic poison is added that specifically and completely inhibits all function of mitochondrial ATP synthase. Draw what you would expect to see for the rest of the graphed line.

For Self-Quiz answers, see Appendix A.

MEDIA Visit the Study Area at **www.masteringbio.com** for a Practice Test.

EVOLUTION CONNECTION

11. ATP synthases are found in the prokaryotic plasma membrane and in mitochondria and chloroplasts. What does this suggest about the evolutionary relationship of these eukaryotic organelles to prokaryotes? How might the amino acid sequences of the ATP synthases from the different sources support or refute your hypothesis?

SCIENTIFIC INQUIRY

12. In the 1940s, some physicians prescribed low doses of a drug called dinitrophenol (DNP) to help patients lose weight. This unsafe method was abandoned after a few patients died. DNP uncouples the chemiosmotic machinery by making the lipid bilayer of the inner mitochondrial membrane leaky to H^+. Explain how this causes weight loss.

SCIENCE, TECHNOLOGY, AND SOCIETY

13. Nearly all human societies use fermentation to produce alcoholic drinks such as beer and wine. The practice dates back to the earliest days of agriculture. How do you suppose this use of fermentation was first discovered? Why did wine prove to be a more useful beverage, especially to a preindustrial culture, than the grape juice from which it was made?

Biological Inquiry: A Workbook of Investigative Cases Explore fermentation further in the case "Bean Brew."

For more **practice test questions** visit the Study Area at **www.masteringbio.com**

The **essay questions** in the Chapter Review give you practice writing about biological topics and making connections between the content of different chapters, as you may be asked to do in class discussions or on exams.

Supplements

Supplements for the Student

MasteringBIOLOGY

www.masteringbio.com

NEW! MasteringBiology™ offers two valuable learning systems:

1. The **Study Area**
2. **MasteringBiology™ Assignments**

Study Area

Media assets in the Study Area include BioFlix, MP3 Tutors, Discovery Videos, Cell Biology Videos, Activities, Investigations, Graph It!, Quizzes, Practice Tests, Cumulative Test, Word Roots, Key Terms, Flashcards, Audio Glossary, Art, an eBook, and the Campbell/Reece Interviews.

In the **Study Area, a** convenient **Chapter Guide** correlates the student media to the Key Concepts of each textbook chapter.

NEW! *BioFlix*

The student versions of **BioFlix** offer engaging 3-D animations plus labeled slide shows, basic tutorials, study sheets, and quizzes.

Discovery Channel™ Videos bring biology to life.

- ■ **MP3 Tutors** can be played from the website or downloaded onto personal MP3 players for studying anytime.
- ■ **NEW! Audio pronunciations** are included for every term in the Audio Glossary, Key Terms, and Flashcards.

MasteringBiology™ Assignments

MasteringBiology™ offers assignable in-depth Tutorials, Chapter Quizzes with ten questions per chapter, and thousands of additional Multiple Choice Test Bank Questions.

The MasteringBiology™ **Tutorials** guide students through difficult concepts with a series of interactive questions that build on each other.

If a student answers incorrectly, the student is given specific **feedback** that addresses the student's misconceptions.

Students can view **hints** for background information, including animations, and additional assistance.

A powerful **Gradebook** automatically records student scores. Shades of red instantly reveal students in trouble or areas of difficulty for the class. Instructors can assign questions to encourage students to read the chapter before class and then adjust their lectures to address student misconceptions. Grades can be exported to another course management system or Excel™, or grades can be imported into the MasteringBiology Gradebook.

For more information about media for students, see the card inserted at the beginning of this book and the **Access Kit for MasteringBiology™**, which is included with every new copy of *BIOLOGY*, Eighth Edition.

NEW! Inquiry in Action: Interpreting Scientific Papers
(978-0-321-53659-4/0-321-53659-2)
Ruth Buskirk, University of Texas, Austin, and Christopher M. Gillen, Kenyan College
Selected Inquiry Figures in the Eighth Edition direct students to read and analyze the complete original research paper. In this new supplement, those articles are reprinted and accompanied by questions that help students analyze the article.

Student Study Guide for *Biology,* Eighth Edition
(978-0-321-50156-1/0-321-50156-X)
Martha R. Taylor, Cornell University
This popular study guide helps students extract key ideas from the textbook and organize their knowledge of biology. Exercises include concept maps for each chapter, chapter summaries, word roots, chapter tests, and a variety of interactive questions in various formats.

Practicing Biology: A Student Workbook, Third Edition
(978-0-321-52293-1/0-321-52293-1)
Jean Heitz and Cynthia Giffen, University of Wisconsin, Madison
This workbook offers a variety of activities to suit different learning styles. Activities such as modeling and mapping allow students to visualize and understand biological processes. New activities focus on basic skills, such as reading and developing graphs.

Biological Inquiry: A Workbook of Investigative Cases, Second Edition (978-0-321-51320-5/0-321-51320-7)
Margaret Waterman, Southeast Missouri State University, and Ethel Stanley, Beloit College and BioQUEST Curriculum Consortium
This workbook offers ten investigative cases, including new cases on avian influenza and hedgehog developmental pathways. Students pose questions, analyze data, think critically, examine the relationship between evidence and conclusions, construct hypotheses, investigate options, graph data, interpret results, and communicate scientific arguments. A student website is at **www.masteringbio.com**.

Study Card for *Biology,* Eighth Edition
(978-0-321-49436-8/0-321-49436-9)
This quick reference card provides an overview of the entire field of biology and helps students quickly review before a test.

Kaplan MCAT®/GRE® Biology Test Preparation Guide for *Biology,* Eighth Edition
(978-0-321-53463-7/0-321-53463-8)
This exclusive supplement includes sample questions from the Kaplan test preparation guides with page references to *Biology,* Eighth Edition.

Spanish Glossary (978-0-321-49434-4/0-321-49434-2)
Laura P. Zanello, University of California, Riverside

NEW! Into the Jungle: Great Adventures in the Search for Evolution
(978-0-321-55671-4/0-321-55671-2)
Sean B. Carroll, University of Wisconsin, Madison
This book of nine short tales vividly depicts key discoveries in evolutionary biology and the excitement of the scientific process.

NEW! Get Ready for Biology
(978-0-321-50057-1/0-321-50057-1)
This engaging workbook helps students brush up on important math and study skills and get up to speed on biological terminology and the basics of chemistry and cell biology.

A Short Guide to Writing About Biology, Sixth Edition
(978-0-321-51716-6/0-321-51716-4)
Jan A. Pechenik, Tufts University
This best-selling writing guide teaches students to think as biologists and to express ideas clearly and concisely through their writing.

An Introduction to Chemistry for Biology Students, Ninth Edition (978-0-8053-9571-6/0-8053-9571-7)
George I. Sackheim, University of Illinois, Chicago
This text/workbook helps students review and master all the basic facts, concepts, and terminology of chemistry that they need for their life science course.

NEW! Pearson Tutor Services
www.masteringbio.com
Access to MasteringBiology™ includes complimentary access to highly interactive one-on-one biology coaching by qualified instructors seven nights per week during peak study hours. Students can "drop-in" for live online help, submit questions to an e-structor anytime, or pre-schedule a tutoring session with an e-structor. (For college students only.)

Special Topics in Biology Series (booklets)
- Alzheimer's Disease (978-0-1318-3834-5/0-1318-3834-2)
- Biological Terrorism (978-0-8053-4868-2/0-8053-4868-9)
- Biology of Cancer (978-0-8053-4867-5/0-8053-4867-0)
- Emerging Infectious Diseases (978-0-8053-3955-0/0-8053-3955-8)
- Gene Therapy (978-0-8053-3819-5/0-8053-3819-5)
- Genetic Testimony: A Guide to Forensic DNA Profiling (978-0-1314-2338-1/0-1314-2338-X)
- HIV and AIDS (978-0-8053-3956-7/0-8053-3956-6)
- Mad Cows and Cannibals: A Guide to the Transmissible Spongiform Encephalopathies (978-0-1314-2339-8/0-1314-2339-8)
- Stem Cells and Cloning (978-0-8053-4864-4/0-8053-4864-6)
- Understanding the Human Genome Project, Second Edition (978-0-8053-4877-4/0-8053-4877-8)

Supplements for the Instructor

Instructor Resource CD/DVD-ROM Set
(978-0-321-52292-4/0-321-52292-3)
The instructor media for Campbell/Reece *Biology*, Eighth Edition, is combined into one chapter-by-chapter resource along with a **Quick Reference Guide**. **DVDs** provide convenient one-stop access to all the visual media for each chapter. Assets are now organized by chapter folders, making it easy to access files. The **Test Bank CD-ROM** includes test bank questions in Word and TestGen. Assets on the DVDs include:

NEW! *BioFlix*
BioFlix™ 3-D Animations invigorate lectures with movie-quality 3-D animations. Topics include: Tour of an Animal Cell, Tour of a Plant Cell, Cellular Respiration, Photosynthesis, Mitosis, Meiosis, Protein Synthesis, Water Transport in Plants, How Neurons Work, and Muscle Contraction. An additional 123 Animations based on student Activities are also included.

NEW! 29 Discovery Channel™ Videos bring biology to life and show students the process of science. Plus, 65 new **Cell Biology Videos** have been added to the video collection, for a total of 182 videos.

PowerPoint® Label Edit Images include all the art, photos, and tables from the book embedded in PowerPoint® plus **Step Edit Art** broken down into steps. These PowerPoint® files are on the DVDs plus the **Quick Start CD-ROM** for easy access. **PowerPoint® Lecture Presentations** include all of the above plus lecture outlines and links to animations and selected videos. In all PowerPoint files, the text and labels can be edited directly in PowerPoint® and have been enlarged for optimal viewing in large lecture halls. Multiple versions of figures are provided to choose from.

JPEG Images include all the art, photos, and tables from the book with and without labels, selected art layered for step-by-step presentation, and hundreds of extra photos in JPEG format, for a total of more than 1600 photos.

MasteringBIOLOGY
www.masteringbio.com

NEW! The **MasteringBiology™ For Instructors** area includes all the media from the Instructor Resource DVDs:
- PowerPoint® Label Edit Images
- PowerPoint® Lecture Presentations
- Extra Photos (jpegs) plus captions
- Labeled Images (jpegs)
- Unlabeled Images (jpegs)
- BioFlix™ Animations
- Animations
- Discovery Channel™ Videos plus scripts
- Videos plus descriptions

Additional Online Resources:
- PowerPoint® Active Lecture Questions
- Lecture Outlines
- Student Misconceptions with Pre-Tests and Post-Tests
- Quick Reference Guide
- *Practicing Biology* Instructor Guide
- *Inquiry in Action* Instructor Guide
- Answers to selected textbook essay questions
- Lab Media for Instructors

Many instructor assets are also available at the Instructor Resource Center for *Biology*, Eighth Edition, at www.pearson-highered.com.

Transparency Acetates
(978-0-321-52328-0/0-321-52328-8)
This transparency package provides all the illustrations and tables from the text, many of which incorporate photos. In addition, key figures are broken down into steps.

Electronic Test Bank

Printed Test Bank (978-0-321-49431-3/0-321-49431-8)
More than 4,500 test questions are available in print, TestGen®, Microsoft® Word, and from within CourseCompass, Blackboard, and WebCT Course Management Systems. Test Bank questions can also be assigned through MasteringBiology™. The questions have been refined through class testing, and over 30% of the questions are new for the Eighth Edition, including three new question types that encourage critical thinking: interpreting art questions, interpreting graphs and data questions focused on quantitative skills, and scenario-based questions.

Instructor Guide for Biological Inquiry: A Workbook of Investigative Cases, Second Edition
(978-0-321-49435-1/0-321-49435-0)
Margaret Waterman, Southeast Missouri State University, and Ethel Stanley, Beloit College and BioQUEST Curriculum Consortium
This Instructor Guide provides insightful coaching for instructors on how to teach using a case-based problem-solving approach, as well as suggested answers.

Course Management Systems
Test Bank questions, quizzes, and selected content from the Study Area of MasteringBiology™ are available in these popular course management systems:
- **CourseCompass**™ (www.aw-bc.com/coursecompass)
- **Blackboard** (www.aw-bc.com/blackboard)
- **WebCT** (www.aw-bc.com/webct)

Supplements for the Lab

NEW! Lab Media at www.masteringbio.com
A new section in the Study Area of MasteringBiology™ brings together all the media assets that can be used to teach scientific inquiry, including Investigating Biology Lab Data Tables in Excel®, Biology Labs On-Line, Investigations, GraphIt!, and LabBench. In the For Instructors area, the Lab Media section includes Investigating Biology Lab Preparation Guide, Answers to Investigations, GraphIt! Instructor Versions, Answers to the LabBench Quizzes, and the *Bio-Explorations* Instructor Guide.

Investigating Biology, Sixth Edition
(978-0-321-53660-0/0-321-53660-6)

Annotated Instructor Edition for Investigating Biology
(978-0-321-54194-9/0-321-54194-4)

Preparation Guide for Investigating Biology
(978-0-321-54166-6/0-321-54166-9)
Judith Giles Morgan, Emory University, and M. Eloise Brown Carter, Oxford College of Emory University
This best-selling laboratory manual encourages students to participate in the process of science and develop creative and critical reasoning skills by posing hypotheses, making predictions, conducting open-ended experiments, collecting data, and applying results to new problems. The Sixth Edition includes a new Bioinformatics Lab and features references to online resources available at www.masteringbio.com, including Lab Data Tables in Excel® for recording data. The Annotated Instructor Edition provides teaching information and marginal notes. A Preparation Guide is also available for instructors in print and online.

New Designs for Bio-Explorations
(978-0-8053-7229-8/0-8053-7229-6)

Instructor Guide for Bio-Explorations
(978-0-8053-7228-1/0-8053-7228-8)
Janet Lanza, University of Arkansas at Little Rock
Eight inquiry-based laboratory exercises offer students creative control over the projects they undertake. Each lab exercise provides students with background information and materials that can be used in the lab projects. The Instructor Guide is provided in the For Instructors area of www.masteringbio.com under Lab Media.

Symbiosis: The Benjamin Cummings Custom Laboratory Program for Biological Sciences
www.pearsoncustom.com/database/symbiosis/bc.html
With Symbiosis, instructors can build a customized lab manual that includes selections from the Benjamin Cummings database along with their own original material.

Biology Labs On-Line
www.biologylabsonline.com
Twelve on-line labs enable students to expand their scientific horizons beyond the traditional wet lab setting and perform potentially dangerous, lengthy, or expensive experiments in an electronic environment. Each experiment can be repeated as often as necessary, employing a unique set of variables each time. The labs are available for purchase individually or in a 12-pack with the printed Student Lab Manual (978-0-8053-7017-1/0-8053-7017-X). An Instructor Lab Manual is also available (978-0-8053-7018-8/0-8053-7018-8).

Reviewers

Eighth Edition Reviewers

Dominique Adriaens, Ghent University
George R. Aliaga, Tarrant County College
J. David Archibald, San Diego State University
David M. Armstrong, University of Colorado-Boulder
Angela S. Aspbury, Texas State University
Ellen Baker, Santa Monica College
Rebecca A. Bartow, Western Kentucky University
Tim Beagley, Salt Lake Community College
Kenneth Birnbaum, New York University
Michael W. Black, California Polytechnic State University, San Luis Obispo
Edward Blumenthal, Marquette University
Jason E. Bond, East Carolina University
Cornelius Bondzi, Hampton University
Oliver Bossdorf, State University of New York, Stony Book
Edward Braun, Iowa State University
Chad Brommer, Emory University
Judith L. Bronstein, University of Arizona
Robb T. Brumfield, Louisiana State University
Richard C. Brusca, University of Arizona, Arizona-Sonora Desert Museum
Jorge Busciglio, University of California, Irvine
Guy A. Caldwell, University of Alabama
Jane Caldwell, West Virginia University
Kim A. Caldwell, University of Alabama
R. Andrew Cameron, California Institute of Technology
W. Zacheus Cande, University of California, Berkeley
Frank R. Cantelmo, St. John's University
Jeffrey Carmichael, University of North Dakota
Laura L. Carruth, Georgia State University
J. Aaron Cassill, University of Texas at San Antonio
P. Bryant Chase, Florida State University
Jung H. Choi, Georgia Institute of Technology
Geoffrey Church, Fairfield University
Patricia J. Clark, Indiana University-Purdue University, Indianapolis
Janice J. Clymer, San Diego Mesa College
Jan Colpaert, Hasselt University
Jay Comeaux, McNeese State University
Gregory Copenhaver, University of North Carolina, Chapel Hill
Karen Curto, University of Pittsburgh
Marymegan Daly, The Ohio State University
Cynthia Dassler, The Ohio State University
Michael A. Davis, Central Connecticut State University
Maria E. de Bellard, California State University, Northridge
Patricia A. DeLeon, University of Delaware
Charles F. Delwiche, University of Maryland
William L. Dentler, University of Kansas
Jean DeSaix, University of North Carolina
Michael Dini, Texas Tech University
Douglas J. Eernisse, California State University, Fullerton
Brad Elder, Doane College
Michelle Elekonich, University of Nevada, Las Vegas
Mary Ellard-Ivey, Pacific Lutheran University
Johnny El-Rady, University of South Florida
John A. Endler, University of California, Santa Barbara
Frederick B. Essig, University of South Florida
Olukemi Fadayomi, Ferris State University
Ellen H. Fanning, Vanderbilt University
Lewis Feldman, University of California, Berkeley

Rebecca Ferrell, Metropolitan State College of Denver
Jonathan S. Fisher, St. Louis University
Kirk Fitzhugh, Natural History Museum of Los Angeles County
Norma Fowler, University of Texas, Austin
Robert Gilbert Fowler, San Jose State University
Jed Fuhrman, University of Southern California
Zofia E. Gagnon, Marist College
Michael Gaines, University of Miami
Stephen Gammie, University of Wisconsin, Madison
Andrea Gargas, University of Wisconsin, Madison
Lauren Garner, California Polytechnic State University, San Luis Obispo
Simon Gilroy, Pennsylvania State University
Alan D. Gishlick, Gustavus Adolphus College
Jessica Gleffe, University of California, Irvine
Tricia Glidewell, Marist School
Elizabeth Godrick, Boston University
Ken Halanych, Auburn University
E. William Hamilton, Washington and Lee University
William F. Hanna, Massasoit Community College
Laszlo Hanzely, Northern Illinois University
Lisa Harper, University of California, Berkeley
Bernard A. Hauser, University of Florida
Evan B. Hazard, Bemidji State University (Emeritus)
S. Blair Hedges, Pennsylvania State University
Brian Hedlund, University of Nevada, Las Vegas
Jean Heitz, University of Wisconsin, Madison
Susan Hengeveld, Indiana University
Albert Herrera, University of Southern California
Kenneth Hillers, California Polytechnic State University, San Luis Obispo
A. Scott Holaday, Texas Tech University
N. Michele Holbrook, Harvard University
Alan R. Holyoak, Brigham Young University, Idaho
Sandra M. Horikami, Daytona Beach Community College
Becky Houck, University of Portland
Daniel J. Howard, New Mexico State University
Cristin Hulslander, University of Oregon
Linda L. Hyde, Gordon College
Jeffrey Ihara, Mira Costa College
Lee Johnson, The Ohio State University
Chad Jordan, North Carolina State University
Walter S. Judd, University of Florida
Thomas W. Jurik, Iowa State University
Caroline M. Kane, University of California, Berkeley
Jennifer Katcher, Pima Community College
Laura A. Katz, Smith College
Maureen Kearney, Field Museum of Natural History
Patrick Keeling, University of British Columbia
Elizabeth A. Kellogg, University of Missouri-St. Louis
Chris Kennedy, Simon Fraser University
Rebecca T. Kimball, University of Florida
Jennifer Knight, University of Colorado
Margareta Krabbe, Uppsala University
Anselm Kratochwil, Universität Osnabrück
Deborah M. Kristan, California State University at San Marcos
William Kroll, Loyola University, Chicago
Justin P. Kumar, Indiana University
Marc-André Lachance, University of Western Ontario
Mohamed Lakrim, Kingsborough Community College
John Latto, University of California, Santa Barbara
Daewoo Lee, Ohio University

Michael R. Leonardo, Coe College
John J. Lepri, University of North Carolina at Greensboro
Graeme Lindbeck, Valencia Community College
Diana Lipscomb, George Washington University
Christopher Little, The University of Texas-Pan American
Kevin D. Livingstone, Trinity University
Andrea Lloyd, Middlebury College
Christopher A. Loretz, State University of New York at Buffalo
Douglas B. Luckie, Michigan State University
Christine R. Maher, University of Southern Maine
Keith Malmos, Valencia Community College – East Campus
Cindy Malone, California State University, Northridge
Carol Mapes, Kutztown University of Pennsylvania
Kathleen A. Marrs, Indiana University-Purdue University, Indianapolis
Diane L. Marshall, University of New Mexico
Andrew McCubbin, Washington State University
Lisa Marie Meffert, Rice University
Scott Meissner, Cornell University
John Merrill, Michigan State University
Michael J. Misamore, Texas Christian University
Alan Molumby, University of Illinois, Chicago
Joseph P. Montoya, Georgia Institute of Technology
Janice Moore, Colorado State University
Jeanette Mowery, Madison Area Technical College
Tom Neils, Grand Rapids Community College
Ray Neubauer, University of Texas, Austin
James Newcomb, New England College
Anders Nilsson, University of Umeå
Mohamed A. F. Noor, Duke University
Shawn Nordell, St. Louis University
Richard S. Norman, University of Michigan, Dearborn (Emeritus)
Gretchen North, Occidental College
Mark P. Oemke, Alma College
Nathan O. Okia, Auburn University, Montgomery
John Oross, University of California, Riverside
Charissa Osborne, Butler University
Thomas G. Owens, Cornell University
Kevin Padian, University of California, Berkeley
Anthony T. Paganini, Michigan State University
Michael A. Palladino, Monmouth University
Imara Y. Perera, North Carolina State University
David S. Pilliod, California Polytechnic State University, San Luis Obispo
J. Chris Pires, University of Missouri-Columbia
Angela R. Porta, Kean University
Daniel Potter, University of California, Davis
Mary V. Price, University of California, Riverside
Mitch Price, Pennsylvania State University
Peter Quinby, University of Pittsburgh
Robert H. Reaves, Glendale Community College
Erin Rempala, San Diego Mesa College
Eric Ribbens, Western Illinois University
Christina Richards, New York University
Loren Rieseberg, University of British Columbia
Bruce B. Riley, Texas A&M University
Laurel Roberts, University of Pittsburgh
Mike Rosenzweig, Virginia Polytechnic Institute and State University
Tyson Sacco, Cornell University
Rowan F. Sage, University of Toronto
Tammy Lynn Sage, University of Toronto
Thomas R. Sawicki, Spartanburg Community College
Inder Saxena, University of Texas, Austin
Maynard H. Schaus, Virginia Wesleyan College
Renate Scheibe, University of Osnabrück
Mark Schlissel, University of California, Berkeley
Christopher J. Schneider, Boston University
Thomas W. Schoener, University of California, Davis
Patricia M. Schulte, University of British Columbia
Karen S. Schumaker, University of Arizona
David J. Schwartz, Houston Community College

Robert W. Seagull, Hofstra University
Duane Sears, University of California, Santa Barbara
Joan Sharp, Simon Fraser University
Timothy E. Shannon, Francis Marion University
Richard M. Showman, University of South Carolina
Rebecca Simmons, University of North Dakota
Anne Simon, University of Maryland, College Park
Robert Simons, University of California, Los Angeles
Julio G. Soto, San Jose State University
John Stachowicz, University of California, Davis
Gail A. Stewart, Camden County College
Michael A. Sypes, Pennsylvania State University
Emily Taylor, California Polytechnic State University, San Luis Obispo
John W. Taylor, University of California, Berkeley
William Thwaites, Tillamook Bay Community College
Eric Toolson, University of New Mexico
Paul Q. Trombley, Florida State University
Nancy J. Trun, Duquesne University
Claudia Uhde-Stone, California State University, East Bay
Saba Valadkhan, Case Western Reserve University School of Medicine
Steven D. Verhey, Central Washington University
Kathleen Verville, Washington College
Sara Via, University of Maryland
Leif Asbjørn Vøllestad, University of Oslo
Linda Walters, University of Central Florida
Nickolas M. Waser, University of California, Riverside
Andrea Weeks, George Mason University
Richard Wetts, University of California, Irvine
Susan Whittemore, Keene State College
Ernest H. Williams, Hamilton College
Kathy Williams, San Diego State University
Paul Wilson, California State University, Northridge
Peter Wimberger, University of Puget Sound
Robert Winning, Eastern Michigan University
E. William Wischusen, Louisiana State University
Vickie L. Wolfe, Marshall University
Denise Woodward, Pennsylvania State University
Sarah E. Wyatt, Ohio University
Ramin Yadegari, University of Arizona
Paul Yancey, Whitman College
Gina M. Zainelli, Loyola University, Chicago
Miriam Zolan, Indiana University

BioFlix Reviewers

Mitch Albers, Minneapolis Community and Technical College
Kirk Bartholomew, Sacred Heart University
Gretchen Bernard, Moraine Valley Community College
Peggy Brickman, University of Georgia
Uriel Buitrago-Suarez, Harper College
Nancy Butler, Kutztown University of Pennsylvania
Guy A. Caldwell, University of Alabama
Kim A. Caldwell, University of Alabama
Jose L. Egremy, Northwest Vista College
Kurt J. Elliott, Northwest Vista College
Gerald G. Farr, Texas State University
Lewis Feldman, University of California, Berkeley
Sandra Gibbons, Moraine Valley Community College
Douglas A. Hamilton, Hartwick College
W. Wyatt Hoback, University of Nebraska at Kearney
Elizabeth Hodgson, York College of Pennsylvania
Kelly Hogan, University of North Carolina at Chapel Hill
Mary Rose Lamb, University of Puget Sound
Cody Locke, University of Alabama
Marvin Brandon Lowery, Sam Houston State University
David Mirman, Mt. San Antonio College
James Newcomb, New England College

Thomas G. Owens, Cornell University
Deb Pires, University of California, Los Angeles
Mitch Price, Pennsylvania State University
David A. Rintoul, Kansas State University
Renee Rivas, University of Alabama
Laurel Roberts, University of Pittsburgh
Chris Romero, Front Range Community College
Juliet Spencer, University of San Francisco
Linda Brooke Stabler, University of Central Oklahoma
Beth Stall, El Centro College
Brian Stout, Northwest Vista College
Diane Sweeney, Crystal Springs Uplands School
Jamey Thompson, Hudson Valley Community College
Paul Q. Trombley, Florida State University
Robert S. Wallace, Iowa State University
Susan Whittemore, Keene State College
Miriam Zolan, Indiana University
Michelle Zurawski, Moraine Valley Community College

MasteringBiology Class-Testers and Reviewers

Peter B. Berget, Carnegie Mellon University
Michael W. Black, California Polytechnic State University, San Luis Obispo
Scott Bowling, Auburn University
Suzanne Butler, Miami Dade College
Alejandro Calderon-Urrea, California State University, Fresno
Kim A. Caldwell, University of Alabama
Jeffrey Carmichael, University of North Dakota
Jung H. Choi, Georgia Institute of Technology
Karen Curto, University of Pittsburgh
Lydia Daniels, University of Pittsburgh
Jill Feinstein, Richland Community College
Donald Glassman, Des Moines Area Community College
Joyce Gordon, University of British Columbia
David Grise, Texas A&M University, Corpus Christi
Douglas A. Hamilton, Hartwick College
Mark Hens, University of North Carolina at Greensboro
John C. Kay, Iolani School
Tracy Kickox, University of Illinois at Urbana-Champaign
Mary Rose Lamb, University of Puget Sound
Deb Maddalena, University of Vermont
C. Smoot Major, University of South Alabama
Nilo Marin, Broward Community College
John Merrill, Michigan State University
Melissa Michael, University of Illinois at Urbana-Champaign
Nancy Rice, Western Kentucky University
Chris Romero, Front Range Community College, Larimer
John Salerno, Kennesaw State University
Brian Stout, Northwest Vista College
Sukanya Subramanian, Collin County Community College
Elizabeth Willott, University of Arizona
Lauren Yaich, University of Pittsburgh at Bradford

Reviewers of Previous Editions

Kenneth Able (State University of New York, Albany), Thomas Adams (Michigan State University), Martin Adamson (University of British Columbia), Shylaja Akkaraju (Bronx Community College of CUNY), John Alcock (Arizona State University), Richard Almon (State University of New York, Buffalo), Bonnie Amos (Angelo State University), Katherine Anderson (University of California, Berkeley),

Richard J. Andren (Montgomery County Community College), Estry Ang (University of Pittsburgh at Greensburg), Jeff Appling (Clemson University), J. David Archibald (San Diego State University), David Armstrong (University of Colorado at Boulder), Howard J. Arnott (University of Texas at Arlington), Mary Ashley (University of Illinois at Chicago), Robert Atherton (University of Wyoming), Karl Aufderheide (Texas A&M University), Leigh Auleb (San Francisco State University), P. Stephen Baenziger (University of Nebraska), Ellen Baker (Santa Monica College), Katherine Baker (Millersville University), William Barklow (Framingham State College), Susan Barman (Michigan State University), Steven Barnhart (Santa Rosa Junior College), Andrew Barton (University of Maine Farmington), Ron Basmajian (Merced College), David Bass (University of Central Oklahoma), Bonnie Baxter (Hobart & William Smith), Tim Beagley (Salt Lake Community College), Margaret E. Beard (College of the Holy Cross), Tom Beatty (University of British Columbia), Chris Beck (Emory University), Wayne Becker (University of Wisconsin, Madison), Patricia Bedinger (Colorado State University), Jane Beiswenger (University of Wyoming), Anne Bekoff (University of Colorado, Boulder), Marc Bekoff (University of Colorado, Boulder), Tania Beliz (College of San Mateo), Adrianne Bendich (Hoffman-La Roche, Inc.), Barbara Bentley (State University of New York, Stony Brook), Darwin Berg (University of California, San Diego), Werner Bergen (Michigan State University), Gerald Bergstrom (University of Wisconsin, Milwaukee), Anna W. Berkovitz (Purdue University), Dorothy Berner (Temple University), Annalisa Berta (San Diego State University), Paulette Bierzychudek (Pomona College), Charles Biggers (Memphis State University), Robert Blanchard (University of New Hampshire), Andrew R. Blaustein (Oregon State University), Judy Bluemer (Morton College), Robert Blystone (Trinity University), Robert Boley (University of Texas, Arlington), Eric Bonde (University of Colorado, Boulder), Richard Boohar (University of Nebraska, Omaha), Carey L. Booth (Reed College), Allan Bornstein (Southeast Missouri State University), James L. Botsford (New Mexico State University), Lisa Boucher (University of Nebraska-Omaha), J. Michael Bowes (Humboldt State University), Richard Bowker (Alma College), Robert Bowker (Glendale Community College - Arizona), Barbara Bowman (Mills College), Barry Bowman (University of California, Santa Cruz), Deric Bownds (University of Wisconsin, Madison), Robert Boyd (Auburn University), Sunny Boyd (University of Notre Dame), Jerry Brand (University of Texas, Austin), Theodore A. Bremner (Howard University), James Brenneman (University of Evansville), Charles H. Brenner (Berkeley, California), Lawrence Brewer (University of Kentucky), Donald P. Briskin (University of Illinois, Urbana), Paul Broady (University of Canterbury), Danny Brower (University of Arizona), Carole Browne (Wake Forest University), Mark Browning (Purdue University), David Bruck (San Jose State University), Herbert Bruneau (Oklahoma State University), Gary Brusca (Humboldt State University), Richard C. Brusca (University of Arizona, Arizona-Sonora Desert Museum), Alan H. Brush (University of Connecticut, Storrs), Howard Buhse (University of Illinois at Chicago), Arthur Buikema (Virginia Tech), Al Burchsted (College of Staten Island), Meg Burke (University of North Dakota), Edwin Burling (De Anza College), William Busa (Johns Hopkins University), John Bushnell (University of Colorado), Linda Butler (University of Texas, Austin), David Byres (Florida Community College, Jacksonville), Alison Campbell (University of Waikato), Iain Campbell (University of Pittsburgh), Robert E. Cannon (University of North Carolina at Greensboro), Deborah Canington (University of California, Davis), Frank Cantelmo (St John's University), John Capeheart (University of Houston-Downtown), Gregory Capelli (College of William and Mary), Richard Cardullo (University of California, Riverside), Nina Caris (Texas A&M University), Robert Carroll (East Carolina University), David Champlin (University of Southern Maine), Bruce Chase (University of Nebraska, Omaha), Doug Cheeseman (De Anza College), Shepley Chen (University of Illinois, Chicago), Giovina Chinchar (Tougaloo College), Joseph P.

Chinnici (Virginia Commonwealth University), Henry Claman (University of Colorado Health Science Center), Anne Clark (Binghamton University), Greg Clark (University of Texas), Ross C. Clark (Eastern Kentucky University), Lynwood Clemens (Michigan State University), William P. Coffman (University of Pittsburgh), Austin Randy Cohen (California State University, Northridge), J. John Cohen (University of Colorado Health Science Center), Jim Colbert (Iowa State University), Robert Colvin (Ohio University), David Cone (Saint Mary's University), Elizabeth Connor (University of Massachusetts), Joanne Conover (University of Connecticut), John Corliss (University of Maryland), James T. Costa (Western Carolina University), Stuart J. Coward (University of Georgia), Charles Creutz (University of Toledo), Bruce Criley (Illinois Wesleyan University), Norma Criley (Illinois Wesleyan University), Joe W. Crim (University of Georgia), Greg Crowther (University of Washington), Karen Curto (University of Pittsburgh), Anne Cusic (University of Alabama at Birmingham), Richard Cyr (Pennsylvania State University), W. Marshall Darley (University of Georgia), Marianne Dauwalder (University of Texas, Austin), Larry Davenport (Samford University), Bonnie J. Davis (San Francisco State University), Jerry Davis (University of Wisconsin, La Crosse), Thomas Davis (University of New Hampshire), John Dearn (University of Canberra), Teresa DeGolier (Bethel College), James Dekloe (University of California, Santa Cruz), Veronique Delesalle (Gettysburg College), T. Delevoryas (University of Texas, Austin), Roger Del Moral (University of Washington), Diane C. DeNagel (Northwestern University), Daniel Dervartanian (University of Georgia), Jean DeSaix (University of North Carolina at Chapel Hill), Michael Dini (Texas Tech University), Biao Ding (Ohio State University), Andrew Dobson (Princeton University), Stanley Dodson (University of Wisconsin-Madison), Mark Drapeau (University of California, Irvine), John Drees (Temple University School of Medicine), Charles Drewes (Iowa State University), Marvin Druger (Syracuse University), Gary Dudley (University of Georgia), Susan Dunford (University of Cincinnati), Betsey Dyer (Wheaton College), Robert Eaton (University of Colorado), Robert S. Edgar (University of California, Santa Cruz), Douglas Eernisse (California State University, Fullerton), Betty J. Eidemiller (Lamar University), Brad Elder (University of Oklahoma), William D. Eldred (Boston University), Norman Ellstrand (University of California, Riverside), Dennis Emery (Iowa State University), John Endler (University of California, Santa Barbara), Margaret T. Erskine (Lansing Community College), Gerald Esch (Wake Forest University), Frederick B. Essig (University of South Florida), Mary Eubanks (Duke University), David Evans (University of Florida), Robert C. Evans (Rutgers University, Camden), Sharon Eversman (Montana State University), Lincoln Fairchild (Ohio State University), Peter Fajer (Florida State University), Bruce Fall (University of Minnesota), Lynn Fancher (College of DuPage), Paul Farnsworth (University of Texas at San Antonio), Larry Farrell (Idaho State University), Jerry F. Feldman (University of California, Santa Cruz), Eugene Fenster (Longview Community College), Russell Fernald (University of Oregon), Kim Finer (Kent State University), Milton Fingerman (Tulane University), Barbara Finney (Regis College), Frank Fish (West Chester University), David Fisher (University of Hawaii, Manoa), Steven Fisher (University of California, Santa Barbara), Lloyd Fitzpatrick (University of North Texas), William Fixsen (Harvard University), Abraham Flexer (Manuscript Consultant, Boulder, Colorado), Kerry Foresman (University of Montana), Norma Fowler (University of Texas, Austin), Robert G. Fowler (San Jose State University), David Fox (University of Tennessee, Knoxville), Carl Frankel (Pennsylvania State University, Hazleton), James Franzen (University of Pittsburgh), Bill Freedman (Dalhousie University), Otto Friesen (University of Virginia), Frank Frisch (Chapman University), Virginia Fry (Monterey Peninsula College), Bernard Frye (University of Texas at Arlington), Alice Fulton (University of Iowa), Chandler Fulton (Brandeis University), Sara Fultz (Stanford University), Berdell Funke (North Dakota State University), Anne Funkhouser (University of

the Pacific), Michael Gaines (University of Miami), Arthur W. Galston (Yale University), Carl Gans (University of Michigan), John Gapter (University of Northern Colorado), Reginald Garrett (University of Virginia), Patricia Gensel (University of North Carolina), Chris George (California Polytechnic State University, San Luis Obispo), Robert George (University of Wyoming), J. Whitfield Gibbons (University of Georgia), J. Phil Gibson (Agnes Scott College), Frank Gilliam (Marshall University), Simon Gilroy (Pennsylvania State University), Alan Gishlick (National Center for Science Education), Todd Gleeson (University of Colorado), John Glendinning (Barnard College), David Glenn-Lewin (Wichita State University), William Glider (University of Nebraska), Elizabeth A. Godrick (Boston University), Lynda Goff (University of California, Santa Cruz), Elliott Goldstein (Arizona State University), Paul Goldstein (University of Texas, El Paso), Sandra Gollnick (State University of New York at Buffalo) Anne Good (University of California, Berkeley), Judith Goodenough (University of Massachusetts, Amherst), Wayne Goodey (University of British Columbia), Robert Goodman (University of Wisconsin-Madison), Ester Goudsmit (Oakland University), Linda Graham (University of Wisconsin, Madison), Robert Grammer (Belmont University), Joseph Graves (Arizona State University), Phyllis Griffard (University of Houston-Downtown), A. J. F. Griffiths (University of British Columbia), William Grimes (University of Arizona), Mark Gromko (Bowling Green State University), Serine Gropper (Auburn University), Katherine L. Gross (Ohio State University), Gary Gussin (University of Iowa), Mark Guyer (National Human Genome Research Institute), Ruth Levy Guyer (Bethesda, Maryland), R. Wayne Habermehl (Montgomery County Community College), Mac Hadley (University of Arizona), Joel Hagen (Radford University), Jack P. Hailman (University of Wisconsin), Leah Haimo (University of California, Riverside), Jody Hall (Brown University), Douglas Hallett, (Northern Arizona University), Rebecca Halyard (Clayton State College), Sam Hammer (Boston University), Penny Hanchey-Bauer (Colorado State University), Laszlo Hanzely (Northern Illinois University), Jeff Hardin (University of Wisconsin, Madison), Richard Harrison (Cornell University), Carla Hass (Pennsylvania State University), Chris Haufler (University of Kansas), Chris Haynes (Shelton State Community College), H. D. Heath (California State University, Hayward), George Hechtel (State University of New York, Stony Brook), Blair Hedges (Pennsylvania State), David Heins (Tulane University), Jean Heitz (University of Wisconsin, Madison), John D. Helmann (Cornell University), Colin Henderson (University of Montana), Michelle Henricks (University of California, Los Angeles), Caroll Henry (Chicago State University), Frank Heppner (University of Rhode Island), Scott Herrick (Missouri Western State College), Ira Herskowitz (University of California, San Francisco), Paul E. Hertz (Barnard College), David Hibbett (Clark University), R. James Hickey (Miami University), William Hillenius (College of Charleston), Ralph Hinegardner (University of California, Santa Cruz), William Hines (Foothill College), Robert Hinrichsen (Indiana University of Pennsylvania), Helmut Hirsch (State University of New York, Albany), Tuan-hua David Ho (Washington University), Carl Hoagstrom (Ohio Northern University), James Hoffman (University of Vermont), A. Scott Holaday (Texas Tech), James Holland (Indiana State University, Bloomington), Charles Holliday (Lafayette College), Lubbock Karl Holte (Idaho State University), Laura Hoopes (Occidental College), Nancy Hopkins (Massachusetts Institute of Technology), Sandra Horikami (Daytona Beach Community College), Kathy Hornberger (Widener University), Pius F. Horner (San Bernardino Valley College), Margaret Houk (Ripon College), Ronald R. Hoy (Cornell University), Donald Humphrey (Emory University School of Medicine), Robert J. Huskey (University of Virginia), Steven Hutcheson (University of Maryland, College Park), Sandra Hsu (Skyline College), Bradley Hyman (University of California, Riverside), Mark Iked (San Bernardino Valley College), Cheryl Ingram-Smith (Clemson University), Alice Jacklet (State University of New York, Albany), John Jackson (North Hennepin

Community College), John C. Jahoda (Bridgewater State College), Dan Johnson (East Tennessee State University), Randall Johnson (University of California, San Diego), Stephen Johnson (William Penn University), Wayne Johnson (Ohio State University), Kenneth C. Jones (California State University, Northridge), Russell Jones (University of California, Berkeley), Alan Journet (Southeast Missouri State University), Walter Judd (University of Florida), Thomas C. Kane (University of Cincinnati), Tamos Kapros (University of Missouri), E. L. Karlstrom (University of Puget Sound), Jennifer Katcher (Pima Community College), Norm Kenkel (University of Manitoba), George Khoury (National Cancer Institute), Mark Kirk (University of Missouri-Columbia), Robert Kitchin (University of Wyoming), Attila O. Klein (Brandeis University), Daniel Klionsky (University of Michigan), Ned Knight (Linfield College), David Kohl (University of California, Santa Barbara), Greg Kopf (University of Pennsylvania School of Medicine), Thomas Koppenheffer (Trinity University), Janis Kuby (San Francisco State University), David Kurijaka (Ohio University), J. A. Lackey (State University of New York, Oswego), Elaine Lai (Brandeis University), Lynn Lamoreux (Texas A&M University), William L'Amoreaux (College of Staten Island), Carmine A. Lanciani (University of Florida), Kenneth Lang (Humboldt State University), Dominic Lannutti (El Paso Community College), Allan Larson (Washington University), Diane K. Lavett (State University of New York, Cortland, and Emory University), Charles Leavell (Fullerton College), C. S. Lee (University of Texas), Robert Leonard (University of California, Riverside), John Lepri (University of North Carolina at Greensboro), Donald Levin (University of Texas), Austin Mike Levine (University of California, Berkeley), Joseph Levine (Boston College), Bill Lewis (Shoreline Community College), John Lewis (Loma Linda University), Lorraine Lica (California State University, Hayward), Harvey Liftin (Broward Community College), Harvey Lillywhite (University of Florida, Gainesville), Clark Lindgren (Grinnell College), Sam Loker (University of New Mexico), Jane Lubchenco (Oregon State University), Margaret A. Lynch (Tufts University), Steven Lynch (Louisiana State University at Shreveport), Richard Machemer Jr. (St. John Fisher College), Elizabeth Machunis-Masuoka (University of Virginia), James MacMahon (Utah State University), Linda Maier (University of Alabama in Huntsville), Jose Maldonado (El Paso Community College), Richard Malkin (University of California, Berkeley), Charles Mallery (University of Miami), William Margolin (University of Texas Medical School), Lynn Margulis (Boston University), Edith Marsh (Angelo State University), Diane Marshall (University of New Mexico), Linda Martin Morris (University of Washington), Karl Mattox (Miami University of Ohio), Joyce Maxwell (California State University, Northridge), Jeffrey D. May (Marshall University), Lee McClenaghan (San Diego State University), Richard McCracken (Purdue University), Kerry McDonald (University of Missouri-Columbia), Jacqueline McLaughlin (Pennsylvania State University, Lehigh Valley), Neal McReynolds (Texas A&M International), Lisa Meffert (Rice University), Michael Meighan (University of California, Berkeley), Scott Meissner (Cornell University), Paul Melchior (North Hennepin Community College), Phillip Meneely (Haverford College), John Merrill (Michigan State University), Brian Metscher (University of California, Irvine), Ralph Meyer (University of Cincinnati), James Mickle (North Carolina State University), Roger Milkman (University of Iowa), Helen Miller (Oklahoma State University), John Miller (University of California, Berkeley), Kenneth R. Miller (Brown University), John E. Minnich (University of Wisconsin, Milwaukee), Michael Misamore (Louisiana State University), Kenneth Mitchell (Tulane University School of Medicine), Alan Molumby (University of Illinois at Chicago), Nicholas Money (Miami University), Russell Monson (University of Colorado, Boulder), Frank Moore (Oregon State University), Randy Moore (Wright State University), William Moore (Wayne State University), Carl Moos (Veterans Administration Hospital, Albany, New York), Michael Mote (Temple University), Alex Motten (Duke University), Deborah Mowshowitz (Columbia University), Rita Moyes (Texas A&M College Station), Darrel L. Murray (University of Illinois at Chicago), John Mutchmor (Iowa State University), Elliot Myerowitz (California Institute of Technology), Gavin Naylor (Iowa State University), John Neess (University of Wisconsin, Madison), Raymond Neubauer (University of Texas, Austin), Todd Newbury (University of California, Santa Cruz), Harvey Nichols (University of Colorado, Boulder), Deborah Nickerson (University of South Florida), Bette Nicotri (University of Washington), Caroline Niederman (Tomball College), Maria Nieto (California State University, Hayward), Greg Nishiyama (College of the Canyons), Charles R. Noback (College of Physicians and Surgeons, Columbia University), Jane Noble-Harvey (Delaware University), Mary C. Nolan (Irvine Valley College), Peter Nonacs (University of California, Los Angeles), Richard Norman (University of Michigan-Dearborn), David O. Norris (University of Colorado, Boulder), Steven Norris (California State, Channel Islands), Cynthia Norton (University of Maine, Augusta), Steve Norton (East Carolina University), Steve Nowicki (Duke University), Bette H. Nybakken (Hartnell College), Brian O'Conner (University of Massachusetts, Amherst), Gerard O'Donovan (University of North Texas), Eugene Odum (University of Georgia), Linda Ogren (University of California, Santa Cruz), Patricia O'Hern (Emory University), Jeanette Oliver (St. Louis Community College Florissant Valley), Gary P. Olivetti (University of Vermont), John Olsen (Rhodes College), Laura J. Olsen (University of Michigan), Sharman O'Neill (University of California, Davis), Wan Ooi (Houston Community College), Gay Ostarello (Diablo Valley College), Catherine Ortega (Fort Lewis College), Charissa Osborne (Butler University), Thomas G. Owens (Cornell University), Penny Padgett (University of North Carolina at Chapel Hill), Kevin Padian (University of California, Berkeley), Dianna Padilla (State University of New York, Stony Brook), Barry Palevitz (University of Georgia), Daniel Papaj (University of Arizona), Peter Pappas (County College of Morris), Bulah Parker (North Carolina State University), Stanton Parmeter (Chemeketa Community College), Robert Patterson (San Francisco State University), Ronald Patterson (Michigan State University), Crellin Pauling (San Francisco State University), Kay Pauling (Foothill Community College), Daniel Pavuk (Bowling Green State University), Debra Pearce (Northern Kentucky University), Patricia Pearson (Western Kentucky University), Shelley Penrod (North Harris College), Beverly Perry (Houston Community College), David Pfennig (University of North Carolina at Chapel Hill), Bob Pittman (Michigan State University), James Platt (University of Denver), Martin Poenie (University of Texas, Austin), Scott Poethig (University of Pennsylvania), Jeffrey Pommerville (Texas A&M University), Warren Porter (University of Wisconsin), Daniel Potter (University of California, Davis), Donald Potts (University of California, Santa Cruz), Andy Pratt (University of Canterbury), David Pratt (University of California, Davis), Halina Presley (University of Illinois, Chicago), Mitch Price (Pennsylvania State University), Rong Sun Pu (Kean University), Rebecca Pyles (East Tennessee State University), Scott Quackenbush (Florida International University), Ralph Quatrano (Oregon State University), Val Raghavan (Ohio State University), Deanna Raineri (University of Illinois, Champaign-Urbana), Talitha Rajah (Indiana University Southeast), Charles Ralph (Colorado State University), Thomas Rand (Saint Mary's University), Kurt Redborg (Coe College), Ahnya Redman (Pennsylvania State), Brian Reeder (Morehead State University), Bruce Reid (Kean University), David Reid (Blackburn College), C. Gary Reiness (Lewis & Clark College), Charles Remington (Yale University), David Reznick (University of California, Riverside), Douglas Rhoads (University of Arkansas), Fred Rhoades (Western Washington State University), Christopher Riegle (Irvine Valley College), Donna Ritch (Pennsylvania State University), Carol Rivin (Oregon State University East), Laurel Roberts (University of Pittsburgh), Thomas Rodella (Merced College), Rodney Rogers (Drake University), William Roosenburg

Acknowledgments

The authors wish to express their gratitude to the global community of instructors, researchers, students, and publishing professionals who have contributed to this edition.

As authors of this text, we are mindful of the daunting challenge of keeping up to date in all areas of our rapidly expanding subject. We are grateful to the numerous scientists who helped shape this edition by discussing their research fields with us, answering specific questions in their areas of expertise, and, often, sharing their ideas about biology education.

For advice in updating the phylogeny of Galápagos finches in Chapter 1, we are indebted to Kevin Burns and Peter Grant. For assistance with the chapters of Units 1 through 3 (chemistry, cell biology, and genetics), we first wish to thank the members of the Mills College Biology and Chemistry/Physics Department, notably Barbara Bowman and Elisabeth Wade. We are also grateful to Tom Owens and Mimi Zolan, who were each exceptionally generous with their time and knowledge, and to Michael Black, Laurie Heyer, and Ed Blake, for noteworthy contributions to figures. And we thank the individuals who took the time to share their expertise on early atmospheric conditions (Laura Schaefer), cell biology (Pat Zambryski, Steve King, Jeremy Reiter, and Jeff Hardin), gene regulation (Phil Zamore, Dave Bartel, Tom Gingeras, Steve Bell, Saba Valadkhan, Joe Heilig, Lorraine Pillus, and Mike Levine), current cloning approaches (Caroline Kane and Andy Cameron), genomics (Nikos Krypides, Emir Khatipov, and Rebekah Rasooly), and homeobox genes (Bill McGinnis). In addition, we thank Lisa Weasel for her feedback on the new "Tips for Genetics Problems."

For the chapters of Units 4 and 5, on evolution and the diversity of life, researchers who generously shared their expertise with us included Richard Anthony, Nick Barton, Toby Bradshaw, Keith Clay, Kevin de Queiroz, Peter and Rosemary Grant, Daniel J. Howard, Patrick Keeling, Andrew H. Knoll, Jon Mallatt, Amy McCune, Axel Meyer, Kevin J. Peterson, Loren Rieseberg, Ole Seehausen, and Mark Webster.

For Units 6 through 8, the units on plant and animal form and function, and ecology, we benefited greatly from the expertise of Charles Michel, Eric Britt, Don Boyer, and Alan French. In addition, Tom Deerinck, Peter Gillespie, Mark Chappell, and Doug DeSimone provided important assistance with figures. We also thank Eric Simon, a coauthor of the Campbell nonmajors texts, for helping us think through some terminology and presentation dilemmas in Unit 7.

And finally, for her many contributions throughout the book, we sincerely thank Marty Taylor, the author of the *Student Study Guide* and a coauthor of *Biology: Concepts & Connections*.

A total of 228 biologists, listed on pages xxiv–xxix, provided detailed reviews of one or more chapters for this edition, helping us ensure the book's scientific accuracy and improve its pedagogical effectiveness. Special thanks for exceptional contributions go to Johnny El-Rady, Graeme Lindbeck, Bruce Riley, Robert Fowler, Alan Gishlick, Alastair Simpson, Ken Halanych, Kevin Padian, John Taylor, Jay Comeaux, Grace Wyngaard, Lauren Garner, Missy Holbrook, Toby Kellogg, Eduardo Zeiger, Richard Norman, Albert Herrera, and Patricia Schulte. Thanks also to the numerous other professors and students, from all over the world, who offered suggestions directly to the authors. Of course, we alone bear the responsibility for any errors that remain in the text, but the dedication of our consultants, reviewers, and other correspondents makes us especially confident in the accuracy and effectiveness of this edition.

Conducting the unit-opening interviews was again one of the great pleasures of revising *BIOLOGY*. For the Eighth Edition, we are proud to include interviews with Deborah Gordon, Paul Nurse, Terry Orr-Weaver, Scott Edwards, Sean Carroll, Pat Zambryski, Masashi Yanagisawa, and Diana Wall (see p. xi). We thank these busy people for generously sharing their experiences with us.

The value of *BIOLOGY* as a learning tool is greatly enhanced by the supplementary materials that have been created for instructors and students. We recognize that the dedicated authors of these materials are essentially writing mini (and not so mini) books. We much appreciate the hard work and creativity of the following: Ruth Buskirk and Christopher Gillen (authors of the new *Inquiry in Action: Interpreting Scientific Papers*); Judith Morgan and Eloise Brown Carter (*Investigating Biology*, 6th Edition); Jean Heitz and Cynthia Giffen (*Practicing Biology*, 3rd Edition); Margaret Waterman and Ethel Stanley (*Biological Inquiry: A Workbook of Investigative Cases*, 2nd Edition); Bill Barstow, Louise Paquin, Michael Dini, John Lepri, John Zarnetske, C. O. Patterson, and Jean DeSaix (*Test Bank*); Ed Zalisko, Margaret Ricci, Lauren Garner, Jung Choi, and Virginia White (*Media Quizzes*); Joan Sharp (*Lecture Outlines, PowerPoint Lectures*, and *Student Misconceptions*); Erin Barley (*PowerPoint Lectures*); Bill Wischusen, Ruth Buskirk, Jung Choi, John Merrill, Melissa Michael, Randy Phillis, Mark Lyford, and Chris Gregg (*Active Learning Questions*); and Laura Zanello (*Spanish Glossary*). Once again, we thank our long-time colleague Marty Taylor for her excellent work on the *Student Study Guide*; she has now completed eight editions of this popular student aid. Special thanks go to Tom Owens for his visionary work on the *BioFlix* animations and his creative, collaborative work as lead author on our new *MasteringBiology* tutorials. We also thank Brad Williamson, Jennifer Yeh, Dawn Keller, and Scott Bowling for their excellent work on the *BioFlix* animations and the accompanying student tools. In addition, we are grateful to the many other people—biology instructors, editors, artists, production experts, and narrators—who are listed in the credits for these and other elements of the electronic media that accompany the book. Finally, we thank the class testers and reviewers of *BioFlix* and *MasteringBiology* who are listed on pages xxv–xxvi.

BIOLOGY, Eighth Edition, results from an unusually strong synergy between a team of scientists and a team of publishing professionals. The expansion of the author team and major revision of many chapters, the creation of new pedagogical features and the improvement of old ones, and the exceptionally rich package of supplements created unprecedented challenges for the publishing team.

The members of our core editorial team at Benjamin Cummings—our Fab Five—brought unmatched talents, commitment, and pedagogical insights to this revision, and working with this team over the past three years has been a great pleasure. Our Editor-in-Chief, Beth Wilbur, continues to be a full colleague in the book's ongoing evolution and a respected advocate for biology education in the academic community. Our extraordinary Supervising Editors, Pat Burner and Beth Winickoff, once again had the awesome responsibility of overseeing in detail the work of all the authors, developmental editors, and developmental artists. Together, Beth and Pat ensured that every page of every chapter has the text, figures, and pedagogy to make this edition the most effective biology textbook ever. Deborah Gale, Executive Director of Development, and our Senior Editorial Manager, the incomparable Ginnie Simione Jutson, oversaw the entire project on a day-by-day basis, a feat equivalent to running a three-ring circus. Ginnie's patience and resourcefulness and Deborah's oversight of the project as a whole have enabled the entire book team to operate at a level of sanity that would not have been possible without their guidance.

We were fortunate to have on our team some of college publishing's top developmental editors. In addition to Beth Winickoff and Pat Burner (who did important hands-on editing themselves, as well as their many other tasks), the primary developmental editors for this edition were John Burner and Matt Lee, joined as the project progressed by Alice Fugate and Suzanne Olivier. We are deeply grateful to all our editors for making us better writers, teachers, and biologists.

Biology is a visual subject, and we are indebted to our developmental artists Hilair Chism, Carla Simmons, Andrew Recher, Connie Balek, and Kelly Murphy for helping us make all our figures better tools for teaching and learning—as well as visually appealing. In addition, the support of our bright, efficient, and good-natured Editorial Assistants—Julia Khait, Ben Pearson, and Logan Triglia—is much appreciated. We couldn't have finished the book without them! We also want to thank Robin Heyden for organizing the annual Benjamin Cummings Biology Leadership Conferences, which always bring us closer to the teaching community and offer a fresh supply of creative teaching ideas from outstanding biology educators.

You would not have a book in your hands today if not for the herculean efforts of the book production team, which has the crucial responsibility of converting the text manuscript and illustrations to pages ready for the printer. For the Eighth Edition, these efforts were headed up by Managing Editor Mike Early. We thank him, as well as our longtime copyeditor Janet Greenblatt, proofreaders Joanna Dinsmore and Marie Dartman, Permissions Editors Sue Ewing and Marcy Lunetta, and indexers Lynn Armstrong and Charlotte Shane. Handling the illustrations were Art Editors Laura Murray and Kelly Murphy; the final rendering of the new and revised illustrations was carried out by the artists of Precision Graphics, working under Kristina Seymour. Senior Photo Editor Donna Kalal and photo researcher Maureen Spuhler obtained a large number of handsome and informative photos for this edition. We are indebted to the entire art and photo team. For the beautiful design of the book's interior, we want to thank Art and Design Director Mark Ong and Design Manager Marilyn Perry for their design of text and art styles that show off the words and pictures in a way that will appeal to readers and help them learn. (And thanks to both of them for their endless patience with all our concerns!) For the user-friendly page layouts, we are grateful to Jennifer Dunn and Jana Anderson. And many thanks to Yvo Riezebos for designing the striking cover. Putting together all the pieces of this complicated book were the staff at S4Carlisle Publishing Services, led by Production Manager Lori Dalberg and Composition Supervisor Holly Paige. Thank you, Lori and Holly!

We are pleased to thank the topnotch publishing professionals who worked on the book's printed supplements: Senior Supplements Project Editor Susan Berge, who coordinated the entire print supplements package; Production Supervisor Jane Brundage; Developmental Editor Susan Weisberg; and Project Editors Mary Douglas, Kim Wimpsett, Elizabeth Campbell, and Melanie Field.

With regard to the wonderful package of electronic media that accompanies the book, we offer special thanks to Senior Media Producer Jon Ballard, Project Editors Nora Lally-Graves and Brienn Buchanan, media correlators Nina Lewallen Hufford and Sarah Kaminker, and proofreader Pete Shanks for their work on the website. We also are grateful to Associate Web Developer Linda Young and Web Technologies Manager Steve Wright. For their work on the *Instructor Resource CD/DVD-ROM*, we thank Project Manager James Bruce; Developmental Artist Hilair Chism; Developmental Editors John Burner, Pat Burner, Matt Lee, and Beth Winickoff; copyeditor John Hammett (*PPT Lectures*); proofreader Pete Shanks (*PPT Lectures*); and Donna King, Production Project Manager at Progressive Information Technologies.

We are especially grateful to the team of publishing professionals whose combined talents are evident in the *BioFlix* animations and student tools: Pat Burner, Russell Chun (storyboard artist extraordinaire), Ginnie Simione Jutson, Jon Ballard, Karen Gulliver (developmental editor), Animated Biomedical Productions (animation production); and Groove 11 (tutorial production). For their work on *MasteringBiology*, we thank the aforementioned Pat Burner, Ginnie Simione Jutson, and Jon Ballard, plus Tania Mlawer, Director of Content Development and Project Management; Mary Catherine Hager, Developmental Editor; Deb Greco, Media Producer; Kristen Sutton, Content Lead; and Developmental Artist Jay McElroy and the artists at Pearson Production Solutions. For their hard work and support, our appreciation goes to the MasteringX Team (in alphabetical order): Ruth Berry, Lewis Costas, Katherine Foley, Julia Henderson, Joseph Ignazi, Jeff King, David Kokorowski, Mary Lee, Claire Masson, Nissi Mathews, Adam Morton, Fred Mueller, Ian Nordby, Maria Panos, Andrea Pascarella, Mary Ann Perry, Caroline Power, Sarah Smith, Margaret Trombley, and Rasil Warnakulasooriya. Last, but not least, we thank Lauren Fogel, Director of Media Development at Benjamin Cummings, for her continued leadership on all things media.

For their important roles in marketing the book, we are very grateful to Director of Marketing Christy Lawrence, Executive Marketing Manager Lauren Harp, and Market Development Manager Josh Frost. For the creation of visually stunning print and electronic promotional materials, we thank Creative Director Lillian Carr; Marketing Communication Specialists Jane Campbell, Kristi Hlaing, and Jessica Perry; Designer Laurie Campbell; Web Designer Mansour Bethoney, who led the creation of the e-brochure; and Webmaster Anna Molodtsova.

Linda Davis, President of Pearson Math, Economics, and Science, has shared our commitment to excellence and provided strong support for four editions now, and we are happy to thank her once again. We also want to thank Paul Corey, now President of Pearson Science, for his enthusiasm, encouragement, and support.

The Pearson Science sales team, which represents *BIOLOGY* on campus, is our living link to the students and professors who use the text. The field representatives tell us what you like and don't like about the book, and they provide prompt service to biology departments. They are strong allies in biology education, and we thank them for their professionalism in communicating the features of our book. For representing our book and its teaching values to our wider international audience, we thank the sustained work of our sales and marketing partners throughout the world, including (but by no means only) Marlene Olsavsky, Ann Oravetz, and Pablo Rendina.

Finally, we wish to thank our families and friends for their encouragement and patience throughout this long project. Our special thanks to: Paul, Dan, Maria, Armelle, and Sean (J.R.); Lily, Grant, Ross, Lilytoo, and Alex (L.U.); Debra and Hannah (M.C.); Harry, Elga, Aaron, Sophie, Noah, and Gabriele (S.W.); Natalie (P.M.); and Sally, Robert, David, and Will (R.J.). And as always, Rochelle and Allison.

Jane Reece, Lisa Urry, Michael Cain,
Steve Wasserman, Peter Minorsky, and Rob Jackson

Detailed Contents

UNIT THREE

Genetics 246

UNIT FOUR

Mechanisms of Evolution   450

Introduction: Themes in the Study of Life

1

▲ **Figure 1.1 What properties of life are demonstrated by this flower?**

OVERVIEW

Inquiring About the World of Life

The flower featured on the cover of this book and in **Figure 1.1** is from a magnolia, a tree of ancient lineage that is native to Asian and American forests. The magnolia blossom is a sign of the plant's status as a living organism, for flowers contain organs of sexual reproduction, and reproduction is a key property of life, as you will learn later.

Like all organisms, the magnolia tree in **Figure 1.2** is living in close association with other organisms, though it is a lone specimen far from its ancestral forest. For example, it depends on beetles to carry pollen from one flower to another, and the beetles, in turn, eat from its flowers. The flowers are adapted to the beetles in several ways: Their bowl shape allows easy access, and their multiple reproductive organs and tough petals (see Figure 1.1) help ensure that some survive the voracious beetles. Such adaptations are the result of **evolution**, the process of change that has transformed life on Earth from its earliest beginnings to the diversity of organisms living today. As discussed later in this chapter, evolution is the fundamental organizing principle of biology and the main theme of this book.

Although biologists know a great deal about magnolias and other plants, many mysteries remain. For instance, what exactly led to the origin of flowering plants? Posing questions about the living world and seeking science-based answers—scientific inquiry—are the central activities of **biology**, the sci-entific study of life. Biologists' questions can be ambitious. They may ask how a single tiny cell becomes a tree or a dog, how the human mind works, or how the different forms of life in a forest interact. Can you think of some questions about living organisms that interest you? When you do, you are already starting to think like a biologist. More than anything else, biology is a quest, an ongoing inquiry about the nature of life.

Perhaps some of your questions relate to health or to societal or environmental issues. Biology is woven into the fabric of our culture more than ever before and can help answer many questions that affect our lives. Research breakthroughs in genetics and cell biology are transforming medicine and agriculture. Neuroscience and evolutionary biology are re-shaping psychology and sociology. New models in ecology are helping societies evaluate environmental issues, such as global warming. There has never been a more important time to embark on a study of life.

▲ **Figure 1.2 A magnolia tree in early spring.**

1

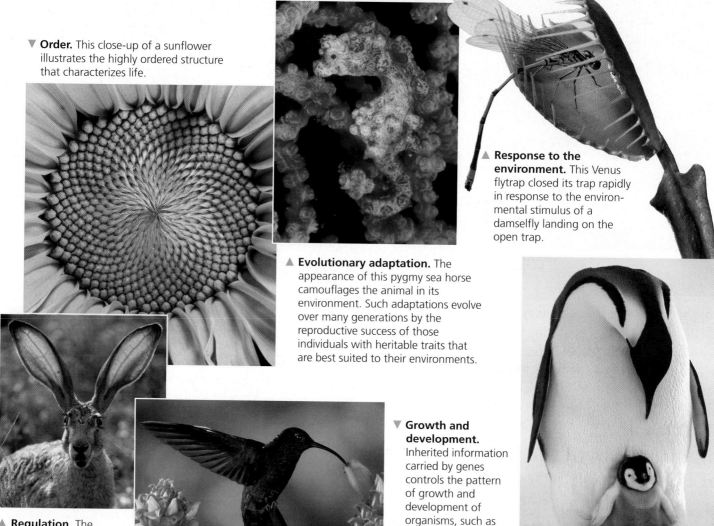

▼ **Order.** This close-up of a sunflower illustrates the highly ordered structure that characterizes life.

▲ **Response to the environment.** This Venus flytrap closed its trap rapidly in response to the environmental stimulus of a damselfly landing on the open trap.

▲ **Evolutionary adaptation.** The appearance of this pygmy sea horse camouflages the animal in its environment. Such adaptations evolve over many generations by the reproductive success of those individuals with heritable traits that are best suited to their environments.

▼ **Growth and development.** Inherited information carried by genes controls the pattern of growth and development of organisms, such as this Nile crocodile.

▲ **Regulation.** The regulation of blood flow through the blood vessels of this jackrabbit's ears helps maintain a constant body temperature by adjusting heat exchange with the surrounding air.

▲ **Energy processing.** This hummingbird obtains fuel in the form of nectar from flowers. The hummingbird will use chemical energy stored in its food to power flight and other work.

▲ **Reproduction.** Organisms (living things) reproduce their own kind. Here an emperor penguin protects its baby.

▲ **Figure 1.3 Some properties of life.**

? *Is a gasoline-powered lawn mower alive? Which of these properties does it have? Which properties does it lack?*

But what is life? Even a small child realizes that a dog or a plant is alive, while a rock is not. Yet the phenomenon we call life defies a simple, one-sentence definition. We recognize life by what living things do. **Figure 1.3** highlights some of the properties and processes we associate with life.

While limited to a handful of images, Figure 1.3 reminds us that the living world is wondrously varied. How do biologists make sense of this diversity and complexity? This opening chapter sets up a framework for answering this question. The first part of the chapter provides a panoramic view of the biological "landscape," organized around some unifying themes. We then focus on biology's overarching theme, evolution, with an introduction to the reasoning that led Charles Darwin to his explanatory theory. Finally, we look at scientific inquiry—how scientists raise and attempt to answer questions about the natural world.

Themes connect the concepts of biology

Biology is a subject of enormous scope, and anyone who follows the news knows that biological knowledge is expanding at an ever-increasing rate. Simply memorizing the factual details of this huge subject is not a reasonable option. How, then, can you, as a student, go beyond the facts to develop a coherent view of life? One approach is to fit the many things you learn into a set of themes that pervade all of biology—ways of thinking about life that will still apply decades from now. Focusing on a few big ideas will help you organize and make sense of all the information you'll encounter as you study biology. To help you, we have selected seven unifying themes to serve as touchstones as you proceed through this book.

Evolution, the Overarching Theme of Biology

Evolution is biology's core theme—the one idea that makes sense of everything we know about living organisms. Life has been evolving on Earth for billions of years, resulting in a vast diversity of past and present organisms. But along with the diversity we find many shared features. For example, while the sea horse, jackrabbit, hummingbird, crocodile, and penguins in Figure 1.3 look very different, their skeletons are basically similar. The scientific explanation for this unity and diversity—and for the suitability of organisms to their environments—is evolution: the idea that the organisms living on Earth today are the modified descendants of common ancestors. In other words, we can explain traits shared by two organisms with the idea that they have descended from a common ancestor, and we can account for differences with the idea that heritable changes have occurred along the way. Many kinds of evidence support the occurrence of evolution and the theory that describes how it takes place. We'll return to evolution later in the chapter, after surveying some other themes and painting a fuller picture of the scope of biology.

Theme: New properties emerge at each level in the biological hierarchy

The study of life extends from the microscopic scale of the molecules and cells that make up organisms to the global scale of the entire living planet. We can divide this enormous range into different levels of biological organization.

Imagine zooming in from space to take a closer and closer look at life on Earth. It is spring, and our destination is a forest in Ontario, Canada, where we will eventually explore a maple leaf right down to the molecular level. **Figure 1.4** (on the next two pages) narrates this journey into life, with the circled numbers leading you through the levels of biological organization illustrated by the photographs.

Emergent Properties

If we now zoom back out from the molecular level in Figure 1.4, we can see that novel properties emerge at each step, properties that are not present at the preceding level. These **emergent properties** are due to the arrangement and interactions of parts as complexity increases. For example, if you make a test-tube mixture of chlorophyll and all the other kinds of molecules found in a chloroplast, photosynthesis will not occur. Photosynthesis can take place only when the molecules are arranged in a specific way in an intact chloroplast. To take another example, if a serious head injury disrupts the intricate architecture of a human brain, the mind may cease to function properly even though all of the brain parts are still present. Our thoughts and memories are emergent properties of a complex network of nerve cells. At a much higher level of biological organization—at the ecosystem level—the recycling of chemical elements essential to life, such as carbon, depends on a network of diverse organisms interacting with each other and with the soil, water, and air.

Emergent properties are not unique to life. We can see the importance of arrangement in the distinction between a box of bicycle parts and a working bicycle. And while graphite and diamonds are both pure carbon, they have very different properties because their carbon atoms are arranged differently. But compared to such nonliving examples, the unrivaled complexity of biological systems makes the emergent properties of life especially challenging to study.

The Power and Limitations of Reductionism

Because the properties of life emerge from complex organization, scientists seeking to understand biological systems confront a dilemma. On the one hand, we cannot fully explain a higher level of order by breaking it down into its parts. A dissected animal no longer functions; a cell reduced to its chemical ingredients is no longer a cell. Disrupting a living system interferes with its functioning. On the other hand, something as complex as an organism or a cell cannot be analyzed without taking it apart.

Reductionism—the reduction of complex systems to simpler components that are more manageable to study—is a powerful strategy in biology. For example, by studying the molecular structure of DNA that had been extracted from cells, James Watson and Francis Crick inferred, in 1953, how this molecule could serve as the chemical basis of inheritance. The central role of DNA in cells and organisms became better understood, however, when scientists were able to study the interactions of DNA with other molecules. Biologists must balance the reductionist strategy with the larger-scale, holistic objective of understanding emergent properties—how the parts of cells, organisms, and higher levels of order, such as ecosystems, work together. At the cutting edge of research today is the approach called systems biology.

Exploring Levels of Biological Organization

◄ 1 The Biosphere

As soon as we are near enough to Earth to make out its continents and oceans, we begin to see signs of life—in the green mosaic of the planet's forests, for example. This is our first view of the biosphere, which consists of all the environments on Earth that are inhabited by life. The biosphere includes most regions of land, most bodies of water, and the atmosphere to an altitude of several kilometers.

◄ 2 Ecosystems

As we approach Earth's surface for an imaginary landing in Ontario, we can begin to make out a forest with an abundance of deciduous trees (trees that lose their leaves in one season and grow new ones in another). Such a deciduous forest is an example of an ecosystem. Grasslands, deserts, and the ocean's coral reefs are other types of ecosystems. An ecosystem consists of all the living things in a particular area, along with all the nonliving components of the environment with which life interacts, such as soil, water, atmospheric gases, and light. All of Earth's ecosystems combined make up the biosphere.

► 3 Communities

The entire array of organisms inhabiting a particular ecosystem is called a biological community. The community in our forest ecosystem includes many kinds of trees and other plants, a diversity of animals, various mushrooms and other fungi, and enormous numbers of diverse microorganisms, which are living forms, such as bacteria, that are too small to see without a microscope. Each of these forms of life is called a *species*.

► 4 Populations

A population consists of all the individuals of a species living within the bounds of a specified area. For example, our Ontario forest includes a population of sugar maple trees and a population of white-tailed deer. We can now refine our definition of a community as the set of populations that inhabit a particular area.

▲ 5 Organisms

Individual living things are called organisms. Each of the maple trees and other plants in the forest is an organism, and so is each forest animal, such as a frog, squirrel, deer, and beetle. The soil teems with microorganisms such as bacteria.

▼ 6 Organs and Organ Systems

The structural hierarchy of life continues to unfold as we explore the architecture of the more complex organisms. A maple leaf is an example of an organ, a body part consisting of two or more tissues (which we'll see upon our next scale change). An organ carries out a particular function in the body. Stems and roots are the other major organs of plants. Examples of human organs are the brain, heart, and kidney. The organs of humans, other complex animals, and plants are organized into organ systems, each a team of organs that cooperate in a specific function. For example, the human digestive system includes such organs as the tongue, stomach, and intestines.

▼ 8 Cells

The cell is life's fundamental unit of structure and function. Some organisms, such as amoebas and most bacteria, are single cells. Other organisms, including plants and animals, are multicellular. Instead of a single cell performing all the functions of life, a multicellular organism has a division of labor among specialized cells. A human body consists of trillions of microscopic cells of many different kinds, such as muscle cells and nerve cells, which are organized into the various specialized tissues. For example, muscle tissue consists of bundles of muscle cells. In the photo below, we see a more highly magnified view of some of the cells in a leaf tissue. Each of the cells is only about 25 micrometers (μm) across. It would take more than 700 of these cells to reach across a penny. As small as these cells are, you can see that each contains numerous green structures called chloroplasts, which are responsible for photosynthesis.

10 μm   Cell

▼ 9 Organelles

Chloroplasts are examples of organelles, the various functional components that make up cells. In this image, a very powerful tool called an electron microscope brings a single chloroplast into sharp focus.

1 μm

Atoms

► 7 Tissues

Our next scale change—to see a leaf's tissues—requires a microscope. The leaf shown here has been cut on an angle. The honeycombed tissue in the interior of the leaf (left portion of photo) is the main location of photosynthesis, the process that converts light energy to the chemical energy of sugar and other food. We are viewing the sliced leaf from a perspective that also enables us to see the jigsaw puzzle–like tissue called epidermis, the "skin" on the surface of the leaf (right part of photo). The pores through the epidermis allow the gas carbon dioxide, a raw material for sugar production, to reach the photosynthetic tissue inside the leaf. At this scale, we can also see that each tissue has a cellular structure. In fact, each kind of tissue is a group of similar cells.

50 μm

► 10 Molecules

Our last scale change vaults us into a chloroplast for a view of life at the molecular level. A molecule is a chemical structure consisting of two or more small chemical units called *atoms*, which are represented as balls in this computer graphic of a chlorophyll molecule. Chlorophyll is the pigment molecule that makes a maple leaf green. One of the most important molecules on Earth, chlorophyll absorbs sunlight during the first step of photosynthesis. Within each chloroplast, millions of chlorophylls and other molecules are organized into the equipment that converts light energy to the chemical energy of food.

Systems Biology

A system is simply a combination of components that function together. A biologist can study a system at any level of organization. A single leaf cell can be considered a system, as can a frog, an ant colony, or a desert ecosytem. To understand how such systems work, it is not enough to have a "parts list," even a complete one. Realizing this, many researchers are now complementing the reductionist approach with new strategies for studying whole systems. This changing perspective is analogous to moving from ground level on a street corner to a helicopter high above a city, from which you can see how variables such as time of day, construction projects, accidents, and traffic-signal malfunctions affect traffic throughout the city.

The goal of **systems biology** is to construct models for the dynamic behavior of whole biological systems. Successful models enable biologists to predict how a change in one or more variables will affect other components and the whole system. Thus, the systems approach enables us to pose new kinds of questions. How might a drug that lowers blood pressure affect the functions of organs throughout the human body? How might increasing a crop's water supply affect processes in the plants, such as the storage of molecules essential for human nutrition? How might a gradual increase in atmospheric carbon dioxide alter ecosystems and the entire biosphere? The ultimate aim of systems biology is to answer big questions like the last one.

Systems biology is relevant to the study of life at all levels. During the early years of the 20th century, biologists studying animal physiology (functioning) began integrating data on how multiple organs coordinate processes such as the regulation of sugar concentration in the blood. And in the 1960s, scientists investigating ecosystems pioneered a more mathematically sophisticated systems approach with elaborate models diagramming the network of interactions between organisms and nonliving components of ecosystems such as salt marshes. Such models have already been useful for predicting the responses of these systems to changing variables. More recently, systems biology has taken hold at the cellular and molecular levels, as we'll describe later when we discuss DNA.

Theme: Organisms interact with their environments, exchanging matter and energy

Turn back again to Figure 1.4, this time focusing on the forest. In this or any other ecosystem, each organism interacts continuously with its environment, which includes both nonliving factors and other organisms. A tree, for example, absorbs water and minerals from the soil, through its roots. At the same time, its leaves take in carbon dioxide from the air and use sunlight absorbed by chlorophyll to drive photosynthesis, converting water and carbon dioxide to sugar and oxygen. The tree releases oxygen to the air, and its roots help form soil by breaking up rocks. Both organism and environment are affected by the interactions between them. The tree also interacts with other organisms, such as soil microorganisms associated with its roots and animals that eat its leaves and fruit.

Ecosystem Dynamics

The operation of any ecosystem involves two major processes. One process is the cycling of nutrients. For example, minerals acquired by a tree will eventually be returned to the soil by organisms that decompose leaf litter, dead roots, and other organic debris. The second major process in an ecosystem is the one-way flow of energy from sunlight to producers to consumers. Producers are plants and other photosynthetic organisms, which use light energy to make sugar. Consumers are organisms, such as animals, that feed on producers and other consumers. The diagram in **Figure 1.5** outlines the two processes acting in an African ecosystem.

Energy Conversion

Moving, growing, reproducing, and the other activities of life are work, and work requires energy. The exchange of energy between an organism and its surroundings often involves the transformation of one form of energy to another. For example, the leaves of a plant absorb light energy and convert it to chemical energy stored in sugar molecules. When an animal's muscle cells use sugar as fuel to power movements, they convert chemical energy to kinetic energy, the energy of motion. And

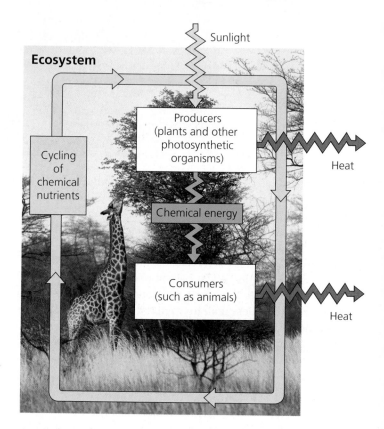

▲ Figure 1.5 **Nutrient cycling and energy flow in an ecosystem.**

(a) A bird's wings have an aerodynamically efficient shape.

(b) Wing bones have a honeycombed internal structure that is strong but lightweight.

100 µm

(c) The flight muscles are controlled by neurons (nerve cells), which transmit signals. With long extensions, neurons are especially well structured for communication within the body.

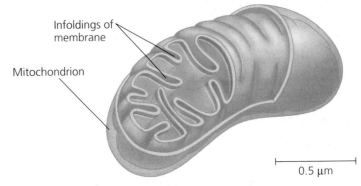

Infoldings of membrane

Mitochondrion

0.5 µm

(d) The flight muscles obtain energy in a usable form from organelles called mitochondria. A mitochondrion has an inner membrane with many infoldings. Molecules embedded in the inner membrane carry out many of the steps in energy production, and the infoldings pack a large amount of this membrane into a small container.

▲ **Figure 1.6 Form fits function in a gull's wing.** A bird's build and the structures of its components make flight possible.
? *How does form fit function in a human hand?*

in all these energy conversions, some of the energy is converted to thermal energy, which dissipates to the surroundings as heat. In contrast to chemical nutrients, which recycle within an ecosystem, energy flows through an ecosystem, usually entering as light and exiting as heat (see Figure 1.5).

Theme: Structure and function are correlated at all levels of biological organization

Another theme evident in Figure 1.4 is the idea that form fits function, which you'll recognize from everyday life. For example, a screwdriver is suited to tighten or loosen screws, a hammer to pound nails. How a device works is correlated with its structure. Applied to biology, this theme is a guide to the anatomy of life at all its structural levels. An example from Figure 1.4 is seen in the leaf: Its thin, flat shape maximizes the amount of sunlight that can be captured by its chloroplasts. Analyzing a biological structure gives us clues about what it does and how it works. Conversely, knowing the function of something provides insight into its construction. An example from the animal kingdom, the wing of a bird, provides additional instances of the structure-function theme **(Figure 1.6)**. In exploring life on its different structural levels, we discover functional beauty at every turn.

Theme: Cells are an organism's basic units of structure and function

In life's structural hierarchy, the cell has a special place as the lowest level of organization that can perform all activities required for life. Moreover, the activities of organisms are all based on the activities of cells. For instance, the division of cells to form new cells is the basis for all reproduction and for the growth and repair of multicellular organisms **(Figure 1.7)**. To

25 µm

▲ **Figure 1.7 A lung cell from a newt divides into two smaller cells that will grow and divide again.**

cite another example, the movement of your eyes as you read this line is based on activities of muscle and nerve cells. Even a global process such as the recycling of carbon is the cumulative product of cellular activities, including the photosynthesis that occurs in the chloroplasts of leaf cells. Understanding how cells work is a major focus of biological research.

All cells share certain characteristics. For example, every cell is enclosed by a membrane that regulates the passage of materials between the cell and its surroundings. And every cell uses DNA as its genetic information. However, we can distinguish between two main forms of cells: prokaryotic cells and eukaryotic cells. The cells of two groups of microorganisms called bacteria and archaea are prokaryotic. All other forms of life, including plants and animals, are composed of eukaryotic cells.

A **eukaryotic cell** is subdivided by internal membranes into various membrane-enclosed organelles, such as the ones you see in **Figure 1.8** and the chloroplast you saw in Figure 1.4. In most eukaryotic cells, the largest organelle is the nucleus, which contains the cell's DNA. The other organelles are located in the cytoplasm, the entire region between the nucleus and outer membrane of the cell. As Figure 1.8 also shows, prokaryotic cells are much simpler and generally smaller than eukaryotic cells. In a **prokaryotic cell**, the DNA is not separated from the rest of the cell by enclosure in a membrane-bounded nucleus. Prokaryotic cells also lack the other kinds of membrane-enclosed organelles that characterize eukaryotic cells. But whether an organism has prokaryotic or eukaryotic cells, its structure and function depend on cells.

Eukaryotic cell

Membrane

Cytoplasm

Organelles

Nucleus (contains DNA)

Prokaryotic cell

DNA
(no nucleus)

Membrane

1 μm

▲ **Figure 1.8 Contrasting eukaryotic and prokaryotic cells in size and complexity.**

Theme: The continuity of life is based on heritable information in the form of DNA

Inside the dividing cell in Figure 1.7 (on the previous page), you can see structures called chromosomes, which are stained with a blue-glowing dye. The chromosomes have almost all of the cell's genetic material, its **DNA** (short for deoxyribonucleic acid). DNA is the substance of **genes**, the units of inheritance that transmit information from parents to offspring. Your blood group (A, B, AB, or O), for example, is the result of certain genes that you inherited from your parents.

DNA Structure and Function

Each chromosome has one very long DNA molecule, with hundreds or thousands of genes arranged along its length. The DNA of chromosomes replicates as a cell prepares to divide, and each of the two cellular offspring inherits a complete set of genes.

Each of us began life as a single cell stocked with DNA inherited from our parents. Replication of that DNA with each round of cell division transmitted copies of it to our trillions of cells. In each cell, the genes along the length of the DNA molecules encode the information for building the cell's other molecules. In this way, DNA controls the development and maintenance of the entire organism and, indirectly, everything it does **(Figure 1.9)**. The DNA serves as a central database.

The molecular structure of DNA accounts for its ability to store information. Each DNA molecule is made up of two long chains arranged in a double helix. Each chain link is one of four kinds of chemical building blocks called nucleotides **(Figure 1.10)**. The way DNA encodes information is analogous to the way we arrange the letters of the alphabet into precise sequences with specific meanings. The word *rat*, for example, evokes a rodent; the words *tar* and *art*, which contain the same letters, mean very different things. Libraries are filled with books containing information encoded in varying sequences of only 26 letters. We can think of nucleotides as the alphabet of inheritance. Specific sequential arrangements of these four chemical letters encode the precise information in genes, which are typically hundreds or thousands of nucleotides long. One gene in a bacterial cell may be translated as "Build a certain component of the cell membrane." A particular human gene may mean "Make growth hormone."

More generally, genes like those just mentioned program the cell's production of large molecules called proteins. Other human proteins include a muscle cell's contraction proteins and the defensive proteins called antibodies. A class of proteins crucial to all cells are enzymes, which catalyze (speed up) specific chemical reactions. Thus, DNA provides the blueprints, and proteins serve as the tools that actually build and maintain the cell and carry out its activities.

The DNA of genes controls protein production indirectly, using a related kind of molecule called RNA as an intermediary.

▲ Figure 1.9 Inherited DNA directs development of an organism.

Sperm cell

Nuclei containing DNA

Egg cell

Fertilized egg with DNA from both parents

Embyro's cells with copies of inherited DNA

Offspring with traits inherited from both parents

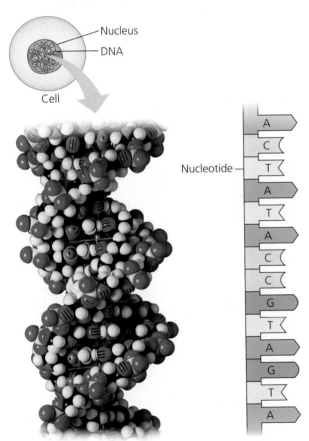

Nucleus

DNA

Cell

Nucleotide

A
C
T
A
T
A
C
C
G
T
A
G
T
A

(a) DNA double helix. This model shows each atom in a segment of DNA. Made up of two long chains of building blocks called nucleotides, a DNA molecule takes the three-dimensional form of a double helix.

(b) Single strand of DNA. These geometric shapes and letters are simple symbols for the nucleotides in a small section of one chain of a DNA molecule. Genetic information is encoded in specific sequences of the four types of nucleotides. (Their names are abbreviated here as A, T, C, and G.)

▲ Figure 1.10 DNA: The genetic material.

The sequence of nucleotides along a gene is transcribed into RNA, which is then translated into a specific protein with a unique shape and function. In the translation process, all forms of life employ essentially the same genetic code. A particular sequence of nucleotides says the same thing to one organism as it does to another. Differences between organisms reflect differences between their nucleotide sequences.

Not all RNA in the cell is translated into protein. We have known for decades that some types of RNA molecules are actually components of the cellular machinery that manufactures proteins. Recently, scientists have discovered whole new classes of RNA that play other roles in the cell, such as regulating the functioning of protein-coding genes.

The entire "library" of genetic instructions that an organism inherits is called its **genome**. A typical human cell has two similar sets of chromosomes, and each set has DNA totaling about 3 billion nucleotides. If the one-letter symbols for these nucleotides were written in letters the size of those you are now reading, the genetic text would fill about 600 books the size of this one. Within this genomic library of nucleotide sequences are genes for about 75,000 kinds of proteins and an as yet unknown number of RNA molecules.

Systems Biology at the Levels of Cells and Molecules

The entire sequence of nucleotides in the human genome is now known, along with the genome sequences of many other organisms, including bacteria, archaea, fungi, plants, and animals. These accomplishments have been made possible by the development of new methods and DNA-sequencing machines, such as those shown in **Figure 1.11**, on the next page.

The sequencing of the human genome is a scientific and technological achievement comparable to landing the *Apollo* astronauts on the moon in 1969. But it is only the beginning of

► **Figure 1.11 Modern biology as an information science.** Automatic DNA-sequencing machines and abundant computing power made the sequencing of the human genome possible. This facility in Walnut Creek, California, was one of many labs that collaborated in the international Human Genome Project.

an even bigger research endeavor, an effort to learn how the activities of the myriad proteins encoded by the DNA are co-ordinated in cells and whole organisms.

The best way to make sense of the deluge of data from genome-sequencing projects and the growing catalog of known protein functions is to apply a systems approach at the cellular and molecular levels. **Figure 1.12** illustrates the re-sults of a large study that mapped a network of protein inter-actions within a cell of a fruit fly, a popular research organism. The model is based on a database of thousands of known pro-teins and their known interactions with other proteins. For ex-ample, protein A may attach to and alter the activities of proteins B, C, and D, which then go on to interact with still other proteins. The figure maps these protein partnerships to their cellular locales.

The basics of the systems strategy are straightforward. First, it is necessary to inventory as many parts of the system as possible, such as all the known genes and proteins in a cell (an application of reductionism). Then it is necessary to in-vestigate how each part behaves in relation to others in the working system—all the protein-protein interactions, in the case of our fly cell example. Finally, with the help of comput-ers and specialized software, it is possible to pool all the data into the kind of system network pictured in Figure 1.12.

Though the basic idea of systems biology is simple, the prac-tice is not, as you would expect from the complexity of biolog-ical systems. It has taken three key research developments to bring systems biology within reach. One is "high-throughput" technology, tools that can analyze biological materials very rapidly and produce enormous amounts of data. The auto-matic DNA-sequencing machines that made the sequencing of

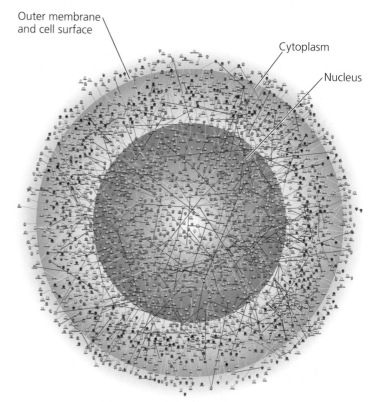

Outer membrane and cell surface

Cytoplasm

Nucleus

▲ **Figure 1.12 A systems map of interactions among proteins in a cell.** This diagram maps 2,346 proteins (dots) and their network of interactions (lines connecting the proteins) in a fruit fly cell. Systems biologists develop such models from huge databases of information about molecules and their interactions in the cell. A major goal of this systems approach is to use the models to predict how one change, such as an increase in the activity of a particular protein, can ripple through the cell's molecular circuitry to cause other changes. The total number of proteins in this type of cell is probably in the range of 4,000 to 7,000.

the human genome possible are examples of high-throughput devices (see Figure 1.11). The second is **bioinformatics**, which is the use of computational tools to store, organize, and analyze the huge volume of data that result from high-throughput methods. The third key development is the formation of inter-disciplinary research teams—melting pots of diverse specialists that may include computer scientists, mathematicians, engineers, chemists, physicists, and, of course, biologists from a variety of fields.

Theme: Feedback mechanisms regulate biological systems

A kind of supply-and-demand economy applies to many biological systems. Consider your muscles, for instance. When your muscle cells require more energy during exercise, they increase their consumption of the sugar molecules that provide fuel. In contrast, when you rest, a different set of chemical reactions converts surplus sugar to storage molecules.

Like most of the cell's chemical processes, those that decompose or store sugar are accelerated, or catalyzed, by the specialized proteins called enzymes. Each type of enzyme catalyzes a specific chemical reaction. In many cases, these reactions are linked into chemical pathways, each step with its own enzyme. How does the cell coordinate its various chemical pathways? In our example of sugar management, how does the cell match fuel supply to demand, regulating its opposing pathways of sugar consumption and storage? The key is the ability of many biological processes to self-regulate by a mechanism called feedback.

In feedback regulation, the output, or product, of a process regulates that very process. In life, the most common form of regulation is **negative feedback**, in which accumulation of an end product of a process slows that process. For example, the cell's breakdown of sugar generates chemical energy in the form of a substance called ATP. When a cell makes more ATP than it can use, the excess ATP "feeds back" and inhibits an enzyme near the beginning of the pathway **(Figure 1.13a)**.

Though less common than processes regulated by negative feedback, there are also many biological processes regulated by **positive feedback**, in which an end product *speeds up* its production **(Figure 1.13b)**. The clotting of your blood in response to injury is an example. When a blood vessel is damaged, structures in the blood called platelets begin to aggregate at the site. Positive feedback occurs as chemicals released by the platelets attract *more* platelets. The platelet pile then initiates a complex process that seals the wound with a clot.

Feedback is a regulatory motif common to life at all levels, from the molecular level to ecosystems and the biosphere. Such regulation is an example of the integration that makes living systems much greater than the sum of their parts.

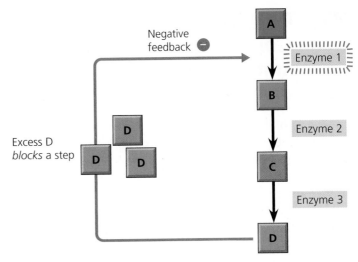

(a) Negative feedback. This three-step chemical pathway converts substance A to substance D. A specific enzyme catalyzes each chemical reaction. Accumulation of the final product (D) inhibits the first enzyme in the sequence, thus slowing down production of more D.

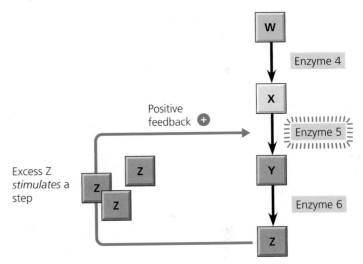

(b) Positive feedback. In a biochemical pathway regulated by positive feedback, a product stimulates an enzyme in the reaction sequence, increasing the rate of production of the product.

▲ **Figure 1.13 Regulation by feedback mechanisms.**
? *What would happen if enzyme 2 were missing?*

CONCEPT CHECK **1.1**

1. For each biological level in Figure 1.4, write a sentence that includes the next "lower" level. Example: "A community consists of *populations* of the various species inhabiting a specific area."
2. What theme or themes are exemplified by (a) the sharp spines of a porcupine, (b) the cloning of a plant from a single cell, and (c) a hummingbird using sugar to power its flight?
3. **WHAT IF?** For each theme discussed in this section, give an example not mentioned in the book.

For suggested answers, see Appendix A.

CONCEPT 1.2
The Core Theme: Evolution accounts for the unity and diversity of life

The list of biological themes discussed under Concept 1.1 is not absolute; some people might find a shorter or longer list more useful. There is consensus among biologists, however, as to the core theme of biology: It is evolution. To quote one of the founders of modern evolutionary theory, Theodosius Dobzhansky, "Nothing in biology makes sense except in the light of evolution."

In addition to encompassing a hierarchy of size scales from molecules to the biosphere, biology extends across the great diversity of species that have ever lived on Earth. To under-stand Dobzhansky's statement, we need to discuss how biologists think about this vast diversity.

Organizing the Diversity of Life

Diversity is a hallmark of life. Biologists have so far identified and named about 1.8 million species. To date, this diversity of life is known to include at least 6,300 species of prokaryotes (organisms with prokaryotic cells), 100,000 fungi, 290,000 plants, 52,000 vertebrates (animals with backbones), and 1 million insects (more than half of all known forms of life). Researchers identify thousands of additional species each year. Estimates of the total number of species range from about 10 million to over 100 million. Whatever the actual number, the enormous variety of life gives biology a very broad scope. Biologists face a major challenge in attempting to make sense of this variety **(Figure 1.14)**.

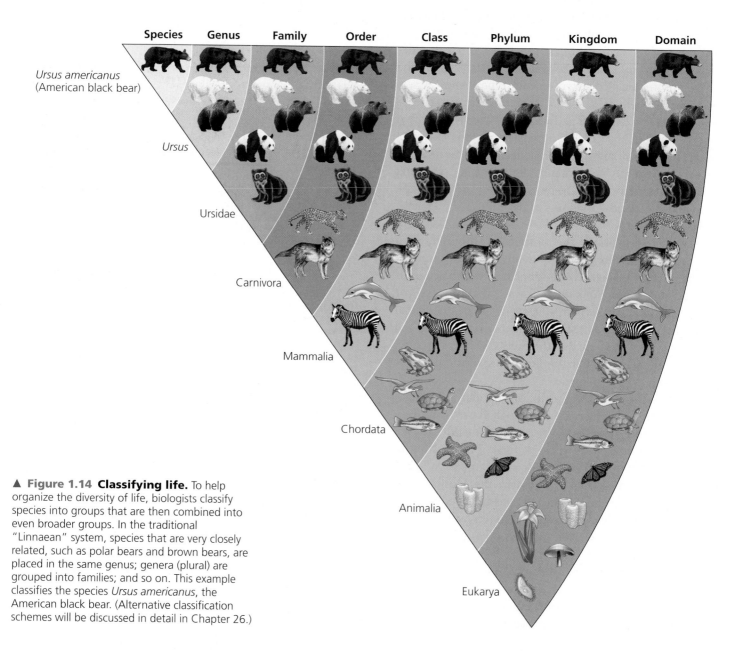

▲ **Figure 1.14 Classifying life.** To help organize the diversity of life, biologists classify species into groups that are then combined into even broader groups. In the traditional "Linnaean" system, species that are very closely related, such as polar bears and brown bears, are placed in the same genus; genera (plural) are grouped into families; and so on. This example classifies the species *Ursus americanus*, the American black bear. (Alternative classification schemes will be discussed in detail in Chapter 26.)

(a) DOMAIN BACTERIA

▼ **Bacteria** are the most diverse and widespread prokaryotes and are now divided among multiple kingdoms. Each of the rod-shaped structures in this photo is a bacterial cell.

2 μm

(b) DOMAIN ARCHAEA

▼ Many of the prokaryotes known as **archaea** live in Earth's extreme environments, such as salty lakes and boiling hot springs. Domain Archaea includes multiple kingdoms. The photo shows a colony composed of many cells.

0.5 μm

(c) DOMAIN EUKARYA

100 μm

▲ **Protists** (multiple kingdoms) are unicellular eukaryotes and their relatively simple multicellular relatives. Pictured here is an assortment of protists inhabiting pond water. Scientists are currently debating how to assign the protists to kingdoms that accurately reflect their evolutionary relationships.

▶ **Kingdom Fungi** is defined in part by the nutritional mode of its members, such as this mushroom, which absorb nutrients from their surroundings.

▲ **Kingdom Plantae** consists of multicellular eukaryotes that carry out photosynthesis, the conversion of light energy to the chemical energy in food.

▼ **Kingdom Animalia** consists of multicellular eukaryotes that ingest other organisms.

▲ **Figure 1.15 The three domains of life.**

Grouping Species: The Basic Idea

There is a human tendency to group diverse items according to similarities. For instance, perhaps you organize your music collection by artist. And then maybe you group the various artists into broader categories, such as rock, jazz, and classical. In the same way, grouping species that are similar is natural for us. We may speak of squirrels and butterflies, though we recognize that many different species belong to each group. We may even sort groups into broader categories, such as rodents (which include squirrels) and insects (which include butterflies). Taxonomy, the branch of biology that names and classifies species, formalizes this ordering of species into groups of increasing breadth (see Figure 1.14). You will learn more about this taxonomic scheme in Chapter 26. For now, we will focus on kingdoms and domains, the broadest units of classification.

The Three Domains of Life

Until a few decades ago, most biologists adopted a taxonomic scheme that divided the diversity of life into five kingdoms: plants, animals, fungi, single-celled eukaryotic organisms, and prokaryotes. Since then, new methods, such as comparisons of DNA sequences from different species, have led to an ongoing reevaluation of the number and boundaries of kingdoms. Researchers have proposed anywhere from six kingdoms to dozens of kingdoms. But as debate continues at the kingdom level, there is a consensus that the kingdoms of life can now be grouped into three even higher levels of classification called domains. The three domains are named Bacteria, Archaea, and Eukarya (**Figure 1.15**).

The organisms making up **domain Bacteria** and **domain Archaea** are all prokaryotic. Most prokaryotes are single-celled and microscopic. In the five-kingdom system, bacteria and archaea were combined in a single kingdom because they shared the prokaryotic form of cell structure. But much evidence now supports the view that bacteria and archaea represent two very distinct branches of prokaryotic life, different in key ways that you'll learn about in Chapter 27. There is also evidence that archaea are at least as closely related to eukaryotic organisms as they are to bacteria.

All the eukaryotes (organisms with eukaryotic cells) are now grouped in **domain Eukarya**. In the era of the five-kingdom scheme, most single-celled eukaryotes, such as the microorganisms known as protozoans, were placed in a single kingdom, "Protista." Many biologists extended the boundaries of kingdom Protista to include some multicellular forms, such as seaweeds, that are closely related to certain unicellular protists. The recent taxonomic trend has been to split the protists into several groups at the kingdom level. In addition to these protistan groups, domain Eukarya includes three kingdoms of multicellular eukaryotes: kingdoms Plantae, Fungi, and Animalia. These three kingdoms are distinguished partly by their modes of nutrition. Plants produce their own sugars and other foods by photosynthesis. Fungi absorb dissolved nutrients from their surroundings; many decompose dead organisms and organic wastes (such as leaf litter and animal feces) and absorb nutrients from these sources. Animals obtain food by ingestion, which is the eating and digesting of other organisms. Animalia is, of course, the kingdom to which we belong.

Unity in the Diversity of Life

As diverse as life is, it also displays remarkable unity. Earlier we mentioned the similar skeletons of different vertebrate animals, but similarities are even more striking at the molecular and cellular levels. For example, the universal genetic language of DNA is common to organisms as different as bacteria and animals. Unity is also evident in many features of cell structure (Figure 1.16).

How can we account for life's dual nature of unity and diversity? The process of evolution, explained next, illuminates both the similarities and differences in the world of life and introduces another dimension of biology: historical time.

Charles Darwin and the Theory of Natural Selection

The history of life, as documented by fossils and other evidence, is a saga of a changing Earth billions of years old, inhabited by an evolving cast of living forms (Figure 1.17). This evolutionary view of life came into sharp focus in November 1859, when Charles Robert Darwin published one of the most important and influential books ever written. Entitled *On the Origin of Species by Means of Natural Selection*, Darwin's book was an immediate bestseller and soon made "Darwinism" almost synonymous with the concept of evolution (Figure 1.18).

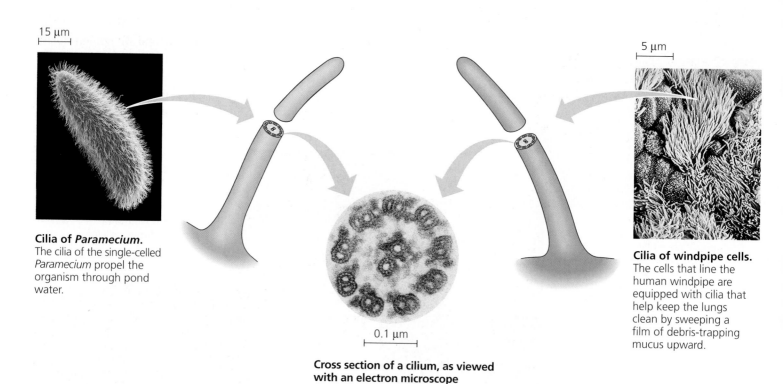

15 μm

Cilia of *Paramecium*. The cilia of the single-celled *Paramecium* propel the organism through pond water.

0.1 μm

Cross section of a cilium, as viewed with an electron microscope

5 μm

Cilia of windpipe cells. The cells that line the human windpipe are equipped with cilia that help keep the lungs clean by sweeping a film of debris-trapping mucus upward.

▲ Figure 1.16 **An example of unity underlying the diversity of life: the architecture of cilia in eukaryotes.** Cilia (singular, *cilium*) are extensions of cells that function in locomotion. They occur in eukaryotes as diverse as paramecia and humans. Even organisms so different share a common architecture for their cilia, which have an elaborate system of tubules that is striking in cross-sectional views.

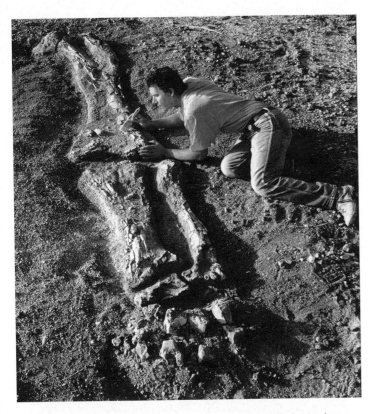

▲ **Figure 1.17 Digging into the past.** Paleontologist Paul Sereno, of the University of Chicago, gingerly excavates the leg bones of a dinosaur fossil in Niger.

The Origin of Species articulated two main points. First, Darwin presented evidence to support his view that contemporary species arose from a succession of ancestors. (We will discuss the evidence for evolution in detail in Chapter 22.) Darwin called this evolutionary history of species "descent with modification." It was an insightful phrase, as it captured the duality of life's unity and diversity—unity in the kinship among species that descended from common ancestors; diversity in the modifications that evolved as species branched from their common ancestors (**Figure 1.19**). Darwin's second main point was to propose a mechanism for descent with modification. He called this evolutionary mechanism natural selection.

Darwin synthesized his theory of natural selection from observations that by themselves were neither new nor profound. Others had the pieces of the puzzle, but Darwin saw how they fit together. He started with the following observations from nature: Individuals in a population vary in their traits, many of which seem to be heritable (passed on from parents to offspring). Also, a population can produce far more offspring than can survive to produce offspring of their own. With more individuals than the environment can support, competition is inevitable. Lastly, species generally suit their environments. For instance, birds living where tough seeds are a good food source may have especially strong beaks.

Darwin made inferences from these observations to arrive at his theory of evolution. He reasoned that individuals with inherited traits that are best suited to the local environment are more likely to survive and reproduce than less fit individuals. Over many generations, a higher and higher proportion

▲ **Figure 1.18 Charles Darwin as a young man.**

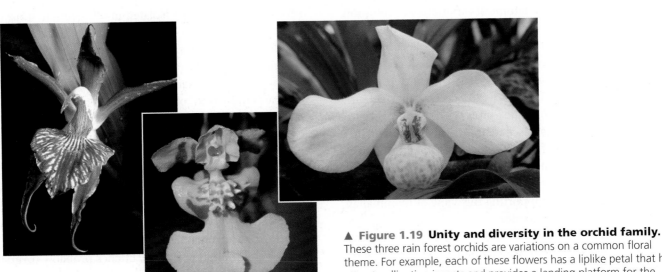

▲ **Figure 1.19 Unity and diversity in the orchid family.** These three rain forest orchids are variations on a common floral theme. For example, each of these flowers has a liplike petal that helps attract pollinating insects and provides a landing platform for the pollinators.

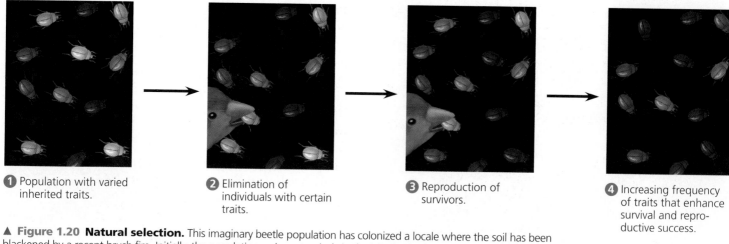

① Population with varied inherited traits.

② Elimination of individuals with certain traits.

③ Reproduction of survivors.

④ Increasing frequency of traits that enhance survival and reproductive success.

▲ **Figure 1.20 Natural selection.** This imaginary beetle population has colonized a locale where the soil has been blackened by a recent brush fire. Initially, the population varies extensively in the inherited coloration of the individuals, from very light gray to charcoal. For hungry birds that prey on the beetles, it is easiest to spot the beetles that are lightest in color.

of individuals in a population will have the advantageous traits. Evolution occurs as the unequal reproductive success of individuals adapts the population to its environment.

Darwin called this mechanism of evolutionary adaptation "natural selection" because the natural environment "selects" for the propagation of certain traits. The example in **Figure 1.20** illustrates the ability of natural selection to "edit" a population's heritable variations in color. We see the products of natural selection in the exquisite adaptations of various organisms to the special circumstances of their way of life and their environment **(Figure 1.21)**.

The Tree of Life

Take another look at the skeletal architecture of the bat's wings in Figure 1.21. These forelimbs, though adapted for flight, actually have all the same bones, joints, nerves, and blood vessels found in other limbs as diverse as the human arm, the horse's foreleg, and the whale's flipper. Indeed, all mammalian forelimbs are anatomical variations of a common architecture, much as the flowers in Figure 1.19 are variations on an underlying "orchid" theme. Such examples of kinship connect life's unity in diversity to the Darwinian concept of descent with modification. In this view, the unity of mammalian limb anatomy reflects inheritance of that structure from a common ancestor—the "prototype" mammal from which all other mammals descended. The diversity of mammalian forelimbs results from modification by natural selection operating over millions of generations in different environmental contexts. Fossils and other evidence corroborate anatomical unity in supporting this view of mammalian descent from a common ancestor.

Darwin proposed that natural selection, by its cumulative effects over long periods of time, could cause an ancestral species to give rise to two or more descendant species. This could occur, for example, if one population fragmented into

▲ **Figure 1.21 Evolutionary adaptation.** Bats, the only mammals capable of active flight, have wings with webbing between extended "fingers." In the Darwinian view of life, such adaptations are refined by natural selection.

several subpopulations isolated in different environments. In these separate arenas of natural selection, one species could gradually radiate into multiple species as the geographically isolated populations adapted over many generations to different sets of environmental factors.

The "family tree" of 14 finches in **Figure 1.22** illustrates a famous example of adaptive radiation of new species from a common ancestor. Darwin collected specimens of these birds during his 1835 visit to the remote Galápagos Islands, 900 kilometers (km) off the Pacific coast of South America. These relatively young, volcanic islands are home to many species of plants and animals found nowhere else in the world, though most Galápagos organisms are clearly related to species on the South American mainland. After volcanism built the Galápagos several million years ago, finches probably diversified on the various islands from an ancestral finch species that by chance reached the archipelago from elsewhere. (Once

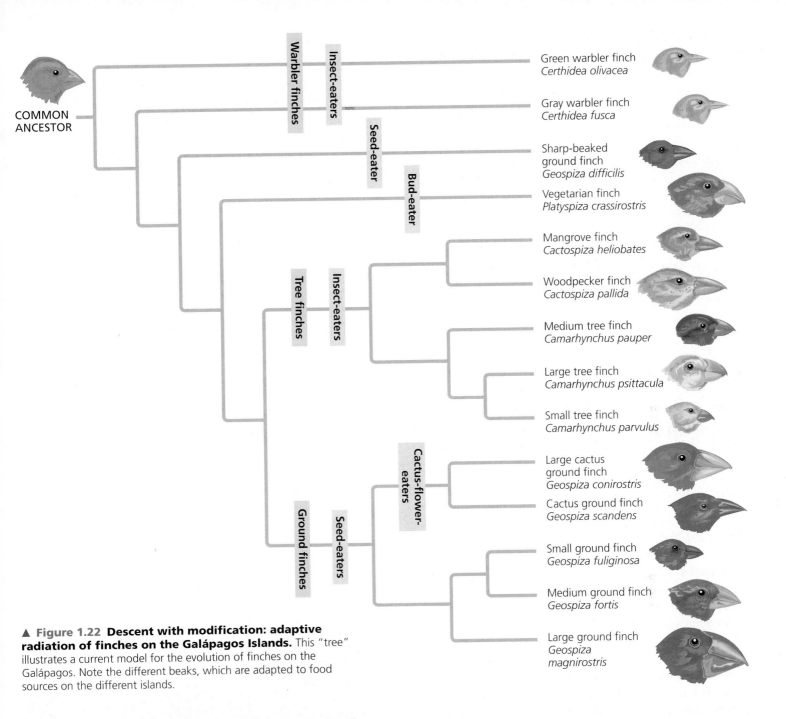

▲ Figure 1.22 Descent with modification: adaptive radiation of finches on the Galápagos Islands. This "tree" illustrates a current model for the evolution of finches on the Galápagos. Note the different beaks, which are adapted to food sources on the different islands.

thought to have originated on the mainland of South America like many Galápagos organisms, the ancestral finches are now thought to have come from islands of the Carribean.) Years after Darwin's collection of Galápagos finches, researchers began to sort out the relationships among the finch species, first from anatomical and geographic data and more recently with the help of DNA sequence comparisons.

Biologists' diagrams of evolutionary relationships generally take treelike forms, though today biologists usually turn the trees sideways as in Figure 1.22. Tree diagrams make sense: Just as an individual has a genealogy that can be diagrammed as a family tree, each species of organism is one twig of a branching tree of life extending back in time through ancestral species

more and more remote. Species that are very similar, such as the Galápagos finches, share a common ancestor at a relatively recent branch point on the tree of life. But through an ancestor that lived much farther back in time, finches are related to sparrows, hawks, penguins, and all other birds. And birds, mammals, and all other vertebrates share a common ancestor even more ancient. We find evidence of still broader relationships in such similarities as the identical construction of all eukaryotic cilia (see Figure 1.16). Trace life back far enough, and there are only fossils of the primeval prokaryotes that inhabited Earth over 3.5 billion years ago. We can recognize their vestiges in our own cells—in the universal genetic code, for example. All of life is connected through its long evolutionary history.

CONCEPT CHECK **1.2**

1. How is a mailing address analogous to biology's hierarchical taxonomic system?
2. Explain why "editing" is an appropriate metaphor for how natural selection acts on a population's heritable variation.
3. **WHAT IF?** The three domains you learned about in Concept 1.2 can be represented in the tree of life as the three main branches. On the eukaryotic branch, three of the subbranches are the kingdoms Plantae, Fungi, and Animalia. What if fungi and animals are more closely related to each other than either of these kingdoms is to plants—as recent evidence strongly suggests? Draw a simple branching pattern that symbolizes the proposed relationship between these three eukaryotic kingdoms.

For suggested answers, see Appendix A.

CONCEPT **1.3**

Scientists use two main forms of inquiry in their study of nature

The word *science* is derived from a Latin verb meaning "to know." Science is a way of knowing about the natural world. It developed out of our curiosity about ourselves, other life-forms, our planet, and the universe. Striving to understand seems to be one of our basic urges.

At the heart of science is **inquiry**, a search for information and explanation, often focusing on specific questions. Inquiry drove Darwin to seek answers in nature for how species adapt to their environments. And today inquiry drives the genome analyses that are helping us understand biological unity and diversity at the molecular level. In fact, the inquisitive mind is the engine that drives all progress in biology.

There is no formula for successful scientific inquiry, no single scientific method with a rule book that researchers must rigidly follow. As in all quests, science includes elements of challenge, adventure, and luck, along with careful planning, reasoning, creativity, cooperation, competition, patience, and the persistence to overcome setbacks. Such diverse elements of inquiry make science far less structured than most people realize. That said, it is possible to distill certain characteristics that help to distinguish science from other ways of describing and explaining nature.

Biologists use two main types of scientific inquiry: discovery science and hypothesis-based science. Discovery science is mostly about *describing* nature. Hypothesis-based science is mostly about *explaining* nature. Most scientific inquiries combine these two research approaches.

Discovery Science

Sometimes called descriptive science, **discovery science** describes natural structures and processes as accurately as possible through careful observation and analysis of data. For example, it is discovery science that has built our understanding of cell structure, and it is discovery science that is expanding our databases of genomes of diverse species.

Types of Data

Observation is the use of the senses to gather information, either directly or indirectly with the help of tools such as microscopes that extend our senses. Recorded observations are called **data**. Put another way, data are items of information on which scientific inquiry is based.

The term *data* implies numbers to many people. But some data are *qualitative*, often in the form of recorded descriptions rather than numerical measurements. For example, Jane Goodall spent decades recording her observations of chimpanzee behavior during field research in a Gambian jungle (**Figure 1.23**). She also documented her observations with photographs and movies. Along with these qualitative data, Goodall also enriched the field of animal behavior with volumes of *quantitative* data, which are generally recorded as measurements. Skim through any of the scientific journals in your college library, and you'll see many examples of quantitative data organized into tables and graphs.

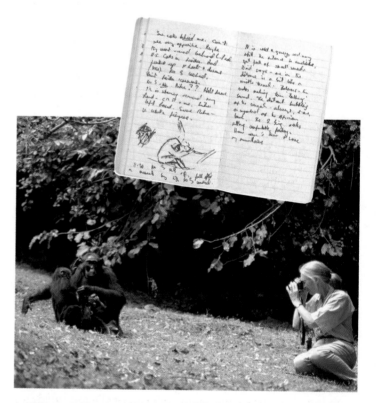

▲ **Figure 1.23 Jane Goodall collecting qualitative data on chimpanzee behavior.** Goodall recorded her observations in field notebooks, often with sketches of the animals' behavior.

Induction in Discovery Science

Discovery science can lead to important conclusions based on a type of logic called induction, or **inductive reasoning**. Through induction, we derive generalizations from a large number of specific observations. "The sun always rises in the east" is an example. And so is "All organisms are made of cells." The latter generalization, part of the so-called cell theory, was based on two centuries of biologists discovering cells in the diverse biological specimens they observed with microscopes. The careful observations and data analyses of discovery science, along with the generalizations reached by induction, are fundamental to our understanding of nature.

Hypothesis-Based Science

The observations and inductions of discovery science stimulate us to seek natural causes and explanations for those observations. What *caused* the diversification of finches on the Galápagos Islands? What *causes* the roots of a plant seedling to grow downward and the leaf-bearing shoot to grow upward? What *explains* the generalization that the sun always rises in the east? In science, such inquiry usually involves the proposing and testing of hypothetical explanations—that is, hypotheses.

The Role of Hypotheses in Inquiry

In science, a **hypothesis** is a tentative answer to a well-framed question—an explanation on trial. It is usually an educated guess, based on experience and on the data available from discovery science. A scientific hypothesis leads to predictions that can be tested by making additional observations or by performing experiments.

We all use hypotheses in solving everyday problems. Let's say, for example, that your flashlight fails during a camp-out. That's an observation. The question is obvious: Why doesn't the flashlight work? Two reasonable hypotheses based on your experience are that (1) the batteries in the flashlight are dead or (2) the bulb is burnt out. Each of these alternative hypotheses leads to predictions you can test with experiments. For example, the dead-battery hypothesis predicts that replacing the batteries will fix the problem. **Figure 1.24** diagrams this campground inquiry. Of course, we rarely dissect our thought processes this way when we are solving a problem using hypotheses, predictions, and experiments. But hypothesis-based science clearly has its origins in the human tendency to figure things out by trial and error.

Deduction: The "If . . . Then" Logic of Hypothesis-Based Science

A type of logic called deduction is built into hypothesis-based science. Deduction contrasts with induction, which, remember, is reasoning from a set of specific observations to reach a general conclusion. In **deductive reasoning**, the logic flows in the opposite direction, from the general to the specific.

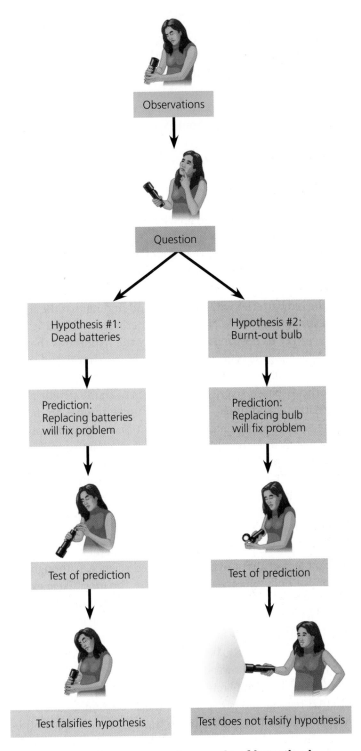

▲ **Figure 1.24 A campground example of hypothesis-based inquiry.**

From general premises, we extrapolate to the specific results we should expect if the premises are true. If all organisms are made of cells (premise 1), and humans are organisms (premise 2), then humans are composed of cells (deductive prediction about a specific case).

In hypothesis-based science, deductions usually take the form of predictions of experimental or observational results that will be found if a particular hypothesis (premise) is correct. We then test the hypothesis by carrying out the experiments or observations to see whether or not the results are as predicted. This deductive testing takes the form of *"If . . . then"* logic. In the case of the flashlight example: *If* the dead-battery hypothesis is correct, and you replace the batteries with new ones, *then* the flashlight should work.

A Closer Look at Hypotheses in Scientific Inquiry

The flashlight example illustrates two important qualities of scientific hypotheses. First, a hypothesis must be *testable*; there must be some way to check the validity of the idea. Second, a hypothesis must be *falsifiable*; there must be some observation or experiment that could reveal if such an idea is actually *not* true. The hypothesis that dead batteries are the sole cause of the broken flashlight could be falsified by replacing the old batteries with new ones and finding that the flashlight still doesn't work. Not all hypotheses meet the criteria of science: Try to devise a test to falsify the hypothesis that invisible campground ghosts are fooling with your flashlight!

The flashlight inquiry illustrates another key point about hypothesis-based science. The ideal is to frame two or more alternative hypotheses and design experiments to falsify those candidate explanations. In addition to the two explanations tested in Figure 1.24, another of the many possible alternative hypotheses is that *both* the batteries *and* the bulb are bad. What does this hypothesis predict about the outcome of the experiments in Figure 1.24? What additional experiment would you design to test this hypothesis of multiple malfunction?

We can mine the flashlight scenario for still one more important lesson about hypothesis-based science. Although the burnt-out bulb hypothesis stands up as the most likely explanation, notice that the testing supports that hypothesis *not* by proving that it is correct, but by not eliminating it through falsification. Perhaps the bulb was simply loose and the new bulb was inserted correctly. We could attempt to falsify the burnt-out bulb hypothesis by trying another experiment—removing the bulb and carefully reinstalling it. But no amount of experimental testing can *prove* a hypothesis beyond a shadow of doubt, because it is impossible to test *all* alternative hypotheses. A hypothesis gains credibility by surviving attempts to falsify it while testing eliminates (falsifies) alternative hypotheses.

The Myth of the Scientific Method

The flashlight example of Figure 1.24 traces an idealized process of inquiry called *the scientific method.* We can recognize the elements of this process in most of the research articles published by scientists, but rarely in such structured form. Very few scientific inquiries adhere rigidly to the sequence of steps prescribed by the "textbook" scientific

method. For example, a scientist may start to design an experiment, but then backtrack upon realizing that more observations are necessary. In other cases, puzzling observations simply don't prompt well-defined questions until other research places those observations in a new context. For example, Darwin collected specimens of the Galápagos finches, but it wasn't until years later, as the idea of natural selection began to gel, that biologists began asking key questions about the history of those birds.

Moreover, scientists sometimes redirect their research when they realize they have been asking the wrong question. For example, in the early 20th century, much research on schizophrenia and manic-depressive disorder (now called bipolar disorder) got sidetracked by focusing too much on the question of how life experiences might cause these serious maladies. Research on the causes and potential treatments became more productive when it was refocused on questions of how certain chemical imbalances in the brain contribute to mental illness. To be fair, we acknowledge that such twists and turns in scientific inquiry become more evident with the advantage of historical perspective.

There is still another reason that good science need not conform exactly to any one method of inquiry: Discovery science has contributed much to our understanding of nature without most of the steps of the so-called scientific method.

It is important for you to get some experience with the power of the scientific method—by using it for some of the laboratory inquiries in your biology course, for example. But it is also important to avoid stereotyping science as lock-step adherence to this method.

A Case Study in Scientific Inquiry: Investigating Mimicry in Snake Populations

Now that we have highlighted the key features of discovery science and hypothesis-based science, you should be able to recognize these forms of inquiry in a case study of actual scientific research.

The story begins with a set of observations and generalizations from discovery science. Many poisonous animals are brightly colored, often with distinctive patterns that stand out against the background. This is called warning coloration because it apparently signals "dangerous species" to potential predators. But there are also mimics. These imposters look like poisonous species but are actually harmless. A question that follows from these observations is: What is the function of such mimicry? A reasonable hypothesis is that such "deception" is an evolutionary adaptation that reduces the harmless animal's risk of being eaten because predators mistake it for the poisonous species. This hypothesis was first formulated by British scientist Henry Bates in 1862.

As obvious as this hypothesis may seem, it has been relatively difficult to test, especially with field experiments. But in

2001, biologists David and Karin Pfennig, of the University of North Carolina, along with William Harcombe, an undergraduate, designed a simple but elegant set of field experiments to test Bates's mimicry hypothesis.

The team investigated a case of mimicry among snakes that live in North and South Carolina (**Figure 1.25**). A poisonous snake called the eastern coral snake has warning coloration: bold, alternating rings of red, yellow (or white), and black. Predators rarely attack these snakes. It is unlikely that the predators learn this avoidance behavior by trial and error, as a first encounter with a coral snake is usually deadly. In areas where coral snakes live, natural selection has apparently increased the frequency of predators that have inherited an instinctive avoidance of the coral snake's coloration. A nonpoisonous snake named the scarlet kingsnake mimics the ringed coloration of the coral snake.

Both types of snakes live in the Carolinas, but the kingsnakes' geographic range also extends into regions where no coral snakes are found (see Figure 1.25). The geographic distribution of the snakes made it possible to test the key prediction of the mimicry hypothesis. Avoiding snakes with warning coloration is an adaptation we expect to be present only in predator populations that evolved in areas where the poisonous coral snakes are present. Therefore, mimicry should help protect kingsnakes from predators, but *only* in regions where coral snakes also live. The mimicry hypothesis predicts that predators adapted to the warning coloration of coral snakes will attack kingsnakes less frequently than will predators in areas where coral snakes are absent.

Field Experiments with Artificial Snakes

To test the prediction, Harcombe made hundreds of artificial snakes out of wire covered with plasticine. He fashioned two versions of fake snakes: an *experimental group* with the red, black, and white ring pattern of kingsnakes; and a *control group* of plain brown artificial snakes as a basis of comparison (**Figure 1.26**).

The researchers placed equal numbers of the two types of artificial snakes in field sites throughout North and South Carolina, including the region where coral snakes are absent. After four weeks, the scientists retrieved the fake snakes and recorded how many had been attacked by looking for bite or claw marks. The most common predators were foxes, coyotes, and raccoons, but black bears also attacked some of the artificial snakes (see Figure 1.26b).

The data fit the key prediction of the mimicry hypothesis. Compared to the brown artificial snakes, the ringed artificial snakes were attacked by predators less frequently *only* in field sites within the geographic range of the poisonous coral

Scarlet kingsnake (nonpoisonous)

Key

▨ Range of scarlet kingsnake only

▧ Overlapping ranges of scarlet kingsnake and eastern coral snake

North Carolina

South Carolina

Eastern coral snake (poisonous)

Scarlet kingsnake (nonpoisonous)

▲ **Figure 1.25 The geographic ranges of a poisonous snake and its mimic.** The scarlet kingsnake (*Lampropeltis triangulum*) mimics the warning coloration of the poisonous eastern coral snake (*Micrurus fulvius*).

(a) Artificial kingsnake

(b) Brown artificial snake that has been attacked

▲ **Figure 1.26 Artificial snakes used in field experiments to test the mimicry hypothesis.** You can see where a bear chomped on the brown artificial snake in (b).

snakes. **Figure 1.27** summarizes the field experiments that the researchers carried out. This figure also introduces a format we will use throughout the book for other examples of biological inquiry.

Designing Controlled Experiments

The snake mimicry experiment is an example of a **controlled experiment**, one that is designed to compare an experimental group (the artificial kingsnakes, in this case) with a control group (the brown artificial snakes). Ideally, the experimental and control groups differ only in the one factor the experiment is designed to test—in our example, the effect of the snakes' coloration on the behavior of predators. Without the control group, the researchers would not have been able to rule out other factors as causes of the more frequent attacks on the artificial kingsnakes—such as different numbers of predators or different temperatures in the different test areas. The clever experimental design left coloration as the only factor that could account for the low predation rate on the artificial kingsnakes placed within the range of coral snakes. It was not the absolute number of attacks on the artificial kingsnakes that counted, but the difference between that number and the number of attacks on the brown snakes.

A common misconception is that the term *controlled experiment* means that scientists control the experimental environment to keep everything constant except the one variable being tested. But that's impossible in field research and not realistic even in highly regulated laboratory environments. Researchers usually "control" unwanted variables not by *eliminating* them through environmental regulation, but by *canceling* their effects by using control groups.

Limitations of Science

Scientific inquiry is a powerful way to learn about nature, but there are limitations to the kinds of questions it can answer. These limits are set by science's requirements that hypotheses be testable and falsifiable and that observations and experimental results be repeatable.

Observations that can't be verified may be interesting or even entertaining, but they cannot count as evidence in scientific inquiry. The headlines of supermarket tabloids would have you believe that humans are occasionally born with the head of a dog and that some of your classmates are extraterrestrials. The unconfirmed eyewitness accounts and the computer-rigged photos are amusing but unconvincing. In science, evidence from observations and experiments is only convincing if it stands up to the criterion of repeatability. The scientists who investigated snake mimicry in the Carolinas obtained similar data when they repeated their experiments with different species of coral snakes and kingsnakes in Arizona. And *you* should be able to obtain similar results if you were to repeat the snake experiments.

▼ **Figure 1.27** **Inquiry**

Does the presence of poisonous coral snakes affect predation rates on their mimics, kingsnakes?

EXPERIMENT David Pfennig and his colleagues made artificial snakes to test a prediction of the mimicry hypothesis: that kingsnakes benefit from mimicking the warning coloration of poisonous coral snakes *only* in regions where coral snakes are present. The researchers placed equal numbers of artificial kingsnakes (experimental group) and brown artificial snakes (control group) at 14 field sites, half in the area the two snakes cohabit and half in the area where coral snakes were absent. The researchers recovered the artificial snakes after four weeks and tabulated predation data based on teeth and claw marks on the snakes.

RESULTS In field sites where coral snakes were present, most attacks were on brown artificial snakes. Where coral snakes were absent, most attacks were on artificial kingsnakes.

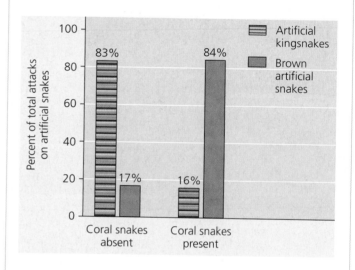

CONCLUSION The field experiments support the mimicry hypothesis by not falsifying the prediction that imitation of coral snakes is only effective where coral snakes are present. The experiments also tested an alternative hypothesis: that predators generally avoid all snakes with brightly colored rings. That hypothesis was falsified by the data showing that the ringed coloration failed to repel predators where coral snakes were absent. (The fake kingsnakes may have been attacked more often in those areas because their bright pattern made them easier to spot than the brown fakes.)

SOURCE D. W. Pfennig, W. R. Harcombe, and K. S. Pfennig, Frequency-dependent Batesian mimicry, *Nature* 410:323 (2001).

Inquiry in Action Read and analyze the original paper in *Inquiry in Action: Interpreting Scientific Papers*.

WHAT IF? What experimental results would you predict if predators throughout the Carolinas avoid all snakes with brightly colored ring patterns?

Because science requires natural explanations for natural phenomena, it can neither support nor falsify hypotheses that angels, ghosts, or spirits, whether benevolent or evil, cause storms, rainbows, illnesses, and cures. Such supernatural explanations are simply outside the bounds of science.

Theories in Science

"It's just a theory!" Our everyday use of the term *theory* often implies an untested speculation. But the term *theory* has a different meaning in science. What is a scientific theory, and how is it different from a hypothesis or from mere speculation?

First, a scientific **theory** is much broader in scope than a hypothesis. *This* is a hypothesis: "Mimicking the coloration of poisonous snakes is an adaptation that protects nonpoisonous snakes from predators." But *this* is a theory: "Evolutionary adaptations arise by natural selection." Darwin's theory of natural selection accounts for an enormous diversity of adaptations, including mimicry.

Second, a theory is general enough to spin off many new, specific hypotheses that can be tested. For example, two researchers at Princeton University, Peter and Rosemary Grant, were motivated by the theory of natural selection to test the specific hypothesis that the beaks of Galápagos finches evolve in response to changes in the types of available food. (Their results supported their hypothesis; see p. 468.)

And third, compared to any one hypothesis, a theory is generally supported by a much greater body of evidence. Those theories that become widely adopted in science (such as the theory of natural selection) explain a great diversity of observations and are supported by a vast accumulation of evidence. In fact, scrutiny of theories continues through testing of the specific, falsifiable hypotheses they spawn.

In spite of the body of evidence supporting a widely accepted theory, scientists must sometimes modify or even reject theories when new research methods produce results that don't fit. For example, the five-kingdom theory of biological diversity began to erode when new methods for comparing cells and molecules made it possible to test some of the hypothetical relationships between organisms that were based on the theory. If there is "truth" in science, it is conditional, based on the preponderance of available evidence.

Model Building in Science

You may work with many models in your biology course this year. Perhaps you'll model cell division by using pipe cleaners as chromosomes. Or maybe you'll practice using mathematical models to predict the growth of a bacterial population. Scientists often construct models as representations of natural phenomena. Scientific **models** can take many forms, including diagrams (such as the evolutionary tree in Figure 1.22), graphs, three-dimensional objects, computer programs, or mathematical equations.

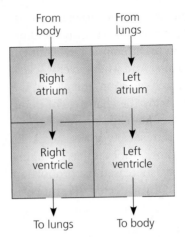

◄ Figure 1.28 A model of the blood flow through the four chambers of a human heart.

? *The blood picks up oxygen (and releases carbon dioxide) in the lungs and releases oxygen (and picks up carbon dioxide) in the rest of the body. From the model shown here, predict what would happen if there were a small hole between the two ventricles.*

Choosing the most appropriate type of model depends on what needs to be communicated and explained about the object, idea, or process the model is to represent. Some models need to be as lifelike as possible. Other models are more useful if they are simple schematics. For example, the simple diagram in **Figure 1.28** does a good job of modeling blood flow through the chambers of a human heart without looking anything like a real heart. A heart model designed to help train a physician to perform heart surgery would look very different. Whatever the design of a model, the test of its success is how well it fits the available data, how comfortably it accommodates new observations, how accurately it predicts the outcomes of new experiments or observations, and how effectively it communicates.

The Culture of Science

Movies and cartoons sometimes portray scientists as loners working in isolated labs. In reality, science is an intensely social activity. Most scientists work in teams, which often include both graduate and undergraduate students **(Figure 1.29)**. And to succeed in science, it helps to be a good communicator. Research results have no impact until shared with a community of peers through seminars, publications, and websites.

◄ Figure 1.29 Science as a social process. In her New York University laboratory, plant biologist Gloria Coruzzi mentors one of her students in the methods of molecular biology.

Both cooperation and competition characterize the scientific culture. Scientists working in the same research field often check one another's claims by attempting to confirm observations or repeat experiments. And when several scientists converge on the same research question, there is all the excitement of a race. Scientists enjoy the challenge of being first with an important discovery or key experiment.

The biology community is part of society at large, embedded in the cultural milieu of the times. For example, changing attitudes about career choices have increased the proportion of women in biology, which has in turn affected the emphasis in certain research fields. A few decades ago, for instance, biologists who studied the mating behavior of animals focused mostly on competition among males for access to females. More recent research, however, emphasizes the important role that females play in choosing mates. For example, in many bird species, females prefer the bright coloration that "advertises" a male's vigorous health, a behavior that enhances the female's probability of having healthy offspring.

Some philosophers of science argue that scientists are so influenced by cultural and political values that science is no more objective than other ways of understanding nature. At the other extreme are people who speak of scientific theories as though they were natural laws instead of human interpretations of nature. The reality of science is probably somewhere in between—rarely perfectly objective, but continuously vetted through the expectation that observations and experiments be repeatable and hypotheses be testable and falsifiable.

Science, Technology, and Society

The relationship of science to society becomes clearer when we add technology to the picture. Though science and technology sometimes employ similar inquiry patterns, their basic goals differ. The goal of science is to understand natural phenomena. In contrast, **technology** generally *applies* scientific knowledge for some specific purpose. Biologists and other scientists often speak of "discoveries," while engineers and other technologists more often speak of "inventions." And the beneficiaries of those inventions include scientists, who put new technology to work in their research; the impact of information technology on systems biology is just one example. Thus, science and technology are interdependent.

The potent combination of science and technology has dramatic effects on society. For example, discovery of the structure of DNA by Watson and Crick half a century ago and subsequent achievements in DNA science led to the technologies of DNA engineering that are transforming many applied fields, including medicine, agriculture, and forensics **(Figure 1.30)**. Perhaps Watson and Crick envisioned that their discovery would someday produce important applications, but it is unlikely that they could have predicted exactly what all those applications would be.

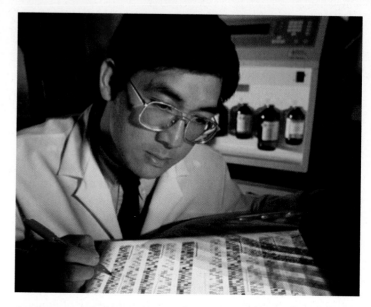

▲ **Figure 1.30 DNA technology and crime scene investigation.** Forensic technicians can use traces of DNA extracted from a blood sample or other body tissue collected at a crime scene to produce molecular "fingerprints." The stained bands you see in this photograph represent fragments of DNA, and the pattern of bands varies from person to person.

The directions that technology takes depend less on the curiosity that drives basic science than on the current needs and wants of people and on the social environment of the times. Debates about technology center more on "*should* we do it" than "*can* we do it." With advances in technology come difficult choices. For example, under what circumstances is it acceptable to use DNA technology to find out if particular people have genes for hereditary diseases? Should such tests always be voluntary, or are there circumstances when genetic testing should be mandatory? Should insurance companies or employers have access to the information, as they do for many other types of personal health data?

Such ethical issues have as much to do with politics, economics, and cultural values as with science and technology. All citizens—not only professional scientists—have a responsibility to be informed about how science works and about the potential benefits and risks of technology. The relationship between science, technology, and society increases the significance and value of any biology course.

CONCEPT CHECK **1.3**

1. Contrast inductive reasoning with deductive reasoning.
2. Why is natural selection called a theory?
3. **WHAT IF?** Suppose you extended the snake mimicry experiment to an area of Virginia where neither type of snake is known to live. What results would you predict at your field site?

For suggested answers, see Appendix A.

SUMMARY OF KEY CONCEPTS

CONCEPT **1.1**

Themes connect the concepts of biology (pp. 3–11)

▶ **Evolution, the Overarching Theme of Biology** Evolution accounts for the unity and diversity of life, and also for the match of organisms to their environments.

▶ *Theme:* **New properties emerge at each level in the biological hierarchy** The hierarchy of life unfolds as follows: biosphere > ecosystem > community > population > organism > organ system > organ > tissue > cell > organelle > molecule > atom. With each step "upward" from atoms, new properties emerge as a result of interactions among components at the lower levels. In an approach called reductionism, complex systems are broken down to simpler components that are more manageable to study. In systems biology, scientists make models of complex biological systems.

▶ *Theme:* **Organisms interact with their environments, exchanging matter and energy** An organism's environment includes other organisms as well as nonliving factors. Whereas chemical nutrients recycle within an ecosystem, energy flows through an ecosystem. All organisms must perform work, which requires energy. Energy flows from sunlight to producers to consumers.

▶ *Theme:* **Structure and function are correlated at all levels of biological organization** The form of a biological structure suits its function and vice versa.

▶ *Theme:* **Cells are an organism's basic units of structure and function** The cell is the lowest level of organization that can perform all activities required for life. Cells are either prokaryotic or eukaryotic. Eukaryotic cells contain membrane-enclosed organelles, including a DNA-containing nucleus. Prokaryotic cells lack such organelles.

▶ *Theme:* **The continuity of life is based on heritable information in the form of DNA** Genetic information is encoded in the nucleotide sequences of DNA. It is DNA that transmits heritable information from parents to offspring. DNA sequences program a cell's protein production by being transcribed into RNA and then translated into specific proteins. RNA that is not translated into protein serves other important functions.

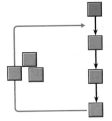

▶ *Theme:* **Feedback mechanisms regulate biological systems** In negative feedback, accumulation of an end product slows the process that makes that product. In positive feedback, the end product stimulates the production of more product. Feedback is a type of regulation common to life at all levels, from molecules to ecosystems.

MEDIA
Activity The Levels of Life Card Game
Activity Energy Flow and Chemical Cycling
Activity Form Fits Function: Cells
Activity Comparing Prokaryotic and Eukaryotic Cells
Activity Heritable Information: DNA
Activity Regulation: Negative and Positive Feedback

CONCEPT **1.2**

***The Core Theme:* Evolution accounts for the unity and diversity of life (pp. 12–18)**

▶ **Organizing the Diversity of Life** Biologists classify species according to a system of broader and broader groups. Domain Bacteria and domain Archaea consist of prokaryotes. Domain Eukarya, the eukaryotes, includes various groups of protists and the kingdoms Plantae, Fungi, and Animalia. As diverse as life is, there is also evidence of remarkable unity, which is revealed in the similarities between different kinds of organisms.

▶ **Charles Darwin and the Theory of Natural Selection** Darwin proposed natural selection as the mechanism for evolutionary adaptation of populations to their environments.

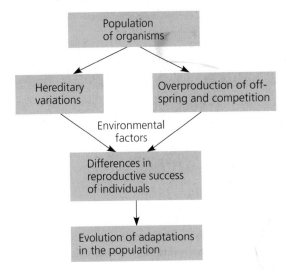

▶ **The Tree of Life** Each species is one twig of a branching tree of life extending back in time through ancestral species more and more remote. All of life is connected through its long evolutionary history.

MEDIA
Activity Classification Schemes
Investigation How Do Environmental Changes Affect a Population?
Biology Labs On-Line EvolutionLab

Scientists use two main forms of inquiry in their study of nature (pp. 18–24)

▶ **Discovery Science** In discovery science, scientists observe and describe some aspect of the world and use inductive reasoning to draw general conclusions.

▶ **Hypothesis-Based Science** Based on observations, scientists propose hypotheses that lead to predictions and then test the hypotheses by seeing if the predictions come true. Deductive reasoning is used in testing hypotheses: If a hypothesis is correct, and we test it, then we can expect a particular outcome. Hypotheses must be testable and falsifiable.

▶ **A Case Study in Scientific Inquiry: Investigating Mimicry in Snake Populations** Experiments must be designed to demonstrate the effect of one variable by testing control groups and experimental groups that differ in only that one variable.

▶ **Limitations of Science** Science cannot address the possibility of supernatural phenomena because hypotheses must be testable and falsifiable, and observations and experimental results must be repeatable.

▶ **Theories in Science** A scientific theory is broad in scope, generates new hypotheses, and is supported by a large body of evidence.

▶ **Model Building in Science** Models of ideas, structures, and processes help us understand scientific phenomena and make predictions.

▶ **The Culture of Science** Science is a social activity characterized by both cooperation and competition.

▶ **Science, Technology, and Society** Technology is a method or device that applies scientific knowledge for some specific purpose.

MEDIA

GraphIt! An Introduction to Graphing
Investigation How Does Acid Precipitation Affect Trees?
Activity Science, Technology, and Society: DDT

TESTING YOUR KNOWLEDGE

SELF-QUIZ

1. All the organisms on your campus make up
   a. an ecosystem.
   b. a community.
   c. a population.
   d. an experimental group.
   e. a taxonomic domain.

2. Which of the following is a correct sequence of levels in life's hierarchy, proceeding downward from an individual animal?
   a. brain, organ system, nerve cell, nervous tissue
   b. organ system, nervous tissue, brain
   c. organism, organ system, tissue, cell, organ
   d. nervous system, brain, nervous tissue, nerve cell
   e. organ system, tissue, molecule, cell

3. Which of the following is *not* an observation or inference on which Darwin's theory of natural selection is based?
   a. Poorly adapted individuals never produce offspring.

   b. There is heritable variation among individuals.
   c. Because of overproduction of offspring, there is competition for limited resources.
   d. Individuals whose inherited characteristics best fit them to the environment will generally produce more offspring.
   e. A population can become adapted to its environment over time.

4. Systems biology is mainly an attempt to
   a. understand the integration of all levels of biological organization from molecules to the biosphere.
   b. simplify complex problems by reducing the system into smaller, less complex units.
   c. construct models of the behavior of entire biological systems.
   d. build high-throughput machines for the rapid acquisition of biological data.
   e. speed up the technological application of scientific knowledge.

5. Protists and bacteria are grouped into different domains because
   a. protists eat bacteria.
   b. bacteria are not made of cells.
   c. protists have a membrane-bounded nucleus, which bacterial cells lack.
   d. bacteria decompose protists.
   e. protists are photosynthetic.

6. Which of the following best demonstrates the unity among all organisms?
   a. matching DNA nucleotide sequences
   b. descent with modification
   c. the structure and function of DNA
   d. natural selection
   e. emergent properties

7. Which of the following is an example of qualitative data?
   a. The temperature decreased from 20°C to 15°C.
   b. The plant's height is 25 centimeters (cm).
   c. The fish swam in a zig-zag motion.
   d. The six pairs of robins hatched an average of three chicks.
   e. The contents of the stomach are mixed every 20 seconds.

8. Which of the following best describes the logic of hypothesis-based science?
   a. If I generate a testable hypothesis, tests and observations will support it.
   b. If my prediction is correct, it will lead to a testable hypothesis.
   c. If my observations are accurate, they will support my hypothesis.
   d. If my hypothesis is correct, I can expect certain test results.
   e. If my experiments are set up right, they will lead to a testable hypothesis.

9. A controlled experiment is one that
   a. proceeds slowly enough that a scientist can make careful records of the results.
   b. may include experimental groups and control groups tested in parallel.

c. is repeated many times to make sure the results are accurate.

d. keeps all environmental variables constant.

e. is supervised by an experienced scientist.

10. Which of the following statements best distinguishes hypotheses from theories in science?

a. Theories are hypotheses that have been proved.

b. Hypotheses are guesses; theories are correct answers.

c. Hypotheses usually are relatively narrow in scope; theories have broad explanatory power.

d. Hypotheses and theories are essentially the same thing.

e. Theories are proved true in all cases; hypotheses are usually falsified by tests.

11. **DRAW IT** With rough sketches, draw a biological hierarchy similar to the one in Figure 1.4 but using a coral reef as the ecosystem, a fish as the organism, its stomach as the organ, and DNA as the molecule. Include all levels in the hierarchy.

For Self-Quiz answers, see Appendix A.

MEDIA Visit the Study Area at **www.masteringbio.com** for a Practice Test.

EVOLUTION CONNECTION

12. A typical prokaryotic cell has about 3,000 genes in its DNA, while a human cell has about 20,500 genes. About 1,000 of these genes are present in both types of cells. Based on your understanding of evolution, explain how such different organisms could have this same subset of genes. What sorts of functions might these shared genes have?

SCIENTIFIC INQUIRY

13. Based on the results of the snake mimicry case study, suggest another hypothesis researchers might use to extend the investigation.

SCIENCE, TECHNOLOGY, AND SOCIETY

14. The fruits of wild species of tomato are tiny compared to the giant beefsteak tomatoes available today. This difference in fruit size is almost entirely due to the larger number of cells in the domesticated fruits. Plant molecular biologists have recently discovered genes that are responsible for controlling cell division in tomatoes. Why would such a discovery be important to producers of other kinds of fruits and vegetables? To the study of human development and disease? To our basic understanding of biology?

The Chemistry of Life

AN INTERVIEW WITH
Deborah M. Gordon

What does an ant sense as it goes about its daily chores? Mainly chemicals—because these are the cues ants use to navigate their environment. The interactions of ants with each other and their surroundings are the research focus of Deborah M. Gordon, a professor of biological sciences at Stanford University. While at Stanford, Dr. Gordon has won several awards for excellence in teaching, as well as recognition for her research in the Arizona desert and the tropics of South America. And through appearances on radio, TV nature shows, and her book *Ants at Work: How an Insect Society Is Organized* (Free Press, 1999), Dr. Gordon has shared her fascination with ant society with people around the world.

How did you get interested in biology?
In my first year in college, thinking of a career in medicine as a possibility, I took introductory chemistry and biology. But those courses just gave me a lot of information that I couldn't really put together. I ended up majoring in French. But I was also very interested in math and in music theory, because I like looking at patterns and understanding how they change over time. Then, in my senior year, I took a course in comparative anatomy, which completely changed my view of biology. That course showed me that evolution is a process that changes patterns in interesting ways.

After graduation, curious about the human body and health, I came to Stanford to take the medical school course in human anatomy. I stayed to complete a master's degree in biology. Then, although I still wasn't sure what I wanted to do with my life, I entered a Ph.D. program at Duke. It was there that I began research on ant behavior—and I loved it.

Students of biology have to study chemistry as well. How is chemistry relevant to ant behavior?
Ants don't see very well; they operate mostly by chemical communication. If you work on ants, you have to think about chemistry because chemicals are critically important in the ant's world. For example, the ants I study in Arizona use long-lasting chemical cues to identify themselves and to mark their nest area. Ants also use many short-term chemical cues called pheromones, which they secrete in certain situations. The best known are alarm pheromones, which are what make ants run around in circles when they're disturbed. Some ants secrete a pheromone from the tip of the abdomen that marks where they walk and creates a trail that other ants can follow. Ants have 12 or 14 different glands that secrete different substances. We really don't know what they're all for, or how many chemical combinations an ant can respond to. In addition to chemicals used in communication, some ants produce antibiotics or chemical defenses against predators. Other ants use chemicals to kill certain plants [see Chapter 2, pp. 30–31].

Why do you study ants?
What interests me about ants is that ants live in societies without any central control. Yet individual ants are very limited in what they can do; each can take in only local information. No ant can figure out what needs to be done for the good of the colony. The big question for me is: How can an ant colony function when nobody's in charge and each ant can only perceive what's right around it?

What about the queens? Please tell us more about how ants live.
There are 10,000 to 12,000 species of ants. They all live in colonies, each with one or a few reproductive females, called queens. The queens lay eggs, using sperm stored from a mating that preceded her establishment of the colony. The rest of the colony—all the ants you see walking around—are her daughters, sterile female workers. These workers do all the work, and they do it without any direction from the queen. Males,

born from unfertilized eggs, are produced only once a year, just in time to join virgin queens in a mating flight. Soon after mating, they die.

What exactly do worker ants do?
The ants I study in Arizona, called harvester ants, perform four kinds of tasks. Some workers forage for food. Some patrol; that is, they go out early in the morning and decide where the foragers should go that day. Others do nest-maintenance work, building chambers underground and then carrying out the excess sand. And still others work on the refuse pile, or midden, which they mark with the colony's specific odor. Different groups of ants perform each of the four tasks.

Tell us about your research in Arizona.
At my research site in Arizona, where I've been working for more than 20 years, I study a population of about 300 colonies of harvester ants. Each year my students and I map the locations of the colonies that make up this population. We identify all the colonies that were there the year before, figure out which ones have died, and map the new ones. In this way I can follow the same colonies year after year. I get to know them quite well. I have found that colonies last 15 to 20 years.

In addition to observing the ant colonies, we do simple experiments where we change the ants' environment in some way and observe how the ants respond. For example, in the last few years we've been studying how a colony regulates the number of ants that go out to forage. We've learned that each ant uses its recent history of interactions with other ants to decide what to do next. An ant uses odors to identify the task of the ants it meets. Each ant is coated with a layer of grease, made of chemicals called hydrocarbons. Each task group—the foragers, the patrollers, the nest maintenance workers, and the midden workers—has a unique mixture of hydrocarbons, which the ants secrete and spread on each other by grooming. We've found that, as an ant spends time outside, the proportions of different hydrocarbons on its body changes.

What causes this change?

The heat of the sun. We learned this from an experiment in which we took ants that had been working inside the nest and exposed them to different conditions. After exposure to high temperatures and low humidity for long enough times, these ants came to smell like foragers. So it's not that foragers secrete something different as they do their task but that doing the task changes them. Just as a carpenter gets calluses from holding tools, an ant comes to smell different from the work it does. The ants of a colony all secrete the same mixture of hydrocarbons, but each ant's chemical profile changes depending on what it does.

What tells an ant what to do? For example, what tells an ant to forage?

We've learned that ants use their recent experience of quick antennal contacts with each other to decide what to do. The antennae are their organs of chemical perception. Anyone who has watched ants has seen them meet and touch antennae, and when they do that, they smell each other, detecting the chemicals on each other's body. But a single interaction is not an instruction; a forager meeting another ant is not saying, "Go forage." It's the *pattern* of encounters that conveys the message.

How did you figure that out?

Working with Michael Greene, who's now at the University of Colorado at Denver, we've been able to extract the hydrocarbons from the ants' bodies and put them on little glass beads, and we've found that the ants respond to a bead coated with ant hydrocarbons as if it were an ant. So by dropping these coated beads into the nest, we can figure out how the ants react to encounters with an ant of a particular task group.

Recently we've been working on how foragers use the rate at which other foragers come in with food to decide whether to go out again. This rate gives feedback about how much food is out there. A forager looking for food won't come back until it finds something; if it has to stay out for 45 minutes, it will. But when there's an abundance of food near the nest, the foragers return quickly. The returning ants provide positive feedback: The faster ants come back, the more ants go out.

We've found that harvester ants respond surprisingly quickly to changes in the frequency of encounters with other ants. This rapid response is probably driven by the ants' short memories—only about 10 seconds.

So the answer to the question of what controls a colony is the aggregate of "decisions" made in the simple interactions between individual ants. Are there analogies in other areas of biology?

A system without central control, built from simple, interacting components, is called a "complex system," and scientists in many areas of biology are interested in such systems. One obvious analog to an ant colony is a brain. Your brain is composed of neurons (nerve cells), but no single neuron knows how to think about, for example, the subject of ants—although your brain as a whole can think about ants. The brain operates without central control, in the sense that there isn't a master neuron in there that says, "OK, you guys, you do ants." Yet somehow all of the simple interactions among the neurons add up to the brain's very complex functioning. Another analogy is the growth of an embryo: The cells of an embryo all have the same DNA, but as the embryo grows, its cells take on different forms and functions. Nobody says, "OK, you become liver, you become bone." Instead, as a result of molecular interactions among cells, the embryo develops tissues of different types.

In your book, the colony is spoken of as if it were an organism. Does evolution operate on the level of the colony?

Yes, because the whole colony cooperates to make more queens and males that go out and start new colonies. A colony's behavior can determine how many offspring colonies it makes. In the long term, I'd like to understand how natural selection is acting on ant behavior (if it is). Why does it matter to the colony that it behaves in a certain way?

Now for a practical question: How can we deal with ant invasions in our homes?

It depends on where you live. In Northern California, the invading ants are usually Argentine ants, whose activity is clearly connected to the weather. The ants come into everybody's houses at the same time—when it rains or is very hot and dry—and they go out at the same time. The most important thing to remember is that putting out pesticide, especially when you don't have ants, sends pesticide into the groundwater but doesn't have much effect on the numbers of ants. I don't like having ants in my kitchen—I always take it personally—but I know that when I do, everybody else does, too. And covering or washing away a trail works only briefly—about 20 minutes for Argentine ants, as I found out in an experiment. Blocking off the places where ants are coming in is the best approach.

Ant-bait devices, from which foraging ants are supposed to carry poison to their nest, can work for ants that have one queen in a central nest. Such ants include carpenter ants, which enter houses in many parts of the United States. These ants nest in decaying wood, though contrary to their reputation, they don't eat wood. Ant baits don't work at all for the Argentine ants because these ants have many queens and many nests and you are unlikely to reach all the queens with the poison.

What advice do you have for undergraduates interested in a research career?

Students should try to experience several kinds of research, involving different kinds of activities. The best way to find out if you like doing research—whether it's working in the field or in the lab—is to try it.

How can an ant colony function when nobody's in charge and each ant can only perceive what's right around it?

Inquiry in Action

Learn about an experiment by Deborah Gordon and her graduate student Megan Frederickson in Inquiry Figure 2.2 on page 31. Read and analyze the original paper in *Inquiry in Action: Interpreting Scientific Papers.*

Left to right: Deborah Gordon, Megan Frederickson, Lisa Urry, and Jane Reece

The Chemical Context of Life

▲ Figure 2.1 **Who tends this garden?**

OVERVIEW

A Chemical Connection to Biology

The Amazon rain forest in South America is a showcase for the diversity of life on Earth. Colorful birds, insects, and other animals live among a myriad of trees, shrubs, vines, and wildflowers, and an excursion along a waterway or a forest path typically reveals a lush variety of plant life. Visitors traveling near the Amazon's headwaters in Peru are therefore surprised to come across tracts of forest like that seen in the foreground of the photo in **Figure 2.1**. This patch is almost completely dominated by a single plant species—a willowy flowering tree called *Duroia hirsuta*. Travelers may wonder if the garden is planted and maintained by local people, but the indigenous people are as mystified as the visitors. They call these stands of *Duroia* trees "devil's gardens," from a legend attributing them to an evil forest spirit.

Seeking a scientific explanation, a research team working under Deborah Gordon, who is interviewed on pages 28–29, recently solved the "devil's garden" mystery. **Figure 2.2** describes their main experiment. The researchers showed that the "farmers" who create and maintain these gardens are actually ants that live in the hollow stems of the *Duroia* trees. The ants do not plant the *Duroia* trees, but they prevent other plant species from growing in the garden by injecting intruders with a poisonous chemical. In this way, the ants create space for the growth of the *Duroia* trees that serve as their home. With the ability to maintain and expand its habitat, a single colony of devil's garden ants can live for hundreds of years.

The chemical the ants use to weed their garden turns out to be formic acid. This substance is produced by many species of ants and in fact got its name from the Latin word for ant, *formica*. In many cases, the formic acid probably serves as a disinfectant that protects the ants against microbial parasites. The devil's garden ant is the first ant species found to use formic acid as a herbicide. This use of a chemical is an important addition to the list of functions mediated by chemicals in the insect world. Scientists already know that chemicals play an important role in insect communication, attraction of mates, and defense against predators.

Research on devil's gardens is only one example of the relevance of chemistry to the study of life. Unlike a list of college courses, nature is not neatly packaged into the individual natural sciences—biology, chemistry, physics, and so forth. Biologists specialize in the study of life, but organisms and their environments are natural systems to which the concepts of chemistry and physics apply. Biology is a multidisciplinary science.

This unit of chapters introduces basic concepts of chemistry that will apply throughout our study of life. We will make many connections to the themes introduced in Chapter 1. One of these themes is the organization of life into a hierarchy of structural levels, with additional properties emerging at each successive level. In this unit, we will see how emergent properties are apparent at the lowest levels of biological organization—such as the ordering of atoms into molecules and the interactions of those molecules within cells. Somewhere in the transition from molecules to cells, we will cross the blurry boundary between nonlife and life. This chapter focuses on the chemical components that make up all matter.

What creates "devil's gardens" in the rain forest?

EXPERIMENT   Working under Deborah Gordon and with Michael Greene, graduate student Megan Frederickson sought the cause of "devil's gardens," stands of a single species of tree, *Duroia hirsuta.* One hypothesis was that ants living in these trees, *Myrmelachista schumanni,* produce a poisonous chemical that kills trees of other species; another was that the *Duroia* trees themselves kill competing trees, perhaps by means of a chemical.

To test these hypotheses, Frederickson did field experiments in Peru. Two saplings of a local nonhost tree species, *Cedrela odorata,* were planted inside each of ten devil's gardens. At the base of one, a sticky insect barrier was applied; the other was unprotected. Two more *Cedrela* saplings, with and without barriers, were planted about 50 meters outside each garden.

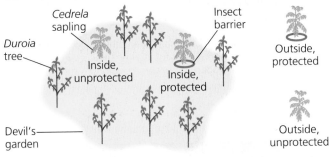

The researchers observed ant activity on the *Cedrela* leaves and measured areas of dead leaf tissue after one day. They also chemically analyzed contents of the ants' poison glands.

RESULTS   The ants made injections from the tips of their abdomens into leaves of unprotected saplings in their gardens (see photo). Within one day, these leaves developed dead areas (see graph). The protected saplings were uninjured, as were the saplings planted outside the gardens. Formic acid was the only chemical detected in the poison glands of the ants.

Cedrela saplings, inside and outside devil's gardens

CONCLUSION   Ants of the species *Myrmelachista schumanni* kill nonhost trees by injecting the leaves with formic acid, thus creating hospitable habitats (devil's gardens) for the ant colony.

SOURCE   M. E. Frederickson, M. J. Greene, and D. M. Gordon, "Devil's gardens" bedevilled by ants, *Nature* 437:495–496 (2005).

Inquiry in Action   Read and analyze the original paper in *Inquiry in Action: Interpreting Scientific Papers.*

WHAT IF?   What would be the results if the unprotected saplings' inability to grow in the devil's gardens was caused by a chemical released by the *Duroia* trees rather than by the ants?

Matter consists of chemical elements in pure form and in combinations called compounds

Organisms are composed of **matter**, which is anything that takes up space and has mass.* Matter exists in many diverse forms. Rocks, metals, oils, gases, and humans are just a few examples of what seems an endless assortment of matter.

Elements and Compounds

Matter is made up of elements. An **element** is a substance that cannot be broken down to other substances by chemical reactions. Today, chemists recognize 92 elements occurring in nature; gold, copper, carbon, and oxygen are examples. Each element has a symbol, usually the first letter or two of its name. Some symbols are derived from Latin or German; for instance, the symbol for sodium is Na, from the Latin word *natrium.*

A **compound** is a substance consisting of two or more different elements combined in a fixed ratio. Table salt, for example, is sodium chloride (NaCl), a compound composed of the elements sodium (Na) and chlorine (Cl) in a 1:1 ratio. Pure sodium is a metal, and pure chlorine is a poisonous gas. When chemically combined, however, sodium and chlorine form an edible compound. Water (H_2O), another compound, consists of the elements hydrogen (H) and oxygen (O) in a 2:1 ratio. These are simple examples of organized matter having emergent properties: A compound has characteristics different from those of its elements **(Figure 2.3).**

Sodium   **Chlorine**   **Sodium chloride**

▲ **Figure 2.3 The emergent properties of a compound.** The metal sodium combines with the poisonous gas chlorine, forming the edible compound sodium chloride, or table salt.

---

* Sometimes we substitute the term *weight* for mass, although the two are not identical. Mass is the amount of matter in an object, whereas the weight of an object is how strongly that mass is pulled by gravity. The weight of an astronaut walking on the moon is approximately ⅙ that of the astronaut's weight on Earth, but his or her mass is the same. However, as long as we are earthbound, the weight of an object is a measure of its mass; in everyday language, therefore, we tend to use the terms interchangeably.

Essential Elements of Life

About 25 of the 92 natural elements are known to be essential to life. Just four of these—carbon (C), oxygen (O), hydrogen (H), and nitrogen (N)—make up 96% of living matter. Phosphorus (P), sulfur (S), calcium (Ca), potassium (K), and a few other elements account for most of the remaining 4% of an organism's weight. **Table 2.1** lists by percentage the elements that make up the human body; the percentages for other organisms are similar. **Figure 2.4a** illustrates the effect of a deficiency of nitrogen, an essential element, in a plant.

Trace elements are those required by an organism in only minute quantities. Some trace elements, such as iron (Fe), are needed by all forms of life; others are required only by certain species. For example, in vertebrates (animals with backbones), the element iodine (I) is an essential ingredient of a hormone produced by the thyroid gland. A daily intake of only 0.15 milligram (mg) of iodine is adequate for normal activity of the human thyroid. An iodine deficiency in the diet causes the thyroid gland to grow to abnormal size, a condition called goiter **(Figure 2.4b)**. Where it is available, iodized salt has reduced the incidence of goiter.

(a) Nitrogen deficiency **(b) Iodine deficiency**

▲ **Figure 2.4 The effects of essential-element deficiencies. (a)** This photo shows the effect of nitrogen deficiency in corn (maize). In this controlled experiment, the taller plants on the left are growing in nitrogen-rich soil, and the shorter plants on the right in nitrogen-poor soil. **(b)** Goiter is an enlargement of the thyroid gland, resulting from a deficiency of the trace element iodine. The goiter of this Malaysian woman can probably be reversed by iodine supplements.

Table 2.1	**Naturally Occurring Elements in the Human Body**		
Symbol	**Element**	**Atomic Number (see p. 33)**	**Percentage of Human Body Weight**
Elements making up about 96% of human body weight			
O	Oxygen	8	65.0
C	Carbon	6	18.5
H	Hydrogen	1	9.5
N	Nitrogen	7	3.3
Elements making up about 4% of human body weight			
Ca	Calcium	20	1.5
P	Phosphorus	15	1.0
K	Potassium	19	0.4
S	Sulfur	16	0.3
Na	Sodium	11	0.2
Cl	Chlorine	17	0.2
Mg	Magnesium	12	0.1

Elements making up less than 0.01% of human body weight (trace elements)

Boron (B), chromium (Cr), cobalt (Co), copper (Cu), fluorine (F), iodine (I), iron (Fe), manganese (Mn), molybdenum (Mo), selenium (Se), silicon (Si), tin (Sn), vanadium (V), zinc (Zn)

CONCEPT CHECK 2.1

1. Explain how table salt has emergent properties.
2. Is a trace element an essential element? Explain.
3. **WHAT IF?** Iron (Fe) is a trace element required for the proper functioning of hemoglobin, the molecule that carries oxygen in red blood cells. What might be the effects of an iron deficiency?

For suggested answers, see Appendix A.

CONCEPT 2.2

An element's properties depend on the structure of its atoms

Each element consists of a certain kind of atom that is different from the atoms of any other element. An **atom** is the smallest unit of matter that still retains the properties of an element. Atoms are so small that it would take about a million of them to stretch across the period printed at the end of this sentence. We symbolize atoms with the same abbreviation used for the element that is made up of those atoms. For example, the symbol C stands for both the element carbon and a single carbon atom.

Subatomic Particles

Although the atom is the smallest unit having the properties of its element, these tiny bits of matter are composed of even smaller parts, called *subatomic particles*. Physicists have split the atom into more than a hundred types of particles, but only

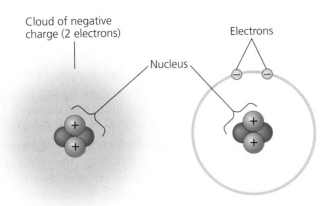

Cloud of negative charge (2 electrons)

Nucleus

Electrons

(a) This model represents the electrons as a cloud of negative charge.

(b) In this even more simplified model, the electrons are shown as two small yellow spheres on a circle around the nucleus.

▲ **Figure 2.5 Simplified models of a helium (He) atom.** The helium nucleus consists of 2 neutrons (brown) and 2 protons (pink). Two electrons (yellow) exist outside the nucleus. These models are not to scale; they greatly overestimate the size of the nucleus in relation to the electron cloud.

three kinds of particles are relevant here: **neutrons, protons,** and **electrons.** Protons and electrons are electrically charged. Each proton has one unit of positive charge, and each electron has one unit of negative charge. A neutron, as its name implies, is electrically neutral.

Protons and neutrons are packed together tightly in a dense core, or **atomic nucleus,** at the center of an atom; protons give the nucleus a positive charge. The electrons form a sort of cloud of negative charge around the nucleus, and it is the attraction between opposite charges that keeps the electrons in the vicinity of the nucleus. **Figure 2.5** shows two models of the structure of the helium atom as an example.

The neutron and proton are almost identical in mass, each about 1.7×10^{-24} gram (g). Grams and other conventional units are not very useful for describing the mass of objects so minuscule. Thus, for atoms and subatomic particles (and for molecules, too), we use a unit of measurement called the **dalton,** in honor of John Dalton, the British scientist who helped develop atomic theory around 1800. (The dalton is the same as the *atomic mass unit,* or *amu,* a unit you may have encountered elsewhere.) Neutrons and protons have masses close to 1 dalton. Because the mass of an electron is only about $\frac{1}{2,000}$ that of a neutron or proton, we can ignore electrons when computing the total mass of an atom.

Atomic Number and Atomic Mass

Atoms of the various elements differ in their number of subatomic particles. All atoms of a particular element have the same number of protons in their nuclei. This number of protons, which is unique to that element, is called the **atomic number** and is written as a subscript to the left of the symbol

for the element. The abbreviation $_2$He, for example, tells us that an atom of the element helium has 2 protons in its nucleus. Unless otherwise indicated, an atom is neutral in electrical charge, which means that its protons must be balanced by an equal number of electrons. Therefore, the atomic number tells us the number of protons and also the number of electrons in an electrically neutral atom.

We can deduce the number of neutrons from a second quantity, the **mass number,** which is the sum of protons plus neutrons in the nucleus of an atom. The mass number is written as a superscript to the left of an element's symbol. For example, we can use this shorthand to write an atom of helium as $_2^4$He. Because the atomic number indicates how many protons there are, we can determine the number of neutrons by subtracting the atomic number from the mass number: The helium atom, $_2^4$He, has 2 neutrons. An atom of sodium, $_{11}^{23}$Na, has 11 protons, 11 electrons, and 12 neutrons. The simplest atom is hydrogen, $_1^1$H, which has no neutrons; it consists of a single proton with a single electron.

As mentioned earlier, the contribution of electrons to mass is negligible. Therefore, almost all of an atom's mass is concentrated in its nucleus. Because neutrons and protons each have a mass very close to 1 dalton, the mass number is an approximation of the total mass of an atom, called its **atomic mass.** So we might say that the atomic mass of sodium ($_{11}^{23}$Na) is 23 daltons, although more precisely it is 22.9898 daltons.

Isotopes

All atoms of a given element have the same number of protons, but some atoms have more neutrons than other atoms of the same element and therefore have greater mass. These different atomic forms are called **isotopes** of the element. In nature, an element occurs as a mixture of its isotopes. For example, consider the three isotopes of the element carbon, which has the atomic number 6. The most common isotope is carbon-12, $_6^{12}$C, which accounts for about 99% of the carbon in nature. The isotope $_6^{12}$C has 6 neutrons. Most of the remaining 1% of carbon consists of atoms of the isotope $_6^{13}$C, with 7 neutrons. A third, even rarer isotope, ^{14}C, has 8 neutrons. Notice that all three isotopes of carbon have 6 protons; otherwise, they would not be carbon. Although the isotopes of an element have slightly different masses, they behave identically in chemical reactions. (The number usually given as the atomic mass of an element, such as 22.9898 daltons for sodium, is actually an average of the atomic masses of all the element's naturally occurring isotopes.)

Both ^{12}C and ^{13}C are stable isotopes, meaning that their nuclei do not have a tendency to lose particles. The isotope ^{14}C, however, is unstable, or radioactive. A **radioactive isotope** is one in which the nucleus decays spontaneously, giving off particles and energy. When the decay leads to a change in the

Research Method

Radioactive Tracers

APPLICATION Scientists use radioactive isotopes to label certain chemical compounds, creating tracers that can be used to follow a metabolic process or locate the compound within an organism. In this example, radioactive tracers are being used to determine the effect of temperature on the rate at which cells make copies of their DNA.

TECHNIQUE

❶ Compounds used by cells to make DNA are added to human cells. One ingredient is labeled with ^3H, a radioactive isotope of hydrogen. Nine dishes of cells are incubated at different temperatures. The cells make new DNA, incorporating the radioactive tracer with ^3H.

❷ The cells are placed in test tubes; their DNA is isolated; and unused labeled compounds are removed.

DNA (old and new)

❸ A solution called scintillation fluid is added to the test tubes and they are placed in a scintillation counter. As the ^3H in the newly made DNA decays, it emits radiation that excites chemicals in the scintillation fluid, causing them to give off light. Flashes of light are recorded by the scintillation counter.

RESULTS The frequency of flashes, which is recorded as counts per minute, is proportional to the amount of the radioactive tracer present, indicating the amount of new DNA. In this experiment, when the counts per minute are plotted against temperature, it is clear that temperature affects the rate of DNA synthesis; the most DNA was made at 35°C.

number of protons, it transforms the atom to an atom of a different element. For example, radioactive carbon decays to form nitrogen.

Radioactive isotopes have many useful applications in biology. In Chapter 25, you will learn how researchers use measurements of radioactivity in fossils to date these relics of past life. Radioactive isotopes are also useful as tracers to follow atoms through metabolism, the chemical processes of an organism. Cells use the radioactive atoms as they would use nonradioactive isotopes of the same element, but the radioactive tracers can be readily detected. **Figure 2.6** presents an example of how biologists use radioactive tracers to monitor biological processes, in this case the synthesis of DNA by human cells.

Radioactive tracers are important diagnostic tools in medicine. For example, certain kidney disorders can be diagnosed by injecting small doses of substances containing radioactive isotopes into the blood and then measuring the amount of tracer excreted in the urine. Radioactive tracers are also used in combination with sophisticated imaging instruments, such as PET scanners, which can monitor chemical processes, such as those involved in cancerous growth, as they actually occur in the body **(Figure 2.7)**.

▲ **Figure 2.7 A PET scan, a medical use for radioactive isotopes.** PET, an acronym for positron-emission tomography, detects locations of intense chemical activity in the body. The patient is first injected with a nutrient such as glucose labeled with a radioactive isotope that emits subatomic particles. These particles collide with electrons made available by chemical reactions in the body. A PET scanner detects the energy released in these collisions and maps "hot spots," the regions of an organ that are most chemically active at the time. The color of the image varies with the amount of the isotope present, with the bright yellow color here identifying a region of cancerous throat tissue.

Although radioactive isotopes are very useful in biological research and medicine, radiation from decaying isotopes also poses a hazard to life by damaging cellular molecules. The severity of this damage depends on the type and amount of radiation an organism absorbs. One of the most serious environmental threats is radioactive fallout from nuclear accidents. The doses of most isotopes used in medical diagnosis, however, are relatively safe.

The Energy Levels of Electrons

The simplified models of the atom in Figure 2.5 greatly exaggerate the size of the nucleus relative to the volume of the whole atom. If an atom of helium were the size of Yankee Stadium, the nucleus would be only the size of a pencil eraser in the center of the field. Moreover, the electrons would be like two tiny gnats buzzing around the stadium. Atoms are mostly empty space.

When two atoms approach each other during a chemical reaction, their nuclei do not come close enough to interact. Of the three kinds of subatomic particles we have discussed, only electrons are directly involved in the chemical reactions between atoms.

An atom's electrons vary in the amount of energy they possess. **Energy** is defined as the capacity to cause change—for instance, by doing work. **Potential energy** is the energy that matter possesses because of its location or structure. For example, water in a reservoir on a hill has potential energy because of its altitude. When the gates of the reservoir's dam are opened and the water runs downhill, the energy can be used to do work, such as turning generators. Because energy has been expended, the water has less energy at the bottom of the hill than it did in the reservoir. Matter has a natural tendency to move to the lowest possible state of potential energy; in this example, the water runs downhill. To restore the potential energy of a reservoir, work must be done to elevate the water against gravity.

The electrons of an atom have potential energy because of how they are arranged in relation to the nucleus. The negatively charged electrons are attracted to the positively charged nucleus. It takes work to move a given electron farther away from the nucleus, so the more distant an electron is from the nucleus, the greater its potential energy. Unlike the continuous flow of water downhill, changes in the potential energy of electrons can occur only in steps of fixed amounts. An electron having a certain amount of energy is something like a ball on a staircase **(Figure 2.8a)**. The ball can have different amounts of potential energy, depending on which step it is on, but it cannot spend much time between the steps. Similarly, an electron's potential energy is determined by its energy level. An electron cannot exist in between energy levels.

An electron's energy level is correlated with its average distance from the nucleus. Electrons are found in different

(a) A ball bouncing down a flight of stairs provides an analogy for energy levels of electrons, because the ball can come to rest only on each step, not between steps.

Third shell (highest energy level)

Second shell (higher energy level)

First shell (lowest energy level)

Energy absorbed

Energy lost

Atomic nucleus

(b) An electron can move from one shell to another only if the energy it gains or loses is exactly equal to the difference in energy between the energy levels of the two shells. Arrows indicate some of the stepwise changes in potential energy that are possible.

▲ **Figure 2.8 Energy levels of an atom's electrons.** Electrons exist only at fixed levels of potential energy called electron shells.

electron shells, each with a characteristic average distance and energy level. In diagrams, shells can be represented by concentric circles **(Figure 2.8b)**. The first shell is closest to the nucleus, and electrons in this shell have the lowest potential energy. Electrons in the second shell have more energy, and electrons in the third shell even more energy. An electron can change the shell it occupies, but only by absorbing or losing an amount of energy equal to the difference in potential energy between its position in the old shell and that in the new shell. When an electron absorbs energy, it moves to a shell farther out from the nucleus. For example, light energy can excite an electron to a higher energy level. (Indeed, this is the first step taken when plants harness the energy of sunlight for photosynthesis, the process that produces food from carbon dioxide and water.) When an electron loses energy, it "falls back" to a shell closer to the nucleus, and the lost energy is usually released to the environment as heat. For example, sunlight excites electrons in the surface of a car to higher energy levels. When the electrons fall back to their original levels, the car's surface heats up. This thermal energy can be transferred to the air or to your hand if you touch the car.

Electron Distribution and Chemical Properties

The chemical behavior of an atom is determined by the distribution of electrons in the atom's electron shells. Beginning with hydrogen, the simplest atom, we can imagine building the atoms of the other elements by adding 1 proton and 1 electron

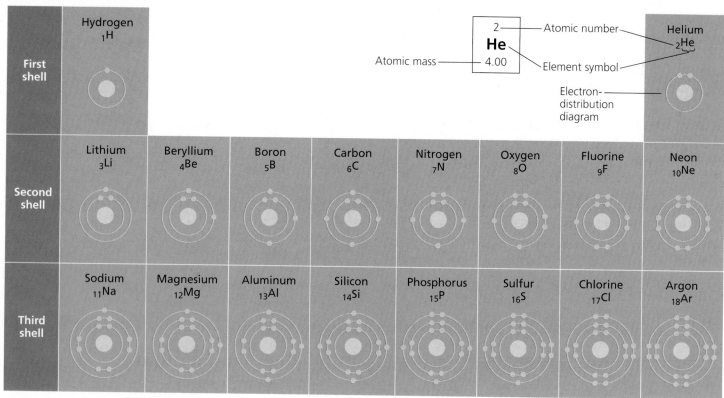

▲ **Figure 2.9 Electron-distribution diagrams for the first 18 elements in the periodic table.** In a standard periodic table (see Appendix B), information for each element is presented as shown for helium in the inset. In the diagrams in this table, electrons are represented as yellow dots and electron shells as concentric circles. These diagrams are a convenient way to picture the distribution of an atom's electrons among its electron shells, but these simplified models do not accurately represent the shape of the atom or the location of its electrons. The elements are arranged in rows, each representing the filling of an electron shell. As electrons are added, they occupy the lowest available shell.

? *What is the atomic number of magnesium? How many protons and electrons does it have? How many electron shells? How many valence electrons?*

at a time (along with an appropriate number of neutrons). **Figure 2.9**, an abbreviated version of what is called the *periodic table of the elements*, shows this distribution of electrons for the first 18 elements, from hydrogen ($_1$H) to argon ($_{18}$Ar). The elements are arranged in three rows, or periods, corresponding to the number of electron shells in their atoms. The left-to-right sequence of elements in each row corresponds to the sequential addition of electrons and protons. (See Appendix B for the complete periodic table.)

Hydrogen's 1 electron and helium's 2 electrons are located in the first shell. Electrons, like all matter, tend to exist in the lowest available state of potential energy. In an atom, this state is in the first shell. However, the first shell can hold no more than 2 electrons; thus, hydrogen and helium are the only elements in the first row of the table. An atom with more than 2 electrons must use higher shells because the first shell is full. The next element, lithium, has 3 electrons. Two of these electrons fill the first shell, while the third electron occupies the second shell. The second shell holds a maximum of 8 electrons. Neon, at the end of the second row, has 8 electrons in the second shell, giving it a total of 10 electrons.

The chemical behavior of an atom depends mostly on the number of electrons in its *outermost* shell. We call those outer electrons **valence electrons** and the outermost electron shell the **valence shell**. In the case of lithium, there is only 1 valence electron, and the second shell is the valence shell. Atoms with the same number of electrons in their valence shells exhibit similar chemical behavior. For example, fluorine (F) and chlorine (Cl) both have 7 valence electrons, and both form compounds when combined with the element sodium (see Figure 2.3). An atom with a completed valence shell is unreactive; that is, it will not interact readily with other atoms. At the far right of the periodic table are helium, neon, and argon, the only three elements shown in Figure 2.9 that have full valence shells. These elements are said to be *inert*, meaning chemically unreactive. All the other atoms in Figure 2.9 are chemically reactive because they have incomplete valence shells.

Electron Orbitals

In the early 1900s, the electron shells of an atom were visualized as concentric paths of electrons orbiting the nucleus, somewhat like planets orbiting the sun. It is still convenient to use two-dimensional concentric-circle diagrams to symbolize electron shells, as in Figure 2.9. However, you need to remember that each concentric circle represents only the

(a) Electron-distribution diagram. An electron-distribution diagram is shown here for a neon atom, which has a total of 10 electrons. Each concentric circle represents an electron shell, which can be subdivided into electron orbitals.

(b) Separate electron orbitals. The three-dimensional shapes represent electron orbitals—the volumes of space where the electrons of an atom are most likely to be found. Each orbital holds a maximum of 2 electrons. The first electron shell, on the left, has one spherical (*s*) orbital, designated 1*s*. The second shell, on the right, has one larger *s* orbital (designated 2*s* for the second shell) plus three dumbbell-shaped orbitals called *p* orbitals (2*p* for the second shell). The three 2*p* orbitals lie at right angles to one another along imaginary *x*-, *y*-, and *z*-axes of the atom. Each 2*p* orbital is outlined here in a different color.

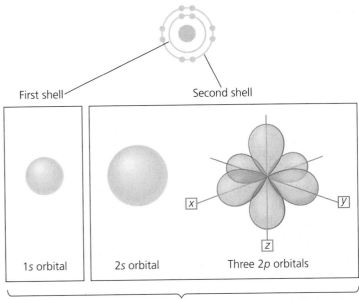

Neon, with two filled shells (10 electrons)

First shell   Second shell

1*s* orbital   2*s* orbital   Three 2*p* orbitals

(c) Superimposed electron orbitals. To show the complete picture of the electron orbitals of neon, we superimpose the 1*s* orbital of the first shell and the 2*s* and three 2*p* orbitals of the second shell.

1*s*, 2*s*, and 2*p* orbitals

▲ **Figure 2.10 Electron orbitals.**

average distance between an electron in that shell and the nucleus. Accordingly, the concentric-circle diagrams do not give a real picture of an atom. In reality, we can never know the exact location of an electron. What we can do instead is describe the space in which an electron spends most of its time. The three-dimensional space where an electron is found 90% of the time is called an **orbital**.

Each electron shell contains electrons at a particular energy level, distributed among a specific number of orbitals of distinctive shapes and orientations. **Figure 2.10** shows the orbitals of neon as an example. You can think of an orbital as a component of an electron shell. The first electron shell has only one spherical *s* orbital (called 1*s*), but the second shell has four orbitals: one large spherical *s* orbital (called 2*s*) and three dumbbell-shaped *p* orbitals (called 2*p* orbitals). (The third shell and other higher electron shells also have *s* and *p* orbitals, as well as orbitals of more complex shapes.)

No more than 2 electrons can occupy a single orbital. The first electron shell can therefore accommodate up to 2 electrons in its *s* orbital. The lone electron of a hydrogen atom occupies the 1*s* orbital, as do the 2 electrons of a helium atom. The four orbitals of the second electron shell can hold up to 8 electrons. Electrons in each of the four orbitals have nearly the same energy, but they move in different volumes of space.

The reactivity of atoms arises from the presence of unpaired electrons in one or more orbitals of their valence shells. As you will see in the next section, atoms interact in a way that completes their valence shells. When they do so, it is the *unpaired* electrons that are involved.

CONCEPT CHECK 2.2

1. A lithium atom has 3 protons and 4 neutrons. What is its atomic mass in daltons?
2. A nitrogen atom has 7 protons, and the most common isotope of nitrogen has 7 neutrons. A radioactive isotope of nitrogen has 8 neutrons. Write the atomic number and mass number of this radioactive nitrogen as a chemical symbol with a subscript and superscript.
3. How many electrons does fluorine have? How many electron shells? Name the orbitals that are occupied. How many electrons are needed to fill the valence shell?
4. **WHAT IF?** In Figure 2.9, if two or more elements are in the same row, what do they have in common? If two or more elements are in the same column, what do they have in common?

For suggested answers, see Appendix A.

The formation and function of molecules depend on chemical bonding between atoms

Now that we have looked at the structure of atoms, we can move up the hierarchy of organization and see how atoms combine to form molecules and ionic compounds. Atoms with incomplete valence shells can interact with certain other atoms in such a way that each partner completes its valence shell: The atoms either share or transfer valence electrons. These interactions usually result in atoms staying close together, held by attractions called **chemical bonds**. The strongest kinds of chemical bonds are covalent bonds and ionic bonds.

Covalent Bonds

A **covalent bond** is the sharing of a pair of valence electrons by two atoms. For example, let's consider what happens when two hydrogen atoms approach each other. Recall that hydrogen has 1 valence electron in the first shell, but the shell's capacity is 2 electrons. When the two hydrogen atoms come close enough for their 1*s* orbitals to overlap, they can share their electrons **(Figure 2.11)**. Each hydrogen atom now has 2 electrons associated with it in what amounts to a completed valence shell. Two or more atoms held together by covalent bonds constitute a **molecule**. In this case, the example is a hydrogen molecule.

Hydrogen atoms (2 H)

❶ In each hydrogen atom, the single electron is held in its orbital by its attraction to the proton in the nucleus.

❷ When two hydrogen atoms approach each other, the electron of each atom is also attracted to the proton in the other nucleus.

❸ The two electrons become shared in a covalent bond, forming an H_2 molecule.

Hydrogen molecule (H_2)

▲ **Figure 2.11 Formation of a covalent bond.**

Electron sharing can be depicted using element symbols, with dots representing the outermost electrons. You have probably seen such diagrams, called Lewis dot structures, in your chemistry book. The Lewis dot structure for a hydrogen molecule, H:H, is shown in **Figure 2.12a**. We can abbreviate the structure of this molecule as H—H, where the line represents a single covalent bond, or simply a **single bond**—that is, a pair of shared electrons. This notation, which represents both atoms and bonding, is called a **structural formula**. We can abbreviate even further by writing H_2, a **molecular formula** indicating simply that the molecule consists of two atoms of hydrogen.

Oxygen has 6 electrons in its second electron shell and therefore needs 2 more electrons to complete its valence shell. Two oxygen atoms form a molecule by sharing *two* pairs of valence electrons **(Figure 2.12b)**. The atoms are thus joined by what is called a double covalent bond, or **double bond**.

Name and Molecular Formula	Electron-distribution Diagram	Lewis Dot Structure and Structural Formula	Space-filling Model
(a) Hydrogen (H_2). Two hydrogen atoms can form a single bond.		H:H H—H	
(b) Oxygen (O_2). Two oxygen atoms share two pairs of electrons to form a double bond.		Ö::Ö O=O	
(c) Water (H_2O). Two hydrogen atoms and one oxygen atom are joined by covalent bonds to produce a molecule of water.		:Ö:H H O—H H	
(d) Methane (CH_4). Four hydrogen atoms can satisfy the valence of one carbon atom, forming methane.		H H:C:H H H H—C—H H	

▲ **Figure 2.12 Covalent bonding in four molecules.** A single covalent bond consists of a pair of shared electrons. The number of electrons required to complete an atom's valence shell generally determines how many bonds that atom will form. Four ways of indicating bonds are shown; the space-filling model comes closest to representing the actual shape of the molecule (see also Figure 2.17).

Each atom that can share valence electrons has a bonding capacity corresponding to the number of covalent bonds the atom can form. When the bonds form, they give the atom a full complement of electrons in the valence shell. The bonding capacity of oxygen, for example, is 2. This bonding capacity is called the atom's **valence** and usually equals the number of unpaired electrons required to complete the atom's outermost (valence) shell. See if you can determine the valences of hydrogen, oxygen, nitrogen, and carbon by studying the electron distribution diagrams in Figure 2.9. You can see that the valence of hydrogen is 1; oxygen, 2; nitrogen, 3; and carbon, 4. However, there are more complicated cases, such as phosphorus (P), another element important to life. Phosphorus can have a valence of 3, as we would predict from the presence of 3 unpaired electrons in its valence shell. In biologically important molecules, however, phosphorus can form three single bonds and one double bond. Therefore, it can also have a valence of 5.

The molecules H_2 and O_2 are pure elements rather than compounds because a compound is a combination of two or more *different* elements. Water, with the molecular formula H_2O, is a compound. Two atoms of hydrogen are needed to satisfy the valence of one oxygen atom. **Figure 2.12c** shows the structure of a water molecule. Water is so important to life that Chapter 3 is devoted entirely to its structure and behavior.

Another molecule that is a compound is methane, the main component of natural gas, with the molecular formula CH_4 **(Figure 2.12d)**. It takes four hydrogen atoms, each with a valence of 1, to complement one atom of carbon, with its valence of 4. We will look at many other compounds of carbon in Chapter 4.

The attraction of a particular kind of atom for the electrons of a covalent bond is called its **electronegativity**. The more electronegative an atom, the more strongly it pulls shared electrons toward itself. In a covalent bond between two atoms of the same element, the outcome of the tug-of-war for common electrons is a standoff; the two atoms are equally electronegative. Such a bond, in which the electrons are shared equally, is a **nonpolar covalent bond**. For example, the covalent bond of H_2 is nonpolar, as is the double bond of O_2. In other compounds, however, where one atom is bonded to a more electronegative atom, the electrons of the bond are not shared equally. This type of bond is called a **polar covalent bond**. Such bonds vary in their polarity, depending on the relative electronegativity of the two atoms. For example, the bonds between the oxygen and hydrogen atoms of a water mol-

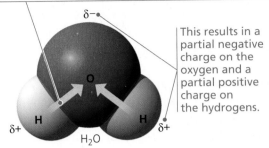

Because oxygen (O) is more electronegative than hydrogen (H), shared electrons are pulled more toward oxygen.

This results in a partial negative charge on the oxygen and a partial positive charge on the hydrogens.

▲ **Figure 2.13 Polar covalent bonds in a water molecule.**

ecule are quite polar **(Figure 2.13)**. Oxygen is one of the most electronegative of all the elements, attracting shared electrons much more strongly than hydrogen does. In a covalent bond between oxygen and hydrogen, the electrons spend more time near the oxygen nucleus than they do near the hydrogen nucleus. Because electrons have a negative charge, the unequal sharing of electrons in water causes the oxygen atom to have a partial negative charge (indicated by the Greek letter δ with a minus sign, δ−, or "delta minus") and each hydrogen atom to have a partial positive charge (δ+, or "delta plus"). In contrast, the individual bonds of methane (CH_4) are much less polar because carbon and hydrogen differ much less in electronegativity than do oxygen and hydrogen.

Ionic Bonds

In some cases, two atoms are so unequal in their attraction for valence electrons that the more electronegative atom strips an electron completely away from its partner. This is what happens when an atom of sodium ($_{11}$Na) encounters an atom of chlorine ($_{17}$Cl) **(Figure 2.14)**. A sodium atom has a total of 11 electrons,

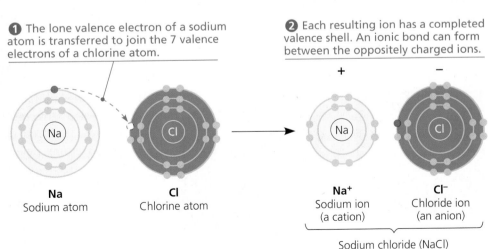

❶ The lone valence electron of a sodium atom is transferred to join the 7 valence electrons of a chlorine atom.

❷ Each resulting ion has a completed valence shell. An ionic bond can form between the oppositely charged ions.

Na
Sodium atom

Cl
Chlorine atom

Na⁺
Sodium ion
(a cation)

Cl⁻
Chloride ion
(an anion)

Sodium chloride (NaCl)

▲ **Figure 2.14 Electron transfer and ionic bonding.** The attraction between oppositely charged atoms, or ions, is an ionic bond. An ionic bond can form between any two oppositely charged ions, even if they have not been formed by transfer of an electron from one to the other.

with its single valence electron in the third electron shell. A chlorine atom has a total of 17 electrons, with 7 electrons in its valence shell. When these two atoms meet, the lone valence electron of sodium is transferred to the chlorine atom, and both atoms end up with their valence shells complete. (Because sodium no longer has an electron in the third shell, the second shell is now the valence shell.)

The electron transfer between the two atoms moves one unit of negative charge from sodium to chlorine. Sodium, now with 11 protons but only 10 electrons, has a net electrical charge of 1+. A charged atom (or molecule) is called an **ion**. When the charge is positive, the ion is specifically called a **cation**; the sodium atom has become a cation. Conversely, the chlorine atom, having gained an extra electron, now has 17 protons and 18 electrons, giving it a net electrical charge of 1−. It has become a chloride ion—an **anion**, or negatively charged ion. Because of their opposite charges, cations and anions attract each other; this attraction is called an **ionic bond**. The transfer of an electron is not the formation of a bond; rather, it allows a bond to form because it results in two ions. Any two ions of opposite charge can form an ionic bond. The ions do not need to have acquired their charge by an electron transfer with each other.

Compounds formed by ionic bonds are called **ionic compounds**, or **salts**. We know the ionic compound sodium chloride (NaCl) as table salt **(Figure 2.15)**. Salts are often found in nature as crystals of various sizes and shapes. Each salt crystal is an aggregate of vast numbers of cations and anions bonded by their electrical attraction and arranged in a three-dimensional lattice. Unlike a covalent compound, which consists of molecules having a definite size and number of atoms, an ionic compound does not consist of molecules in the same sense. The formula for an ionic compound, such as NaCl, indicates only the ratio of elements in a crystal of the salt. "NaCl" by itself is not a molecule.

Not all salts have equal numbers of cations and anions. For example, the ionic compound magnesium chloride ($MgCl_2$) has two chloride ions for each magnesium ion. Magnesium ($_{12}Mg$) must lose 2 outer electrons if the atom is to have a complete valence shell, so it tends to become a cation with a net charge of 2+ (Mg^{2+}). One magnesium cation can therefore form ionic bonds with two chloride anions.

The term *ion* also applies to entire molecules that are electrically charged. In the salt ammonium chloride (NH_4Cl), for instance, the anion is a single chloride ion (Cl^-), but the cation is ammonium (NH_4^+), a nitrogen atom with four covalently bonded hydrogen atoms. The whole ammonium ion has an electrical charge of 1+ because it is 1 electron short.

Environment affects the strength of ionic bonds. In a dry salt crystal, the bonds are so strong that it takes a hammer and chisel to break enough of them to crack the crystal in two. If the same salt crystal is dissolved in water, however, the ionic bonds are much weaker because each ion is partially shielded by its interactions with water molecules. Most drugs are manufactured as salts because they are quite stable when dry but can dissociate easily in water. In the next chapter, you will learn how water dissolves salts.

Weak Chemical Bonds

In organisms, most of the strongest chemical bonds are covalent bonds, which link atoms to form a cell's molecules. But weaker bonding within and between molecules is also indispensable in the cell, contributing greatly to the emergent properties of life. Most important large biological molecules are held in their functional form by weak bonds. In addition, when two molecules in the cell make contact, they may adhere temporarily by weak bonds. The reversibility of weak bonding can be an advantage: Two molecules can come together, respond to one another in some way, and then separate.

Certain types of weak chemical bonds are important in organisms. One is the ionic bond as it exists between ions dissociated in water, which we just discussed. Another type of weak bond, known as a hydrogen bond, is also crucial to life.

Hydrogen Bonds

Among the various kinds of weak chemical bonds, hydrogen bonds are so important in the chemistry of life that they deserve special attention. A **hydrogen bond** forms when a hydrogen atom covalently bonded to one electronegative atom is also attracted to another electronegative atom. In living cells, the electronegative partners are usually oxygen or nitrogen atoms. Refer to **Figure 2.16** to examine the simple case of hydrogen bonding between water (H_2O) and ammonia (NH_3). In the next chapter, we'll see how the hydrogen bonds between water molecules allow some insects to walk on water.

Van der Waals Interactions

Even a molecule with nonpolar covalent bonds may have positively and negatively charged regions. Electrons are not always symmetrically distributed in such a molecule; at any

▲ **Figure 2.15 A sodium chloride crystal.** The sodium ions (Na^+) and chloride ions (Cl^-) are held together by ionic bonds. The formula NaCl tells us that the ratio of Na^+ to Cl^- is 1:1.

Na⁺
Cl⁻

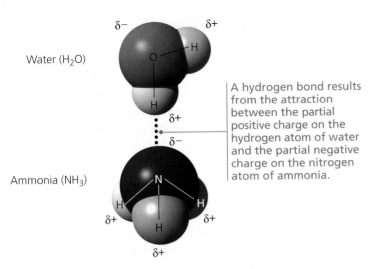

Water (H₂O)

Ammonia (NH₃)

A hydrogen bond results from the attraction between the partial positive charge on the hydrogen atom of water and the partial negative charge on the nitrogen atom of ammonia.

▲ Figure 2.16 A hydrogen bond.

DRAW IT *Draw five water molecules using structural formulas and indicating partial charges, and show how they can make hydrogen bonds with each other.*

instant, they may accumulate by chance in one part of the molecule or another. The results are ever-changing regions of positive and negative charge that enable all atoms and molecules to stick to one another. These **van der Waals interactions** are weak and occur only when atoms and molecules are very close together. In spite of their weakness, van der Waals interactions were recently shown to be responsible for the ability of a gecko lizard (left) to walk up a wall. Each gecko toe has hundreds of thousands of tiny hairs, with multiple projections at the hair's tip that increase surface area. Apparently, the van der Waals interactions between the hair tip molecules and the molecules of the wall's surface are so numerous that despite their individual weakness, together they can support the gecko's body weight.

Van der Waals interactions, hydrogen bonds, ionic bonds in water, and other weak bonds may form not only between molecules but also between different regions of a single large molecule, such as a protein. Although these bonds are individually weak, their cumulative effect is to reinforce the three-dimensional shape of a large molecule. You will learn more about the very important biological roles of weak bonds in Chapter 5.

Molecular Shape and Function

A molecule has a characteristic size and shape. The precise shape of a molecule is usually very important to its function in the living cell.

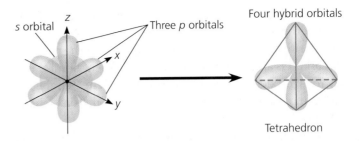

s orbital Three p orbitals Four hybrid orbitals

Tetrahedron

(a) Hybridization of orbitals. The single s and three p orbitals of a valence shell involved in covalent bonding combine to form four teardrop-shaped hybrid orbitals. These orbitals extend to the four corners of an imaginary tetrahedron (outlined in red).

Space-filling Model	Ball-and-stick Model	Hybrid-orbital Model (with ball-and-stick model superimposed)

Water (H₂O)

Unbonded electron pair

104.5°

Methane (CH₄)

(b) Molecular-shape models. Three models representing molecular shape are shown for water and methane. The positions of the hybrid orbitals determine the shapes of the molecules.

▲ Figure 2.17 Molecular shapes due to hybrid orbitals.

A molecule consisting of two atoms, such as H₂ or O₂, is always linear, but molecules with more than two atoms have more complicated shapes. These shapes are determined by the positions of the atoms' orbitals. When an atom forms covalent bonds, the orbitals in its valence shell rearrange. For atoms with valence electrons in both s and p orbitals (review Figure 2.10), the single s and three p orbitals hybridize to form four new hybrid orbitals shaped like identical teardrops extending from the region of the atomic nucleus **(Figure 2.17a)**. If we connect the larger ends of the teardrops with lines, we have the outline of a geometric shape called a tetrahedron, similar to a pyramid.

For the water molecule (H₂O), two of the hybrid orbitals in the oxygen atom's valence shell are shared with hydrogen atoms **(Figure 2.17b)**. The result is a molecule shaped roughly like a V, with its two covalent bonds spread apart at an angle of 104.5°.

The methane molecule (CH₄) has the shape of a completed tetrahedron because all four hybrid orbitals of carbon are shared with hydrogen atoms (see Figure 2.17b). The nucleus of the carbon is at the center, with its four covalent bonds radiating to hydrogen nuclei at the corners of the tetrahedron. Larger molecules containing multiple carbon atoms, including many of the molecules that make up living matter, have more complex overall shapes. However, the tetrahedral shape of a carbon atom bonded to four other atoms is often a repeating motif within such molecules.

Molecular shape is crucial in biology because it determines how biological molecules recognize and respond to one another with specificity. Only molecules with complementary shapes can form weak bonds with each other. We can see this specificity in the effects of opiates, drugs derived from opium. Opium's narcotic effects have been known since ancient times. During the 1800s, morphine was isolated from opium,

and heroin was synthesized from morphine. These opiates relieve pain and alter mood by binding to specific receptor molecules on the surface of brain cells. Why would brain cells carry receptors for opiates, compounds not made by our bodies? The discovery of endorphins in 1975 answered this question. Endorphins are signaling molecules made by the pituitary gland that bind to the receptors, relieving pain and producing euphoria during times of stress, such as intense exercise. It turns out that opiates have shapes similar to endorphins and mimic them by binding to endorphin receptors in the brain. That is why opiates and endorphins have similar effects (**Figure 2.18**). The role of molecular shape in brain chemistry illustrates the relationship between structure and function, one of biology's unifying themes.

CONCEPT CHECK 2.3

1. Why does the following structure fail to make sense chemically?

$$H—C{=}C—H$$

2. Explain what holds together the atoms in a crystal of magnesium chloride (MgCl₂).

3. **WHAT IF?** If you were a pharmaceutical researcher, why would you want to learn the three-dimensional shapes of naturally occurring signaling molecules?

For suggested answers, see Appendix A.

Key

- ■ Carbon
- ■ Hydrogen
- ■ Nitrogen
- ■ Sulfur
- ■ Oxygen

Natural endorphin

Morphine

(a) Structures of endorphin and morphine. The boxed portion of the endorphin molecule (left) binds to receptor molecules on target cells in the brain. The boxed portion of the morphine molecule (right) is a close match.

Natural endorphin
Morphine
Endorphin receptors
Brain cell

(b) Binding to endorphin receptors. Both endorphin and morphine can bind to endorphin receptors on the surface of a brain cell.

▲ **Figure 2.18 A molecular mimic.** Morphine affects pain perception and emotional state by mimicking the brain's natural endorphins.

CONCEPT 2.4

Chemical reactions make and break chemical bonds

The making and breaking of chemical bonds, leading to changes in the composition of matter, are called **chemical reactions**. An example is the reaction between hydrogen and oxygen that forms water:

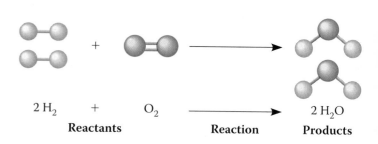

2 H₂	+	O₂	→	2 H₂O
Reactants			**Reaction**	**Products**

This reaction breaks the covalent bonds of H₂ and O₂ and forms the new bonds of H₂O. When we write a chemical reaction, we use an arrow to indicate the conversion of the starting materials, called the **reactants**, to the **products**. The coefficients indicate the number of molecules involved; for example, the coefficient 2 in front of the H_2 means that the reaction starts with two molecules of hydrogen. Notice that all atoms of the reactants must be accounted for in the products. Matter is conserved in a chemical reaction: Reactions cannot create or destroy matter but can only rearrange it.

Photosynthesis, which takes place within the cells of green plant tissues, is a particularly important example of how chemical reactions rearrange matter. Humans and other animals ultimately depend on photosynthesis for food and oxygen, and this process is at the foundation of almost all ecosystems. The following chemical shorthand summarizes the process of photosynthesis:

$$6\ CO_2 + 6\ H_2O \longrightarrow C_6H_{12}O_6 + 6\ O_2$$

The raw materials of photosynthesis are carbon dioxide (CO_2), which is taken from the air, and water (H_2O), which is absorbed from the soil. Within the plant cells, sunlight powers the conversion of these ingredients to a sugar called glucose ($C_6H_{12}O_6$) and oxygen molecules (O_2), a by-product that the plant releases into the surroundings **(Figure 2.19)**. Although photosynthesis is actually a sequence of many chemical reactions, we still end up with the same number and kinds

of atoms we had when we started. Matter has simply been rearranged, with an input of energy provided by sunlight.

All chemical reactions are reversible, with the products of the forward reaction becoming the reactants for the reverse reaction. For example, hydrogen and nitrogen molecules can combine to form ammonia, but ammonia can also decompose to regenerate hydrogen and nitrogen:

$$3\ H_2 + N_2 \rightleftharpoons 2\ NH_3$$

The two opposite-headed arrows indicate that the reaction is reversible.

One of the factors affecting the rate of a reaction is the concentration of reactants. The greater the concentration of reactant molecules, the more frequently they collide with one another and have an opportunity to react and form products. The same holds true for products. As products accumulate, collisions resulting in the reverse reaction become more frequent. Eventually, the forward and reverse reactions occur at the same rate, and the relative concentrations of products and reactants stop changing. The point at which the reactions offset one another exactly is called **chemical equilibrium**. This is a dynamic equilibrium; reactions are still going on, but with no net effect on the concentrations of reactants and products. Equilibrium does *not* mean that the reactants and products are equal in concentration, but only that their concentrations have stabilized at a particular ratio. The reaction involving ammonia reaches equilibrium when ammonia decomposes as rapidly as it forms. In some chemical reactions, the equilibrium point may lie so far to the right that these reactions go essentially to completion; that is, virtually all the reactants are converted to products.

We will return to the subject of chemical reactions after more detailed study of the various types of molecules that are important to life. In the next chapter, we focus on water, the substance in which all the chemical processes of organisms occur.

▲ **Figure 2.19 Photosynthesis: a solar-powered rearrangement of matter.** *Elodea*, a freshwater plant, produces sugar by rearranging the atoms of carbon dioxide and water in the chemical process known as photosynthesis, which is powered by sunlight. Much of the sugar is then converted to other food molecules. Oxygen gas (O_2) is a by-product of photosynthesis; notice the bubbles of oxygen escaping from the leaves in the photo.

? *Explain how this photo relates to the reactants and products in the equation for photosynthesis given in the above text. (You will learn more about photosynthesis in Chapter 10.)*

CONCEPT CHECK 2.4

1. Refer to the reaction between hydrogen and oxygen that forms water, shown with ball-and-stick models on page 42. Draw the Lewis dot structures representing this reaction.
2. Which types of chemical reactions occur faster at equilibrium, the formation of products from reactants, or reactants from products?
3. **WHAT IF?** Write an equation that uses the products of photosynthesis as reactants and uses the reactants as products. Add energy as another product. This new equation describes a process that occurs in your cells. Describe this equation in words. How does this equation relate to breathing?

For suggested answers, see Appendix A.

Chapter 2 Review

SUMMARY OF KEY CONCEPTS

CONCEPT 2.1

Matter consists of chemical elements in pure form and in combinations called compounds (pp. 31–32)

► **Elements and Compounds** Elements cannot be broken down chemically to other substances. A compound contains two or more different elements in a fixed ratio.

► **Essential Elements of Life** Carbon, oxygen, hydrogen, and nitrogen make up approximately 96% of living matter.

   MEDIA

   Investigation How Are Space Rocks Analyzed for Signs of Life?

CONCEPT 2.2

An element's properties depend on the structure of its atoms (pp. 32–37)

► **Subatomic Particles** An atom, the smallest unit of an element, has the following components:

► **Atomic Number and Atomic Mass** An electrically neutral atom has equal numbers of electrons and protons; the number of protons determines the atomic number. The atomic mass is measured in daltons and is roughly equal to the sum of protons plus neutrons.

► **Isotopes** Isotopes of an element differ from each other in neutron number and therefore mass. Unstable isotopes give off particles and energy as radioactivity.

► **The Energy Levels of Electrons** In an atom, electrons occupy specific energy shells; the electrons in a shell have a characteristic energy level.

► **Electron Distribution and Chemical Properties** Electron distribution in shells determines the chemical behavior of an atom. An atom that has an incomplete valence shell is reactive.

► **Electron Orbitals** Electrons exist in orbitals, three-dimensional spaces with specific shapes that are components of electron shells.

   MEDIA

   Activity Structure of the Atomic Nucleus
   Activity Electron Arrangement
   Activity Build an Atom

CONCEPT 2.3

The formation and function of molecules depend on chemical bonding between atoms (pp. 38–42)

► **Covalent Bonds** Chemical bonds form when atoms interact and complete their valence shells. Covalent bonds form when pairs of electrons are shared.

Molecules consist of two or more covalently bonded atoms. Electrons of a polar covalent bond are pulled closer to the more electronegative atom. If both atoms are the same, they have the same electronegativity, and the covalent bond is nonpolar.

► **Ionic Bonds**

Ionic bond

Na Sodium atom	**Cl** Chlorine atom

Electron transfer forms ions →

+	−
Na⁺ Sodium ion (a cation)	**Cl⁻** Chloride ion (an anion)

► **Weak Chemical Bonds** A hydrogen bond is an attraction between a hydrogen atom carrying a partial positive charge ($\delta+$) and an electronegative atom ($\delta-$). Van der Waals interactions occur between transiently positive and negative regions of molecules. Weak bonds reinforce the shapes of large molecules and help molecules adhere to each other.

► **Molecular Shape and Function** A molecule's shape is determined by the positions of its atoms' valence orbitals. Covalent bonds result in hybrid orbitals, which are responsible for the shapes of H_2O, CH_4, and many more complex biological molecules. Shape is usually the basis for the recognition of one biological molecule by another.

   MEDIA

   Activity Covalent Bonds
   Activity Nonpolar and Polar Molecules
   Activity Ionic Bonds
   Activity Hydrogen Bonds

CONCEPT 2.4

Chemical reactions make and break chemical bonds (pp. 42–43)

► Chemical reactions change reactants into products while conserving matter. All chemical reactions are theoretically reversible. Chemical equilibrium is reached when the forward and reverse reaction rates are equal.

TESTING YOUR KNOWLEDGE

SELF-QUIZ

1. In the term *trace element,* the modifier *trace* means
   a. the element is required in very small amounts.
   b. the element can be used as a label to trace atoms through an organism's metabolism.
   c. the element is very rare on Earth.
   d. the element enhances health but is not essential for the organism's long-term survival.
   e. the element passes rapidly through the organism.

2. Compared with ^{31}P, the radioactive isotope ^{32}P has
   a. a different atomic number.
   b. one more neutron.
   c. one more proton.
   d. one more electron.
   e. a different charge.

3. Atoms can be represented by simply listing the number of protons, neutrons, and electrons—for example, $2p^+; 2n^0; 2e^-$ for helium. Which one of the following lists represents the ^{18}O isotope of oxygen?
   a. $6p^+; 8n^0; 6e^-$
   b. $8p^+; 10n^0; 8e^-$
   c. $9p^+; 9n^0; 9e^-$
   d. $7p^+; 2n^0; 9e^-$
   e. $10p^+; 8n^0; 9e^-$

4. The atomic number of sulfur is 16. Sulfur combines with hydrogen by covalent bonding to form a compound, hydrogen sulfide. Based on the number of valence electrons in a sulfur atom, predict the molecular formula of the compound:
   a. HS   b. HS_2 c. H_2S d. H_3S_2 e. H_4S

5. The reactivity of an atom arises from
   a. the average distance of the outermost electron shell from the nucleus.
   b. the existence of unpaired electrons in the valence shell.
   c. the sum of the potential energies of all the electron shells.
   d. the potential energy of the valence shell.
   e. the energy difference between the s and p orbitals.

6. Which statement is true of all atoms that are anions?
   a. The atom has more electrons than protons.
   b. The atom has more protons than electrons.
   c. The atom has fewer protons than does a neutral atom of the same element.
   d. The atom has more neutrons than protons.
   e. The net charge is $1-$.

7. What coefficients must be placed in the following blanks so that all atoms are accounted for in the products?

   $$C_6H_{12}O_6 \longrightarrow \underline{\quad}C_2H_6O + \underline{\quad}CO_2$$

   a. 1; 2   b. 2; 2   c. 1; 3   d. 1; 1   e. 3; 1

8. Which of the following statements correctly describes any chemical reaction that has reached equilibrium?
   a. The concentrations of products and reactants are equal.
   b. The rates of the forward and reverse reactions are equal.
   c. Both forward and reverse reactions have halted.
   d. The reaction is now irreversible.
   e. No reactants remain.

9. **DRAW IT** Draw Lewis structures for each hypothetical molecule shown below, using the correct number of valence electrons for each atom. Determine which molecule makes sense because each atom has a complete valence shell and each bond has the correct number of electrons. Explain what makes the other molecules nonsensical, considering the number of bonds each type of atom can make.

   a. $O=C-H$

   c.
   $$H-\overset{\displaystyle \overset{H}{|}}{\underset{\displaystyle \underset{H}{|}}{C}}-H-\overset{\displaystyle \overset{H}{|}}{C}=O$$

   b. $H-O-\overset{\displaystyle \overset{H}{|}}{\underset{\displaystyle \underset{H}{|}}{C}}-\overset{\displaystyle \overset{H}{|}}{C}=O$

   d. $H-N=H$ with $\overset{\displaystyle O}{|}$ above N

For Self-Quiz answers, see Appendix A.

MEDIA Visit the Study Area at **www.masteringbio.com** for a Practice Test.

EVOLUTION CONNECTION

10. The percentages of naturally occurring elements making up the human body (see Table 2.1) are similar to the percentages of these elements found in other organisms. How could you account for this similarity among organisms?

SCIENTIFIC INQUIRY

11. Female silkworm moths (*Bombyx mori*) attract males by emitting chemical signals that spread through the air. A male hundreds of meters away can detect these molecules and fly toward their source. The sensory organs responsible for this behavior are the comblike antennae visible in the photograph here. Each filament of an antenna is equipped with thousands of receptor cells that detect the sex attractant. Based on what you learned in this chapter, propose a hypothesis to account for the ability of the male moth to detect a specific molecule in the presence of many other molecules in the air. What predictions does your hypothesis make? Design an experiment to test one of these predictions.

SCIENCE, TECHNOLOGY, AND SOCIETY

12. While waiting at an airport, Neil Campbell once overheard this claim: "It's paranoid and ignorant to worry about industry or agriculture contaminating the environment with their chemical wastes. After all, this stuff is just made of the same atoms that were already present in our environment." How would you counter this argument?

Water and the Fitness of the Environment

3

OVERVIEW

The Molecule That Supports All of Life

As astronomers study newly discovered planets orbiting distant stars, they hope to find evidence of water on these far-off celestial bodies, for water is the substance that makes possible life as we know it here on Earth. All organisms familiar to us are made mostly of water and live in an environment dominated by water. Water is the biological medium here on Earth, and possibly on other planets as well.

Three-quarters of Earth's surface is submerged in water **(Figure 3.1)**. Although most of this water is in liquid form, water is also present on Earth as ice and vapor. Water is the only common substance to exist in the natural environment in all three physical states of matter: solid, liquid, and gas. The abundance of water is a major reason Earth is habitable. In a classic book called *The Fitness of the Environment,* ecologist Lawrence Henderson highlights the importance of water to life. While acknowledging that life adapts to its environment through natural selection, Henderson emphasizes that for life to exist at all, the environment must first be a suitable abode.

Life on Earth began in water and evolved there for 3 billion years before spreading onto land. Modern life, even terrestrial (land-dwelling) life, remains tied to water. All living organisms require water more than any other substance. Human beings, for example, can survive for quite a few weeks without food, but only a week or so without water. Molecules of water par-

▲ **Figure 3.1 Why does the abundance of water allow life to exist on the planet Earth?**

ticipate in many chemical reactions necessary to sustain life. Most cells are surrounded by water, and cells themselves are about 70–95% water.

What properties of the simple water molecule allow it to function as a support to all living organisms? In this chapter, you will learn how the structure of a water molecule allows it to interact with other molecules, including other water molecules. This ability leads to unique emergent properties that support and maintain living systems on our planet. Your objective in this chapter is to develop a conceptual understanding of how water contributes to the fitness of Earth for life.

CONCEPT **3.1**

The polarity of water molecules results in hydrogen bonding

Water is so common that it is easy to overlook the fact that it is an exceptional substance with many extraordinary qualities. Following the theme of emergent properties, we can trace water's unique behavior to the structure and interactions of its molecules.

Studied in isolation, the water molecule is deceptively simple. It is shaped something like a wide V, with its two hydrogen atoms joined to the oxygen atom by single covalent bonds. Because oxygen is more electronegative than hydrogen, the electrons of the covalent bonds spend more time closer to oxygen than to hydrogen; in other words, they are polar covalent bonds (see Figure 2.13). This unequal distribution of electrons makes water a **polar molecule**, meaning that the two ends of the molecule have opposite charges: The oxygen region of the molecule has a partial negative charge ($\delta-$), and the hydrogens have a partial positive charge ($\delta+$).

The anomalous properties of water arise from attractions between its polar molecules: The slightly positive hydrogen of

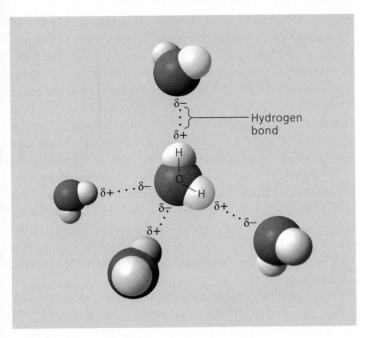

▲ **Figure 3.2 Hydrogen bonds between water molecules.**
The charged regions of a polar water molecule are attracted to oppositely charged parts of neighboring molecules. Each molecule can hydrogen-bond to multiple partners, and these associations are constantly changing.

one molecule is attracted to the slightly negative oxygen of a nearby molecule. The two molecules are thus held together by a hydrogen bond **(Figure 3.2)**. When water is in its liquid form, its hydrogen bonds are very fragile, each about ¹⁄₂₀ as strong as a covalent bond. The hydrogen bonds form, break, and re-form with great frequency. Each lasts only a few trillionths of a second, but the molecules are constantly forming new hydrogen bonds with a succession of partners. Therefore, at any instant, a substantial percentage of all the water molecules are hydrogen-bonded to their neighbors. The extraordinary qualities of water are emergent properties resulting from the hydrogen bonding that orders molecules into a higher level of structural organization.

CONCEPT CHECK 3.1

1. What is electronegativity, and how does it affect interactions between water molecules?
2. Why is it unlikely that two neighboring water molecules would be arranged like this?

$$O \diagdown{}^{H\ H}\diagup O$$
$$\diagup{}_{H\ H}\diagdown$$

3. **WHAT IF?** What would be the effect on the properties of the water molecule if oxygen and hydrogen had equal electronegativity?

For suggested answers, see Appendix A.

CONCEPT 3.2
Four emergent properties of water contribute to Earth's fitness for life

We will examine four emergent properties of water that contribute to Earth's suitability as an environment for life: cohesive behavior, ability to moderate temperature, expansion upon freezing, and versatility as a solvent.

Cohesion

Water molecules stay close to each other as a result of hydrogen bonding. Although the arrangement of molecules in a sample of liquid water is constantly changing, at any given moment many of the molecules are linked by multiple hydrogen bonds. These linkages make water more structured than most other liquids. Collectively, the hydrogen bonds hold the substance together, a phenomenon called **cohesion**.

Cohesion due to hydrogen bonding contributes to the transport of water and dissolved nutrients against gravity in plants **(Figure 3.3)**. Water from the roots reaches the leaves through a network of water-conducting cells. As water evaporates from a leaf, hydrogen bonds cause water molecules leaving the veins to tug on molecules farther down, and the upward pull is transmitted through the water-conducting cells all the way to the roots. **Adhesion**, the clinging of one substance to

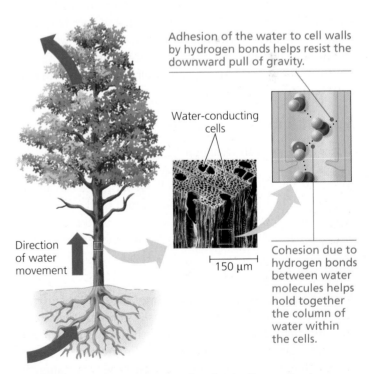

Adhesion of the water to cell walls by hydrogen bonds helps resist the downward pull of gravity.

Water-conducting cells

Direction of water movement

150 μm

Cohesion due to hydrogen bonds between water molecules helps hold together the column of water within the cells.

▲ **Figure 3.3 Water transport in plants.** Evaporation from leaves pulls water upward from the roots through water-conducting cells. Because of the properties of cohesion and adhesion, the tallest trees can transport water more than 100 m upward—approximately one-quarter the height of the Empire State Building in New York City.

▲ **Figure 3.4 Walking on water.** The high surface tension of water, resulting from the collective strength of its hydrogen bonds, allows the water strider to walk on the surface of a pond.

another, also plays a role. Adhesion of water to cell walls by hydrogen bonds helps counter the downward pull of gravity (see Figure 3.3).

Related to cohesion is **surface tension**, a measure of how difficult it is to stretch or break the surface of a liquid. Water has a greater surface tension than most other liquids. At the interface between water and air is an ordered arrangement of water molecules, hydrogen-bonded to one another and to the water below. This makes the water behave as though coated with an invisible film. You can observe the surface tension of water by slightly overfilling a drinking glass; the water will stand above the rim. In a more biological example, some animals can stand, walk, or run on water without breaking the surface **(Figure 3.4)**.

Moderation of Temperature

Water moderates air temperature by absorbing heat from air that is warmer and releasing the stored heat to air that is cooler. Water is effective as a heat bank because it can absorb or release a relatively large amount of heat with only a slight change in its own temperature. To understand this capability of water, we must first look briefly at heat and temperature.

Heat and Temperature

Anything that moves has **kinetic energy**, the energy of motion. Atoms and molecules have kinetic energy because they are always moving, although not necessarily in any particular direction. The faster a molecule moves, the greater its kinetic energy. **Heat** is a form of energy. For a given body of matter, the amount of heat is a measure of the matter's *total* kinetic energy due to motion of its molecules; thus, heat depends in part on the matter's volume. Although heat is related to temperature,

they are not the same thing. **Temperature** is a measure of heat intensity that represents the *average* kinetic energy of the molecules, regardless of volume. When water is heated in a coffeemaker, the average speed of the molecules increases, and the thermometer records this as a rise in temperature of the liquid. The amount of heat also increases in this case. Note, however, that although the pot of coffee has a much higher temperature than, say, the water in a swimming pool, the swimming pool contains more heat because of its much greater volume.

Whenever two objects of different temperature are brought together, heat passes from the warmer to the cooler object until the two are the same temperature. Molecules in the cooler object speed up at the expense of the kinetic energy of the warmer object. An ice cube cools a drink not by adding coldness to the liquid, but by absorbing heat from the liquid as the ice itself melts.

Throughout this book, we will use the **Celsius scale** to indicate temperature (Celsius degrees are abbreviated °C). At sea level, water freezes at 0°C and boils at 100°C. The temperature of the human body averages 37°C, and comfortable room temperature is about 20–25°C.

One convenient unit of heat used in this book is the **calorie (cal)**. A calorie is the amount of heat it takes to raise the temperature of 1 g of water by 1°C. Conversely, a calorie is also the amount of heat that 1 g of water releases when it cools by 1°C. A **kilocalorie (kcal)**, 1,000 cal, is the quantity of heat required to raise the temperature of 1 kilogram (kg) of water by 1°C. (The "calories" on food packages are actually kilocalories.) Another energy unit used in this book is the **joule (J)**. One joule equals 0.239 cal; one calorie equals 4.184 J.

Water's High Specific Heat

The ability of water to stabilize temperature stems from its relatively high specific heat. The **specific heat** of a substance is defined as the amount of heat that must be absorbed or lost for 1 g of that substance to change its temperature by 1°C. We already know water's specific heat because we have defined a calorie as the amount of heat that causes 1 g of water to change its temperature by 1°C. Therefore, the specific heat of water is 1 calorie per gram per degree Celsius, abbreviated as 1 cal/g/°C. Compared with most other substances, water has an unusually high specific heat. For example, ethyl alcohol, the type of alcohol in alcoholic beverages, has a specific heat of 0.6 cal/g/°C; that is, only 0.6 cal is required to raise the temperature of 1 g of ethyl alcohol 1°C.

Because of the high specific heat of water relative to other materials, water will change its temperature less when it absorbs or loses a given amount of heat. The reason you can burn your fingers by touching the side of a metal pot on the stove when the water in the pot is still lukewarm is that the specific heat of water is ten times greater than that of iron. In other words, the same amount of heat will raise the temperature of

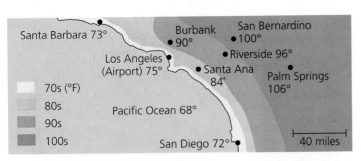

▲ Figure 3.5 Effect of a large body of water on climate. By absorbing or releasing heat, oceans moderate coastal climates. In this example from an August day in Southern California, the relatively cool ocean reduces coastal air temperatures by absorbing heat.

1 g of the iron much faster than the temperature of 1 g of the water. Specific heat can be thought of as a measure of how well a substance resists changing its temperature when it absorbs or releases heat. Water resists changing its temperature; when it does change its temperature, it absorbs or loses a relatively large quantity of heat for each degree of change.

We can trace water's high specific heat, like many of its other properties, to hydrogen bonding. Heat must be absorbed in order to break hydrogen bonds, and heat is released when hydrogen bonds form. A calorie of heat causes a relatively small change in the temperature of water because much of the heat is used to disrupt hydrogen bonds before the water molecules can begin moving faster. And when the temperature of water drops slightly, many additional hydrogen bonds form, releasing a considerable amount of energy in the form of heat.

What is the relevance of water's high specific heat to life on Earth? A large body of water can absorb and store a huge amount of heat from the sun in the daytime and during summer while warming up only a few degrees. And at night and during winter, the gradually cooling water can warm the air. This is the reason coastal areas generally have milder climates than inland regions (Figure 3.5). The high specific heat of water also tends to stabilize ocean temperatures, creating a favorable environment for marine life. Thus, because of its high specific heat, the water that covers most of Earth keeps temperature fluctuations on land and in water within limits that permit life. Also, because organisms are made primarily of water, they are more able to resist changes in their own temperature than if they were made of a liquid with a lower specific heat.

Evaporative Cooling

Molecules of any liquid stay close together because they are attracted to one another. Molecules moving fast enough to overcome these attractions can depart the liquid and enter the air as gas. This transformation from a liquid to a gas is called vaporization, or *evaporation*. Recall that the speed of molecular movement varies and that temperature is the *average* kinetic energy of molecules. Even at low temperatures, the speediest molecules can escape into the air. Some evaporation

occurs at any temperature; a glass of water at room temperature, for example, will eventually evaporate. If a liquid is heated, the average kinetic energy of molecules increases and the liquid evaporates more rapidly.

Heat of vaporization is the quantity of heat a liquid must absorb for 1 g of it to be converted from the liquid to the gaseous state. For the same reason that water has a high specific heat, it also has a high heat of vaporization relative to most other liquids. To evaporate 1 g of water at 25°C, about 580 cal of heat is needed—nearly double the amount needed to vaporize a gram of alcohol or ammonia. Water's high heat of vaporization is another emergent property caused by hydrogen bonds, which must be broken before the molecules can make their exodus from the liquid.

The high amount of energy required to vaporize water has a wide range of effects. On a global scale, for example, it helps moderate Earth's climate. A considerable amount of solar heat absorbed by tropical seas is consumed during the evaporation of surface water. Then, as moist tropical air circulates poleward, it releases heat as it condenses and forms rain. On an organismal level, water's high heat of vaporization accounts for the severity of steam burns. These burns are caused by the heat energy released when steam condenses into liquid on the skin.

As a liquid evaporates, the surface of the liquid that remains behind cools down. This **evaporative cooling** occurs because the "hottest" molecules, those with the greatest kinetic energy, are the most likely to leave as gas. It is as if the hundred fastest runners at a college transferred to another school; the average speed of the remaining students would decline.

Evaporative cooling of water contributes to the stability of temperature in lakes and ponds and also provides a mechanism that prevents terrestrial organisms from overheating. For example, evaporation of water from the leaves of a plant helps keep the tissues in the leaves from becoming too warm in the sunlight. Evaporation of sweat from human skin dissipates body heat and helps prevent overheating on a hot day or when excess heat is generated by strenuous activity. High humidity on a hot day increases discomfort because the high concentration of water vapor in the air inhibits the evaporation of sweat from the body.

Insulation of Bodies of Water by Floating Ice

Water is one of the few substances that are less dense as a solid than as a liquid. In other words, ice floats in liquid water. While other materials contract when they solidify, water expands. The cause of this exotic behavior is, once again, hydrogen bonding. At temperatures above 4°C, water behaves like other liquids, expanding as it warms and contracting as it cools. Water begins to freeze when its molecules are no longer moving vigorously enough to break their hydrogen bonds. As the temperature falls to 0°C, the water becomes locked into a crystalline lattice, each water molecule hydrogen-bonded to

Ice
Hydrogen bonds are stable

Liquid water
Hydrogen bonds break and re-form

▲ **Figure 3.6 Ice: crystalline structure and floating barrier.** In ice, each molecule is hydrogen-bonded to four neighbors in a three-dimensional crystal. Because the crystal is spacious, ice has fewer molecules than an equal volume of liquid water. In other words, ice is less dense than liquid water. Floating ice becomes a barrier that protects the liquid water below from the colder air. The marine organism shown here is a type of shrimp called krill; it was photographed beneath floating ice in the Antarctic Ocean.

? *If water did not form hydrogen bonds, what would happen to the shrimp's environment?*

four partners **(Figure 3.6)**. The hydrogen bonds keep the molecules at "arm's length," far enough apart to make ice about 10% less dense (10% fewer molecules for the same volume) than liquid water at 4°C. When ice absorbs enough heat for its temperature to rise above 0°C, hydrogen bonds between molecules are disrupted. As the crystal collapses, the ice melts, and molecules are free to slip closer together. Water reaches its greatest density at 4°C and then begins to expand as the molecules move faster. Keep in mind, however, that even in liquid water, many of the molecules are connected by hydrogen bonds, though only transiently: The hydrogen bonds are constantly breaking and re-forming.

The ability of ice to float because of the expansion of water as it solidifies is an important factor in the fitness of the environment. If ice sank, then eventually all ponds, lakes, and even oceans would freeze solid, making life as we know it impossible on Earth. During summer, only the upper few inches of the ocean would thaw. Instead, when a deep body of water cools, the floating ice insulates the liquid water below, preventing it from freezing and allowing life to exist under the frozen surface, as shown in the photo in Figure 3.6.

The Solvent of Life

A sugar cube placed in a glass of water will dissolve. The glass will then contain a uniform mixture of sugar and water; the concentration of dissolved sugar will be the same everywhere in the mixture. A liquid that is a completely homogeneous mixture of two or more substances is called a **solution**. The dissolving agent of a solution is the **solvent**, and the substance that is dissolved is the **solute**. In this case, water is the solvent and sugar is the solute. An **aqueous solution** is one in which water is the solvent.

The medieval alchemists tried to find a universal solvent, one that would dissolve anything. They learned that nothing works better than water. However, water is not a universal solvent; if it were, it would dissolve any container in which it was stored, including our cells. But water is a very versatile solvent, a quality we can trace to the polarity of the water molecule.

Suppose, for example, that a spoonful of table salt, the ionic compound sodium chloride (NaCl), is placed in water **(Figure 3.7)**. At the surface of each grain, or crystal, of salt, the sodium and chloride ions are exposed to the solvent. These ions and the water molecules have a mutual affinity owing to the attraction between opposite charges. The oxygen

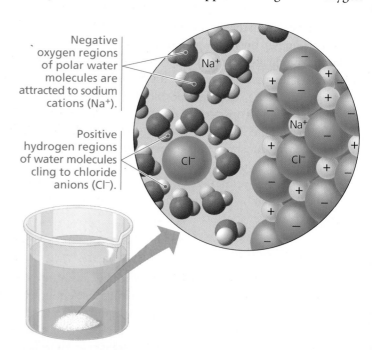

Negative oxygen regions of polar water molecules are attracted to sodium cations (Na⁺).

Positive hydrogen regions of water molecules cling to chloride anions (Cl⁻).

▲ **Figure 3.7 Table salt dissolving in water.** A sphere of water molecules, called a hydration shell, surrounds each solute ion.

? *What would happen if you heated this solution for a long time?*

This oxygen is attracted to a slight positive charge on the lysozyme molecule.

This hydrogen is attracted to a slight negative charge on the lysozyme molecule.

(a) Lysozyme molecule in a nonaqueous environment

(b) Lysozyme molecule (purple) in an aqueous environment such as tears or saliva

(c) Ionic and polar regions on the protein's surface attract water molecules.

▲ **Figure 3.8 A water-soluble protein.** This figure shows human lysozyme, a protein found in tears and saliva that has antibacterial action.

regions of the water molecules are negatively charged and cling to sodium cations. The hydrogen regions are positively charged and are attracted to chloride anions. As a result, water molecules surround the individual sodium and chloride ions, separating and shielding them from one another. The sphere of water molecules around each dissolved ion is called a **hydration shell**. Working inward from the surface of each salt crystal, water eventually dissolves all the ions. The result is a solution of two solutes, sodium cations and chloride anions, homogeneously mixed with water, the solvent. Other ionic compounds also dissolve in water. Seawater, for instance, contains a great variety of dissolved ions, as do living cells.

A compound does not need to be ionic to dissolve in water; many compounds made up of nonionic polar molecules, such as sugars, are also water-soluble. Such compounds dissolve when water molecules surround each of the solute molecules, forming hydrogen bonds with them. Even molecules as large as proteins can dissolve in water if they have ionic and polar regions on their surface **(Figure 3.8)**. Many different kinds of polar compounds are dissolved (along with ions) in the water of such biological fluids as blood, the sap of plants, and the liquid within all cells. Water is the solvent of life.

Hydrophilic and Hydrophobic Substances

Any substance that has an affinity for water is said to be **hydrophilic** (from the Greek *hydro*, water, and *philios*, loving). In some cases, substances can be hydrophilic without actually dissolving. For example, some molecules in cells are so large that they do not dissolve. Instead, they remain suspended in the aqueous liquid of the cell. Such a mixture is an example of a **colloid**, a stable suspension of fine particles in a liquid. Another example of a hydrophilic substance that does not dissolve is cotton, a plant product. Cotton consists of giant molecules of cellulose, a compound with numerous

regions of partial positive and partial negative charges that can form hydrogen bonds with water. Water adheres to the cellulose fibers. Thus, a cotton towel does a great job of drying the body, yet does not dissolve in the washing machine. Cellulose is also present in the walls of water-conducting cells in a plant; you read earlier how the adhesion of water to these hydrophilic walls allows water transport to occur.

There are, of course, substances that do not have an affinity for water. Substances that are nonionic and nonpolar (or for some other reason cannot form hydrogen bonds) actually seem to repel water; these substances are said to be **hydrophobic** (from the Greek *phobos*, fearing). An example from the kitchen is vegetable oil, which, as you know, does not mix stably with water-based substances such as vinegar. The hydrophobic behavior of the oil molecules results from a prevalence of relatively nonpolar bonds, in this case bonds between carbon and hydrogen, which share electrons almost equally. Hydrophobic molecules related to oils are major ingredients of cell membranes. (Imagine what would happen to a cell if its membrane dissolved!)

Solute Concentration in Aqueous Solutions

Biological chemistry is "wet" chemistry. Most of the chemical reactions in organisms involve solutes dissolved in water. To understand such reactions, we must know how many atoms and molecules are involved and be able to calculate the concentration of solutes in an aqueous solution (the number of solute molecules in a volume of solution).

When carrying out experiments, we use mass to calculate the number of molecules. We know the mass of each atom in a given molecule, so we can calculate its **molecular mass**, which is simply the sum of the masses of all the atoms in a molecule. As an example, let's calculate the molecular mass of table sugar (sucrose), which has the molecular formula

$C_{12}H_{22}O_{11}$. In round numbers of daltons, the mass of a carbon atom is 12, the mass of a hydrogen atom is 1, and the mass of an oxygen atom is 16. Thus, sucrose has a molecular mass of 342 daltons. Of course, weighing out small numbers of molecules is not practical. For this reason, we usually measure substances in units called moles. Just as a dozen always means 12 objects, a **mole (mol)** represents an exact number of objects—6.02×10^{23}, which is called Avogadro's number. Because of the way in which Avogadro's number and the unit *dalton* were originally defined, there are 6.02×10^{23} daltons in 1 g. This is significant because once we determine the molecular mass of a molecule such as sucrose, we can use the same number (342), but with the unit *gram*, to represent the mass of 6.02×10^{23} molecules of sucrose, or 1 mol of sucrose (this is sometimes called the *molar mass*). To obtain 1 mol of sucrose in the lab, therefore, we weigh out 342 g.

The practical advantage of measuring a quantity of chemicals in moles is that a mole of one substance has exactly the same number of molecules as a mole of any other substance. If the molecular mass of substance A is 342 daltons and that of substance B is 10 daltons, then 342 g of A will have the same number of molecules as 10 g of B. A mole of ethyl alcohol (C_2H_6O) also contains 6.02×10^{23} molecules, but its mass is only 46 g because the mass of a molecule of ethyl alcohol is less than that of a molecule of sucrose. Measuring in moles makes it convenient for scientists working in the laboratory to combine substances in fixed ratios of molecules.

How would we make a liter (L) of solution consisting of 1 mol of sucrose dissolved in water? We would measure out 342 g of sucrose and then gradually add water, while stirring, until the sugar was completely dissolved. We would then add enough water to bring the total volume of the solution up to 1 L. At that point, we would have a 1-molar ($1\,M$) solution of sucrose. **Molarity**—the number of moles of solute per liter of solution—is the unit of concentration most often used by biologists for aqueous solutions.

CONCEPT CHECK 3.2

1. Describe how properties of water contribute to the upward movement of water in a tree.
2. Explain the saying "It's not the heat; it's the humidity."
3. How can the freezing of water crack boulders?
4. If you were a pharmacist, how would you make a 0.5-molar ($0.5\,M$) solution of sodium chloride (NaCl)? (The atomic mass of Na is 23 daltons and that of Cl is 35.5 daltons.)
5. **WHAT IF?** A water strider's legs (see Figure 3.4) are coated with a hydrophobic substance. What might be the benefit? What would happen if the substance were hydrophilic?

For suggested answers, see Appendix A.

CONCEPT 3.3

Acidic and basic conditions affect living organisms

Occasionally, a hydrogen atom participating in a hydrogen bond between two water molecules shifts from one molecule to the other. When this happens, the hydrogen atom leaves its electron behind, and what is actually transferred is a **hydrogen ion** (H^+), a single proton with a charge of $1+$. The water molecule that lost a proton is now a **hydroxide ion** (OH^-), which has a charge of $1-$. The proton binds to the other water molecule, making that molecule a **hydronium ion** (H_3O^+). We can picture the chemical reaction this way:

$2H_2O$ ⇌ Hydronium ion (H_3O^+) + Hydroxide ion (OH^-)

By convention, H^+ (the hydrogen ion) is used to represent H_3O^+ (the hydronium ion), and we follow that practice here. Keep in mind, though, that H^+ does not exist on its own in an aqueous solution. It is always associated with another water molecule in the form of H_3O^+.

As indicated by the double arrows, this is a reversible reaction that reaches a state of dynamic equilibrium when water molecules dissociate at the same rate that they are being re-formed from H^+ and OH^- At this equilibrium point, the concentration of water molecules greatly exceeds the concentrations of H^+ and OH^-. In pure water, only one water molecule in every 554 million is dissociated. The concentration of each ion in pure water is $10^{-7}\,M$ (at 25°C). This means there is only one ten-millionth of a mole of hydrogen ions per liter of pure water and an equal number of hydroxide ions.

Although the dissociation of water is reversible and statistically rare, it is exceedingly important in the chemistry of life. H^+ and OH^- are very reactive. Changes in their concentrations can drastically affect a cell's proteins and other complex molecules. As we have seen, the concentrations of H^+ and OH^- are equal in pure water, but adding certain kinds of solutes, called acids and bases, disrupts this balance. Biologists use something called the pH scale to describe how acidic or basic (the opposite of acidic) a solution is. In the remainder of this chapter, you will learn about acids, bases, and pH and why changes in pH can adversely affect organisms.

Effects of Changes in pH

Before discussing the pH scale, let's see what acids and bases are and how they interact with water.

Acids and Bases

What would cause an aqueous solution to have an imbalance in H^+ and OH^- concentrations? When acids dissolve in water, they donate additional H^+ to the solution. An **acid** is a substance that increases the hydrogen ion concentration of a solution. For example, when hydrochloric acid (HCl) is added to water, hydrogen ions dissociate from chloride ions:

$$HCl \longrightarrow H^+ + Cl^-$$

This source of H^+ (dissociation of water is the other source) results in an acidic solution—one having more H^+ than OH^-.

A substance that reduces the hydrogen ion concentration of a solution is called a **base**. Some bases reduce the H^+ concentration directly by accepting hydrogen ions. Ammonia (NH_3), for instance, acts as a base when the unshared electron pair in nitrogen's valence shell attracts a hydrogen ion from the solution, resulting in an ammonium ion (NH_4^+):

$$NH_3 + H^+ \rightleftharpoons NH_4^+$$

Other bases reduce the H^+ concentration indirectly by dissociating to form hydroxide ions, which combine with hydrogen ions and form water. One such base is sodium hydroxide (NaOH), which in water dissociates into its ions:

$$NaOH \longrightarrow Na^+ + OH^-$$

In either case, the base reduces the H^+ concentration. Solutions with a higher concentration of OH^- than H^+ are known as basic solutions. A solution in which the H^+ and OH^- concentrations are equal is said to be neutral.

Notice that single arrows were used in the reactions for HCl and NaOH. These compounds dissociate completely when mixed with water, and so hydrochloric acid is called a strong acid and sodium hydroxide a strong base. In contrast, ammonia is a relatively weak base. The double arrows in the reaction for ammonia indicate that the binding and release of hydrogen ions are reversible reactions, although at equilibrium there will be a fixed ratio of NH_4^+ to NH_3.

There are also weak acids, which reversibly release and accept back hydrogen ions. An example is carbonic acid:

$$\underset{\substack{\text{Carbonic} \\ \text{acid}}}{H_2CO_3} \rightleftharpoons \underset{\substack{\text{Bicarbonate} \\ \text{ion}}}{HCO_3^-} + \underset{\substack{\text{Hydrogen} \\ \text{ion}}}{H^+}$$

Here the equilibrium so favors the reaction in the left direction that when carbonic acid is added to water, only 1% of the molecules are dissociated at any particular time. Still, that is enough to shift the balance of H^+ and OH^- from neutrality.

The pH Scale

In any aqueous solution at 25°C, the *product* of the H^+ and OH^- concentrations is constant at 10^{-14}. This can be written

$$[H^+][OH^-] = 10^{-14}$$

In such an equation, brackets indicate molar concentration. In a neutral solution at room temperature (25°C), $[H^+] = 10^{-7}$ and $[OH^-] = 10^{-7}$, so in this case, 10^{-14} is the product of $10^{-7} \times 10^{-7}$. If enough acid is added to a solution to increase $[H^+]$ to $10^{-5} M$, then $[OH^-]$ will decline by an equivalent amount to $10^{-9} M$ (note that $10^{-5} \times 10^{-9} = 10^{-14}$). This constant relationship expresses the behavior of acids and bases in an aqueous solution. An acid not only adds hydrogen ions to a solution, but also removes hydroxide ions because of the tendency for H^+ to combine with OH^-, forming water. A base has the opposite effect, increasing OH^- concentration but also reducing H^+ concentration by the formation of water. If enough of a base is added to raise the OH^- concentration to $10^{-4} M$, it will cause the H^+ concentration to drop to $10^{-10} M$. Whenever we know the concentration of either H^+ or OH^- in an aqueous solution, we can deduce the concentration of the other ion.

Because the H^+ and OH^- concentrations of solutions can vary by a factor of 100 trillion or more, scientists have developed a way to express this variation more conveniently than in moles per liter. The pH scale (Figure 3.9) compresses the

▲ Figure 3.9 **The pH scale and pH values of some aqueous solutions.**

range of H^+ and OH^- concentrations by employing logarithms. The **pH** of a solution is defined as the negative logarithm (base 10) of the hydrogen ion concentration:

$$pH = -\log [H^+]$$

For a neutral aqueous solution, $[H^+]$ is 10^{-7} M, giving us

$$-\log 10^{-7} = -(-7) = 7$$

Notice that pH *declines* as H^+ concentration *increases*. Notice, too, that although the pH scale is based on H^+ concentration, it also implies OH^- concentration. A solution of pH 10 has a hydrogen ion concentration of 10^{-10} M and a hydroxide ion concentration of 10^{-4} M.

The pH of a neutral aqueous solution at 25°C is 7, the midpoint of the scale. A pH value less than 7 denotes an acidic solution; the lower the number, the more acidic the solution. The pH for basic solutions is above 7. Most biological fluids are within the range pH 6–8. There are a few exceptions, however, including the strongly acidic digestive juice of the human stomach, which has a pH of about 2.

Remember that each pH unit represents a tenfold difference in H^+ and OH^- concentrations. It is this mathematical feature that makes the pH scale so compact. A solution of pH 3 is not twice as acidic as a solution of pH 6, but a thousand times more acidic. When the pH of a solution changes slightly, the actual concentrations of H^+ and OH^- in the solution change substantially.

Buffers

The internal pH of most living cells is close to 7. Even a slight change in pH can be harmful, because the chemical processes of the cell are very sensitive to the concentrations of hydrogen and hydroxide ions.

The pH of human blood is very close to 7.4, which is slightly basic. A person cannot survive for more than a few minutes if the blood pH drops to 7 or rises to 7.8, and a chemical system exists in the blood that maintains a stable pH. If you add 0.01 mol of a strong acid to a liter of pure water, the pH drops from 7.0 to 2.0. If the same amount of acid is added to a liter of blood, however, the pH decrease is only from 7.4 to 7.3. Why does the addition of acid have so much less of an effect on the pH of blood than it does on the pH of water? The presence of substances called buffers allows for a relatively constant pH in biological fluids despite the addition of acids or bases. **Buffers** are substances that minimize changes in the concentrations of H^+ and OH^- in a solution. They do so by accepting hydrogen ions from the solution when they are in excess and donating hydrogen ions to the solution when they have been depleted. Most buffer solutions contain a weak acid and its corresponding base, which combine reversibly with hydrogen ions. There are several buffers that contribute to pH stability in human blood and many other biological solutions. One of these is carbonic

acid (H_2CO_3), formed when CO_2 reacts with water in blood plasma. As mentioned earlier, carbonic acid dissociates to yield a bicarbonate ion (HCO_3^-) and a hydrogen ion (H^+):

$$\underset{\substack{H^+ \text{ donor} \\ \text{(acid)}}}{H_2CO_3} \underset{\substack{\text{Response to} \\ \text{a drop in pH}}}{\overset{\substack{\text{Response} \\ \text{to a rise in pH}}}{\rightleftharpoons}} \underset{\substack{H^+ \text{ acceptor} \\ \text{(base)}}}{HCO_3^-} + \underset{\substack{\text{Hydrogen} \\ \text{ion}}}{H^+}$$

The chemical equilibrium between carbonic acid and bicarbonate acts as a pH regulator, the reaction shifting left or right as other processes in the solution add or remove hydrogen ions. If the H^+ concentration in blood begins to fall (that is, if pH rises), the reaction proceeds to the right and more carbonic acid dissociates, replenishing hydrogen ions. But when H^+ concentration in blood begins to rise (when pH drops), the reaction proceeds to the left, with HCO_3^- (the base) removing the hydrogen ions from the solution and forming H_2CO_3. Thus, the carbonic acid–bicarbonate buffering system consists of an acid and a base in equilibrium with each other. Most other buffers are also acid-base pairs.

Threats to Water Quality on Earth

Considering the dependence of all life on water, contamination of rivers, lakes, seas, and rain is a dire environmental problem. Many threats to water quality have been posed by human activities. Consider, for example, the burning of fossil fuels (coal, oil, and gas). This practice, which has been increasing since the Industrial Revolution in the 1800s, releases gaseous compounds into the atmosphere, including prodigious amounts of CO_2. The chemical reactions of these compounds with water alter the delicate balance of conditions for life on Earth by affecting water pH and temperature.

The burning of fossil fuels is a major source of sulfur oxides and nitrous oxides. These react with water in the air to form strong acids, which fall to Earth with rain or snow. **Acid precipitation** refers to rain, snow, or fog with a pH lower (more acidic) than pH 5.2. (Uncontaminated rain has a pH of about 5.6, slightly acidic, owing to the formation of carbonic acid from carbon dioxide and water.) Electric power plants that burn coal produce more of these oxides than any other single source. Winds carry the pollutants away, and acid rain may fall hundreds of kilometers away from industrial centers. In certain sites in Pennsylvania and New York, the pH of rainfall in December 2001 averaged 4.3, about 20 times more acidic than normal rain. Acid precipitation falls on many other regions, including eastern Canada, the Cascade Mountains of the Pacific Northwest, and certain parts of Europe and Asia **(Figure 3.10)**.

Acid precipitation can damage life in lakes and streams. Also, acid precipitation falling on land adversely affects soil chemistry and has taken a toll on some North American and European forests (see Figure 3.10). Nevertheless, studies indicate that the majority of North American forests are not

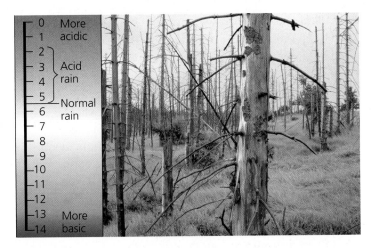

▲ **Figure 3.10 Acid precipitation and its effects on a forest.** Acid rain is thought to be responsible for killing trees in many forests, including the fir forest shown here in the Czech Republic.

currently suffering substantially from acid precipitation, in large part due to amendments made in 1990 to the Clean Air Act.

Carbon dioxide, the main product of fossil fuel combustion, causes other problems. Its release into the atmosphere has been increasing steadily and is expected to double by the year 2065, relative to 1880 levels. About half of the CO_2 stays in the atmosphere, acting like a reflective blanket over the planet that prevents heat from radiating into outer space. This "greenhouse" effect and the problems associated with it will be discussed in Chapter 55. A portion of the CO_2 is taken up by trees and other organisms during photosynthesis, as mentioned in Chapter 2. The remainder—about 30% or so—is absorbed by the oceans. In spite of the huge volume of water in the oceans, scientists worry that this absorption of so much CO_2 will harm marine life and ecosystems.

When CO_2 dissolves in seawater, it reacts with water (H_2O) to form carbonic acid (H_2CO_3). Almost all of the carbonic acid in turn dissociates, producing protons and a balance between two ions, bicarbonate (HCO_3^-) and carbonate (CO_3^{2-}). As seawater acidifies due to the extra protons, the balance shifts toward HCO_3^-, lowering the concentration of CO_3^{2-}. Many studies have shown that calcification, the production of calcium carbonate ($CaCO_3$) by corals and other organisms, is directly affected by the concentration of CO_3^{2-}. Any decrease in CO_3^{2-} is therefore of great concern because calcification accounts for the formation of coral reefs in our tropical seas. These sensitive ecosystems act as havens for a great diversity of organisms.

Perhaps one of the best-known and longest studies on coral reef calcification was carried out by scientists at the ecosystem center in Arizona known as Biosphere-2. The center includes an artificial coral reef system in which the temperature and chemistry of the seawater can be controlled and manipulated. Chris Langdon and colleagues used this system to test the effects of varying the concentration of CO_3^{2-} on the rate of calcification in the coral reef **(Figure 3.11)**. Together with

▼ Figure 3.11 Inquiry

What is the effect of carbonate ion concentration on coral reef calcification?

EXPERIMENT   Chris Langdon and colleagues at Columbia University wondered how the increase in CO_2 emissions due to burning of fossil fuels and the resulting decrease in CO_3^{2-} concentration in the oceans affect coral reefs. They took advantage of the artificial coral reef system at Biosphere-2. This 2,650-cubic-meter (m^3) aquarium behaves like a natural coral reef community. For almost four years, these researchers varied the carbonate concentration in the seawater under controlled conditions and measured the rate of calcification by reef organisms.

RESULTS   The calcification rate was observed to be lower at lower concentrations of carbonate ion ($[CO_3^{2-}]$).

CONCLUSION   Coral reefs could be endangered by reduced $[CO_3^{2-}]$. Other studies have predicted a doubling of CO_2 emissions from 1880 to 2065 and a resulting decrease in carbonate ion concentration. Combining those predictions with the results of this study, the authors predict that by 2065 the rate of coral reef calcification may decrease by 40% relative to preindustrial levels.

SOURCE   C. Langdon et al., Effect of calcium carbonate saturation state on the calcification rate of an experimental coral reef, *Global Biogeochemical Cycles* 14:639–654 (2000).

WHAT IF?   The data above were for a particular concentration of calcium (Ca^{2+}). The series of experiments included measurements at two higher concentrations of Ca^{2+}. Given that the following reaction represents calcification, predict how the $[Ca^{2+}]$ would affect the results and explain why.

$$Ca^{2+} + CO_3^{2-} \longrightarrow CaCO_3$$

conclusions from other studies, their results led them to predict that the expected doubling of CO_2 emissions by the year 2065 could lead to a 40% decrease in coral reef calcification. Although scientists may not agree on the exact percentage, most concur that this and other studies provide cause for grave concern.

If there is reason for optimism about the future quality of water resources on our planet, it is that we have made progress in learning about the delicate chemical balances in oceans and other bodies of water. Continued progress can come only from the actions of people who are concerned about environmental quality. This requires understanding the crucial role that water plays in the environment's fitness for continued life on Earth.

CONCEPT CHECK 3.3

1. Compared with a basic solution at pH 9, the same volume of an acidic solution at pH 4 has ___ times as many hydrogen ions (H^+).
2. HCl is a strong acid that dissociates in water: $HCl \longrightarrow H^+ + Cl^-$. What is the pH of 0.01 M HCl?
3. Acetic acid (CH_3COOH) can be a buffer, similar to carbonic acid. Write the dissociation reaction, identifying the acid, base, H^+ acceptor, and H^+ donor.
4. **WHAT IF?** Given a liter of pure water and a liter solution of acetic acid, what would happen to the pH if you added 0.01 mol of a strong acid to each? Use the reaction equation to explain the result.

For suggested answers, see Appendix A.

Chapter 3 Review

MB **MEDIA** Go to the Study Area at **www.masteringbio.com** for BioFlix 3-D Animations, MP3 Tutors, Videos, Practice Tests, an eBook, and more.

SUMMARY OF KEY CONCEPTS

CONCEPT 3.1

The polarity of water molecules results in hydrogen bonding (pp. 46–47)

▶ A hydrogen bond forms when the slightly negatively charged oxygen of one water molecule is attracted to the slightly positively charged hydrogen of a nearby molecule. Hydrogen bonding between water molecules is the basis for water's unusual properties.

MEDIA

Activity The Polarity of Water

CONCEPT 3.2

Four emergent properties of water contribute to Earth's fitness for life (pp. 47–52)

▶ **Cohesion** Hydrogen bonding keeps water molecules close to each other, and this cohesion helps pull water upward in the microscopic water-conducting cells of plants. Hydrogen bonding is also responsible for water's surface tension.

▶ **Moderation of Temperature** Water has a high specific heat: Heat is absorbed when hydrogen bonds break and is released when hydrogen bonds form. This helps keep temperatures relatively steady, within limits that permit life. Evaporative cooling is based on water's high heat of vaporization. The evaporative loss of the most energetic water molecules cools a surface.

▶ **Insulation of Bodies of Water by Floating Ice** Ice floats because it is less dense than liquid water. This allows life to exist under the frozen surfaces of lakes and polar seas.

Ice: stable hydrogen bonds

Liquid water: transient hydrogen bonds

▶ **The Solvent of Life** Water is an unusually versatile solvent because its polar molecules are attracted to charged and polar substances capable of forming hydrogen bonds. Hydrophilic substances have an affinity for water; hydrophobic substances do not. Molarity, the number of moles of solute per liter of solution, is used as a measure of solute concentration in solutions. A mole is a certain number of molecules of a substance. The mass of a mole of the substance in grams is the same as the molecular mass in daltons.

MEDIA

MP3 Tutor The Properties of Water
Activity Cohesion of Water

CONCEPT 3.3

Acidic and basic conditions affect living organisms (pp. 52–56)

▶ A water molecule can transfer an H^+ to another water molecule to form H_3O^+ (represented simply by H^+) and OH^-.

▶ **Effects of Changes in pH** The concentration of H^+ is expressed as pH, where $pH = -\log [H^+]$. Buffers in biological fluids resist changes in pH. A buffer consists of an acid-base pair that combines reversibly with hydrogen ions.

▶ **Threats to Water Quality on Earth** The burning of fossil fuels results in

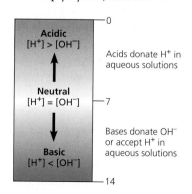

Acids donate H^+ in aqueous solutions

Bases donate OH^- or accept H^+ in aqueous solutions

emission of oxides (leading to acid precipitation) and increasing amounts of CO_2. Some CO_2 becomes dissolved in the oceans, lowering pH and potentially affecting the rate of calcification on coral reefs.

MEDIA

Activity Dissociation of Water Molecules
Activity Acids, Bases, and pH
Investigation How Does Acid Precipitation Affect Trees?

TESTING YOUR KNOWLEDGE

SELF-QUIZ

1. Many mammals control their body temperature by sweating. Which property of water is most directly responsible for the ability of sweat to lower body temperature?
   a. water's change in density when it condenses
   b. water's ability to dissolve molecules in the air
   c. the release of heat by the formation of hydrogen bonds
   d. the absorption of heat by the breaking of hydrogen bonds
   e. water's high surface tension

2. A slice of pizza has 500 kcal. If we could burn the pizza and use all the heat to warm a 50-L container of cold water, what would be the approximate increase in the temperature of the water? (*Note:* A liter of cold water weighs about 1 kg.)
   a. 50°C   d. 100°C
   b. 5°C   e. 1°C
   c. 10°C

3. The bonds that are broken when water vaporizes are
   a. ionic bonds.
   b. hydrogen bonds between water molecules.
   c. covalent bonds between atoms within water molecules.
   d. polar covalent bonds.
   e. nonpolar covalent bonds.

4. Which of the following is a hydrophobic material?
   a. paper   d. sugar
   b. table salt   e. pasta
   c. wax

5. We can be sure that a mole of table sugar and a mole of vitamin C are equal in their
   a. mass in daltons.   d. number of atoms.
   b. mass in grams.   e. volume.
   c. number of molecules.

6. How many grams of acetic acid ($C_2H_4O_2$) would you use to make 10 L of a 0.1 M aqueous solution of acetic acid? (*Note:* The atomic masses, in daltons, are approximately 12 for carbon, 1 for hydrogen, and 16 for oxygen.)
   a. 10.0 g   d. 60.0 g
   b. 0.1 g   e. 0.6 g
   c. 6.0 g

7. Measurements show that the pH of a particular lake is 4.0. What is the hydrogen ion concentration of the lake?
   a. 4.0 M d. $10^4 M$
   b. $10^{-10} M$ e. 4%
   c. $10^{-4} M$

8. What is the *hydroxide* ion concentration of the lake described in question 7?
   a. $10^{-7} M$ d. $10^{-14} M$
   b. $10^{-4} M$ e. 10 M
   c. $10^{-10} M$

9. **DRAW IT** Draw three water molecules, using space-filling models, and label the atoms. Draw solid lines to indicate covalent bonds and dotted lines for hydrogen bonds. Add partial-charge labels as appropriate.

For Self-Quiz answers, see Appendix A.

MEDIA Visit the Study Area at **www.masteringbio.com** for a Practice Test.

EVOLUTION CONNECTION

10. The surface of the planet Mars has many landscape features reminiscent of those formed by flowing water on Earth, including what appear to be meandering channels and outwash areas. In 2004, images of Meridiani Planum

Surface of Mars   Surface of Earth

on Mars taken by NASA's *Opportunity* rover suggested that liquid water was once present on its surface. For example, one image (left, above) shows polygonal fractures in the rock. Similar fracture patterns in rocks on Earth's surface (above, right) correlate with the earlier presence of water. Ice exists at the Martian poles today, and some scientists suspect a great deal more water may be present beneath the Martian surface. Why has there been so much interest in the presence of water on Mars? Does the presence of water make it more likely that life arose there? What other physical factors might also be important?

SCIENTIFIC INQUIRY

11. Design a controlled experiment to test the hypothesis that acid precipitation inhibits the growth of *Elodea*, a common freshwater plant (see Figure 2.19).

12. In agricultural areas, farmers pay close attention to the weather forecast. Right before a predicted overnight freeze, farmers spray water on crops to protect the plants. Use the properties of water to explain how this method works. Be sure to mention why hydrogen bonds are responsible for this phenomenon.

SCIENCE, TECHNOLOGY, AND SOCIETY

13. Agriculture, industry, and the growing populations of cities all compete, through political influence, for water. If you were in charge of water resources in an arid region, what would your priorities be for allocating the limited water supply for various uses? How would you try to build consensus among the different special-interest groups?

Carbon and the Molecular Diversity of Life

▲ Figure 4.1 **What properties of carbon underlie its role as the molecular basis of life?**

OVERVIEW
Carbon: The Backbone of Life

Although water is the universal medium for life on Earth, living organisms, such as the plants and trilobite beetle in **Figure 4.1**, are made up of chemicals that are based mostly on the element carbon. Carbon enters the biosphere through the action of plants, which use solar energy to transform atmospheric CO_2 into the molecules of life. These molecules are passed along to animals that feed on plants.

Of all chemical elements, carbon is unparalleled in its ability to form molecules that are large, complex, and diverse, and this molecular diversity has made possible the diversity of organisms that have evolved on Earth. Proteins, DNA, carbohydrates, and other molecules that distinguish living matter from inanimate material are all composed of carbon atoms bonded to one another and to atoms of other elements. Hydrogen (H), oxygen (O), nitrogen (N), sulfur (S), and phosphorus (P) are other common ingredients of these compounds, but it is the element carbon (C) that accounts for the large diversity of biological molecules.

Proteins and other very large molecules are the main focus of Chapter 5. Here we investigate the properties of smaller molecules. We will use these molecules to illustrate concepts of molecular architecture that will help explain why carbon is so important to life, at the same time highlighting the theme that emergent properties arise from the organization of matter in living organisms.

CONCEPT **4.1**
Organic chemistry is the study of carbon compounds

For historical reasons, compounds containing carbon are said to be organic, and the branch of chemistry that specializes in the study of carbon compounds is called **organic chemistry**. Organic compounds range from simple molecules, such as methane (CH_4), to colossal ones, such as proteins, with thousands of atoms. Most organic compounds contain hydrogen atoms in addition to carbon atoms.

The overall percentages of the major elements of life—C, H, O, N, S, and P—are quite uniform from one organism to another. Because of carbon's versatility, however, this limited assortment of atomic building blocks, taken in roughly the same proportions, can be used to build an inexhaustible variety of organic molecules. Different species of organisms, and different individuals within a species, are distinguished by variations in their organic molecules.

Since the dawn of human history, people have used other organisms as sources of valued substances—from foods and medicines to fabrics. The science of organic chemistry originated in attempts to purify and improve the yield of such products. By the early 1800s, chemists had learned to make many simple compounds in the laboratory by combining elements under the right conditions. Artificial synthesis of the complex molecules extracted from living matter seemed impossible, however. At that time, the Swedish chemist Jöns Jakob Berzelius made the distinction between organic compounds, those thought to arise only in living organisms, and inorganic compounds, those found only in the nonliving world. *Vitalism*, the belief in a life force outside the jurisdiction of physical and chemical laws, provided the foundation for the new discipline of organic chemistry.

Chemists began to chip away at the foundation of vitalism when they finally learned to synthesize organic compounds in laboratories. In 1828, Friedrich Wöhler, a German chemist who had studied with Berzelius, attempted to make an "inorganic" salt, ammonium cyanate, by mixing solutions of ammonium ions (NH_4^+) and cyanate ions (CNO^-). Wöhler was astonished to find that instead he had made urea, an organic compound present in the urine of animals. Wöhler challenged the vitalists when he wrote, "I must tell you that I can prepare urea without requiring a kidney or an animal, either man or dog." However, one of the ingredients used in the synthesis, the cyanate, had been extracted from animal blood, and the vitalists were not swayed by Wöhler's discovery. A few years later, however, Hermann Kolbe, a student of Wöhler's, made the organic compound acetic acid from inorganic substances that could be prepared directly from pure elements.

Vitalism crumbled completely after several decades of laboratory synthesis of some increasingly complex organic compounds. In 1953, Stanley Miller, a graduate student of Harold Urey at the University of Chicago, helped bring this abiotic (nonliving) synthesis of organic compounds into the context of evolution in a classic experiment described in **Figure 4.2**. Miller's experiment, testing whether complex organic molecules could arise spontaneously under conditions thought to have existed on the early Earth, stimulated interest and further research on the origin of organic compounds. Some scientists have questioned whether the gases Miller used as starting materials were really present in the primitive Earth's atmosphere. Recent work supports a slightly different recipe for early Earth's conditions; when used in the experiment, it led to the compounds Miller found. Although the jury is still out, these experiments support the idea that abiotic synthesis of organic compounds could have been an early stage in the origin of life.

The pioneers of organic chemistry helped shift the mainstream of biological thought from vitalism to *mechanism*, the view that physical and chemical laws govern all natural phenomena, including the processes of life. Organic chemistry was redefined as the study of carbon compounds, regardless of origin. Organisms produce most of the naturally occurring organic compounds, and these molecules represent a diversity and range of complexity unrivaled by inorganic compounds. However, the rules of chemistry apply to all molecules. The foundation of organic chemistry is not some intangible life force, but the unique chemical versatility of the element carbon.

CONCEPT CHECK **4.1**

1. What conclusion did Stanley Miller draw when he found amino acids in the products of his experiment?
2. **WHAT IF?** When Miller tried the experiment in Figure 4.2 without the electrical discharge, no organic compounds were found. What might explain this result?

For suggested answers, see Appendix A.

▼ Figure 4.2 **Inquiry**

Can organic molecules form under conditions believed to simulate those on the early Earth?

EXPERIMENT In 1953, Stanley Miller set up a closed system to simulate conditions thought to have existed on the early Earth. A flask of water simulated the primeval sea. The water was heated so that some vaporized and moved into a second, higher flask containing the "atmosphere"—a mixture of gases. Sparks were discharged in the synthetic atmosphere to mimic lightning.

❷ The "atmosphere" contained a mixture of hydrogen gas (H_2), methane (CH_4), ammonia (NH_3), and water vapor.

❸ Sparks were discharged to mimic lightning.

"Atmosphere"

CH_4

Water vapor

Electrode

❶ The water mixture in the "sea" flask was heated; vapor entered the "atmosphere" flask.

NH_3 H_2

Condenser

Cooled water containing organic molecules

Cold water

H_2O "sea"

Sample for chemical analysis

❺ As material cycled through the apparatus, Miller periodically collected samples for analysis.

❹ A condenser cooled the atmosphere, raining water and any dissolved molecules down into the sea flask.

RESULTS Miller identified a variety of organic molecules that are common in organisms. These included simple compounds such as formaldehyde (CH_2O) and hydrogen cyanide (HCN) and more complex molecules such as amino acids and long chains of carbon and hydrogen known as hydrocarbons.

CONCLUSION Organic molecules, a first step in the origin of life, may have been synthesized abiotically on the early Earth. (We will explore this hypothesis in more detail in Chapter 25.)

SOURCE S. Miller, A production of amino acids under possible primitive Earth conditions, *Science* 117:528–529 (1953).

WHAT IF? If Miller had increased the concentration of NH_3 in his experiment, how might the relative amounts of the products HCN and CH_2O have differed?

Carbon atoms can form diverse molecules by bonding to four other atoms

The key to an atom's chemical characteristics is its electron configuration. This configuration determines the kinds and number of bonds an atom will form with other atoms.

The Formation of Bonds with Carbon

Carbon has 6 electrons, with 2 in the first electron shell and 4 in the second shell. Having 4 valence electrons in a shell that holds 8, carbon would have to donate or accept 4 electrons to complete its valence shell and become an ion. Instead, a carbon atom usually completes its valence shell by sharing its 4 electrons with other atoms in covalent bonds so that 8 electrons are present. These bonds may include single and double covalent bonds. Each carbon atom thus acts as an intersection point from which a molecule can branch off in as many as four directions. This *tetravalence* is one facet of carbon's versatility that makes large, complex molecules possible.

When a carbon atom forms four single covalent bonds, the arrangement of its four hybrid orbitals causes the bonds to angle toward the corners of an imaginary tetrahedron (see Figure 2.17b). The bond angles in methane (CH_4) are 109.5° **(Figure 4.3a)**, and they are roughly the same in any group of atoms where carbon has four single bonds. For example, ethane (C_2H_6) is shaped like two overlapping tetrahedrons

(Figure 4.3b). In molecules with more carbons, every grouping of a carbon bonded to four other atoms has a tetrahedral shape. But when two carbon atoms are joined by a double bond, all bonds around those carbons are in the same plane. For example, ethene (C_2H_4) is a flat molecule; its atoms all lie in the same plane **(Figure 4.3c)**. We find it convenient to write all structural formulas as though the molecules represented were flat, but keep in mind that molecules are three-dimensional and that the shape of a molecule often determines its function.

The electron configuration of carbon gives it covalent compatibility with many different elements. **Figure 4.4** shows the valences of carbon and its most frequent partners—oxygen, hydrogen, and nitrogen. These are the four major atomic components of organic molecules. These valences are the basis for the rules of covalent bonding in organic chemistry—the building code for the architecture of organic molecules.

Let's consider how the rules of covalent bonding apply to carbon atoms with partners other than hydrogen. We'll look at two examples, the simple molecules carbon dioxide and urea.

In the carbon dioxide molecule (CO_2), a single carbon atom is joined to two atoms of oxygen by double covalent bonds. The structural formula for CO_2 is shown here:

$$O=C=O$$

Each line in a structural formula represents a pair of shared electrons. The two double bonds formed by the carbon atom are the equivalent of four single covalent bonds. The arrangement completes the valence shells of all atoms in the molecule. Because CO_2 is a very simple molecule and lacks hydrogen, it is often considered inorganic, even though it contains carbon.

Name and Comment	Molecular Formula	Structural Formula	Ball-and-Stick Model	Space-Filling Model
(a) Methane. When a carbon atom has four single bonds to other atoms, the molecule is tetrahedral.	CH_4			
(b) Ethane. A molecule may have more than one tetrahedral group of single-bonded atoms. (Ethane consists of two such groups.)	C_2H_6			
(c) Ethene (ethylene). When two carbon atoms are joined by a double bond, all atoms attached to those carbons are in the same plane; the molecule is flat.	C_2H_4			

▲ **Figure 4.3 The shapes of three simple organic molecules.**

Hydrogen
(valence = 1)

Oxygen
(valence = 2)

Nitrogen
(valence = 3)

Carbon
(valence = 4)

▲ **Figure 4.4 Valences of the major elements of organic molecules.** Valence is the number of covalent bonds an atom can form. It is generally equal to the number of electrons required to complete the valence (outermost) shell (see Figure 2.9). All the electrons are shown for each atom in the electron distribution diagrams (top). Only the electrons in the valence shell are presented in the Lewis dot structures.

DRAW IT *Refer to Figure 2.9 and draw the Lewis dot structures for sodium, phosphorus, sulfur, and chlorine.*

Whether we call CO_2 organic or inorganic, however, it is clearly important to the living world as the source of carbon for all organic molecules in organisms.

Urea, $CO(NH_2)_2$, is the organic compound found in urine that Wöhler synthesized in the early 1800s. The structural formula for urea is shown at the right. Again, each atom has the required number of covalent bonds. In this case, one carbon atom is involved in both single and double bonds.

Urea and carbon dioxide are molecules with one carbon atom. But as Figure 4.3 shows, a carbon atom can also use one or more valence electrons to form covalent bonds to other carbon atoms, linking the atoms into chains of seemingly infinite variety.

Molecular Diversity Arising from Carbon Skeleton Variation

Carbon chains form the skeletons of most organic molecules (**Figure 4.5**). The skeletons vary in length and may be straight, branched, or arranged in closed rings. Some carbon skeletons have double bonds, which vary in number and location. Such variation in carbon skeletons is one important source of the molecular complexity and diversity that characterize living matter. In addition, atoms of other elements can be bonded to the skeletons at available sites.

Hydrocarbons

All of the molecules that are shown in Figures 4.3 and 4.5 are **hydrocarbons**, organic molecules consisting of only carbon and hydrogen. Atoms of hydrogen are attached to the carbon skeleton wherever electrons are available for covalent bonding. Hydrocarbons are the major components of petroleum, which is called a fossil fuel because it consists of the partially decomposed remains of organisms that lived millions of years ago.

Although hydrocarbons are not prevalent in living organisms, many of a cell's organic molecules have regions consisting of only carbon and hydrogen. For example, the molecules known as fats have long hydrocarbon tails attached to a non-hydrocarbon component (**Figure 4.6**, on next page). Neither petroleum nor fat dissolves in water; both are hydrophobic compounds because the great majority of their bonds are relatively nonpolar carbon-to-hydrogen linkages. Another characteristic of hydrocarbons is that they can undergo reactions that release a relatively large amount of energy. The gasoline that fuels a car consists of hydrocarbons, and the hydrocarbon tails of fat molecules serve as stored fuel for animal bodies.

(c) **Double bonds.** The skeleton may have double bonds, which can vary in location.

(a) **Length.** Carbon skeletons vary in length.

(b) **Branching.** Skeletons may be unbranched or branched.

(d) **Rings.** Some carbon skeletons are arranged in rings. In the abbreviated structural formula for each compound (at the right), each corner represents a carbon and its attached hydrogens.

▲ **Figure 4.5 Variations in carbon skeletons.** Hydrocarbons, organic molecules consisting only of carbon and hydrogen, illustrate the diversity of the carbon skeletons of organic molecules.

Fat droplets (stained red)

100 μm

(a) Mammalian adipose cells   **(b) A fat molecule**

▲ **Figure 4.6 The role of hydrocarbons in fats. (a)** Mammalian adipose cells stockpile fat molecules as a fuel reserve. Each adipose cell in this micrograph is almost filled by a large fat droplet, which contains a huge number of fat molecules. **(b)** A fat molecule consists of a small, nonhydrocarbon component joined to three hydrocarbon tails. The tails can be broken down to provide energy. They also account for the hydrophobic behavior of fats. (Black = carbon; gray = hydrogen; red = oxygen.)

Isomers

Variation in the architecture of organic molecules can be seen in **isomers**, compounds that have the same numbers of atoms of the same elements but different structures and hence different properties. Compare, for example, the two five-carbon compounds in **Figure 4.7a**. Both have the molecular formula C_5H_{12}, but they differ in the covalent arrangement of their carbon skeletons. The skeleton is straight in one compound but branched in the other. We will examine three types of isomers: structural isomers, geometric isomers, and enantiomers.

Structural isomers differ in the covalent arrangements of their atoms. The number of possible isomers increases tremendously as carbon skeletons increase in size. There are only 3 forms of C_5H_{12} (2 are shown in Figure 4.7a), but there are 18 variations of C_8H_{18} and 366,319 possible structural isomers of $C_{20}H_{42}$. Structural isomers may also differ in the location of double bonds.

Geometric isomers have the same covalent partnerships, but they differ in their spatial arrangements. The differences arise from the inflexibility of double bonds. Single bonds allow the atoms they join to rotate freely about the bond axis without changing the compound. In contrast, double bonds do not permit such rotation, resulting in the possibility of geometric isomers. If a double bond joins two carbon atoms, and each C also has two different atoms (or groups of atoms) attached to it, then two distinct geometric isomers are possible. Consider a simple molecule with two double-bonded carbons, each of which has an H and an X attached to it **(Figure 4.7b)**. The arrangement with both Xs on the same side of the double bond is called a *cis* isomer, and the arrangement with the Xs on opposite sides is called a *trans* isomer. The subtle difference in shape between geometric isomers can dramatically affect the biological activities of organic molecules. For example, the biochemistry of vision involves a light-induced

(a) Structural isomers differ in covalent partners, as shown in this example of two isomers of C_5H_{12}: pentane (left) and 2-methyl butane (right).

cis isomer: The two Xs are on the same side.   *trans* isomer: The two Xs are on opposite sides.

(b) Geometric isomers differ in arrangement about a double bond. In these diagrams, X represents an atom or group of atoms attached to a double-bonded carbon.

L isomer   D isomer

(c) Enantiomers differ in spatial arrangement around an asymmetric carbon, resulting in molecules that are mirror images, like left and right hands. The two isomers are designated the L and D isomers from the Latin for left and right (*levo* and *dextro*). Enantiomers cannot be superimposed on each other.

▲ **Figure 4.7 Three types of isomers.** Compounds with the same molecular formula but different structures, isomers are a source of diversity in organic molecules.

DRAW IT *There are three structural isomers of C_5H_{12}; draw the one not shown in (a).*

change of rhodopsin, a chemical compound in the eye, from the *cis* isomer to the *trans* isomer (see Chapter 50).

Enantiomers are isomers that are mirror images of each other. In the ball-and-stick models shown in **Figure 4.7c**, the middle carbon is called an *asymmetric carbon* because it is attached to four different atoms or groups of atoms. The four groups can be arranged in space around the asymmetric carbon in two different ways that are mirror images. Enantiomers are, in a way, left-handed and right-handed versions of the molecule. Just as your right hand won't fit into a left-handed glove, the working molecules in a cell can distinguish the two versions by shape. Usually, one isomer is biologically active, and the other is inactive.

The concept of enantiomers is important in the pharmaceutical industry because the two enantiomers of a drug may not be equally

Drug	Condition	Effective Enantiomer	Ineffective Enantiomer
Ibuprofen	Pain; inflammation	S-Ibuprofen	R-Ibuprofen
Albuterol	Asthma	R-Albuterol	S-Albuterol

▲ **Figure 4.8 The pharmacological importance of enantiomers.** Ibuprofen and albuterol are examples of drugs whose enantiomers have different effects. (*S* and *R* are letters used in one system to distinguish two enantiomers.) Ibuprofen reduces inflammation and pain. It is commonly sold as a mixture of the two enantiomers. The *S* enantiomer is 100 times more effective than the other. Albuterol is used to relax bronchial muscles, improving airflow in asthma patients. Only *R*-albuterol is synthesized and sold as a drug; the *S* form counteracts the active *R* form.

▲ **Figure 4.9 A comparison of chemical groups of female (estradiol) and male (testosterone) sex hormones.** The two molecules differ only in the chemical groups attached to a common carbon skeleton of four fused rings, shown here in abbreviated form. These subtle variations in molecular architecture (shaded in blue) influence the development of the anatomical and physiological differences between female and male vertebrates.

effective **(Figure 4.8)**. In some cases, one of the isomers may even produce harmful effects. This was the case with thalidomide, a drug prescribed for thousands of pregnant women in the late 1950s and early 1960s. The drug was a mixture of two enantiomers. One enantiomer reduced morning sickness, the desired effect, but the other caused severe birth defects. (Unfortunately, even if the "good" thalidomide enantiomer is used in purified form, some of it soon converts to the "bad" enantiomer in the patient's body.) The differing effects of enantiomers in the body demonstrate that organisms are sensitive to even the most subtle variations in molecular architecture. Once again, we see that molecules have emergent properties that depend on the specific arrangement of their atoms.

CONCEPT CHECK 4.2

1. Draw a structural formula for C_2H_4.
2. Which molecules in Figure 4.5 are isomers? For each pair, identify the type of isomer.
3. How are gasoline and fat chemically similar?
4. **WHAT IF?** Can propane (C_3H_8) form isomers?

For suggested answers, see Appendix A.

CONCEPT 4.3

A small number of chemical groups are key to the functioning of biological molecules

The distinctive properties of an organic molecule depend not only on the arrangement of its carbon skeleton but also on the molecular components attached to that skeleton. We can think of hydrocarbons, the simplest organic molecules, as the underlying framework for more complex organic molecules. A number of chemical groups can replace one or more of the hydrogens bonded to the carbon skeleton of the hydrocarbon. (Some groups include atoms of the carbon skeleton, as we will see.) These groups may participate in chemical reactions or may contribute to function indirectly by their effects on molecular shape. The number and arrangement of the groups help give each molecule its unique properties.

The Chemical Groups Most Important in the Processes of Life

Consider the differences between testosterone and estradiol (a type of estrogen). These compounds are male and female sex hormones, respectively, in humans and other vertebrates **(Figure 4.9)**. Both are steroids, organic molecules with a common carbon skeleton in the form of four fused rings. These sex hormones differ only in the chemical groups attached to the rings. The different actions of these two molecules on many targets throughout the body help produce the contrasting features of males and females. Thus, even our sexuality has its biological basis in variations of molecular architecture.

In the example of sex hormones, different chemical groups contribute to function by affecting the molecule's shape. In other cases, the chemical groups affect molecular function by being directly involved in chemical reactions; these important chemical groups are known as **functional groups**. Each functional group participates in chemical reactions in a characteristic way, from one organic molecule to another.

The seven chemical groups most important in biological processes are the hydroxyl, carbonyl, carboxyl, amino, sulfhydryl, phosphate, and methyl groups. The first six groups can act as functional groups; they are also hydrophilic and thus increase the solubility of organic compounds in water. The methyl group is not reactive, but instead often acts as a recognizable tag on biological molecules. Before reading further, study **Figure 4.10** on the next two pages to familiarize yourself with these biologically important chemical groups.

Exploring Some Biologically Important Chemical Groups

CHEMICAL GROUP	Hydroxyl	Carbonyl	Carboxyl
STRUCTURE	 (may be written HO—) In a **hydroxyl group** (—OH), a hydrogen atom is bonded to an oxygen atom, which in turn is bonded to the carbon skeleton of the organic molecule. (Do not confuse this functional group with the hydroxide ion, OH⁻.)	 The **carbonyl group** (>CO) consists of a carbon atom joined to an oxygen atom by a double bond.	 When an oxygen atom is double-bonded to a carbon atom that is also bonded to an —OH group, the entire assembly of atoms is called a **carboxyl group** (—COOH).
NAME OF COMPOUND	**Alcohols** (their specific names usually end in -ol)	**Ketones** if the carbonyl group is within a carbon skeleton **Aldehydes** if the carbonyl group is at the end of the carbon skeleton	**Carboxylic acids**, or organic acids
EXAMPLE	 **Ethanol**, the alcohol present in alcoholic beverages	 **Acetone**, the simplest ketone **Propanal**, an aldehyde	 **Acetic acid**, which gives vinegar its sour taste
FUNCTIONAL PROPERTIES	• Is polar as a result of the electrons spending more time near the electronegative oxygen atom. • Can form hydrogen bonds with water molecules, helping dissolve organic compounds such as sugars (see Figure 5.3).	• A ketone and an aldehyde may be structural isomers with different properties, as is the case for acetone and propanal. • These two groups are also found in sugars, giving rise to two major groups of sugars: aldoses (containing an aldehyde) and ketoses (containing a ketone).	• Has acidic properties (is a source of hydrogen ions) because the covalent bond between oxygen and hydrogen is so polar; for example, Acetic acid ⇌ Acetate ion + H⁺ • Found in cells in the ionized form with a charge of 1− and called a carboxylate ion (here, specifically, the acetate ion).

Amino

$$-N\begin{matrix}H\\\ \\H\end{matrix}$$

The **amino group** (—NH₂) consists of a nitrogen atom bonded to two hydrogen atoms and to the carbon skeleton.

Sulfhydryl

—SH

(may be written HS —)

The **sulfhydryl group** consists of a sulfur atom bonded to an atom of hydrogen; resembles a hydroxyl group in shape.

Phosphate

$$-O-\overset{\overset{O}{|}}{\underset{\underset{O^-}{|}}{P}}-O^-$$

In a **phosphate group**, a phosphorus atom is bonded to four oxygen atoms; one oxygen is bonded to the carbon skeleton; two oxygens carry negative charges. The phosphate group (—OPO₃²⁻, abbreviated ⓟ) is an ionized form of a phosphoric acid group (—OPO₃H₂; note the two hydrogens).

Methyl

$$-C\begin{matrix}H\\|\\|\\H\end{matrix}H$$

A **methyl group** consists of a carbon bonded to three hydrogen atoms. The methyl group may be attached to a carbon or to a different atom.

Amines

Glycine

Because it also has a carboxyl group, glycine is both an amine and a carboxylic acid; compounds with both groups are called **amino acids**.

Thiols

Cysteine

Cysteine is an important sulfur-containing amino acid.

Organic phosphates

Glycerol phosphate

In addition to taking part in many important chemical reactions in cells, glycerol phosphate provides the backbone for phospholipids, the most prevalent molecules in cell membranes.

Methylated compounds

5-Methyl cytidine

5-Methyl cytidine is a component of DNA that has been modified by addition of the methyl group.

- Acts as a base; can pick up an H⁺ from the surrounding solution (water, in living organisms).

$$-N\begin{matrix}H\\\ \\H\end{matrix} \qquad -\overset{+}{N}\begin{matrix}H\\|\\H\end{matrix}-H$$

(nonionized)   (ionized)

- Ionized, with a charge of 1+, under cellular conditions.

- Two sulfhydryl groups can react, forming a covalent bond. This "cross-linking" helps stabilize protein structure (see Figure 5.21).

- Cross-linking of cysteines in hair proteins maintains the curliness or straightness of hair. Straight hair can be "permanently" curled by shaping it around curlers, then breaking and re-forming the cross-linking bonds.

- Contributes negative charge to the molecule of which it is a part (2− when at the end of a molecule, as above; 1− when located internally in a chain of phosphates).

- Has the potential to react with water, releasing energy.

- Addition of a methyl group to DNA, or to molecules bound to DNA, affects expression of genes.

- Arrangement of methyl groups in male and female sex hormones affects their shape and function (see Figure 4.9).

? *Given the information in this figure and what you know about the electronegativity of oxygen, predict which of the following molecules would be the stronger acid. Explain your answer.*

a. $H-\overset{\overset{H}{|}}{\underset{\underset{H}{|}}{C}}-\overset{\overset{H}{|}}{\underset{\underset{H}{|}}{C}}-\overset{\overset{O}{\|}}{C}-OH$

b. $H-\overset{\overset{H}{|}}{\underset{\underset{H}{|}}{C}}-\overset{\overset{O}{\|}}{C}-\overset{\overset{O}{\|}}{C}-OH$

ATP: An Important Source of Energy for Cellular Processes

The "Phosphate" column in Figure 4.10 shows a simple example of an organic phosphate molecule. A more complicated organic phosphate, **adenosine triphosphate**, or **ATP**, is worth mentioning because its function in the cell is so important. ATP consists of an organic molecule called adenosine attached to a string of three phosphate groups:

$$
\begin{array}{ccccc}
& O & & O & & O \\
& \| & & \| & & \| \\
{}^-O-P & -O-P & -O-P & -O-\boxed{\text{Adenosine}} \\
& | & & | & & | \\
& O^- & & O^- & & O^-
\end{array}
$$

Where three phosphates are present in series, as in ATP, one phosphate may be split off as a result of a reaction with water. This inorganic phosphate ion, $HOPO_3^{2-}$, is often abbreviated $\textcircled{P}_i$ in this book. Having lost one phosphate, ATP becomes adenosine *di*phosphate, or ADP. Although ATP is sometimes said to "store" energy, it is more accurate to think of it as "storing" the potential to react with water. This reaction releases energy that can be used by the cell. You will learn about this in more detail in Chapter 8.

Reacts
with H_2O

$\textcircled{P}-\textcircled{P}-\textcircled{P}-\boxed{\text{Adenosine}} \longrightarrow \textcircled{P}_i + \textcircled{P}-\textcircled{P}-\boxed{\text{Adenosine}} +$ Energy

ATP   Inorganic   ADP
       phosphate

CONCEPT CHECK 4.3

1. What does the term *amino acid* signify about the structure of such a molecule?
2. What chemical change occurs when ATP reacts with water and releases energy?
3. **WHAT IF?** Suppose you had an organic molecule such as glycine (see Figure 4.10, amino group example), and you chemically removed the —NH_2 group and replaced it with —COOH. Draw the structural formula for this molecule and speculate about its chemical properties.

For suggested answers, see Appendix A.

The Chemical Elements of Life: *A Review*

Living matter, as you have learned, consists mainly of carbon, oxygen, hydrogen, and nitrogen, with smaller amounts of sulfur and phosphorus. These elements all form strong covalent bonds, an essential characteristic in the architecture of complex organic molecules. Of all these elements, carbon is the virtuoso of the covalent bond. The versatility of carbon makes possible the great diversity of organic molecules, each with particular properties that emerge from the unique arrangement of its carbon skeleton and the chemical groups appended to that skeleton. At the foundation of all biological diversity lies this variation at the molecular level.

Chapter 4 Review

SUMMARY OF KEY CONCEPTS

CONCEPT 4.1

Organic chemistry is the study of carbon compounds (pp. 58–59)

▶ Organic compounds were once thought to arise only within living organisms, but this idea (vitalism) was disproved when chemists were able to synthesize organic compounds in the laboratory.

CONCEPT 4.2

Carbon atoms can form diverse molecules by bonding to four other atoms (pp. 60–63)

▶ **The Formation of Bonds with Carbon** Carbon, with a valence of 4, can bond to various other atoms, including O, H, and N. Carbon can also bond to other carbon atoms, forming the carbon skeletons of organic compounds.

▶ **Molecular Diversity Arising from Carbon Skeleton Variation** The carbon skeletons of organic molecules vary in length and shape and have bonding sites for atoms of other elements. Hydrocarbons consist only of carbon and hydrogen. Isomers are compounds with the same molecular formula but different structures and properties. Three types of isomers are structural isomers, geometric isomers, and enantiomers.

MEDIA

Activity Diversity of Carbon-Based Molecules
Activity Isomers
Investigation What Factors Determine the Effectiveness of Drugs?

CONCEPT 4.3

A small number of chemical groups are key to the functioning of biological molecules (pp. 63–66)

▶ **The Chemical Groups Most Important in the Processes of Life** Chemical groups attached to the carbon skeletons of organic molecules participate in chemical reactions (functional groups) or contribute to function by affecting molecular shape.

ATP: An Important Source of Energy for Cellular Processes

Reacts with H_2O

ⓅⓅⓅ–Adenosine ⟶ Ⓟᵢ + ⓅⓅ–Adenosine + Energy

ATP   Inorganic   ADP
             phosphate

MEDIA

Activity Functional Groups

► **The Chemical Elements of Life: *A Review*** Living matter is made mostly of carbon, oxygen, hydrogen, and nitrogen, with some sulfur and phosphorus. Biological diversity has its molecular basis in carbon's ability to form a huge number of molecules with particular shapes and chemical properties.

TESTING YOUR KNOWLEDGE

SELF-QUIZ

1. Organic chemistry is currently defined as
  a. the study of compounds made only by living cells.
  b. the study of carbon compounds.
  c. the study of vital forces.
  d. the study of natural (as opposed to synthetic) compounds.
  e. the study of hydrocarbons.

2. Which of the following hydrocarbons has a double bond in its carbon skeleton?
  a. C_3H_8 d. C_2H_4
  b. C_2H_6 e. C_2H_2
  c. CH_4

3. Choose the term that correctly describes the relationship between these two sugar molecules:

  a. structural isomers   c. enantiomers
  b. geometric isomers   d. isotopes

4. Identify the asymmetric carbon in this molecule:

5. Which functional group is *not* present in this molecule?

  a. carboxyl   b. sulfhydryl   c. hydroxyl   d. amino

6. Which action could produce a carbonyl group?
  a. the replacement of the —OH of a carboxyl group with hydrogen
  b. the addition of a thiol to a hydroxyl
  c. the addition of a hydroxyl to a phosphate
  d. the replacement of the nitrogen of an amine with oxygen
  e. the addition of a sulfhydryl to a carboxyl

7. Which chemical group is most likely to be responsible for an organic molecule behaving as a base?
  a. hydroxyl   d. amino
  b. carbonyl   e. phosphate
  c. carboxyl

For Self-Quiz answers, see Appendix A.

MEDIA Visit the Study Area at **www.masteringbio.com** for a Practice Test.

EVOLUTION CONNECTION

8. **DRAW IT** Some scientists believe that life elsewhere in the universe might be based on the element silicon, rather than on carbon, as on Earth. Look at the electron distribution diagram for silicon in Figure 2.9 and draw the Lewis dot structure for silicon. What properties does silicon share with carbon that would make silicon-based life more likely than, say, neon-based life or aluminum-based life?

SCIENTIFIC INQUIRY

9. In 1918, an epidemic of sleeping sickness caused an unusual rigid paralysis in some survivors, similar to symptoms of advanced Parkinson's disease. Years later, L-dopa (below, left), a chemical used to treat Parkinson's disease, was given to some of these patients, as dramatized in the movie *Awakenings.* L-dopa was remarkably effective at eliminating the paralysis, at least temporarily. However, its enantiomer, D-dopa (right), was subsequently shown to have no effect at all, as is the case for Parkinson's disease. Suggest a hypothesis to explain why, for both diseases, one enantiomer is effective and the other is not.

L-dopa   **D-dopa**

SCIENCE, TECHNOLOGY, AND SOCIETY

10. Thalidomide achieved notoriety 50 years ago because of a wave of birth defects among children born to women who took thalidomide during pregnancy as a treatment for morning sickness. However, in 1998 the U.S. Food and Drug Administration (FDA) approved this drug for the treatment of certain conditions associated with Hansen's disease (leprosy). In clinical trials, thalidomide also shows promise for use in treating patients suffering from AIDS, tuberculosis, and some types of cancer. Do you think approval of this drug is appropriate? If so, under what conditions? What criteria do you think the FDA should use in weighing a drug's benefits against its dangers?

The Structure and Function of Large Biological Molecules

▲ **Figure 5.1 Why do scientists study the structures of macromolecules?**

OVERVIEW

The Molecules of Life

Given the rich complexity of life on Earth, we might expect organisms to have an enormous diversity of molecules. Remarkably, however, the critically important large molecules of all living things—from bacteria to elephants—fall into just four main classes: carbohydrates, lipids, proteins, and nucleic acids. On the molecular scale, members of three of these classes—carbohydrates, proteins, and nucleic acids—are huge and are thus called **macromolecules**. For example, a protein may consist of thousands of atoms that form a molecular colossus with a mass well over 100,000 daltons. Considering the size and complexity of macromolecules, it is noteworthy that biochemists have determined the detailed structures of so many of them **(Figure 5.1)**.

The architecture of a large biological molecule helps explain how that molecule works. Like water and simple organic molecules, large biological molecules exhibit unique emergent properties arising from the orderly arrangement of their atoms. In this chapter, we'll first consider how macromolecules are built. Then we'll examine the structure and function of all four classes of large biological molecules: carbohydrates, lipids, proteins, and nucleic acids.

CONCEPT 5.1

Macromolecules are polymers, built from monomers

The macromolecules in three of the four classes of life's organic compounds—carbohydrates, proteins, and nucleic acids—are chain-like molecules called polymers (from the Greek *polys*, many, and *meris*, part). A **polymer** is a long molecule consisting of many similar or identical building blocks linked by covalent bonds, much as a train consists of a chain of cars. The repeating units that serve as the building blocks of a polymer are smaller molecules called **monomers**. Some of the molecules that serve as monomers also have other functions of their own.

The Synthesis and Breakdown of Polymers

The classes of polymers differ in the nature of their monomers, but the chemical mechanisms by which cells make and break down polymers are basically the same in all cases **(Figure 5.2)**. Monomers are connected by a reaction in which two molecules are covalently bonded to each other through loss of a water molecule; this is known as a **condensation reaction**, specifically a **dehydration reaction**, because water is the molecule that is lost **(Figure 5.2a)**. When a bond forms between two monomers, each monomer contributes part of the water molecule that is lost: One molecule provides a hydroxyl group (—OH), while the other provides a hydrogen (—H). This reaction can be repeated as monomers are added to the chain one by one, making a polymer. The dehydration process is facilitated by **enzymes**, specialized macromolecules that speed up chemical reactions in cells.

Polymers are disassembled to monomers by **hydrolysis**, a process that is essentially the reverse of the dehydration

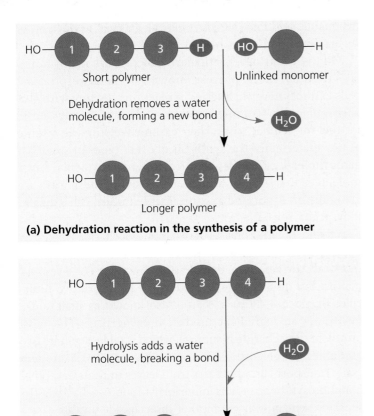

(a) Dehydration reaction in the synthesis of a polymer

Short polymer

Unlinked monomer

Dehydration removes a water molecule, forming a new bond

H_2O

Longer polymer

(b) Hydrolysis of a polymer

Hydrolysis adds a water molecule, breaking a bond

H_2O

▲ **Figure 5.2 The synthesis and breakdown of polymers.**

als are more extensive and those between species greater still. The diversity of macromolecules in the living world is vast, and the possible variety is effectively limitless.

What is the basis for such diversity in life's polymers? These molecules are constructed from only 40 to 50 common monomers and some others that occur rarely. Building a huge variety of polymers from such a limited number of monomers is analogous to constructing hundreds of thousands of words from only 26 letters of the alphabet. The key is arrangement—the particular linear sequence that the units follow. However, this analogy falls far short of describing the great diversity of macromolecules because most biological polymers have many more monomers than the number of letters in the longest word. Proteins, for example, are built from 20 kinds of amino acids arranged in chains that are typically hundreds of amino acids long. The molecular logic of life is simple but elegant: Small molecules common to all organisms are ordered into unique macromolecules.

Despite this immense diversity, molecular structure and function can still be grouped roughly by class. Let's look at each of the four major classes of large biological molecules. For each class, the large molecules have emergent properties not found in their individual building blocks.

CONCEPT CHECK 5.1

1. What are the four main classes of large biological molecules?
2. How many molecules of water are needed to completely hydrolyze a polymer that is ten monomers long?
3. **WHAT IF?** Suppose you eat a serving of green beans. What reactions must occur for the amino acid monomers in the protein of the beans to be converted to proteins in your body?

For suggested answers, see Appendix A.

reaction **(Figure 5.2b)**. Hydrolysis means to break using water (from the Greek *hydro*, water, and *lysis*, break). Bonds between the monomers are broken by the addition of water molecules, with a hydrogen from the water attaching to one monomer and a hydroxyl group attaching to the adjacent monomer. An example of hydrolysis working within our bodies is the process of digestion. The bulk of the organic material in our food is in the form of polymers that are much too large to enter our cells. Within the digestive tract, various enzymes attack the polymers, speeding up hydrolysis. The released monomers are then absorbed into the bloodstream for distribution to all body cells. Those cells can then use dehydration reactions to assemble the monomers into new, different polymers that can perform specific functions required by the cell.

The Diversity of Polymers

Each cell has thousands of different kinds of macromolecules; the collection varies from one type of cell to another even in the same organism. The inherent differences between human siblings reflect variations in polymers, particularly DNA and proteins. Molecular differences between unrelated individu-

CONCEPT 5.2

Carbohydrates serve as fuel and building material

Carbohydrates include both sugars and polymers of sugars. The simplest carbohydrates are the monosaccharides, also known as simple sugars. Disaccharides are double sugars, consisting of two monosaccharides joined by a covalent bond. Carbohydrates also include macromolecules called polysaccharides, polymers composed of many sugar building blocks.

Sugars

Monosaccharides (from the Greek *monos*, single, and *sacchar*, sugar) generally have molecular formulas that are some multiple of the unit CH_2O **(Figure 5.3)**. Glucose ($C_6H_{12}O_6$), the most common monosaccharide, is of central importance in the chemistry of life. In the structure of glucose, we can see the trademarks of a sugar: The molecule has a carbonyl group ($>C=O$) and multiple hydroxyl groups (—OH). Depending on the location of the carbonyl group, a sugar is either an aldose (aldehyde sugar) or a ketose (ketone sugar). Glucose, for example, is an aldose; fructose, a structural isomer of glucose, is a ketose. (Most names for sugars end in -ose.) Another criterion for classifying sugars is the size of the carbon skeleton, which ranges from three to seven carbons long. Glucose, fructose, and other sugars that have six carbons are called hexoses. Trioses (three-carbon sugars) and pentoses (five-carbon sugars) are also common.

Still another source of diversity for simple sugars is in the spatial arrangement of their parts around asymmetric carbons. (Recall that an asymmetric carbon is a carbon attached to four different atoms or groups of atoms.) Glucose and galactose, for example, differ only in the placement of parts around one asymmetric carbon (see the purple boxes in Figure 5.3). What seems like a small difference is significant enough to give the two sugars distinctive shapes and behaviors.

Although it is convenient to draw glucose with a linear carbon skeleton, this representation is not completely accurate.

In aqueous solutions, glucose molecules, as well as most other sugars, form rings **(Figure 5.4)**.

Monosaccharides, particularly glucose, are major nutrients for cells. In the process known as cellular respiration, cells extract energy in a series of reactions starting with glucose molecules. Not only are simple-sugar molecules a major fuel for cellular work; their carbon skeletons also serve as raw material for the synthesis of other types of small organic molecules, such as amino acids and fatty acids. Sugar molecules that are not immediately used in these ways are generally incorporated as monomers into disaccharides or polysaccharides.

A **disaccharide** consists of two monosaccharides joined by a **glycosidic linkage**, a covalent bond formed between two monosaccharides by a dehydration reaction. For example, maltose is a disaccharide formed by the linking of two molecules of glucose **(Figure 5.5a)**. Also known as malt sugar, maltose is an ingredient used in brewing beer. The most prevalent disaccharide is sucrose, which is table sugar. Its two monomers are glucose and fructose **(Figure 5.5b)**. Plants generally transport carbohydrates from leaves to roots and other nonphotosynthetic organs in the form of sucrose. Lactose, the sugar present in milk, is another disaccharide, in this case a glucose molecule joined to a galactose molecule.

▶ **Figure 5.3 The structure and classification of some monosaccharides.** Sugars may be aldoses (aldehyde sugars, top row) or ketoses (ketone sugars, bottom row), depending on the location of the carbonyl group (dark orange). Sugars are also classified according to the length of their carbon skeletons. A third point of variation is the spatial arrangement around asymmetric carbons (compare, for example, the purple portions of glucose and galactose).

(a) **Linear and ring forms.** Chemical equilibrium between the linear and ring structures greatly favors the formation of rings. The carbons of the sugar are numbered 1 to 6, as shown. To form the glucose ring, carbon 1 bonds to the oxygen attached to carbon 5.

(b) **Abbreviated ring structure.** Each corner represents a carbon. The ring's thicker edge indicates that you are looking at the ring edge-on; the components attached to the ring lie above or below the plane of the ring.

▲ **Figure 5.4 Linear and ring forms of glucose.**

DRAW IT   *Start with the linear form of fructose (see Figure 5.3) and draw the formation of the fructose ring in two steps. Number the carbons. Attach carbon 5 via oxygen to carbon 2. Compare the number of carbons in the fructose and glucose rings.*

(a) **Dehydration reaction in the synthesis of maltose.** The bonding of two glucose units forms maltose. The glycosidic linkage joins the number 1 carbon of one glucose to the number 4 carbon of the second glucose. Joining the glucose monomers in a different way would result in a different disaccharide.

Glucose + Glucose → Maltose

(b) **Dehydration reaction in the synthesis of sucrose.** Sucrose is a disaccharide formed from glucose and fructose. Notice that fructose, though a hexose like glucose, forms a five-sided ring.

Glucose + Fructose → Sucrose

▲ **Figure 5.5 Examples of disaccharide synthesis.**

Polysaccharides

Polysaccharides are macromolecules, polymers with a few hundred to a few thousand monosaccharides joined by glycosidic linkages. Some polysaccharides serve as storage material, hydrolyzed as needed to provide sugar for cells. Other polysaccharides serve as building material for structures that protect the cell or the whole organism. The architecture and function of a polysaccharide are determined by its sugar monomers and by the positions of its glycosidic linkages.

Storage Polysaccharides

Both plants and animals store sugars for later use in the form of storage polysaccharides. Plants store **starch**, a polymer of

glucose monomers, as granules within cellular structures known as plastids, which include chloroplasts. Synthesizing starch enables the plant to stockpile surplus glucose. Because glucose is a major cellular fuel, starch represents stored energy. The sugar can later be withdrawn from this carbohydrate "bank" by hydrolysis, which breaks the bonds between the glucose monomers. Most animals, including humans, also have enzymes that can hydrolyze plant starch, making glucose available as a nutrient for cells. Potato tubers and grains—the fruits of wheat, maize (corn), rice, and other grasses—are the major sources of starch in the human diet.

Most of the glucose monomers in starch are joined by 1–4 linkages (number 1 carbon to number 4 carbon), like the glucose units in maltose (see Figure 5.5a). The angle of these

(a) Starch: a plant polysaccharide. Two forms of starch are amylose (unbranched) and amylopectin (branched). The light ovals in the micrograph are granules of starch within a chloroplast of a plant cell.

(b) Glycogen: an animal polysaccharide. Glycogen is more branched than amylopectin. Animal cells stockpile glycogen as dense clusters of granules within liver and muscle cells. (The micrograph shows part of a liver cell; mitochondria are organelles that help break down sugars.)

▲ **Figure 5.6 Storage polysaccharides of plants and animals.** These examples, starch and glycogen, are composed entirely of glucose monomers, represented here by hexagons. Because of their molecular structure, the polymer chains tend to form helices.

bonds makes the polymer helical. The simplest form of starch, amylose, is unbranched **(Figure 5.6a)**. Amylopectin, a more complex starch, is a branched polymer with 1–6 linkages at the branch points.

Animals store a polysaccharide called **glycogen**, a polymer of glucose that is like amylopectin but more extensively branched **(Figure 5.6b)**. Humans and other vertebrates store glycogen mainly in liver and muscle cells. Hydrolysis of glycogen in these cells releases glucose when the demand for sugar increases. This stored fuel cannot sustain an animal for long, however. In humans, for example, glycogen stores are depleted in about a day unless they are replenished by consumption of food. This is an issue of concern in low-carbohydrate diets.

Structural Polysaccharides

Organisms build strong materials from structural polysaccharides. For example, the polysaccharide called **cellulose** is a major component of the tough walls that enclose plant cells. On a global scale, plants produce almost 10^{14} kg (100 billion tons) of cellulose per year; it is the most abundant organic compound on Earth. Like starch, cellulose is a polymer of glucose, but the glycosidic linkages in these two polymers differ. The difference is based on the fact that there are actually two slightly different ring structures for glucose **(Figure 5.7a)**. When glucose forms a ring, the hydroxyl group attached to the number 1 carbon is positioned either below or above the plane of the ring. These two ring forms for glucose are called alpha (α) and beta (β), respectively. In starch, all the glucose monomers are in the α configuration **(Figure 5.7b)**, the arrangement we saw in Figures 5.4 and 5.5. In contrast, the glucose monomers of cellulose are all in the β configuration, making every other glucose monomer upside down with respect to its neighbors **(Figure 5.7c)**.

The differing glycosidic linkages in starch and cellulose give the two molecules distinct three-dimensional shapes. Whereas a starch molecule is mostly helical, a cellulose molecule is straight. Cellulose is never branched, and some hydroxyl groups on its glucose monomers are free to hydrogen-bond with the hydroxyls of other cellulose molecules lying parallel to it. In plant cell walls, parallel cellulose molecules held together in this way are grouped into units called microfibrils **(Figure 5.8)**. These cable-like

(a) α and β glucose ring structures. These two interconvertible forms of glucose differ in the placement of the hydroxyl group (highlighted in blue) attached to the number 1 carbon.

α Glucose

β Glucose

(b) Starch: 1–4 linkage of α glucose monomers. All monomers are in the same orientation. Compare the positions of the —OH groups highlighted in yellow with those in cellulose (c).

(c) Cellulose: 1–4 linkage of β glucose monomers. In cellulose, every other β glucose monomer is upside down with respect to its neighbors.

▲ Figure 5.7 **Starch and cellulose structures.**

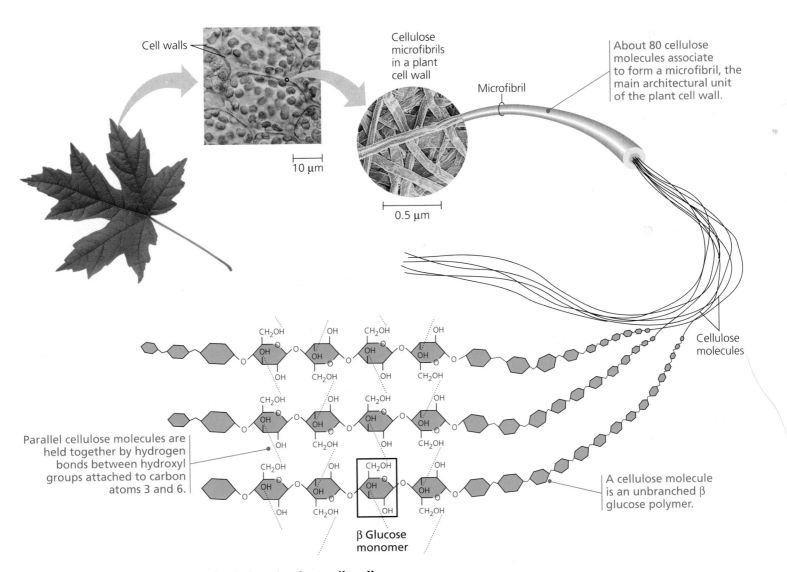

Cell walls

Cellulose microfibrils in a plant cell wall

10 μm

Microfibril

0.5 μm

About 80 cellulose molecules associate to form a microfibril, the main architectural unit of the plant cell wall.

Cellulose molecules

Parallel cellulose molecules are held together by hydrogen bonds between hydroxyl groups attached to carbon atoms 3 and 6.

A cellulose molecule is an unbranched β glucose polymer.

β Glucose monomer

▲ Figure 5.8 **The arrangement of cellulose in plant cell walls.**

▲ **Figure 5.9 Cellulose-digesting prokaryotes are found in grazing animals such as this cow.**

microfibrils are a strong building material for plants and an important substance for humans because cellulose is the major constituent of paper and the only component of cotton.

Enzymes that digest starch by hydrolyzing its α linkages are unable to hydrolyze the β linkages of cellulose because of the distinctly different shapes of these two molecules. In fact, few organisms possess enzymes that can digest cellulose. Humans do not; the cellulose in our food passes through the digestive tract and is eliminated with the feces. Along the way, the cellulose abrades the wall of the digestive tract and stimulates the lining to secrete mucus, which aids in the smooth passage of food through the tract. Thus, although cellulose is not a nutrient for humans, it is an important part of a healthful diet. Most fresh fruits, vegetables, and whole grains are rich in cellulose. On food packages, "insoluble fiber" refers mainly to cellulose.

Some prokaryotes can digest cellulose, breaking it down into glucose monomers. A cow harbors cellulose-digesting prokaryotes in its rumen, the first compartment in its stomach **(Figure 5.9)**. The prokaryotes hydrolyze the cellulose of hay and grass and convert the glucose to other nutrients that nourish the cow. Similarly, a termite, which is unable to digest cellulose by itself, has prokaryotes living in its gut that can make a meal of wood. Some fungi can also digest cellulose, thereby helping recycle chemical elements within Earth's ecosystems.

Another important structural polysaccharide is **chitin**, the carbohydrate used by arthropods (insects, spiders, crustaceans, and related animals) to build their exoskeletons **(Figure 5.10)**. An exoskeleton is a hard case that surrounds the soft parts of an animal. Pure chitin is leathery and flexible, but it becomes hardened when encrusted with calcium carbonate, a salt. Chitin is also found in many fungi, which use this polysaccharide rather than cellulose as the building material for their cell walls. Chitin is similar to cellulose, except that the glucose monomer of chitin has a nitrogen-containing appendage (see Figure 5.10a).

CONCEPT CHECK 5.2

1. Write the formula for a monosaccharide that has three carbons.
2. A dehydration reaction joins two glucose molecules to form maltose. The formula for glucose is $C_6H_{12}O_6$. What is the formula for maltose?
3. **WHAT IF?**   What would happen if a cow were given antibiotics that killed all the prokaryotes in its stomach?

For suggested answers, see Appendix A.

CONCEPT 5.3

Lipids are a diverse group of hydrophobic molecules

Lipids are the one class of large biological molecules that does not include true polymers, and they are generally not big enough to be considered macromolecules. The compounds called **lipids** are grouped together because they share one important trait: They mix poorly, if at all, with water. The hydrophobic behavior of lipids is based on their molecular structure. Although they may have some polar bonds associated with oxygen, lipids consist mostly of hydrocarbon regions.

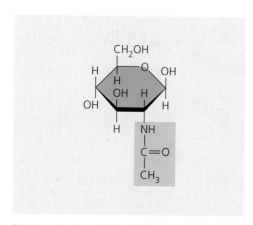

(a) The structure of the chitin monomer.

(b) Chitin forms the exoskeleton of arthropods. This cicada is molting, shedding its old exoskeleton and emerging in adult form.

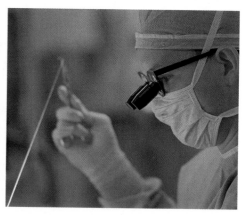

(c) Chitin is used to make a strong and flexible surgical thread that decomposes after the wound or incision heals.

▲ **Figure 5.10 Chitin, a structural polysaccharide.**

Lipids are varied in form and function. They include waxes and certain pigments, but we will focus on the most biologically important types of lipids: fats, phospholipids, and steroids.

Fats

Although fats are not polymers, they are large molecules assembled from a few smaller molecules by dehydration reactions. A **fat** is constructed from two kinds of smaller molecules: glycerol and fatty acids **(Figure 5.11a)**. Glycerol is an alcohol with three carbons, each bearing a hydroxyl group. A **fatty acid** has a long carbon skeleton, usually 16 or 18 carbon atoms in length. The carbon at one end of the fatty acid is part of a carboxyl group, the functional group that gives these molecules the name fatty *acid*. Attached to the carboxyl group is a long hydrocarbon chain. The relatively nonpolar C—H bonds in the hydrocarbon chains of fatty acids are the reason fats are hydrophobic. Fats separate from water because the water molecules hydrogen-bond to one another and exclude the fats. This is the reason that vegetable oil (a liquid fat) separates from the aqueous vinegar solution in a bottle of salad dressing.

In making a fat, three fatty acid molecules each join to glycerol by an ester linkage, a bond between a hydroxyl group and a carboxyl group. The resulting fat, also called a **triacylglycerol**, thus consists of three fatty acids linked to one glycerol molecule. (Still another name for a fat is *triglyceride*, a word often found in the list of ingredients on packaged foods.) The fatty acids in a fat can be the same, as in **Figure 5.11b**, or they can be of two or three different kinds.

Fatty acids vary in length and in the number and locations of double bonds. The terms *saturated fats* and *unsaturated fats* are commonly used in the context of nutrition **(Figure 5.12)**.

Glycerol

(a) Dehydration reaction in the synthesis of a fat

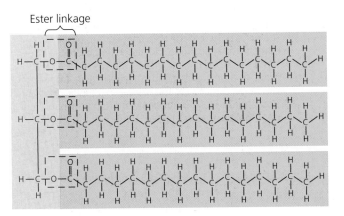

(b) Fat molecule (triacylglycerol)

▲ **Figure 5.11 The synthesis and structure of a fat, or triacylglycerol.** The molecular building blocks of a fat are one molecule of glycerol and three molecules of fatty acids. **(a)** One water molecule is removed for each fatty acid joined to the glycerol. **(b)** A fat molecule with three identical fatty acid units. The carbons of the fatty acids are arranged zig-zag to suggest the actual orientations of the four single bonds extending from each carbon (see Figure 4.3a).

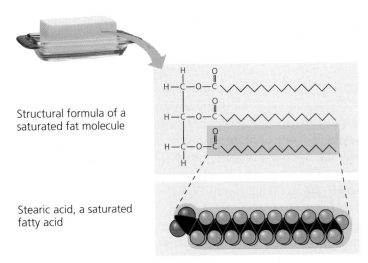

Structural formula of a saturated fat molecule

Stearic acid, a saturated fatty acid

(a) Saturated fat. At room temperature, the molecules of a saturated fat such as this butter are packed closely together, forming a solid.

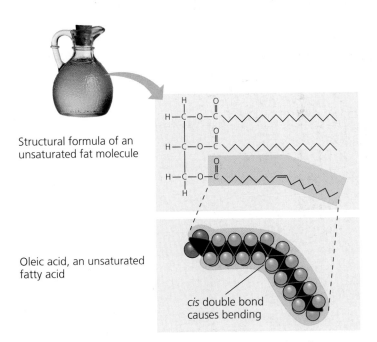

Structural formula of an unsaturated fat molecule

Oleic acid, an unsaturated fatty acid

cis double bond causes bending

(b) Unsaturated fat. At room temperature, the molecules of an unsaturated fat such as this olive oil cannot pack together closely enough to solidify because of the kinks in some of their fatty acid hydrocarbon chains.

▲ **Figure 5.12 Examples of saturated and unsaturated fats and fatty acids.** The structural formula for each fat follows a common chemical convention of omitting the carbons and attached hydrogens of the hydrocarbon regions. In the space-filling models of the fatty acids, black = carbon, gray = hydrogen, and red = oxygen.

These terms refer to the structure of the hydrocarbon chains of the fatty acids. If there are no double bonds between carbon atoms composing the chain, then as many hydrogen atoms as possible are bonded to the carbon skeleton. Such a structure is described as being *saturated* with hydrogen, so the resulting fatty acid is called a **saturated fatty acid (Figure 5.12a)**. An **unsaturated fatty acid** has one or more double bonds, formed by the removal of hydrogen atoms from the carbon skeleton. The fatty acid will have a kink in its hydrocarbon chain wherever a *cis* double bond occurs **(Figure 5.12b)**.

A fat made from saturated fatty acids is called a saturated fat. Most animal fats are saturated: The hydrocarbon chains of their fatty acids—the "tails" of the fat molecules—lack double bonds, and their flexibility allows the fat molecules to pack together tightly. Saturated animal fats—such as lard and butter—are solid at room temperature. In contrast, the fats of plants and fishes are generally unsaturated, meaning that they are built of one or more types of unsaturated fatty acids. Usually liquid at room temperature, plant and fish fats are referred to as oils—olive oil and cod liver oil are examples. The kinks where the *cis* double bonds are located prevent the molecules from packing together closely enough to solidify at room temperature. The phrase "hydrogenated vegetable oils" on food labels means that unsaturated fats have been synthetically converted to saturated fats by adding hydrogen. Peanut butter, margarine, and many other products are hydrogenated to prevent lipids from separating out in liquid (oil) form.

A diet rich in saturated fats is one of several factors that may contribute to the cardiovascular disease known as atherosclerosis. In this condition, deposits called plaques develop within the walls of blood vessels, causing inward bulges that impede blood flow and reduce the resilience of the vessels. Recent studies have shown that the process of hydrogenating vegetable oils produces not only saturated fats but also unsaturated fats with *trans* double bonds. These **trans fats** may contribute more than saturated fats to atherosclerosis (see Chapter 42) and other problems. Because trans fats are especially common in baked goods and processed foods, the USDA requires trans fat content information on nutritional labels.

Fat has come to have such a negative connotation in our culture that you might wonder what useful purpose fats serve. The major function of fats is energy storage. The hydrocarbon chains of fats are similar to gasoline molecules and just as rich in energy. A gram of fat stores more than twice as much energy as a gram of a polysaccharide, such as starch. Because plants are relatively immobile, they can function with bulky energy storage in the form of starch. (Vegetable oils are generally obtained from seeds, where more compact storage is an asset to the plant.) Animals, however, must carry their energy stores with them, so there is an advantage to having a more compact reservoir of fuel—fat. Humans and other mammals stock their long-term food reserves in adipose cells (see Figure 4.6a), which swell and shrink as fat is deposited and withdrawn from storage. In addition to storing energy, adipose tissue also cushions such vital organs as the kidneys, and a layer of fat beneath the skin insulates the body. This subcutaneous layer is especially thick in whales, seals, and most other marine mammals, protecting them from cold ocean water.

Phospholipids

Cells could not exist without another type of lipid—**phospholipids (Figure 5.13)**. Phospholipids are essential

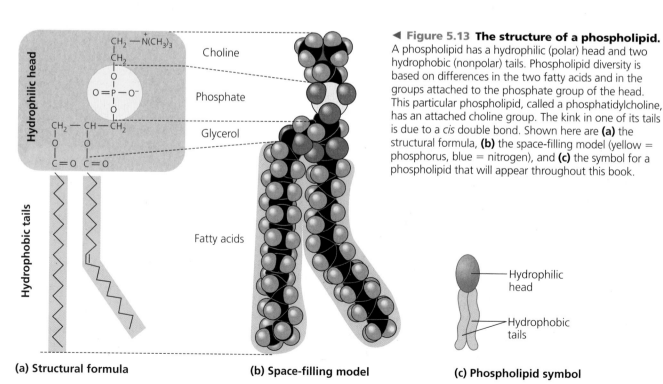

◄ **Figure 5.13 The structure of a phospholipid.** A phospholipid has a hydrophilic (polar) head and two hydrophobic (nonpolar) tails. Phospholipid diversity is based on differences in the two fatty acids and in the groups attached to the phosphate group of the head. This particular phospholipid, called a phosphatidylcholine, has an attached choline group. The kink in one of its tails is due to a *cis* double bond. Shown here are **(a)** the structural formula, **(b)** the space-filling model (yellow = phosphorus, blue = nitrogen), and **(c)** the symbol for a phospholipid that will appear throughout this book.

(a) Structural formula   (b) Space-filling model   (c) Phospholipid symbol

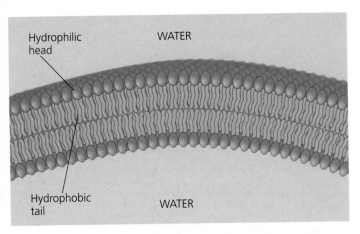

▲ Figure 5.14 Bilayer structure formed by self-assembly of phospholipids in an aqueous environment. The phospholipid bilayer shown here is the main fabric of biological membranes. Note that the hydrophilic heads of the phospholipids are in contact with water in this structure, whereas the hydrophobic tails are in contact with each other and remote from water.

▲ Figure 5.15 Cholesterol, a steroid. Cholesterol is the molecule from which other steroids, including the sex hormones, are synthesized. Steroids vary in the chemical groups attached to their four interconnected rings (shown in gold).

for cells because they make up cell membranes. Their structure provides a classic example of how form fits function at the molecular level. As shown in Figure 5.13, a phospholipid is similar to a fat molecule but has only two fatty acids attached to glycerol rather than three. The third hydroxyl group of glycerol is joined to a phosphate group, which has a negative electrical charge. Additional small molecules, which are usually charged or polar, can be linked to the phosphate group to form a variety of phospholipids.

The two ends of phospholipids show different behavior toward water. The hydrocarbon tails are hydrophobic and are excluded from water. However, the phosphate group and its attachments form a hydrophilic head that has an affinity for water. When phospholipids are added to water, they self-assemble into double-layered aggregates—bilayers—that shield their hydrophobic portions from water (**Figure 5.14**).

At the surface of a cell, phospholipids are arranged in a similar bilayer. The hydrophilic heads of the molecules are on the outside of the bilayer, in contact with the aqueous solutions inside and outside of the cell. The hydrophobic tails point toward the interior of the bilayer, away from the water. The phospholipid bilayer forms a boundary between the cell and its external environment; in fact, cells could not exist without phospholipids.

Steroids

Many hormones, as well as cholesterol, are **steroids**, which are lipids characterized by a carbon skeleton consisting of four fused rings (**Figure 5.15**). Different steroids vary in the chemical groups attached to this ensemble of rings. **Cholesterol** is a common component of animal cell membranes and is also the precursor from which other steroids are synthesized. In

vertebrates, cholesterol is synthesized in the liver. Many hormones, including vertebrate sex hormones, are steroids produced from cholesterol (see Figure 4.9). Thus, cholesterol is a crucial molecule in animals, although a high level of it in the blood may contribute to atherosclerosis. Both saturated fats and trans fats exert their negative impact on health by affecting cholesterol levels.

CONCEPT CHECK 5.3

1. Compare the structure of a fat (triglyceride) with that of a phospholipid.
2. Why are human sex hormones considered lipids?
3. **WHAT IF?** Suppose a membrane surrounded an oil droplet, as it does in the cells of plant seeds. Describe and explain the form it might take.

For suggested answers, see Appendix A.

CONCEPT 5.4
Proteins have many structures, resulting in a wide range of functions

Nearly every dynamic function of a living being depends on proteins. In fact, the importance of proteins is underscored by their name, which comes from the Greek word *proteios*, meaning "first place." Proteins account for more than 50% of the dry mass of most cells, and they are instrumental in almost everything organisms do. Some proteins speed up chemical reactions, while others play a role in structural support,

Table 5.1 An Overview of Protein Functions

Type of Protein	Function	Examples
Enzymatic proteins	Selective acceleration of chemical reactions	Digestive enzymes catalyze the hydrolysis of the polymers in food.
Structural proteins	Support	Insects and spiders use silk fibers to make their cocoons and webs, respectively. Collagen and elastin provide a fibrous framework in animal connective tissues. Keratin is the protein of hair, horns, feathers, and other skin appendages.
Storage proteins	Storage of amino acids	Ovalbumin is the protein of egg white, used as an amino acid source for the developing embryo. Casein, the protein of milk, is the major source of amino acids for baby mammals. Plants have storage proteins in their seeds.
Transport proteins	Transport of other substances	Hemoglobin, the iron-containing protein of vertebrate blood, transports oxygen from the lungs to other parts of the body. Other proteins transport molecules across cell membranes.
Hormonal proteins	Coordination of an organism's activities	Insulin, a hormone secreted by the pancreas, helps regulate the concentration of sugar in the blood of vertebrates.
Receptor proteins	Response of cell to chemical stimuli	Receptors built into the membrane of a nerve cell detect chemical signals released by other nerve cells.
Contractile and motor proteins	Movement	Actin and myosin are responsible for the contraction of muscles. Other proteins are responsible for the undulations of the organelles called cilia and flagella.
Defensive proteins	Protection against disease	Antibodies combat bacteria and viruses.

storage, transport, cellular communication, movement, and defense against foreign substances (**Table 5.1**).

Life would not be possible without **enzymes**, most of which are proteins. Enzymatic proteins regulate metabolism by acting as **catalysts**, chemical agents that selectively speed up chemical reactions without being consumed by the reaction (**Figure 5.16**).

❶ Active site is available for a molecule of substrate, the reactant on which the enzyme acts.

❷ Substrate binds to enzyme.

Substrate (sucrose)

Glucose

OH

Enzyme (sucrase)

Fructose

HO

H_2O

❹ Products are released.

❸ Substrate is converted to products.

▲ **Figure 5.16 The catalytic cycle of an enzyme.** The enzyme sucrase accelerates hydrolysis of sucrose into glucose and fructose. Acting as a catalyst, the sucrase protein is not consumed during the cycle, but remains available for further catalysis.

Because an enzyme can perform its function over and over again, these molecules can be thought of as workhorses that keep cells running by carrying out the processes of life.

A human has tens of thousands of different proteins, each with a specific structure and function; proteins, in fact, are the most structurally sophisticated molecules known. Consistent with their diverse functions, they vary extensively in structure, each type of protein having a unique three-dimensional shape.

Polypeptides

Diverse as proteins are, they are all polymers constructed from the same set of 20 amino acids. Polymers of amino acids are called **polypeptides**. A **protein** consists of one or more polypeptides, each folded and coiled into a specific three-dimensional structure.

Amino Acid Monomers

All amino acids share a common structure. **Amino acids** are organic molecules possessing both carboxyl and amino groups (see Chapter 4). The illustration at the right shows the general formula for an amino acid. At the center of the amino acid is an asymmetric carbon atom called the *alpha (α) carbon*. Its four different partners are an amino group, a carboxyl group, a hydrogen atom, and a variable group symbolized by R. The R group, also called the side chain, differs with each amino acid.

α carbon

Amino group

Carboxyl group

Figure 5.17 shows the 20 amino acids that cells use to build their thousands of proteins. Here the amino and carboxyl

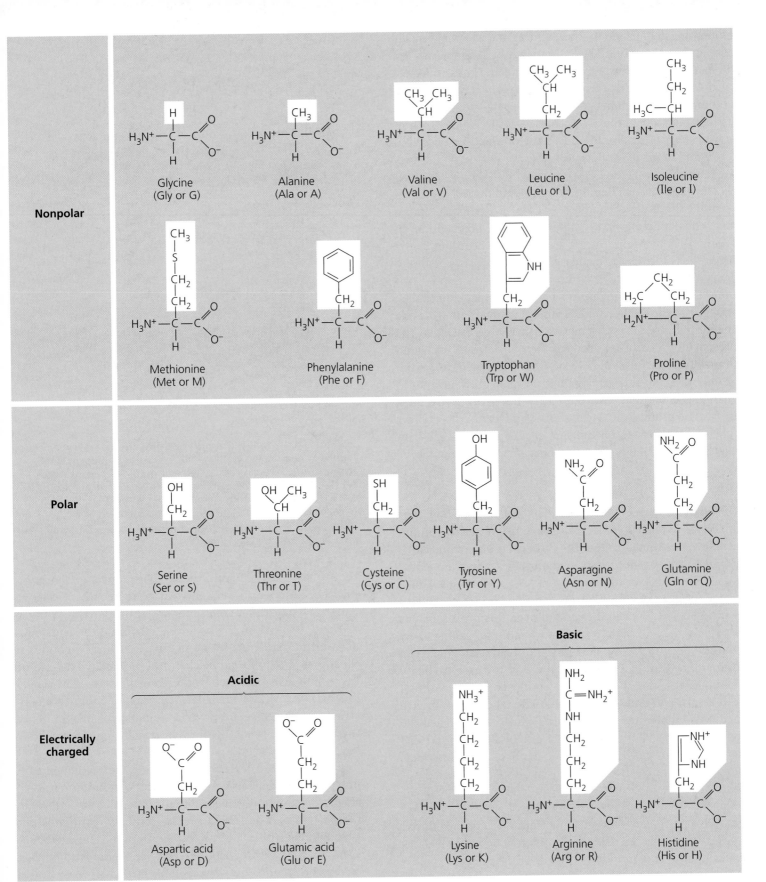

▲ **Figure 5.17 The 20 amino acids of proteins.** The amino acids are grouped here according to the properties of their side chains (R groups), highlighted in white. The amino acids are shown in their prevailing ionic forms at pH 7.2, the pH within a cell. The three-letter and more commonly used one-letter abbreviations for the amino acids are in parentheses. All the amino acids used in proteins are the same enantiomer, called the L form, as shown here (see Figure 4.7).

groups are all depicted in ionized form, the way they usually exist at the pH in a cell. The R group may be as simple as a hydrogen atom, as in the amino acid glycine (the one amino acid lacking an asymmetric carbon, since two of its α carbon's partners are hydrogen atoms), or it may be a carbon skeleton with various functional groups attached, as in glutamine. (Organisms do have other amino acids, some of which are occasionally found in proteins. Because these are relatively rare, they are not shown in Figure 5.17.)

The physical and chemical properties of the side chain determine the unique characteristics of a particular amino acid, thus affecting its functional role in a polypeptide. In Figure 5.17, the amino acids are grouped according to the properties of their side chains. One group consists of amino acids with nonpolar side chains, which are hydrophobic. Another group consists of amino acids with polar side chains, which are hydrophilic. Acidic amino acids are those with side chains that are generally negative in charge owing to the presence of a carboxyl group, which is usually dissociated (ionized) at cellular pH. Basic amino acids have amino groups in their side chains that are generally positive in charge. (Notice that *all* amino acids have carboxyl groups and amino groups; the terms *acidic* and *basic* in this context refer only to groups on the side chains.) Because they are charged, acidic and basic side chains are also hydrophilic.

Amino Acid Polymers

Now that we have examined amino acids, let's see how they are linked to form polymers **(Figure 5.18)**. When two amino acids are positioned so that the carboxyl group of one is adjacent to the amino group of the other, they can become joined by a dehydration reaction, with the removal of a water molecule. The resulting covalent bond is called a **peptide bond**. Repeated over and over, this process yields a polypeptide, a polymer of many amino acids linked by peptide bonds. At one end of the polypeptide chain is a free amino group; at the opposite end is a free carboxyl group. Thus, the chain has an amino end (N-terminus) and a carboxyl end (C-terminus). The repeating sequence of atoms highlighted in purple in Figure 5.18b is called the polypeptide backbone. Extending from this backbone are different kinds of appendages, the side chains of the amino acids. Polypeptides range in length from a few monomers to a thousand or more. Each specific polypeptide has a unique linear sequence of amino acids. The immense variety of polypeptides in nature illustrates an important concept introduced earlier—that cells can make many different polymers by linking a limited set of monomers into diverse sequences.

Protein Structure and Function

The specific activities of proteins result from their intricate three-dimensional architecture, the simplest level of which is

▲ **Figure 5.18 Making a polypeptide chain. (a)** Peptide bonds formed by dehydration reactions link the carboxyl group of one amino acid to the amino group of the next. **(b)** The peptide bonds are formed one at a time, starting with the amino acid at the amino end (N-terminus). The polypeptide has a repetitive backbone (purple) to which the amino acid side chains are attached.

DRAW IT *In (a), circle and label the carboxyl and amino groups that will form the peptide bond shown in (b).*

the sequence of their amino acids. The pioneer in determining the amino acid sequence of proteins was Frederick Sanger, who, with his colleagues at Cambridge University in England, worked on the hormone insulin in the late 1940s and early 1950s. He used agents that break polypeptides at specific places, followed by chemical methods to determine the amino acid sequence in these small fragments. Sanger and his co-workers were able, after years of effort, to reconstruct the complete amino acid sequence of insulin. Since then, most of the steps involved in sequencing a polypeptide have been automated.

Once we have learned the amino acid sequence of a polypeptide, what can it tell us about the three-dimensional structure (commonly referred to simply as the "structure") of the protein and its function? The term *polypeptide* is not synonymous with the term *protein*. Even for a protein consisting of a single polypeptide, the relationship is somewhat analogous to that between a long strand of yarn and a sweater of particular size and shape that can be knit from the yarn. A functional protein is not *just* a polypeptide chain, but one or more polypeptides precisely twisted, folded, and coiled into a molecule of unique shape **(Figure 5.19)**. And it

(a) A **ribbon model** shows how the single polypeptide chain folds and coils to form the functional protein. (The yellow lines represent cross-linking bonds between cysteines that stabilize the protein's shape.)

(b) A **space-filling model** shows more clearly the globular shape seen in many proteins, as well as the specific three-dimensional structure unique to lysozyme.

▲ **Figure 5.19 Structure of a protein, the enzyme lysozyme.** Present in our sweat, tears, and saliva, lysozyme is an enzyme that helps prevent infection by binding to and destroying specific molecules on the surface of many kinds of bacteria. The groove is the part of the protein that recognizes and binds to the target molecules on bacterial walls.

is the amino acid sequence of each polypeptide that determines what three-dimensional structure the protein will have.

When a cell synthesizes a polypeptide, the chain generally folds spontaneously, assuming the functional structure for that protein. This folding is driven and reinforced by the formation of a variety of bonds between parts of the chain, which in turn depends on the sequence of amino acids. Many proteins are roughly spherical (*globular proteins*), while others are shaped like long fibers (*fibrous proteins*). Even within these broad categories, countless variations exist.

A protein's specific structure determines how it works. In almost every case, the function of a protein depends on its ability to recognize and bind to some other molecule. In an especially striking example of the marriage of form and function, **Figure 5.20** shows the exact match of shape between an antibody (a protein in the body) and the particular foreign substance on a flu virus that the antibody binds to and marks for destruction. A second example is an enzyme, which must recognize and bind closely to its substrate, the substance the enzyme works on (see Figure 5.16). Also, you learned in Chapter 2 that natural signaling molecules called endorphins bind to specific receptor proteins on the surface of brain cells in humans, producing euphoria and relieving pain. Morphine, heroin, and other opiate drugs are able to mimic endorphins because they all share a similar shape with endorphins and can thus fit into and bind to endorphin receptors in the brain. This fit is very specific, something like a lock and key (see Figure 2.18). Thus, the function of a protein—for instance, the ability of a receptor protein to bind to a particular pain-relieving signaling molecule—is an emergent property resulting from exquisite molecular order.

Four Levels of Protein Structure

With the goal of understanding the function of a protein, learning about its structure is often productive. In spite of their great diversity, all proteins share three superimposed levels of structure, known as primary, secondary, and tertiary structure. A fourth level, quaternary structure, arises when a protein consists of two or more polypeptide chains. **Figure 5.21**, on the following two pages, describes these four levels of protein structure. Be sure to study this figure thoroughly before going on to the next section.

Antibody protein   Protein from flu virus

▲ **Figure 5.20 An antibody binding to a protein from a flu virus.** A technique called X-ray crystallography was used to generate a computer model of an antibody protein (blue and orange, left) bound to a flu virus protein (green and yellow, right). Computer software was then used to back the images away from each other, revealing the exact complementarity of shape between the two protein surfaces.

Exploring Levels of Protein Structure

Primary Structure

The **primary structure** of a protein is its unique sequence of amino acids. As an example, let's consider transthyretin, a globular protein found in the blood that transports vitamin A and one of the thyroid hormones throughout the body. Each of the four identical polypeptide chains that together make up transthyretin is composed of 127 amino acids. Shown here is one of these chains unraveled for a closer look at its primary structure. Each of the 127 positions along the chain is occupied by one of the 20 amino acids, indicated here by its three-letter abbreviation. The primary structure is like the order of letters in a very long word. If left to chance, there would be 20^{127} different ways of making a polypeptide chain 127 amino acids long. However, the precise primary structure of a protein is determined not by the random linking of amino acids, but by inherited genetic information.

Secondary Structure

β pleated sheet

α helix

Most proteins have segments of their polypeptide chains repeatedly coiled or folded in patterns that contribute to the protein's overall shape. These coils and folds, collectively referred to as **secondary structure**, are the result of hydrogen bonds between the repeating constituents of the polypeptide backbone (not the amino acid side chains). Both the oxygen and the nitrogen atoms of the backbone are electronegative, with partial negative charges (see Figure 2.16). The weakly positive hydrogen atom attached to the nitrogen atom has an affinity for the oxygen atom of a nearby peptide bond. Individually, these hydrogen bonds are weak, but because they are repeated many times over a relatively long region of the polypeptide chain, they can support a particular shape for that part of the protein.

One such secondary structure is the **α helix**, a delicate coil held together by hydrogen bonding between every fourth amino acid, shown above. Although transthyretin has only one α helix region (see tertiary structure), other globular proteins have multiple stretches of α helix separated by nonhelical regions. Some fibrous proteins, such as α-keratin, the structural protein of hair, have the α helix formation over most of their length.

The other main type of secondary structure is the **β pleated sheet**. As shown above, in this structure two or more regions of the polypeptide chain lying side by side are connected by hydrogen bonds between parts of the two parallel polypeptide backbones. Pleated sheets make up the core of many globular proteins, as is the case for transthyretin, and dominate some fibrous proteins, including the silk protein of a spider's web. The teamwork of so many hydrogen bonds makes each spider silk fiber stronger than a steel strand of the same weight.

Abdominal glands of the spider secrete silk fibers made of a structural protein containing β pleated sheets.

The radiating strands, made of dry silk fibers, maintain the shape of the web.

The spiral strands (capture strands) are elastic, stretching in response to wind, rain, and the touch of insects.

Superimposed on the patterns of secondary structure is a protein's **tertiary structure**, shown above for the transthyretin polypeptide. While secondary structure involves interactions between backbone constituents, tertiary structure is the overall shape of a polypeptide resulting from interactions between the side chains (R groups) of the various amino acids. One type of interaction that contributes to tertiary structure is—somewhat misleadingly—called a **hydrophobic interaction**. As a polypeptide folds into its functional shape, amino acids with hydrophobic (nonpolar) side chains usually end up in clusters at the core of the protein, out of contact with water. Thus, what we call a hydrophobic interaction is actually caused by the action of water molecules, which exclude nonpolar substances as they form hydrogen bonds with each other and with hydrophilic parts of the protein. Once nonpolar amino acid side chains are close together, van der Waals interactions help hold them together. Meanwhile, hydrogen bonds between polar side chains and ionic bonds between positively and negatively charged side chains also help stabilize tertiary structure. These are all weak interactions, but their cumulative effect helps give the protein a unique shape.

The shape of a protein may be reinforced further by covalent bonds called **disulfide bridges**. Disulfide bridges form where two cysteine monomers, amino acids with sulfhydryl groups (—SH) on their side chains (see Figure 4.10), are brought close together by the folding of the protein. The sulfur of one cysteine bonds to the sulfur of the second, and the disulfide bridge (—S—S—) rivets parts of the protein together (see yellow lines in Figure 5.19a). All of these different kinds of bonds can occur in one protein, as shown here in a small part of a hypothetical protein.

Some proteins consist of two or more polypeptide chains aggregated into one functional macromolecule. **Quaternary structure** is the overall protein structure that results from the aggregation of these polypeptide subunits. For example, shown above is the complete, globular transthyretin protein, made up of its four polypeptides. Another example is collagen, shown below left, which is a fibrous protein that has helical subunits intertwined into a larger triple helix, giving the long fibers great strength. This suits collagen fibers to their function as the girders of connective tissue in skin, bone, tendons, ligaments, and other body parts (collagen accounts for 40% of the protein in a human body). Hemoglobin, the oxygen-binding protein of red blood cells shown below right, is another example of a globular protein with quaternary structure. It consists of four polypeptide subunits, two of one kind ("α chains") and two of another kind ("β chains"). Both α and β subunits consist primarily of α-helical secondary structure. Each subunit has a nonpolypeptide component, called heme, with an iron atom that binds oxygen.

Hydrophobic interactions and van der Waals interactions

Polypeptide backbone

Hydrogen bond

Disulfide bridge

Ionic bond

Polypeptide chain

Collagen

β Chains

Iron

Heme

α Chains

Hemoglobin

Sickle-Cell Disease: A Change in Primary Structure

Even a slight change in primary structure can affect a protein's shape and ability to function. For instance, *sickle-cell disease,* an inherited blood disorder, is caused by the substitution of one amino acid (valine) for the normal one (glutamic acid) at a particular position in the primary structure of hemoglobin, the protein that carries oxygen in red blood cells. Normal red blood cells are disk-shaped, but in sickle-cell disease, the abnormal hemoglobin molecules tend to crystallize, deforming some of the cells into a sickle shape **(Figure 5.22)**. The life of someone with the disease is punctuated by "sickle-cell crises," which occur when the angular cells clog tiny blood vessels, impeding blood flow. The toll taken on such patients is a dramatic example of how a simple change in protein structure can have devastating effects on protein function.

What Determines Protein Structure?

You've learned that a unique shape endows each protein with a specific function. But what are the key factors determining protein structure? You already know most of the answer: A polypeptide chain of a given amino acid sequence can spontaneously arrange itself into a three-dimensional shape determined and maintained by the interactions responsible for secondary and tertiary structure. This folding normally occurs as the protein is being synthesized within the cell. However, protein structure also depends on the physical and chemical conditions of the protein's environment. If the pH, salt concentration, temperature, or other aspects of its environment are altered, the protein may unravel and lose its native shape, a change called **denaturation (Figure 5.23)**. Because it is misshapen, the denatured protein is biologically inactive.

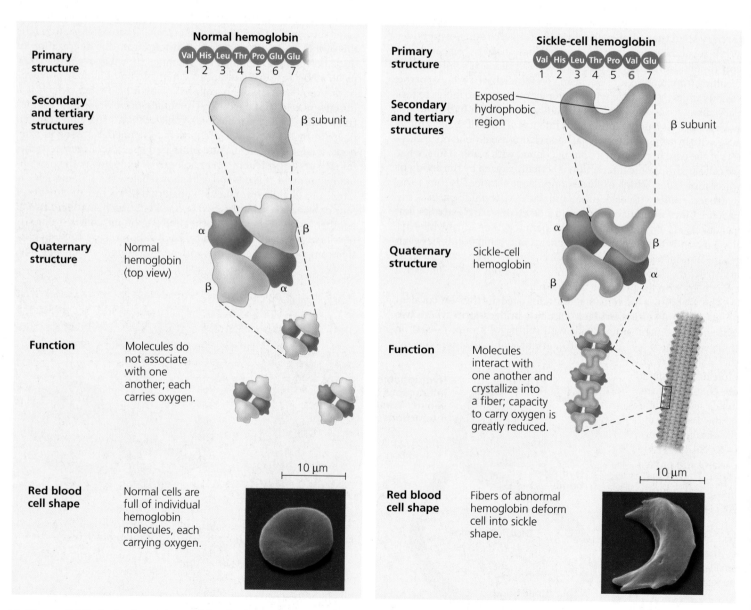

▲ **Figure 5.22 A single amino acid substitution in a protein causes sickle-cell disease.** To show fiber formation clearly, the orientation of the hemoglobin molecule here is different from that in Figure 5.21.

Denaturation

Normal protein

Renaturation

Denatured protein

▲ **Figure 5.23 Denaturation and renaturation of a protein.** High temperatures or various chemical treatments will denature a protein, causing it to lose its shape and hence its ability to function. If the denatured protein remains dissolved, it can often renature when the chemical and physical aspects of its environment are restored to normal.

Most proteins become denatured if they are transferred from an aqueous environment to an organic solvent, such as ether or chloroform; the polypeptide chain refolds so that its hydrophobic regions face outward toward the solvent. Other denaturation agents include chemicals that disrupt the hydrogen bonds, ionic bonds, and disulfide bridges that maintain a protein's shape. Denaturation can also result from excessive heat, which agitates the polypeptide chain enough to overpower the weak interactions that stabilize the structure. The white of an egg becomes opaque during cooking because the denatured proteins are insoluble and solidify. This also explains why excessively high fevers can be fatal: Proteins in the blood can denature at very high body temperatures.

When a protein in a test-tube solution has been denatured by heat or chemicals, it can sometimes return to its functional shape when the denaturing agent is removed. We can conclude that the information for building specific shape is intrinsic to the protein's primary structure. The sequence of amino acids determines the protein's shape—where an α helix can form, where β pleated sheets can occur, where disulfide bridges are located, where ionic bonds can form, and so on. In the crowded environment inside a cell, there are also specific proteins that aid in the folding of other proteins.

Protein Folding in the Cell

Biochemists now know the amino acid sequences of more than 1.2 million proteins and the three-dimensional shapes of about 8,500. One would think that by correlating the primary structures of many proteins with their three-dimensional structures, it would be relatively easy to discover the rules of protein folding. Unfortunately, the protein-folding process is not that simple. Most proteins probably go through several intermediate structures on their way to a stable shape, and looking at the mature structure does not reveal the stages of folding required to achieve that form. However, biochemists have developed methods for tracking a protein through such stages. Researchers have also discovered **chaperonins** (also called chaperone proteins), protein molecules that assist in the proper folding of other proteins **(Figure 5.24)**. Chaperonins do not specify the final structure of a polypeptide. Instead, they keep the new polypeptide segregated from "bad influences" in the cytoplasmic environment while it folds spontaneously. The chaperonin shown in Figure 5.24, from the bacterium *E. coli*, is a giant multiprotein complex shaped like a hollow cylinder. The cavity provides a shelter for folding polypeptides.

Misfolding of polypeptides is a serious problem in cells. Many diseases, such as Alzheimer's and Parkinson's, are associated with an accumulation of misfolded proteins. Recently, researchers have begun to shed light on molecular systems in the cell that interact with chaperonins and check whether proper folding has occurred. Such systems either refold the misfolded proteins correctly or mark them for destruction.

Even when scientists have a correctly folded protein in hand, determining its exact three-dimensional structure is not simple, for a single protein molecule has thousands of atoms. The first 3-D structures were worked out in 1959, for hemoglobin and a related protein. The method that made these feats possible was **X-ray crystallography**, which has since been used to determine the 3-D structures of many other proteins. In a recent example, Roger Kornberg and his colleagues at Stanford University used this method in order to elucidate the structure of RNA polymerase, an enzyme that plays a crucial role in the expression

▶ **Figure 5.24 A chaperonin in action.** The computer graphic (left) shows a large chaperonin protein complex. It has an interior space that provides a shelter for the proper folding of newly made polypeptides. The complex consists of two proteins: One protein is a hollow cylinder; the other is a cap that can fit on either end.

Cap

Hollow cylinder

Chaperonin (fully assembled)

Polypeptide

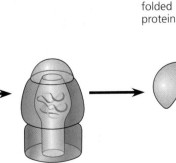

Correctly folded protein

Steps of Chaperonin Action:

1 An unfolded polypeptide enters the cylinder from one end.

2 The cap attaches, causing the cylinder to change shape in such a way that it creates a hydrophilic environment for the folding of the polypeptide.

3 The cap comes off, and the properly folded protein is released.

of genes **(Figure 5.25)**. Another method now in use is nuclear magnetic resonance (NMR) spectroscopy, which does not require protein crystallization.

A still newer approach uses bioinformatics (see Chapter 1) to predict the 3-D structures of polypeptides from their amino acid sequences. In 2005, researchers in Austria used comput-

ers to analyze the sequences and structures of 129 common plant protein allergens. They were able to classify all of these allergens into 20 families of proteins out of 3,849 families and 65% into just 4 families. This result suggests that the shared structures in these protein families may play a role in generating allergic reactions. These structures may provide targets for new allergy medications.

X-ray crystallography, NMR spectroscopy, and bioinformatics are complementary approaches to understanding protein structure. Together they have also given us valuable hints about protein function.

CONCEPT CHECK 5.4

1. Why does a denatured protein no longer function normally?
2. What parts of a polypeptide chain participate in the bonds that hold together secondary structure? What parts participate in tertiary structure?
3. **WHAT IF?** If a genetic mutation changes primary structure, how might it destroy the protein's function?

For suggested answers, see Appendix A.

CONCEPT 5.5

Nucleic acids store and transmit hereditary information

If the primary structure of polypeptides determines a protein's shape, what determines primary structure? The amino acid sequence of a polypeptide is programmed by a unit of inheritance known as a **gene**. Genes consist of DNA, a polymer belonging to the class of compounds known as **nucleic acids**.

The Roles of Nucleic Acids

The two types of nucleic acids, **deoxyribonucleic acid (DNA)** and **ribonucleic acid (RNA)**, enable living organisms to reproduce their complex components from one generation to the next. Unique among molecules, DNA provides directions for its own replication. DNA also directs RNA synthesis and, through RNA, controls protein synthesis **(Figure 5.26)**.

DNA is the genetic material that organisms inherit from their parents. Each chromosome contains one long DNA molecule, usually carrying several hundred or more genes. When a cell reproduces itself by dividing, its DNA molecules are copied and passed along from one generation of cells to the next. Encoded in the structure of DNA is the information that programs all the cell's activities. The DNA, however, is not directly involved in running the operations of the cell, any more than computer software by itself can print a bank statement or read the bar code on a box of cereal. Just as a printer is needed to print out a statement and a scanner is needed to read a bar code, proteins are required

---

▼ Figure 5.25 **Inquiry**

What can the 3-D shape of the enzyme RNA polymerase II tell us about its function?

EXPERIMENT In 2006, Roger Kornberg was awarded the Nobel Prize in Chemistry for using X-ray crystallography to determine the 3-D shape of RNA polymerase II, which binds to the DNA double helix and synthesizes RNA. After crystallizing a complex of all three components, Kornberg and his colleagues aimed an X-ray beam through the crystal. The atoms of the crystal diffracted (bent) the X-rays into an orderly array that a digital detector recorded as a pattern of spots called an X-ray diffraction pattern.

RESULTS Using data from X-ray diffraction patterns, as well as the amino acid sequence determined by chemical methods, Kornberg and colleagues built a 3-D model of the complex with the help of computer software.

CONCLUSION By analyzing their model, the researchers developed a hypothesis about the functions of different regions of RNA polymerase II. For example, the region above the DNA may act as a clamp that holds the nucleic acids in place. (You'll learn more about this enzyme in Chapter 17.)

SOURCE A. L. Gnatt et al., Structural basis of transcription: an RNA polymerase II elongation complex at 3.3Å, *Science* 292:1876–1882 (2001).

WHAT IF? If you were an author of the paper and were describing the model, what type of protein structure would you call the small green polypeptide spiral in the center?

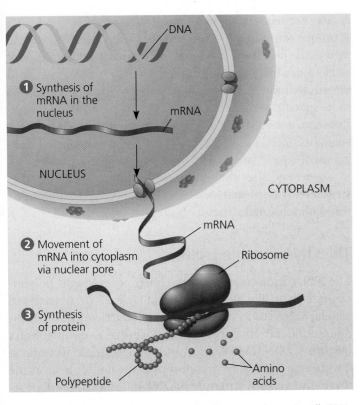

① Synthesis of mRNA in the nucleus

② Movement of mRNA into cytoplasm via nuclear pore

③ Synthesis of protein

DNA

mRNA

NUCLEUS

CYTOPLASM

mRNA

Ribosome

Polypeptide

Amino acids

▲ **Figure 5.26 DNA → RNA → protein.** In a eukaryotic cell, DNA in the nucleus programs protein production in the cytoplasm by dictating synthesis of messenger RNA (mRNA). (The cell nucleus is actually much larger relative to the other elements of this figure.)

to implement genetic programs. The molecular hardware of the cell—the tools for biological functions—consists mostly of proteins. For example, the oxygen carrier in red blood cells is the protein hemoglobin, not the DNA that specifies its structure.

How does RNA, the other type of nucleic acid, fit into the flow of genetic information from DNA to proteins? Each gene along a DNA molecule directs synthesis of a type of RNA called *messenger RNA* (*mRNA*). The mRNA molecule interacts with the cell's protein-synthesizing machinery to direct production of a polypeptide, which folds into all or part of a protein. We can summarize the flow of genetic information as DNA → RNA → protein (see Figure 5.26). The sites of protein synthesis are tiny structures called ribosomes. In a eukaryotic cell, ribosomes are in the cytoplasm, but DNA resides in the nucleus. Messenger RNA conveys genetic instructions for building proteins from the nucleus to the cytoplasm. Prokaryotic cells lack nuclei but still use RNA to convey a message from the DNA to ribosomes and other cellular equipment that translate the coded information into amino acid sequences. RNA also plays many other roles in the cell.

The Structure of Nucleic Acids

Nucleic acids are macromolecules that exist as polymers called **polynucleotides (Figure 5.27a)**. As indicated by the

5′ end

5′C
3′C

5′C
3′C

OH

3′ end

(a) Polynucleotide, or nucleic acid

Nucleoside

Nitrogenous base

Phosphate group

Sugar (pentose)

5′C

3′C

(b) Nucleotide

Nitrogenous bases

Pyrimidines

Cytosine (C)   Thymine (T, in DNA)   Uracil (U, in RNA)

Purines

Adenine (A)   Guanine (G)

Sugars

Deoxyribose (in DNA)   Ribose (in RNA)

(c) Nucleoside components

▲ **Figure 5.27 Components of nucleic acids. (a)** A polynucleotide has a sugar-phosphate backbone with variable appendages, the nitrogenous bases. **(b)** A nucleotide monomer includes a nitrogenous base, a sugar, and a phosphate group. Without the phosphate group, the structure is called a nucleoside. **(c)** A nucleoside includes a nitrogenous base (purine or pyrimidine) and a five-carbon sugar (deoxyribose or ribose).

name, each polynucleotide consists of monomers called **nucleotides**. A nucleotide is itself composed of three parts: a nitrogenous base, a five-carbon sugar (a pentose), and a phosphate group **(Figure 5.27b)**. The portion of this unit without the phosphate group is called a *nucleoside*.

Nucleotide Monomers

To build a nucleotide, let's first consider the two components of the nucleoside: the nitrogenous base and the sugar **(Figure 5.27c)**. There are two families of nitrogenous bases: pyrimidines and purines. A **pyrimidine** has a six-membered ring of carbon and nitrogen atoms. (The nitrogen atoms tend to take up H^+ from solution, which explains why it's called a nitrogenous *base*.) The members of the pyrimidine family are cytosine (C), thymine (T), and uracil (U). **Purines** are larger, with a six-membered ring fused to a five-membered ring. The purines are adenine (A) and guanine (G). The specific pyrimidines and purines differ in the chemical groups attached to the rings. Adenine, guanine, and cytosine are found in both types of nucleic acid; thymine is found only in DNA and uracil only in RNA.

The sugar connected to the nitrogenous base is **ribose** in the nucleotides of RNA and **deoxyribose** in DNA (see Figure 5.27c). The only difference between these two sugars is that deoxyribose lacks an oxygen atom on the second carbon in the ring; hence the name *deoxy*ribose. Because the atoms in both the nitrogenous base and the sugar are numbered, the sugar atoms have a prime (′) after the number to distinguish them. Thus, the second carbon in the sugar ring is the 2′ ("2 prime") carbon, and the carbon that sticks up from the ring is called the 5′ carbon.

So far, we have built a nucleoside. To complete the construction of a nucleotide, we attach a phosphate group to the 5′ carbon of the sugar (see Figure 5.27b). The molecule is now a nucleoside monophosphate, better known as a nucleotide.

Nucleotide Polymers

Now we can see how these nucleotides are linked together to build a polynucleotide. Adjacent nucleotides are joined by a phosphodiester linkage, which consists of a phosphate group that links the sugars of two nucleotides. This bonding results in a backbone with a repeating pattern of sugar-phosphate units (see Figure 5.27a). The two free ends of the polymer are distinctly different from each other. One end has a phosphate attached to a 5′ carbon, and the other end has a hydroxyl group on a 3′ carbon; we refer to these as the 5′ end and the 3′ end, respectively. We can say that the DNA strand has a built-in directionality along its sugar-phosphate backbone, from 5′ to 3′, somewhat like a one-way street. All along this sugar-phosphate backbone are appendages consisting of the nitrogenous bases.

The sequence of bases along a DNA (or mRNA) polymer is unique for each gene and provides very specific information to the cell. Because genes are hundreds to thousands of nucleotides long, the number of possible base sequences is effectively limitless. A gene's meaning to the cell is encoded in its specific sequence of the four DNA bases. For example, the sequence AGGTAACTT means one thing, whereas the sequence CGCTTTAAC has a different meaning. (Entire genes, of course, are much longer.) The linear order of bases in a gene specifies the amino acid sequence—the primary structure—of a protein, which in turn specifies that protein's three-dimensional structure and function in the cell.

The DNA Double Helix

The RNA molecules of cells consist of a single polynucleotide chain like the one shown in Figure 5.27. In contrast, cellular DNA molecules have two polynucleotides that spiral around an imaginary axis, forming a **double helix** **(Figure 5.28)**. James Watson and Francis Crick, working at Cambridge University, first proposed the double helix as the three-dimensional structure of DNA in 1953. The two sugar-phosphate backbones run in opposite 5′ → 3′ directions from each other, an arrangement referred to as **antiparallel**, somewhat like a divided highway. The sugar-phosphate backbones are on the outside of the helix, and the nitrogenous bases are paired in the interior of the helix. The two polynucleotides, or strands, as they are called, are held together by hydrogen bonds between the paired bases and by van der Waals interactions between the stacked bases. Most DNA molecules are very long, with thousands or even millions of base pairs connecting the two chains. One long DNA double helix includes many genes, each one a particular segment of the molecule.

Only certain bases in the double helix are compatible with each other. Adenine (A) always pairs with thymine (T), and guanine (G) always pairs with cytosine (C). If we were to read the sequence of bases along one strand as we traveled the length of the double helix, we would know the sequence of bases along the other strand. If a stretch of one strand has the base sequence 5′-AGGTCCG-3′, then the base-pairing rules tell us that the same stretch of the other strand must have the sequence 3′-TCCAGGC-5′. The two strands of the double helix are *complementary*, each the predictable counterpart of the other. It is this feature of DNA that makes possible the precise copying of genes that is responsible for inheritance (see Figure 5.28). In preparation for cell division, each of the two strands of a DNA molecule serves as a template to order nucleotides into a new complementary strand. The result is two identical copies of the original double-stranded DNA molecule, which are then distributed to the two daughter cells. Thus, the structure of DNA accounts for its function in transmitting genetic information whenever a cell reproduces.

DNA and Proteins as Tape Measures of Evolution

We are accustomed to thinking of shared traits, such as hair and milk production in mammals, as evidence of shared ancestors. Because we now understand that DNA carries heritable information in the form of genes, we can see that genes and their products (proteins) document the hereditary background of an organism. The linear sequences of nucleotides in DNA molecules are passed from parents to offspring; these sequences determine the amino acid sequences of proteins. Siblings have greater similarity in their DNA and proteins than do unrelated individuals of the same species. If the evolutionary view of life is valid, we should be able to extend this concept of "molecular genealogy" to relationships *between* species: We should expect two species that appear to be closely related based on fossil and anatomical evidence to also share a greater proportion of their DNA and protein sequences than do more distantly related species. In fact, that is the case. An example is the comparison of a polypeptide chain of human hemoglobin with the corresponding hemoglobin polypeptide in five other vertebrates. In this chain of 146 amino acids, humans and gorillas differ in just 1 amino acid, while humans and frogs differ in 67 amino acids. (Clearly, these changes do not make the protein nonfunctional.)

Molecular biology has added a new tape measure to the toolkit biologists use to assess evolutionary kinship.

▶ **Figure 5.28 The DNA double helix and its replication.** The DNA molecule is usually double-stranded, with the sugar-phosphate backbone of the antiparallel polynucleotide strands (symbolized here by blue ribbons) on the outside of the helix. Holding the two strands together are pairs of nitrogenous bases attached to each other by hydrogen bonds. As illustrated here with symbolic shapes for the bases, adenine (A) can pair only with thymine (T), and guanine (G) can pair only with cytosine (C). When a cell prepares to divide, the two strands of the double helix separate, and each serves as a template for the precise ordering of nucleotides into new complementary strands (orange). Each DNA strand in this figure is the structural equivalent of the polynucleotide diagrammed in Figure 5.27a.

CONCEPT CHECK 5.5

1. Go to Figure 5.27a and number all the carbons in the sugars for the top three nucleotides; circle the nitrogenous bases and star the phosphates.
2. In a DNA double helix, a region along one DNA strand has this sequence of nitrogenous bases: 5'-TAGGCCT-3'. Write down this strand and its complementary strand, clearly indicating the 5' and 3' ends of the complementary strand.
3. **WHAT IF?** (a) Suppose a substitution occurred in one DNA strand of the double helix in question 2, resulting in:

   5'-TAAGCCT-3'
   3'-ATCCGGA-5'

   Draw the two strands; circle and label the mismatched bases. (b) If the modified top strand is replicated, what would its matching strand be?

   For suggested answers, see Appendix A.

The Theme of Emergent Properties in the Chemistry of Life: *A Review*

Recall that life is organized along a hierarchy of structural levels (see Figure 1.4). With each increasing level of order, new properties emerge. In Chapters 2–5, we have dissected the chemistry of life. But we have also begun to develop a more integrated view of life, exploring how properties emerge with increasing order.

We have seen that water's behavior results from interactions of its molecules, each an ordered arrangement of hydrogen and oxygen atoms. We reduced the complexity and diversity of organic compounds to carbon skeletons and appended chemical groups. We saw that macromolecules are assembled from small organic molecules, taking on new properties. By completing our overview with an introduction to macromolecules and lipids, we have built a bridge to Unit Two, where we will study cell structure and function. We will keep a balance between the need to reduce life to simpler processes and the ultimate satisfaction of viewing those processes in their integrated context.

MEDIA Go to the Study Area at **www.masteringbio.com** for BioFlix 3-D Animations, MP3 Tutors, Videos, Practice Tests, an eBook, and more.

SUMMARY OF KEY CONCEPTS

CONCEPT 5.1

Macromolecules are polymers, built from monomers (pp. 68–69)

▶ **The Synthesis and Breakdown of Polymers** Carbohydrates, proteins, and nucleic acids are polymers, chains of monomers. The components of lipids vary. Monomers form larger molecules by dehydration reactions, in which water molecules are released. Polymers can disassemble by the reverse process, hydrolysis.

▶ **The Diversity of Polymers** An immense variety of polymers can be built from a small set of monomers.

MEDIA

Activity Making and Breaking Polymers

Large Biological Molecules	Components	Examples	Functions
Concept 5.2 **Carbohydrates serve as fuel and building material (pp. 69–74)** **MEDIA** Activity Models of Glucose Activity Carbohydrates	Monosaccharide monomer	Monosaccharides: glucose, fructose	Fuel; carbon sources that can be converted to other molecules or combined into polymers
		Disaccharides: lactose, sucrose	
		Polysaccharides: • Cellulose (plants) • Starch (plants) • Glycogen (animals) • Chitin (animals and fungi)	• Strengthens plant cell walls • Stores glucose for energy • Stores glucose for energy • Strengthens exoskeletons and fungal cell walls
Concept 5.3 **Lipids are a diverse group of hydrophobic molecules (pp. 74–77)** **MEDIA** Activity Lipids	Glycerol / 3 fatty acids	Triacylglycerols (fats or oils): glycerol + 3 fatty acids	Important energy source
	Head with ℗ / 2 fatty acids	Phospholipids: phosphate group + 2 fatty acids	Lipid bilayers of membranes
	Steroid backbone	Steroids: four fused rings with attached chemical groups	• Component of cell membranes (cholesterol) • Signaling molecules that travel through the body (hormones)
Concept 5.4 **Proteins have many structures, resulting in a wide range of functions (pp. 77–86)** **MEDIA** MP3 Tutor Protein Structure and Function Activity Protein Functions Activity Protein Structure Biology Labs On-Line HemoglobinLab	Amino acid monomer (20 types)	• Enzymes • Structural proteins • Storage proteins • Transport proteins • Hormones • Receptor proteins • Motor proteins • Defensive proteins	• Catalyze chemical reactions • Provide structural support • Store amino acids • Transport substances • Coordinate organismal responses • Receive signals from outside cell • Function in cell movement • Protect against disease
Concept 5.5 **Nucleic acids store and transmit hereditary information (pp. 86–89)** **MEDIA** Activity Nucleic Acid Functions Activity Nucleic Acid Structure	Nucleotide monomer	DNA: • Sugar = deoxyribose • Nitrogenous bases = C, G, A, T • Usually double-stranded	Stores all hereditary information
		RNA: • Sugar = ribose • Nitrogenous bases = C, G, A, U • Usually single-stranded	Carries protein-coding instructions from DNA to protein-synthesizing machinery

SELF-QUIZ

1. Which term includes all others in the list?
   a. monosaccharide
   b. disaccharide
   c. starch
   d. carbohydrate
   e. polysaccharide

2. The molecular formula for glucose is $C_6H_{12}O_6$. What would be the molecular formula for a polymer made by linking ten glucose molecules together by dehydration reactions?
   a. $C_{60}H_{120}O_{60}$
   b. $C_6H_{12}O_6$
   c. $C_{60}H_{102}O_{51}$
   d. $C_{60}H_{100}O_{50}$
   e. $C_{60}H_{111}O_{51}$

3. The enzyme amylase can break glycosidic linkages between glucose monomers only if the monomers are the α form. Which of the following could amylase break down?
   a. glycogen, starch, and amylopectin
   b. glycogen and cellulose
   c. cellulose and chitin
   d. starch and chitin
   e. starch, amylopectin, and cellulose

4. Which of the following statements concerning *unsaturated* fats is true?
   a. They are more common in animals than in plants.
   b. They have double bonds in the carbon chains of their fatty acids.
   c. They generally solidify at room temperature.
   d. They contain more hydrogen than saturated fats having the same number of carbon atoms.
   e. They have fewer fatty acid molecules per fat molecule.

5. The structural level of a protein least affected by a disruption in hydrogen bonding is the
   a. primary level.
   b. secondary level.
   c. tertiary level.
   d. quaternary level.
   e. All structural levels are equally affected.

6. Which of the following pairs of base sequences could form a short stretch of a normal double helix of DNA?
   a. 5'-purine-pyrimidine-purine-pyrimidine-3' with 3'-purine-pyrimidine-purine-pyrimidine-5'
   b. 5'-AGCT-3' with 5'-TCGA-3'
   c. 5'-GCGC-3' with 5'-TATA-3'
   d. 5'-ATGC-3' with 5'-GCAT-3'
   e. All of these pairs are correct.

7. Enzymes that break down DNA catalyze the hydrolysis of the covalent bonds that join nucleotides together. What would happen to DNA molecules treated with these enzymes?
   a. The two strands of the double helix would separate.
   b. The phosphodiester linkages between deoxyribose sugars would be broken.
   c. The purines would be separated from the deoxyribose sugars.
   d. The pyrimidines would be separated from the deoxyribose sugars.
   e. All bases would be separated from the deoxyribose sugars.

8. Construct a table that organizes the following terms, and label the columns and rows.

phosphodiester linkages	polypeptides	monosaccharides
peptide bonds	triacylglycerols	nucleotides
glycosidic linkages	polynucleotides	amino acids
ester linkages	polysaccharides	fatty acids

9. **DRAW IT** Draw the polynucleotide strand in Figure 5.27a and label the bases G, T, C, and T, starting from the 5' end. Now draw the complementary strand of the double helix, using the same symbols for phosphates (circles), sugars (pentagons), and bases. Label the bases. Draw arrows showing the 5' → 3' direction of each strand. Use the arrows to make sure the second strand is antiparallel to the first. *Hint:* After you draw the first strand vertically, turn the paper upside down; it is easier to draw the second strand from the 5' toward the 3' direction as you go from top to bottom.

For Self-Quiz answers, see Appendix A.

MEDIA Visit the Study Area at **www.masteringbio.com** for a Practice Test.

EVOLUTION CONNECTION

10. Comparisons of amino acid sequences can shed light on the evolutionary divergence of related species. Would you expect all the proteins of a given set of living species to show the same degree of divergence? Why or why not?

SCIENTIFIC INQUIRY

11. During the Napoleonic Wars in the early 1800s, there was a sugar shortage in Europe because supply ships could not enter blockaded harbors. To create artificial sweeteners, German scientists hydrolyzed wheat starch. They did this by adding hydrochloric acid to heated starch solutions, breaking some of the glycosidic linkages between the glucose monomers. The graph here shows the percentage of glycosidic linkages broken over time. Why do you think consumers found the sweetener to be less sweet than sugar? Sketch a glycosidic linkage in starch using Figures 5.5a and 5.7b for reference. Show how the acid was able to break this bond. Why do you think the acid broke only 50% of the linkages in the wheat starch?

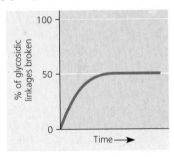

Biological Inquiry: A Workbook of Investigative Cases Explore large biological molecules further with the case "Picture Perfect."

SCIENCE, TECHNOLOGY, AND SOCIETY

12. Some amateur and professional athletes take anabolic steroids to help them "bulk up" or build strength. The health risks of this practice are extensively documented. Apart from health considerations, how do you feel about the use of chemicals to enhance athletic performance? Is an athlete who takes anabolic steroids cheating, or is such use part of the preparation that is required to succeed in competition? Explain.

The Cell

AN INTERVIEW WITH

Paul Nurse

British biologist Sir Paul Nurse shared a Nobel Prize in 2001 with Leland H. Hartwell and R. Timothy Hunt for groundbreaking discoveries about how the eukaryotic cell controls its reproduction. Educated at the Universities of Birmingham and East Anglia, Dr. Nurse was a professor at the University of Oxford and a researcher at the Imperial Cancer Research Fund (now called Cancer Research UK), eventually heading up the latter organization. In 2003, he left the United Kingdom for Rockefeller University in New York City, where he serves as president while also running an active research laboratory.

Tell us about Rockefeller University.
Rockefeller is basically a research institute that gives Ph.D.'s. We have no departments; instead, we have between 70 and 80 independent laboratories. Our sole purpose is to do the highest-quality research relevant to biomedicine. We have physicists, chemists, and mathematicians, as well as biologists and biomedical scientists, but they all tend to be interested in biological problems. It's a wonderfully stimulating environment— and rather anarchic, but I'm happy with that. In my role as president, I focus very much on having the best people around, and then just letting them loose to investigate what they want. I'm very privileged to be here.

How did you first become interested in science, and biology in particular?
When I was a child, I had a long walk to my school through a couple of parks, and I liked to look at the plants, the birds, and the insects. I remember wondering why certain plants seemed to have big leaves when they grew in the shade and small leaves when they grew in sunlight. I also had an interest in astronomy, which I still have. So the origin of my interest in science was really through natural history.

I wasn't the greatest of students at school. My parents were working class, and we didn't

have many books at home. It took me quite a while to get up to speed. But I had a tremendous curiosity to learn about the world around me. Then, as a teenager, I had a science teacher who really encouraged me, named Keith Neil. I did a number of biology projects with him—a fruit fly project, censuses of butterflies and beetles, and a trout egg-laying project in the lab. After I got the Nobel Prize, I nominated him for a mentoring award and did a TV program with him. I think my interest in biology was also influenced by a sense that there were so many unanswered questions in biology that even an ordinary mortal could contribute to the field in some way!

At university, I was at first going to concentrate on ecology and evolution, but I ended up going for subjects that seemed easier to study in a laboratory—cell biology and genetics.

What led you to study the cell cycle?
As a graduate student, I asked myself, "What's really important in biology?" I thought it would be important to focus on the features that distinguish life from nonlife, and a key one of those is the ability of an organism to reproduce itself. You see reproduction in its simplest form in the division of a cell because the cell is the simplest unit of life.

What did you want to find out about cell division?
The cell cycle is a series of events from the "birth" of a cell to its later division into two cells. I wanted to understand how the different events in the cell cycle were coordinated—what controlled the progression of cell-cycle events. In fact, I have ended up spending most of my life trying to answer that question!

There were two alternative ideas about how the cell cycle works: One was that the cell simply proceeds automatically through the events in the pathway, from A to B to C to D, and so forth. Another was that a smaller number of rate-limiting steps within the pathway serve as control points. These control points would determine how rapidly the cell cycle progressed.

How did you proceed to figure out which hypothesis was correct?
My inspiration came from Lee Hartwell, who had used genetics in budding yeast (the yeast used by bakers and brewers) to find mutants with defects in the cell cycle. This is the classical genetic approach. You look for what stops a system from working to tell you how it should be working. I used Lee's work as a template, but I used a different sort of yeast, called fission yeast, which is actually not closely related to budding yeast. Like Lee, I isolated mutants with defects in genes that defined particular steps in the cell-cycle process. We called them *cdc* genes—*cdc* for *c*ell *d*ivision *c*ycle.

In reproducing, a cell of fission yeast first grows to twice its starting size and then divides in two. I looked for mutants that couldn't divide, where the cells just got bigger and bigger. Finding such mutants told us that the genes defective in these cells were necessary for the cells to divide. And when you find a number of different kinds of mutants that are defective in a process, the obvious interpretation is that the process is a pathway of events, each of which is controlled by one or more genes. So the cell cycle could have worked like a straightforward pathway, with each step simply leading to the next.

But one day I happened to notice a different sort of mutant under the microscope: yeast cells that were dividing but at an unusually small size. I realized that if a cell went through the cell cycle faster than normal, it would reach the end of the cell cycle before it had doubled in size. The mutant I'd spotted had only a single mutation, in a single gene, but it was sufficient to make the whole cell cycle go faster. That meant there had to be at least some major rate-limiting steps in the cell cycle, because if they didn't exist you couldn't make the cell cycle go faster. So the second hypothesis seemed to be correct.

All of that came out of just looking at those small mutant cells for five minutes. I could say that most of the next twenty years of my career was based on those five minutes!

It's essential to add that many other scientists have contributed to the field of cell cycle regulation, working in many different places. In addition to Lee Hartwell, who is in Seattle, these people included Yoshio Masui in Toronto and Jim Maller in Colorado, who both worked with frog eggs, and my longtime friend Tim Hunt, in England, who studied the eggs of sea urchins.

You focused in on a mutant with a defect in a gene you called *cdc2*. What does this gene do?
It turned out that the *cdc2* gene codes for an enzyme called a protein kinase. Protein kinases are heavily used by cells as a means of regulating what other proteins do. There are hundreds of different kinds of these enzymes—over 500 in human cells, for example. What they do is phosphorylate other proteins: They take phosphates from ATP molecules and transfer them to proteins. Phosphate groups are big lumps of negative charge, and they can change the shape of a protein and therefore its properties. So showing that *cdc2* coded for a protein kinase was important in identifying protein phosphorylation as a key regulatory mechanism in the cell cycle. Eventually we showed that, in fission yeast, the *cdc2* protein kinase is used fairly early in the cell cycle, where it controls the replication of DNA, and then again later in the cycle, when the replicated chromosomes are ready to separate from each other in mitosis. This is soon before the cell divides in two.

Do similar enzymes control the cell cycle in other kinds of organisms?
A postdoc in my lab, Melanie Lee, was able to track down the human equivalent of the yeast *cdc2* gene, by showing that it was able to substitute for a defective *cdc2* gene in a yeast cell. After we put the human gene in a yeast cell that had a defective *cdc2* gene, the yeast cell was able to divide normally!

It turns out that the Cdc2 protein and many others involved in cell-cycle regulation are very similar in all eukaryotic organisms. What this has to mean is that this system of controlling cell division must have evolved very soon after eukaryotic cells first appeared on the planet, and that it was so crucial to cell survival that it remained unchanged. We have found the *cdc2* gene, for example, in every eukaryotic organism we've looked at.

What is the medical relevance of research on the cell cycle?
The main medical relevance is to cancer, because cancer occurs when cells grow and divide out of control. Now, growth and division is a good thing in the right place at the right time; it's how a fertilized human egg develops into a baby and how wounds in the body are repaired. But if you start getting growth and division in the wrong place at the wrong time, then you can get tumors that destroy the function of the organs or tissue in which they are located.

But maybe, in the end, the more important connection to cancer has to do with what's called genome stability. You have to precisely replicate all your genes in every cell cycle and then separate them precisely into the two progeny cells—that's what the cell cycle is all about. If there are mistakes, if the DNA does not replicate properly or the chromosomes don't separate properly, you end up generating genome instability, in which the number of chromosomes may be altered and parts of chromosomes rearranged. Such changes can lead to cancer. So understanding how genome stability is maintained is crucial for understanding how cancer arises.

What is your approach to mentoring young scientists in your lab? And what about collaboration with other labs?
I've always run a pretty disorganized lab. With students and postdocs, I look upon my job as not so much directing them as helping them follow their own interests, although I do try to keep them from falling into too many elephant traps. The lab is a bit inefficient, to be honest, because we're constantly starting new projects. But since people take these projects away with them when they leave, this practice helps the field expand very fast.

My collaboration with people outside my own lab is mostly in the form of talking. I find I think much better when I can bounce around ideas with other people. This sort of conversation is especially useful when there is a very honest and open relationship—it's good to be sufficiently comfortable with someone to be able to say, "What you just said was stupid." I've benefited from such frank discussions for decades with Tim Hunt, for example, but we've never published a paper together. Tim discovered another kind of cell-cycle control protein, called cyclin, which works in partnership with protein kinases like Cdc2. The protein kinases we've been talking about in this interview are therefore called cyclin-dependent kinases, or CDKs.

What responsibilities do scientists have toward society?
I always say that scientists need to have a "license to operate." We have to earn that license; we cannot assume society will be pro-science. When I was younger, I used to think: Well, I'm doing this because I'm curious, and science should be supported because it's an important cultural endeavor, something like art or music. But we have to realize that if we can justify science only in cultural terms, science budgets will plummet. The public and their governmental representatives want to use scientific discoveries to benefit humankind, and that's completely reasonable. I think it's critical that scientists communicate effectively with the public so that we can influence policymakers in government. Most importantly, we scientists have to listen to the public and understand how they see the issues; we need to have a dialogue with the public. Without that dialogue, we just don't know what misunderstandings are out there. I think we need more grassroots involvement by scientists.

... this system of controlling cell division must have evolved very soon after eukaryotic cells first appeared on the planet.

Inquiry in Action

Learn about an experiment by Paul Nurse and colleagues in Inquiry Figure 12.16 on page 240.

Paul Nurse and Jane Reece

A Tour of the Cell

6

▲ **Figure 6.1 How do cellular components cooperate to help the cell function?**

OVERVIEW

The Fundamental Units of Life

What do a small compartment in a honeycomb, a prison room, and the area covered by a mobile phone tower have in common with a microscopic part of your body? Each is the simplest unit of function in a larger system, and each is described by the word *cell*. The cell is as fundamental to the living systems of biology as the atom is to chemistry: All organisms are made of cells.

In the hierarchy of biological organization, the cell is the simplest collection of matter that can live. Indeed, there are diverse forms of life existing as single-celled organisms. More complex organisms, including plants and animals, are multicellular; their bodies are cooperatives of many kinds of specialized cells that could not survive for long on their own. However, even when they are arranged into higher levels of organization, such as tissues and organs, cells are an organism's basic units of structure and function. The contraction of muscle cells moves your eyes as you read this sentence; when you decide to turn the next page, nerve cells will transmit that decision from your brain to the muscle cells of your hand. Each action of an organism begins at the cellular level.

The cell is a microcosm that demonstrates most of the themes introduced in Chapter 1. Life at the cellular level arises from structural order, reflecting emergent properties and the correlation between structure and function. For example, the movement of an animal cell depends on an intricate interplay of the structures that make up a cellular skeleton (the colored fibers in the micrograph in **Figure 6.1**). Another recurring theme in biology is the interaction of organisms with their environment. Cells sense and respond to environmental fluctuations. And keep in mind the one biological theme that unifies all others: evolution. All cells are related by their descent from earlier cells. However, they have been modified in many different ways during the long evolutionary history of life on Earth.

Although cells can differ substantially from one another, they share certain common characteristics. In this chapter, we'll first examine the tools and experimental approaches that allow us to understand subcellular details; then we'll tour the cell and become acquainted with its components.

CONCEPT 6.1

To study cells, biologists use microscopes and the tools of biochemistry

It can be difficult to understand how a cell, usually too small to be seen by the unaided eye, can be so complex. How can cell biologists possibly investigate the inner workings of such tiny entities? Before we tour the cell, it will be helpful to learn how cells are studied.

Microscopy

The development of instruments that extend the human senses has gone hand in hand with the advance of science. The discovery and early study of cells progressed with the invention of microscopes in 1590 and their refinement during the 1600s. Microscopes are still indispensable for the study of cells.

The microscopes first used by Renaissance scientists, as well as the microscopes you are likely to use in the laboratory, are all light microscopes. In a **light microscope (LM)**, visible light is passed through the specimen and then through glass lenses. The lenses refract (bend) the light in such a way that the image of the specimen is magnified as it is projected into the eye, onto photographic film or a digital sensor, or onto a video screen. (See the diagram of microscope structure in Appendix D.)

Two important parameters in microscopy are magnification and resolving power, or resolution. *Magnification* is the ratio of an object's image size to its real size. *Resolution* is a measure of the clarity of the image; it is the minimum distance two points can be separated and still be distinguished as two points. For example, what appears to the unaided eye as one star in the sky may be resolved as twin stars with a telescope.

Just as the resolving power of the human eye is limited, the light microscope cannot resolve detail finer than about 0.2 micrometer (μm), or 200 nanometers (nm), the size of a small bacterium, regardless of the magnification factor **(Figure 6.2)**. This resolution is limited by the shortest wavelength of light used to illuminate the specimen. Light microscopes can magnify effectively to about 1,000 times the actual size of the specimen; at greater magnifications, additional details cannot be seen clearly. A third important parameter in microscopy is *contrast*, which accentuates differences in parts of the sample. In fact, most improvements in light microscopy in the last hundred years have involved new methods for enhancing contrast, such as staining or labeling cell components to stand out visually **(Figure 6.3**, on the next page).

Cell walls were first seen by Robert Hooke in 1665 as he looked through a microscope at dead cells from the bark of an oak tree. But it took the wonderfully crafted lenses of Antoni van Leeuwenhoek to visualize living cells. Imagine Hooke's awe when he visited van Leeuwenhoek in 1674 and the world of microorganisms—what his host called "very little animalcules"—was revealed to him. In spite of these early observations, the cell's geography remained largely uncharted for some time. Most subcellular structures—including **organelles**, which are membrane-enclosed compartments—are simply too small to be resolved by the light microscope.

Cell biology advanced rapidly in the 1950s with the introduction of the electron microscope. Instead of using light, the **electron microscope (EM)** focuses a beam of electrons through the specimen or onto its surface (see Appendix D). Resolution is inversely related to the wavelength of the radiation a microscope uses for imaging, and electron beams have much shorter wavelengths than visible light. Modern electron

microscopes can theoretically achieve a resolution of about 0.002 nm, although for practical purposes they usually cannot resolve biological structures smaller than about 2 nm. Still, this resolution is a hundredfold improvement over the light

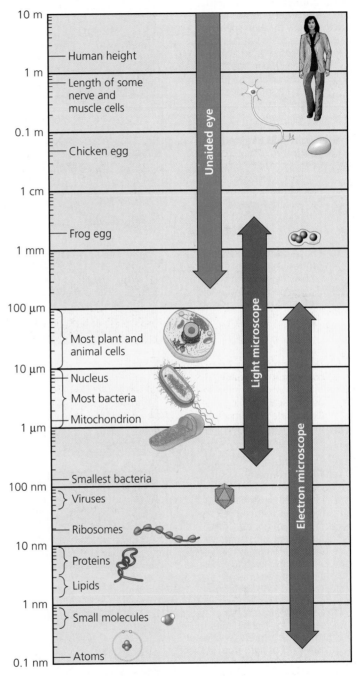

1 centimeter (cm) = 10^{-2} meter (m) = 0.4 inch
1 millimeter (mm) = 10^{-3} m
1 micrometer (μm) = 10^{-3} mm = 10^{-6} m
1 nanometer (nm) = 10^{-3} μm = 10^{-9} m

▲ **Figure 6.2 The size range of cells.** Most cells are between 1 and 100 μm in diameter (yellow region of chart) and are therefore visible only under a microscope. Notice that the scale along the left side is logarithmic to accommodate the range of sizes shown. Starting at the top of the scale with 10 m and going down, each reference measurement marks a tenfold decrease in diameter or length. For a complete table of the metric system, see Appendix C.

Light Microscopy

TECHNIQUE	RESULTS

(a) Brightfield (unstained specimen). Passes light directly through specimen. Unless cell is naturally pigmented or artificially stained, image has little contrast. [Parts (a)–(d) show a human cheek epithelial cell.]

50 μm

(b) Brightfield (stained specimen). Staining with various dyes enhances contrast. Most staining procedures require that cells be fixed (preserved).

(c) Phase-contrast. Enhances contrast in unstained cells by amplifying variations in density within specimen; especially useful for examining living, unpigmented cells.

(d) Differential-interference-contrast (Nomarski). Like phase-contrast microscopy, uses optical modifications to exaggerate differences in density, making the image appear almost 3-D.

(e) Fluorescence. Shows the locations of specific molecules in the cell by tagging the molecules with fluorescent dyes or antibodies. These fluorescent substances absorb ultraviolet radiation and emit visible light, as shown here in a cell from an artery.

50 μm

(f) Confocal. A fluorescent "optical sectioning" technique that uses a pinhole aperture to eliminate out-of-focus light from a thick sample, creating a single plane of fluorescence in the image. By capturing sharp images at many different planes, a 3-D reconstruction can be created. At the right are confocal (top) and standard fluorescent micrographs of stained nervous tissue, where nerve cells are green, support cells are red, and regions of overlap are yellow. The standard image is blurry because the out-of-focus light is not excluded.

50 μm

microscope. The term *cell ultrastructure* refers to the cellular anatomy revealed by an electron microscope.

The **scanning electron microscope (SEM)** is especially useful for detailed study of the surface of a specimen (**Figure 6.4a**). The electron beam scans the surface of the sample, which is usually coated with a thin film of gold. The beam excites electrons on the surface, and these secondary electrons are detected by a device that translates the pattern of electrons into an electronic signal to a video screen. The result is an image of the specimen's topography. The SEM has great depth of field, resulting in an image that appears three-dimensional.

The **transmission electron microscope (TEM)** is used to study the internal ultrastructure of cells (**Figure 6.4b**). The TEM aims an electron beam through a very thin section of the specimen, similar to the way a light microscope transmits light through a slide. The specimen has been stained with atoms of heavy metals, which attach to certain cellular structures, thus enhancing the electron density of some parts of the cell more than others. The electrons passing through the specimen are scattered more in the denser regions, so fewer are transmitted. The image displays the pattern of transmitted electrons. Instead of using glass lenses, the TEM uses electromagnets as lenses to bend the paths of the electrons, ultimately focusing the image onto a screen for viewing or onto photographic film. Some microscopes are equipped with a digital camera to photograph the image on the screen; others have a digital detector in place of both screen and camera.

Electron Microscopy

TECHNIQUE	RESULTS

(a) Scanning electron microscopy (SEM). Micrographs taken with a scanning electron microscope show a 3-D image of the surface of a specimen. This SEM shows the surface of a cell from a rabbit trachea (windpipe) covered with motile organelles called cilia. Beating of the cilia helps move inhaled debris upward toward the throat.

Cilia

1 μm

(b) Transmission electron microscopy (TEM). A transmission electron microscope profiles a thin section of a specimen. Here we see a section through a tracheal cell, revealing its ultrastructure. In preparing the TEM, some cilia were cut along their lengths, creating longitudinal sections, while other cilia were cut straight across, creating cross sections.

Longitudinal section of cilium   Cross section of cilium

1 μm

Electron microscopes reveal many organelles and other subcellular structures that are impossible to resolve with the light microscope. But the light microscope offers advantages, especially in studying living cells. A disadvantage of electron microscopy is that the methods used to prepare the specimen kill the cells. Also, specimen preparation can introduce artifacts, structural features seen in micrographs that do not exist in the living cell (as is true for all microscopy techniques). From this point on in the book, micrographs are identified by the type of microscopy: LM for a light micrograph, SEM for a scanning electron micrograph, and TEM for a transmission electron micrograph. Also, micrograph images may be artificially "colorized" to highlight particular structures.

Microscopes are the most important tools of *cytology*, the study of cell structure. But simply describing the diverse organelles and other structures within the cell reveals little about their function. Modern cell biology developed from an integration of cytology with *biochemistry*, the study of the molecules and chemical processes (metabolism) of cells.

Cell Fractionation

A useful technique for studying cell structure and function is **cell fractionation**, which takes cells apart and separates the major organelles and other subcellular structures from one another **(Figure 6.5)**. The instrument used is the centrifuge, which spins test tubes holding mixtures of disrupted cells at various speeds. The resulting forces cause a fraction of the cell components to settle to the bottom of the tube, forming a pellet. At lower speeds, the pellet consists of larger components, and higher speeds yield a pellet with smaller components. The most powerful machines, called *ultracentrifuges*, spin up to 130,000 revolutions per minute (rpm) and apply forces on particles of more than 1 million times the force of gravity (1,000,000 *g*).

Cell fractionation enables researchers to prepare specific cell components in bulk and identify their functions, a task that would be far more difficult with intact cells. For example, biochemical tests showed that one of the cell fractions produced by centrifugation included enzymes involved in cellular respiration. Electron microscopy revealed that this fraction contained large numbers of the organelles called mitochondria. Together, these data helped biologists determine that mitochondria are the sites of cellular respiration. Biochemistry and cytology thus complement each other in correlating cell function with structure.

▼ Figure 6.5 **Research Method**

Cell Fractionation

APPLICATION   Cell fractionation is used to isolate (fractionate) cell components based on size and density.

TECHNIQUE   First, cells are homogenized in a blender to break them up. The resulting mixture (cell homogenate) is then centrifuged at various speeds and durations to fractionate the cell components, forming a series of pellets, overlaid by the remaining homogenate (supernatant).

Homogenization

Tissue cells

Homogenate

1,000 *g*
(1,000 times the force of gravity)
10 min

Differential centrifugation

Supernatant poured into next tube

20,000 *g*
20 min

80,000 *g*
60 min

150,000 *g*
3 hr

Pellet rich in nuclei and cellular debris

Pellet rich in mitochondria (and chloroplasts if cells are from a plant)

Pellet rich in "microsomes" (pieces of plasma membranes and cells' internal membranes)

Pellet rich in ribosomes

RESULTS   In early experiments, researchers used microscopy to identify the organelles in each pellet and biochemical methods to determine their metabolic functions. These identifications established a baseline for this method, enabling today's researchers to know which cell fraction they should collect in order to isolate and study particular organelles.

Eukaryotic cells have internal membranes that compartmentalize their functions

The basic structural and functional unit of every organism is one of two types of cells—prokaryotic or eukaryotic. Only organisms of the domains Bacteria and Archaea consist of prokaryotic cells. Protists, fungi, animals, and plants all consist of eukaryotic cells. This chapter focuses on generalized animal and plant cells after first comparing them with prokaryotic cells.

Comparing Prokaryotic and Eukaryotic Cells

All cells have several basic features in common: They are all bounded by a selective barrier, called the *plasma membrane.* Enclosed by the membrane is a semifluid, jellylike substance called **cytosol**, in which organelles and other components are found. All cells contain *chromosomes*, which carry genes in the form of DNA. And all cells have *ribosomes*, tiny complexes that make proteins according to instructions from the genes.

A major difference between prokaryotic and eukaryotic cells is the location of their DNA, as reflected in their names. In a **eukaryotic cell**, most of the DNA is in an organelle called the *nucleus,* which is bounded by a double membrane (see Figure 6.9, on pp. 100–101). (The word *eukaryotic* is from the Greek *eu,*

true, and *karyon*, kernel, here referring to the nucleus.) In a **prokaryotic cell** (from the Greek *pro*, before, and *karyon*), the DNA is concentrated in a region that is not membrane-enclosed, called the **nucleoid (Figure 6.6)**. The interior of a prokaryotic cell is called the **cytoplasm**; this term is also used for the region between the nucleus and the plasma membrane of a eukaryotic cell. Within the cytoplasm of a eukaryotic cell, suspended in cytosol, are a variety of organelles of specialized form and function. These membrane-bounded structures are absent in prokaryotic cells. Thus, the presence or absence of a true nucleus is just one example of the disparity in structural complexity between the two types of cells.

Eukaryotic cells are generally much larger than prokaryotic cells (see Figure 6.2). Size is a general aspect of cell structure that relates to function. The logistics of carrying out cellular metabolism sets limits on cell size. At the lower limit, the smallest cells known are bacteria called mycoplasmas, which have diameters between 0.1 and 1.0 µm. These are perhaps the smallest packages with enough DNA to program metabolism and enough enzymes and other cellular equipment to carry out the activities necessary for a cell to sustain itself and reproduce. Typical bacteria are 1–5 µm in diameter, a dimension about ten times greater than that of mycoplasmas. Eukaryotic cells are typically 10–100 µm in diameter.

Metabolic requirements also impose theoretical upper limits on the size that is practical for a single cell. At the boundary of every cell, the **plasma membrane** functions as a selective barrier that allows sufficient passage of oxygen, nutrients, and wastes to

Fimbriae: attachment structures on the surface of some prokaryotes

Nucleoid: region where the cell's DNA is located (not enclosed by a membrane)

Ribosomes: complexes that synthesize proteins

Plasma membrane: membrane enclosing the cytoplasm

Cell wall: rigid structure outside the plasma membrane

Capsule: jellylike outer coating of many prokaryotes

Bacterial chromosome

(a) **A typical rod-shaped bacterium**

Flagella: locomotion organelles of some bacteria

0.5 µm

(b) **A thin section through the bacterium *Bacillus coagulans* (TEM)**

▲ **Figure 6.6 A prokaryotic cell.** Lacking a true nucleus and the other membrane-enclosed organelles of the eukaryotic cell, the prokaryotic cell is much simpler in structure. Only bacteria and archaea are prokaryotes.

(a) TEM of a plasma membrane. The plasma membrane, here in a red blood cell, appears as a pair of dark bands separated by a light band.

Outside of cell

Inside of cell
0.1 μm

Carbohydrate side chain

Hydrophilic region

Hydrophobic region

Hydrophilic region

Phospholipid

Proteins

(b) Structure of the plasma membrane

▲ **Figure 6.7 The plasma membrane.** The plasma membrane and the membranes of organelles consist of a double layer (bilayer) of phospholipids with various proteins attached to or embedded in it. In the interior of a membrane, the phospholipid tails are hydrophobic, as are the interior portions of membrane proteins in contact with them. The phospholipid heads are hydrophilic, as are proteins or parts of proteins in contact with the aqueous solution on either side of the membrane. (Channels through certain proteins are also hydrophilic.) Carbohydrate side chains are found only attached to proteins or lipids on the outer surface of the plasma membrane.

? *Describe the components of a phospholipid (see Figure 5.13) that allow it to function as the major element in the plasma membrane.*

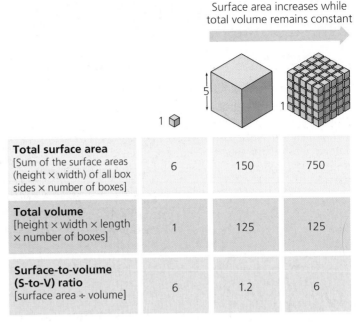

Surface area increases while total volume remains constant

	1	5	1
Total surface area [Sum of the surface areas (height × width) of all box sides × number of boxes]	6	150	750
Total volume [height × width × length × number of boxes]	1	125	125
Surface-to-volume (S-to-V) ratio [surface area ÷ volume]	6	1.2	6

▲ **Figure 6.8 Geometric relationships between surface area and volume.** In this diagram, cells are represented as boxes. Using arbitrary units of length, we can calculate the cell's surface area (in square units, or units^2), volume (in cubic units, or units^3), and ratio of surface area to volume. A high surface-to-volume ratio facilitates the exchange of materials between a cell and its environment.

A Panoramic View of the Eukaryotic Cell

In addition to the plasma membrane at its outer surface, a eukaryotic cell has extensive and elaborately arranged internal membranes, which divide the cell into compartments—the organelles mentioned earlier. The cell's compartments provide different local environments that facilitate specific metabolic functions, so incompatible processes can go on simultaneously inside a single cell. The plasma and organelle membranes also participate directly in the cell's metabolism, because many enzymes are built right into the membranes.

Because membranes are fundamental to the organization of the cell, Chapter 7 will discuss them in detail. In general, biological membranes consist of a double layer of phospholipids and other lipids. Embedded in this lipid bilayer or attached to its surfaces are diverse proteins (see Figure 6.7). However, each type of membrane has a unique composition of lipids and proteins suited to that membrane's specific functions. For example, enzymes embedded in the membranes of the organelles called mitochondria function in cellular respiration.

Before continuing with this chapter, examine the overviews of eukaryotic cells in **Figure 6.9**, on the next two pages. These generalized cell diagrams introduce the various organelles and provide a map of the cell for the detailed tour upon which we will now embark. Figure 6.9 also contrasts animal and plant cells. As eukaryotic cells, they have much more in common than either has with any prokaryotic cell. As you will see, however, there are important differences between animal and plant cells.

service the entire cell! **(Figure 6.7).** For each square micrometer of membrane, only a limited amount of a particular substance can cross per second, so the ratio of surface area to volume is critical. As a cell (or any other object) increases in size, its volume grows proportionately more than its surface area. (Area is proportional to a linear dimension squared, whereas volume is proportional to the linear dimension cubed.) Thus, a smaller object has a greater ratio of surface area to volume **(Figure 6.8).**

The need for a surface area sufficiently large to accommodate the volume helps explain the microscopic size of most cells and the narrow, elongated shapes of others, such as nerve cells. Larger organisms do not generally have *larger* cells than smaller organisms—simply *more* cells (see Figure 6.8). A sufficiently high ratio of surface area to volume is especially important in cells that exchange a lot of material with their surroundings, such as intestinal cells. Such cells may have many long, thin projections from their surface called microvilli, which increase surface area without an appreciable increase in volume.

The possible evolutionary relationships between prokaryotic and eukaryotic cells will be discussed in Chapter 26, and prokaryotic cells will be described in detail in Chapter 27. Most of the discussion of cell structure that follows in this chapter applies to eukaryotic cells.

Exploring Animal and Plant Cells

Animal Cell

This drawing of a generalized animal cell incorporates the most common structures of animal cells (no cell actually looks just like this). As shown by this cutaway view, the cell has a variety of components, including organelles ("little organs"), which are bounded by membranes. The most prominent organelle in an animal cell is usually the nucleus. Most of the cell's metabolic activities occur in the cytoplasm, the entire region between the nucleus and the plasma membrane. The cytoplasm contains many organelles and other cell components suspended in a semifluid medium, the cytosol. Pervading much of the cytoplasm is a labyrinth of membranes called the endoplasmic reticulum (ER).

Flagellum: locomotion organelle present in some animal cells; composed of a cluster of microtubules within an extension of the plasma membrane

Centrosome: region where the cell's microtubules are initiated; contains a pair of centrioles (function unknown)

CYTOSKELETON: reinforces cell's shape, functions in cell movement; components are made of protein. Includes:

Microfilaments

Intermediate filaments

Microtubules

Microvilli: projections that increase the cell's surface area

Peroxisome: organelle with various specialized metabolic functions; produces hydrogen peroxide as a by-product, then converts it to water

ENDOPLASMIC RETICULUM (ER): network of membranous sacs and tubes; active in membrane synthesis and other synthetic and metabolic processes; has rough (ribosome-studded) and smooth regions

Rough ER   **Smooth ER**

Nuclear envelope: double membrane enclosing the nucleus; perforated by pores; continuous with ER

Nucleolus: structure involved in production of ribosomes; a nucleus has one or more nucleoli

Chromatin: material consisting of DNA and proteins; visible as individual chromosomes in a dividing cell

NUCLEUS

Plasma membrane: membrane enclosing the cell

Ribosomes: complexes (small brown dots) that make proteins; free in cytosol or bound to rough ER or nuclear envelope

Golgi apparatus: organelle active in synthesis, modification, sorting, and secretion of cell products

Mitochondrion: organelle where cellular respiration occurs and most ATP is generated

Lysosome: digestive organelle where macromolecules are hydrolyzed

In animal cells but not plant cells:
Lysosomes
Centrosomes, with centrioles
Flagella (but present in some plant sperm)

Plant Cell

This drawing of a generalized plant cell reveals the similarities and differences between an animal cell and a plant cell. In addition to most of the features seen in an animal cell, a plant cell has organelles called plastids. The most important type of plastid is the chloroplast, which carries out photosynthesis. Many plant cells have a large central vacuole; some may have one or more smaller vacuoles. Among other tasks, vacuoles carry out functions performed by lysosomes in animal cells. Outside a plant cell's plasma membrane is a thick cell wall, perforated by channels called plasmodesmata.

 MEDIA **BioFlix** Visit the Study Area at **www.masteringbio.com** for the BioFlix 3-D Animations called Tour of an Animal Cell and Tour of a Plant Cell.

If you preview the rest of the chapter now, you'll see Figure 6.9 repeated in miniature as orientation diagrams. In each case, a particular organelle is highlighted, color-coded to its appearance in Figure 6.9. As we take a closer look at individual organelles, the orientation diagrams will help you place those structures in the context of the whole cell.

NUCLEUS
- Nuclear envelope
- Nucleolus
- Chromatin

Rough endoplasmic reticulum

Smooth endoplasmic reticulum

Ribosomes (small brown dots)

Golgi apparatus

Central vacuole: prominent organelle in older plant cells; functions include storage, breakdown of waste products, hydrolysis of macromolecules; enlargement of vacuole is a major mechanism of plant growth

CYTOSKELETON
- Microfilaments
- Intermediate filaments
- Microtubules

Mitochondrion

Peroxisome

Plasma membrane

Cell wall: outer layer that maintains cell's shape and protects cell from mechanical damage; made of cellulose, other polysaccharides, and protein

Wall of adjacent cell

Plasmodesmata: channels through cell walls that connect the cytoplasms of adjacent cells

Chloroplast: photosynthetic organelle; converts energy of sunlight to chemical energy stored in sugar molecules

In plant cells but not animal cells:
Chloroplasts
Central vacuole
Cell wall
Plasmodesmata

1. After carefully reviewing Figure 6.9, briefly describe the structure and function of the nucleus, the mitochondrion, the chloroplast, and the endoplasmic reticulum.

2. **WHAT IF?** Imagine an elongated cell (such as a nerve cell) that is $125 \times 1 \times 1$, using arbitrary units similar to the ones in Figure 6.8. Predict where its surface-to-volume ratio would lie in Figure 6.8. Then calculate and check your prediction.

For suggested answers, see Appendix A.

CONCEPT 6.3

The eukaryotic cell's genetic instructions are housed in the nucleus and carried out by the ribosomes

On the first stop of our detailed tour of the cell, let's look at two cellular components involved in the genetic control of the cell: the nucleus, which houses most of the cell's DNA, and the ribosomes, which use information from the DNA to make proteins.

The Nucleus: Information Central

The **nucleus** contains most of the genes in the eukaryotic cell (some genes are located in mitochondria and chloroplasts). It is generally the most conspicuous organelle in a eukaryotic cell, averaging about 5 µm in diameter. The **nuclear envelope** encloses the nucleus **(Figure 6.10)**, separating its contents from the cytoplasm.

The nuclear envelope is a *double* membrane. The two membranes, each a lipid bilayer with associated proteins, are separated by a space of 20–40 nm. The envelope is perforated by pore structures that are about 100 nm in diameter. At the lip of each pore, the inner and outer membranes of the nuclear envelope are continuous. An intricate protein structure called a *pore complex* lines each pore and plays an important role in the cell by regulating the entry and exit of most proteins and RNAs, as well as large complexes of macromolecules. Except at the pores, the nuclear side of the envelope is lined by the **nuclear lamina**, a netlike array of protein filaments that maintains the shape of the nucleus by mechanically supporting the nuclear envelope. There is also much evidence for a *nuclear matrix*, a framework of fibers extending throughout the nuclear interior. (On page 322, we will touch on possible functions of the nuclear lamina and matrix in organizing the genetic material.)

Within the nucleus, the DNA is organized into discrete units called **chromosomes**, structures that carry the genetic information. Each chromosome is made up of a material called **chromatin**, a complex of proteins and DNA. Stained chromatin usually appears as a diffuse mass through both light microscopes and electron microscopes. As a cell prepares to divide, however, the thin chromatin fibers coil up (condense), becoming thick enough to be distinguished as the familiar separate structures we know as chromosomes. Each eukaryotic species has a characteristic number of chromosomes. A typical human cell, for example, has 46 chromosomes in its nucleus; the exceptions are the sex cells (eggs and sperm), which have only 23 chromosomes in humans. A fruit fly cell has 8 chromosomes in most cells and 4 in the sex cells.

A prominent structure within the nondividing nucleus is the **nucleolus** (plural, *nucleoli*), which appears through the electron microscope as a mass of densely stained granules and fibers adjoining part of the chromatin. Here a type of RNA called *ribosomal RNA* (rRNA) is synthesized from instructions in the DNA. Also in the nucleolus, proteins imported from the cytoplasm are assembled with rRNA into large and small ribosomal subunits. These subunits then exit the nucleus through the nuclear pores to the cytoplasm, where a large and a small subunit can assemble into a ribosome. Sometimes there are two or more nucleoli; the number depends on the species and the stage in the cell's reproductive cycle. Recent studies suggest that the nucleolus also functions in regulation of some cellular processes, such as cell division.

As we saw in Figure 5.26, the nucleus directs protein synthesis by synthesizing messenger RNA (mRNA) according to instructions provided by the DNA. The mRNA is then transported to the cytoplasm via the nuclear pores. Once an mRNA molecule reaches the cytoplasm, ribosomes translate the mRNA's genetic message into the primary structure of a specific polypeptide. This process of transcribing and translating genetic information is described in detail in Chapter 17.

Ribosomes: Protein Factories

Ribosomes, which are complexes made of ribosomal RNA and protein, are the cellular components that carry out protein synthesis **(Figure 6.11)**. Cells that have high rates of protein synthesis have particularly large numbers of ribosomes. For example, a human pancreas cell has a few million ribosomes. Not surprisingly, cells active in protein synthesis also have prominent nucleoli.

Ribosomes build proteins in two cytoplasmic locales (see Figure 6.11). At any given time, *free ribosomes* are suspended in the cytosol, while *bound ribosomes* are attached to the outside of the endoplasmic reticulum or nuclear envelope. Bound and free ribosomes are structurally identical, and ribosomes can alternate between the two roles. Most of the proteins

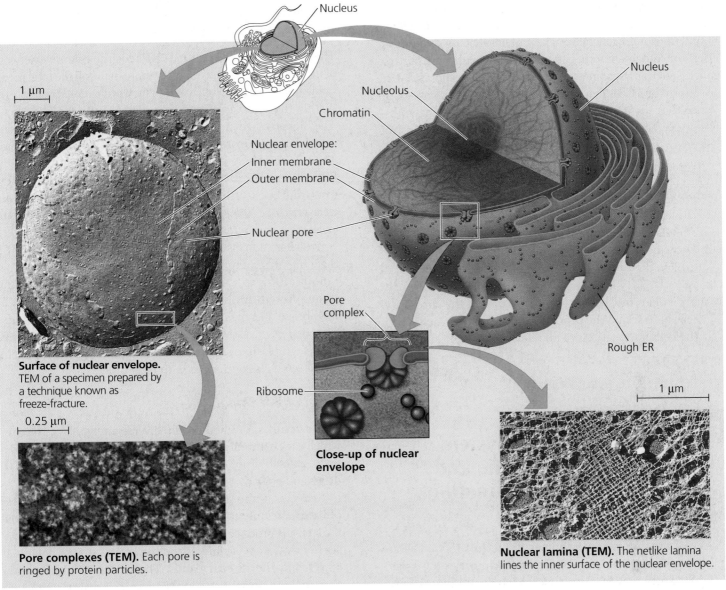

Nucleus

Nucleus

Nucleolus

Chromatin

Nuclear envelope:
Inner membrane
Outer membrane

Nuclear pore

Rough ER

1 µm

Surface of nuclear envelope.
TEM of a specimen prepared by
a technique known as
freeze-fracture.

0.25 µm

Pore
complex

Ribosome

**Close-up of nuclear
envelope**

1 µm

Nuclear lamina (TEM). The netlike lamina
lines the inner surface of the nuclear envelope.

Pore complexes (TEM). Each pore is
ringed by protein particles.

▲ **Figure 6.10 The nucleus and its
envelope.** Within the nucleus are the
chromosomes, which appear as a mass of
chromatin (DNA and associated proteins), and
one or more nucleoli (singular, *nucleolus*), which
function in ribosome synthesis. The nuclear
envelope, which consists of two membranes
separated by a narrow space, is perforated with
pores and lined by the nuclear lamina.

▶ **Figure 6.11 Ribosomes.** This electron
micrograph of part of a pancreas cell shows
many ribosomes, both free (in the cytosol) and
bound (to the endoplasmic reticulum). The
simplified diagram of a ribosome shows its two
subunits.

Ribosomes

ER

Cytosol

Endoplasmic reticulum (ER)

Free ribosomes

Bound ribosomes

Large
subunit

Small
subunit

0.5 µm

TEM showing ER and ribosomes

Diagram of a ribosome

made on free ribosomes function within the cytosol; examples are enzymes that catalyze the first steps of sugar breakdown. Bound ribosomes generally make proteins that are destined for insertion into membranes, for packaging within certain organelles such as lysosomes (see Figure 6.9), or for export from the cell (secretion). Cells that specialize in protein secretion—for instance, the cells of the pancreas that secrete digestive enzymes—frequently have a high proportion of bound ribosomes. You will learn more about ribosome structure and function in Chapter 17.

CONCEPT CHECK 6.3

1. What role do the ribosomes play in carrying out genetic instructions?
2. Describe the molecular composition of nucleoli and explain their function.
3. **WHAT IF?** If the function of a particular protein in a eukaryotic cell is to make up part of the chromatin, describe the process of its synthesis. Include the cellular locations of all relevant molecules.

For suggested answers, see Appendix A.

CONCEPT 6.4

The endomembrane system regulates protein traffic and performs metabolic functions in the cell

Many of the different membranes of the eukaryotic cell are part of an **endomembrane system**, which carries out a variety of tasks in the cell. These tasks include synthesis of proteins and their transport into membranes and organelles or out of the cell, metabolism and movement of lipids, and detoxification of poisons. The membranes of this system are related either through direct physical continuity or by the transfer of membrane segments as tiny **vesicles** (sacs made of membrane). Despite these relationships, the various membranes are not identical in structure and function. Moreover, the thickness, molecular composition, and types of chemical reactions carried out in a given membrane are not fixed, but may be modified several times during the membrane's life. The endomembrane system includes the nuclear envelope, the endoplasmic reticulum, the Golgi apparatus, lysosomes, various kinds of vacuoles, and the plasma membrane (not actually an *endo*membrane in physical location, but nevertheless related to the endoplasmic reticulum and other internal membranes). Having already discussed the nuclear envelope, we will now focus on the endoplasmic reticulum and the other endomembranes to which the endoplasmic reticulum gives rise.

The Endoplasmic Reticulum: Biosynthetic Factory

The **endoplasmic reticulum (ER)** is such an extensive network of membranes that it accounts for more than half the total membrane in many eukaryotic cells. (The word *endoplasmic* means "within the cytoplasm," and *reticulum* is Latin for "little net.") The ER consists of a network of membranous tubules and sacs called cisternae (from the Latin *cisterna*, a reservoir for a liquid). The ER membrane separates the internal compartment of the ER, called the ER lumen (cavity) or cisternal space, from the cytosol. And because the ER membrane is continuous with the nuclear envelope, the space between the two membranes of the envelope is continuous with the lumen of the ER (**Figure 6.12**).

There are two distinct, though connected, regions of the ER that differ in structure and function: smooth ER and rough ER. **Smooth ER** is so named because its outer surface lacks ribosomes. **Rough ER** has ribosomes on the outer surface of the membrane and thus appears rough through the electron microscope. As already mentioned, ribosomes are also attached to the cytoplasmic side of the nuclear envelope's outer membrane, which is continuous with rough ER.

Functions of Smooth ER

The smooth ER functions in diverse metabolic processes, which vary with cell type. These processes include synthesis of lipids, metabolism of carbohydrates, and detoxification of drugs and poisons.

Enzymes of the smooth ER are important in the synthesis of lipids, including oils, phospholipids, and steroids. Among the steroids produced by the smooth ER in animal cells are the sex hormones of vertebrates and the various steroid hormones secreted by the adrenal glands. The cells that synthesize and secrete these hormones—in the testes and ovaries, for example—are rich in smooth ER, a structural feature that fits the function of these cells.

Other enzymes of the smooth ER help detoxify drugs and poisons, especially in liver cells. Detoxification usually involves adding hydroxyl groups to drug molecules, making them more soluble and easier to flush from the body. The sedative phenobarbital and other barbiturates are examples of drugs metabolized in this manner by smooth ER in liver cells. In fact, barbiturates, alcohol, and many other drugs induce the proliferation of smooth ER and its associated detoxification enzymes, thus increasing the rate of detoxification. This, in turn, increases tolerance to the drugs, meaning that higher doses are required to achieve a particular effect, such as sedation. Also, because some of the detoxification enzymes have relatively broad action, the proliferation of smooth ER in response to one drug can increase tolerance to other drugs as well. Barbiturate abuse, for example, can decrease the effectiveness of certain antibiotics and other useful drugs.

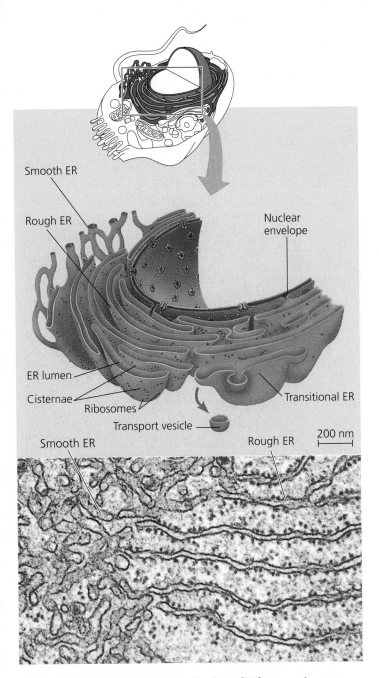

Smooth ER

Rough ER

Nuclear
envelope

ER lumen

Cisternae

Ribosomes

Transport vesicle

Smooth ER

Rough ER

200 nm

▲ **Figure 6.12 Endoplasmic reticulum (ER).** A membranous system of interconnected tubules and flattened sacs called cisternae, the ER is also continuous with the nuclear envelope. (The drawing is a cutaway view.) The membrane of the ER encloses a continuous compartment called the ER lumen (or cisternal space). Rough ER, which is studded on its outer surface with ribosomes, can be distinguished from smooth ER in the electron micrograph (TEM). Transport vesicles bud off from a region of the rough ER called transitional ER and travel to the Golgi apparatus and other destinations.

The smooth ER also stores calcium ions. In muscle cells, for example, a specialized smooth ER membrane pumps calcium ions from the cytosol into the ER lumen. When a muscle cell is stimulated by a nerve impulse, calcium ions rush back across the ER membrane into the cytosol and

trigger contraction of the muscle cell. In other cell types, calcium ion release from the smooth ER triggers different responses.

Functions of Rough ER

Many types of cells secrete proteins produced by ribosomes attached to rough ER. For example, certain pancreatic cells synthesize the protein insulin on the ER and secrete this hormone into the bloodstream. As a polypeptide chain grows from a bound ribosome, it is threaded into the ER lumen through a pore formed by a protein complex in the ER membrane. As the new protein enters the ER lumen, it folds into its native shape. Most secretory proteins are **glycoproteins**, proteins that have carbohydrates covalently bonded to them. The carbohydrates are attached to the proteins in the ER by specialized molecules built into the ER membrane.

After secretory proteins are formed, the ER membrane keeps them separate from proteins that are produced by free ribosomes and will remain in the cytosol. Secretory proteins depart from the ER wrapped in the membranes of vesicles that bud like bubbles from a specialized region called transitional ER (see Figure 6.12). Vesicles in transit from one part of the cell to another are called **transport vesicles**; we will discuss their fate shortly.

In addition to making secretory proteins, rough ER is a membrane factory for the cell; it grows in place by adding membrane proteins and phospholipids to its own membrane. As polypeptides destined to be membrane proteins grow from the ribosomes, they are inserted into the ER membrane itself and are anchored there by their hydrophobic portions. The rough ER also makes its own membrane phospholipids; enzymes built into the ER membrane assemble phospholipids from precursors in the cytosol. The ER membrane expands and is transferred in the form of transport vesicles to other components of the endomembrane system.

The Golgi Apparatus: Shipping and Receiving Center

After leaving the ER, many transport vesicles travel to the **Golgi apparatus**. We can think of the Golgi as a center of manufacturing, warehousing, sorting, and shipping. Here, products of the ER, such as proteins, are modified and stored and then sent to other destinations. Not surprisingly, the Golgi apparatus is especially extensive in cells specialized for secretion.

The Golgi apparatus consists of flattened membranous sacs—cisternae—looking like a stack of pita bread (**Figure 6.13**, on the next page). A cell may have many, even hundreds, of these stacks. The membrane of each cisterna in a stack separates its internal space from the cytosol. Vesicles concentrated in the vicinity of the Golgi apparatus are engaged in the transfer of material between parts of the Golgi and other structures.

Golgi
apparatus

cis face
("receiving" side of
Golgi apparatus)

6 Vesicles also transport certain proteins back to ER, their site of function.

1 Vesicles move from ER to Golgi.

2 Vesicles coalesce to form new *cis* Golgi cisternae.

Cisternae

3 Cisternal maturation: Golgi cisternae move in a *cis*-to-*trans* direction.

4 Vesicles form and leave Golgi, carrying specific proteins to other locations or to the plasma membrane for secretion.

5 Vesicles transport some proteins backward to less mature Golgi cisternae, where they function.

trans face ("shipping" side of Golgi apparatus)

0.1 μm

TEM of Golgi apparatus

▲ **Figure 6.13 The Golgi apparatus.** The Golgi apparatus consists of stacks of flattened sacs, or cisternae, which, unlike ER cisternae, are not physically connected. (The drawing is a cutaway view.) A Golgi stack receives and dispatches transport vesicles and the products they contain. A Golgi stack has a structural and functional polarity, with a *cis* face that receives vesicles containing ER products and a *trans* face that dispatches vesicles. The cisternal maturation model proposes that the Golgi cisternae themselves "mature," moving from the *cis* to the *trans* face while carrying some proteins along. In addition, some vesicles recycle enzymes that had been carried forward in moving cisternae, transporting them "backward" to a less mature region where their functions are needed.

A Golgi stack has a distinct structural polarity, with the membranes of cisternae on opposite sides of the stack differing in thickness and molecular composition. The two poles of a Golgi stack are referred to as the *cis* face and the *trans* face; these act, respectively, as the receiving and shipping departments of the Golgi apparatus. The *cis* face is usually located near the ER. Transport vesicles move material from the ER to the Golgi apparatus. A vesicle that buds from the ER can add its membrane and the contents of its lumen to the *cis* face by fusing with a Golgi membrane. The *trans* face gives rise to vesicles, which pinch off and travel to other sites.

Products of the ER are usually modified during their transit from the *cis* region to the *trans* region of the Golgi. For example, various Golgi enzymes modify the carbohydrate portions of glycoproteins. Carbohydrates are first added to proteins in the rough ER, often during the process of polypeptide synthesis. The carbohydrate on the resulting glycoprotein is then modified as it passes through the rest of the ER and the Golgi. The Golgi removes some sugar monomers and substitutes others, producing a large variety of carbohydrates. Membrane phospholipids may also be altered in the Golgi.

In addition to its finishing work, the Golgi apparatus manufactures certain macromolecules by itself. Many polysaccharides secreted by cells are Golgi products, including pectins and certain other noncellulose polysaccharides made by plant cells and incorporated along with cellulose into their cell walls. (Cellulose is made by enzymes located within the plasma membrane, which directly deposit this polysaccharide on the outside surface.) Like secretory proteins, non-protein Golgi products that will be secreted depart from the *trans* face of the Golgi inside transport vesicles that eventually fuse with the plasma membrane.

The Golgi manufactures and refines its products in stages, with different cisternae containing unique teams of enzymes. Until recently, biologists viewed the Golgi as a static structure, with products in various stages of processing transferred from one cisterna to the next by vesicles. While this may occur, recent research has given rise to a new model of the Golgi as a more dynamic structure. According to the model called the *cisternal maturation model*, the cisternae of the Golgi actually progress forward from the *cis* to the *trans* face of the Golgi, carrying and modifying their cargo as they move. Figure 6.13 shows the details of this model.

Before a Golgi stack dispatches its products by budding vesicles from the *trans* face, it sorts these products and targets them for various parts of the cell. Molecular identification tags, such as phosphate groups added to the Golgi products, aid in sorting by acting like ZIP codes on mailing labels. Finally, transport vesicles budded from the Golgi may have external molecules on their membranes that recognize "docking sites" on the surface of specific organelles or on the plasma membrane, thus targeting the vesicles appropriately.

Lysosomes: Digestive Compartments

A **lysosome** is a membranous sac of hydrolytic enzymes that an animal cell uses to digest macromolecules. Lysosomal enzymes work best in the acidic environment found in lysosomes. If a lysosome breaks open or leaks its contents, the released enzymes are not very active because the cytosol has a neutral pH. However, excessive leakage from a large number of lysosomes can destroy a cell by autodigestion.

Hydrolytic enzymes and lysosomal membrane are made by rough ER and then transferred to the Golgi apparatus for further processing. At least some lysosomes probably arise by budding from the *trans* face of the Golgi apparatus (see Figure 6.13). Proteins of the inner surface of the lysosomal membrane and the digestive enzymes themselves are thought to be spared from destruction by having three-dimensional shapes that protect vulnerable bonds from enzymatic attack.

Lysosomes carry out intracellular digestion in a variety of circumstances. Amoebas and many other protists eat by engulfing smaller organisms or other food particles, a process called **phagocytosis** (from the Greek *phagein*, to eat, and *kytos*, vessel, referring here to the cell). The *food vacuole* formed in this way then fuses with a lysosome, whose enzymes digest the food (**Figure 6.14a**, bottom). Digestion products, including simple sugars, amino acids, and other monomers, pass into the cytosol and become nutrients for the cell. Some human cells also carry out phagocytosis. Among them are macrophages, a type of white blood cell that helps defend the body by engulfing and destroying bacteria and other invaders (see Figure 6.14a, top, and Figure 6.33).

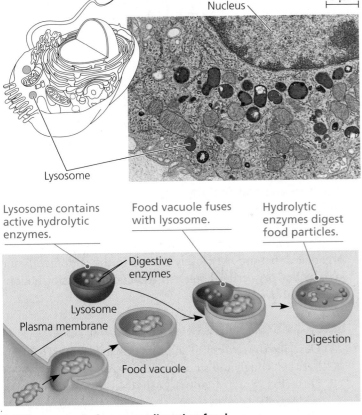

(a) **Phagocytosis: lysosome digesting food**

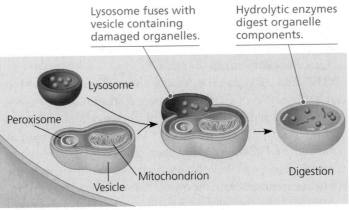

(b) **Autophagy: lysosome breaking down damaged organelles**

▲ **Figure 6.14 Lysosomes.** Lysosomes digest (hydrolyze) materials taken into the cell and recycle intracellular materials. **(a)** *Top:* In this macrophage (a type of white blood cell) from a rat, the lysosomes are very dark because of a stain that reacts with one of the products of digestion within the lysosome (TEM). Macrophages ingest bacteria and viruses and destroy them using lysosomes. *Bottom:* This diagram shows one lysosome fusing with a food vacuole during the process of phagocytosis by a protist. **(b)** *Top:* In the cytoplasm of this rat liver cell is a vesicle containing two disabled organelles; the vesicle will fuse with a lysosome in the process of autophagy (TEM). *Bottom:* This diagram shows fusion of such a vesicle with a lysosome. This type of vesicle has a double membrane of unknown origin. The outer membrane fuses with the lysosome, and the inner membrane is degraded along with the damaged organelles.

Lysosomes also use their hydrolytic enzymes to recycle the cell's own organic material, a process called *autophagy*. During autophagy, a damaged organelle or small amount of cytosol becomes surrounded by a double membrane, which is of unknown origin, and a lysosome fuses with the outer membrane of this vesicle (**Figure 6.14b**). The lysosomal enzymes dismantle the enclosed material, and the organic monomers are returned to the cytosol for reuse. With the help of lysosomes, the cell continually renews itself. A human liver cell, for example, recycles half of its macromolecules each week.

The cells of people with inherited lysosomal storage diseases lack a functioning hydrolytic enzyme normally present in lysosomes. The lysosomes become engorged with indigestible substrates, which begin to interfere with other cellular activities. In Tay-Sachs disease, for example, a lipid-digesting enzyme is missing or inactive, and the brain becomes impaired by an accumulation of lipids in the cells. Fortunately, lysosomal storage diseases are rare in the general population.

Vacuoles: Diverse Maintenance Compartments

Vacuoles are membrane-bounded vesicles whose functions vary in different kinds of cells. **Food vacuoles**, formed by phagocytosis, have already been mentioned (see Figure 6.14a). Many freshwater protists have **contractile vacuoles** that pump excess water out of the cell, thereby maintaining a suitable concentration of ions and molecules inside the cell (see Figure 7.14). In plants and fungi, which lack lysosomes, vacuoles carry out hydrolysis; however, they play other roles as well. Mature plant cells generally contain a large **central vacuole** (**Figure 6.15**). The central vacuole develops by the coalescence of smaller vacuoles, themselves derived from the endoplasmic reticulum and Golgi apparatus. The vacuole is thus an integral part of a plant cell's endomembrane system. Like all cellular membranes, the vacuolar membrane is selective in transporting solutes; as a result, the solution inside the central vacuole, called cell sap, differs in composition from the cytosol.

The plant cell's central vacuole is a versatile compartment. It can hold reserves of important organic compounds, such as the proteins stockpiled in the vacuoles of storage cells in seeds. It is also the plant cell's main repository of inorganic ions, such as potassium and chloride. Many plant cells use their vacuoles as disposal sites for metabolic by-products that would endanger the cell if they accumulated in the cytosol. Some vacuoles contain pigments that color the cells, such as the red and blue pigments of petals that help attract pollinating insects to flowers. Vacuoles may also help protect the plant against predators by containing compounds that are poisonous or unpalatable to animals. The vacuole has a major role in the growth of plant cells, which enlarge as their vacuoles absorb water, enabling the cell to become larger with a minimal investment in new cytoplasm. The cytosol often occupies only a thin layer between the central vacuole and the

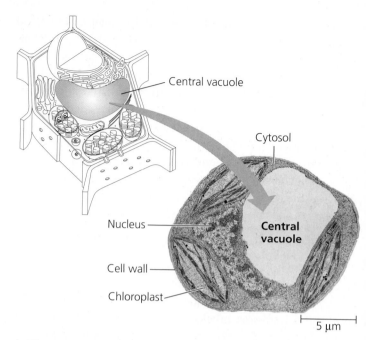

▲ **Figure 6.15 The plant cell vacuole.** The central vacuole is usually the largest compartment in a plant cell; the rest of the cytoplasm is generally confined to a narrow zone between the vacuolar membrane and the plasma membrane (TEM).

plasma membrane, so the ratio of plasma membrane surface to cytosolic volume is great, even for a large plant cell.

The Endomembrane System: *A Review*

Figure 6.16 reviews the endomembrane system, which shows the flow of membrane lipids and proteins through the various organelles. As the membrane moves from the ER to the Golgi and then elsewhere, its molecular composition and metabolic functions are modified, along with those of its contents. The endomembrane system is a complex and dynamic player in the cell's compartmental organization.

We'll continue our tour of the cell with some membranous organelles that are *not* closely related to the endomembrane system but play crucial roles in the energy transformations carried out by cells.

CONCEPT CHECK 6.4

1. Describe the structural and functional distinctions between rough and smooth ER.
2. Describe how transport vesicles integrate the endomembrane system.
3. **WHAT IF?** Imagine a protein that functions in the ER but requires modification in the Golgi apparatus before it can achieve that function. Describe the protein's path through the cell, starting with the mRNA molecule that specifies the protein.

For suggested answers, see Appendix A.

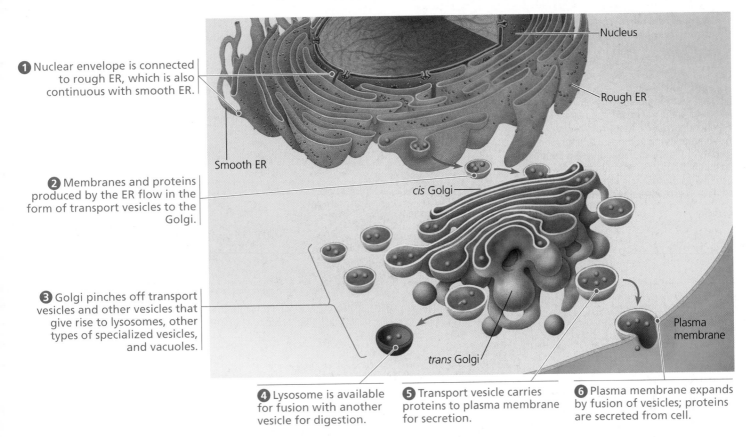

① Nuclear envelope is connected to rough ER, which is also continuous with smooth ER.

Nucleus

Rough ER

Smooth ER

② Membranes and proteins produced by the ER flow in the form of transport vesicles to the Golgi.

cis Golgi

③ Golgi pinches off transport vesicles and other vesicles that give rise to lysosomes, other types of specialized vesicles, and vacuoles.

Plasma membrane

trans Golgi

④ Lysosome is available for fusion with another vesicle for digestion.

⑤ Transport vesicle carries proteins to plasma membrane for secretion.

⑥ Plasma membrane expands by fusion of vesicles; proteins are secreted from cell.

▲ Figure 6.16 **Review: relationships among organelles of the endomembrane system.** The red arrows show some of the migration pathways for membranes and the materials they enclose.

CONCEPT 6.5

Mitochondria and chloroplasts change energy from one form to another

Organisms transform the energy they acquire from their surroundings. In eukaryotic cells, mitochondria and chloroplasts are the organelles that convert energy to forms that cells can use for work. **Mitochondria** (singular, *mitochondrion*) are the sites of cellular respiration, the metabolic process that generates ATP by extracting energy from sugars, fats, and other fuels with the help of oxygen. **Chloroplasts**, found in plants and algae, are the sites of photosynthesis. They convert solar energy to chemical energy by absorbing sunlight and using it to drive the synthesis of organic compounds such as sugars from carbon dioxide and water.

Although mitochondria and chloroplasts are enclosed by membranes, they are not part of the endomembrane system. In contrast to organelles of the endomembrane system, mitochondria have two membranes separating their innermost space from the cytosol, and chloroplasts typically have three. (Chloroplasts and related organelles in some algae have *four* membranes.) The membrane proteins of mitochondria and

chloroplasts are made not by ribosomes bound to the ER, but by free ribosomes in the cytosol and by ribosomes contained within these organelles themselves. These organelles also contain a small amount of DNA. It is this DNA that programs the synthesis of the proteins made on the organelle's ribosomes. (Proteins imported from the cytosol—most of the organelle's proteins—are programmed by nuclear DNA.) Mitochondria and chloroplasts are semiautonomous organelles that grow and reproduce within the cell. In Chapters 9 and 10, we will focus on how mitochondria and chloroplasts function. We will consider the evolution of these organelles in Chapter 25. Here we are concerned mainly with the structure of these energy transformers.

In this section, we will also consider the **peroxisome**, an oxidative organelle that is not part of the endomembrane system. Like mitochondria and chloroplasts, the peroxisome imports its proteins primarily from the cytosol.

Mitochondria: Chemical Energy Conversion

Mitochondria are found in nearly all eukaryotic cells, including those of plants, animals, fungi, and most protists. Even in exceptions, such as the human intestinal parasite *Giardia* and some other protists, recent studies have identified closely related organelles that probably evolved from mitochondria.

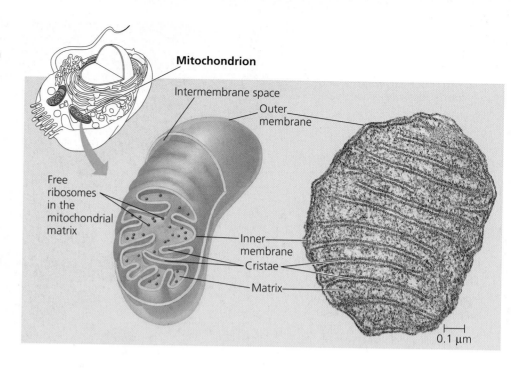

► **Figure 6.17 The mitochondrion, site of cellular respiration.** The inner and outer membranes of the mitochondrion are evident in the drawing and micrograph (TEM). The cristae are infoldings of the inner membrane, which increase its surface area. The cutaway drawing shows the two compartments bounded by the membranes: the intermembrane space and the mitochondrial matrix. Many respiratory enzymes are found in the inner membrane and the matrix. Free ribosomes are also present in the matrix. The DNA molecules, too small to be seen here, are usually circular and are attached to the inner mitochondrial membrane.

Some cells have a single large mitochondrion, but more often a cell has hundreds or even thousands of mitochondria; the number correlates with the cell's level of metabolic activity. For example, motile or contractile cells have proportionally more mitochondria per volume than less active cells. Mitochondria are about 1–10 μm long. Time-lapse films of living cells reveal mitochondria moving around, changing their shapes, and fusing or dividing in two, unlike the static cylinders seen in electron micrographs of dead cells.

The mitochondrion is enclosed by two membranes, each a phospholipid bilayer with a unique collection of embedded proteins **(Figure 6.17)**. The outer membrane is smooth, but the inner membrane is convoluted, with infoldings called **cristae**. The inner membrane divides the mitochondrion into two internal compartments. The first is the intermembrane space, the narrow region between the inner and outer membranes. The second compartment, the **mitochondrial matrix**, is enclosed by the inner membrane. The matrix contains many different enzymes as well as the mitochondrial DNA and ribosomes. Enzymes in the matrix catalyze some steps of cellular respiration. Other proteins that function in respiration, including the enzyme that makes ATP, are built into the inner membrane. As highly folded surfaces, the cristae give the inner mitochondrial membrane a large surface area, thus enhancing the productivity of cellular respiration. This is another example of structure fitting function.

Chloroplasts: Capture of Light Energy

The chloroplast is a specialized member of a family of closely related plant organelles called **plastids**. Some others are amyloplasts, colorless plastids that store starch (amylose),

particularly in roots and tubers, and chromoplasts, which have pigments that give fruits and flowers their orange and yellow hues. Chloroplasts contain the green pigment chlorophyll, along with enzymes and other molecules that function in the photosynthetic production of sugar. These lens-shaped organelles, measuring about 2 μm by 5 μm, are found in leaves and other green organs of plants and in algae **(Figure 6.18)**.

The contents of a chloroplast are partitioned from the cytosol by an envelope consisting of two membranes separated by a very narrow intermembrane space. Inside the chloroplast is another membranous system in the form of flattened, interconnected sacs called **thylakoids**. In some regions, thylakoids are stacked like poker chips; each stack is called a **granum** (plural, *grana*). The fluid outside the thylakoids is the **stroma**, which contains the chloroplast DNA and ribosomes as well as many enzymes. The membranes of the chloroplast divide the chloroplast space into three compartments: the intermembrane space, the stroma, and the thylakoid space. In Chapter 10, you will learn how this compartmental organization enables the chloroplast to convert light energy to chemical energy during photosynthesis.

As with mitochondria, the static and rigid appearance of chloroplasts in micrographs or schematic diagrams is not true to their dynamic behavior in the living cell. Their shapes are changeable, and they grow and occasionally pinch in two, reproducing themselves. They are mobile and, with mitochondria and other organelles, move around the cell along tracks of the cytoskeleton, a structural network we will consider later in this chapter.

Peroxisomes: Oxidation

The peroxisome is a specialized metabolic compartment that is bounded by a single membrane **(Figure 6.19)**. Peroxisomes

◄ **Figure 6.18 The chloroplast, site of photosynthesis.** A typical chloroplast is enclosed by two membranes separated by a narrow intermembrane space that constitutes an outer compartment. The inner membrane encloses a second compartment containing the fluid called stroma. The stroma surrounds a third compartment, the thylakoid space, delineated by the thylakoid membrane. Interconnected thylakoid sacs (thylakoids) are stacked to form structures called grana (singular, *granum*), which are further connected by thin tubules between individual thylakoids. Photosynthetic enzymes are embedded in the thylakoid membranes. Free ribosomes are present in the stroma, along with copies of the chloroplast genome (DNA), too small to be seen here (TEM).

contain enzymes that transfer hydrogen from various substrates to oxygen (O_2), producing hydrogen peroxide (H_2O_2) as a by-product, from which the organelle derives its name. These reactions may have many different functions. Some peroxisomes use oxygen to break fatty acids down into smaller molecules that can then be transported to mitochondria, where they are used as fuel for cellular respiration. Peroxisomes in the liver detoxify alcohol and other harmful compounds by transferring hydrogen from the poisons to oxygen. The H_2O_2 formed by peroxisomes is itself toxic, but the organelle also contains an enzyme that converts H_2O_2 to water. This is an excellent example of how the cell's compartmental structure is crucial to its functions: The enzymes that produce hydrogen peroxide and those that dispose of this toxic compound are sequestered in the same space, away from other cellular components that could otherwise be damaged.

Specialized peroxisomes called *glyoxysomes* are found in the fat-storing tissues of plant seeds. These organelles contain enzymes that initiate the conversion of fatty acids to sugar, which the emerging seedling uses as a source of energy and carbon until it can produce its own sugar by photosynthesis.

Unlike lysosomes, peroxisomes do not bud from the endomembrane system. They grow larger by incorporating proteins made primarily in the cytosol, lipids made in the ER, and lipids synthesized within the peroxisome itself. Peroxisomes may increase in number by splitting in two when they reach a certain size.

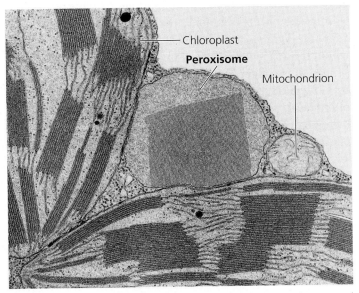

▲ **Figure 6.19 A peroxisome.** Peroxisomes are roughly spherical and often have a granular or crystalline core that is thought to be a dense collection of enzyme molecules. This peroxisome is in a leaf cell (TEM). Notice its proximity to two chloroplasts and a mitochondrion. These organelles cooperate with peroxisomes in certain metabolic functions.

CONCEPT CHECK **6.5**

1. Describe two common characteristics of chloroplasts and mitochondria. Consider both function and membrane structure.
2. **WHAT IF?** A classmate proposes that mitochondria, chloroplasts, and peroxisomes should be classified in the endomembrane system. Argue against the proposal.

For suggested answers, see Appendix A.

CONCEPT 6.6

The cytoskeleton is a network of fibers that organizes structures and activities in the cell

In the early days of electron microscopy, biologists thought that the organelles of a eukaryotic cell floated freely in the cytosol. But improvements in both light microscopy and electron microscopy have revealed the **cytoskeleton**, a network of fibers extending throughout the cytoplasm (**Figure 6.20**). The cytoskeleton, which plays a major role in organizing the structures and activities of the cell, is composed of three types of molecular structures: microtubules, microfilaments, and intermediate filaments.

Roles of the Cytoskeleton: Support, Motility, and Regulation

The most obvious function of the cytoskeleton is to give mechanical support to the cell and maintain its shape. This is especially important for animal cells, which lack walls. The remarkable strength and resilience of the cytoskeleton as a whole is based on its architecture. Like a geodesic dome, the cytoskeleton is stabilized by a balance between opposing forces exerted by its elements. And just as the skeleton of an animal helps fix the positions of other body parts, the cytoskeleton provides anchorage for many organelles and even cytosolic enzyme molecules. The cytoskeleton is more dynamic than an animal skeleton, however. It can be quickly dismantled in one part of the cell and reassembled in a new location, changing the shape of the cell.

Several types of cell motility (movement) also involve the cytoskeleton. The term *cell motility* encompasses both changes in cell location and more limited movements of parts of the cell. Cell motility generally requires the interaction of the cytoskeleton with **motor proteins**. Examples of such cell motility

(a) Motor proteins that attach to receptors on vesicles can "walk" the vesicles along microtubules or, in some cases, microfilaments.

(b) Vesicles containing neurotransmitters migrate to the tips of nerve cell axons via the mechanism in (a). In this SEM of a squid giant axon, two vesicles can be seen moving along a microtubule. (A separate part of the experiment provided the evidence that they were in fact moving.)

▲ **Figure 6.21 Motor proteins and the cytoskeleton.**

abound. Cytoskeletal elements and motor proteins work together with plasma membrane molecules to allow whole cells to move along fibers outside the cell. Motor proteins bring about the bending of cilia and flagella by gripping microtubules within those organelles and sliding them against each other. A similar mechanism involving microfilaments causes muscle cells to contract. Inside the cell, vesicles and other organelles often travel to their destinations along "monorails" provided by the cytoskeleton. For example, this is how vesicles containing neurotransmitter molecules migrate to the tips of axons, the long extensions of nerve cells that release these molecules as chemical signals to adjacent nerve cells (**Figure 6.21**). The vesicles that bud off from the ER travel to the Golgi along cytoskeletal tracks. The cytoskeleton also manipulates the plasma membrane in a way that forms food vacuoles or other phagocytic vesicles. And the streaming of cytoplasm that circulates materials within many large plant cells is yet another kind of cellular movement brought about by the cytoskeleton.

The cytoskeleton is also involved in regulating biochemical activities in the cell in response to mechanical stimulation. Forces exerted by extracellular molecules via cell-surface proteins are apparently transmitted into the cell by cytoskeletal elements, and the forces may even reach the nucleus. In one experiment, investigators used a micromanipulation device to

▲ **Figure 6.20 The cytoskeleton.** In this TEM, prepared by a method known as deep-etching, the thicker, hollow microtubules and the thinner, solid microfilaments are visible. A third component of the cytoskeleton, intermediate filaments, is not evident here.

Table 6.1 The Structure and Function of the Cytoskeleton

Property	Microtubules (Tubulin Polymers)	Microfilaments (Actin Filaments)	Intermediate Filaments
Structure	Hollow tubes; wall consists of 13 columns of tubulin molecules	Two intertwined strands of actin, each a polymer of actin subunits	Fibrous proteins supercoiled into thicker cables
Diameter	25 nm with 15-nm lumen	7 nm	8–12 nm
Protein subunits	Tubulin, a dimer consisting of α-tubulin and β-tubulin	Actin	One of several different proteins of the keratin family, depending on cell type
Main functions	Maintenance of cell shape (compression-resisting "girders") Cell motility (as in cilia or flagella) Chromosome movements in cell division Organelle movements	Maintenance of cell shape (tension-bearing elements) Changes in cell shape Muscle contraction Cytoplasmic streaming Cell motility (as in pseudopodia) Cell division (cleavage furrow formation)	Maintenance of cell shape (tension-bearing elements) Anchorage of nucleus and certain other organelles Formation of nuclear lamina

Micrographs of fibroblasts, a favorite cell type for cell biology studies. Each has been experimentally treated to fluorescently tag the structure of interest.

10 μm

10 μm

5 μm

Column of tubulin dimers
25 nm
α β Tubulin dimer

Actin subunit
7 nm

Keratin proteins
Fibrous subunit (keratins coiled together)
8–12 nm

pull on certain plasma membrane proteins attached to the cytoskeleton. A video microscope captured the almost instantaneous rearrangements of nucleoli and other structures in the nucleus. In this way, cytoskeletal transmission of naturally occurring mechanical signals may help regulate and coordinate the cell's response.

Components of the Cytoskeleton

Now let's look more closely at the three main types of fibers that make up the cytoskeleton **(Table 6.1)**. *Microtubules* are the thickest of the three types; *microfilaments* (also called actin filaments) are the thinnest; and *intermediate filaments* are fibers with diameters in a middle range.

Microtubules

All eukaryotic cells have **microtubules**, hollow rods measuring about 25 nm in diameter and from 200 nm to 25 μm in length. The wall of the hollow tube is constructed from a globular protein called tubulin. Each tubulin protein is a *dimer*, a molecule made up of two subunits. A tubulin dimer consists of two slightly different polypeptides, α-tubulin and β-tubulin. Microtubules grow in length by adding tubulin dimers; they can also be disassembled and their tubulin used to build microtubules elsewhere in the cell. Because of the architecture of a microtubule, its two ends are slightly different. One end can accumulate or release tubulin dimers at a much higher rate than the other, thus growing and shrinking significantly during cellular activities. (This is called the "plus end," not because it can only add tubulin proteins but because it's the end where both "on" and "off" rates are much higher.)

Microtubules shape and support the cell and also serve as tracks along which organelles equipped with motor proteins can move. To mention an example different from the one in Figure 6.21, microtubules guide secretory vesicles from the Golgi apparatus to the plasma membrane. Microtubules also separate chromosomes during cell division (see Chapter 12).

Centrosomes and Centrioles In animal cells, microtubules grow out from a **centrosome**, a region that is often located near the nucleus and is considered a "microtubule-organizing center." These microtubules function as compression-resisting girders of the cytoskeleton. Within the centrosome are a pair of **centrioles**, each composed of nine sets of triplet microtubules arranged in a ring **(Figure 6.22)**. Before an animal cell divides, the centrioles replicate. Although centrosomes with centrioles may help organize microtubule assembly in animal cells, they are not essential for this function in all eukaryotes; yeast cells and plant cells lack centrosomes with centrioles but have well-organized microtubules. Clearly, other microtubule-organizing centers must play the role of centrosomes in these cells.

Cilia and Flagella In eukaryotes, a specialized arrangement of microtubules is responsible for the beating of **flagella** (singular, *flagellum*) and **cilia** (singular, *cilium*), microtubule-containing extensions that project from some cells. Many unicellular eukaryotes are propelled through water by cilia or flagella that act as locomotor appendages, and the sperm of animals, algae, and some plants have flagella. When cilia or flagella extend from cells that are held in place as part of a tissue layer, they can move fluid over the surface of the tissue. For example, the ciliated lining of the trachea (windpipe) sweeps mucus containing trapped debris out of the lungs (see Figure 6.4). In a woman's reproductive tract, the cilia lining the oviducts help move an egg toward the uterus.

Motile cilia usually occur in large numbers on the cell surface. They are about 0.25 μm in diameter and about 2–20 μm long. Flagella are the same diameter but longer, 10–200 μm. Also, flagella are usually limited to just one or a few per cell.

Flagella and cilia differ in their beating patterns **(Figure 6.23)**. A flagellum has an undulating motion that generates force in the same direction as the flagellum's axis. In contrast, cilia work more like oars, with alternating power and recovery strokes generating force in a direction perpendicular to the cilium's axis, much as the oars of a crew boat extend outward at right angles to the boat's forward movement.

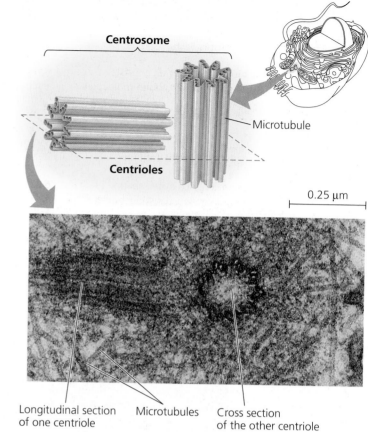

▲ **Figure 6.22 Centrosome containing a pair of centrioles.** Most animal cells have a centrosome, a region near the nucleus where the cell's microtubules are initiated. Within the centrosome is a pair of centrioles, each about 250 nm (0.25 μm) in diameter. The two centrioles are at right angles to each other, and each is made up of nine sets of three microtubules. The blue portions of the drawing represent nontubulin proteins that connect the microtubule triplets (TEM).

? *How many microtubules are in a centrosome? In the drawing, circle and label one microtubule and describe its structure.*

A cilium may also act as a signal-receiving "antenna" for the cell. Cilia that have this function are generally nonmotile, and there is only one per cell. (In fact, in vertebrate animals, almost all cells seem to have such a cilium, which is called a *primary cilium.*) Membrane proteins on this kind of cilium transmit molecular signals from the cell's environment to its interior, triggering signaling pathways that may lead to changes in the cell's activities. Cilia-based signaling appears to be crucial to brain function and to embryonic development.

Though different in length, number per cell, and beating pattern, motile cilia and flagella share a common ultrastructure. Each has a core of microtubules sheathed in an extension of the plasma membrane **(Figure 6.24)**. Nine doublets of microtubules, the members of each pair sharing part of their walls, are arranged in a ring. In the center of the ring are two single microtubules. This arrangement, referred to as the "9 + 2" pattern, is found in nearly all eukaryotic flagella and motile cilia. (Nonmotile primary cilia have a "9 + 0" pattern, lacking the central pair of microtubules.) The microtubule assembly of a cilium or

▶ **Figure 6.23**
A comparison of the beating of flagella and cilia.

(a) Motion of flagella. A flagellum usually undulates, its snakelike motion driving a cell in the same direction as the axis of the flagellum. Propulsion of a human sperm cell is an example of flagellate locomotion (LM).

Direction of swimming

5 μm

(b) Motion of cilia. Cilia have a back-and-forth motion. The rapid power stroke moves the cell in a direction perpendicular to the axis of the cilium. Then, during the slower recovery stroke, the cilium bends and sweeps sideways, closer to the surface. A dense nap of cilia, beating at a rate of about 40 to 60 strokes a second, covers this *Colpidium*, a freshwater protozoan (colorized SEM).

Direction of organism's movement

Power stroke   Recovery stroke

15 μm

0.1 μm

Outer microtubule doublet

Plasma membrane

Dynein proteins

Central microtubule

Radial spoke

Protein cross-linking outer doublets

Microtubules

Plasma membrane

Basal body

0.5 μm

(a) A longitudinal section of a motile cilium shows microtubules running the length of the structure (TEM).

(b) A cross section through a motile cilium shows the "9 + 2" arrangement of microtubules (TEM). The outer microtubule doublets and the two central microtubules are held together by flexible cross-linking proteins (blue in art), including the radial spokes. The doublets also have attached motor proteins called dyneins (red in art). In the drawing, the plasma membrane has been peeled away to reveal a longitudinal view of two of the doublets.

0.1 μm

Triplet

(c) Basal body: The nine outer doublets of a cilium or flagellum extend into the basal body, where each doublet joins another microtubule to form a ring of nine triplets. Each triplet is connected to the next triplet and to the center by nontubulin proteins (the blue lines in diagram). The two central microtubules are not shown because they terminate above the basal body (TEM).

Cross section of basal body

▲ **Figure 6.24 Ultrastructure of a eukaryotic flagellum or motile cilium.**

flagellum is anchored in the cell by a **basal body**, which is structurally very similar to a centriole. In fact, in many animals (including humans), the basal body of the fertilizing sperm's flagellum enters the egg and becomes a centriole.

In flagella and motile cilia, flexible cross-linking proteins, evenly spaced along the length of the cilium or flagellum, connect the outer doublets to each other and to the two central microtubules. Each outer doublet also has pairs of protruding proteins spaced along its length and reaching toward the neighboring doublet; these are large motor proteins called **dyneins**, each composed of several polypeptides. Dyneins are responsible for the bending movements of the organelle. A dynein molcule performs a complex cycle of movements caused by changes in the shape of the protein, with ATP providing the energy for these changes (**Figure 6.25**).

The mechanics of dynein-based bending involve a process that resembles walking. A typical dynein protein has two "feet" that "walk" along the microtubule of the adjacent doublet, one foot maintaining contact while the other releases and reattaches one step further along the microtubule. Without any restraints on the movement of the microtubule doublets, one doublet would continue to "walk" along and slide past the surface of the other, elongating the cilium or flagellum rather than bending it (see Figure 6.25a). For lateral movement of a cilium or flagellum, the dynein "walking" must have something to pull against, as when the muscles in your leg pull against your bones to move your knee. In cilia and flagella, the microtubule doublets seem to be held in place by the cross-linking proteins just inside the outer doublets and by the radial spokes and other structural elements. Thus, neighboring doublets cannot slide past each other very far. Instead, the forces exerted by dynein "walking" cause the doublets to curve, bending the cilium or flagellum (see Figure 6.25b and c).

Microfilaments (Actin Filaments)

Microfilaments are solid rods about 7 nm in diameter. They are also called actin filaments because they are built from molecules of **actin**, a globular protein. A microfilament is a twisted double chain of actin subunits (see Table 6.1). Besides occurring as linear filaments, microfilaments can form structural networks, due to the presence of proteins that bind along the side of an actin filament and allow a new filament to extend as a branch. Microfilaments seem to be present in all eukaryotic cells.

In contrast to the compression-resisting role of microtubules, the structural role of microfilaments in the cytoskeleton is to bear tension (pulling forces). A three-dimensional network formed by microfilaments just inside the plasma membrane (*cortical microfilaments*) helps support the cell's shape. This network gives the outer cytoplasmic layer of a cell, called the **cortex**, the semisolid consistency of a gel, in contrast with the more fluid (sol) state of the interior cytoplasm.

(a) Effect of unrestrained dynein movement. If a cilium or flagellum had no cross-linking proteins, the two feet of each dynein along one doublet (powered by ATP) would alternately grip and release the adjacent doublet. This "walking" motion would push the adjacent doublet up. Instead of bending, the doublets would slide past each other.

(b) Effect of cross-linking proteins. In a cilium or flagellum, two adjacent doublets cannot slide far because they are physically restrained by proteins, so they bend. (Only two of the nine outer doublets in Figure 6.24b are shown here.)

(c) Wavelike motion. Synchronized cycles of movement of many dyneins probably cause a bend to begin at the base of the cilium or flagellum and move outward toward the tip. Many successive bends, such as the ones shown here to the left and right, result in a wavelike motion. In this diagram, the two central microtubules and the cross-linking proteins are not shown.

▲ **Figure 6.25 How dynein "walking" moves flagella and cilia.**

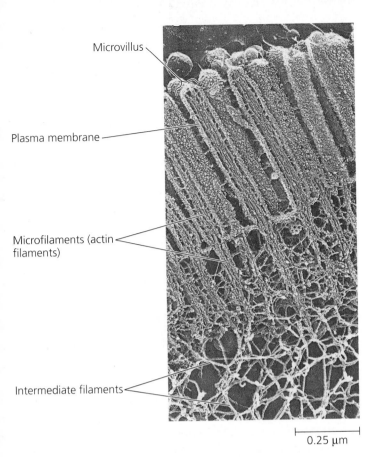

Microvillus

Plasma membrane

Microfilaments (actin filaments)

Intermediate filaments

0.25 μm

▲ **Figure 6.26 A structural role of microfilaments.** The surface area of this nutrient-absorbing intestinal cell is increased by its many microvilli (singular, *microvillus*), cellular extensions reinforced by bundles of microfilaments. These actin filaments are anchored to a network of intermediate filaments (TEM).

In animal cells specialized for transporting materials across the plasma membrane, such as intestinal cells, bundles of microfilaments make up the core of microvilli, the previously mentioned delicate projections that increase the cell surface area there **(Figure 6.26)**.

Microfilaments are well known for their role in cell motility, particularly as part of the contractile apparatus of muscle cells. Thousands of actin filaments are arranged parallel to one another along the length of a muscle cell, interdigitated with thicker filaments made of a protein called **myosin** **(Figure 6.27a)**. Like dynein when it interacts with microtubules, myosin acts as a microfilament-based motor protein by means of projections that "walk" along the actin filaments. Contraction of the muscle cell results from the actin and myosin filaments sliding past one another in this way, shortening the cell. In other kinds of cells, actin filaments are associated with myosin in miniature and less elaborate versions of the arrangement in muscle cells. These actin-myosin aggregates are responsible for localized contractions of cells. For example, a contracting belt of microfilaments forms a cleavage furrow that pinches a dividing animal cell into two daughter cells.

Muscle cell

Actin filament

Myosin filament
Myosin arm

(a) Myosin motors in muscle cell contraction. The "walking" of myosin arms drives the parallel myosin and actin filaments past each other so that the actin filaments approach each other in the middle (red arrows). This shortens the muscle cell. Muscle contraction involves the shortening of many muscle cells at the same time.

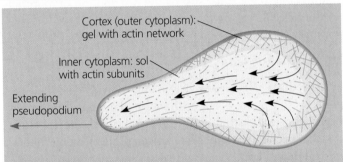

Cortex (outer cytoplasm): gel with actin network

Inner cytoplasm: sol with actin subunits

Extending pseudopodium

(b) Amoeboid movement. Interaction of actin filaments with myosin near the cell's trailing end (at right) squeezes the interior, more fluid cytoplasm forward (to the left) into the pseudopodium.

Nonmoving cortical cytoplasm (gel)

Chloroplast

Streaming cytoplasm (sol)

Vacuole

Parallel actin filaments

Cell wall

(c) Cytoplasmic streaming in plant cells. A layer of cytoplasm cycles around the cell, moving over a carpet of parallel actin filaments. Myosin motors attached to organelles in the fluid cytosol may drive the streaming by interacting with the actin.

▲ **Figure 6.27 Microfilaments and motility.** In the three examples shown in this figure, cell nuclei and most other organelles have been omitted for clarity.

Localized contraction brought about by actin and myosin also plays a role in amoeboid movement **(Figure 6.27b)**, in which a cell such as an amoeba crawls along a surface by extending and flowing into cellular extensions called **pseudopodia** (from the Greek *pseudes*, false, and *pod*, foot).

Pseudopodia extend and contract through the reversible assembly of actin subunits into microfilaments and of microfilaments into networks that convert cytoplasm from a sol to a gel. According to a widely accepted model, filaments near the cell's trailing end interact with myosin, causing contraction. Like squeezing on a toothpaste tube, this contraction forces the interior, more fluid cytoplasm into the pseudopodium, where the actin network has been weakened. The pseudopodium extends until the actin reassembles into a network. Amoebas are not the only cells that move by crawling; so do many cells in the animal body, including some white blood cells.

In plant cells, both actin-myosin interactions and sol-gel transformations brought about by actin may be involved in **cytoplasmic streaming**, a circular flow of cytoplasm within cells **(Figure 6.27c)**. This movement, which is especially common in large plant cells, speeds the distribution of materials within the cell.

Intermediate Filaments

Intermediate filaments are named for their diameter, which, at 8–12 nm, is larger than the diameter of microfilaments but smaller than that of microtubules (see Table 6.1, p. 113). Specialized for bearing tension (like microfilaments), intermediate filaments are a diverse class of cytoskeletal elements. Each type is constructed from a different molecular subunit belonging to a family of proteins whose members include the keratins. Microtubules and microfilaments, in contrast, are consistent in diameter and composition in all eukaryotic cells.

Intermediate filaments are more permanent fixtures of cells than are microfilaments and microtubules, which are often disassembled and reassembled in various parts of a cell. Even after cells die, intermediate filament networks often persist; for example, the outer layer of our skin consists of dead skin cells full of keratin proteins. Chemical treatments that remove microfilaments and microtubules from the cytoplasm of living cells leave a web of intermediate filaments that retains its original shape. Such experiments suggest that intermediate filaments are especially important in reinforcing the shape of a cell and fixing the position of certain organelles. For instance, the nucleus commonly sits within a cage made of intermediate filaments, fixed in location by branches of the filaments that extend into the cytoplasm. Other intermediate filaments make up the nuclear lamina that lines the interior of the nuclear envelope (see Figure 6.10). In cases where the shape of the entire cell is correlated with function, intermediate filaments support that shape. A case in point is the long extensions (axons) of nerve cells that transmit impulses, which are strengthened by one class of intermediate filament. Thus, the various kinds of intermediate filaments may function as the framework of the entire cytoskeleton.

CONCEPT 6.7

Extracellular components and connections between cells help coordinate cellular activities

Having crisscrossed the interior of the cell to explore its interior components, we complete our tour of the cell by returning to the surface of this microscopic world, where there are additional structures with important functions. The plasma membrane is usually regarded as the boundary of the living cell, but most cells synthesize and secrete materials that are external to the plasma membrane. Although these materials and the structures they form are outside the cell, their study is central to cell biology because they are involved in a great many cellular functions.

Cell Walls of Plants

The **cell wall** is an extracellular structure of plant cells that distinguishes them from animal cells. The wall protects the plant cell, maintains its shape, and prevents excessive uptake of water. On the level of the whole plant, the strong walls of specialized cells hold the plant up against the force of gravity. Prokaryotes, fungi, and some protists also have cell walls, but we will postpone discussion of them until Unit Five.

Plant cell walls are much thicker than the plasma membrane, ranging from 0.1 µm to several micrometers. The exact chemical composition of the wall varies from species to species and even from one cell type to another in the same plant, but the basic design of the wall is consistent. Microfibrils made of the polysaccharide cellulose (see Figure 5.8) are synthesized by an enzyme called cellulose synthase and secreted to the extracellular space, where they become embedded in a matrix of other polysaccharides and proteins. This combination of materials, strong fibers in a "ground substance" (matrix), is the same basic architectural design found in steel-reinforced concrete and in fiberglass.

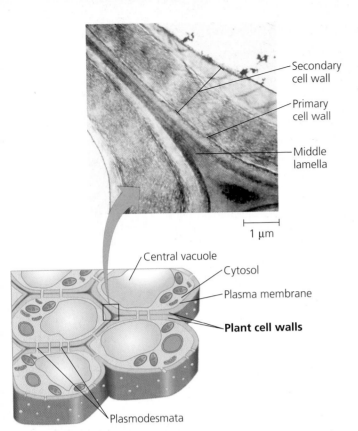

Secondary cell wall

Primary cell wall

Middle lamella

1 μm

Central vacuole

Cytosol

Plasma membrane

Plant cell walls

Plasmodesmata

▲ **Figure 6.28 Plant cell walls.** The drawing shows several cells, each with a large vacuole, a nucleus, and several chloroplasts and mitochondria. The transmission electron micrograph (TEM) shows the cell walls where two cells come together. The multilayered partition between plant cells consists of adjoining walls individually secreted by the cells.

A young plant cell first secretes a relatively thin and flexible wall called the **primary cell wall (Figure 6.28)**. In actively growing cells, the cellulose fibrils are oriented at right angles to the direction of cell expansion, possibly affecting the growth pattern. David Ehrhardt and colleagues investigated the role of microtubules in orienting these fibrils **(Figure 6.29)**. Their observations strongly supported the idea that microtubules in the cell cortex guide cellulose synthase as it synthesizes and deposits the fibrils. By orienting cellulose deposition, microtubules thus affect the growth pattern of the cells.

Between primary walls of adjacent cells is the **middle lamella**, a thin layer rich in sticky polysaccharides called pectins. The middle lamella glues adjacent cells together (pectin is used as a thickening agent in jams and jellies). When the cell matures and stops growing, it strengthens its wall. Some plant cells do this simply by secreting hardening substances into the primary wall. Other cells add a **secondary cell wall** between the plasma membrane and the primary wall. The secondary wall, often deposited in several laminated layers, has a strong and durable matrix that affords the cell protection and support. Wood, for example, consists mainly of secondary walls. Plant cell walls are commonly perforated by channels be-

▼ **Figure 6.29 Inquiry**

What role do microtubules play in orienting deposition of cellulose in cell walls?

EXPERIMENT Previous experiments on preserved plant tissues had shown alignment of microtubules in the cell cortex with cellulose fibrils in the cell wall. Also, drugs that disrupted microtubules were observed to cause disoriented cellulose fibrils. To further investigate the possible role of cortical microtubules in guiding fibril deposition, David Ehrhardt and colleagues at Stanford University used a type of confocal microscopy to study cell wall deposition in living cells. In these cells, they labeled both cellulose synthase and microtubules with fluorescent markers and observed them over time.

RESULTS The path of cellulose synthase movement and the positions of existing microtubules coincided highly over time. The fluorescent micrographs below represent an average of five images, taken 10 seconds apart. The labeling molecules caused cellulose synthase to fluoresce green and the microtubules to fluoresce red. The arrowheads indicate prominent areas where the two are seen to align.

10 μm

Distribution of cellulose synthase over time

Distribution of microtubules over time

CONCLUSION The organization of microtubules appears to directly guide the path of cellulose synthase as it lays down cellulose, thus determining the orientation of cellulose fibrils.

SOURCE A. R. Paradez et al., Visualization of cellulose synthase demonstrates functional association with microtubules, *Science* 312:1491–1495 (2006).

WHAT IF? In a second experiment, the researchers exposed the plant cells to blue light, previously shown to cause reorientation of microtubules. What events would you predict would follow blue light exposure?

tween adjacent cells called plasmodesmata (see Figure 6.28), which will be discussed shortly.

The Extracellular Matrix (ECM) of Animal Cells

Although animal cells lack walls akin to those of plant cells, they do have an elaborate **extracellular matrix (ECM) (Figure 6.30,** on the next page). The main ingredients of the ECM are glycoproteins secreted by the cells. (Recall that glycoproteins are proteins with covalently bonded carbohydrate, usually short chains of sugars.) The most abundant glycoprotein in the ECM of most animal cells is **collagen**, which forms strong fibers outside the

▲ **Figure 6.30 Extracellular matrix (ECM) of an animal cell.** The molecular composition and structure of the ECM varies from one cell type to another. In this example, three different types of glycoproteins are present: proteoglycans, collagen, and fibronectin.

cells (see Figure 5.21). In fact, collagen accounts for about 40% of the total protein in the human body. The collagen fibers are embedded in a network woven from **proteoglycans**. A proteoglycan molecule consists of a small core protein with many carbohydrate chains covalently attached, so that it may be up to 95% carbohydrate. Large proteoglycan complexes can form when hundreds of proteoglycans become noncovalently attached to a single long polysaccharide molecule, as shown in Figure 6.30. Some cells are attached to the ECM by still other ECM glycoproteins, such as **fibronectin**. Fibronectin and other ECM proteins bind to cell surface receptor proteins called **integrins** that are built into the plasma membrane. Integrins span the membrane and bind on their cytoplasmic side to associated proteins attached to microfilaments of the cytoskeleton. The name *integrin* is based on the word *integrate*: Integrins are in a position to transmit signals between the ECM and the cytoskeleton and thus to integrate changes occurring outside and inside the cell.

Current research on fibronectin, other ECM molecules, and integrins is revealing the influential role of the extracellular matrix in the lives of cells. By communicating with a cell through integrins, the ECM can regulate a cell's behavior. For example, some cells in a developing embryo migrate along specific pathways by matching the orientation of their microfilaments to the "grain" of fibers in the extracellular matrix. Researchers are also learning that the extracellular matrix around a cell can influence the activity of genes in the nucleus. Information about the ECM probably reaches the nucleus by a combination of mechanical and chemical signaling pathways. Mechanical signaling involves fibronectin, integrins, and microfilaments of the cytoskeleton. Changes in the cytoskeleton may in turn trigger

chemical signaling pathways inside the cell, leading to changes in the set of proteins being made by the cell and therefore changes in the cell's function. In this way, the extracellular matrix of a particular tissue may help coordinate the behavior of all the cells within that tissue. Direct connections between cells also function in this coordination, as we discuss next.

Intercellular Junctions

Cells in an animal or plant are organized into tissues, organs, and organ systems. Cells often adhere, interact, and communicate through direct physical contact.

Plasmodesmata in Plant Cells

It might seem that the nonliving cell walls of plants would isolate cells from one another. But in fact, as shown in **Figure 6.31**, cell walls are perforated with channels called **plasmodesmata**

▲ **Figure 6.31 Plasmodesmata between plant cells.** The cytoplasm of one plant cell is continuous with the cytoplasm of its neighbors via plasmodesmata, channels through the cell walls (TEM).

(singular, *plasmodesma*; from the Greek *desmos*, to bind). Cytosol passes through the plasmodesmata and connects the chemical environments of adjacent cells. These connections unify most of the plant into one living continuum. The plasma membranes of adjacent cells line the channel of each plasmodesma and thus are continuous. Water and small solutes can pass freely from cell to cell, and recent experiments have shown that in some circumstances, certain proteins and RNA molecules can also do this (see Concept 36.6). The macromolecules transported to neighboring cells seem to reach the plasmodesmata by moving along fibers of the cytoskeleton.

Tight Junctions, Desmosomes, and Gap Junctions in Animal Cells

In animals, there are three main types of intercellular junctions: *tight junctions*, *desmosomes*, and *gap junctions* (the latter of which are most like the plasmodesmata of plants). All three types of intercellular junctions are especially common in epithelial tissue, which lines the external and internal surfaces of the body. **Figure 6.32** uses epithelial cells of the intestinal lining to illustrate these junctions; you should study this figure before moving on.

▼ **Figure 6.32**

Exploring Intercellular Junctions in Animal Tissues

Tight junctions prevent fluid from moving across a layer of cells

Tight junction

Tight junction

Intermediate filaments

Desmosome

Gap junction

Space between cells

Plasma membranes of adjacent cells

Extracellular matrix

Tight junction

0.5 µm

1 µm

0.1 µm

Tight Junctions

At **tight junctions**, the plasma membranes of neighboring cells are very tightly pressed against each other, bound together by specific proteins (purple). Forming continuous seals around the cells, tight junctions prevent leakage of extracellular fluid across a layer of epithelial cells. For example, tight junctions between skin cells make us watertight by preventing leakage between cells in our sweat glands.

Desmosomes

Desmosomes (also called *anchoring junctions*) function like rivets, fastening cells together into strong sheets. Intermediate filaments made of sturdy keratin proteins anchor desmosomes in the cytoplasm. Desmosomes attach muscle cells to each other in a muscle. Some "muscle tears" involve the rupture of desmosomes.

Gap Junctions

Gap junctions (also called *communicating junctions*) provide cytoplasmic channels from one cell to an adjacent cell and in this way are similar in their function to the plasmodesmata in plants. Gap junctions consist of membrane proteins that surround a pore through which ions, sugars, amino acids, and other small molecules may pass. Gap junctions are necessary for communication between cells in many types of tissues, including heart muscle, and in animal embryos.

▲ **Figure 6.33 The emergence of cellular functions.** The ability of this macrophage (brown) to recognize, apprehend, and destroy bacteria (yellow) is a coordinated activity of the whole cell. Its cytoskeleton, lysosomes, and plasma membrane are among the components that function in phagocytosis (colorized SEM).

The Cell: A Living Unit Greater Than the Sum of Its Parts

From our panoramic view of the cell's overall compartmental organization to our close-up inspection of each organelle's architecture, this tour of the cell has provided many opportunities to correlate structure with function. (This would be a good time to review cell structure by returning to Figure 6.9, on pp. 100 and 101.) But even as we dissect the cell, remember that none of its components works alone. As an example of cellular integration, consider the microscopic scene in **Figure 6.33**. The large cell is a macrophage (see Figure 6.14a). It helps defend the mammalian body against infections by ingesting bacteria (the smaller cells) into phagocytic vesicles. The macrophage crawls along a surface and reaches out to the bacteria with thin pseudopodia (called filopodia). Actin filaments interact with other elements of the cytoskeleton in these movements. After the macrophage engulfs the bacteria, they are destroyed by lysosomes. The elaborate endomembrane system produces the lysosomes. The digestive enzymes of the lysosomes and the proteins of the cytoskeleton are all made on ribosomes. And the synthesis of these proteins is programmed by genetic messages dispatched from the DNA in the nucleus. All these processes require energy, which mitochondria supply in the form of ATP. Cellular functions arise from cellular order: The cell is a living unit greater than the sum of its parts.

Chapter 6 Review

 MEDIA Go to the Study Area at **www.masteringbio.com** for BioFlix 3-D Animations, MP3 Tutors, Videos, Practice Tests, an eBook, and more.

SUMMARY OF KEY CONCEPTS

CONCEPT 6.1

To study cells, biologists use microscopes and the tools of biochemistry (pp. 94–97)

▶ **Microscopy** Improvements in microscopy that affect the parameters of magnification, resolution, and contrast have catalyzed progress in the study of cell structure. Light and electron microscopy (LM and EM) remain important tools.

▶ **Cell Fractionation** Cell biologists can obtain pellets enriched in particular cellular components by centrifuging disrupted cells at sequential speeds. Larger components are in the pellet after lower speed centrifugation, and smaller components after higher speed centrifugation.

MEDIA
Activity Metric System Review
Investigation What Is the Size and Scale of Our World?

CONCEPT 6.2

Eukaryotic cells have internal membranes that compartmentalize their functions (pp. 98–102)

▶ **Comparing Prokaryotic and Eukaryotic Cells** All cells are bounded by a plasma membrane. Unlike eukaryotic cells, prokaryotic cells lack nuclei and other membrane-enclosed organelles. The surface-to-volume ratio is an important parameter affecting cell size and shape.

▶ **A Panoramic View of the Eukaryotic Cell** Plant and animal cells have most of the same organelles.

MEDIA
BioFlix 3-D Animations A Tour of an Animal Cell and A Tour of a Plant Cell
Activity Prokaryotic Cell Structure and Function
Activity Comparing Prokaryotic and Eukaryotic Cells
Activity Build an Animal Cell and a Plant Cell

	Cell Component	Structure	Function
Concept 6.3 **The eukaryotic cell's genetic instructions are housed in the nucleus and carried out by the ribosomes** (pp. 102–104) **MEDIA** **Activity** Role of the Nucleus and Ribosomes in Protein Synthesis	Nucleus (ER)	Surrounded by nuclear envelope (double membrane) perforated by nuclear pores. The nuclear envelope is continuous with the endoplasmic reticulum (ER).	Houses chromosomes, made of chromatin (DNA, the genetic material, and proteins); contains nucleoli, where ribosomal subunits are made. Pores regulate entry and exit of materials.
	Ribosome	Two subunits made of ribosomal RNA and proteins; can be free in cytosol or bound to ER	Protein synthesis
Concept 6.4 **The endomembrane system regulates protein traffic and performs metabolic functions in the cell** (pp. 104–108) **MEDIA** **Activity** The Endomembrane System	Endoplasmic reticulum (Nuclear envelope)	Extensive network of membrane-bounded tubules and sacs; membrane separates lumen from cytosol; continuous with the nuclear envelope	Smooth ER: synthesis of lipids, metabolism of carbohydrates, Ca^{2+} storage, detoxification of drugs and poisons Rough ER: Aids in synthesis of secretory and other proteins from bound ribosomes; adds carbohydrates to glycoproteins; produces new membrane
	Golgi apparatus	Stacks of flattened membranous sacs; has polarity (*cis* and *trans* faces)	Modification of proteins, carbohydrates on proteins, and phospholipids; synthesis of many polysaccharides; sorting of Golgi products, which are then released in vesicles
	Lysosome	Membranous sac of hydrolytic enzymes (in animal cells)	Breakdown of ingested substances, cell macromolecules, and damaged organelles for recycling
	Vacuole	Large membrane-bounded vesicle in plants	Digestion, storage, waste disposal, water balance, cell growth, and protection
Concept 6.5 **Mitochondria and chloroplasts change energy from one form to another** (pp. 109–111) **MEDIA** **Activity** Build a Chloroplast and a Mitochondrion	Mitochondrion	Bounded by double membrane; inner membrane has infoldings (cristae)	Cellular respiration
	Chloroplast	Typically two membranes around fluid stroma, which contains membranous thylakoids stacked into grana (in plants)	Photosynthesis
	Peroxisome	Specialized metabolic compartment bounded by a single membrane	Contains enzymes that transfer hydrogen to water, producing hydrogen peroxide (H_2O_2) as a by-product, which is converted to water by other enzymes in the peroxisome

CONCEPT 6.6

The cytoskeleton is a network of fibers that organizes structures and activities in the cell (pp. 112–118)

▶ **Roles of the Cytoskeleton: Support, Motility, and Regulation** The cytoskeleton functions in structural support for the cell and in motility and signal transmission.

▶ **Components of the Cytoskeleton** Microtubules shape the cell, guide organelle movement, and separate chromosomes in dividing cells. Cilia and flagella are motile appendages containing microtubules. Primary cilia also play sensory and signaling roles. Microfilaments are thin rods functioning in muscle contraction, amoeboid movement, cytoplasmic streaming, and microvillus support. Intermediate filaments support cell shape and fix organelles in place.

MEDIA
Activity Cilia and Flagella

CONCEPT 6.7

Extracellular components and connections between cells help coordinate cellular activities (pp. 118–122)

▶ **Cell Walls of Plants** Plant cell walls are made of cellulose fibers embedded in other polysaccharides and proteins. Cellulose deposition is oriented along microtubules.

▶ **The Extracellular Matrix (ECM) of Animal Cells** Animal cells secrete glycoproteins that form the ECM, which functions in support, adhesion, movement, and regulation.

▶ **Intercellular Junctions** Plants have plasmodesmata that pass through adjoining cell walls. Animal cells have tight junctions, desmosomes, and gap junctions.

▶ **The Cell: A Living Unit Greater Than the Sum of Its Parts**

MEDIA
Activity Cell Junctions
Activity Review: Animal Cell Structure and Function
Activity Review: Plant Cell Structure and Function

TESTING YOUR KNOWLEDGE

SELF-QUIZ

1. Which statement correctly characterizes bound ribosomes?
   a. Bound ribosomes are enclosed in their own membrane.
   b. Bound and free ribosomes are structurally different.
   c. Bound ribosomes generally synthesize membrane proteins and secretory proteins.
   d. The most common location for bound ribosomes is the cytoplasmic surface of the plasma membrane.
   e. All of the above.

2. Which structure is *not* part of the endomembrane system?
   a. nuclear envelope   d. plasma membrane
   b. chloroplast   e. ER
   c. Golgi apparatus

3. Cells of the pancreas will incorporate radioactively labeled amino acids into proteins. This "tagging" of newly synthesized proteins enables a researcher to track their location. In this

case, we are tracking an enzyme secreted by pancreatic cells. What is its most likely pathway?
   a. ER→Golgi→nucleus
   b. Golgi→ER→lysosome
   c. nucleus→ER→Golgi
   d. ER→Golgi→vesicles that fuse with plasma membrane
   e. ER→lysosomes→vesicles that fuse with plasma membrane

4. Which structure is common to plant *and* animal cells?
   a. chloroplast   d. mitochondrion
   b. wall made of cellulose e. centriole
   c. central vacuole

5. Which of the following is present in a prokaryotic cell?
   a. mitochondrion   d. chloroplast
   b. ribosome   e. ER
   c. nuclear envelope

6. Which cell would be best for studying lysosomes?
   a. muscle cell   d. leaf cell of a plant
   b. nerve cell   e. bacterial cell
   c. phagocytic white blood cell

7. Which structure-function pair is *mismatched*?
   a. nucleolus; production of ribosomal subunits
   b. lysosome; intracellular digestion
   c. ribosome; protein synthesis
   d. Golgi; protein trafficking
   e. microtubule; muscle contraction

8. Cyanide binds with at least one molecule involved in producing ATP. If a cell is exposed to cyanide, most of the cyanide would be found within the
   a. mitochondria.   d. lysosomes.
   b. ribosomes.   e. endoplasmic reticulum.
   c. peroxisomes.

9. **DRAW IT** From memory, draw two cells, showing the structures below and any connections between them.

   nucleus, rough ER, smooth ER, mitochondrion, centrosome, chloroplast, vacuole, lysosome, microtubule, cell wall, ECM, microfilament, Golgi apparatus, intermediate filament, plasma membrane, peroxisome, ribosome, nucleolus, nuclear pore, vesicle, flagellum, microvilli, plasmodesma

For Self-Quiz Answers, see Appendix A.

MEDIA Visit the Study Area at **www.masteringbio.com** for a Practice Test.

EVOLUTION CONNECTION

10. Which aspects of cell structure best reveal evolutionary unity? What are some examples of specialized modifications?

SCIENTIFIC INQUIRY

11. Imagine protein X, destined to go to the plasma membrane. Assume that the mRNA carrying the genetic message for protein X has already been translated by ribosomes in a cell culture. If you fractionate the cell (see Figure 6.5), in which fraction would you find protein X? Explain by describing its transit.

Membrane Structure and Function

▲ Figure 7.1 **How do cell membrane proteins help regulate chemical traffic?**

KEY CONCEPTS

7.1 Cellular membranes are fluid mosaics of lipids and proteins

7.2 Membrane structure results in selective permeability

7.3 Passive transport is diffusion of a substance across a membrane with no energy investment

7.4 Active transport uses energy to move solutes against their gradients

7.5 Bulk transport across the plasma membrane occurs by exocytosis and endocytosis

OVERVIEW
Life at the Edge

The plasma membrane is the edge of life, the boundary that separates the living cell from its surroundings. A remarkable film only about 8 nm thick—it would take over 8,000 to equal the thickness of this page—the plasma membrane controls traffic into and out of the cell it surrounds. Like all biological membranes, the plasma membrane exhibits **selective permeability**; that is, it allows some substances to cross it more easily than others. One of the earliest episodes in the evolution of life may have been the formation of a membrane that enclosed a solution different from the surrounding solution while still permitting the uptake of nutrients and elimination of waste products. The ability of the cell to discriminate in its chemical exchanges with its environment is fundamental to life, and it is the plasma membrane and its component molecules that make this selectivity possible.

In this chapter, you will learn how cellular membranes control the passage of substances. The image in **Figure 7.1** shows the elegant structure of a eukaryotic plasma membrane protein that plays a crucial role in nerve cell signaling. This protein restores the ability of the nerve cell to fire again by providing a channel for a stream of potassium ions (K^+) to exit the cell at a precise moment after nerve stimulation. (The green ball in the center represents one K^+ moving through the channel.) In this case, the plasma membrane and its proteins not only act as an outer boundary but also enable the cell to carry out its functions. The same applies to the many varieties of internal membranes that partition the eukaryotic cell: The molecular makeup of each membrane allows compartmentalized specialization in cells. To understand how membranes work, we'll begin by examining their architecture.

CONCEPT 7.1
Cellular membranes are fluid mosaics of lipids and proteins

Lipids and proteins are the staple ingredients of membranes, although carbohydrates are also important. The most abundant lipids in most membranes are phospholipids. The ability of phospholipids to form membranes is inherent in their molecular structure. A phospholipid is an **amphipathic** molecule, meaning it has both a hydrophilic region and a hydrophobic region (see Figure 5.13). Other types of membrane lipids are also amphipathic. Furthermore, most of the proteins within membranes have both hydrophobic and hydrophilic regions.

How are phospholipids and proteins arranged in the membranes of cells? You encountered the currently accepted model for the arrangement of these molecules in Chapter 6 (see Figure 6.7). In this **fluid mosaic model**, the membrane is a fluid structure with a "mosaic" of various proteins embedded in or attached to a double layer (bilayer) of phospholipids. Scientists propose models as hypotheses, ways of organizing and explaining existing information. We'll discuss the fluid mosaic model in detail, starting with the story of how it was developed.

Membrane Models: *Scientific Inquiry*

Scientists began building molecular models of the membrane decades before membranes were first seen with the electron microscope in the 1950s. In 1915, membranes isolated from red blood cells were chemically analyzed and found to be composed of lipids and proteins. Ten years later, two Dutch scientists, E. Gorter and F. Grendel, reasoned that cell membranes must be phospholipid bilayers. Such a double layer of molecules could exist as a stable boundary between two aqueous compartments because the molecular arrangement shelters the hydrophobic tails of the phospholipids from water while exposing the hydrophilic heads to water (Figure 7.2).

Building on the idea that a phospholipid bilayer was the main fabric of a membrane, the next question was where the proteins were located. Although the heads of phospholipids are hydrophilic, the surface of a membrane consisting of a pure phospholipid bilayer adheres less strongly to water than does the surface of a biological membrane. Given these data, Hugh Davson and James Danielli suggested in 1935 that this difference could be accounted for if the membrane were coated on both sides with hydrophilic proteins. They proposed a sandwich model: a phospholipid bilayer between two layers of proteins.

When researchers first used electron microscopes to study cells in the 1950s, the pictures seemed to support the Davson-Danielli model. By the 1960s, the Davson-Danielli sandwich had become widely accepted as the structure not only of the plasma membrane but also of all the cell's internal membranes. By the end of that decade, however, many cell biologists recognized two problems with the model. The first problem was the generalization that all membranes of the cell are identical. Whereas the plasma membrane is 7–8 nm thick and has a three-layered structure in electron micrographs, the inner membrane of the mitochondrion is only 6 nm thick and looks like a row of beads. Mitochondrial membranes also have a higher percentage of proteins and different kinds of phospholipids and other lipids. In short, membranes with different functions differ in chemical composition and structure.

A second, more serious problem with the sandwich model was the protein placement. Unlike proteins dissolved in the cytosol, membrane proteins are not very soluble in water, because they are amphipathic; that is,

they have hydrophobic regions as well as hydrophilic regions. If such proteins were layered on the surface of the membrane, their hydrophobic parts would be in aqueous surroundings.

In 1972, S. J. Singer and G. Nicolson proposed that membrane proteins are dispersed, individually inserted into the phospholipid bilayer with their hydrophilic regions protruding (Figure 7.3). This molecular arrangement would maximize contact of hydrophilic regions of proteins and phospholipids with water in the cytosol and extracellular fluid, while providing their hydrophobic parts with a nonaqueous environment. In this fluid mosaic model, the membrane is a mosaic of protein molecules bobbing in a fluid bilayer of phospholipids.

A method of preparing cells for electron microscopy called freeze-fracture has demonstrated visually that proteins are indeed embedded in the phospholipid bilayer of the membrane. Freeze-fracture splits a membrane along the middle of the phospholipid bilayer, somewhat like pulling apart a chunky peanut butter sandwich. When the membrane layers are viewed in the electron microscope, the interior of the bilayer appears cobblestoned, with protein particles interspersed in a smooth matrix, as in the fluid mosaic model (Figure 7.4). Some proteins travel with one layer or the other, like the peanut chunks in the sandwich.

Because models are hypotheses, replacing one model of membrane structure with another does not imply that the original model was worthless. The acceptance or rejection of a model depends on how well it fits observations and explains experimental results. A good model also makes predictions that shape future research. Models inspire experiments, and few models survive these tests without modification. New findings may make a model obsolete; even then, it may not be totally scrapped, but revised to incorporate the new observations. The fluid mosaic model is continually being refined. For example, recent research suggests that membranes may be "more mosaic than fluid." Often, multiple proteins semipermanently associate in specialized patches, where they carry out common functions. Also, the membrane may be much more packed with proteins than imagined in the classic fluid mosaic model. Let's now take a closer look at membrane structure.

Hydrophilic head

Hydrophobic tail

WATER

WATER

▲ **Figure 7.2 Phospholipid bilayer (cross section).**

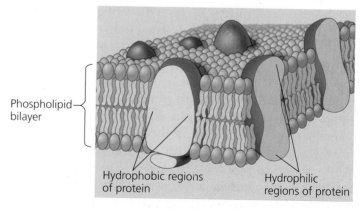

Phospholipid bilayer

Hydrophobic regions of protein

Hydrophilic regions of protein

▲ **Figure 7.3 The fluid mosaic model for membranes.**

Figure 7.4 Research Method

Freeze-Fracture

APPLICATION A cell membrane can be split into its two layers, revealing the ultrastructure of the membrane's interior.

TECHNIQUE A cell is frozen and fractured with a knife. The fracture plane often follows the hydrophobic interior of a membrane, splitting the phospholipid bilayer into two separated layers. The membrane proteins go wholly with one of the layers.

RESULTS These SEMs show membrane proteins (the "bumps") in the two layers, demonstrating that proteins are embedded in the phospholipid bilayer.

Inside of extracellular layer

Inside of cytoplasmic layer

The Fluidity of Membranes

Membranes are not static sheets of molecules locked rigidly in place. A membrane is held together primarily by hydrophobic interactions, which are much weaker than covalent bonds (see Figure 5.21). Most of the lipids and some of the proteins can shift about laterally—that is, in the plane of the membrane, like party-goers elbowing their way through a crowded room (**Figure 7.5a**). It is quite rare, however, for a molecule to flip-flop transversely across the membrane, switching from one phospholipid layer to the other; to do so, the hydrophilic part of the molecule must cross the hydrophobic core of the membrane.

The lateral movement of phospholipids within the membrane is rapid. Adjacent phospholipids switch positions about 10^7 times per second, which means that a phospholipid can travel about 2 μm—the length of many bacterial cells—in 1 second. Proteins are much larger than lipids and move more slowly, but some membrane proteins do drift, as shown in a classic experiment by David Frye and Michael Edidin (**Figure 7.6**, on the next page). And some membrane proteins seem to move in a highly directed manner, perhaps driven along cytoskeletal fibers by motor proteins connected to the membrane proteins' cytoplasmic regions. However, many other membrane proteins seem to be held virtually immobile by their attachment to the cytoskeleton.

(a) Movement of phospholipids. Lipids move laterally in a membrane, but flip-flopping across the membrane is quite rare.

(b) Membrane fluidity. Unsaturated hydrocarbon tails of phospholipids have kinks that keep the molecules from packing together, enhancing membrane fluidity.

(c) Cholesterol within the animal cell membrane. Cholesterol reduces membrane fluidity at moderate temperatures by reducing phospholipid movement, but at low temperatures it hinders solidification by disrupting the regular packing of phospholipids.

▲ **Figure 7.5 The fluidity of membranes.**

A membrane remains fluid as temperature decreases until finally the phospholipids settle into a closely packed arrangement and the membrane solidifies, much as bacon grease forms lard when it cools. The temperature at which a membrane solidifies depends on the types of lipids it is made of. The membrane remains fluid to a lower temperature if it is rich in phospholipids with unsaturated hydrocarbon tails (see Figures 5.12 and 5.13). Because of kinks in the tails where double bonds are located, unsaturated hydrocarbon tails cannot pack together as closely as saturated hydrocarbon tails, and this makes the membrane more fluid (**Figure 7.5b**).

The steroid cholesterol, which is wedged between phospholipid molecules in the plasma membranes of animal cells, has different effects on membrane fluidity at different temperatures (**Figure 7.5c**). At relatively higher temperatures—at 37°C, the

▼ Figure 7.6 Inquiry

Do membrane proteins move?

EXPERIMENT David Frye and Michael Edidin, at Johns Hopkins University, labeled the plasma membrane proteins of a mouse cell and a human cell with two different markers and fused the cells. Using a microscope, they observed the markers on the hybrid cell.

RESULTS

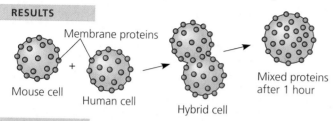

Membrane proteins

Mouse cell + Human cell → Hybrid cell → Mixed proteins after 1 hour

CONCLUSION The mixing of the mouse and human membrane proteins indicates that at least some membrane proteins move sideways within the plane of the plasma membrane.

SOURCE L. D. Frye and M. Edidin, The rapid intermixing of cell surface antigens after formation of mouse-human heterokaryons, *J. Cell Sci.* 7:319 (1970).

WHAT IF? If, after many hours, the protein distribution still looked like that in the third image above, would you be able to conclude that proteins don't move within the membrane? What other explanation could there be?

body temperature of humans, for example—cholesterol makes the membrane less fluid by restraining phospholipid movement. However, because cholesterol also hinders the close packing of phospholipids, it lowers the temperature required for the membrane to solidify. Thus, cholesterol can be thought of as a "temperature buffer" for the membrane, resisting changes in membrane fluidity that can be caused by changes in temperature.

Membranes must be fluid to work properly; they are usually about as fluid as salad oil. When a membrane solidifies, its permeability changes, and enzymatic proteins in the membrane may become inactive—for example, if their activity requires them to be able to move laterally in the membrane. The lipid composition of cell membranes can change as an adjustment to changing temperature. For instance, in many plants that tolerate extreme cold, such as winter wheat, the percentage of unsaturated phospholipids increases in autumn, an adaptation that keeps the membranes from solidifying during winter.

Membrane Proteins and Their Functions

Now we come to the *mosaic* aspect of the fluid mosaic model. A membrane is a collage of different proteins embedded in the fluid matrix of the lipid bilayer **(Figure 7.7)**. More than 50 kinds of proteins have been found so far in the plasma mem-

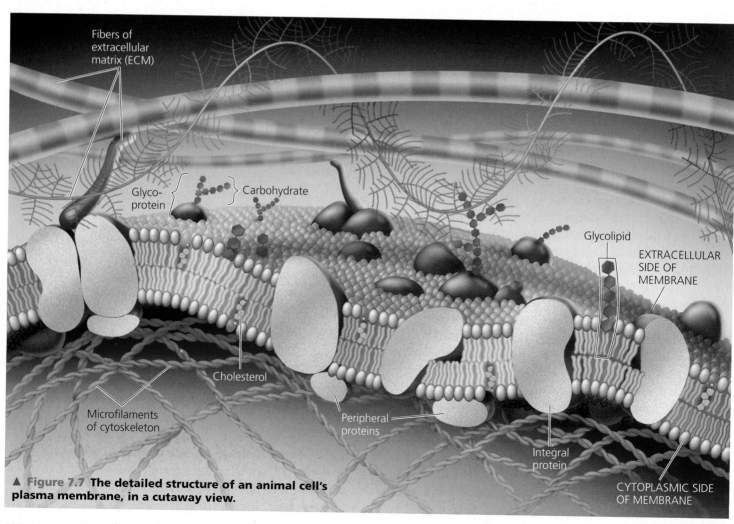

▲ **Figure 7.7 The detailed structure of an animal cell's plasma membrane, in a cutaway view.**

brane of red blood cells, for example. Phospholipids form the main fabric of the membrane, but proteins determine most of the membrane's functions. Different types of cells contain different sets of membrane proteins, and the various membranes within a cell each have a unique collection of proteins.

Notice in Figure 7.7 that there are two major populations of membrane proteins: integral proteins and peripheral proteins. **Integral proteins** penetrate the hydrophobic core of the lipid bilayer. Many are *transmembrane proteins*, which span the membrane; other integral proteins extend only partway into the hydrophobic core. The hydrophobic regions of an integral protein consist of one or more stretches of nonpolar amino acids (see Figure 5.17), usually coiled into α helices **(Figure 7.8)**. The hydrophilic parts of the molecule are exposed to the aqueous solutions on either side of the membrane. Some proteins also have a hydrophilic channel through their center that allows passage of hydrophilic substances (see Figure 7.1). **Peripheral proteins** are not embedded in the lipid bilayer at all; they are appendages loosely bound to the surface of the membrane, often to exposed parts of integral proteins (see Figure 7.7).

On the cytoplasmic side of the plasma membrane, some membrane proteins are held in place by attachment to the cytoskeleton. And on the extracellular side, certain membrane proteins are attached to fibers of the extracellular matrix (see Figure 6.30; *integrins* are one type of integral protein). These attachments combine to give animal cells a stronger framework than the plasma membrane alone could provide.

Figure 7.9 gives an overview of six major functions performed by proteins of the plasma membrane. A single cell may

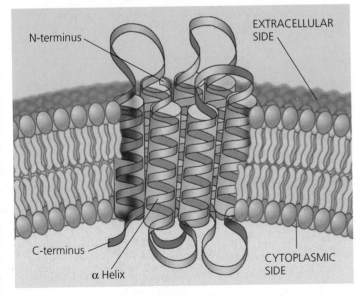

▲ **Figure 7.8 The structure of a transmembrane protein.** This protein, bacteriorhodopsin (a bacterial transport protein), has a distinct orientation in the membrane, with the N-terminus outside the cell and the C-terminus inside. This ribbon model highlights the α-helical secondary structure of the hydrophobic parts, which lie mostly within the hydrophobic core of the membrane. The protein includes seven transmembrane helices (outlined with cylinders for emphasis). The nonhelical hydrophilic segments are in contact with the aqueous solutions on the extracellular and cytoplasmic sides of the membrane.

(a) Transport. *Left:* A protein that spans the membrane may provide a hydrophilic channel across the membrane that is selective for a particular solute. *Right:* Other transport proteins shuttle a substance from one side to the other by changing shape. Some of these proteins hydrolyze ATP as an energy source to actively pump substances across the membrane.

(b) Enzymatic activity. A protein built into the membrane may be an enzyme with its active site exposed to substances in the adjacent solution. In some cases, several enzymes in a membrane are organized as a team that carries out sequential steps of a metabolic pathway.

(c) Signal transduction. A membrane protein (receptor) may have a binding site with a specific shape that fits the shape of a chemical messenger, such as a hormone. The external messenger (signaling molecule) may cause a shape change in the protein that relays the message to the inside of the cell, usually by binding to a cytoplasmic protein. (See Figure 11.6.)

(d) Cell-cell recognition. Some glycoproteins serve as identification tags that are specifically recognized by membrane proteins of other cells.

(e) Intercellular joining. Membrane proteins of adjacent cells may hook together in various kinds of junctions, such as gap junctions or tight junctions (see Figure 6.32).

(f) Attachment to the cytoskeleton and extracellular matrix (ECM). Microfilaments or other elements of the cytoskeleton may be noncovalently bound to membrane proteins, a function that helps maintain cell shape and stabilizes the location of certain membrane proteins. Proteins that can bind to ECM molecules can coordinate extracellular and intracellular changes (see Figure 6.30).

▲ **Figure 7.9 Some functions of membrane proteins.** In many cases, a single protein performs multiple tasks.

? *Some transmembrane proteins can bind to a particular ECM molecule and, when bound, transmit a signal into the cell. Use the proteins shown here to explain how this might occur.*

have membrane proteins carrying out several of these functions, and a single membrane protein may have multiple functions. In this way, the membrane is a functional mosaic as well as a structural one.

The Role of Membrane Carbohydrates in Cell-Cell Recognition

Cell-cell recognition, a cell's ability to distinguish one type of neighboring cell from another, is crucial to the functioning of an organism. It is important, for example, in the sorting of cells into tissues and organs in an animal embryo. It is also the basis for the rejection of foreign cells (including those of transplanted organs) by the immune system, an important line of defense in vertebrate animals (see Chapter 43). Cells recognize other cells by binding to surface molecules, often to carbohydrates, on the plasma membrane (see Figure 7.9d).

Membrane carbohydrates are usually short, branched chains of fewer than 15 sugar units. Some are covalently bonded to lipids, forming molecules called **glycolipids**. (Recall that *glyco* refers to the presence of carbohydrate.) However, most are covalently bonded to proteins, which are thereby **glycoproteins** (see Figure 7.7).

The carbohydrates on the extracellular side of the plasma membrane vary from species to species, among individuals of the same species, and even from one cell type to another in a single individual. The diversity of the molecules and their location on the cell's surface enable membrane carbohydrates to function as markers that distinguish one cell from another. For example, the four human blood types designated A, B, AB, and O reflect variation in the carbohydrates on the surface of red blood cells.

Synthesis and Sidedness of Membranes

Membranes have distinct inside and outside faces. The two lipid layers may differ in specific lipid composition, and each protein has directional orientation in the membrane (see Figure 7.8). When a vesicle fuses with the plasma membrane, the outside layer of the vesicle becomes continuous with the cytoplasmic (inner) layer of the plasma membrane. Therefore, molecules that start out on the *inside* face of the ER end up on the *outside* face of the plasma membrane.

The process, shown in **Figure 7.10**, starts with ❶ the synthesis of membrane proteins and lipids in the endoplasmic reticulum. Carbohydrates (green) are added to the proteins (purple), making them glycoproteins. The carbohydrate portions may then be modified. ❷ Inside the Golgi apparatus, the glycoproteins undergo further carbohydrate modification, and lipids acquire carbohydrates, becoming glycolipids. ❸ The transmembrane proteins (purple dumbbells), membrane glycolipids, and secretory proteins (purple spheres) are transported in vesicles to the plasma membrane. ❹ There the vesicles fuse with the membrane, releasing secretory proteins from the cell. Vesicle fusion positions the carbohydrates of mem-

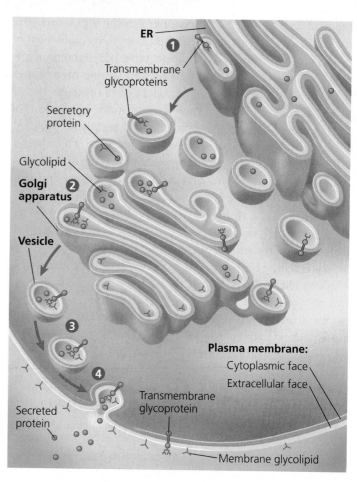

▲ Figure 7.10 **Synthesis of membrane components and their orientation on the resulting membrane.** The plasma membrane has distinct cytoplasmic (orange) and extracellular (aqua) faces, with the extracellular face arising from the inside face of ER, Golgi, and vesicle membranes.

brane glycoproteins and glycolipids on the outside of the plasma membrane. Thus, the asymmetrical arrangement of proteins, lipids, and their associated carbohydrates in the plasma membrane is determined as the membrane is being built by the ER and Golgi apparatus.

CONCEPT CHECK 7.1

1. The carbohydrates attached to some proteins and lipids of the plasma membrane are added as the membrane is made and refined in the ER and Golgi apparatus; the new membrane then forms transport vesicles that travel to the cell surface. On which side of the vesicle membrane are the carbohydrates?

2. **WHAT IF?** How would you expect the saturation levels of membrane phospholipid fatty acids to differ in plants adapted to cold environments and plants adapted to hot environments?

For suggested answers, see Appendix A.

CONCEPT 7.2

Membrane structure results in selective permeability

The biological membrane is an exquisite example of a supramolecular structure—many molecules ordered into a higher level of organization—with emergent properties beyond those of the individual molecules. The remainder of this chapter focuses on one of the most important of those properties: the ability to regulate transport across cellular boundaries, a function essential to the cell's existence. We will see once again that form fits function: The fluid mosaic model helps explain how membranes regulate the cell's molecular traffic.

A steady traffic of small molecules and ions moves across the plasma membrane in both directions. Consider the chemical exchanges between a muscle cell and the extracellular fluid that bathes it. Sugars, amino acids, and other nutrients enter the cell, and metabolic waste products leave it. The cell takes in oxygen for use in cellular respiration and expels carbon dioxide. Also, the cell regulates its concentrations of inorganic ions, such as Na^+, K^+, Ca^{2+}, and Cl^-, by shuttling them one way or the other across the plasma membrane. Although traffic through the membrane is extensive, cell membranes are selectively permeable, and substances do not cross the barrier indiscriminately. The cell is able to take up many varieties of small molecules and ions and exclude others. Moreover, substances that move through the membrane do so at different rates.

The Permeability of the Lipid Bilayer

Nonpolar molecules, such as hydrocarbons, carbon dioxide, and oxygen, are hydrophobic and can therefore dissolve in the lipid bilayer of the membrane and cross it easily, without the aid of membrane proteins. However, the hydrophobic core of the membrane impedes the direct passage of ions and polar molecules, which are hydrophilic, through the membrane. Polar molecules such as glucose and other sugars pass only slowly through a lipid bilayer, and even water, an extremely small polar molecule, does not cross very rapidly. A charged atom or molecule and its surrounding shell of water (see Figure 3.7) find the hydrophobic layer of the membrane even more difficult to penetrate. Furthermore, the lipid bilayer is only one aspect of the gatekeeper system responsible for the selective permeability of a cell. Proteins built into the membrane play key roles in regulating transport.

Transport Proteins

Cell membranes *are* permeable to specific ions and a variety of polar molecules. These hydrophilic substances can avoid contact with the lipid bilayer by passing through **transport proteins** that span the membrane.

Some transport proteins, called *channel proteins*, function by having a hydrophilic channel that certain molecules or atomic ions use as a tunnel through the membrane (see Figure 7.9a, left). For example, the passage of water molecules through the membrane in certain cells is greatly facilitated by channel proteins known as **aquaporins**. Each aquaporin allows entry of up to 3 *billion* (3×10^9) water molecules per second, passing single file through its central channel, which fits ten at a time. Without aquaporins, only a tiny fraction of these water molecules would diffuse through the same area of the cell membrane in a second, so the channel protein brings about a tremendous increase in rate. Other transport proteins, called *carrier proteins*, hold onto their passengers and change shape in a way that shuttles them across the membrane (see Figure 7.9a, right). A transport protein is specific for the substance it translocates (moves), allowing only a certain substance (or substances) to cross the membrane. For example, glucose, carried in the blood and needed by red blood cells for cellular activities, enters the red blood cells rapidly via specific carrier proteins in the plasma membrane. The glucose passes through the membrane 50,000 times faster than if diffusing through on its own. This "glucose transporter" is so selective as a carrier protein that it even rejects fructose, a structural isomer of glucose.

Thus, the selective permeability of a membrane depends on both the discriminating barrier of the lipid bilayer and the specific transport proteins built into the membrane. But what establishes the *direction* of traffic across a membrane? At a given time, what determines whether a particular substance will enter the cell or leave the cell? And what mechanisms actually drive molecules across membranes? We will address these questions next as we explore two modes of membrane traffic: passive transport and active transport.

CONCEPT CHECK 7.2

1. Two molecules that can cross a lipid bilayer without help from membrane proteins are O_2 and CO_2. What properties allow this to occur?
2. Why would water molecules need a transport protein to move rapidly and in large quantities across a membrane?
3. **WHAT IF?** Aquaporins exclude passage of hydronium ions (H_3O^+). But recent research has revealed a role for some aquaporins in fat metabolism, in which they allow passage of glycerol, a three-carbon alcohol (see Figure 5.11), as well as H_2O. Since H_3O^+ is much closer in size to water than is glycerol, what do you suppose is the basis of this selectivity?

For suggested answers, see Appendix A.

Passive transport is diffusion of a substance across a membrane with no energy investment

Molecules have a type of energy called thermal motion (heat). One result of thermal motion is **diffusion**, the movement of molecules of any substance so that they spread out evenly into the available space. Each molecule moves randomly, yet diffusion of a *population* of molecules may be directional. To understand this process, let's imagine a synthetic membrane separating pure water from a solution of a dye in water. Assume that this membrane has microscopic pores and is permeable to the dye molecules **(Figure 7.11a)**. Each dye molecule wanders randomly, but there will be a *net* movement of the dye molecules across the membrane to the side that began as pure water. The dye molecules will continue to spread across the membrane until both solutions have equal concentrations of the dye. Once that point is reached, there will be a dynamic equilibrium, with as many dye molecules crossing the membrane each second in one direction as in the other.

We can now state a simple rule of diffusion: In the absence of other forces, a substance will diffuse from where it is more concentrated to where it is less concentrated. Put another way, any substance will diffuse down its **concentration gradient**, the region along which the density of a chemical substance decreases.

No work must be done in order to make this happen; diffusion is a spontaneous process, needing no input of energy. Note that each substance diffuses down its *own* concentration gradient, unaffected by the concentration differences of other substances **(Figure 7.11b)**.

Much of the traffic across cell membranes occurs by diffusion. When a substance is more concentrated on one side of a membrane than on the other, there is a tendency for the substance to diffuse across the membrane down its concentration gradient (assuming that the membrane is permeable to that substance). One important example is the uptake of oxygen by a cell performing cellular respiration. Dissolved oxygen diffuses into the cell across the plasma membrane. As long as cellular respiration consumes the O_2 as it enters, diffusion into the cell will continue because the concentration gradient favors movement in that direction.

The diffusion of a substance across a biological membrane is called **passive transport** because the cell does not have to expend energy to make it happen. The concentration gradient itself represents potential energy (see Chapter 2, p. 35) and drives diffusion. Remember, however, that membranes are selectively permeable and therefore have different effects on the rates of diffusion of various molecules. In the case of water, aquaporins allow water to diffuse very rapidly across the membranes of certain cells. As we'll see next, the movement of water across the plasma membrane has important consequences for cells.

(a) Diffusion of one solute. The membrane has pores large enough for molecules of dye to pass through. Random movement of dye molecules will cause some to pass through the pores; this will happen more often on the side with more molecules. The dye diffuses from where it is more concentrated to where it is less concentrated (called diffusing down a concentration gradient). This leads to a dynamic equilibrium: The solute molecules continue to cross the membrane, but at equal rates in both directions.

Molecules of dye — Membrane (cross section)

WATER

Net diffusion   Net diffusion   Equilibrium

(b) Diffusion of two solutes. Solutions of two different dyes are separated by a membrane that is permeable to both. Each dye diffuses down its own concentration gradient. There will be a net diffusion of the purple dye toward the left, even though the *total* solute concentration was initially greater on the left side.

▲ **Figure 7.11 The diffusion of solutes across a membrane.** Each of the large arrows under the diagrams shows the net diffusion of the dye molecules of that color.

Net diffusion   Net diffusion   Equilibrium
Net diffusion   Net diffusion   Equilibrium

Effects of Osmosis on Water Balance

To see how two solutions with different solute concentrations interact, picture a U-shaped glass tube with a selectively permeable membrane separating two sugar solutions (Figure 7.12). Pores in this synthetic membrane are too small for sugar molecules to pass through but large enough for water molecules. How does this affect the *water* concentration? It seems logical that the solution with the higher concentration of solute would have the lower concentration of water and that water would diffuse into it from the other side for that reason. However, for a dilute solution like most biological fluids, solutes do not affect the water concentration significantly. Instead, tight clustering of water molecules around the hydrophilic solute molecules makes some of the water unavailable to cross the membrane. It is the difference in *free* water concentration that is important. In the end, the effect is the same: Water diffuses across the membrane from the region of lower solute concentration to that of higher solute concentration until the solute concentrations on both sides of the membrane are equal. The diffusion of water across a selectively permeable membrane is called **osmosis**. The movement of water across cell membranes and the balance of water between the cell and its environment are crucial to organisms. Let's now apply to living cells what we have learned about osmosis in artificial systems.

Water Balance of Cells Without Walls

When considering the behavior of a cell in a solution, both solute concentration and membrane permeability must be considered. Both factors are taken into account in the concept of **tonicity**, the ability of a solution to cause a cell to gain or lose water. The tonicity of a solution depends in part on its concentration of solutes that cannot cross the membrane (nonpenetrating solutes), relative to that inside the cell. If there is a higher concentration of nonpenetrating solutes in the surrounding solution, water will tend to leave the cell, and vice versa.

If a cell without a wall, such as an animal cell, is immersed in an environment that is **isotonic** to the cell (*iso* means "same"), there will be no *net* movement of water across the plasma membrane. Water flows across the membrane, but at the same rate in both directions. In an isotonic environment, the volume of an animal cell is stable (Figure 7.13a).

Now let's transfer the cell to a solution that is **hypertonic** to the cell (*hyper* means "more," in this case referring to nonpenetrating solutes). The cell will lose water to its environment, shrivel, and probably die. This is one way an

▲ **Figure 7.12 Osmosis.** Two sugar solutions of different concentrations are separated by a membrane, which the solvent (water) can pass through but the solute (sugar) cannot. Water molecules move randomly and may cross in either direction, but overall, water diffuses from the solution with less concentrated solute to that with more concentrated solute. This transport of water, or osmosis, equalizes the sugar concentrations on both sides.

WHAT IF? *If an orange dye capable of passing through the membrane was added to the left side of the tube above, how would it be distributed at the end of the process? (See Figure 7.11.) Would the solution levels in the tube on the right be affected?*

(a) Animal cell. An animal cell fares best in an isotonic environment unless it has special adaptations that offset the osmotic uptake or loss of water.

(b) Plant cell. Plant cells are turgid (firm) and generally healthiest in a hypotonic environment, where the uptake of water is eventually balanced by the wall pushing back on the cell.

▲ **Figure 7.13 The water balance of living cells.** How living cells react to changes in the solute concentration of their environment depends on whether or not they have cell walls. **(a)** Animal cells, such as this red blood cell, do not have cell walls. **(b)** Plant cells do. (Arrows indicate net water movement after the cells were first placed in these solutions.)

increase in the salinity (saltiness) of a lake can kill animals there; if the lake water becomes hypertonic to the animals' cells, the cells might shrivel and die. However, taking up too much water can be just as hazardous to an animal cell as losing water. If we place the cell in a solution that is **hypotonic** to the cell (*hypo* means "less"), water will enter the cell faster than it leaves, and the cell will swell and lyse (burst) like an overfilled water balloon.

A cell without rigid walls can tolerate neither excessive uptake nor excessive loss of water. This problem of water balance is automatically solved if such a cell lives in isotonic surroundings. Seawater is isotonic to many marine invertebrates. The cells of most terrestrial (land-dwelling) animals are bathed in an extracellular fluid that is isotonic to the cells. Animals and other organisms without rigid cell walls living in hypertonic or hypotonic environments must have special adaptations for **osmoregulation**, the control of water balance. For example, the protist *Paramecium* lives in pond water, which is hypotonic to the cell. *Paramecium* has a plasma membrane that is much less permeable to water than the membranes of most other cells, but this only slows the uptake of water, which continually enters the cell. The *Paramecium* cell doesn't burst because it is also equipped with a contractile vacuole, an organelle that functions as a bilge pump to force water out of the cell as fast as it enters by osmosis **(Figure 7.14)**. We will examine other evolutionary adaptations for osmoregulation in Chapter 44.

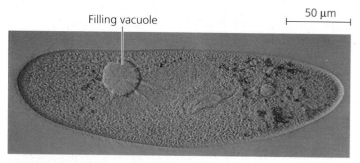

Filling vacuole

50 µm

(a) A contractile vacuole fills with fluid that enters from a system of canals radiating throughout the cytoplasm.

Contracting vacuole

(b) When full, the vacuole and canals contract, expelling fluid from the cell.

▲ **Figure 7.14 The contractile vacuole of *Paramecium*: an evolutionary adaptation for osmoregulation.** The contractile vacuole of this freshwater protist offsets osmosis by pumping water out of the cell (LM).

Water Balance of Cells with Walls

The cells of plants, prokaryotes, fungi, and some protists have walls (see Figure 6.28). When such a cell is immersed in a hypotonic solution—bathed in rainwater, for example—the wall helps maintain the cell's water balance. Consider a plant cell. Like an animal cell, the plant cell swells as water enters by osmosis **(Figure 7.13b)**. However, the relatively inelastic wall will expand only so much before it exerts a back pressure on the cell that opposes further water uptake. At this point, the cell is **turgid** (very firm), which is the healthy state for most plant cells. Plants that are not woody, such as most houseplants, depend for mechanical support on cells kept turgid by a surrounding hypotonic solution. If a plant's cells and their surroundings are isotonic, there is no net tendency for water to enter, and the cells become **flaccid** (limp).

However, a wall is of no advantage if the cell is immersed in a hypertonic environment. In this case, a plant cell, like an animal cell, will lose water to its surroundings and shrink. As the plant cell shrivels, its plasma membrane pulls away from the wall. This phenomenon, called **plasmolysis**, causes the plant to wilt and can lead to plant death. The walled cells of bacteria and fungi also plasmolyze in hypertonic environments.

Facilitated Diffusion: Passive Transport Aided by Proteins

Let's look more closely at how water and certain hydrophilic solutes cross a membrane. As mentioned earlier, many polar molecules and ions impeded by the lipid bilayer of the membrane diffuse passively with the help of transport proteins that span the membrane. This phenomenon is called **facilitated diffusion**. Cell biologists are still trying to learn exactly how various transport proteins facilitate diffusion. Most transport proteins are very specific: They transport some substances but not others.

As described earlier, the two types of transport proteins are channel proteins and carrier proteins. Channel proteins simply provide corridors that allow a specific molecule or ion to cross the membrane **(Figure 7.15a)**. The hydrophilic passageways provided by these proteins can allow water molecules or small ions to flow very quickly from one side of the membrane to the other. Although water molecules are small enough to cross through the phospholipid bilayer, the rate of water movement by this route is relatively slow because of the polarity of the water molecules. Aquaporins, the water channel proteins, facilitate the massive amounts of diffusion that occur in plant cells and in animal cells such as red blood cells (see Figure 7.13). Kidney cells also have a high number of aquaporins, allowing them to reclaim water from urine before it is excreted. It has been estimated that a person would have to drink 50 gallons of water a day and excrete the same volume if the kidneys did not perform this function.

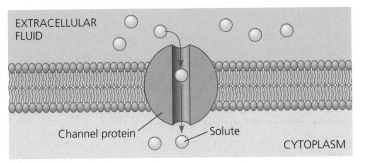

(a) A channel protein (purple) has a channel through which water molecules or a specific solute can pass.

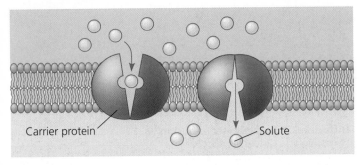

(b) A carrier protein alternates between two shapes, moving a solute across the membrane during the shape change.

▲ **Figure 7.15 Two types of transport proteins that carry out facilitated diffusion.** In both cases, the protein can transport the solute in either direction, but the net movement is down the concentration gradient of the solute.

Another group of channel proteins are **ion channels**, many of which function as **gated channels**, which open or close in response to a stimulus. The stimulus may be electrical or chemical; if chemical, the stimulus is a substance other than the one to be transported. For example, stimulation of a nerve cell by certain neurotransmitter molecules opens gated channels that allow sodium ions into the cell. Later, an electrical stimulus activates the ion channel protein shown in Figure 7.1, and potassium ions rush out of the cell.

Carrier proteins, such as the glucose transporter mentioned earlier, seem to undergo a subtle change in shape that somehow translocates the solute-binding site across the membrane **(Figure 7.15b)**. These changes in shape may be triggered by the binding and release of the transported molecule.

In certain inherited diseases, specific transport systems are either defective or missing altogether. An example is cystinuria, a human disease characterized by the absence of a carrier protein that transports cysteine and some other amino acids across the membranes of kidney cells. Kidney cells normally reabsorb these amino acids from the urine and return them to the blood, but an individual afflicted with cystinuria develops painful stones from amino acids that accumulate and crystallize in the kidneys.

CONCEPT 7.4

Active transport uses energy to move solutes against their gradients

Despite the help of transport proteins, facilitated diffusion is considered passive transport because the solute is moving down its concentration gradient. Facilitated diffusion speeds transport of a solute by providing efficient passage through the membrane, but it does not alter the direction of transport. Some transport proteins, however, can move solutes against their concentration gradients, across the plasma membrane from the side where they are less concentrated (whether inside or outside) to the side where they are more concentrated.

The Need for Energy in Active Transport

To pump a solute across a membrane against its gradient requires work; the cell must expend energy. Therefore, this type of membrane traffic is called **active transport**. The transport proteins that move solutes against a concentration gradient are all carrier proteins, rather than channel proteins. This makes sense because when channel proteins are open, they merely allow solutes to flow down their concentration gradient, rather than picking them up and transporting them against their gradient.

Active transport enables a cell to maintain internal concentrations of small solutes that differ from concentrations in its environment. For example, compared with its surroundings, an animal cell has a much higher concentration of potassium ions and a much lower concentration of sodium ions. The plasma membrane helps maintain these steep gradients by pumping sodium out of the cell and potassium into the cell.

As in other types of cellular work, ATP supplies the energy for most active transport. One way ATP can power active transport is by transferring its terminal phosphate group directly to the transport protein. This can induce the protein to change its shape in a manner that translocates a solute bound to the protein across the membrane. One transport system that works this way is the **sodium-potassium pump**, which exchanges sodium (Na^+) for

① Cytoplasmic Na⁺ binds to the sodium-potassium pump. The affinity for Na⁺ is high when the protein has this shape.

② Na⁺ binding stimulates phosphorylation (addition of a phosphate group) of the protein by ATP.

③ Phosphorylation causes the protein to change its shape, decreasing its affinity for Na⁺, which is expelled to the outside.

④ The new shape has a high affinity for K⁺, which binds on the extracellular side and triggers release of the phosphate group.

⑤ Loss of the phosphate restores the protein's original shape, which has a lower affinity for K⁺.

⑥ K⁺ is released; affinity for Na⁺ is high again, and the cycle repeats.

▲ **Figure 7.16 The sodium-potassium pump: a specific case of active transport.** This transport system pumps ions against steep concentration gradients: Sodium ion concentration (represented as [Na⁺]) is high outside the cell and low inside, while potassium ion concentration ([K⁺]) is low outside the cell and high inside. The pump oscillates between two shapes in a pumping cycle that translocates three sodium ions out of the cell for every two potassium ions pumped into the cell. The two shapes have different affinities for the two types of ions. ATP powers the shape change by phosphorylating the transport protein (that is, by transferring a phosphate group to the protein).

potassium (K⁺) across the plasma membrane of animal cells **(Figure 7.16).** The distinction between passive transport and active transport is reviewed in **Figure 7.17.**

Passive transport. Substances diffuse spontaneously down their concentration gradients, crossing a membrane with no expenditure of energy by the cell. The rate of diffusion can be greatly increased by transport proteins in the membrane.

Active transport. Some transport proteins act as pumps, moving substances across a membrane against their concentration (or electrochemical) gradients. Energy for this work is usually supplied by ATP.

Diffusion. Hydrophobic molecules and (at a slow rate) very small uncharged polar molecules can diffuse through the lipid bilayer.

Facilitated diffusion. Many hydrophilic substances diffuse through membranes with the assistance of transport proteins, either channel or carrier proteins.

▲ **Figure 7.17 Review: passive and active transport.**

How Ion Pumps Maintain Membrane Potential

All cells have voltages across their plasma membranes. Voltage is electrical potential energy—a separation of opposite charges. The cytoplasm is negative in charge relative to the extracellular fluid because of an unequal distribution of anions and cations on opposite sides of the membrane. The voltage across a membrane, called a **membrane potential**, ranges from about −50 to −200 millivolts (mV). (The minus sign indicates that the inside of the cell is negative relative to the outside.)

The membrane potential acts like a battery, an energy source that affects the traffic of all charged substances across the membrane. Because the inside of the cell is negative compared with the outside, the membrane potential favors the passive transport of cations into the cell and anions out of the cell. Thus, *two* forces drive the diffusion of ions across a membrane: a chemical force (the ion's concentration gradient) and an electrical force (the effect of the membrane potential on the ion's movement). This combination of forces acting on an ion is called the **electrochemical gradient**.

In the case of ions, then, we must refine our concept of passive transport: An ion diffuses not simply down its *concentration* gradient but, more exactly, down its *electrochemical* gradient. For example, the concentration of sodium ions (Na⁺) inside a resting nerve cell is much lower than outside it. When the cell is stimulated, gated channels open that facilitate Na$^+$ diffusion. Sodium ions then "fall" down their electrochemical gradient, driven by the concentration gradient of Na$^+$ and by the attraction of these cations to the negative side of the membrane. In this example, both electrical and chemical contributions to the electrochemical gradient act in the same direction across the membrane, but this is not always so. In cases where electrical forces due to the membrane potential oppose the simple diffusion of an ion down its concentration gradient, active transport may be necessary. In Chapter 48, you'll learn about the importance of electrochemical gradients and membrane potentials in the transmission of nerve impulses.

Some membrane proteins that actively transport ions contribute to the membrane potential. An example is the sodium-potassium pump. Notice in Figure 7.16 that the pump does not translocate Na$^+$ and K$^+$ one for one, but pumps three sodium ions out of the cell for every two potassium ions it pumps into the cell. With each "crank" of the pump, there is a net transfer of one positive charge from the cytoplasm to the extracellular fluid, a process that stores energy as voltage. A transport protein that generates voltage across a membrane is called an **electrogenic pump**. The sodium-potassium pump seems to be the major electrogenic pump of animal cells. The main electrogenic pump of plants, fungi, and bacteria is a **proton pump**, which actively transports hydrogen ions (protons) out of the cell. The pumping of H$^+$ transfers positive charge from the cytoplasm to the extracellular solution **(Figure 7.18)**. By generating voltage across membranes, electrogenic pumps store energy that can be tapped for cellular work. One important use of proton gradients in the cell is for ATP synthesis during cellular respiration, as you will see in Chapter 9. Another is a type of membrane traffic called cotransport.

Cotransport: Coupled Transport by a Membrane Protein

A single ATP-powered pump that transports a specific solute can indirectly drive the active transport of several other solutes in a mechanism called **cotransport**. A substance that has been pumped across a membrane can do work as it moves back across the membrane by diffusion, analogous to water that has been pumped uphill and performs work as it flows back down. Another transport protein, a cotransporter separate from the pump, can couple the "downhill" diffusion of this substance to the "uphill" transport of a second substance against its own concentration gradient. For example, a plant cell uses the gradient of hydrogen ions generated by its proton pumps to drive the active transport of amino acids, sugars, and several other nutrients into the cell. One transport protein couples the return of hydrogen ions to the transport of sucrose into the cell **(Figure 7.19)**. This protein can translocate sucrose into the cell against a concentration gradient, but only if the sucrose molecule travels in the company of a hydrogen ion. The hydrogen ion uses the transport protein as an avenue to diffuse down the electrochemical gradient maintained by the proton pump. Plants use sucrose-H$^+$ cotransport to load sucrose produced by photosynthesis into cells in the veins of leaves. The vascular tissue of the plant can then distribute the sugar to nonphotosynthetic organs, such as roots.

What we know about cotransport proteins, osmosis, and water balance in animal cells has helped us find more effective treat-

▲ **Figure 7.18 An electrogenic pump.** Proton pumps, the main electrogenic pumps of plants, fungi, and bacteria, are membrane proteins that store energy by generating voltage (charge separation) across membranes. Using ATP for power, a proton pump translocates positive charge in the form of hydrogen ions. The voltage and H$^+$ concentration gradient represent a dual energy source that can drive other processes, such as the uptake of nutrients.

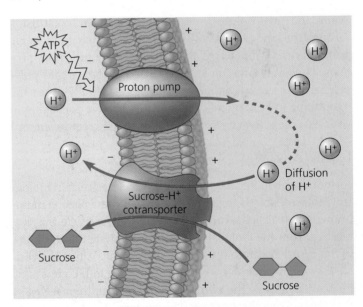

▲ **Figure 7.19 Cotransport: active transport driven by a concentration gradient.** A carrier protein such as this sucrose-H$^+$ cotransporter is able to use the diffusion of H$^+$ down its electrochemical gradient into the cell to drive the uptake of sucrose. The H$^+$ gradient is maintained by an ATP-driven proton pump that concentrates H$^+$ outside the cell, thus storing potential energy that can be used for active transport, in this case of sucrose. Thus, ATP is indirectly providing the energy necessary for cotransport.

ments for the dehydration resulting from diarrhea, a serious problem in developing countries where intestinal parasites are prevalent. Patients are given a solution to drink containing a high concentration of glucose and salt. The solutes are taken up by transport proteins on the surface of intestinal cells and passed through the cells into the blood. The increase in the blood's solute concentration causes a flow of water from the intestine through the intestinal cells into the blood, rehydrating the patient. Because of the transport proteins involved, both glucose *and* sodium ions from salt must be present. This is why athletes consume solute-rich sports drinks.

CONCEPT CHECK 7.4

1. When nerve cells establish a voltage across their membrane with a sodium-potassium pump, does this pump use ATP or does it produce ATP? Why?
2. Explain why the sodium-potassium pump in Figure 7.16 would not be considered a cotransporter.
3. WHAT IF? What would happen if cells had a channel protein allowing unregulated passage of hydrogen ions?

For suggested answers, see Appendix A.

CONCEPT 7.5

Bulk transport across the plasma membrane occurs by exocytosis and endocytosis

Water and small solutes enter and leave the cell by diffusing through the lipid bilayer of the plasma membrane or by being pumped or carried across the membrane by transport proteins. However, large molecules, such as proteins and polysaccharides, as well as larger particles, generally cross the membrane in bulk by mechanisms that involve packaging in vesicles. Like active transport, these processes require energy.

Exocytosis

As we described in Chapter 6, the cell secretes certain biological molecules by the fusion of vesicles with the plasma membrane; this is called **exocytosis**. A transport vesicle that has budded from the Golgi apparatus moves along microtubules of the cytoskeleton to the plasma membrane. When the vesicle membrane and plasma membrane come into contact, the lipid molecules of the two bilayers rearrange themselves so that the two membranes fuse. The contents of the vesicle then spill to the outside of the cell, and the vesicle membrane becomes part of the plasma membrane (see Figure 7.10).

Many secretory cells use exocytosis to export products. For example, some cells in the pancreas make insulin and secrete it into the extracellular fluid by exocytosis. Another example is the neuron (nerve cell), which uses exocytosis to release neurotransmitters that signal other neurons or muscle cells.

When plant cells are making walls, exocytosis delivers proteins and carbohydrates from Golgi vesicles to the outside of the cell.

Endocytosis

In **endocytosis**, the cell takes in biological molecules and particulate matter by forming new vesicles from the plasma membrane. Although the proteins involved in the processes are different, the events of endocytosis look like the reverse of exocytosis. A small area of the plasma membrane sinks inward to form a pocket. As the pocket deepens, it pinches in, forming a vesicle containing material that had been outside the cell. There are three types of endocytosis: **phagocytosis** ("cellular eating"), **pinocytosis** ("cellular drinking"), and **receptor-mediated endocytosis**. (Study **Figure 7.20**.)

Human cells use receptor-mediated endocytosis to take in cholesterol for use in the synthesis of membranes and other steroids. Cholesterol travels in the blood in particles called low-density lipoproteins (LDLs), complexes of lipids and proteins. LDLs act as **ligands** (a term for any molecule that binds specifically to a receptor site of another molecule) by binding to LDL receptors on plasma membranes and then entering the cells by endocytosis. In humans with familial hypercholesterolemia, an inherited disease characterized by a very high level of cholesterol in the blood, the LDL receptor proteins are defective or missing, and the LDL particles cannot enter cells. Instead, cholesterol accumulates in the blood, where it contributes to early atherosclerosis, the buildup of lipid deposits within the walls of blood vessels. This buildup causes the walls to bulge inward, thereby narrowing the vessel and impeding blood flow.

Vesicles not only transport substances between the cell and its surroundings but also provide a mechanism for rejuvenating or remodeling the plasma membrane. Endocytosis and exocytosis occur continually in most eukaryotic cells, yet the amount of plasma membrane in a nongrowing cell remains fairly constant. Apparently, the addition of membrane by one process offsets the loss of membrane by the other.

Energy and cellular work have figured prominently in our study of membranes. We have seen, for example, that active transport is powered by ATP. In the next three chapters, you will learn more about how cells acquire chemical energy to do the work of life.

CONCEPT CHECK 7.5

1. As a cell grows, its plasma membrane expands. Does this involve endocytosis or exocytosis? Explain.
2. WHAT IF? To send a signal, a neuron may carry out exocytosis of signaling molecules that are recognized by a second neuron. In some cases, the first neuron ends the signal by taking up the molecules by endocytosis. Would you expect this to occur by pinocytosis or by receptor-mediated endocytosis? Explain.

For suggested answers, see Appendix A.

Exploring Endocytosis in Animal Cells

Phagocytosis

In **phagocytosis**, a cell engulfs a particle by wrapping pseudopodia (singular, *pseudopodium*) around it and packaging it within a membrane-enclosed sac that can be large enough to be classified as a vacuole. The particle is digested after the vacuole fuses with a lysosome containing hydrolytic enzymes.

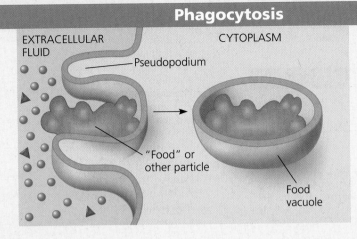

EXTRACELLULAR FLUID — Pseudopodium

CYTOPLASM

"Food" or other particle

Food vacuole

1 µm

Pseudopodium of amoeba

Bacterium

Food vacuole

An amoeba engulfing a bacterium via phagocytosis (TEM)

Pinocytosis

In **pinocytosis**, the cell "gulps" droplets of extracellular fluid into tiny vesicles. It is not the fluid itself that is needed by the cell, but the molecules dissolved in the droplets. Because any and all included solutes are taken into the cell, pinocytosis is nonspecific in the substances it transports.

Plasma membrane

Vesicle

0.5 µm

Pinocytosis vesicles forming (arrows) in a cell lining a small blood vessel (TEM)

Receptor-Mediated Endocytosis

Receptor-mediated endocytosis enables the cell to acquire bulk quantities of specific substances, even though those substances may not be very concentrated in the extracellular fluid. Embedded in the membrane are proteins with specific receptor sites exposed to the extracellular fluid. The receptor proteins are usually already clustered in regions of the membrane called coated pits, which are lined on their cytoplasmic side by a fuzzy layer of coat proteins. The specific substances (ligands) bind to these receptors. When binding occurs, the coated pit forms a vesicle containing the ligand molecules. Notice that there are relatively more bound molecules (purple) inside the vesicle, but other molecules (green) are also present. After this ingested material is liberated from the vesicle, the receptors are recycled to the plasma membrane by the same vesicle.

Coat protein

Receptor

Coated vesicle

Coated pit

Ligand

Coat protein

Plasma membrane

A coated pit and a coated vesicle formed during receptor-mediated endocytosis (TEMs)

0.25 µm

MEDIA Go to the Study Area at **www.masteringbio.com** for BioFlix 3-D Animations, MP3 Tutors, Videos, Practice Tests, an eBook, and more.

SUMMARY OF KEY CONCEPTS

CONCEPT 7.1

Cellular membranes are fluid mosaics of lipids and proteins (pp. 125–130)

▶ **Membrane Models: *Scientific Inquiry*** The Davson-Danielli sandwich model of the membrane has been replaced by the fluid mosaic model, in which amphipathic proteins are embedded in the phospholipid bilayer.

▶ **The Fluidity of Membranes** Phospholipids and, to a lesser extent, proteins move laterally within the membrane. The unsaturated hydrocarbon tails of some phospholipids keep membranes fluid at lower temperatures, while cholesterol acts as a temperature buffer, resisting changes in fluidity caused by temperature changes.

▶ **Membrane Proteins and Their Functions** Integral proteins are embedded in the lipid bilayer; peripheral proteins are attached to the surfaces. The functions of membrane proteins include transport, enzymatic activity, signal transduction, cell-cell recognition, intercellular joining, and attachment to the cytoskeleton and extracellular matrix.

▶ **The Role of Membrane Carbohydrates in Cell-Cell Recognition** Short chains of sugars are linked to proteins and lipids on the exterior side of the plasma membrane, where they interact with surface molecules of other cells.

▶ **Synthesis and Sidedness of Membranes** Membrane proteins and lipids are synthesized in the ER and modified in the ER and Golgi apparatus. The inside and outside faces of the membrane differ in molecular composition.

MEDIA
Activity Membrane Structure

CONCEPT 7.2

Membrane structure results in selective permeability (p. 131)

▶ A cell must exchange molecules and ions with its surroundings, a process controlled by the plasma membrane.

▶ **The Permeability of the Lipid Bilayer** Hydrophobic substances are soluble in lipid and pass through membranes rapidly.

▶ **Transport Proteins** To cross the membrane, polar molecules and ions generally require specific transport proteins.

MEDIA
Activity Selective Permeability of Membranes

CONCEPT 7.3

Passive transport is diffusion of a substance across a membrane with no energy investment (pp. 132–135)

▶ Diffusion is the spontaneous movement of a substance down its concentration gradient.

▶ **Effects of Osmosis on Water Balance** Water diffuses out of a cell if the solution outside has a higher solute concentration (hypertonic) than the cytosol and enters the cell if the solution has a lower solute concentration (hypotonic). If the concentrations are equal (isotonic), no net osmosis occurs. Cell survival depends on balancing water uptake and loss. Cells lacking walls (as in animals and some protists) are isotonic with their environments or have adaptations for osmoregulation. Plants, prokaryotes, fungi, and some protists have relatively inelastic cell walls, so the cells don't burst when in a hypotonic environment.

▶ **Facilitated Diffusion: Passive Transport Aided by Proteins** In facilitated diffusion, a transport protein speeds the movement of water or a solute across a membrane down its concentration gradient.

Passive transport: Facilitated diffusion

Channel protein — Carrier protein

MEDIA
Activity Diffusion
Activity Osmosis and Water Balance in Cells
Investigation How Do Salt Concentrations Affect Cells?
Activity Facilitated Diffusion

CONCEPT 7.4

Active transport uses energy to move solutes against their gradients (pp. 135–138)

Active transport:

▶ **The Need for Energy in Active Transport** Specific membrane proteins use energy, usually in the form of ATP, to do the work of active transport.

▶ **How Ion Pumps Maintain Membrane Potential** Ions can have both a concentration (chemical) gradient and an electrical gradient (voltage). These forces combine in the electrochemical gradient, which determines the net direction of ionic diffusion. Electrogenic pumps, such as sodium-potassium pumps and proton pumps, are transport proteins that contribute to electrochemical gradients.

▶ **Cotransport: Coupled Transport by a Membrane Protein** One solute's "downhill" diffusion drives the other's "uphill" transport.

MEDIA
Activity Active Transport

CONCEPT 7.5

Bulk transport across the plasma membrane occurs by exocytosis and endocytosis (pp. 138–139)

▶ **Exocytosis** In exocytosis, transport vesicles migrate to the plasma membrane, fuse with it, and release their contents.

▶ **Endocytosis** In endocytosis, molecules enter cells within vesicles that pinch inward from the plasma membrane. The three types of endocytosis are phagocytosis, pinocytosis, and receptor-mediated endocytosis.

MEDIA
Activity Exocytosis and Endocytosis

TESTING YOUR KNOWLEDGE

SELF-QUIZ

1. In what way do the membranes of a eukaryotic cell vary?
   a. Phospholipids are found only in certain membranes.
   b. Certain proteins are unique to each membrane.
   c. Only certain membranes of the cell are selectively permeable.
   d. Only certain membranes are constructed from amphipathic molecules.
   e. Some membranes have hydrophobic surfaces exposed to the cytoplasm, while others have hydrophilic surfaces facing the cytoplasm.

2. According to the fluid mosaic model of membrane structure, proteins of the membrane are mostly
   a. spread in a continuous layer over the inner and outer surfaces of the membrane.
   b. confined to the hydrophobic core of the membrane.
   c. embedded in a lipid bilayer.
   d. randomly oriented in the membrane, with no fixed inside-outside polarity.
   e. free to depart from the fluid membrane and dissolve in the surrounding solution.

3. Which of the following factors would tend to increase membrane fluidity?
   a. a greater proportion of unsaturated phospholipids
   b. a greater proportion of saturated phospholipids
   c. a lower temperature
   d. a relatively high protein content in the membrane
   e. a greater proportion of relatively large glycolipids compared with lipids having smaller molecular masses

4. Which of the following processes includes all others?
   a. osmosis
   b. diffusion of a solute across a membrane
   c. facilitated diffusion
   d. passive transport
   e. transport of an ion down its electrochemical gradient

5. Based on Figure 7.19, which of these experimental treatments would increase the rate of sucrose transport into the cell?
   a. decreasing extracellular sucrose concentration
   b. decreasing extracellular pH
   c. decreasing cytoplasmic pH
   d. adding an inhibitor that blocks the regeneration of ATP
   e. adding a substance that makes the membrane more permeable to hydrogen ions

6. **DRAW IT** An artificial cell consisting of an aqueous solution enclosed in a selectively permeable membrane is immersed in a beaker containing a different solution. The membrane is permeable to water and to the simple sugars glucose and fructose but impermeable to the disaccharide sucrose.

   a. Draw solid arrows to indicate the net movement of solutes into and/or out of the cell.
   b. Is the solution outside the cell isotonic, hypotonic, or hypertonic?
   c. Draw a dashed arrow to show the net osmotic movement of water, if any.
   d. Will the artificial cell become more flaccid, more turgid, or stay the same?
   e. Eventually, will the two solutions have the same or different solute concentrations?

For Self-Quiz answers, see Appendix A.

MEDIA Visit the Study Area at **www.masteringbio.com** for a Practice Test.

EVOLUTION CONNECTION

7. *Paramecium* and other protists that live in hypotonic environments have cell membranes that slow osmotic water uptake, while those living in isotonic environments have more permeable cell membranes. What water regulation adaptations might have evolved in protists in hypertonic habitats such as Great Salt Lake? In habitats with changing salt concentration?

SCIENTIFIC INQUIRY

8. An experiment is designed to study the mechanism of sucrose uptake by plant cells. Cells are immersed in a sucrose solution, and the pH of the solution is monitored. Samples of the cells are taken at intervals, and their sucrose concentration is measured. Their sucrose uptake correlates with a rise in the solution's pH. This rise is proportional to the starting concentration of sucrose in the solution. A metabolic poison that blocks the ability of cells to regenerate ATP is found to inhibit the pH changes in the solution. Propose a hypothesis accounting for these results. Suggest an experiment to test it.

SCIENCE, TECHNOLOGY, AND SOCIETY

9. Extensive irrigation in arid regions causes salts to accumulate in the soil. (When water evaporates, salts are left behind to concentrate in the soil.) Based on what you learned about water balance in plant cells, why might increased soil salinity (saltiness) be harmful to crops? Suggest ways to minimize damage. What costs are attached to your solutions?

An Introduction to Metabolism

8

▲ **Figure 8.1 What causes the bioluminescence in these fungi?**

8.1 An organism's metabolism transforms matter and energy, subject to the laws of thermodynamics

8.2 The free-energy change of a reaction tells us whether or not the reaction occurs spontaneously

8.3 ATP powers cellular work by coupling exergonic reactions to endergonic reactions

8.4 Enzymes speed up metabolic reactions by lowering energy barriers

8.5 Regulation of enzyme activity helps control metabolism

OVERVIEW

The Energy of Life

The living cell is a chemical factory in miniature, where thousands of reactions occur within a microscopic space. Sugars can be converted to amino acids that are linked together into proteins when needed, and proteins are dismantled into amino acids that can be converted to sugars when food is digested. Small molecules are assembled into polymers, which may be hydrolyzed later as the needs of the cell change. In multicellular organisms, many cells export chemical products that are used in other parts of the organism. The process known as cellular respiration drives the cellular economy by extracting the energy stored in sugars and other fuels. Cells apply this energy to perform various types of work, such as the transport of solutes across the plasma membrane, which we discussed in Chapter 7. In a more exotic example, cells of the fungus in **Figure 8.1** convert the energy stored in certain organic molecules to light, a process called bioluminescence. (The glow may attract insects that benefit the fungus by dispersing its

▲ **Figure 8.1 What causes the bioluminescence in these fungi?**

spores.) Bioluminescence and all other metabolic activities carried out by a cell are precisely coordinated and controlled. In its complexity, its efficiency, its integration, and its responsiveness to subtle changes, the cell is peerless as a chemical factory. The concepts of metabolism that you learn in this chapter will help you understand how matter and energy flow during life's processes and how that flow is regulated.

CONCEPT 8.1

An organism's metabolism transforms matter and energy, subject to the laws of thermodynamics

The totality of an organism's chemical reactions is called **metabolism** (from the Greek *metabole*, change). Metabolism is an emergent property of life that arises from interactions between molecules within the orderly environment of the cell.

Organization of the Chemistry of Life into Metabolic Pathways

We can picture a cell's metabolism as an elaborate road map of the thousands of chemical reactions that occur in a cell, arranged as intersecting metabolic pathways. A **metabolic pathway** begins with a specific molecule, which is then altered in a series of defined steps, resulting in a certain product. Each step of the pathway is catalyzed by a specific enzyme:

Analogous to the red, yellow, and green stoplights that control the flow of automobile traffic, mechanisms that regulate enzymes balance metabolic supply and demand, averting deficits or surpluses of important cellular molecules.

Metabolism as a whole manages the material and energy resources of the cell. Some metabolic pathways release energy by breaking down complex molecules to simpler compounds. These degradative processes are called **catabolic pathways**, or breakdown pathways. A major pathway of catabolism is cellular respiration, in which the sugar glucose and other organic fuels are broken down in the presence of oxygen to carbon dioxide and water. (Pathways can have more than one starting molecule and/or product.) Energy that was stored in the organic molecules becomes available to do the work of the cell, such as ciliary beating or membrane transport. **Anabolic pathways**, in contrast, consume energy to build complicated molecules from simpler ones; they are sometimes called biosynthetic pathways. An example of anabolism is the synthesis of a protein from amino acids. Catabolic and anabolic pathways are the "downhill" and "uphill" avenues of the metabolic map. Energy released from the downhill reactions of catabolic pathways can be stored and then used to drive the uphill reactions of anabolic pathways.

In this chapter, we will focus on mechanisms common to metabolic pathways. Because energy is fundamental to all metabolic processes, a basic knowledge of energy is necessary to understand how the living cell works. Although we will use some nonliving examples to study energy, the concepts demonstrated by these examples also apply to **bioenergetics**, the study of how energy flows through living organisms.

Forms of Energy

Energy is the capacity to cause change. In everyday life, energy is important because some forms of energy can be used to do work—that is, to move matter against opposing forces, such as gravity and friction. Put another way, energy is the ability to rearrange a collection of matter. For example, you expend energy to turn the pages of this book, and your cells expend energy in transporting certain substances across membranes. Energy exists in various forms, and the work of life depends on the ability of cells to transform energy from one form into another.

Energy can be associated with the relative motion of objects; this energy is called **kinetic energy**. Moving objects can perform work by imparting motion to other matter: A pool player uses the motion of the cue stick to push the cue ball, which in turn moves the other balls; water gushing through a dam turns turbines; and the contraction of leg muscles pushes bicycle pedals. **Heat**, or **thermal energy**, is kinetic energy associated with the random movement of atoms or molecules. Light is also a type of energy that can be harnessed to perform work, such as powering photosynthesis in green plants.

An object not presently moving may still possess energy. Energy that is not kinetic is called **potential energy**; it is energy that matter possesses because of its location or structure. Water behind a dam, for instance, possesses energy because of its altitude above sea level. Molecules possess energy because of the arrangement of their atoms. **Chemical energy** is a term used by biologists to refer to the potential energy available for release in a chemical reaction. Recall that catabolic pathways release energy by breaking down complex molecules. Biologists say that these complex molecules, such as glucose, are high in chemical energy. During a catabolic reaction, atoms are rearranged and energy is released, resulting in lower-energy breakdown products. This transformation also occurs, for example, in the engine of a car when the hydrocarbons of gasoline react explosively with oxygen, releasing the energy that pushes the pistons and producing exhaust. Although less explosive, a similar reaction of food molecules with oxygen provides chemical energy in biological systems, producing carbon dioxide and water as waste products. It is the structures and biochemical pathways of cells that enable them to release chemical energy from food molecules, powering life processes.

How is energy converted from one form to another? Consider the divers in **Figure 8.2**. The young man climbing the steps to the diving platform is releasing chemical energy from the food he ate for lunch and using some of that energy to perform the work

A diver has more potential energy on the platform than in the water.

Diving converts potential energy to kinetic energy.

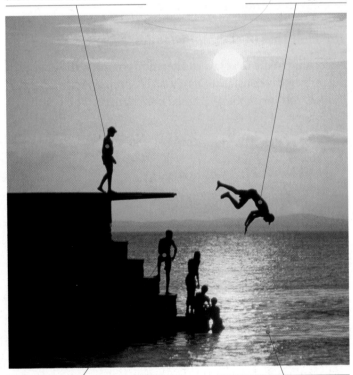

Climbing up converts the kinetic energy of muscle movement to potential energy.

A diver has less potential energy in the water than on the platform.

▲ **Figure 8.2 Transformations between potential and kinetic energy.**

of climbing. The kinetic energy of muscle movement is thus being transformed into potential energy due to his increasing height above the water. The young man diving is converting his potential energy to kinetic energy, which is then transferred to the water as he enters it. A small amount of energy is lost as heat due to friction.

Now let's go back one step and consider the original source of the organic food molecules that provided the necessary chemical energy for the diver to climb the steps. This chemical energy was itself derived from light energy by plants during photosynthesis. Organisms are energy transformers.

The Laws of Energy Transformation

The study of the energy transformations that occur in a collection of matter is called **thermodynamics**. Scientists use the word *system* to denote the matter under study; they refer to the rest of the universe—everything outside the system—as the *surroundings*. An *isolated system*, such as that approximated by liquid in a thermos bottle, is unable to exchange either energy or matter with its surroundings. In an *open system*, energy and matter can be transferred between the system and its surroundings. Organisms are open systems. They absorb energy—for instance, light energy or chemical energy in the form of organic molecules—and release heat and metabolic waste products, such as carbon dioxide, to the surroundings. Two laws of thermodynamics govern energy transformations in organisms and all other collections of matter.

The First Law of Thermodynamics

According to the **first law of thermodynamics**, the energy of the universe is constant. *Energy can be transferred and transformed, but it cannot be created or destroyed.* The first law is also known as the *principle of conservation of energy.* The electric company does not make energy, but merely converts it to a form that is convenient for us to use. By converting sunlight to chemical energy, a plant acts as an energy transformer, not an energy producer.

The cheetah in **Figure 8.3a** will convert the chemical energy of the organic molecules in its food to kinetic and other forms of energy as it carries out biological processes. What happens to this energy after it has performed work? The second law helps to answer this question.

The Second Law of Thermodynamics

If energy cannot be destroyed, why can't organisms simply recycle their energy over and over again? It turns out that during every energy transfer or transformation, some energy becomes unusable energy, unavailable to do work. In most energy transformations, more usable forms of energy are at least partly converted to heat, which is the energy associated with the random motion of atoms or molecules. Only a small fraction of the chemical energy from the food in Figure 8.3a is transformed into the motion of the cheetah shown in **Figure 8.3b**; most is lost as heat, which dissipates rapidly through the surroundings.

In the process of carrying out chemical reactions that perform various kinds of work, living cells unavoidably convert other forms of energy to heat. A system can put heat to work only when there is a temperature difference that results in the heat flowing from a warmer location to a cooler one. If temperature is uniform, as it is in a living cell, then the only use for heat energy generated during a chemical reaction is to warm a body of matter, such as the organism. (This can make a room crowded with people uncomfortably warm, as each person is carrying out a multitude of chemical reactions!)

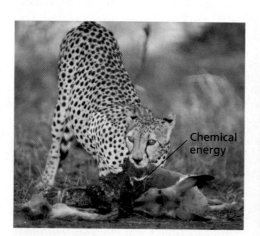

(a) First law of thermodynamics: Energy can be transferred or transformed but neither created nor destroyed. For example, the chemical (potential) energy in food will be converted to the kinetic energy of the cheetah's movement in (b).

(b) Second law of thermodynamics: Every energy transfer or transformation increases the disorder (entropy) of the universe. For example, disorder is added to the cheetah's surroundings in the form of heat and the small molecules that are the by-products of metabolism.

▲ Figure 8.3 **The two laws of thermodynamics.**

A logical consequence of the loss of usable energy during energy transfer or transformation is that each such event makes the universe more disordered. Scientists use a quantity called **entropy** as a measure of disorder, or randomness. The more randomly arranged a collection of matter is, the greater its entropy. We can now state the **second law of thermodynamics** as follows: *Every energy transfer or transformation increases the entropy of the universe.* Although order can increase locally, there is an unstoppable trend toward randomization of the universe as a whole.

In many cases, increased entropy is evident in the physical disintegration of a system's organized structure. For example, you can observe increasing entropy in the gradual decay of an unmaintained building. Much of the increasing entropy of the universe is less apparent, however, because it appears as increasing amounts of heat and less ordered forms of matter. As the cheetah in Figure 8.3b converts chemical energy to kinetic energy, it is also increasing the disorder of its surroundings by producing heat and the small molecules, such as the CO_2 it exhales, that are the breakdown products of food.

The concept of entropy helps us understand why certain processes occur. It turns out that for a process to occur on its own, without outside help (an input of energy), it must increase the entropy of the universe. Let's first agree to use the word *spontaneous* for a process that can occur without an input of energy. Note that as we're using it here, the word *spontaneous* does not imply that such a process would occur quickly. Some spontaneous processes may be virtually instantaneous, such as an explosion, while others may be much slower, such as the rusting of an old car over time. A process that cannot occur on its own is said to be nonspontaneous; it will happen only if energy is added to the system. We know from experience that certain events occur spontaneously and others do not. For instance, we know that water flows downhill spontaneously, but moves uphill only with an input of energy, such as when a machine pumps the water against gravity. In fact, another way to state the second law is: *For a process to occur spontaneously, it must increase the entropy of the universe.*

Biological Order and Disorder

Living systems increase the entropy of their surroundings, as predicted by thermodynamic law. It is true that cells create ordered structures from less organized starting materials. For example, amino acids are ordered into the specific sequences of polypeptide chains. At the organismal level, **Figure 8.4** shows the extremely symmetrical anatomy of a plant's root, formed by biological processes from simpler starting materials. However, an organism also takes in organized forms of matter and energy from the surroundings and replaces them with less ordered forms. For example, an animal obtains starch, proteins, and other complex molecules from the food it eats. As catabolic pathways break these molecules down, the animal releases car-

|— 50 μm —|

▲ **Figure 8.4 Order as a characteristic of life.** Order is evident in the detailed anatomy of this root tissue from a buttercup plant (LM, cross section). As open systems, organisms can increase their order as long as the order of their surroundings decreases.

bon dioxide and water—small molecules that possess less chemical energy than the food did. The depletion of chemical energy is accounted for by heat generated during metabolism. On a larger scale, energy flows into an ecosystem in the form of light and exits in the form of heat (see Figure 1.5).

During the early history of life, complex organisms evolved from simpler ancestors. For example, we can trace the ancestry of the plant kingdom from much simpler organisms called green algae to more complex flowering plants. However, this increase in organization over time in no way violates the second law. The entropy of a particular system, such as an organism, may actually decrease as long as the total entropy of the *universe*—the system plus its surroundings—increases. Thus, organisms are islands of low entropy in an increasingly random universe. The evolution of biological order is perfectly consistent with the laws of thermodynamics.

CONCEPT CHECK 8.1

1. How does the second law of thermodynamics help explain the diffusion of a substance across a membrane?
2. Describe the forms of energy found in an apple as it grows on a tree, then falls and is digested by someone who eats it.
3. **WHAT IF?** If you place a teaspoon of sugar in the bottom of a glass of water, it will dissolve completely over time. Left longer, eventually the water will disappear and the sugar crystals will reappear. Explain these observations in terms of entropy.

For suggested answers, see Appendix A.

CONCEPT 8.2

The free-energy change of a reaction tells us whether or not the reaction occurs spontaneously

The laws of thermodynamics that we've just discussed apply to the universe as a whole. As biologists, we want to understand the chemical reactions of life—for example, which reactions occur spontaneously and which ones require some input of energy from outside. But how can we know this without assessing the energy and entropy changes in the entire universe for each separate reaction?

Free-Energy Change, ΔG

Recall that the universe is really equivalent to "the system" plus "the surroundings." In 1878, J. Willard Gibbs, a professor at Yale, defined a very useful function called the Gibbs free energy of a system (without considering its surroundings), symbolized by the letter G. We'll refer to the Gibbs free energy simply as free energy. **Free energy** is the portion of a system's energy that can perform work when temperature and pressure are uniform throughout the system, as in a living cell. Let's consider how we determine the free-energy change that occurs when a system changes—for example, during a chemical reaction.

The change in free energy, ΔG, can be calculated for a chemical reaction with the following formula:

$$\Delta G = \Delta H - T\Delta S$$

This formula uses only properties of the system (the reaction) itself: ΔH symbolizes the change in the system's *enthalpy* (in biological systems, equivalent to total energy); ΔS is the change in the system's entropy; and T is the absolute temperature in Kelvin (K) units (K = °C + 273; see Appendix C).

Once we know the value of ΔG for a process, we can use it to predict whether the process will be spontaneous (that is, whether it will occur without an input of energy from outside). More than a century of experiments has shown that only processes with a negative ΔG are spontaneous. For a process to occur spontaneously, therefore, the system must either give up enthalpy (H must decrease), give up order (TS must increase), or both: When the changes in H and TS are tallied, ΔG must have a negative value ($\Delta G < 0$) for a process to be spontaneous. This means that every spontaneous process decreases the system's free energy. Processes that have a positive or zero ΔG are never spontaneous.

This information is immensely interesting to biologists, for it gives us the power to predict which kinds of change can happen without help. Such spontaneous changes can be har-

nessed to perform work. This principle is very important in the study of metabolism, where a major goal is to determine which reactions can supply energy for cellular work.

Free Energy, Stability, and Equilibrium

As we saw in the previous section, when a process occurs spontaneously in a system, we can be sure that ΔG is negative. Another way to think of ΔG is to realize that it represents the difference between the free energy of the final state and the free energy of the initial state:

$$\Delta G = G_{\text{final state}} - G_{\text{initial state}}$$

Thus, ΔG can be negative only when the process involves a loss of free energy during the change from initial state to final state. Because it has less free energy, the system in its final state is less likely to change and is therefore more stable than it was previously.

We can think of free energy as a measure of a system's instability—its tendency to change to a more stable state. Unstable systems (higher G) tend to change in such a way that they become more stable (lower G). For example, a diver on top of a platform is less stable (more likely to fall) than when floating in the water, a drop of concentrated dye is less stable (more likely to disperse) than when the dye is spread randomly through the liquid, and a sugar molecule is less stable (more likely to break down) than the simpler molecules into which it can be split **(Figure 8.5)**. Unless something prevents it, each of these systems will move toward greater stability: The diver falls, the solution becomes uniformly colored, and the sugar molecule is broken down.

Another term that describes a state of maximum stability is *equilibrium*, which you learned about in Chapter 2 in connection with chemical reactions. There is an important relationship between free energy and equilibrium, including chemical equilibrium. Recall that most chemical reactions are reversible and proceed to a point at which the forward and backward reactions occur at the same rate. The reaction is then said to be at chemical equilibrium, and there is no further net change in the relative concentration of products and reactants.

As a reaction proceeds toward equilibrium, the free energy of the mixture of reactants and products decreases. Free energy increases when a reaction is somehow pushed away from equilibrium, perhaps by removing some of the products (and thus changing their concentration relative to that of the reactants). For a system at equilibrium, G is at its lowest possible value in that system. We can think of the equilibrium state as a free-energy valley. Any change from the equilibrium position will have a positive ΔG and will not be spontaneous. For this reason, systems never spontaneously move away from equilibrium. Because a system at equilibrium cannot spontaneously change, it can do no work. A process is spontaneous and can perform work only when it is moving toward equilibrium.

- More free energy (higher G)
- Less stable
- Greater work capacity

In a **spontaneous change**
- The free energy of the system decreases ($\Delta G < 0$)
- The system becomes more stable
- The released free energy can be harnessed to do work

- Less free energy (lower G)
- More stable
- Less work capacity

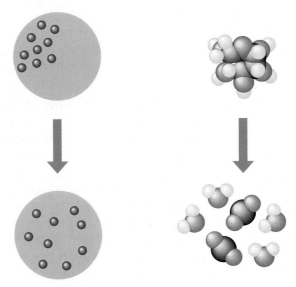

(a) Gravitational motion. Objects move spontaneously from a higher altitude to a lower one.

(b) Diffusion. Molecules in a drop of dye diffuse until they are randomly dispersed.

(c) Chemical reaction. In a cell, a sugar molecule is broken down into simpler molecules.

▲ **Figure 8.5 The relationship of free energy to stability, work capacity, and spontaneous change.** Unstable systems (top diagrams) are rich in free energy, G. They have a tendency to change spontaneously to a more stable state (bottom), and it is possible to harness this "downhill" change to perform work.

Free Energy and Metabolism

We can now apply the free-energy concept more specifically to the chemistry of life's processes.

Exergonic and Endergonic Reactions in Metabolism

Based on their free-energy changes, chemical reactions can be classified as either exergonic ("energy outward") or endergonic ("energy inward"). An **exergonic reaction** proceeds with a net release of free energy **(Figure 8.6a)**. Because the chemical mixture loses free energy (G decreases), ΔG is negative for an exergonic reaction. Using ΔG as a standard for spontaneity, exergonic reactions are those that occur spontaneously. (Remember, the word *spontaneous* does not imply that a reaction will occur instantaneously or even rapidly.) The magnitude of ΔG for an exergonic reaction represents the maximum amount of work the reaction can perform.* The greater the decrease in free energy, the greater the amount of work that can be done.

We can use the overall reaction for cellular respiration as an example:

$$C_6H_{12}O_6 + 6\ O_2 \rightarrow 6\ CO_2 + 6\ H_2O$$
$$\Delta G = -686 \text{ kcal/mol } (-2{,}870 \text{ kJ/mol})$$

---

* The word *maximum* qualifies this statement, because some of the free energy is released as heat and cannot do work. Therefore, ΔG represents a theoretical upper limit of available energy.

(a) Exergonic reaction: energy released

(b) Endergonic reaction: energy required

▲ **Figure 8.6 Free energy changes (ΔG) in exergonic and endergonic reactions.**

For each mole (180 g) of glucose broken down by respiration under what are called "standard conditions" (1 M of each reactant and product, 25°C, pH 7), 686 kcal (2,870 kJ) of energy are made available for work. Because energy must be conserved, the chemical products of respiration store 686 kcal less free energy per mole than the reactants. The products are, in a sense, the spent exhaust of a process that tapped the free energy stored in the sugar molecules.

An **endergonic reaction** is one that absorbs free energy from its surroundings **(Figure 8.6b)**. Because this kind of reaction essentially *stores* free energy in molecules (G increases), ΔG is positive. Such reactions are nonspontaneous, and the magnitude of ΔG is the quantity of energy required to drive the reaction. If a chemical process is exergonic (downhill), releasing energy in one direction, then the reverse process must be endergonic (uphill), using energy. A reversible process cannot be downhill in both directions. If ΔG = −686 kcal/mol for respiration, which converts sugar and oxygen to carbon dioxide and water, then the reverse process—the conversion of carbon dioxide and water to sugar and oxygen—must be strongly endergonic, with ΔG = +686 kcal/mol. Such a reaction would never happen by itself.

How, then, do plants make the sugar that organisms use for energy? They get the required energy—686 kcal to make a mole of sugar—from the environment by capturing light and converting its energy to chemical energy. Next, in a long series of exergonic steps, they gradually spend that chemical energy to assemble sugar molecules.

Equilibrium and Metabolism

Reactions in an isolated system eventually reach equilibrium and can then do no work, as illustrated by the isolated hydroelectric system in **Figure 8.7a**. The chemical reactions of metabolism are reversible, and they, too, would reach equilibrium if they occurred in the isolation of a test tube. Because systems at equilibrium are at a minimum of G and can do no work, a cell that has reached metabolic equilibrium is dead! The fact that metabolism as a whole is never at equilibrium is one of the defining features of life.

Like most systems, a living cell is not in equilibrium. The constant flow of materials in and out of the cell keeps the metabolic pathways from ever reaching equilibrium, and the cell continues to do work throughout its life. This principle is illustrated by the open (and more realistic) hydroelectric system in **Figure 8.7b**. However, unlike this simple single-step system, a catabolic pathway in a cell releases free energy in a series of reactions. An example is cellular respiration, illustrated by analogy in **Figure 8.7c**. Some of the reversible reactions of respiration are constantly "pulled" in one direction—that is, they are kept out of equilibrium. The key to maintaining this lack of equilibrium is that the product of a reaction does not accumulate, but instead becomes a reactant in the next step; finally, waste products are expelled from the cell.

(a) An isolated hydroelectric system. Water flowing downhill turns a turbine that drives a generator providing electricity to a light bulb, but only until the system reaches equilibrium.

(b) An open hydroelectric system. Flowing water keeps driving the generator because intake and outflow of water keep the system from reaching equilibrium.

(c) A multistep open hydroelectric system. Cellular respiration is analogous to this system: Glucose is broken down in a series of exergonic reactions that power the work of the cell. The product of each reaction becomes the reactant for the next, so no reaction reaches equilibrium.

▲ **Figure 8.7 Equilibrium and work in isolated and open systems.**

The overall sequence of reactions is kept going by the huge free-energy difference between glucose and oxygen at the top of the energy "hill" and carbon dioxide and water at the "downhill" end. As long as our cells have a steady supply of glucose or other fuels and oxygen and are able to expel waste products to the surroundings, their metabolic pathways never reach equilibrium and can continue to do the work of life.

We see once again how important it is to think of organisms as open systems. Sunlight provides a daily source of free energy for an ecosystem's plants and other photosynthetic organisms. Animals and other nonphotosynthetic organisms in an ecosystem must have a source of free energy in the form of the organic products of photosynthesis. Now that we have applied the free-energy concept to metabolism, we are ready to see how a cell actually performs the work of life.

1. Cellular respiration uses glucose and oxygen, which have high levels of free energy, and releases CO_2 and water, which have low levels of free energy. Is respiration spontaneous or not? Is it exergonic or endergonic? What happens to the energy released from glucose?

2. A key process in metabolism is the transport of hydrogen ions (H^+) across a membrane to create a concentration gradient. Other processes can result in an equal concentration of hydrogen ions on each side. Which arrangement of hydrogen ions allows the H^+ to perform work in this system?

3. **WHAT IF?** At nighttime celebrations, revelers can sometimes be seen wearing glow-in-the-dark necklaces. The necklaces start glowing once they are "activated," which usually involves snapping the necklace in a way that allows two chemicals to react and emit light in the form of "chemiluminescence." Is the chemical reaction exergonic or endergonic? Explain your answer.

For suggested answers, see Appendix A.

ATP powers cellular work by coupling exergonic reactions to endergonic reactions

A cell does three main kinds of work:

▶ *Chemical work*, the pushing of endergonic reactions, which would not occur spontaneously, such as the synthesis of polymers from monomers (chemical work will be discussed further here and will come up again in Chapters 9 and 10)

▶ *Transport work*, the pumping of substances across membranes against the direction of spontaneous movement (see Chapter 7)

▶ *Mechanical work*, such as the beating of cilia (see Chapter 6), the contraction of muscle cells, and the movement of chromosomes during cellular reproduction

A key feature in the way cells manage their energy resources to do this work is **energy coupling**, the use of an exergonic process to drive an endergonic one. ATP is responsible for mediating most energy coupling in cells, and in most cases it acts as the immediate source of energy that powers cellular work.

The Structure and Hydrolysis of ATP

ATP (adenosine triphosphate) was introduced in Chapter 4 when we discussed the phosphate group as a functional group. ATP contains the sugar ribose, with the nitrogenous base ade-

nine and a chain of three phosphate groups bonded to it **(Figure 8.8)**. In addition to its role in energy coupling, ATP is also one of the nucleoside triphosphates used to make RNA (see Figure 5.27).

The bonds between the phosphate groups of ATP can be broken by hydrolysis. When the terminal phosphate bond is broken, a molecule of inorganic phosphate ($HOPO_3^{2-}$, abbreviated $\textcircled{P}_i$ throughout this book) leaves the ATP, which becomes adenosine diphosphate, or ADP **(Figure 8.9)**. The reaction is exergonic and releases 7.3 kcal of energy per mole of ATP hydrolyzed:

$$ATP + H_2O \rightarrow ADP + \textcircled{P}_i$$
$$\Delta G = -7.3 \text{ kcal/mol } (-30.5 \text{ kJ/mol})$$

This is the free-energy change measured under standard conditions. In the cell, conditions do not conform to standard conditions, primarily because reactant and product concentrations differ from 1 M. For example, when ATP hydrolysis occurs under cellular conditions, the actual ΔG is about -13 kcal/mol, 78% greater than the energy released by ATP hydrolysis under standard conditions.

Because their hydrolysis releases energy, the phosphate bonds of ATP are sometimes referred to as high-energy phosphate bonds, but the term is misleading. The phosphate bonds of ATP

▲ **Figure 8.8 The structure of adenosine triphosphate (ATP).** In the cell, most hydroxyl groups of phosphates are ionized ($—O^-$).

▲ **Figure 8.9 The hydrolysis of ATP.** The reaction of ATP and water yields inorganic phosphate ($\textcircled{P}_i$) and ADP and releases energy.

are not unusually strong bonds, as "high-energy" may imply; rather, the reactants (ATP and water) themselves have high energy relative to the energy of the products (ADP and P_i). The release of energy during the hydrolysis of ATP comes from the chemical change to a state of lower free energy, not from the phosphate bonds themselves.

ATP is useful to the cell because the energy it releases on losing a phosphate group is somewhat greater than the energy most other molecules could deliver. But why does this hydrolysis release so much energy? If we reexamine the ATP molecule in Figure 8.8, we can see that all three phosphate groups are negatively charged. These like charges are crowded together, and their mutual repulsion contributes to the instability of this region of the ATP molecule. The triphosphate tail of ATP is the chemical equivalent of a compressed spring.

How ATP Performs Work

When ATP is hydrolyzed in a test tube, the release of free energy merely heats the surrounding water. In an organism, this same generation of heat can sometimes be beneficial. For instance, the process of shivering uses ATP hydrolysis during muscle contraction to generate heat and warm the body. In most cases in the cell, however, the generation of heat alone would be an inefficient (and potentially dangerous) use of a valuable energy resource. Instead, the cell's proteins harness the energy released during ATP hydrolysis in several ways to perform the three types of cellular work—chemical, transport, and mechanical.

For example, with the help of specific enzymes, the cell is able to use the energy released by ATP hydrolysis directly to drive chemical reactions that, by themselves, are endergonic. If the ΔG of an endergonic reaction is less than the amount of energy released by ATP hydrolysis, then the two reactions can be coupled so that, overall, the coupled reactions are exergonic **(Figure 8.10)**. This usually involves the transfer of a phosphate group from ATP to some other molecule, such as the reactant. The recipient of the phosphate group is then said to be **phosphorylated**. The key to coupling exergonic and endergonic reactions is the formation of this phosphorylated intermediate, which is more reactive (less stable) than the original unphosphorylated molecule.

Transport and mechanical work in the cell are also nearly always powered by the hydrolysis of ATP. In these cases, ATP hydrolysis leads to a change in a protein's shape and often its ability to bind another molecule. Sometimes this occurs via a phosphorylated intermediate, as seen for the transport protein in **Figure 8.11a**. In most instances of mechanical work involving motor proteins "walking" along cytoskeletal elements **(Figure 8.11b)**, a cycle occurs in which ATP is first bound noncovalently to the motor protein. Next, ATP is hydrolyzed, releasing ADP and P_i; another ATP molecule can then bind. At each stage, the motor protein changes its shape and ability

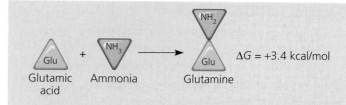

(a) Endergonic reaction. Amino acid conversion by itself is endergonic (ΔG is positive), so it is not spontaneous.

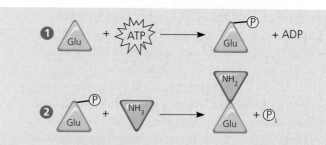

(b) Coupled with ATP hydrolysis, an exergonic reaction. In the cell, glutamine synthesis occurs in two steps, coupled by a phosphorylated intermediate. ❶ ATP phosphorylates glutamic acid, making the amino acid less stable. ❷ Ammonia displaces the phosphate group, forming glutamine.

Glu + NH$_3$	⟶	Glu—NH$_2$	$\Delta G = +3.4$ kcal/mol
ATP	⟶	ADP + P$_i$	$\Delta G = -7.3$ kcal/mol
			Net $\Delta G = -3.9$ kcal/mol

(c) Overall free-energy change. Adding the ΔG (under standard conditions) for the amino acid conversion to the ΔG for ATP hydrolysis gives the free-energy change for the overall reaction. Because the overall process is exergonic (ΔG is negative), it occurs spontaneously.

▲ **Figure 8.10 How ATP drives chemical work: Energy coupling using ATP hydrolysis.** In this example, the exergonic process of ATP hydrolysis is used to drive an endergonic process—the cellular synthesis of the amino acid glutamine from glutamic acid and ammonia.

to bind the cytoskeleton, resulting in movement of the protein along the cytoskeletal track.

The Regeneration of ATP

An organism at work uses ATP continuously, but ATP is a renewable resource that can be regenerated by the addition of phosphate to ADP **(Figure 8.12)**. The free energy required to phosphorylate ADP comes from exergonic breakdown reactions (catabolism) in the cell. This shuttling of inorganic phosphate and energy is called the ATP cycle, and it couples the cell's energy-yielding (exergonic) processes to the energy-consuming (endergonic) ones. The ATP cycle moves at an astonishing pace. For example, a working muscle cell recycles its entire pool of ATP in less than a minute. That turnover represents 10 million molecules of ATP consumed and regenerated per second per cell. If ATP could not be regenerated by the phosphorylation of ADP, humans would use up nearly their body weight in ATP each day.

(a) **Transport work:** ATP phosphorylates transport proteins

Membrane protein

Solute   Solute transported

ATP

ADP + Ⓟᵢ

Vesicle   Cytoskeletal track

ATP

Motor protein   Protein moved

(b) **Mechanical work:** ATP binds noncovalently to motor proteins, then is hydrolyzed

▲ **Figure 8.11 How ATP drives transport and mechanical work.** ATP hydrolysis causes changes in the shapes and binding affinities of proteins. This can occur either **(a)** directly, by phosphorylation, as shown for membrane proteins involved in active transport of solutes, or **(b)** indirectly, via noncovalent binding of ATP and its hydrolytic products, as is the case for motor proteins that move vesicles (and organelles) along cytoskeletal "tracks" in the cell.

ATP synthesis from ADP + Ⓟᵢ requires energy

ATP hydrolysis to ADP + Ⓟᵢ yields energy

$ATP + H_2O$

Energy from catabolism (exergonic, energy-releasing processes)

Energy for cellular work (endergonic, energy-consuming processes)

$ADP + Ⓟ_i$

▲ **Figure 8.12 The ATP cycle.** Energy released by breakdown reactions (catabolism) in the cell is used to phosphorylate ADP, regenerating ATP. Chemical potential energy stored in ATP drives most cellular work.

Because both directions of a reversible process cannot go downhill, the regeneration of ATP from ADP and $Ⓟ_i$ is necessarily endergonic:

$$ADP + Ⓟ_i \rightarrow ATP + H_2O$$

$\Delta G = +7.3$ kcal/mol ($+30.5$ kJ/mol) (standard conditions)

Because ATP formation from ADP and $Ⓟ_i$ is not spontaneous, free energy must be spent to make it occur. Catabolic (exergonic) pathways, especially cellular respiration, provide the energy for the endergonic process of making ATP. Plants also use light energy to produce ATP.

Thus, the ATP cycle is a turnstile through which energy passes during its transfer from catabolic to anabolic pathways. In fact, the chemical potential energy temporarily stored in ATP drives most cellular work.

CONCEPT CHECK 8.3

1. In most cases, how does ATP transfer energy from exergonic to endergonic reactions in the cell?
2. **WHAT IF?** Which of the following combinations has more free energy: glutamic acid + ammonia + ATP, or glutamine + ADP + $Ⓟ_i$? Explain your answer.

For suggested answers, see Appendix A.

CONCEPT 8.4
Enzymes speed up metabolic reactions by lowering energy barriers

The laws of thermodynamics tell us what will and will not happen under given conditions but say nothing about the rate of these processes. A spontaneous chemical reaction occurs without any requirement for outside energy, but it may occur so slowly that it is imperceptible. For example, even though the hydrolysis of sucrose (table sugar) to glucose and fructose is exergonic, occurring spontaneously with a release of free energy ($\Delta G = -7$ kcal/mol), a solution of sucrose dissolved in sterile water will sit for years at room temperature with no appreciable hydrolysis. However, if we add a small amount of the enzyme sucrase to the solution, then all the sucrose may be hydrolyzed within seconds **(Figure 8.13)**. How does the enzyme do this?

Sucrose ($C_{12}H_{22}O_{11}$)

H_2O

Sucrase

Glucose ($C_6H_{12}O_6$)   Fructose ($C_6H_{12}O_6$)

▲ **Figure 8.13 Example of an enzyme-catalyzed reaction: hydrolysis of sucrose by sucrase.**

An **enzyme** is a macromolecule that acts as a **catalyst**, a chemical agent that speeds up a reaction without being consumed by the reaction. In this chapter, we are focusing on enzymes that are proteins. (RNA enzymes, also called ribozymes, are discussed in Chapters 17 and 25.) In the absence of regulation by enzymes, chemical traffic through the pathways of metabolism would become terribly congested because many chemical reactions would take such a long time. In the next two sections, we will see what impedes a spontaneous reaction from occurring faster and how an enzyme changes the situation.

The Activation Energy Barrier

Every chemical reaction between molecules involves both bond breaking and bond forming. For example, the hydrolysis of sucrose involves breaking the bond between glucose and fructose and one of the bonds of a water molecule and then forming two new bonds, as shown in Figure 8.13. Changing one molecule into another generally involves contorting the starting molecule into a highly unstable state before the reaction can proceed. This contortion can be compared to the bending of a metal key ring when you pry it open to add a new key. The key ring is highly unstable in its opened form but returns to a stable state once the key is threaded all the way onto the ring. To reach the contorted state where bonds can change, reactant molecules must absorb energy from their surroundings. When the new bonds of the product molecules form, energy is released as heat, and the molecules return to stable shapes with lower energy than the contorted state.

The initial investment of energy for starting a reaction—the energy required to contort the reactant molecules so the bonds can break—is known as the *free energy of activation,* or **activation energy**, abbreviated E_A in this book. We can think of activation energy as the amount of energy needed to push the reactants over an energy barrier, or hill, so that the "downhill" part of the reaction can begin. **Figure 8.14** graphs the energy changes for a hypothetical exergonic reaction that swaps portions of two reactant molecules:

$$AB + CD \rightarrow AC + BD$$

The energizing, or activation, of the reactants is represented by the uphill portion of the graph, in which the free-energy content of the reactant molecules is increasing. At the summit, the reactants are in an unstable condition known as the *transition state*: They are activated, and their bonds can be broken. The subsequent bond-forming phase of the reaction corresponds to the downhill part of the curve, which shows the loss of free energy by the molecules.

Activation energy is often supplied in the form of heat that the reactant molecules absorb from the surroundings. The bonds of the reactants break only when the molecules have absorbed enough energy to become unstable—to enter the transition state. The absorption of thermal energy increases the speed of

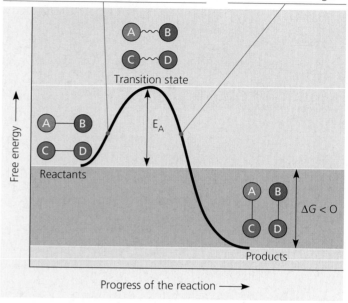

The reactants AB and CD must absorb enough energy from the surroundings to reach the unstable transition state, where bonds can break.

After bonds have broken, new bonds form, releasing energy to the surroundings.

▲ **Figure 8.14 Energy profile of an exergonic reaction.** The "molecules" are hypothetical, with A, B, C, and D representing portions of the molecules. Thermodynamically, this is an exergonic reaction, with a negative ΔG, and the reaction occurs spontaneously. However, the activation energy (E_A) provides a barrier that determines the rate of the reaction.

DRAW IT *Graph the progress of an endergonic reaction in which EF and GH form products EG and FH, assuming that the reactants must pass through a transition state.*

the reactant molecules, so they collide more often and more forcefully. Also, thermal agitation of the atoms within the molecules makes the bonds more likely to break. As the atoms settle into their new, more stable bonding arrangements, energy is released to the surroundings. If the reaction is exergonic, E_A will be repaid with interest, as the formation of new bonds releases more energy than was invested in the breaking of old bonds.

The reaction shown in Figure 8.14 is exergonic and occurs spontaneously. However, the activation energy provides a barrier that determines the rate of the reaction. The reactants must absorb enough energy to reach the top of the activation energy barrier before the reaction can occur. For some reactions, E_A is modest enough that even at room temperature there is sufficient thermal energy for many of the reactants to reach the transition state in a short time. In most cases, however, E_A is so high and the transition state is reached so rarely that the reaction will hardly proceed at all. In these cases, the reaction will occur at a noticeable rate only if the reactants are heated. For example, the reaction of gasoline and oxygen is exergonic and will occur spontaneously, but energy is required for the molecules to reach the transition state and react. Only when the spark plugs fire in an automobile engine can there be the explosive release of energy that pushes the pistons. Without a spark, a mixture of gasoline

▲ Figure 8.15 The effect of an enzyme on activation energy. Without affecting the free-energy change (ΔG) for a reaction, an enzyme speeds the reaction by reducing its activation energy (E_A).

hydrocarbons and oxygen will not react because the E_A barrier is too high.

How Enzymes Lower the E_A Barrier

Proteins, DNA, and other complex molecules of the cell are rich in free energy and have the potential to decompose spontaneously; that is, the laws of thermodynamics favor their breakdown. These molecules persist only because at temperatures typical for cells, few molecules can make it over the hump of activation energy. However, the barriers for selected reactions must occasionally be surmounted for cells to carry out the processes needed for life. Heat speeds a reaction by allowing reactants to attain the transition state more often, but this solution would be inappropriate for biological systems. First, high temperature denatures proteins and kills cells. Second, heat would speed up *all* reactions, not just those that are needed. Organisms therefore use an alternative: catalysis.

An enzyme catalyzes a reaction by lowering the E_A barrier **(Figure 8.15)**, enabling the reactant molecules to absorb enough energy to reach the transition state even at moderate temperatures. An enzyme cannot change the ΔG for a reaction; it cannot make an endergonic reaction exergonic. Enzymes can only hasten reactions that would occur eventually anyway, but this function makes it possible for the cell to have a dynamic metabolism, routing chemicals smoothly through the cell's metabolic pathways. And because enzymes are very specific for the reactions they catalyze, they determine which chemical processes will be going on in the cell at any particular time.

Substrate Specificity of Enzymes

The reactant an enzyme acts on is referred to as the enzyme's **substrate**. The enzyme binds to its substrate (or substrates, when there are two or more reactants), forming an **enzyme-substrate complex**. While enzyme and substrate are joined, the catalytic action of the enzyme converts the substrate to the product (or products) of the reaction. The overall process can be summarized as follows:

$$\text{Enzyme} + \text{Substrate(s)} \rightleftharpoons \begin{array}{c}\text{Enzyme-}\\\text{substrate}\\\text{complex}\end{array} \rightleftharpoons \text{Enzyme} + \text{Product(s)}$$

For example, the enzyme sucrase (most enzyme names end in *-ase*) catalyzes the hydrolysis of the disaccharide sucrose into its two monosaccharides, glucose and fructose (see Figure 8.13):

$$\begin{array}{c}\text{Sucrase} +\\\text{Sucrose} +\\\text{H}_2\text{O}\end{array} \rightleftharpoons \begin{array}{c}\text{Sucrase-}\\\text{sucrose-H}_2\text{O}\\\text{complex}\end{array} \rightleftharpoons \begin{array}{c}\text{Sucrase} +\\\text{Glucose} +\\\text{Fructose}\end{array}$$

The reaction catalyzed by each enzyme is very specific; an enzyme can recognize its specific substrate even among closely related compounds, such as isomers. For instance, sucrase will act only on sucrose and will not bind to other disaccharides, such as maltose. What accounts for this molecular recognition? Recall that most enzymes are proteins, and proteins are macromolecules with unique three-dimensional configurations. The specificity of an enzyme results from its shape, which is a consequence of its amino acid sequence.

Only a restricted region of the enzyme molecule actually binds to the substrate. This region, called the **active site**, is typically a pocket or groove on the surface of the protein where catalysis occurs **(Figure 8.16a)**. Usually, the active site is formed by

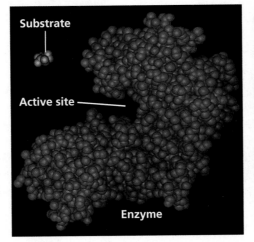

(a) In this computer graphic model, the active site of this enzyme (hexokinase, shown in blue) forms a groove on its surface. Its substrate is glucose (red).

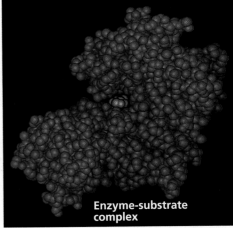

(b) When the substrate enters the active site, it induces a change in the shape of the protein. This change allows more weak bonds to form, causing the active site to enfold the substrate and hold it in place.

▲ Figure 8.16 Induced fit between an enzyme and its substrate.

only a few of the enzyme's amino acids, with the rest of the protein molecule providing a framework that determines the configuration of the active site. The specificity of an enzyme is attributed to a compatible fit between the shape of its active site and the shape of the substrate. The active site, however, is not a rigid receptacle for the substrate. As the substrate enters the active site, interactions between its chemical groups and those on the R groups (side chains) of the amino acids that form the active site of the protein cause the enzyme to change its shape slightly so that the active site fits even more snugly around the substrate **(Figure 8.16b)**. This **induced fit** is like a clasping handshake. Induced fit brings chemical groups of the active site into positions that enhance their ability to catalyze the chemical reaction.

Catalysis in the Enzyme's Active Site

In most enzymatic reactions, the substrate is held in the active site by so-called weak interactions, such as hydrogen bonds and ionic bonds. R groups of a few of the amino acids that make up the active site catalyze the conversion of substrate to product, and the product departs from the active site. The enzyme is then free to take another substrate molecule into its active site. The entire cycle happens so fast that a single enzyme molecule typically acts on about a thousand substrate molecules per second. Some enzymes are much faster. Enzymes, like other catalysts, emerge from the reaction in their original form. Therefore, very small amounts of enzyme can have a huge metabolic impact by functioning over and over again in catalytic cycles. **Figure 8.17** shows a catalytic cycle involving two substrates and two products.

Most metabolic reactions are reversible, and an enzyme can catalyze either the forward or the reverse reaction, depending on which direction has a negative ΔG. This in turn depends mainly on the relative concentrations of reactants and products. The net effect is always in the direction of equilibrium.

Enzymes use a variety of mechanisms that lower activation energy and speed up a reaction (see Figure 8.17, step ❸). First, in reactions involving two or more reactants, the active site provides a template on which the substrates can come together in the proper orientation for a reaction to occur between them. Second, as the active site of an enzyme clutches the bound substrates, the enzyme may stretch the substrate molecules toward their transition-state form, stressing and bending critical chemical bonds that must be broken during the reaction. Because E_A is proportional to the difficulty of breaking the bonds, distorting the substrate helps it approach the transition state and thus reduces the amount of free energy that must be absorbed to achieve that state.

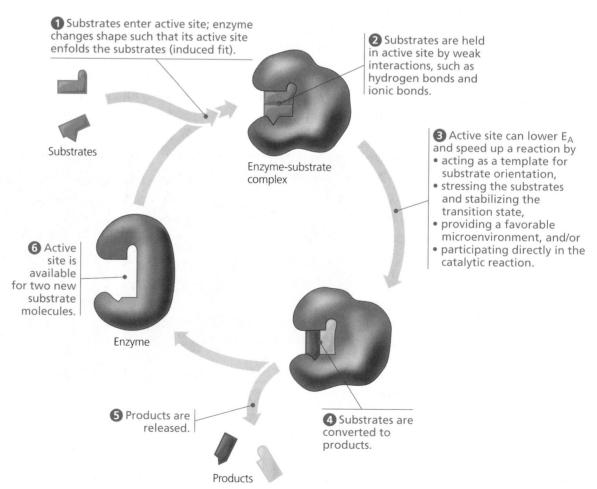

▶ **Figure 8.17 The active site and catalytic cycle of an enzyme.** An enzyme can convert one or more reactant molecules to one or more product molecules. The enzyme shown here converts two substrate molecules to two product molecules.

❶ Substrates enter active site; enzyme changes shape such that its active site enfolds the substrates (induced fit).

Substrates

❷ Substrates are held in active site by weak interactions, such as hydrogen bonds and ionic bonds.

Enzyme-substrate complex

❸ Active site can lower E_A and speed up a reaction by
• acting as a template for substrate orientation,
• stressing the substrates and stabilizing the transition state,
• providing a favorable microenvironment, and/or
• participating directly in the catalytic reaction.

❻ Active site is available for two new substrate molecules.

Enzyme

❺ Products are released.

❹ Substrates are converted to products.

Products

Third, the active site may also provide a microenvironment that is more conducive to a particular type of reaction than the solution itself would be without the enzyme. For example, if the active site has amino acids with acidic R groups, the active site may be a pocket of low pH in an otherwise neutral cell. In such cases, an acidic amino acid may facilitate H^+ transfer to the substrate as a key step in catalyzing the reaction.

A fourth mechanism of catalysis is the direct participation of the active site in the chemical reaction. Sometimes this process even involves brief covalent bonding between the substrate and an R group of an amino acid of the enzyme. Subsequent steps of the reaction restore the R groups to their original states, so that the active site is the same after the reaction as it was before.

The rate at which a particular amount of enzyme converts substrate to product is partly a function of the initial concentration of the substrate: The more substrate molecules that are available, the more frequently they access the active sites of the enzyme molecules. However, there is a limit to how fast the reaction can be pushed by adding more substrate to a fixed concentration of enzyme. At some point, the concentration of substrate will be high enough that all enzyme molecules have their active sites engaged. As soon as the product exits an active site, another substrate molecule enters. At this substrate concentration, the enzyme is said to be *saturated*, and the rate of the reaction is determined by the speed at which the active site converts substrate to product. When an enzyme population is saturated, the only way to increase the rate of product formation is to add more enzyme. Cells sometimes increase the rate of a reaction by producing more enzyme molecules.

Effects of Local Conditions on Enzyme Activity

The activity of an enzyme—how efficiently the enzyme functions—is affected by general environmental factors, such as temperature and pH. It can also be affected by chemicals that specifically influence that enzyme. In fact, researchers have learned much about enzyme function by employing such chemicals.

Effects of Temperature and pH

Recall from Chapter 5 that the three-dimensional structures of proteins are sensitive to their environment. As a consequence, each enzyme works better under some conditions than under others, because these *optimal conditions* favor the most active shape for the enzyme molecule.

Temperature and pH are environmental factors important in the activity of an enzyme. Up to a point, the rate of an enzymatic reaction increases with increasing temperature, partly because substrates collide with active sites more frequently when the molecules move rapidly. Above that temperature, however, the speed of the enzymatic reaction drops sharply.

The thermal agitation of the enzyme molecule disrupts the hydrogen bonds, ionic bonds, and other weak interactions that stabilize the active shape of the enzyme, and the protein molecule eventually denatures. Each enzyme has an optimal temperature at which its reaction rate is greatest. Without denaturing the enzyme, this temperature allows the greatest number of molecular collisions and the fastest conversion of the reactants to product molecules. Most human enzymes have optimal temperatures of about 35–40°C (close to human body temperature). The thermophilic bacteria that live in hot springs contain enzymes with optimal temperatures of 70°C or higher **(Figure 8.18a)**.

Just as each enzyme has an optimal temperature, it also has a pH at which it is most active. The optimal pH values for most enzymes fall in the range of pH 6–8, but there are exceptions. For example, pepsin, a digestive enzyme in the human stomach, works best at pH 2. Such an acidic environment denatures most enzymes, but pepsin is adapted to maintain its functional three-dimensional structure in the acidic environment of the stomach. In contrast, trypsin, a digestive enzyme residing in the alkaline environment of the human intestine, has an optimal pH of 8 and would be denatured in the stomach **(Figure 8.18b)**.

(a) **Optimal temperature for two enzymes**

(b) **Optimal pH for two enzymes**

▲ **Figure 8.18 Environmental factors affecting enzyme activity.** Each enzyme has an optimal **(a)** temperature and **(b)** pH that favor the most active shape of the protein molecule.
DRAW IT *Given that a mature lysosome has an internal pH of around 4.5, draw a curve in (b) showing what you would predict for a lysosomal enzyme, labeling its optimal pH.*

Cofactors

Many enzymes require nonprotein helpers for catalytic activity. These adjuncts, called **cofactors**, may be bound tightly to the enzyme as permanent residents, or they may bind loosely and reversibly along with the substrate. The cofactors of some enzymes are inorganic, such as the metal atoms zinc, iron, and copper in ionic form. If the cofactor is an organic molecule, it is more specifically called a **coenzyme**. Most vitamins are important in nutrition because they act as coenzymes or raw materials from which coenzymes are made. Cofactors function in various ways, but in all cases where they are used, they perform a crucial function in catalysis. You'll encounter examples of cofactors later in the book.

Enzyme Inhibitors

Certain chemicals selectively inhibit the action of specific enzymes, and we have learned a lot about enzyme function by studying the effects of these molecules. If the inhibitor attaches to the enzyme by covalent bonds, inhibition is usually irreversible.

Many enzyme inhibitors, however, bind to the enzyme by weak interactions, in which case inhibition is reversible. Some reversible inhibitors resemble the normal substrate molecule and compete for admission into the active site **(Figure 8.19a and b)**. These mimics, called **competitive inhibitors**, reduce the productivity of enzymes by blocking substrates from entering active sites. This kind of inhibition can be overcome by increasing the concentration of substrate so that as active sites become available, more substrate molecules than inhibitor molecules are around to gain entry to the sites.

In contrast, **noncompetitive inhibitors** do not directly compete with the substrate to bind to the enzyme at the active site **(Figure 8.19c)**. Instead, they impede enzymatic reactions by binding to another part of the enzyme. This interaction causes the enzyme molecule to change its shape in such a way that the active site becomes less effective at catalyzing the conversion of substrate to product.

Toxins and poisons are often irreversible enzyme inhibitors. An example is sarin, a nerve gas that caused the death of several people and injury to many others when it was released by terrorists in the Tokyo subway in 1995. This small molecule binds covalently to the R group on the amino acid serine, which is found in the active site of acetylcholinesterase, an enzyme important in the nervous system. Other examples include the pesticides DDT and parathion, inhibitors of key enzymes in the nervous system. Finally, many antibiotics are inhibitors of specific enzymes in bacteria. For instance, penicillin blocks the active site of an enzyme that many bacteria use to make their cell walls.

Citing enzyme inhibitors that are metabolic poisons may give the impression that enzyme inhibition is generally abnormal and harmful. In fact, molecules naturally present in the

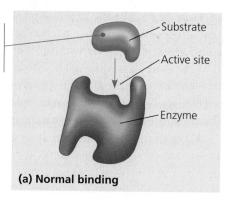

A substrate can bind normally to the active site of an enzyme.

Substrate
Active site
Enzyme

(a) Normal binding

A competitive inhibitor mimics the substrate, competing for the active site.

Competitive inhibitor

(b) Competitive inhibition

A noncompetitive inhibitor binds to the enzyme away from the active site, altering the shape of the enzyme so that even if the substrate can bind, the active site functions less effectively.

Noncompetitive inhibitor

(c) Noncompetitive inhibition

▲ **Figure 8.19 Inhibition of enzyme activity.**

cell often regulate enzyme activity by acting as inhibitors. Such regulation—selective inhibition—is essential to the control of cellular metabolism, as we discuss next.

CONCEPT CHECK 8.4

1. Many spontaneous reactions occur very slowly. Why don't all spontaneous reactions occur instantly?
2. Why do enzymes act only on very specific substrates?
3. **WHAT IF?** Malonate is an inhibitor of the enzyme succinate dehydrogenase. How would you determine whether malonate is a competitive or noncompetitive inhibitor?

For suggested answers, see Appendix A.

Regulation of enzyme activity helps control metabolism

Chemical chaos would result if all of a cell's metabolic pathways were operating simultaneously. Intrinsic to the process of life is a cell's ability to tightly regulate its metabolic pathways by controlling when and where its various enzymes are active. It does this either by switching on and off the genes that encode specific enzymes (as we will discuss in Unit Three) or, as we discuss here, by regulating the activity of enzymes once they are made.

Allosteric Regulation of Enzymes

In many cases, the molecules that naturally regulate enzyme activity in a cell behave something like reversible noncompetitive inhibitors (see Figure 8.19c): These regulatory molecules change an enzyme's shape and the functioning of its active site by binding to a site elsewhere on the molecule, via noncovalent interactions. **Allosteric regulation** is the term used to describe any case in which a protein's function at one site is affected by the binding of a regulatory molecule to a separate site. It may result in either inhibition or stimulation of an enzyme's activity.

Allosteric Activation and Inhibition

Most enzymes known to be allosterically regulated are constructed from two or more subunits, each composed of a polypeptide chain and having its own active site (Figure 8.20). Each subunit has its own active site. The entire complex oscillates between two different shapes, one catalytically active and the other inactive (Figure 8.20a). In the simplest case of allosteric regulation, an activating or inhibiting regulatory molecule binds to a regulatory site (sometimes called an allosteric site), often located where subunits join. The binding of an *activator* to a regulatory site stabilizes the shape that has functional active sites, whereas the binding of an *inhibitor* stabilizes the inactive form of the enzyme. The subunits of an allosteric enzyme fit together in such a way that a shape change in one subunit is transmitted to all others. Through this interaction of subunits, a single activator or inhibitor molecule that binds to one regulatory site will affect the active sites of all subunits.

Fluctuating concentrations of regulators can cause a sophisticated pattern of response in the activity of cellular enzymes. The products of ATP hydrolysis (ADP and $\circled{P}_i$), for example, play a complex role in balancing the flow of traffic between anabolic and catabolic pathways by their effects on key enzymes. ATP binds to several catabolic enzymes allosterically, lowering their affinity for substrate and thus inhibiting their activity. ADP, however, functions as an activator of the same enzymes. This is logical because a major function of catabolism is to regenerate ATP. If ATP production lags behind its use, ADP ac-

cumulates and activates the enzymes that speed up catabolism, producing more ATP. If the supply of ATP exceeds demand, then catabolism slows down as ATP molecules accumulate and bind these same enzymes, inhibiting them. (You'll see specific examples of this type of regulation when you learn about cellular respiration in the next chapter.) ATP, ADP, and other related

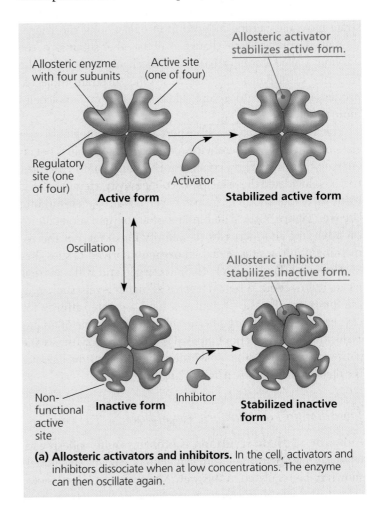

(a) **Allosteric activators and inhibitors.** In the cell, activators and inhibitors dissociate when at low concentrations. The enzyme can then oscillate again.

(b) **Cooperativity: another type of allosteric activation.** The inactive form shown on the left oscillates back and forth with the active form when the active form is not stabilized by substrate.

▲ Figure 8.20 **Allosteric regulation of enzyme activity.**

molecules also affect key enzymes in anabolic pathways. In this way, allosteric enzymes control the rates of key reactions in both sorts of metabolic pathways.

In another kind of allosteric activation, a *substrate* molecule binding to one active site may stimulate the catalytic powers of a multisubunit enzyme by affecting the other active sites **(Figure 8.20b)**. If an enzyme has two or more subunits, a substrate molecule causing induced fit in one subunit can trigger the same favorable shape change in all the other subunits of the enzyme. Called **cooperativity**, this mechanism amplifies the response of enzymes to substrates: One substrate molecule primes an enzyme to accept additional substrate molecules more readily.

The vertebrate oxygen transport protein hemoglobin is a classic example of cooperativity. Although hemoglobin is not an enzyme, the study of how cooperative binding works in this protein has elucidated the principle of cooperativity. Hemoglobin is made up of four subunits, each of which has an oxygen-binding site (see Figure 5.21). The binding of an oxygen molecule to each binding site increases the affinity for oxygen of the remaining binding sites. Thus, in oxygen-deprived tissues, hemoglobin will be less likely to bind oxygen and will release it where it is needed. Where oxygen is at higher levels, such as in the lungs or gills, the protein will have a greater affinity for oxygen as more binding sites are filled. An example of an enzyme that exhibits cooperativity is the first enzyme in the pathway for pyrimidine biosynthesis in bacteria (this enzyme is called aspartyl transcarbamoylase).

Identification of Allosteric Regulators

Although allosteric regulation is probably quite widespread, relatively few of the many known metabolic enzymes have been shown to be regulated in this way. Allosteric regulatory molecules are hard to characterize, in part because they tend to bind the enzyme at low affinity and are thus hard to isolate. Recently, however, pharmaceutical companies have turned their attention to allosteric regulators. These molecules are attractive drug candidates for enzyme regulation because they exhibit higher specificity for particular enzymes than do inhibitors that bind to the active site. (An active site may be similar to the active site in another, related enzyme, whereas allosteric regulatory sites appear to be quite distinct between enzymes.)

Figure 8.21 describes a search for allosteric regulators, carried out as a collaboration between researchers at the University of California at San Francisco and a company called Sunesis Pharmaceuticals. The study was designed to find allosteric inhibitors of *caspases*, protein-digesting enzymes that play an active role in inflammation and cell death. (You'll learn more about caspases and cell death in Chapter 11.) By specifically regulating these enzymes, we may be able to better manage inappropriate inflammatory responses, such as those commonly seen in vascular and neurodegenerative diseases.

▼ **Figure 8.21** **Inquiry**

Are there allosteric inhibitors of caspase enzymes?

EXPERIMENT   In an effort to identify allosteric inhibitors of caspases, Justin Scheer and co-workers screened close to 8,000 compounds for their ability to bind to a possible allosteric binding site in caspase 1 and inhibit the enzyme's activity. Each compound was designed to form a disulfide bond with a cysteine near the site in order to stabilize the low-affinity interaction that is expected of an allosteric inhibitor. As the caspases are known to exist in both active and inactive forms, the researchers hypothesized that this linkage might lock the enzyme in the inactive form.

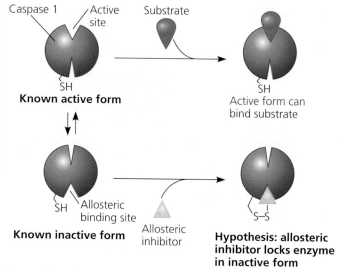

To test this model, X-ray diffraction analysis was used to determine the structure of caspase 1 when bound to one of the inhibitors and to compare it with the active and inactive structures.

RESULTS   Fourteen compounds were identified that could bind to the proposed allosteric site (red) of caspase 1 and block enzymatic activity. The enzyme's shape when one such inhibitor was bound resembled the inactive caspase 1 more than the active form.

| Active form | Allosterically inhibited form | Inactive form |

CONCLUSION   The inhibitory compound that was studied apparently locks the enzyme in its inactive form, as expected for a true allosteric regulator. The data therefore support the existence of an allosteric inhibitory site on caspase 1, which can be used to control enzymatic activity.

SOURCE   J. M. Scheer et al., A common allosteric site and mechanism in caspases, *PNAS* 103:7595–7600 (2006).

WHAT IF?   As a control, the researchers broke the disulfide linkage between one of the inhibitors and the caspase. Assuming that the experimental solution contains no other inhibitors, how would you expect the resulting caspase 1 activity to be affected?

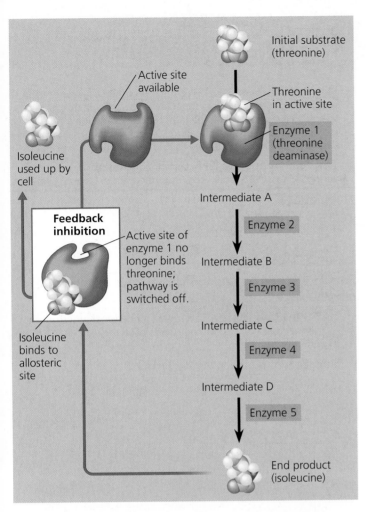

▲ **Figure 8.22 Feedback inhibition in isoleucine synthesis.**

Feedback Inhibition

When ATP allosterically inhibits an enzyme in an ATP-generating pathway, as we discussed earlier, the result is feedback inhibition, a common method of metabolic control. In **feedback inhibition**, a metabolic pathway is switched off by the inhibitory binding of its end product to an enzyme that acts early in the pathway. **Figure 8.22** shows an example of this control mechanism operating on an anabolic pathway. Some cells use this five-step pathway to synthesize the amino acid isoleucine from threonine, another amino acid. As isoleucine accumulates, it slows down its own synthesis by allosterically inhibiting the enzyme for the first step of the pathway. Feedback inhibition thereby prevents the cell from wasting chemical resources by making more isoleucine than is necessary.

Specific Localization of Enzymes Within the Cell

The cell is not just a bag of chemicals with thousands of different kinds of enzymes and substrates in a random mix. The cell is compartmentalized, and cellular structures help bring order to metabolic pathways. In some cases, a team of enzymes for several steps of a metabolic pathway are assembled

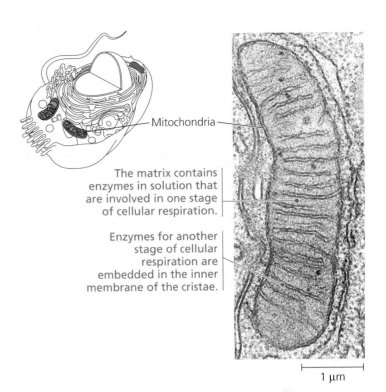

▲ **Figure 8.23 Organelles and structural order in metabolism.** Organelles such as these mitochondria (TEM) contain enzymes that carry out specific functions, in this case cellular respiration.

into a multienzyme complex. The arrangement facilitates the sequence of reactions, with the product from the first enzyme becoming the substrate for an adjacent enzyme in the complex, and so on, until the end product is released. Some enzymes and enzyme complexes have fixed locations within the cell and act as structural components of particular membranes. Others are in solution within specific membrane-enclosed eukaryotic organelles, each with its own internal chemical environment. For example, in eukaryotic cells, the enzymes for cellular respiration reside in specific locations within mitochondria **(Figure 8.23)**.

In this chapter, you have learned that metabolism, the intersecting set of chemical pathways characteristic of life, is a choreographed interplay of thousands of different kinds of cellular molecules. In the next chapter, we explore cellular respiration, the major catabolic pathway that breaks down organic molecules, releasing energy for the crucial processes of life.

CONCEPT CHECK 8.5

1. How can an activator and an inhibitor have different effects on an allosterically regulated enzyme?
2. **WHAT IF?** Imagine you are a pharmacological researcher who wants to design a drug that inhibits a particular enzyme. Upon reading the scientific literature, you find that the enzyme's active site is similar to that of several other enzymes. What might be the best approach to developing your inhibitor drug?

For suggested answers, see Appendix A.

Chapter 8 Review

SUMMARY OF KEY CONCEPTS

CONCEPT 8.1

An organism's metabolism transforms matter and energy, subject to the laws of thermodynamics (pp. 142–145)

▶ **Organization of the Chemistry of Life into Metabolic Pathways** Metabolism is the collection of chemical reactions that occur in an organism. Aided by enzymes, it follows intersecting pathways, which may be catabolic (breaking down molecules, releasing energy) or anabolic (building molecules, consuming energy).

▶ **Forms of Energy** Energy is the capacity to cause change; some forms of energy do work by moving matter. Kinetic energy is associated with motion. Potential energy is related to the location or structure of matter and includes chemical energy possessed by a molecule due to its structure.

▶ **The Laws of Energy Transformation** The first law, conservation of energy, states that energy cannot be created or destroyed, only transferred or transformed. The second law states that spontaneous changes, those requiring no outside input of energy, increase the entropy (disorder) of the universe.

MEDIA
MP3 Tutor Basic Energy Concepts
Activity Energy Transformations

CONCEPT 8.2

The free-energy change of a reaction tells us whether or not the reaction occurs spontaneously (pp. 146–149)

▶ **Free-Energy Change, ΔG** A living system's free energy is energy that can do work under cellular conditions. The change in free energy (ΔG) during a biological process is related directly to enthalpy change (ΔH) and to the change in entropy (ΔS): $\Delta G = \Delta H - T\Delta S$.

▶ **Free Energy, Stability, and Equilibrium** Organisms live at the expense of free energy. During a spontaneous change, free energy decreases and the stability of a system increases. At maximum stability, the system is at equilibrium and can do no work.

▶ **Free Energy and Metabolism** In an exergonic (spontaneous) chemical reaction, the products have less free energy than the reactants ($-\Delta G$). Endergonic (nonspontaneous) reactions require an input of energy ($+\Delta G$). The addition of starting materials and the removal of end products prevent metabolism from reaching equilibrium.

CONCEPT 8.3

ATP powers cellular work by coupling exergonic reactions to endergonic reactions (pp. 149–151)

▶ **The Structure and Hydrolysis of ATP** ATP is the cell's energy shuttle. Hydrolysis at its terminal phosphate group produces ADP and phosphate and releases free energy.

▶ **How ATP Performs Work** ATP hydrolysis drives endergonic reactions by phosphorylation, the transfer of a phosphate group to specific reactants, making them more reactive. ATP hydrolysis (sometimes with protein phosphorylation) also causes changes in the shape and binding affinities of transport and motor proteins.

▶ **The Regeneration of ATP** Catabolic pathways drive the regeneration of ATP from ADP and phosphate.

MEDIA
Activity The Structure of ATP
Activity Chemical Reactions and ATP

CONCEPT 8.4

Enzymes speed up metabolic reactions by lowering energy barriers (pp. 151–156)

▶ **The Activation Energy Barrier** In a chemical reaction, the energy necessary to break the bonds of the reactants is the activation energy, E_A.

▶ **How Enzymes Lower the E_A Barrier**

▶ **Substrate Specificity of Enzymes** Each type of enzyme has a unique active site that combines specifically with its substrate, the reactant molecule on which it acts. The enzyme changes shape slightly when it binds the substrate (induced fit).

▶ **Catalysis in the Enzyme's Active Site** The active site can lower an E_A barrier by orienting substrates correctly, straining their bonds, providing a favorable microenvironment, and even covalently bonding with the substrate.

▶ **Effects of Local Conditions on Enzyme Activity** Each enzyme has an optimal temperature and pH. Inhibitors reduce enzyme function. A competitive inhibitor binds to the active site, while a noncompetitive inhibitor binds to a different site on the enzyme.

MEDIA
Activity How Enzymes Work
Investigation How Is the Rate of Enzyme Catalysis Measured?
Biology Labs On-Line EnzymeLab

CONCEPT 8.5

Regulation of enzyme activity helps control metabolism (pp. 157–159)

▶ **Allosteric Regulation of Enzymes** Many enzymes are allosterically regulated: Regulatory molecules, either activators or inhibitors, bind to specific regulatory sites, affecting the shape and function of the enzyme. In cooperativity, binding of one substrate molecule can stimulate binding or activity at other active sites. In feedback inhibition, the end product of a metabolic pathway allosterically inhibits the enzyme for a previous step in the pathway.

▶ **Specific Localization of Enzymes Within the Cell** Some enzymes are grouped into complexes, some are incorporated into membranes, and some are contained inside organelles, increasing the efficiency of metabolic processes.

TESTING YOUR KNOWLEDGE

SELF-QUIZ

1. Choose the pair of terms that correctly completes this sentence: Catabolism is to anabolism as _____ is to _____.
   a. exergonic; spontaneous
   b. exergonic; endergonic
   c. free energy; entropy
   d. work; energy
   e. entropy; enthalpy

2. Most cells cannot harness heat to perform work because
   a. heat is not a form of energy.
   b. cells do not have much heat; they are relatively cool.
   c. temperature is usually uniform throughout a cell.
   d. heat can never be used to do work.
   e. heat must remain constant during work.

3. Which of the following metabolic processes can occur without a net influx of energy from some other process?
   a. $ADP + \textcircled{P}_i \rightarrow ATP + H_2O$
   b. $C_6H_{12}O_6 + 6\,O_2 \rightarrow 6\,CO_2 + 6\,H_2O$
   c. $6\,CO_2 + 6\,H_2O \rightarrow C_6H_{12}O_6 + 6\,O_2$
   d. amino acids $\rightarrow$ protein
   e. glucose + fructose $\rightarrow$ sucrose

4. If an enzyme in solution is saturated with substrate, the most effective way to obtain a faster yield of products is to
   a. add more of the enzyme.
   b. heat the solution to 90°C.
   c. add more substrate.
   d. add an allosteric inhibitor.
   e. add a noncompetitive inhibitor.

5. If an enzyme is added to a solution where its substrate and product are in equilibrium, what would occur?
   a. Additional product would be formed.
   b. Additional substrate would be formed.
   c. The reaction would change from endergonic to exergonic.
   d. The free energy of the system would change.
   e. Nothing; the reaction would stay at equilibrium.

6. Some bacteria are metabolically active in hot springs because
   a. they are able to maintain a lower internal temperature.
   b. high temperatures make catalysis unnecessary.
   c. their enzymes have high optimal temperatures.
   d. their enzymes are completely insensitive to temperature.
   e. they use molecules other than proteins or RNAs as their main catalysts.

7. **DRAW IT** Using a series of arrows, draw the branched metabolic reaction pathway described by the following statements, and then answer the question at the end. Use red arrows and minus signs to indicate inhibition.

   L can form either M or N.
   M can form O.
   O can form either P or R.
   P can form Q.
   R can form S.
   O inhibits the reaction of L to form M.
   Q inhibits the reaction of O to form P.
   S inhibits the reaction of O to form R.

   Which reaction would prevail if both Q and S were present in the cell in high concentrations?
   a. $L \rightarrow M$
   b. $M \rightarrow O$
   c. $L \rightarrow N$
   d. $O \rightarrow P$
   e. $R \rightarrow S$

For Self-Quiz answers, see Appendix A.

MEDIA Visit the Study Area at **www.masteringbio.com** for a Practice Test.

EVOLUTION CONNECTION

8. A recent revival of the antievolutionary "intelligent design" argument holds that biochemical pathways are too complex to have evolved, because all intermediate steps in a given pathway must be present to produce the final product. Critique this argument. How could you use the diversity of metabolic pathways that produce the same or similar products to support your case?

SCIENTIFIC INQUIRY

9. **DRAW IT** A researcher has developed an assay to measure the activity of an important enzyme present in liver cells being grown in culture. She adds the enzyme's substrate to a dish of cells and then measures the appearance of reaction products. The results are graphed as the amount of product on the y-axis versus time on the x-axis. The researcher notes four sections of the graph. For a short period of time, no products appear (section A). Then (section B) the reaction rate is quite high (the slope of the line is steep). Next, the reaction gradually slows down (section C). Finally, the graph line becomes flat (section D). Draw and label the graph, and propose a model to explain the molecular events occurring at each stage of this reaction profile.

SCIENCE, TECHNOLOGY, AND SOCIETY

10. The EPA is evaluating the safety of the most commonly used organophosphate insecticides (organic compounds containing phosphate groups). Organophosphates typically interfere with nerve transmission by inhibiting the enzymes that degrade transmitter molecules diffusing from one neuron to another. Noxious insects are not uniquely susceptible; humans and other vertebrates can be affected as well. Thus, the use of organophosphate pesticides creates some health risks. As a consumer, what level of risk are you willing to accept in exchange for an abundant and affordable food supply?

Cellular Respiration
Harvesting Chemical Energy

9

OVERVIEW

Life Is Work

Living cells require transfusions of energy from outside sources to perform their many tasks—for example, assembling polymers, pumping substances across membranes, moving, and reproducing. The giant panda in **Figure 9.1** obtains energy for its cells by eating plants; some animals feed on other organisms that eat plants. The energy stored in the organic molecules of food ultimately comes from the sun. Energy flows into an ecosystem as sunlight and leaves as heat **(Figure 9.2)**. In contrast, the chemical elements essential to life are recycled. Photosynthesis generates oxygen and organic molecules used by the mitochondria of eukaryotes (including plants and algae) as fuel for cellular respiration. Respiration breaks this fuel down, generating ATP. The waste products of this type of respiration, carbon dioxide and water, are the raw materials for photosynthesis. In this chapter, we consider how cells harvest the chemical energy stored in organic molecules and use it to generate ATP, the molecule that drives most cellular work. After presenting some basics about respiration, we will focus on the three key pathways of respiration: glycolysis, the citric acid cycle, and oxidative phosphorylation.

▲ **Figure 9.1 How do these leaves power the work of life for the giant panda?**

▲ **Figure 9.2 Energy flow and chemical recycling in ecosystems.** Energy flows into an ecosystem as sunlight and ultimately leaves as heat, while the chemical elements essential to life are recycled.

CONCEPT 9.1
Catabolic pathways yield energy by oxidizing organic fuels

As you learned in Chapter 8, metabolic pathways that release stored energy by breaking down complex molecules are called catabolic pathways. Electron transfer plays a major role in these pathways. In this section, we consider these processes, which are central to cellular respiration.

Catabolic Pathways and Production of ATP

Organic compounds possess potential energy as a result of their arrangement of atoms. Compounds that can participate in exergonic reactions can act as fuels. With the help of enzymes, a cell systematically degrades complex organic molecules that are rich in potential energy to simpler waste products that have less energy. Some of the energy taken out of chemical storage can be used to do work; the rest is dissipated as heat.

One catabolic process, **fermentation**, is a partial degradation of sugars that occurs without the use of oxygen. However, the most prevalent and efficient catabolic pathway is **aerobic respiration**, in which oxygen is consumed as a reactant along with the organic fuel (*aerobic* is from the Greek *aer*, air, and *bios*, life). The cells of most eukaryotic and many prokaryotic organisms can carry out aerobic respiration. Some prokaryotes use substances other than oxygen as reactants in a similar process that harvests chemical energy without using any oxygen at all; this process is called *anaerobic respiration* (the prefix *an-* means "without"). Technically, the term **cellular respiration** includes both aerobic and anaerobic processes. However, it originated as a synonym for aerobic respiration because of the relationship of that process to organismal respiration, in which an animal breathes in oxygen. Thus, *cellular respiration* is often used to refer to the aerobic process, a practice we follow in most of this chapter.

Although very different in mechanism, aerobic respiration is in principle similar to the combustion of gasoline in an automobile engine after oxygen is mixed with the fuel (hydrocarbons). Food provides the fuel for respiration, and the exhaust is carbon dioxide and water. The overall process can be summarized as follows:

$$\text{Organic compounds} + \text{Oxygen} \longrightarrow \text{Carbon dioxide} + \text{Water} + \text{Energy}$$

Although carbohydrates, fats, and proteins can all be processed and consumed as fuel, it is helpful to learn the steps of cellular respiration by tracking the degradation of the sugar glucose ($C_6H_{12}O_6$):

$$C_6H_{12}O_6 + 6\,O_2 \longrightarrow 6\,CO_2 + 6\,H_2O + \text{Energy (ATP + heat)}$$

Glucose is the fuel that cells most often use; we will discuss other organic molecules contained in foods later in the chapter.

This breakdown of glucose is exergonic, having a free-energy change of −686 kcal (2,870 kJ) per mole of glucose decomposed ($\Delta G = -686$ kcal/mol). Recall that a negative ΔG indicates that the products of the chemical process store less energy than the reactants and that the reaction can happen spontaneously—in other words, without an input of energy.

Catabolic pathways do not directly move flagella, pump solutes across membranes, polymerize monomers, or perform other cellular work. Catabolism is linked to work by a chemical drive shaft—ATP, which you learned about in Chapter 8. To keep working, the cell must regenerate its supply of ATP from ADP and P_i (see Figure 8.12). To understand how cellular respiration accomplishes this, let's examine the fundamental chemical processes known as oxidation and reduction.

Redox Reactions: Oxidation and Reduction

How do the catabolic pathways that decompose glucose and other organic fuels yield energy? The answer is based on the transfer of electrons during the chemical reactions. The relocation of electrons releases energy stored in organic molecules, and this energy ultimately is used to synthesize ATP.

The Principle of Redox

In many chemical reactions, there is a transfer of one or more electrons (e^-) from one reactant to another. These electron transfers are called oxidation-reduction reactions, or **redox reactions** for short. In a redox reaction, the loss of electrons from one substance is called **oxidation**, and the addition of electrons to another substance is known as **reduction**. (Note that *adding* electrons is called *reduction*; negatively charged electrons added to an atom *reduce* the amount of positive charge of that atom.) To take a simple, non-biological example, consider the reaction between the elements sodium (Na) and chlorine (Cl) that forms table salt:

$$
\begin{array}{c}
\overbrace{}^{\text{becomes oxidized (loses electron)}} \\
Na + Cl \longrightarrow Na^+ + Cl^- \\
\underbrace{}_{\text{becomes reduced (gains electron)}}
\end{array}
$$

We could generalize a redox reaction this way:

$$
\begin{array}{c}
\overbrace{}^{\text{becomes oxidized}} \\
Xe^- + Y \longrightarrow X + Ye^- \\
\underbrace{}_{\text{becomes reduced}}
\end{array}
$$

In the generalized reaction, substance Xe^-, the electron donor, is called the **reducing agent**; it reduces Y, which accepts the donated electron. Substance Y, the electron acceptor, is the **oxidizing agent**; it oxidizes Xe^- by removing its electron. Because an electron transfer requires both a donor and an acceptor, oxidation and reduction always go together.

Not all redox reactions involve the complete transfer of electrons from one substance to another; some change the degree of electron sharing in covalent bonds. The reaction between methane and oxygen, shown in **Figure 9.3** on the next page, is an example. As explained in Chapter 2, the covalent electrons in methane are shared nearly equally between the bonded atoms because carbon and hydrogen have about the same affinity for valence electrons; they are about equally electronegative. But when methane reacts with oxygen, forming carbon dioxide, electrons end up shared less equally between the carbon atom and its new covalent partners, the oxygen atoms, which are very electronegative. In effect, the carbon atom has partially "lost" its shared electrons; thus, methane has been oxidized.

Reactants **Products**

becomes oxidized

$$CH_4 + 2 O_2 \longrightarrow CO_2 + Energy + 2 H_2O$$

becomes reduced

Methane (reducing agent) Oxygen (oxidizing agent) Carbon dioxide Water

▲ **Figure 9.3 Methane combustion as an energy-yielding redox reaction.** The reaction releases energy to the surroundings because the electrons lose potential energy when they end up being shared unequally, spending more time near electronegative atoms such as oxygen.

Now let's examine the fate of the reactant O_2. The two atoms of the oxygen molecule (O_2) share their electrons equally. But when oxygen reacts with the hydrogen from methane, forming water, the electrons of the covalent bonds spend more time near the oxygen (see Figure 9.3). In effect, each oxygen atom has partially "gained" electrons, so the oxygen molecule has been reduced. Because oxygen is so electronegative, it is one of the most potent of all oxidizing agents.

Energy must be added to pull an electron away from an atom, just as energy is required to push a ball uphill. The more electronegative the atom (the stronger its pull on electrons), the more energy is required to take an electron away from it. An electron loses potential energy when it shifts from a less electronegative atom toward a more electronegative one, just as a ball loses potential energy when it rolls downhill. A redox reaction that moves electrons closer to oxygen, such as the burning (oxidation) of methane, therefore releases chemical energy that can be put to work.

Oxidation of Organic Fuel Molecules During Cellular Respiration

The oxidation of methane by oxygen is the main combustion reaction that occurs at the burner of a gas stove. The combustion of gasoline in an automobile engine is also a redox reaction; the energy released pushes the pistons. But the energy-yielding redox process of greatest interest to biologists is respiration: the oxidation of glucose and other molecules in food. Examine again the summary equation for cellular respiration, but this time think of it as a redox process:

becomes oxidized

$$C_6H_{12}O_6 + 6 O_2 \longrightarrow 6 CO_2 + 6 H_2O + Energy$$

becomes reduced

As in the combustion of methane or gasoline, the fuel (glucose) is oxidized and oxygen is reduced. The electrons lose potential energy along the way, and energy is released.

In general, organic molecules that have an abundance of hydrogen are excellent fuels because their bonds are a source of "hilltop" electrons, whose energy may be released as these electrons "fall" down an energy gradient when they are transferred to oxygen. The summary equation for respiration indicates that hydrogen is transferred from glucose to oxygen. But the important point, not visible in the summary equation, is that the energy state of the electron changes as hydrogen (with its electron) is transferred to oxygen. In respiration, the oxidation of glucose transfers electrons to a lower energy state, liberating energy that becomes available for ATP synthesis.

The main energy foods, carbohydrates and fats, are reservoirs of electrons associated with hydrogen. Only the barrier of activation energy holds back the flood of electrons to a lower energy state (see Figure 8.14). Without this barrier, a food substance like glucose would combine almost instantaneously with O_2. When we supply the activation energy by igniting glucose, it burns in air, releasing 686 kcal (2,870 kJ) of heat per mole of glucose (about 180 g). Body temperature is not high enough to initiate burning, of course. Instead, if you swallow some glucose, enzymes in your cells will lower the barrier of activation energy, allowing the sugar to be oxidized in a series of steps.

Stepwise Energy Harvest via NAD$^+$ and the Electron Transport Chain

If energy is released from a fuel all at once, it cannot be harnessed efficiently for constructive work. For example, if a gasoline tank explodes, it cannot drive a car very far. Cellular respiration does not oxidize glucose in a single explosive step either. Rather, glucose and other organic fuels are broken down in a series of steps, each one catalyzed by an enzyme. At key steps, electrons are stripped from the glucose. As is often the case in oxidation reactions, each electron travels with a proton—thus, as a hydrogen atom. The hydrogen atoms are not transferred directly to oxygen, but instead are usually passed first to an electron carrier, a coenzyme called **NAD$^+$** (nicotinamide adenine dinucleotide, a derivative of the vitamin niacin). As an electron acceptor, NAD$^+$ functions as an oxidizing agent during respiration.

How does NAD$^+$ trap electrons from glucose and other organic molecules? Enzymes called dehydrogenases remove a pair of hydrogen atoms (2 electrons and 2 protons) from the substrate (glucose, in this example), thereby oxidizing it. The enzyme delivers the 2 electrons along with 1 proton to its coenzyme, NAD$^+$ **(Figure 9.4)**. The other proton is released as a hydrogen ion (H$^+$) into the surrounding solution:

$$H-\underset{|}{\overset{|}{C}}-OH + NAD^+ \xrightarrow{\text{Dehydrogenase}} \underset{|}{\overset{|}{C}}=O + NADH + H^+$$

By receiving 2 negatively charged electrons but only 1 positively charged proton, NAD$^+$ has its charge neutralized when it is reduced to NADH. The name NADH shows the hydrogen that has been received in the reaction. NAD$^+$ is the most versatile electron

NAD⁺

Nicotinamide
(oxidized form)

Dehydrogenase

Reduction of NAD⁺

Oxidation of NADH

$+ \; 2[H]$
(from food)

NADH

Nicotinamide
(reduced form)

▲ **Figure 9.4 NAD⁺ as an electron shuttle.** The full name for NAD^+, nicotinamide adenine dinucleotide, describes its structure: the molecule consists of two nucleotides joined together at their phosphate groups (shown in yellow). (Nicotinamide is a nitrogenous base, although not one that is present in DNA or RNA.) The enzymatic transfer of 2 electrons and 1 proton (H^+) from an organic molecule in food to NAD^+ reduces the NAD^+ to NADH; the second proton (H^+) is released. Most of the electrons removed from food are transferred initially to NAD^+.

acceptor in cellular respiration and functions in several of the redox steps during the breakdown of glucose.

Electrons lose very little of their potential energy when they are transferred from glucose to NAD^+. Each NADH molecule formed during respiration represents stored energy that can be tapped to make ATP when the electrons complete their "fall" down an energy gradient from NADH to oxygen.

How do electrons that are extracted from glucose and stored as potential energy in NADH finally reach oxygen? It will help to compare the redox chemistry of cellular respiration to a much simpler reaction: the reaction between hydrogen and oxygen to form water **(Figure 9.5a)**. Mix H_2 and O_2, provide a spark for activation energy, and the gases combine explosively. In fact, combustion of liquid H_2 and O_2 is harnessed to power the main engines of the space shuttle after it is launched, boosting it into orbit. The explosion represents a release of energy as the electrons of hydrogen "fall" closer to the electronegative oxygen atoms. Cellular respiration also brings hydrogen and oxygen together to form water, but there are two important differences. First, in cellular respiration, the hydrogen that reacts with oxygen is derived from organic molecules rather than H_2. Second, instead of occurring in one explosive reaction, respiration uses an **electron transport chain** to break the fall of electrons to oxygen into several energy-releasing steps **(Figure 9.5b)**. An electron transport chain consists of a number of

molecules, mostly proteins, built into the inner membrane of mitochondria of eukaryotic cells and the plasma membrane of aerobically respiring prokaryotes. Electrons removed from glucose are shuttled by NADH to the "top," higher-energy end of the chain. At the "bottom," lower-energy end, O_2 captures these electrons along with hydrogen nuclei (H^+), forming water.

Electron transfer from NADH to oxygen is an exergonic reaction with a free-energy change of -53 kcal/mol (-222 kJ/mol). Instead of this energy being released and wasted in a single explosive step, electrons cascade down the chain from

(a) Uncontrolled reaction

(b) Cellular respiration

▲ **Figure 9.5 An introduction to electron transport chains. (a)** The one-step exergonic reaction of hydrogen with oxygen to form water releases a large amount of energy in the form of heat and light: an explosion. **(b)** In cellular respiration, the same reaction occurs in stages: An electron transport chain breaks the "fall" of electrons in this reaction into a series of smaller steps and stores some of the released energy in a form that can be used to make ATP. (The rest of the energy is released as heat.)

one carrier molecule to the next in a series of redox reactions, losing a small amount of energy with each step until they finally reach oxygen, the terminal electron acceptor, which has a very great affinity for electrons. Each "downhill" carrier is more electronegative than, and thus capable of oxidizing, its "uphill" neighbor, with oxygen at the bottom of the chain. Therefore, the electrons removed from glucose by NAD^+ fall down an energy gradient in the electron transport chain to a far more stable location in the electronegative oxygen atom. Put another way, oxygen pulls electrons down the chain in an energy-yielding tumble analogous to gravity pulling objects downhill.

In summary, during cellular respiration, most electrons travel the following "downhill" route: glucose → NADH → electron transport chain → oxygen. Later in this chapter, you will learn more about how the cell uses the energy released from this exergonic electron fall to regenerate its supply of ATP. For now, having covered the basic redox mechanisms of cellular respiration, let's look at the entire process.

The Stages of Cellular Respiration: *A Preview*

Respiration is a cumulative function of three metabolic stages:

1. **Glycolysis (color-coded teal throughout the chapter)**
2. **The citric acid cycle (color-coded salmon)**
3. **Oxidative phosphorylation: electron transport and chemiosmosis (color-coded violet)**

Cellular respiration is sometimes defined as including only the citric acid cycle and oxidative phosphorylation. We include glycolysis, however, because most respiring cells deriving energy from glucose use this process to produce starting material for the citric acid cycle.

As diagrammed in **Figure 9.6**, the first two stages of cellular respiration, glycolysis and the citric acid cycle, are the catabolic pathways that break down glucose and other organic fuels. **Glycolysis**, which occurs in the cytosol, begins the degradation process by breaking glucose into two molecules of a compound called pyruvate. The **citric acid cycle**, which takes place within the mitochondrial matrix of eukaryotic cells or simply in the cytosol of prokaryotes, completes the breakdown of glucose by oxidizing a derivative of pyruvate to carbon dioxide. Thus, the carbon dioxide produced by respiration represents fragments of oxidized organic molecules.

Some of the steps of glycolysis and the citric acid cycle are redox reactions in which dehydrogenases transfer electrons from substrates to NAD^+, forming NADH. In the third stage of respiration, the electron transport chain accepts electrons from the breakdown products of the first two stages (most often via NADH) and passes these electrons from one molecule to another. At the end of the chain, the electrons are combined with molecular oxygen and hydrogen ions (H^+), forming water (see Figure 9.5b). The energy released at each step of the chain is stored in a form the mitochondrion (or prokaryotic cell) can use to make ATP. This mode of ATP synthesis is called **oxidative phosphorylation** because it is powered by the redox reactions of the electron transport chain.

In eukaryotic cells, the inner membrane of the mitochondrion is the site of electron transport and chemiosmosis, the processes that together constitute oxidative phosphorylation. In prokaryotes, these processes take place in the plasma membrane. Oxidative phosphorylation accounts for almost 90% of the ATP generated by respiration. A smaller amount of ATP is formed directly in a few reactions of glycolysis and the citric acid cycle by a mechanism called **substrate-level phosphorylation (Figure 9.7)**. This mode of ATP synthesis occurs when an enzyme transfers a phosphate group from a substrate molecule to ADP, rather than adding an inorganic phosphate to ADP as in oxidative phosphorylation.

▶ **Figure 9.6 An overview of cellular respiration.** During glycolysis, each glucose molecule is broken down into two molecules of the compound pyruvate. In eukaryotic cells, as shown here, the pyruvate enters the mitochondrion, where the citric acid cycle oxidizes it to carbon dioxide. NADH and a similar electron carrier, a coenzyme called $FADH_2$, transfer electrons derived from glucose to electron transport chains, which are built into the inner mitochondrial membrane. (In prokaryotes, the electron transport chains are located in the plasma membrane.) During oxidative phosphorylation, electron transport chains convert the chemical energy to a form used for ATP synthesis in the process called chemiosmosis.

MEDIA **BioFlix** Visit the Study Area at **www.masteringbio.com** for the BioFlix 3-D Animation on Cellular Respiration.

Figure 9.7 Substrate-level phosphorylation. Some ATP is made by direct transfer of a phosphate group from an organic substrate to ADP by an enzyme. (For examples in glycolysis, see Figure 9.9, steps 7 and 10.)

? *Do you think the potential energy is higher for the reactants or the products? Explain.*

"Substrate molecule" here refers to an organic molecule generated as an intermediate during the catabolism of glucose.

For each molecule of glucose degraded to carbon dioxide and water by respiration, the cell makes up to about 38 molecules of ATP, each with 7.3 kcal/mol of free energy. Respiration cashes in the large denomination of energy banked in a single molecule of glucose (686 kcal/mol) for the small change of many molecules of ATP, which is more practical for the cell to spend on its work.

This preview has introduced you to how glycolysis, the citric acid cycle, and oxidative phosphorylation fit into the process of cellular respiration. We are now ready to take a closer look at each of these three stages of respiration.

CONCEPT CHECK 9.1

1. Compare and contrast aerobic and anaerobic respiration.
2. **WHAT IF?** If the following redox reaction occurred, which compound would be oxidized and which reduced?

   $C_4H_6O_5 + NAD^+ \rightarrow C_4H_4O_5 + NADH + H^+$

   For suggested answers, see Appendix A.

CONCEPT 9.2

Glycolysis harvests chemical energy by oxidizing glucose to pyruvate

The word *glycolysis* means "sugar splitting," and that is exactly what happens during this pathway. Glucose, a six-carbon sugar, is split into two three-carbon sugars. These smaller sugars are then oxidized and their remaining atoms rearranged to form two molecules of pyruvate. (Pyruvate is the ionized form of pyruvic acid.)

As summarized in **Figure 9.8**, glycolysis can be divided into two phases: energy investment and energy payoff. During the energy investment phase, the cell actually spends ATP. This investment is repaid with interest during the energy payoff phase, when ATP is produced by substrate-level phosphorylation and NAD^+ is reduced to NADH by electrons released

Energy investment phase

Glucose

2 ADP + 2 (P) ⟵ 2 ATP used

Energy payoff phase

4 ADP + 4 (P) ⟶ 4 ATP formed

$2 NAD^+ + 4 e^- + 4 H^+$ ⟶ 2 NADH + 2 H⁺

2 Pyruvate + 2 H_2O

Net

Glucose ⟶ 2 Pyruvate + 2 H_2O

4 ATP formed – 2 ATP used ⟶ 2 ATP

$2 NAD^+ + 4 e^- + 4 H^+$ ⟶ 2 NADH + 2 H⁺

Figure 9.8 The energy input and output of glycolysis.

from the oxidation of glucose. The net energy yield from glycolysis, per glucose molecule, is 2 ATP plus 2 NADH. The ten steps of the glycolytic pathway are described in more detail in **Figure 9.9**, on the next two pages, which you should study carefully before continuing.

In the end, all of the carbon originally present in glucose is accounted for in the two molecules of pyruvate; no CO_2 is released during glycolysis. Glycolysis occurs whether or not O_2 is present. However, if O_2 *is* present, the chemical energy stored in pyruvate and NADH can be extracted by the citric acid cycle and oxidative phosphorylation.

CONCEPT CHECK 9.2

1. During the redox reaction in glycolysis (step 6 in Figure 9.9), which molecule acts as the oxidizing agent? The reducing agent?
2. **WHAT IF?** Step 3 in Figure 9.9 is a major point of regulation of glycolysis. The enzyme phosphofructokinase is allosterically regulated by ATP and related molecules. Considering the overall result of glycolysis, would you expect ATP to inhibit or stimulate activity of this enzyme? (*Hint:* Make sure you consider the role of ATP as an allosteric regulator, not as a substrate of the enzyme.)

   For suggested answers, see Appendix A.

▼ **Figure 9.9** **A closer look at glycolysis.** The orientation diagram at the right relates glycolysis to the entire process of respiration. Do not let the chemical detail in the main diagram block your view of glycolysis as a source of ATP and NADH.

ENERGY INVESTMENT PHASE

1 Glucose enters the cell and is phosphorylated by the enzyme hexokinase, which transfers a phosphate group from ATP to the sugar. The charge of the phosphate group traps the sugar in the cell because the plasma membrane is impermeable to large ions. Phosphorylation also makes glucose more chemically reactive. In this diagram, the transfer of a phosphate group or pair of electrons from one reactant to another is indicated by coupled arrows: ⇗⇛

2 Glucose-6-phosphate is converted to its isomer, fructose-6-phosphate.

3 This enzyme transfers a phosphate group from ATP to the sugar, investing another molecule of ATP in glycolysis. So far, 2 ATP have been used. With phosphate groups on its opposite ends, the sugar is now ready to be split in half. This is a key step for regulation of glycolysis; phosphofructokinase is allosterically regulated by ATP and its products.

4 This is the reaction from which glycolysis gets its name. The enzyme cleaves the sugar molecule into two different three-carbon sugars: dihydroxyacetone phosphate and glyceraldehyde-3-phosphate. These two sugars are isomers of each other.

5 Isomerase catalyzes the reversible conversion between the two three-carbon sugars. This reaction never reaches equilibrium in the cell because the next enzyme in glycolysis uses only glyceraldehyde-3-phosphate as its substrate (and not dihydroxyacetone phosphate). This pulls the equilibrium in the direction of glyceraldehyde-3-phosphate, which is removed as fast as it forms. Thus, the net result of steps 4 and 5 is cleavage of a six-carbon sugar into two molecules of glyceraldehyde-3-phosphate; each will progress through the remaining steps of glycolysis.

WHAT IF? *What would happen if you removed dihydroxyacetone phosphate as fast as it was produced?*

ENERGY PAYOFF PHASE

6 This enzyme catalyzes two sequential reactions while it holds glyceraldehyde-3-phosphate in its active site. First, the sugar is oxidized by the transfer of electrons and H$^+$ to NAD$^+$, forming NADH (a redox reaction). This reaction is very exergonic, and the enzyme uses the released energy to attach a phosphate group to the oxidized substrate, making a product of very high potential energy. The source of the phosphates is the pool of inorganic phosphate ions that are always present in the cytosol. Notice that the coefficient 2 precedes all molecules in the energy payoff phase; these steps occur after glucose has been split into two three-carbon sugars (step 4).

7 Glycolysis produces some ATP by substrate-level phosphorylation. The phosphate group added in the previous step is transferred to ADP in an exergonic reaction. For each glucose molecule that began glycolysis, step 7 produces 2 ATP, since every product after the sugar-splitting step (step 4) is doubled. Recall that 2 ATP were invested to get sugar ready for splitting; this ATP debt has now been repaid. Glucose has been converted to two molecules of 3-phosphoglycerate, which is not a sugar. The carbonyl group that characterizes a sugar has been oxidized to a carboxyl group (— COO$^-$), the hallmark of an organic acid. The sugar was oxidized in step 6, and now the energy made available by that oxidation has been used to make ATP.

8 This enzyme relocates the remaining phosphate group, preparing the substrate for the next reaction.

9 This enzyme causes a double bond to form in the substrate by extracting a water molecule, yielding phosphoenolpyruvate (PEP). The electrons of the substrate are rearranged in such a way that the resulting phosphorylated compound has a very high potential energy, allowing step 10 to occur.

10 The last reaction of glycolysis produces more ATP by transferring the phosphate group from PEP to ADP, a second instance of substrate-level phosphorylation. Since this step occurs twice for each glucose molecule, 2 ATP are produced. Overall, glycolysis has used 2 ATP in the energy investment phase (steps 1 and 3) and produced 4 ATP in the energy payoff phase (steps 7 and 10), for a net gain of 2 ATP. Glycolysis has repaid the ATP investment with 100% interest. Additional energy was stored by step 6 in NADH, which can be used to make ATP by oxidative phosphorylation if oxygen is present. Glucose has been broken down and oxidized to two molecules of pyruvate, the end product of the glycolytic pathway. If oxygen is present, the chemical energy in pyruvate can be extracted by the citric acid cycle. If oxygen is not present, fermentation may occur; this will be described later.

CONCEPT 9.3

The citric acid cycle completes the energy-yielding oxidation of organic molecules

Glycolysis releases less than a quarter of the chemical energy stored in glucose; most of the energy remains stockpiled in the two molecules of pyruvate. If molecular oxygen is present, the pyruvate enters a mitochondrion (in eukaryotic cells), where the enzymes of the citric acid cycle complete the oxidation of glucose. (In prokaryotic cells, this process occurs in the cytosol.)

Upon entering the mitochondrion via active transport, pyruvate is first converted to a compound called acetyl coenzyme A, or **acetyl CoA (Figure 9.10)**. This step, the junction between glycolysis and the citric acid cycle, is accomplished by a multi-enzyme complex that catalyzes three reactions: ❶ Pyruvate's carboxyl group ($-COO^-$), which is already fully oxidized and thus has little chemical energy, is removed and given off as a molecule of CO_2. (This is the first step in which CO_2 is released during respiration.) ❷ The remaining two-carbon fragment is oxidized, forming a compound named acetate (the ionized form of acetic acid). An enzyme transfers the extracted electrons to NAD^+, storing energy in the form of NADH. ❸ Finally, coenzyme A (CoA), a sulfur-containing compound derived from a B vitamin, is attached to the acetate by an unstable bond (the wavy line in Figure 9.10) that makes the acetyl group (the attached acetate) very reactive. Because of the chemical nature of the CoA group, the product of this chemical grooming, acetyl CoA, has a high potential energy; in other words, the reaction of acetyl CoA to yield lower-energy products is highly exergonic. This molecule is now ready to feed its acetyl group into the citric acid cycle for further oxidation.

The citric acid cycle is also called the tricarboxylic acid cycle or the Krebs cycle, the latter honoring Hans Krebs, the German-British scientist who was largely responsible for working out the pathway in the 1930s. The cycle functions as a metabolic furnace that oxidizes organic fuel derived from pyruvate. **Figure 9.11** summarizes the inputs and outputs as pyruvate is broken down to three CO_2 molecules, including the molecule of CO_2 released during the conversion of pyruvate to acetyl CoA. The cycle generates 1 ATP per turn by substrate-level phosphorylation, but most of the chemical energy is transferred to NAD^+ and a related electron carrier, the coenzyme FAD (flavin adenine dinucleotide, derived from riboflavin, a B vitamin), during the redox reactions. The reduced coenzymes, NADH and $FADH_2$, shuttle their cargo of high-energy electrons to the electron transport chain.

Now let's look at the citric acid cycle in more detail. The cycle has eight steps, each catalyzed by a specific enzyme. You can see in **Figure 9.12** that for each turn of the citric acid cycle, two

▲ **Figure 9.11 An overview of the citric acid cycle.** To calculate the inputs and outputs on a per-glucose basis, multiply by 2, because each glucose molecule is split during glycolysis into two pyruvate molecules.

▲ **Figure 9.10 Conversion of pyruvate to acetyl CoA, the junction between glycolysis and the citric acid cycle.**
Pyruvate is a charged molecule, so in eukaryotic cells it must enter the mitochondrion via active transport, with the help of a transport protein. Next, a complex of several enzymes (the pyruvate dehydrogenase complex) catalyzes the three numbered steps, which are described in the text. The acetyl group of acetyl CoA will enter the citric acid cycle. The CO_2 molecule will diffuse out of the cell.

1 Acetyl CoA adds its two-carbon acetyl group to oxaloacetate, producing citrate.

2 Citrate is converted to its isomer, isocitrate, by removal of one water molecule and addition of another.

3 Isocitrate is oxidized, reducing NAD^+ to NADH. Then the resulting compound loses a CO_2 molecule.

4 Another CO_2 is lost, and the resulting compound is oxidized, reducing NAD^+ to NADH. The remaining molecule is then attached to coenzyme A by an unstable bond.

5 CoA is displaced by a phosphate group, which is transferred to GDP, forming GTP, a molecule with functions similar to ATP that, in some cases, is used to generate ATP.

6 Two hydrogens are transferred to FAD, forming $FADH_2$ and oxidizing succinate.

7 Addition of a water molecule rearranges bonds in the substrate.

8 The substrate is oxidized, reducing NAD^+ to NADH and regenerating oxaloacetate.

Acetyl CoA
Oxaloacetate
Citrate
Isocitrate
α-Ketoglutarate
Succinyl CoA
Succinate
Fumarate
Malate
Citric acid cycle

▲ **Figure 9.12 A closer look at the citric acid cycle.** In the chemical structures, red type traces the fate of the two carbon atoms that enter the cycle via acetyl CoA (step 1), and blue type indicates the two carbons that exit the cycle as CO_2 in steps 3 and 4. (The red labeling goes only through step 5 because the succinate molecule is symmetrical; the two ends cannot be distinguished from each other.) Notice that the carbon atoms that enter the cycle from acetyl CoA do not leave the cycle in the same turn. They remain in the cycle, occupying a different location in the molecules on their next turn, after another acetyl group is added. As a consequence, the oxaloacetate that is regenerated at step 8 is composed of different carbon atoms each time around. In eukaryotic cells, all the citric acid cycle enzymes are located in the mitochondrial matrix except for the enzyme that catalyzes step 6, which resides in the inner mitochondrial membrane. Carboxylic acids are represented in their ionized forms, as —COO⁻, because the ionized forms prevail at the pH within the mitochondrion. For example, citrate is the ionized form of citric acid.

carbons (red) enter in the relatively reduced form of an acetyl group (step 1), and two different carbons (blue) leave in the completely oxidized form of CO_2 molecules (steps 3 and 4). The acetyl group of acetyl CoA joins the cycle by combining with the compound oxaloacetate, forming citrate (step 1). (Citrate is the ionized form of citric acid, for which the cycle is named.) The next seven steps decompose the citrate back to oxaloacetate. It is this regeneration of oxaloacetate that makes this process a *cycle*.

Now let's tally the energy-rich molecules produced by the citric acid cycle. For each acetyl group entering the cycle, $3 NAD^+$ are reduced to NADH (steps 3, 4, and 8). In step 6, electrons are transferred not to NAD^+, but to FAD, which accepts 2 electrons and 2 protons to become $FADH_2$. In many animal tissue cells, step 5 produces a guanosine triphosphate (GTP) molecule by substrate-level phosphorylation as shown in Figure 9.12. GTP is a molecule similar to ATP in its structure and cellular function. This GTP may be used to make an ATP molecule (as shown) or directly power work in the cell. In the cells of plants, bacteria, and some animal tissues, step 5 forms an ATP molecule directly by substrate-level phosphorylation. The output from step 5 represents the only ATP generated directly by the citric acid cycle.

Most of the ATP produced by respiration results from oxidative phosphorylation, when the NADH and $FADH_2$ produced by the citric acid cycle relay the electrons extracted from food to the electron transport chain. In the process, they supply the necessary energy for the phosphorylation of ADP to ATP. We will explore this process in the next section.

CONCEPT 9.4
During oxidative phosphorylation, chemiosmosis couples electron transport to ATP synthesis

Our main objective in this chapter is to learn how cells harvest the energy of glucose and other nutrients in food to make ATP. But the metabolic components of respiration we have dissected so far, glycolysis and the citric acid cycle, produce only 4 ATP molecules per glucose molecule, all by substrate-level phosphorylation: 2 net ATP from glycolysis and 2 ATP from the citric acid cycle. At this point, molecules of NADH (and $FADH_2$) account for most of the energy extracted from the glucose. These electron escorts link glycolysis and the citric acid cycle to the machinery of oxidative phosphorylation, which uses energy released by the electron transport chain to power ATP synthesis. In this section, you will learn first how the electron transport chain works, then how electron flow down the chain is coupled to ATP synthesis.

The Pathway of Electron Transport

The electron transport chain is a collection of molecules embedded in the inner membrane of the mitochondrion in eukaryotic cells (in prokaryotes, they reside in the plasma membrane). The folding of the inner membrane to form cristae increases its surface area, providing space for thousands of copies of the chain in each mitochondrion. (Once again, we see that structure fits function.) Most components of the chain are proteins, which exist in multiprotein complexes numbered I through IV. Tightly bound to these proteins are *prosthetic groups*, nonprotein components essential for the catalytic functions of certain enzymes.

Figure 9.13 shows the sequence of electron carriers in the electron transport chain and the drop in free energy as electrons travel down the chain. During electron transport along the chain, electron carriers alternate between reduced and oxidized states as they accept and donate electrons. Each component of the chain becomes reduced when it accepts electrons from its "uphill" neighbor, which has a lower affinity for electrons (is less electronegative). It then returns to its oxidized form as it passes electrons to its "downhill," more electronegative neighbor.

Now let's take a closer look at the electron transport chain in Figure 9.13. We'll first describe the passage of electrons through complex I in some detail, as an illustration of the general principles involved in electron transport. Electrons removed from glucose by NAD^+, during glycolysis and the citric acid cycle, are transferred from NADH to the first molecule of the electron transport chain in complex I. This molecule is a flavoprotein, so named because it has a prosthetic group called flavin mononucleotide (FMN). In the next redox reaction, the flavoprotein returns to its oxidized form as it passes electrons to an iron-sulfur protein (Fe·S in complex I), one of a family of proteins with both iron and sulfur tightly bound. The iron-sulfur protein then passes the electrons to a compound called ubiquinone (Q in Figure 9.13). This electron carrier is a small hydrophobic molecule, the only member of the electron transport chain that is not a protein. Ubiquinone is individually mobile within the membrane rather than residing in a particular complex. (Another name for ubiquinone is coenzyme Q, or CoQ; you may have seen it sold as a nutritional supplement.)

Most of the remaining electron carriers between ubiquinone and oxygen are proteins called **cytochromes**. Their prosthetic

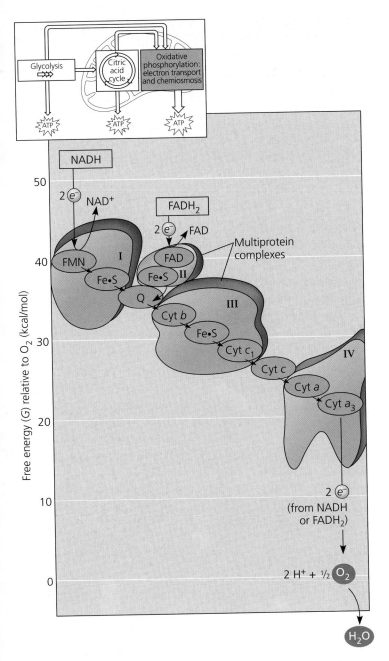

▲ Figure 9.13 Free-energy change during electron transport. The overall energy drop (ΔG) for electrons traveling from NADH to oxygen is 53 kcal/mol, but this "fall" is broken up into a series of smaller steps by the electron transport chain. (An oxygen atom is represented here as $\frac{1}{2} O_2$ to emphasize that the electron transport chain reduces molecular oxygen, O_2, not individual oxygen atoms.)

group, called a heme group, has an iron atom that accepts and donates electrons. (It is similar to the heme group in hemoglobin, the protein of red blood cells, except that the iron in hemoglobin carries oxygen, not electrons.) The electron transport chain has several types of cytochromes, each a different protein with a slightly different electron-carrying heme group. The last cytochrome of the chain, cyt a_3, passes its electrons to oxygen,

which is *very* electronegative. Each oxygen atom also picks up a pair of hydrogen ions from the aqueous solution, forming water.

Another source of electrons for the transport chain is $FADH_2$, the other reduced product of the citric acid cycle. Notice in Figure 9.13 that $FADH_2$ adds its electrons to the electron transport chain at complex II, at a lower energy level than NADH does. Consequently, although NADH and $FADH_2$ each donate an equivalent number of electrons (2) for oxygen reduction, the electron transport chain provides about one-third less energy for ATP synthesis when the electron donor is $FADH_2$ rather than NADH. We'll see why in the next section.

The electron transport chain makes no ATP directly. Instead, it eases the fall of electrons from food to oxygen, breaking a large free-energy drop into a series of smaller steps that release energy in manageable amounts. How does the mitochondrion (or the prokaryotic plasma membrane) couple this electron transport and energy release to ATP synthesis? The answer is a mechanism called chemiosmosis.

Chemiosmosis: The Energy-Coupling Mechanism

Populating the inner membrane of the mitochondrion or the prokaryotic plasma membrane are many copies of a protein complex called **ATP synthase**, the enzyme that actually makes ATP from ADP and inorganic phosphate. ATP synthase works like an ion pump running in reverse. Recall from Chapter 7 that ion pumps usually use ATP as an energy source to transport ions against their gradients. In fact, the proton pump shown in Figure 7.19 is an ATP synthase. As we mentioned in Chapter 8, enzymes can catalyze a reaction in either direction, depending on the ΔG for the reaction, which is affected by the local concentrations of reactants and products. Rather than hydrolyzing ATP to pump protons against their concentration gradient, under the conditions of cellular respiration, ATP synthase uses the energy of an existing ion gradient to power ATP synthesis. The power source for the ATP synthase is a difference in the concentration of H^+ on opposite sides of the inner mitochondrial membrane. (We can also think of this gradient as a difference in pH, since pH is a measure of H^+ concentration.) This process, in which energy stored in the form of a hydrogen ion gradient across a membrane is used to drive cellular work such as the synthesis of ATP, is called **chemiosmosis** (from the Greek *osmos*, push). We have previously used the word *osmosis* in discussing water transport, but here it refers to the flow of H^+ across a membrane.

From studying the structure of ATP synthase, scientists have learned how the flow of H^+ through this large enzyme powers ATP generation. ATP synthase is a multisubunit complex with four main parts, each made up of multiple polypeptides. Protons move one by one into binding sites on one of the parts (the rotor), causing it to spin in a way that catalyzes ATP production from ADP and inorganic phosphate. The flow of

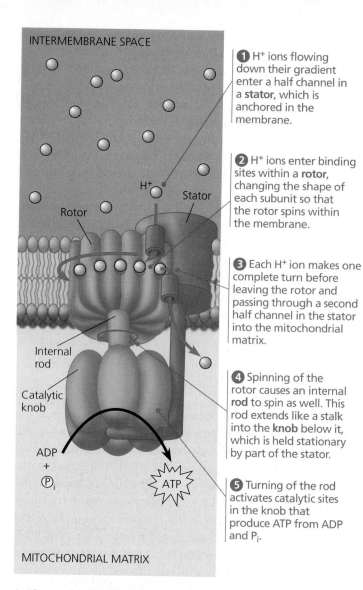

INTERMEMBRANE SPACE

1 H+ ions flowing down their gradient enter a half channel in a **stator**, which is anchored in the membrane.

2 H+ ions enter binding sites within a **rotor**, changing the shape of each subunit so that the rotor spins within the membrane.

3 Each H+ ion makes one complete turn before leaving the rotor and passing through a second half channel in the stator into the mitochondrial matrix.

4 Spinning of the rotor causes an internal **rod** to spin as well. This rod extends like a stalk into the **knob** below it, which is held stationary by part of the stator.

5 Turning of the rod activates catalytic sites in the knob that produce ATP from ADP and P$_i$.

Stator

Rotor

H+

Internal rod

Catalytic knob

ADP + P$_i$

ATP

MITOCHONDRIAL MATRIX

▲ **Figure 9.14 ATP synthase, a molecular mill.** The ATP synthase protein complex functions as a mill, powered by the flow of hydrogen ions. This complex resides in mitochondrial and chloroplast membranes of eukaryotes and in the plasma membranes of prokaryotes. Each of the four parts of ATP synthase consists of a number of polypeptide subunits.

protons thus behaves somewhat like a rushing stream that turns a waterwheel **(Figure 9.14)**.

ATP synthase is the smallest molecular rotary motor known in nature. The research that led to a detailed description of this enzyme's activity first showed that part of the complex actually spun around in the membrane when the reaction proceeded in the direction of ATP *hydrolysis*. Although biochemists assumed that the same rotational mechanism was responsible for ATP *synthesis*, there was no definitive support for this model until 2004, when several research institutions in collaboration with a private company were able to tackle this issue using *nanotechnology* (techniques involving control of matter on the molecular scale; from the Greek *nanos*, meaning "dwarf"). **Figure 9.15** describes the elegant experiment performed by these investigators to demonstrate that the direction of rotation of one part of

▼ **Figure 9.15 Inquiry**

Is the rotation of the internal rod in ATP synthase responsible for ATP synthesis?

EXPERIMENT Previous experiments on ATP synthase had demonstrated that the "internal rod" rotated when ATP was hydrolyzed (see Figure 9.14). Hiroyasu Itoh and colleagues set out to investigate whether simply rotating the rod in the opposite direction would cause ATP synthesis to occur. They isolated the internal rod and catalytic knob, which was then anchored to a nickel plate. A magnetic bead was bound to the rod. This complex was placed in a chamber containing an array of electromagnets, and the bead was manipulated by the sequential activation of the magnets to rotate the internal rod in either direction. The investigators hypothesized that if the bead were rotated in the direction opposite to that observed during hydrolysis, ATP synthesis would occur. ATP levels were monitored by a "reporter enzyme" in the solution that emits a discrete amount of light (a photon) when it cleaves ATP. Their hypothesis was that rotation in one direction would result in more photons than rotation in the other direction or no rotation at all.

Magnetic bead

Electromagnet

Sample

Internal rod

Catalytic knob

Nickel plate

RESULTS More photons were emitted by spinning the rod for 5 minutes in one direction (yellow bars) than by no rotation (gray bars) or rotation in the opposite direction (blue bars).

□ Rotation in one direction
▨ Rotation in opposite direction
▨ No rotation

Number of photons detected ($\times 10^3$)

Sequential trials

CONCLUSION The researchers concluded that the mechanical rotation of the internal rod in a particular direction within ATP synthase appears to be all that is required for generating ATP. As ATP synthase is the smallest rotary motor known, one of the goals in this type of research is to learn how to use its activity in artificial ways.

SOURCE H. Itoh et al., Mechanically driven ATP synthesis by F$_1$-ATPase, *Nature* 427:465–468 (2004).

Inquiry in Action Read and analyze the original paper in *Inquiry in Action: Interpreting Scientific Papers.*

WHAT IF? The "no rotation" (gray) bars represent the background level of ATP in the experiment. When the enzyme is rotated one way (yellow bars), the increase in ATP level suggests synthesis is occurring. For enzymes rotating the other way (blue bars), what level of ATP would you expect compared to the gray bars? (Note: this may not be what is observed.)

the protein complex in relation to another is solely responsible for either ATP synthesis or ATP hydrolysis.

How does the inner mitochondrial membrane or the prokaryotic plasma membrane generate and maintain the H^+ gradient that drives ATP synthesis by the ATP synthase protein complex? Establishing the H^+ gradient is a major function of the electron transport chain, which is shown in its mitochondrial location in **Figure 9.16**. The chain is an energy converter that uses the exergonic flow of electrons from NADH and $FADH_2$ to pump H^+ across the membrane, from the mitochondrial matrix into the intermembrane space. The H^+ has a tendency to move back across the membrane, diffusing down its gradient. And the ATP synthases are the only sites that pro-

vide a route through the membrane for H^+. As we described previously, their passage through ATP synthase uses the exergonic flow of H^+ to drive the phosphorylation of ADP. Thus, the energy stored in an H^+ gradient across a membrane couples the redox reactions of the electron transport chain to ATP synthesis, an example of chemiosmosis.

At this point, you may be wondering how the electron transport chain pumps hydrogen ions. Researchers have found that certain members of the electron transport chain accept and release protons (H^+) along with electrons. (The aqueous solutions inside and surrounding the cell are a ready source of H^+.) At certain steps along the chain, electron transfers cause H^+ to be taken up and released into the

▲ **Figure 9.16 Chemiosmosis couples the electron transport chain to ATP synthesis.** ❶ NADH and $FADH_2$ shuttle high-energy electrons extracted from food during glycolysis and the citric acid cycle to an electron transport chain built into the inner mitochondrial membrane. The gold arrows trace the transport of electrons, which finally pass to oxygen at the "downhill" end of the chain, forming water. As Figure 9.13 showed, most of the electron carriers of the chain are grouped into four complexes. Two mobile

carriers, ubiquinone (Q) and cytochrome c (Cyt c), move rapidly, ferrying electrons between the large complexes. As complexes I, III, and IV accept and then donate electrons, they pump protons from the mitochondrial matrix into the intermembrane space. (In prokaryotes, protons are pumped outside the plasma membrane.) Note that $FADH_2$ deposits its electrons via complex II and so results in fewer protons being pumped into the intermembrane space than occurs with NADH. Chemical energy originally harvested from food is transformed into a

proton-motive force, a gradient of H^+ across the membrane. ❷ During chemiosmosis, the protons flow back down their gradient via ATP synthase, which is built into the membrane nearby. The ATP synthase harnesses the proton-motive force to phosphorylate ADP, forming ATP. Together, electron transport and chemiosmosis make up oxidative phosphorylation.

WHAT IF? *If complex IV were nonfunctional, could chemiosmosis produce any ATP, and if so, how would the rate of synthesis differ?*

surrounding solution. In eukaryotic cells, the electron carriers are spatially arranged in the membrane in such a way that H^+ is accepted from the mitochondrial matrix and deposited in the intermembrane space (see Figure 9.16). The H^+ gradient that results is referred to as a **proton-motive force**, emphasizing the capacity of the gradient to perform work. The force drives H^+ back across the membrane through the H^+ channels provided by ATP synthases.

In general terms, *chemiosmosis is an energy-coupling mechanism that uses energy stored in the form of an H^+ gradient across a membrane to drive cellular work*. In mitochondria, the energy for gradient formation comes from exergonic redox reactions, and ATP synthesis is the work performed. But chemiosmosis also occurs elsewhere and in other variations. Chloroplasts use chemiosmosis to generate ATP during photosynthesis; in these organelles, light (rather than chemical energy) drives both electron flow down an electron transport chain and the resulting H^+ gradient formation. Prokaryotes, as already mentioned, generate H^+ gradients across their plasma membranes. They then tap the proton-motive force not only to make ATP inside the cell but also to rotate their flagella and to pump nutrients and waste products across the membrane. Because of its central importance to energy conversions in prokaryotes and eukaryotes, chemiosmosis has helped unify the study of bioenergetics. Peter Mitchell was awarded the Nobel Prize in 1978 for originally proposing the chemiosmotic model.

An Accounting of ATP Production by Cellular Respiration

In the last few sections, we have looked more closely at the key processes of cellular respiration. Now, let's take a step back and remind ourselves of its overall function: harvesting the energy of glucose for ATP synthesis.

During respiration, most energy flows in this sequence: glucose → NADH → electron transport chain → proton-motive force → ATP. We can do some bookkeeping to calculate the ATP profit when cellular respiration oxidizes a molecule of glucose to six molecules of carbon dioxide. The three main departments of this metabolic enterprise are glycolysis, the citric acid cycle, and the electron transport chain, which drives oxidative phosphorylation. **Figure 9.17** gives a detailed accounting of the ATP yield per glucose molecule oxidized. The tally adds the 4 ATP produced directly by substrate-level phosphorylation during glycolysis and the citric acid cycle to the many more molecules of ATP generated by oxidative phosphorylation. Each NADH that transfers a pair of electrons from glucose to the electron transport chain contributes enough to the proton-motive force to generate a maximum of about 3 ATP.

Why are the numbers in Figure 9.17 inexact? There are three reasons we cannot state an exact number of ATP molecules generated by the breakdown of one molecule of glucose. First, phosphorylation and the redox reactions are not directly coupled to

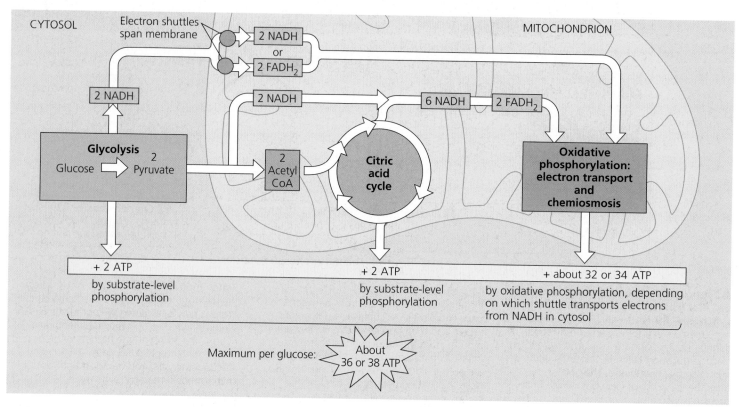

▲ **Figure 9.17 ATP yield per molecule of glucose at each stage of cellular respiration.**

each other, so the ratio of number of NADH molecules to number of ATP molecules is not a whole number. We know that 1 NADH results in 10 H^+ being transported out across the inner mitochondrial membrane, and we also know that somewhere between 3 and 4 H^+ must reenter the mitochondrial matrix via ATP synthase to generate 1 ATP. Therefore, a single molecule of NADH generates enough proton-motive force for synthesis of 2.5 to 3.3 ATP; generally, we round off and say that 1 NADH can generate about 3 ATP. The citric acid cycle also supplies electrons to the electron transport chain via $FADH_2$, but since it enters later in the chain, each molecule of this electron carrier is responsible for transport of only enough H^+ for the synthesis of 1.5 to 2 ATP. These numbers also take into account the slight energetic cost of moving the ATP formed in the mitochondrion out into the rest of the cytoplasm where it will be used.

Second, the ATP yield varies slightly depending on the type of shuttle used to transport electrons from the cytosol into the mitochondrion. The mitochondrial inner membrane is impermeable to NADH, so NADH in the cytosol is segregated from the machinery of oxidative phosphorylation. The two electrons of NADH captured in glycolysis must be conveyed into the mitochondrion by one of several electron shuttle systems. Depending on the type of shuttle in a particular cell type, the electrons are passed either to NAD^+ or to FAD in the mitochondrial matrix (see Figure 9.17). If the electrons are passed to FAD, as in brain cells, only about 2 ATP can result from each cytosolic NADH. If the electrons are passed to mitochondrial NAD^+, as in liver cells and heart cells, the yield is about 3 ATP.

A third variable that reduces the yield of ATP is the use of the proton-motive force generated by the redox reactions of respiration to drive other kinds of work. For example, the proton-motive force powers the mitochondrion's uptake of pyruvate from the cytosol. However, if *all* the proton-motive force generated by the electron transport chain were used to drive ATP synthesis, one glucose molecule could generate a maximum of 34 ATP produced by oxidative phosphorylation plus 4 ATP (net) from substrate-level phosphorylation to give a total yield of about 38 ATP (or only about 36 ATP if the less efficient shuttle were functioning).

We can now make a rough estimate of the efficiency of respiration—that is, the percentage of chemical energy possessed by glucose that has been transferred to ATP. Recall that the complete oxidation of a mole of glucose releases 686 kcal of energy under standard conditions ($\Delta G = -686$ kcal/mol). Phosphorylation of ADP to form ATP stores at least 7.3 kcal per mole of ATP. Therefore, the efficiency of respiration is 7.3 kcal per mole of ATP times 38 moles of ATP per mole of glucose divided by 686 kcal per mole of glucose, which equals 0.4. Thus, about 40% of the potential chemical energy in glucose has been transferred to ATP; the actual percentage is probably higher because ΔG is lower under cellular conditions. The rest of the stored energy is lost as heat. We humans use some of this heat to maintain our relatively high body temperature (37°C), and we dissipate the rest through sweating and other cooling mechanisms. Cellular respiration is remarkably efficient in its energy conversion. By comparison, the most efficient automobile converts only about 25% of the energy stored in gasoline to energy that moves the car.

CONCEPT CHECK 9.4

1. What effect would an absence of O_2 have on the process shown in Figure 9.16?
2. **WHAT IF?** In the absence of O_2, as in question 1, what do you think would happen if you decreased the pH of the intermembrane space of the mitochondrion? Explain your answer.

For suggested answers, see Appendix A.

CONCEPT 9.5

Fermentation and anaerobic respiration enable cells to produce ATP without the use of oxygen

Because most of the ATP generated by cellular respiration is due to the work of oxidative phosphorylation, our estimate of ATP yield from aerobic respiration is contingent on an adequate supply of oxygen to the cell. Without the electronegative oxygen to pull electrons down the transport chain, oxidative phosphorylation ceases. However, there are two general mechanisms by which certain cells can oxidize organic fuel and generate ATP *without* the use of oxygen: anaerobic respiration and fermentation. The distinction between these two is based on whether an electron transport chain is present. (The electron transport chain is also called the respiratory chain because of its role in cellular respiration.)

We have already mentioned anaerobic respiration, which takes place in certain prokaryotic organisms that live in environments without oxygen. These organisms have an electron transport chain but do not use oxygen as a final electron acceptor at the end of the chain. Oxygen performs this function very well because it is extremely electronegative, but other, less electronegative substances can also serve as final electron acceptors. Some "sulfate-reducing" marine bacteria, for instance, use the sulfate ion (SO_4^{2-}) at the end of their respiratory chain. Operation of the chain builds up a proton-motive force used to produce ATP, but H_2S (hydrogen sulfide) is produced as a by-product rather than water.

Fermentation is a way of harvesting chemical energy without using either oxygen or any electron transport chain—in other words, without cellular respiration. How can food be oxidized without cellular respiration? Remember, oxidation simply refers to the loss of electrons to an electron acceptor, so it does not need to involve oxygen. Glycolysis oxidizes glucose to two molecules of pyruvate. The oxidizing agent of glycolysis is NAD^+, and neither oxygen nor any electron transfer chain is involved. Overall, glycolysis is exergonic, and some of the energy made available is used to produce 2 ATP (net) by substrate-level phosphorylation. If oxygen *is* present, then additional ATP is made by oxidative phosphorylation when NADH passes electrons removed from glucose to the electron transport chain. But glycolysis generates 2 ATP whether oxygen is present or not—that is, whether conditions are aerobic or anaerobic.

As an alternative to respiratory oxidation of organic nutrients, fermentation is an expansion of glycolysis that allows continuous generation of ATP by the substrate-level phosphorylation of glycolysis. For this to occur, there must be a sufficient supply of NAD^+ to accept electrons during the oxidation step of glycolysis. Without some mechanism to recycle NAD^+ from NADH, glycolysis would soon deplete the cell's pool of NAD^+ by reducing it all to NADH and would shut itself down for lack of an oxidizing agent. Under aerobic conditions, NAD^+ is recycled from NADH by the transfer of electrons to the electron transport chain. An anaerobic alternative is to transfer electrons from NADH to pyruvate, the end product of glycolysis.

Types of Fermentation

Fermentation consists of glycolysis plus reactions that regenerate NAD^+ by transferring electrons from NADH to pyruvate or derivatives of pyruvate. The NAD^+ can then be reused to oxidize sugar by glycolysis, which nets two molecules of ATP by substrate-level phosphorylation. There are many types of fermentation, differing in the end products formed from pyruvate. Two common types are alcohol fermentation and lactic acid fermentation.

In **alcohol fermentation (Figure 9.18a)**, pyruvate is converted to ethanol (ethyl alcohol) in two steps. The first step releases carbon dioxide from the pyruvate, which is converted to the two-carbon compound acetaldehyde. In the second step, acetaldehyde is reduced by NADH to ethanol. This regenerates the supply of NAD^+ needed for the continuation of glycolysis. Many bacteria carry out alcohol fermentation under anaerobic conditions. Yeast (a fungus) also carries out alcohol fermentation. For thousands of years, humans have used yeast in brewing, winemaking, and baking. The CO_2 bubbles generated by baker's yeast during alcohol fermentation allow bread to rise.

During **lactic acid fermentation (Figure 9.18b)**, pyruvate is reduced directly by NADH to form lactate as an end product, with no release of CO_2. (Lactate is the ionized form of lactic acid.) Lactic acid fermentation by certain fungi and bacteria is used in the dairy industry to make cheese and yogurt.

(a) Alcohol fermentation

(b) Lactic acid fermentation

▲ **Figure 9.18 Fermentation.** In the absence of oxygen, many cells use fermentation to produce ATP by substrate-level phosphorylation. Pyruvate, the end product of glycolysis, serves as an electron acceptor for oxidizing NADH back to NAD^+, which can then be reused in glycolysis. Two of the common end products formed from fermentation are **(a)** ethanol and **(b)** lactate, the ionized form of lactic acid.

Human muscle cells make ATP by lactic acid fermentation when oxygen is scarce. This occurs during the early stages of strenuous exercise, when sugar catabolism for ATP production outpaces the muscle's supply of oxygen from the blood. Under these conditions, the cells switch from aerobic respiration to fermentation. The lactate that accumulates was previously thought to cause muscle fatigue and pain, but recent research suggests instead that increased levels of potassium ions (K^+) may be to blame, while lactate appears to enhance muscle performance. In any case, the excess lactate is gradually carried away by the blood to the liver. Lactate is converted back to pyruvate by liver cells.

Fermentation and Aerobic Respiration Compared

Fermentation and aerobic cellular respiration are anaerobic and aerobic alternatives, respectively, for producing ATP by harvesting the chemical energy of food. Both pathways use glycolysis to oxidize glucose and other organic fuels to pyruvate, with a net production of 2 ATP by substrate-level phosphorylation. And in both fermentation and respiration, NAD^+ is the oxidizing agent that accepts electrons from food during glycolysis. A key difference is the contrasting mechanisms for oxidizing NADH back to NAD^+, which is required to sustain glycolysis. In fermentation, the final electron acceptor is an organic molecule such as pyruvate (lactic acid fermentation) or acetaldehyde (alcohol fermentation). In aerobic respiration, by contrast, the final acceptor for electrons from NADH is oxygen. This process not only regenerates the NAD^+ required for glycolysis but pays an ATP bonus when the stepwise electron transport from this NADH to oxygen drives oxidative phosphorylation. An even bigger ATP payoff comes from the oxidation of pyruvate in the citric acid cycle, which is unique to respiration. Without oxygen, the energy still stored in pyruvate is unavailable to the cell. Thus, cellular respiration harvests much more energy from each sugar molecule than fermentation can. In fact, respiration yields up to 19 times as much ATP per glucose molecule as does fermentation—up to 38 molecules of ATP for respiration, compared with 2 molecules of ATP produced by substrate-level phosphorylation in fermentation.

Some organisms, called **obligate anaerobes**, carry out only fermentation or anaerobic respiration and in fact cannot survive in the presence of oxygen. A few cell types, such as cells of the vertebrate brain, can carry out only aerobic oxidation of pyruvate, but not fermentation. Other organisms, including yeasts and many bacteria, can make enough ATP to survive using either fermentation or respiration. Such species are called **facultative anaerobes**. On the cellular level, our muscle cells behave as facultative anaerobes. In such cells, pyruvate is a fork in the metabolic road that leads to two alternative catabolic routes **(Figure 9.19)**. Under aerobic conditions, pyruvate can be converted to acetyl CoA, and oxidation continues in the citric acid cycle. Under anaerobic conditions, pyruvate is diverted from the citric acid cycle, serving instead as an electron acceptor to recycle NAD^+. To make the same amount of ATP, a facultative anaerobe would have to consume sugar at a much faster rate when fermenting than when respiring.

The Evolutionary Significance of Glycolysis

The role of glycolysis in both fermentation and respiration has an evolutionary basis. Ancient prokaryotes probably used glycolysis to make ATP long before oxygen was present in Earth's atmosphere. The oldest known fossils of bacteria date

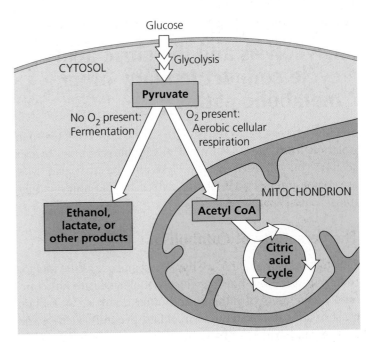

▲ **Figure 9.19 Pyruvate as a key juncture in catabolism.** Glycolysis is common to fermentation and cellular respiration. The end product of glycolysis, pyruvate, represents a fork in the catabolic pathways of glucose oxidation. In a facultative anaerobe, which is capable of both aerobic cellular respiration and fermentation, pyruvate is committed to one of those two pathways, usually depending on whether or not oxygen is present.

back 3.5 billion years, but appreciable quantities of oxygen probably did not begin to accumulate in the atmosphere until about 2.7 billion years ago. Cyanobacteria produced this O_2 as a by-product of photosynthesis. Therefore, early prokaryotes may have generated ATP exclusively from glycolysis. The fact that glycolysis is today the most widespread metabolic pathway among Earth's organisms suggests that it evolved very early in the history of life. The cytosolic location of glycolysis also implies great antiquity; the pathway does not require any of the membrane-bounded organelles of the eukaryotic cell, which evolved approximately 1 billion years after the prokaryotic cell. Glycolysis is a metabolic heirloom from early cells that continues to function in fermentation and as the first stage in the breakdown of organic molecules by respiration.

CONCEPT CHECK 9.5

1. Consider the NADH formed during glycolysis. What is the final acceptor for its electrons during fermentation? What is the final acceptor for its electrons during aerobic respiration?
2. **WHAT IF?** A glucose-fed yeast cell is moved from an aerobic environment to an anaerobic one. For the cell to continue generating ATP at the same rate, how would its rate of glucose consumption need to change?

For suggested answers, see Appendix A.

Glycolysis and the citric acid cycle connect to many other metabolic pathways

So far, we have treated the oxidative breakdown of glucose in isolation from the cell's overall metabolic economy. In this section, you will learn that glycolysis and the citric acid cycle are major intersections of the cell's catabolic and anabolic (biosynthetic) pathways.

The Versatility of Catabolism

Throughout this chapter, we have used glucose as the fuel for cellular respiration. But free glucose molecules are not common in the diets of humans and other animals. We obtain most of our calories in the form of fats, proteins, sucrose and other disaccharides, and starch, a polysaccharide. All these organic molecules in food can be used by cellular respiration to make ATP (Figure 9.20).

Glycolysis can accept a wide range of carbohydrates for catabolism. In the digestive tract, starch is hydrolyzed to glucose, which can then be broken down in the cells by glycolysis and the citric acid cycle. Similarly, glycogen, the polysaccharide that humans and many other animals store in their liver and muscle cells, can be hydrolyzed to glucose between meals as fuel for respiration. The digestion of disaccharides, including sucrose, provides glucose and other monosaccharides as fuel for respiration.

Proteins can also be used for fuel, but first they must be digested to their constituent amino acids. Many of the amino acids, of course, are used by the organism to build new proteins. Amino acids present in excess are converted by enzymes to intermediates of glycolysis and the citric acid cycle. Before amino acids can feed into glycolysis or the citric acid cycle, their amino groups must be removed, a process called deamination. The nitrogenous refuse is excreted from the animal in the form of ammonia, urea, or other waste products.

Catabolism can also harvest energy stored in fats obtained either from food or from storage cells in the body. After fats are digested to glycerol and fatty acids, the glycerol is converted to glyceraldehyde-3-phosphate, an intermediate of glycolysis. Most of the energy of a fat is stored in the fatty acids. A metabolic sequence called **beta oxidation** breaks the fatty acids down to two-carbon fragments, which enter the citric acid cycle as acetyl CoA. NADH and $FADH_2$ are also generated during beta oxidation; they can enter the electron transport chain, leading to further ATP production. Fats make excellent fuel, in large part due to their chemical structure and the high energy level of their electrons compared to those of carbohydrates. A gram of fat oxidized by

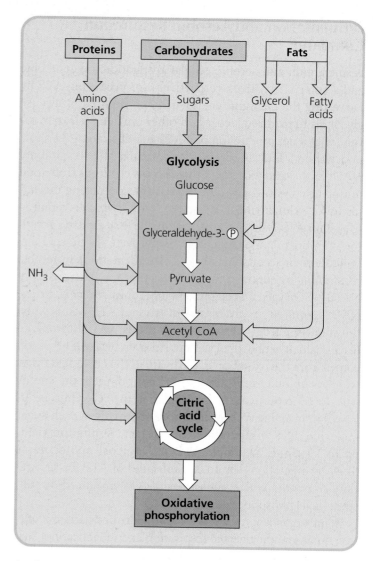

▲ **Figure 9.20 The catabolism of various molecules from food.** Carbohydrates, fats, and proteins can all be used as fuel for cellular respiration. Monomers of these molecules enter glycolysis or the citric acid cycle at various points. Glycolysis and the citric acid cycle are catabolic funnels through which electrons from all kinds of organic molecules flow on their exergonic fall to oxygen.

respiration produces more than twice as much ATP as a gram of carbohydrate. Unfortunately, this also means that a person trying to lose weight must work hard to use up fat stored in the body because so many calories are stockpiled in each gram of fat.

Biosynthesis (Anabolic Pathways)

Cells need substance as well as energy. Not all the organic molecules of food are destined to be oxidized as fuel to make ATP. In addition to calories, food must also provide the carbon skeletons that cells require to make their own molecules. Some organic monomers obtained from digestion can be used directly. For example, as previously mentioned, amino acids from the hydrolysis of proteins in food can be incorporated into the organism's own proteins. Often, however, the body needs specific molecules that are not present as such in food. Compounds formed as intermediates of glycolysis and the citric acid cycle can be diverted into anabolic pathways as precursors from which the cell can synthesize the molecules it requires. For example, humans can make about half of the 20 amino acids in proteins by modifying compounds siphoned away from the citric acid cycle; the rest are "essential amino acids" that must be obtained in the diet. Also, glucose can be made from pyruvate, and fatty acids can be synthesized from acetyl CoA. Of course, these anabolic, or biosynthetic, pathways do not generate ATP, but instead consume it.

In addition, glycolysis and the citric acid cycle function as metabolic interchanges that enable our cells to convert some kinds of molecules to others as we need them. For example, an intermediate compound generated during glycolysis, dihydroxyacetone phosphate (see Figure 9.9, step 5), can be converted to one of the major precursors of fats. If we eat more food than we need, we store fat even if our diet is fat-free. Metabolism is remarkably versatile and adaptable.

Regulation of Cellular Respiration via Feedback Mechanisms

Basic principles of supply and demand regulate the metabolic economy. The cell does not waste energy making more of a particular substance than it needs. If there is a glut of a certain amino acid, for example, the anabolic pathway that synthesizes that amino acid from an intermediate of the citric acid cycle is switched off. The most common mechanism for this control is feedback inhibition: The end product of the anabolic pathway inhibits the enzyme that catalyzes an early step of the pathway (see Figure 8.22). This prevents the needless diversion of key metabolic intermediates from uses that are more urgent.

The cell also controls its catabolism. If the cell is working hard and its ATP concentration begins to drop, respiration speeds up. When there is plenty of ATP to meet demand, respiration slows down, sparing valuable organic molecules for other functions. Again, control is based mainly on regulating the activity of enzymes at strategic points in the catabolic pathway. As shown in **Figure 9.21**, one important switch is phosphofructokinase, the enzyme that catalyzes step 3 of glycolysis (see Figure 9.9). That is the first step that commits substrate irreversibly to the glycolytic pathway. By controlling the rate of this step, the cell can speed up or slow down the entire catabolic process. Phosphofructokinase can thus be considered the pacemaker of respiration.

Phosphofructokinase is an allosteric enzyme with receptor sites for specific inhibitors and activators. It is inhibited by ATP and stimulated by AMP (adenosine monophosphate), which the cell derives from ADP. As

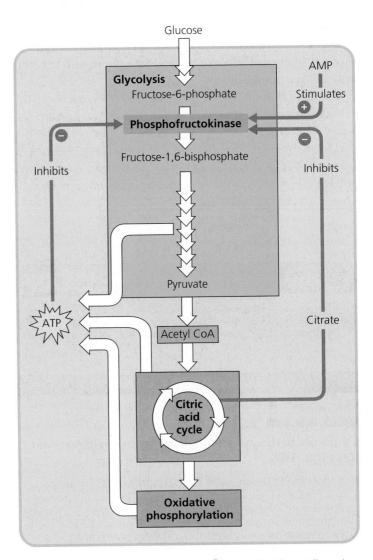

▲ **Figure 9.21 The control of cellular respiration.** Allosteric enzymes at certain points in the respiratory pathway respond to inhibitors and activators that help set the pace of glycolysis and the citric acid cycle. Phosphofructokinase, which catalyzes an early step in glycolysis (see Figure 9.9), is one such enzyme. It is stimulated by AMP (derived from ADP) but is inhibited by ATP and by citrate. This feedback regulation adjusts the rate of respiration as the cell's catabolic and anabolic demands change.

ATP accumulates, inhibition of the enzyme slows down glycolysis. The enzyme becomes active again as cellular work converts ATP to ADP (and AMP) faster than ATP is being regenerated. Phosphofructokinase is also sensitive to citrate, the first product of the citric acid cycle. If citrate accumulates in mitochondria, some of it passes into the cytosol and inhibits phosphofructokinase. This mechanism helps synchronize the rates of glycolysis and the citric acid cycle. As citrate accumulates, glycolysis slows down, and the supply of acetyl groups to the citric acid cycle decreases. If citrate consumption increases, either because of a demand for more ATP or because anabolic pathways are draining off intermediates of the citric acid cycle, glycolysis accelerates and meets the demand.

Metabolic balance is augmented by the control of enzymes that catalyze other key steps of glycolysis and the citric acid cycle. Cells are thrifty, expedient, and responsive in their metabolism.

Examine Figure 9.2 again to put cellular respiration into the broader context of energy flow and chemical cycling in ecosystems. The energy that keeps us alive is *released*, but not *produced*, by cellular respiration. We are tapping energy that was stored in food by photosynthesis. In the next chapter, you will learn how photosynthesis captures light and converts it to chemical energy.

Chapter 9 Review

 MEDIA Go to the Study Area at www.masteringbio.com for BioFlix 3-D Animations, MP3 Tutors, Videos, Practice Tests, an eBook, and more.

SUMMARY OF KEY CONCEPTS

CONCEPT 9.1
Catabolic pathways yield energy by oxidizing organic fuels (pp. 162–167)

▶ **Catabolic Pathways and Production of ATP** To keep working, a cell must regenerate the ATP it uses. The breakdown of glucose and other organic fuels is exergonic. Starting with glucose or another organic molecule and using O_2, aerobic respiration yields H_2O, CO_2, and energy in the form of ATP and heat. Cellular respiration includes both aerobic and anaerobic respiration; the latter uses another electron acceptor at the end of the electron transport chain instead of O_2, but also yields ATP.

▶ **Redox Reactions: Oxidation and Reduction** The cell taps the energy stored in food molecules through redox reactions, in which one substance partially or totally shifts electrons to another. The substance receiving electrons is reduced; the substance losing electrons is oxidized. During cellular respiration, glucose ($C_6H_{12}O_6$) is oxidized to CO_2, and O_2 is reduced to H_2O. Electrons lose potential energy during their transfer from organic compounds to oxygen. Electrons from organic compounds are usually passed first to NAD^+, reducing it to NADH. NADH passes the electrons to an electron transport chain, which conducts them to O_2 in energy-releasing steps. The energy is used to make ATP.

▶ **The Stages of Cellular Respiration: *A Preview***
Glycolysis and the citric acid cycle supply electrons (via NADH or $FADH_2$) to the electron transport chain, which drives oxidative phosphorylation. Oxidative phosphorylation generates ATP.

MEDIA
BioFlix 3-D Animation Cellular Respiration
Activity Build a Chemical Cycling System
Activity Overview of Cellular Respiration

CONCEPT 9.2
Glycolysis harvests chemical energy by oxidizing glucose to pyruvate (pp. 167–169)

MEDIA
MP3 Tutor Cellular Respiration Part 1—Glycolysis
Activity Glycolysis

CONCEPT 9.3
The citric acid cycle completes the energy-yielding oxidation of organic molecules (pp. 170–172)

▶ In eukaryotic cells, the import of pyruvate into the mitochondrion and its conversion to acetyl CoA links glycolysis to the citric acid cycle. (In prokaryotic cells, the citric acid cycle occurs in the cytosol.)

MEDIA
Activity The Citric Acid Cycle

CONCEPT 9.4

During oxidative phosphorylation, chemiosmosis couples electron transport to ATP synthesis (pp. 172–177)

▶ NADH and FADH$_2$ donate electrons to the electron transport chain, which powers ATP synthesis via oxidative phosphorylation.

▶ **The Pathway of Electron Transport** In the electron transport chain, electrons from NADH and FADH$_2$ lose energy in several energy-releasing steps. At the end of the chain, electrons are passed to O$_2$, reducing it to H$_2$O.

▶ **Chemiosmosis: The Energy-Coupling Mechanism** At certain steps along the electron transport chain, electron transfer causes protein complexes in eukaryotes to move H$^+$ from the mitochondrial matrix to the intermembrane space, storing energy as a proton-motive force (H$^+$ gradient). As H$^+$ diffuses back into the matrix through ATP synthase, its passage drives the phosphorylation of ADP. Prokaryotes generate an H$^+$ gradient across their plasma membrane and use this gradient to synthesize ATP in the cell.

▶ **An Accounting of ATP Production by Cellular Respiration** About 40% of the energy stored in a glucose molecule is transferred to ATP during cellular respiration, producing a maximum of about 38 ATP.

> **MEDIA**
> **MP3 Tutor** Cellular Respiration Part 2—Citric Acid Cycle and Electron Transport
> **Activity** Electron Transport
> **Biology Labs On-Line** MitochondriaLab
> **Investigation** How Is the Rate of Cellular Respiration Measured?

CONCEPT 9.5

Fermentation and anaerobic respiration enable cells to produce ATP without the use of oxygen (pp. 177–179)

▶ **Types of Fermentation** Glycolysis nets 2 ATP by substrate-level phosphorylation, whether oxygen is present or not. Under anaerobic conditions, either anaerobic respiration or fermentation can take place. In anaerobic respiration, an electron transport chain is present with a final electron acceptor other than oxygen. In fermentation, the electrons from NADH are passed to pyruvate or a derivative of pyruvate, regenerating the NAD$^+$ required to oxidize more glucose. Two common types of fermentation are alcohol fermentation and lactic acid fermentation.

▶ **Fermentation and Aerobic Respiration Compared** Both use glycolysis to oxidize glucose but differ in their final electron acceptor. Respiration yields more ATP.

▶ **The Evolutionary Significance of Glycolysis** Glycolysis occurs in nearly all organisms and probably evolved in ancient prokaryotes before there was O$_2$ in the atmosphere.

> **MEDIA**
> **Activity** Fermentation

CONCEPT 9.6

Glycolysis and the citric acid cycle connect to many other metabolic pathways (pp. 180–182)

▶ **The Versatility of Catabolism** Catabolic pathways funnel electrons from many kinds of organic molecules into cellular respiration.

▶ **Biosynthesis (Anabolic Pathways)** Cells can use small molecules from food directly or use them to build other substances through glycolysis or the citric acid cycle.

▶ **Regulation of Cellular Respiration via Feedback Mechanisms** Cellular respiration is controlled by allosteric enzymes at key points in glycolysis and the citric acid cycle.

TESTING YOUR KNOWLEDGE

SELF-QUIZ

1. What is the reducing agent in the following reaction?

   Pyruvate + NADH + H$^+$ → Lactate + NAD$^+$

   a. oxygen   d. lactate
   b. NADH   e. pyruvate
   c. NAD$^+$

2. The *immediate* energy source that drives ATP synthesis by ATP synthase during oxidative phosphorylation is the
   a. oxidation of glucose and other organic compounds.
   b. flow of electrons down the electron transport chain.
   c. affinity of oxygen for electrons.
   d. H$^+$ concentration across the membrane holding ATP synthase.
   e. transfer of phosphate to ADP.

3. Which metabolic pathway is common to both fermentation and cellular respiration of a glucose molecule?
   a. the citric acid cycle
   b. the electron transport chain
   c. glycolysis
   d. synthesis of acetyl CoA from pyruvate
   e. reduction of pyruvate to lactate

4. In mitochondria, exergonic redox reactions
   a. are the source of energy driving prokaryotic ATP synthesis.
   b. are directly coupled to substrate-level phosphorylation.
   c. provide the energy that establishes the proton gradient.
   d. reduce carbon atoms to carbon dioxide.
   e. are coupled via phosphorylated intermediates to endergonic processes.

5. The final electron acceptor of the electron transport chain that functions in aerobic oxidative phosphorylation is
   a. oxygen.
   b. water.
   c. NAD^+.
   d. pyruvate.
   e. ADP.

6. When electrons flow along the electron transport chains of mitochondria, which of the following changes occurs?
   a. The pH of the matrix increases.
   b. ATP synthase pumps protons by active transport.
   c. The electrons gain free energy.
   d. The cytochromes phosphorylate ADP to form ATP.
   e. NAD^+ is oxidized.

7. Cells do not catabolize carbon dioxide because
   a. its double bonds are too stable to be broken.
   b. CO_2 has fewer bonding electrons than other organic compounds.
   c. CO_2 is already completely reduced.
   d. CO_2 is already completely oxidized.
   e. the molecule has too few atoms.

8. Which of the following is a true distinction between fermentation and cellular respiration?
   a. Only respiration oxidizes glucose.
   b. NADH is oxidized by the electron transport chain in respiration only.
   c. Fermentation, but not respiration, is an example of a catabolic pathway.
   d. Substrate-level phosphorylation is unique to fermentation.
   e. NAD^+ functions as an oxidizing agent only in respiration.

9. Most CO_2 from catabolism is released during
   a. glycolysis.
   b. the citric acid cycle.
   c. lactate fermentation.
   d. electron transport.
   e. oxidative phosphorylation.

10. **DRAW IT** The graph here shows the pH difference across the inner mitochondrial membrane over time in an actively respiring cell. At the time indicated by the vertical arrow, a metabolic poison is added that specifically and completely inhibits all function of mitochondrial ATP synthase. Draw what you would expect to see for the rest of the graphed line.

For Self-Quiz answers, see Appendix A.

MEDIA Visit the Study Area at **www.masteringbio.com** for a Practice Test.

EVOLUTION CONNECTION

11. ATP synthases are found in the prokaryotic plasma membrane and in mitochondria and chloroplasts. What does this suggest about the evolutionary relationship of these eukaryotic organelles to prokaryotes? How might the amino acid sequences of the ATP synthases from the different sources support or refute your hypothesis?

SCIENTIFIC INQUIRY

12. In the 1940s, some physicians prescribed low doses of a drug called dinitrophenol (DNP) to help patients lose weight. This unsafe method was abandoned after a few patients died. DNP uncouples the chemiosmotic machinery by making the lipid bilayer of the inner mitochondrial membrane leaky to H^+. Explain how this causes weight loss.

SCIENCE, TECHNOLOGY, AND SOCIETY

13. Nearly all human societies use fermentation to produce alcoholic drinks such as beer and wine. The practice dates back to the earliest days of agriculture. How do you suppose this use of fermentation was first discovered? Why did wine prove to be a more useful beverage, especially to a preindustrial culture, than the grape juice from which it was made?

Biological Inquiry: A Workbook of Investigative Cases Explore fermentation further in the case "Bean Brew."

Photosynthesis

10

OVERVIEW

The Process That Feeds the Biosphere

Life on Earth is solar powered. The chloroplasts of plants capture light energy that has traveled 150 million kilometers from the sun and convert it to chemical energy stored in sugar and other organic molecules. This conversion process is called **photosynthesis**. Let's begin by placing photosynthesis in its ecological context.

Photosynthesis nourishes almost the entire living world directly or indirectly. An organism acquires the organic compounds it uses for energy and carbon skeletons by one of two major modes: autotrophic nutrition or heterotrophic nutrition. **Autotrophs** are "self-feeders" (*auto* means "self," and *trophos* means "feed"); they sustain themselves without eating anything derived from other living beings. Autotrophs produce their organic molecules from CO_2 and other inorganic raw materials obtained from the environment. They are the ultimate sources of organic compounds for all nonautotrophic organisms, and for this reason, biologists refer to autotrophs as the *producers* of the biosphere.

▲ **Figure 10.1 How can sunlight, seen here as a spectrum of colors in a rainbow, power the synthesis of organic substances?**

Almost all plants are autotrophs; the only nutrients they require are water and minerals from the soil and carbon dioxide from the air. Specifically, plants are *photo*autotrophs, organisms that use light as a source of energy to synthesize organic substances **(Figure 10.1)**. Photosynthesis also occurs in algae, certain other protists, and some prokaryotes **(Figure 10.2,** on the next page**)**. In this chapter, we will touch on these other groups in passing, but our emphasis will be on plants. Variations in autotrophic nutrition that occur in prokaryotes and algae will be detailed in Chapters 27 and 28.

Heterotrophs obtain their organic material by the second major mode of nutrition. Unable to make their own food, they live on compounds produced by other organisms (*hetero* means "other"). Heterotrophs are the biosphere's *consumers*. The most obvious form of this "other-feeding" occurs when an animal eats plants or other animals. But heterotrophic nutrition may be more subtle. Some heterotrophs consume the remains of dead organisms by decomposing and feeding on organic litter such as carcasses, feces, and fallen leaves; they are known as decomposers. Most fungi and many types of prokaryotes get their nourishment this way. Almost all heterotrophs, including humans, are completely dependent, either directly or indirectly, on photoautotrophs for food—and also for oxygen, a by-product of photosynthesis.

In this chapter, you will learn how photosynthesis works. After a discussion of the general principles of photosynthesis, we will consider the two stages of photosynthesis: the light reactions, in which solar energy is captured and transformed into chemical energy; and the Calvin cycle, in which the chemical energy is used to make organic molecules of food. Finally, we will consider a few aspects of photosynthesis from an evolutionary perspective.

▼ **Figure 10.2 Photoautotrophs.** These organisms use light energy to drive the synthesis of organic molecules from carbon dioxide and (in most cases) water. They feed not only themselves, but the entire living world. **(a)** On land, plants are the predominant producers of food. In aquatic environments, photosynthetic organisms include **(b)** multicellular algae, such as this kelp; **(c)** some unicellular protists, such as *Euglena*; **(d)** the prokaryotes called cyanobacteria; and **(e)** other photosynthetic prokaryotes, such as these purple sulfur bacteria, which produce sulfur (spherical globules) (c, d, e: LMs).

(a) Plants

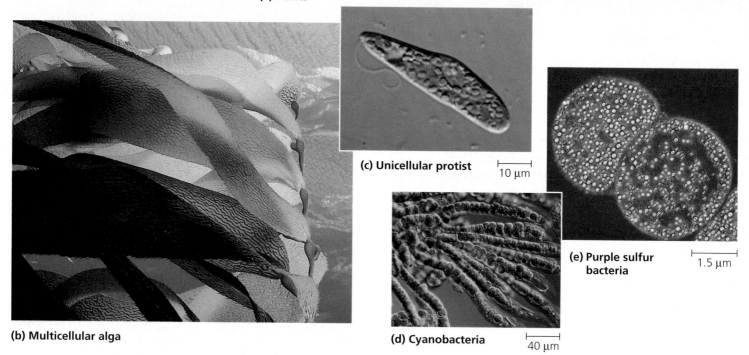

(b) Multicellular alga

(c) Unicellular protist   10 μm

(d) Cyanobacteria   40 μm

(e) Purple sulfur bacteria   1.5 μm

CONCEPT **10.1**

Photosynthesis converts light energy to the chemical energy of food

The remarkable ability of an organism to harness light energy and use it to drive the synthesis of organic compounds emerges from structural organization in the cell: Photosynthetic enzymes and other molecules are grouped together in a biological membrane, enabling the necessary series of chemical reactions to be carried out efficiently. The process of photosynthesis most likely originated in a group of bacteria that had infolded regions of the plasma membrane containing clusters of such molecules. In existing photosynthetic bacteria, infolded photosynthetic membranes function similarly to the internal membranes of the chloroplast, a eukaryotic organelle you learned about in Chapter 6. In fact, the original chloroplast is believed to have been a photosynthetic prokaryote that lived inside a eukaryotic cell. (You'll learn more about this hypothesis in Chapter 25.) Chloroplasts are present in a variety of photosynthesizing organisms (see Figure 10.2), but here we will focus on plants.

Chloroplasts: The Sites of Photosynthesis in Plants

All green parts of a plant, including green stems and unripened fruit, have chloroplasts, but the leaves are the major sites of photosynthesis in most plants **(Figure 10.3)**. There are about half a million chloroplasts per square millimeter of leaf surface. The color of the leaf is from **chlorophyll**, the green pigment located within chloroplasts. It is the light energy absorbed by chlorophyll that drives the synthesis of organic molecules in the chloroplast. Chloroplasts are found mainly in the cells of the **mesophyll**, the tissue in the interior of the leaf.

Carbon dioxide enters the leaf, and oxygen exits, by way of microscopic pores called **stomata** (singular, *stoma*; from the Greek, meaning "mouth"). Water absorbed by the roots is delivered to the leaves in veins. Leaves also use veins to export sugar to roots and other nonphotosynthetic parts of the plant.

A typical mesophyll cell has about 30 to 40 chloroplasts, each organelle measuring about 2–4 μm by 4–7 μm. An envelope of two membranes encloses the **stroma**, the dense fluid within the chloroplast. An elaborate system of interconnected membranous sacs called **thylakoids** segregates the stroma from another compartment, the interior of the thylakoids, or *thylakoid space.* In some places, thylakoid sacs are stacked in columns called *grana* (singular, *granum*). Chlorophyll resides in the thylakoid membranes. (The infolded photosynthetic membranes of prokaryotes are also called thylakoid membranes; see Figure 27.7b.) Now that we have looked at the sites of photosynthesis in plants, we are ready to look more closely at the process of photosynthesis.

Tracking Atoms Through Photosynthesis: *Scientific Inquiry*

Scientists have tried for centuries to piece together the process by which plants make food. Although some of the steps are still not completely understood, the overall photosynthetic equation has been known since the 1800s: In the presence of light, the green parts of plants produce organic compounds and oxygen from carbon dioxide and water. Using molecular formulas, we can summarize the complex series of chemical reactions in photosynthesis with this chemical equation:

$$6 CO_2 + 12 H_2O + \text{Light energy} \rightarrow C_6H_{12}O_6 + 6 O_2 + 6 H_2O$$

We use glucose ($C_6H_{12}O_6$) here to simplify the relationship between photosynthesis and respiration, but the direct product of photosynthesis is actually a three-carbon sugar that can be used to make glucose. Water appears on both sides of the equation because 12 molecules are consumed and 6 molecules are newly formed during photosynthesis. We can simplify the equation by indicating only the net consumption of water:

$$6 CO_2 + 6 H_2O + \text{Light energy} \rightarrow C_6H_{12}O_6 + 6 O_2$$

Writing the equation in this form, we can see that the overall chemical change during photosynthesis is the reverse of the one that occurs during cellular respiration. Both of these metabolic processes occur in plant cells. However, as you will soon learn, chloroplasts do not synthesize sugars by simply reversing the steps of respiration.

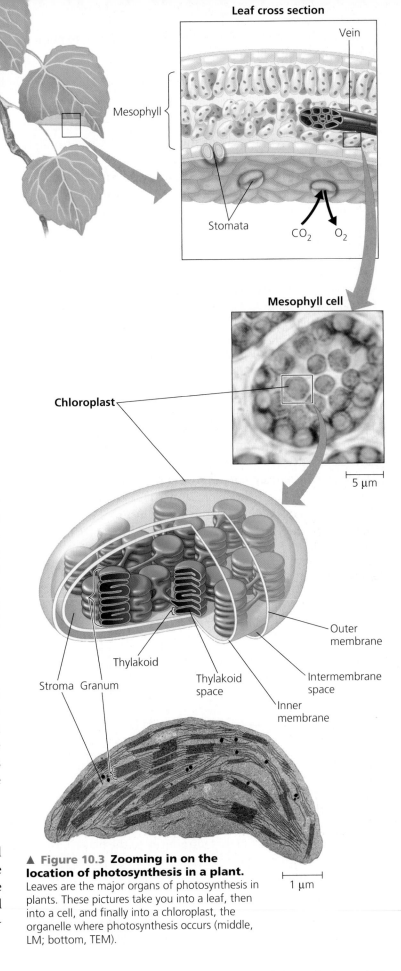

▲ Figure 10.3 Zooming in on the location of photosynthesis in a plant.
Leaves are the major organs of photosynthesis in plants. These pictures take you into a leaf, then into a cell, and finally into a chloroplast, the organelle where photosynthesis occurs (middle, LM; bottom, TEM).

Now let's divide the photosynthetic equation by 6 to put it in its simplest possible form:

$$CO_2 + H_2O \rightarrow [CH_2O] + O_2$$

Here, the brackets indicate that CH_2O is not an actual sugar but represents the general formula for a carbohydrate. In other words, we are imagining the synthesis of a sugar molecule one carbon at a time. Six repetitions would theoretically produce a glucose molecule. Let's now use this simplified formula to see how researchers tracked the elements C, H, and O from the reactants of photosynthesis to the products.

The Splitting of Water

One of the first clues to the mechanism of photosynthesis came from the discovery that the O_2 given off by plants is derived from H_2O and not from CO_2. The chloroplast splits water into hydrogen and oxygen. Before this discovery, the prevailing hypothesis was that photosynthesis split carbon dioxide ($CO_2 \rightarrow C + O_2$) and then added water to the carbon ($C + H_2O \rightarrow [CH_2O]$). This hypothesis predicted that the O_2 released during photosynthesis came from CO_2. This idea was challenged in the 1930s by C. B. van Niel, of Stanford University. Van Niel was investigating photosynthesis in bacteria that make their carbohydrate from CO_2 but do not release O_2. Van Niel concluded that, at least in these bacteria, CO_2 is not split into carbon and oxygen. One group of bacteria used hydrogen sulfide (H_2S) rather than water for photosynthesis, forming yellow globules of sulfur as a waste product (these globules are visible in Figure 10.2e). Here is the chemical equation for photosynthesis in these sulfur bacteria:

$$CO_2 + 2\,H_2S \rightarrow [CH_2O] + H_2O + 2\,S$$

Van Niel reasoned that the bacteria split H_2S and used the hydrogen atoms to make sugar. He then generalized that idea, proposing that all photosynthetic organisms require a hydrogen source but that the source varies:

Sulfur bacteria: $CO_2 + 2\,H_2S \rightarrow [CH_2O] + H_2O + 2\,S$
Plants: $CO_2 + 2\,H_2O \rightarrow [CH_2O] + H_2O + O_2$
General: $CO_2 + 2\,H_2X \rightarrow [CH_2O] + H_2O + 2\,X$

Thus, van Niel hypothesized that plants split H_2O as a source of electrons from hydrogen atoms, releasing O_2 as a by-product.

Nearly 20 years later, scientists confirmed van Niel's hypothesis by using oxygen-18 (^{18}O), a heavy isotope, as a tracer to follow the fate of oxygen atoms during photosynthesis. The experiments showed that the O_2 from plants was labeled with ^{18}O *only* if water was the source of the tracer (experiment 1). If the ^{18}O was introduced to the plant in the form of CO_2, the label did not turn up in the released O_2 (experiment 2). In the following summary, red denotes labeled atoms of oxygen (^{18}O):

Experiment 1: $CO_2 + 2\,H_2O \rightarrow [CH_2O] + H_2O + O_2$
Experiment 2: $CO_2 + 2\,H_2O \rightarrow [CH_2O] + H_2O + O_2$

▲ **Figure 10.4 Tracking atoms through photosynthesis.** The atoms from CO_2 are shown in orange, and the atoms from H_2O are shown in blue.

A significant result of the shuffling of atoms during photosynthesis is the extraction of hydrogen from water and its incorporation into sugar. The waste product of photosynthesis, O_2, is released to the atmosphere. **Figure 10.4** shows the fates of all atoms in photosynthesis.

Photosynthesis as a Redox Process

Let's briefly compare photosynthesis with cellular respiration. Both processes involve redox reactions. During cellular respiration, energy is released from sugar when electrons associated with hydrogen are transported by carriers to oxygen, forming water as a by-product. The electrons lose potential energy as they "fall" down the electron transport chain toward electronegative oxygen, and the mitochondrion harnesses that energy to synthesize ATP (see Figure 9.16). Photosynthesis reverses the direction of electron flow. Water is split, and electrons are transferred along with hydrogen ions from the water to carbon dioxide, reducing it to sugar. Because the electrons increase in potential energy as they move from water to sugar, this process requires energy, in other words is endergonic. This energy boost is provided by light.

The Two Stages of Photosynthesis: *A Preview*

The equation for photosynthesis is a deceptively simple summary of a very complex process. Actually, photosynthesis is not a single process, but two processes, each with multiple steps. These two stages of photosynthesis are known as the **light reactions** (the *photo* part of photosynthesis) and the **Calvin cycle** (the *synthesis* part) **(Figure 10.5)**.

The light reactions are the steps of photosynthesis that convert solar energy to chemical energy. Water is split, providing a source of electrons and protons (hydrogen ions, H^+) and giving off O_2 as a by-product. Light absorbed by chlorophyll drives a transfer of the electrons and hydrogen ions from water to an acceptor called **NADP$^+$** (nicotinamide adenine dinucleotide phosphate), where they are temporarily stored. The electron acceptor NADP$^+$ is first cousin to NAD$^+$, which functions as an electron carrier in cellular respiration; the two molecules differ only by the presence of an extra phosphate group in the NADP$^+$ molecule. The light reactions use solar power to reduce NADP$^+$ to NADPH by adding a

▶ **Figure 10.5** **An overview of photosynthesis: cooperation of the light reactions and the Calvin cycle.** In the chloroplast, the thylakoid membranes are the sites of the light reactions, whereas the Calvin cycle occurs in the stroma. The light reactions use solar energy to make ATP and NADPH, which supply chemical energy and reducing power, respectively, to the Calvin cycle. The Calvin cycle incorporates CO_2 into organic molecules, which are converted to sugar. (Recall that most simple sugars have formulas that are some multiple of CH_2O.)

A smaller version of this diagram will reappear in several subsequent figures as a reminder of whether the events being described occur in the light reactions or in the Calvin cycle.

MEDIA ***BioFlix*** Visit the Study Area at **www.masteringbio.com** for the BioFlix 3-D Animation on Photosynthesis.

pair of electrons along with an H^+. The light reactions also generate ATP, using chemiosmosis to power the addition of a phosphate group to ADP, a process called **photophosphorylation**. Thus, light energy is initially converted to chemical energy in the form of two compounds: NADPH, a source of electrons as "reducing power" that can be passed along to an electron acceptor, reducing it, and ATP, the versatile energy currency of cells. Notice that the light reactions produce no sugar; that happens in the second stage of photosynthesis, the Calvin cycle.

The Calvin cycle is named for Melvin Calvin, who, along with his colleagues, began to elucidate its steps in the late 1940s. The cycle begins by incorporating CO_2 from the air into organic molecules already present in the chloroplast. This initial incorporation of carbon into organic compounds is known as **carbon fixation**. The Calvin cycle then reduces the fixed carbon to carbohydrate by the addition of electrons. The reducing power is provided by NADPH, which acquired its cargo of electrons in the light reactions. To convert CO_2 to carbohydrate, the Calvin cycle also requires chemical energy in the form of ATP, which is also generated by the light reactions. Thus, it is the Calvin cycle that makes sugar, but it can do so only with the help of the NADPH and ATP produced by the light reactions. The metabolic steps of the Calvin cycle are sometimes referred to as the dark reactions, or light-independent reactions, because none of the steps requires light *directly*. Nevertheless, the Calvin cycle in most plants occurs during daylight, for only then can the light reactions

provide the NADPH and ATP that the Calvin cycle requires. In essence, the chloroplast uses light energy to make sugar by coordinating the two stages of photosynthesis.

As Figure 10.5 indicates, the thylakoids of the chloroplast are the sites of the light reactions, while the Calvin cycle occurs in the stroma. In the thylakoids, molecules of $NADP^+$ and ADP pick up electrons and phosphate, respectively, and NADPH and ATP are then released to the stroma, where they play crucial roles in the Calvin cycle. The two stages of photosynthesis are treated in this figure as metabolic modules that take in ingredients and crank out products. Our next step toward understanding photosynthesis is to look more closely at how the two stages work, beginning with the light reactions.

CONCEPT CHECK 10.1

1. How do the reactant molecules of photosynthesis reach the chloroplasts in leaves?
2. How did the use of an oxygen isotope help elucidate the chemistry of photosynthesis?
3. **WHAT IF?** The Calvin cycle clearly requires the products of the light reactions, ATP and NADPH. Suppose a classmate asserts that the converse is not true—that the light reactions don't depend on the Calvin cycle and, with continual light, could just keep on producing ATP and NADPH. Do you agree or disagree? Explain.

For suggested answers, see Appendix A.

CONCEPT 10.2

The light reactions convert solar energy to the chemical energy of ATP and NADPH

Chloroplasts are chemical factories powered by the sun. Their thylakoids transform light energy into the chemical energy of ATP and NADPH. To understand this conversion better, we need to know about some important properties of light.

The Nature of Sunlight

Light is a form of energy known as electromagnetic energy, also called electromagnetic radiation. Electromagnetic energy travels in rhythmic waves analogous to those created by dropping a pebble into a pond. Electromagnetic waves, however, are disturbances of electric and magnetic fields rather than disturbances of a material medium such as water.

The distance between the crests of electromagnetic waves is called the **wavelength**. Wavelengths range from less than a nanometer (for gamma rays) to more than a kilometer (for radio waves). This entire range of radiation is known as the **electromagnetic spectrum (Figure 10.6)**. The segment most important to life is the narrow band from about 380 nm to 750 nm in wavelength. This radiation is known as **visible light** because it can be detected as various colors by the human eye.

The model of light as waves explains many of light's properties, but in certain respects light behaves as though it consists of discrete particles, called **photons**. Photons are not tangible objects, but they act like objects in that each of them has a fixed quantity of energy. The amount of energy is in-versely related to the wavelength of the light: the shorter the wavelength, the greater the energy of each photon of that light. Thus, a photon of violet light packs nearly twice as much energy as a photon of red light.

Although the sun radiates the full spectrum of electromagnetic energy, the atmosphere acts like a selective window, allowing visible light to pass through while screening out a substantial fraction of other radiation. The part of the spectrum we can see—visible light—is also the radiation that drives photosynthesis.

Photosynthetic Pigments: The Light Receptors

When light meets matter, it may be reflected, transmitted, or absorbed. Substances that absorb visible light are known as *pigments*. Different pigments absorb light of different wavelengths, and the wavelengths that are absorbed disappear. If a pigment is illuminated with white light, the color we see is the color most reflected or transmitted by the pigment. (If a pigment absorbs all wavelengths, it appears black.) We see green when we look at a leaf because chlorophyll absorbs violet-blue and red light while transmitting and reflecting green light **(Figure 10.7)**. The ability of a pigment to absorb various wavelengths of light can be measured with an instrument called a **spectrophotometer**. This machine directs beams of light of different wavelengths through a solution of the pigment and measures the fraction of the light transmitted at each wavelength. A graph plotting

▲ **Figure 10.6 The electromagnetic spectrum.** White light is a mixture of all wavelengths of visible light. A prism can sort white light into its component colors by bending light of different wavelengths at different angles. (Droplets of water in the atmosphere can act as prisms, forming a rainbow; see Figure 10.1.) Visible light drives photosynthesis.

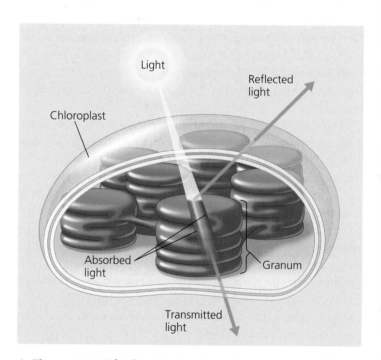

▲ **Figure 10.7 Why leaves are green: interaction of light with chloroplasts.** The chlorophyll molecules of chloroplasts absorb violet-blue and red light (the colors most effective in driving photosynthesis) and reflect or transmit green light. This is why leaves appear green.

a pigment's light absorption versus wavelength is called an **absorption spectrum (Figure 10.8)**.

The absorption spectra of chloroplast pigments provide clues to the relative effectiveness of different wavelengths for driving photosynthesis, since light can perform work in chloroplasts only if it is absorbed. **Figure 10.9a** shows the absorption spectra of three types of pigments in chloroplasts: **chlorophyll a**, which participates directly in the light reactions; the accessory pigment *chlorophyll b*; and a group of accessory pigments called carotenoids. The spectrum of chlorophyll *a* suggests that

Determining an Absorption Spectrum

APPLICATION An absorption spectrum is a visual representation of how well a particular pigment absorbs different wavelengths of visible light. Absorption spectra of various chloroplast pigments help scientists decipher each pigment's role in a plant.

TECHNIQUE A spectrophotometer measures the relative amounts of light of different wavelengths absorbed and transmitted by a pigment solution.

❶ White light is separated into colors (wavelengths) by a prism.

❷ One by one, the different colors of light are passed through the sample (chlorophyll in this example). Green light and blue light are shown here.

❸ The transmitted light strikes a photoelectric tube, which converts the light energy to electricity.

❹ The electrical current is measured by a galvanometer. The meter indicates the fraction of light transmitted through the sample, from which we can determine the amount of light absorbed.

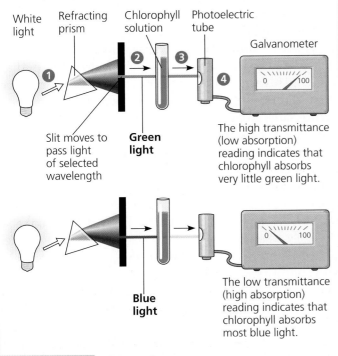

White light — Refracting prism — Chlorophyll solution — Photoelectric tube — Galvanometer

Slit moves to pass light of selected wavelength

Green light

The high transmittance (low absorption) reading indicates that chlorophyll absorbs very little green light.

Blue light

The low transmittance (high absorption) reading indicates that chlorophyll absorbs most blue light.

RESULTS See Figure 10.9a for absorption spectra of three types of chloroplast pigments.

Which wavelengths of light are most effective in driving photosynthesis?

EXPERIMENT Absorption and action spectra, along with a classic experiment by Theodor W. Engelmann, reveal which wavelengths of light are photosynthetically important.

RESULTS

Absorption of light by chloroplast pigments

Chlorophyll a — Chlorophyll b — Carotenoids

400   500   600   700

Wavelength of light (nm)

(a) Absorption spectra. The three curves show the wavelengths of light best absorbed by three types of chloroplast pigments.

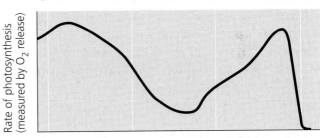

Rate of photosynthesis (measured by O_2 release)

(b) Action spectrum. This graph plots the rate of photosynthesis versus wavelength. The resulting action spectrum resembles the absorption spectrum for chlorophyll *a* but does not match exactly (see part a). This is partly due to the absorption of light by accessory pigments such as chlorophyll *b* and carotenoids.

Aerobic bacteria

Filament of alga

400   500   600   700

(c) Engelmann's experiment. In 1883, Theodor W. Engelmann illuminated a filamentous alga with light that had been passed through a prism, exposing different segments of the alga to different wavelengths. He used aerobic bacteria, which concentrate near an oxygen source, to determine which segments of the alga were releasing the most O_2 and thus photosynthesizing most. Bacteria congregated in greatest numbers around the parts of the alga illuminated with violet-blue or red light.

CONCLUSION Light in the violet-blue and red portions of the spectrum is most effective in driving photosynthesis.

SOURCE T. W. Engelmann, *Bacterium photometricum. Ein Betrag zur vergleichenden Physiologie des Licht- und farbensinnes, Archiv. für Physiologie.* 30:95–124 (1883).

WHAT IF? If Engelmann had placed a red-colored filter between the prism and the alga, how would the results have differed?

violet-blue and red light work best for photosynthesis, since they are absorbed, while green is the least effective color. This is confirmed by an **action spectrum** for photosynthesis (**Figure 10.9b**), which profiles the relative effectiveness of different wavelengths of radiation in driving the process. An action spectrum is prepared by illuminating chloroplasts with light of different colors and then plotting wavelength against some measure of photosynthetic rate, such as CO_2 consumption or O_2 release. The action spectrum for photosynthesis was first demonstrated by a German botanist in 1883. Before equipment for measuring O_2 levels had even been invented, Theodor W. Engelmann performed a clever experiment in which he used bacteria to measure rates of photosynthesis in filamentous algae (**Figure 10.9c**). His results are a striking match to the modern action spectrum shown in Figure 10.9b.

Notice by comparing Figures 10.9a and 10.9b that the action spectrum for photosynthesis does not exactly match the absorption spectrum of chlorophyll *a*. The absorption spectrum of chlorophyll *a* alone underestimates the effectiveness of certain wavelengths in driving photosynthesis. This is partly because accessory pigments with different absorption spectra are also photosynthetically important in chloroplasts and broaden the spectrum of colors that can be used for photosynthesis. **Figure 10.10** shows chlorophyll *a* compared to one

of these accessory pigments, **chlorophyll *b***. A slight structural difference between them is enough to cause the two pigments to absorb at slightly different wavelengths in the red and blue parts of the spectrum (see Figure 10.9a). As a result, chlorophyll *a* is blue green and chlorophyll *b* is olive green.

Other accessory pigments include **carotenoids**, hydrocarbons that are various shades of yellow and orange because they absorb violet and blue-green light (see Figure 10.9a). Carotenoids may broaden the spectrum of colors that can drive photosynthesis. However, a more important function of at least some carotenoids seems to be *photoprotection*: These compounds absorb and dissipate excessive light energy that would otherwise damage chlorophyll or interact with oxygen, forming reactive oxidative molecules that are dangerous to the cell. Interestingly, carotenoids similar to the photoprotective ones in chloroplasts have a photoprotective role in the human eye. These and related molecules, often found in health food products, are valued as "phytochemicals" (from the Greek *phyton*, plant), compounds with antioxidant properties. Plants can synthesize all the antioxidants they require, but humans and other animals must obtain some of them from their diets.

Excitation of Chlorophyll by Light

What exactly happens when chlorophyll and other pigments absorb light? The colors corresponding to the absorbed wavelengths disappear from the spectrum of the transmitted and reflected light, but energy cannot disappear. When a molecule absorbs a photon of light, one of the molecule's electrons is elevated to an orbital where it has more potential energy. When the electron is in its normal orbital, the pigment molecule is said to be in its ground state. Absorption of a photon boosts an electron to an orbital of higher energy, and the pigment molecule is then said to be in an excited state. The only photons absorbed are those whose energy is exactly equal to the energy difference between the ground state and an excited state, and this energy difference varies from one kind of molecule to another. Thus, a particular compound absorbs only photons corresponding to specific wavelengths, which is why each pigment has a unique absorption spectrum.

Once absorption of a photon raises an electron from the ground state to an excited state, the electron cannot remain there long. The excited state, like all high-energy states, is unstable. Generally, when isolated pigment molecules absorb light, their excited electrons drop back down to the ground-state orbital in a billionth of a second, releasing their excess energy as heat. This conversion of light energy to heat is what makes the top of an automobile so hot on a sunny day. (White cars are coolest because their paint reflects all wavelengths of visible light, although it may absorb ultraviolet and other invisible radiation.) In isolation, some pigments, including chlorophyll, emit light as well as heat after absorbing photons. As excited electrons fall back to the ground state, photons are given off. This afterglow is called

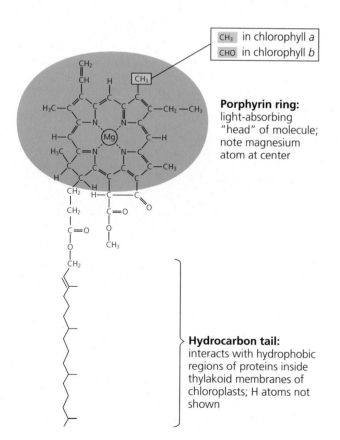

CH₃ in chlorophyll *a*
CHO in chlorophyll *b*

Porphyrin ring: light-absorbing "head" of molecule; note magnesium atom at center

Hydrocarbon tail: interacts with hydrophobic regions of proteins inside thylakoid membranes of chloroplasts; H atoms not shown

▲ **Figure 10.10 Structure of chlorophyll molecules in chloroplasts of plants.** Chlorophyll *a* and chlorophyll *b* differ only in one of the functional groups bonded to the organic structure called a porphyrin ring.

(a) Excitation of isolated chlorophyll molecule

(b) Fluorescence

◄ **Figure 10.11 Excitation of isolated chlorophyll by light. (a)** Absorption of a photon causes a transition of the chlorophyll molecule from its ground state to its excited state. The photon boosts an electron to an orbital where it has more potential energy. If the illuminated molecule exists in isolation, its excited electron immediately drops back down to the ground-state orbital, and its excess energy is given off as heat and fluorescence (light). **(b)** A chlorophyll solution excited with ultraviolet light fluoresces with a red-orange glow.

WHAT IF? *If a leaf containing a similar concentration of chlorophyll as the solution was exposed to the same ultraviolet light, no fluorescence would be seen. Explain the difference in fluorescence emission between the solution and the leaf.*

fluorescence. If a solution of chlorophyll isolated from chloroplasts is illuminated, it will fluoresce in the red-orange part of the spectrum and also give off heat **(Figure 10.11)**.

A Photosystem: A Reaction-Center Complex Associated with Light-Harvesting Complexes

Chlorophyll molecules excited by the absorption of light energy produce very different results in an intact chloroplast than they do in isolation (see Figure 10.11). In their native environment of the thylakoid membrane, chlorophyll molecules are organized along with other small organic molecules and proteins into photosystems.

A **photosystem** is composed of a protein complex called a **reaction-center complex** surrounded by several light-harvesting complexes **(Figure 10.12)**. The reaction-center complex includes a special pair of chlorophyll *a* molecules. Each **light-harvesting complex** consists of various pigment molecules (which may include chlorophyll *a*, chlorophyll *b*, and carotenoids) bound to proteins. The number and variety of pigment molecules enable a photosystem to harvest light over a larger surface and a larger portion of the spectrum than any single pigment molecule alone could. Together, these light-harvesting complexes act as an antenna for the reaction-center complex. When a pigment molecule absorbs a photon, the energy is transferred from pigment molecule to pigment molecule within a light-harvesting complex, somewhat like a human "wave" at a sports arena, until it is passed into the reaction-center complex. The reaction-center complex contains a molecule capable of accepting electrons and becoming reduced; it is called the **primary electron acceptor**. The pair of chlorophyll *a* molecules in the reaction-center complex are special because their molecular environment—their location and the other molecules with which they are associated—enables

▲ **Figure 10.12 How a photosystem harvests light.** When a photon strikes a pigment molecule in a light-harvesting complex, the energy is passed from molecule to molecule until it reaches the reaction-center complex. Here, an excited electron from the special pair of chlorophyll *a* molecules is transferred to the primary electron acceptor.

them to use the energy from light not only to boost one of their electrons to a higher energy level, but also to transfer it to a different molecule—the primary electron acceptor.

The solar-powered transfer of an electron from the reaction-center chlorophyll *a* pair to the primary electron acceptor is the first step of the light reactions. As soon as the chlorophyll electron is excited to a higher energy level, the primary electron acceptor captures it; this is a redox reaction. Isolated chlorophyll fluoresces because there is no electron acceptor, so electrons of photoexcited chlorophyll drop right back to the ground state. In a chloroplast, the potential energy represented by the excited electron is not lost. Thus, each photosystem—a reaction-center complex surrounded by light-harvesting complexes—functions in the chloroplast as a unit. It converts light energy to chemical energy, which will ultimately be used for the synthesis of sugar.

The thylakoid membrane is populated by two types of photosystems that cooperate in the light reactions of photosynthesis. They are called **photosystem II (PS II)** and **photosystem I (PS I)**. (They were named in order of their discovery, but photosystem II functions first in the light reactions.) Each has a characteristic reaction-center complex—a particular kind of primary electron acceptor next to a special pair of chlorophyll *a* molecules associated with specific proteins. The reaction-center chlorophyll *a* of photosystem II is known as P680 because this pigment is best at absorbing light having a wavelength of 680 nm (in the red part of the spectrum). The chlorophyll *a* at the reaction-center complex of photosystem I is called P700 because it most effectively absorbs light of wavelength 700 nm (in the far-red part of the spectrum). These two pigments, P680 and P700, are nearly identical chlorophyll *a* molecules. However, their association with different proteins in the thylakoid membrane affects the electron distribution in the two pigments and accounts for the slight differences in their light-absorbing properties. Now let's see how the two photosystems work together in using light energy to generate ATP and NADPH, the two main products of the light reactions.

Linear Electron Flow

Light drives the synthesis of ATP and NADPH by energizing the two photosystems embedded in the thylakoid membranes of chloroplasts. The key to this energy transformation is a flow of electrons through the photosystems and other molecular components built into the thylakoid membrane. This is called **linear electron flow**, and it occurs during the light reactions of photosynthesis, as shown in **Figure 10.13**. The numbers in the text description correspond to the numbered steps in the figure.

❶ A photon of light strikes a pigment molecule in a light-harvesting complex, boosting one of its electrons to a higher energy level. As this electron falls back to its ground state, an electron in a nearby pigment molecule is simultaneously raised to an excited state. The process continues, with the energy being relayed to other pigment molecules until it reaches the P680 pair of chlorophyll *a* molecules in the PS II reaction-center complex. It excites an electron in this pair of chlorophylls to a higher energy state.

❷ This electron is transferred from the excited P680 to the primary electron acceptor. We can refer to the resulting form of P680, missing an electron, as P680$^+$.

❸ An enzyme catalyzes the splitting of a water molecule into two electrons, two hydrogen ions, and an oxygen atom. The electrons are supplied one by one to the P680$^+$ pair, each electron replacing one transferred to the primary electron acceptor. (P680$^+$ is the strongest biological oxidizing agent known; its electron "hole" must be filled. This greatly facilitates the transfer of electrons from the split water molecule.) The oxygen atom immediately combines with an oxygen atom generated by the splitting of another water molecule, forming O_2.

❹ Each photoexcited electron passes from the primary electron acceptor of PS II to PS I via an electron transport chain, the components of which are similar to those of the electron transport chain that functions in cellular respiration. The electron transport chain between PS II and PS I is made up of the electron carrier plastoquinone (Pq), a cytochrome complex, and a protein called plastocyanin (Pc).

❺ The exergonic "fall" of electrons to a lower energy level provides energy for the synthesis of ATP. As electrons pass through the cytochrome complex, the pumping of protons builds a proton gradient that is subsequently used in chemiosmosis.

❻ Meanwhile, light energy was transferred via light-harvesting complex pigments to the PS I reaction-center complex, exciting an electron of the P700 pair of chlorophyll *a* molecules located there. The photoexcited electron was then transferred to PS I's primary electron acceptor, creating an electron "hole" in the P700—which we now can call P700$^+$. In other words, P700$^+$ can now act as an electron acceptor, accepting an electron that reaches the bottom of the electron transport chain from PS II.

❼ Photoexcited electrons are passed in a series of redox reactions from the primary electron acceptor of PS I down a second electron transport chain through the protein ferredoxin (Fd). (This chain does not create a proton gradient and thus does not produce ATP.)

❽ The enzyme NADP$^+$ reductase catalyzes the transfer of electrons from Fd to NADP$^+$. Two electrons are required for its reduction to NADPH. This molecule is at a higher energy level than water, and its electrons are more readily available for the reactions of the Calvin cycle than were those of water.

As complicated as the scheme shown in Figure 10.13 is, do not lose track of its functions. The light reactions use solar power to generate ATP and NADPH, which provide chemical energy and reducing power, respectively, to the carbohydrate-synthesizing reactions of the Calvin cycle. The energy changes of electrons as they flow through the light reactions are shown in a mechanical analogy in **Figure 10.14**.

▼ Figure 10.13 **How linear electron flow during the light reactions generates ATP and NADPH.** The gold arrows trace the current of light-driven electrons from water to NADPH.

▲ **Figure 10.14 A mechanical analogy for the light reactions.**

Cyclic Electron Flow

In certain cases, photoexcited electrons can take an alternative path called **cyclic electron flow**, which uses photosystem I but not photosystem II. You can see in **Figure 10.15**, on the next page, that cyclic flow is a short circuit: The electrons cycle back from ferredoxin (Fd) to the cytochrome complex and from there continue on to a P700 chlorophyll in the PS I reaction-center complex. There is no production of NADPH and no release of oxygen. Cyclic flow does, however, generate ATP.

Several of the currently existing groups of photosynthetic bacteria are known to have photosystem I but not photosystem II; for these species, which include the purple sulfur bacteria (see Figure 10.2e), cyclic electron flow is the sole means of generating ATP in photosynthesis. Evolutionary biologists believe that these bacterial groups are descendants of the bacteria in which photosynthesis first evolved, in a form similar to cyclic electron flow.

Cyclic electron flow can also occur in photosynthetic species that possess both photosystems; this includes some prokaryotes, such as the cyanobacteria shown in Figure 10.2d, as well as the eukaryotic photosynthetic species that have been tested to

▶ **Figure 10.15 Cyclic electron flow.** Photoexcited electrons from PS I are occasionally shunted back from ferredoxin (Fd) to chlorophyll via the cytochrome complex and plastocyanin (Pc). This electron shunt supplements the supply of ATP (via chemiosmosis) but produces no NADPH. The "shadow" of linear electron flow is included in the diagram for comparison with the cyclic route. The two ferredoxin molecules shown in this diagram are actually one and the same—the final electron carrier in the electron transport chain of PS I.

date. Although the process is probably in part an "evolutionary leftover," it clearly plays at least one beneficial role for these organisms. Mutant plants that are not able to carry out cyclic electron flow are capable of growing well in low light, but do not grow well where light is intense. This is evidence for the idea that cyclic electron flow may be photoprotective, protecting cells from light-induced damage. Later you'll learn more about cyclic electron flow as it relates to a particular adaptation of photosynthesis (C_4 plants; see Concept 10.4).

Whether ATP synthesis is driven by linear or cyclic electron flow, the actual mechanism is the same. Before we move on to consider the Calvin cycle, let's review chemiosmosis, the process that uses membranes to couple redox reactions to ATP production.

A Comparison of Chemiosmosis in Chloroplasts and Mitochondria

Chloroplasts and mitochondria generate ATP by the same basic mechanism: chemiosmosis. An electron transport chain assembled in a membrane pumps protons across the membrane as electrons are passed through a series of carriers that are progressively more electronegative. In this way, electron transport chains transform redox energy to a proton-motive force, potential energy stored in the form of an H^+ gradient across a membrane. Built into the same membrane is an ATP synthase complex that couples the diffusion of hydrogen ions down their gradient to the phosphorylation of ADP. Some of the electron carriers, including the iron-containing proteins called cytochromes, are very similar in chloroplasts and mitochondria. The ATP synthase complexes of the two organelles are also very much alike. But there are noteworthy differences between oxidative phosphorylation in mitochondria and photophosphorylation in chloroplasts. In mitochondria, the high-energy electrons dropped down the transport chain are extracted from organic molecules (which are thus oxidized), while in chloroplasts, the source of electrons is water. Chloroplasts do not need molecules from food to make ATP; their

photosystems capture light energy and use it to drive the electrons from water to the top of the transport chain. In other words, mitochondria use chemiosmosis to transfer chemical energy from food molecules to ATP, whereas chloroplasts transform light energy into chemical energy in ATP.

Although the spatial organization of chemiosmosis differs slightly between chloroplasts and mitochondria, it is easy to see similarities in the two **(Figure 10.16)**. The inner membrane of

▲ **Figure 10.16 Comparison of chemiosmosis in mitochondria and chloroplasts.** In both kinds of organelles, electron transport chains pump protons (H^+) across a membrane from a region of low H^+ concentration (light gray in this diagram) to one of high H^+ concentration (dark gray). The protons then diffuse back across the membrane through ATP synthase, driving the synthesis of ATP.

the mitochondrion pumps protons from the mitochondrial matrix out to the intermembrane space, which then serves as a reservoir of hydrogen ions. The thylakoid membrane of the chloroplast pumps protons from the stroma into the thylakoid space (interior of the thylakoid), which functions as the H^+ reservoir. If you imagine the cristae of mitochondria pinching off from the inner membrane, this may help you see how the thylakoid space and the intermembrane space are comparable spaces in the two organelles, while the mitochondrial matrix is analogous to the stroma of the chloroplast. In the mitochondrion, protons diffuse down their concentration gradient from the intermembrane space through ATP synthase to the matrix,

driving ATP synthesis. In the chloroplast, ATP is synthesized as the hydrogen ions diffuse from the thylakoid space back to the stroma through ATP synthase complexes, whose catalytic knobs are on the stroma side of the membrane. Thus, ATP forms in the stroma, where it is used to help drive sugar synthesis during the Calvin cycle (Figure 10.17).

The proton (H^+) gradient, or pH gradient, across the thylakoid membrane is substantial. When chloroplasts in an experimental setting are illuminated, the pH in the thylakoid space drops to about 5 (the H^+ concentration increases), and the pH in the stroma increases to about 8 (the H^+ concentration decreases). This gradient of three pH units corresponds to a thousandfold

▲ **Figure 10.17 The light reactions and chemiosmosis: the organization of the thylakoid membrane.** This diagram shows a current model for the organization of the thylakoid membrane. The gold arrows track the linear electron flow outlined in Figure 10.13. As electrons pass from carrier to carrier in redox reactions, hydrogen ions removed from the stroma are deposited in the thylakoid space, storing energy as a proton-motive force (H^+ gradient). At least three steps in the light reactions contribute to the proton gradient: ❶ Water is split by photosystem II on the side of the membrane facing the thylakoid space; ❷ as plastoquinone (Pq), a mobile carrier, transfers electrons to the cytochrome complex, four protons are translocated across the membrane into the thylakoid space; and ❸ a hydrogen ion is removed from the stroma when it is taken up by $NADP^+$. Notice how, as in Figure 10.16, hydrogen ions are being pumped from the stroma into the thylakoid space. The diffusion of H^+ from the thylakoid space back to the stroma (along the H^+ concentration gradient) powers the ATP synthase. These light-driven reactions store chemical energy in NADPH and ATP, which shuttle the energy to the carbohydrate-producing Calvin cycle.

difference in H^+ concentration. If in the laboratory the lights are turned off, the pH gradient is abolished, but it can quickly be restored by turning the lights back on. Experiments such as this provided strong evidence in support of the chemiosmotic model.

Based on studies in several laboratories, Figure 10.17 shows a current model for the organization of the light-reaction "machinery" within the thylakoid membrane. Each of the molecules and molecular complexes in the figure is present in numerous copies in each thylakoid. Notice that NADPH, like ATP, is produced on the side of the membrane facing the stroma, where the Calvin cycle reactions take place.

Let's summarize the light reactions. Electron flow pushes electrons from water, where they are at a low state of potential energy, ultimately to NADPH, where they are stored at a high state of potential energy. The light-driven electron current also generates ATP. Thus, the equipment of the thylakoid membrane converts light energy to chemical energy stored in ATP and NADPH. (Oxygen is a by-product.) Let's now see how the Calvin cycle uses the products of the light reactions to synthesize sugar from CO_2.

CONCEPT CHECK 10.2

1. What color of light is *least* effective in driving photosynthesis? Explain.
2. Compared to a solution of isolated chlorophyll, why do intact chloroplasts release less heat and fluorescence when illuminated?
3. In the light reactions, what is the initial electron donor? Where do the electrons end up?
4. **WHAT IF?** In an experiment, isolated chloroplasts placed in a solution with the appropriate components can carry out ATP synthesis. Predict what would happen to the rate of synthesis if a compound is added to the solution that makes membranes freely permeable to hydrogen ions.

For suggested answers, see Appendix A.

CONCEPT 10.3
The Calvin cycle uses ATP and NADPH to convert CO_2 to sugar

The Calvin cycle is similar to the citric acid cycle in that a starting material is regenerated after molecules enter and leave the cycle. However, while the citric acid cycle is catabolic, oxidizing glucose and using the energy to synthesize ATP, the Calvin cycle is anabolic, building carbohydrates from smaller molecules and consuming energy. Carbon enters the Calvin cycle in the form of CO_2 and leaves in the form of sugar. The cycle spends ATP as an energy source and consumes NADPH as reducing power for adding high-energy electrons to make the sugar.

As we mentioned previously, the carbohydrate produced directly from the Calvin cycle is actually not glucose, but a three-carbon sugar; the name of this sugar is **glyceraldehyde-3-phosphate (G3P)**. For the net synthesis of one molecule of G3P, the cycle must take place three times, fixing three molecules of CO_2. (Recall that carbon fixation refers to the initial incorporation of CO_2 into organic material.) As we trace the steps of the cycle, keep in mind that we are following three molecules of CO_2 through the reactions. **Figure 10.18** divides the Calvin cycle into three phases: carbon fixation, reduction, and regeneration of the CO_2 acceptor.

Phase 1: Carbon fixation. The Calvin cycle incorporates each CO_2 molecule, one at a time, by attaching it to a five-carbon sugar named ribulose bisphosphate (abbreviated RuBP). The enzyme that catalyzes this first step is RuBP carboxylase, or **rubisco**. (This is the most abundant protein in chloroplasts and is also said to be the most abundant protein on Earth.) The product of the reaction is a six-carbon intermediate so unstable that it immediately splits in half, forming two molecules of 3-phosphoglycerate (for each CO_2 fixed).

Phase 2: Reduction. Each molecule of 3-phosphoglycerate receives an additional phosphate group from ATP, becoming 1,3-bisphosphoglycerate. Next, a pair of electrons donated from NADPH reduces 1,3-bisphosphoglycerate, which also loses a phosphate group, becoming G3P. Specifically, the electrons from NADPH reduce a carboxyl group on 1,3-bisphosphoglycerate to the aldehyde group of G3P, which stores more potential energy. G3P is a sugar—the same three-carbon sugar formed in glycolysis by the splitting of glucose (see Figure 9.9). Notice in Figure 10.18 that for every *three* molecules of CO_2 that enter the cycle, there are *six* molecules of G3P formed. But only one molecule of this three-carbon sugar can be counted as a net gain of carbohydrate. The cycle began with 15 carbons' worth of carbohydrate in the form of three molecules of the five-carbon sugar RuBP. Now there are 18 carbons' worth of carbohydrate in the form of six molecules of G3P. One molecule exits the cycle to be used by the plant cell, but the other five molecules must be recycled to regenerate the three molecules of RuBP.

Phase 3: Regeneration of the CO_2 acceptor (RuBP). In a complex series of reactions, the carbon skeletons of five molecules of G3P are rearranged by the last steps of the Calvin cycle into three molecules of RuBP. To accomplish this, the cycle spends three more molecules of ATP. The RuBP is now prepared to receive CO_2 again, and the cycle continues.

For the net synthesis of one G3P molecule, the Calvin cycle consumes a total of nine molecules of ATP and six molecules

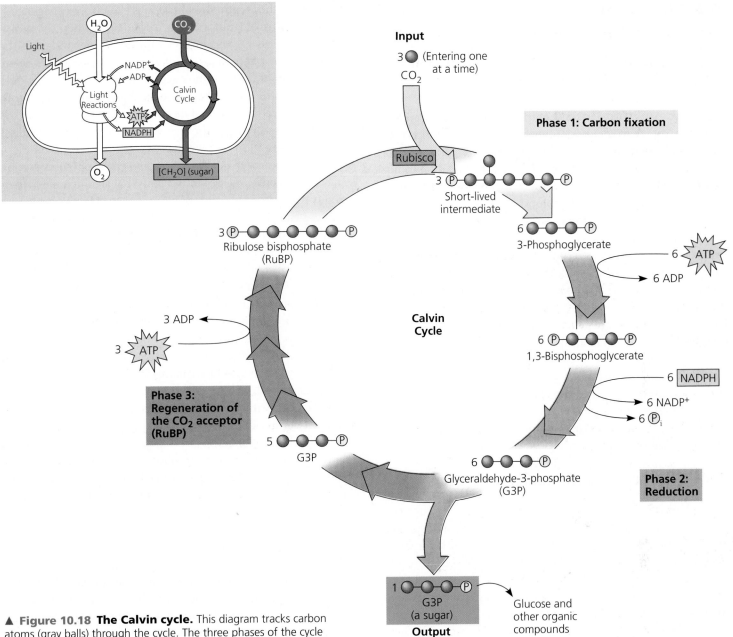

Input

3 ● (Entering one at a time)
CO₂

Phase 1: Carbon fixation

Rubisco

3 ℗ ●●●●● ℗
Short-lived intermediate

6 ●●● ℗
3-Phosphoglycerate

6 ATP
6 ADP

Calvin Cycle

3 ℗ ●●●●● ℗
Ribulose bisphosphate (RuBP)

3 ADP

3 ATP

Phase 3: Regeneration of the CO₂ acceptor (RuBP)

6 ℗ ●●● ℗
1,3-Bisphosphoglycerate

6 NADPH
6 NADP⁺
6 ℗ᵢ

5 ●●● ℗
G3P

6 ●●● ℗
Glyceraldehyde-3-phosphate (G3P)

Phase 2: Reduction

1 ●●● ℗
G3P (a sugar)
Output

Glucose and other organic compounds

▲ **Figure 10.18 The Calvin cycle.** This diagram tracks carbon atoms (gray balls) through the cycle. The three phases of the cycle correspond to the phases discussed in the text. For every three molecules of CO₂ that enter the cycle, the net output is one molecule of glyceraldehyde-3-phosphate (G3P), a three-carbon sugar. The light reactions sustain the Calvin cycle by regenerating ATP and NADPH.
DRAW IT *Redraw this cycle using numerals to indicate the numbers of carbons instead of gray balls, multiplying at each step to ensure that you have accounted for all carbons. In what forms do the carbon atoms enter and leave the cycle?*

of NADPH. The light reactions regenerate the ATP and NADPH. The G3P spun off from the Calvin cycle becomes the starting material for metabolic pathways that synthesize other organic compounds, including glucose and other carbohydrates. Neither the light reactions nor the Calvin cycle alone can make sugar from CO₂. Photosynthesis is an emergent property of the intact chloroplast, which integrates the two stages of photosynthesis.

CONCEPT CHECK 10.3

1. To synthesize one glucose molecule, the Calvin cycle uses _____ molecules of CO₂, _____ molecules of ATP, and _____ molecules of NADPH.
2. Explain why the large numbers of ATP and NADPH molecules used during the Calvin cycle are consistent with the high value of glucose as an energy source.
3. **WHAT IF?** Explain why a poison that inhibits an enzyme of the Calvin cycle will also inhibit the light reactions.

For suggested answers, see Appendix A.

CONCEPT 10.4

Alternative mechanisms of carbon fixation have evolved in hot, arid climates

Ever since plants first moved onto land about 475 million years ago, they have been adapting to the problems of terrestrial life, particularly the problem of dehydration. In Chapters 29 and 36, we will consider anatomical adaptations that help plants conserve water. Here we are concerned with metabolic adaptations. The solutions often involve trade-offs. An important example is the compromise between photosynthesis and the prevention of excessive water loss from the plant. The CO_2 required for photosynthesis enters a leaf via stomata, the pores through the leaf surface (see Figure 10.3). However, stomata are also the main avenues of transpiration, the evaporative loss of water from leaves. On a hot, dry day, most plants close their stomata, a response that conserves water. This response also reduces photosynthetic yield by limiting access to CO_2. With stomata even partially closed, CO_2 concentrations begin to decrease in the air spaces within the leaf, and the concentration of O_2 released from the light reactions begins to increase. These conditions within the leaf favor an apparently wasteful process called photorespiration.

Photorespiration: An Evolutionary Relic?

In most plants, initial fixation of carbon occurs via rubisco, the Calvin cycle enzyme that adds CO_2 to ribulose bisphosphate. Such plants are called **C$_3$ plants** because the first organic product of carbon fixation is a three-carbon compound, 3-phosphoglycerate (see Figure 10.18). Rice, wheat, and soybeans are C_3 plants that are important in agriculture. When their stomata partially close on hot, dry days, C_3 plants produce less sugar because the declining level of CO_2 in the leaf starves the Calvin cycle. In addition, rubisco can bind O_2 in place of CO_2. As CO_2 becomes scarce within the air spaces of the leaf, rubisco adds O_2 to the Calvin cycle instead of CO_2. The product splits, and a two-carbon compound leaves the chloroplast. Peroxisomes and mitochondria rearrange and split this compound, releasing CO_2. The process is called **photorespiration** because it occurs in the light (*photo*) and consumes O_2 while producing CO_2 (*respiration*). However, unlike normal cellular respiration, photorespiration generates no ATP; in fact, photorespiration consumes ATP. And unlike photosynthesis, photorespiration produces no sugar. In fact, photorespiration *decreases* photosynthetic output by siphoning organic material from the Calvin cycle and releasing CO_2 that would otherwise be fixed.

How can we explain the existence of a metabolic process that seems to be counterproductive for the plant? According to one hypothesis, photorespiration is evolutionary baggage—a metabolic relic from a much earlier time when the atmosphere had less O_2 and more CO_2 than it does today. In the ancient atmosphere that prevailed when rubisco first evolved, the inability of the enzyme's active site to exclude O_2 would have made little difference. The hypothesis suggests that modern rubisco retains some of its chance affinity for O_2, which is now so concentrated in the atmosphere that a certain amount of photorespiration is inevitable.

We now know that, at least in some cases, photorespiration plays a protective role in plants. Plants that are impaired in their ability to carry out photorespiration (due to defective genes) are more susceptible to damage induced by excess light. Researchers consider this clear evidence that photorespiration acts to neutralize the otherwise damaging products of the light reactions, which build up when a low CO_2 concentration limits the progress of the Calvin cycle. Whether there are other benefits of photorespiration is still unknown. In many types of plants—including a significant number of crop plants—photorespiration drains away as much as 50% of the carbon fixed by the Calvin cycle. As heterotrophs that depend on carbon fixation in chloroplasts for our food, we naturally view photorespiration as wasteful. Indeed, if photorespiration could be reduced in certain plant species without otherwise affecting photosynthetic productivity, crop yields and food supplies might increase.

In some plant species, alternate modes of carbon fixation have evolved that minimize photorespiration and optimize the Calvin cycle—even in hot, arid climates. The two most important of these photosynthetic adaptations are C_4 photosynthesis and CAM.

C$_4$ Plants

The **C$_4$ plants** are so named because they preface the Calvin cycle with an alternate mode of carbon fixation that forms a four-carbon compound as its first product. Several thousand species in at least 19 plant families use the C_4 pathway. Among the C_4 plants important to agriculture are sugarcane and corn, members of the grass family.

A unique leaf anatomy is correlated with the mechanism of C_4 photosynthesis (**Figure 10.19**; compare with Figure 10.3). In C_4 plants, there are two distinct types of photosynthetic cells: bundle-sheath cells and mesophyll cells. **Bundle-sheath cells** are arranged into tightly packed sheaths around the veins of the leaf. Between the bundle sheath and the leaf surface are the more loosely arranged **mesophyll cells**. The Calvin cycle is confined to the chloroplasts of the bundle-sheath cells. However, the cycle is preceded by incorporation of CO_2 into organic compounds in the mesophyll cells (see the numbered steps in Figure 10.19). ❶ The first step is carried out by an enzyme present only in mesophyll cells called **PEP carboxylase**. This enzyme adds CO_2 to phosphoenolpyruvate (PEP), forming the four-carbon product oxaloacetate. PEP carboxylase

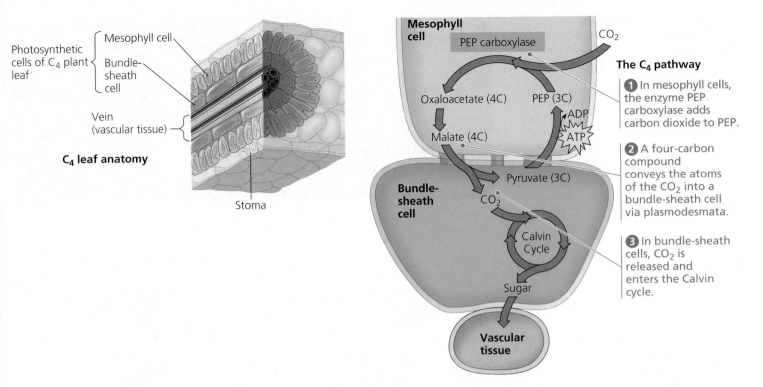

Photosynthetic cells of C_4 plant leaf
- Mesophyll cell
- Bundle-sheath cell

Vein (vascular tissue)

C_4 leaf anatomy

Stoma

Mesophyll cell

PEP carboxylase

CO_2

The C_4 pathway

Oxaloacetate (4C)   PEP (3C)

Malate (4C)   ADP   ATP

Bundle-sheath cell

Pyruvate (3C)

CO_2

Calvin Cycle

Sugar

Vascular tissue

❶ In mesophyll cells, the enzyme PEP carboxylase adds carbon dioxide to PEP.

❷ A four-carbon compound conveys the atoms of the CO_2 into a bundle-sheath cell via plasmodesmata.

❸ In bundle-sheath cells, CO_2 is released and enters the Calvin cycle.

▲ **Figure 10.19 C_4 leaf anatomy and the C_4 pathway.** The structure and biochemical functions of the leaves of C_4 plants are an evolutionary adaptation to hot, dry climates. This adaptation maintains a CO_2 concentration in the bundle sheath that favors photosynthesis over photorespiration.

has a much higher affinity for CO_2 than does rubisco and no affinity for O_2. Therefore, PEP carboxylase can fix carbon efficiently when rubisco cannot—that is, when it is hot and dry and stomata are partially closed, causing CO_2 concentration in the leaf to fall and O_2 concentration to rise. ❷ After the C_4 plant fixes carbon from CO_2, the mesophyll cells export their four-carbon products (malate in the example shown in Figure 10.19) to bundle-sheath cells through plasmodesmata (see Figure 6.31). ❸ Within the bundle-sheath cells, the four-carbon compounds release CO_2, which is reassimilated into organic material by rubisco and the Calvin cycle. The same reaction regenerates pyruvate, which is transported to mesophyll cells. There, ATP is used to convert pyruvate to PEP, allowing the reaction cycle to continue; this ATP can be thought of as the "price" of concentrating CO_2 in the bundle-sheath cells. To generate this extra ATP, bundle-sheath cells carry out cyclic electron flow, the process described earlier in this chapter (see Figure 10.15). In fact, these cells contain PS I but no PS II, so cyclic electron flow is their only photosynthetic mode of generating ATP.

In effect, the mesophyll cells of a C_4 plant pump CO_2 into the bundle sheath, keeping the CO_2 concentration in the bundle-sheath cells high enough for rubisco to bind carbon dioxide rather than oxygen. The cyclic series of reactions involving PEP carboxylase and the regeneration of PEP can be thought of as a CO_2-concentrating pump that is powered by ATP. In

this way, C_4 photosynthesis minimizes photorespiration and enhances sugar production. This adaptation is especially advantageous in hot regions with intense sunlight, where stomata partially close during the day, and it is in such environments that C_4 plants evolved and thrive today.

CAM Plants

A second photosynthetic adaptation to arid conditions has evolved in many succulent (water-storing) plants, numerous cacti, pineapples, and representatives of several other plant families. These plants open their stomata during the night and close them during the day, just the reverse of how other plants behave. Closing stomata during the day helps desert plants conserve water, but it also prevents CO_2 from entering the leaves. During the night, when their stomata are open, these plants take up CO_2 and incorporate it into a variety of organic acids. This mode of carbon fixation is called **crassulacean acid metabolism**, or **CAM**, after the plant family Crassulaceae, the succulents in which the process was first discovered. The mesophyll cells of **CAM plants** store the organic acids they make during the night in their vacuoles until morning, when the stomata close. During the day, when the light reactions can supply ATP and NADPH for the Calvin cycle, CO_2 is released from the organic acids made the night before to become incorporated into sugar in the chloroplasts.

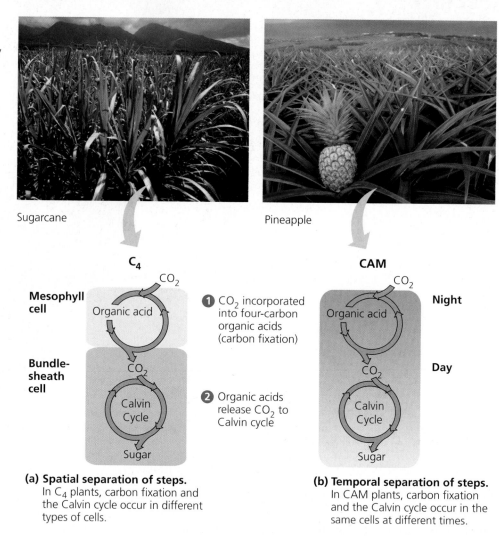

► **Figure 10.20 C₄ and CAM photosynthesis compared.** Both adaptations are characterized by ❶ preliminary incorporation of CO₂ into organic acids, followed by ❷ transfer of CO₂ to the Calvin cycle. The C₄ and CAM pathways are two evolutionary solutions to the problem of maintaining photosynthesis with stomata partially or completely closed on hot, dry days.

Sugarcane

Pineapple

C₄

Mesophyll cell

CO₂

Organic acid

Bundle-sheath cell

CO₂

Calvin Cycle

Sugar

❶ CO₂ incorporated into four-carbon organic acids (carbon fixation)

❷ Organic acids release CO₂ to Calvin cycle

CAM

CO₂

Organic acid

Night

CO₂

Calvin Cycle

Day

Sugar

(a) Spatial separation of steps.
In C₄ plants, carbon fixation and the Calvin cycle occur in different types of cells.

(b) Temporal separation of steps.
In CAM plants, carbon fixation and the Calvin cycle occur in the same cells at different times.

Notice in **Figure 10.20** that the CAM pathway is similar to the C₄ pathway in that carbon dioxide is first incorporated into organic intermediates before it enters the Calvin cycle. The difference is that in C₄ plants, the initial steps of carbon fixation are separated structurally from the Calvin cycle, whereas in CAM plants, the two steps occur at separate times but within the same cell. (Keep in mind that CAM, C₄, and C₃ plants all eventually use the Calvin cycle to make sugar from carbon dioxide.)

CONCEPT CHECK 10.4

1. Explain why photorespiration lowers photosynthetic output for plants.
2. The presence of only PS I, not PS II, in the bundle-sheath cells of C₄ plants has an effect on O₂ concentration. What is that effect, and how might that benefit the plant?
3. **WHAT IF?** How would you expect the relative abundance of C₃ versus C₄ and CAM species to change in a geographic region whose climate becomes much hotter and drier?

For suggested answers, see Appendix A.

The Importance of Photosynthesis: *A Review*

In this chapter, we have followed photosynthesis from photons to food. The light reactions capture solar energy and use it to make ATP and transfer electrons from water to NADP⁺, forming NADPH. The Calvin cycle uses the ATP and NADPH to produce sugar from carbon dioxide. The energy that enters the chloroplasts as sunlight becomes stored as chemical energy in organic compounds. See **Figure 10.21** for a review of the entire process.

What are the fates of photosynthetic products? The sugar made in the chloroplasts supplies the entire plant with chemical energy and carbon skeletons for the synthesis of all the major organic molecules of plant cells. About 50% of the organic material made by photosynthesis is consumed as fuel for cellular respiration in the mitochondria of the plant cells. Sometimes there is a loss of photosynthetic products to photorespiration.

Technically, green cells are the only autotrophic parts of the plant. The rest of the plant depends on organic molecules exported from leaves via veins. In most plants, carbohydrate is transported out of the leaves in the form of

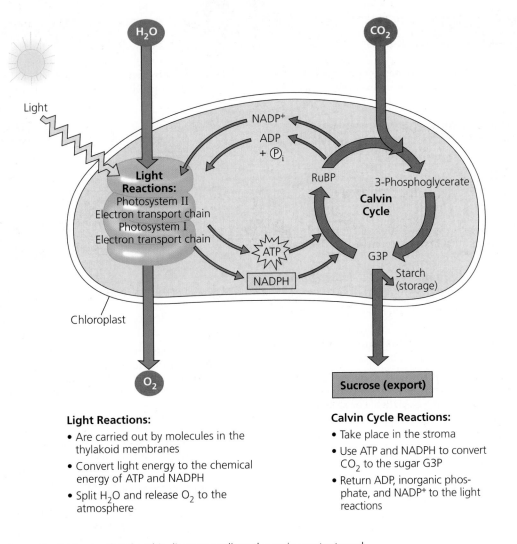

Light Reactions:

- Are carried out by molecules in the thylakoid membranes
- Convert light energy to the chemical energy of ATP and NADPH
- Split H_2O and release O_2 to the atmosphere

Calvin Cycle Reactions:

- Take place in the stroma
- Use ATP and NADPH to convert CO_2 to the sugar G3P
- Return ADP, inorganic phosphate, and $NADP^+$ to the light reactions

▲ **Figure 10.21 A review of photosynthesis.** This diagram outlines the main reactants and products of the light reactions and the Calvin cycle as they occur in the chloroplasts of plant cells. The entire ordered operation depends on the structural integrity of the chloroplast and its membranes. Enzymes in the chloroplast and cytosol convert glyceraldehyde-3-phosphate (G3P), the direct product of the Calvin cycle, to many other organic compounds.

sucrose, a disaccharide. After arriving at nonphotosynthetic cells, the sucrose provides raw material for cellular respiration and a multitude of anabolic pathways that synthesize proteins, lipids, and other products. A considerable amount of sugar in the form of glucose is linked together to make the polysaccharide cellulose, especially in plant cells that are still growing and maturing. Cellulose, the main ingredient of cell walls, is the most abundant organic molecule in the plant—and probably on the surface of the planet.

Most plants manage to make more organic material each day than they need to use as respiratory fuel and precursors for biosynthesis. They stockpile the extra sugar by synthesizing starch, storing some in the chloroplasts themselves and some in storage cells of roots, tubers, seeds, and fruits. In accounting for the consumption of the food mol-

ecules produced by photosynthesis, let's not forget that most plants lose leaves, roots, stems, fruits, and sometimes their entire bodies to heterotrophs, including humans.

On a global scale, photosynthesis is the process responsible for the presence of oxygen in our atmosphere. Furthermore, in terms of food production, the collective productivity of the minuscule chloroplasts is prodigious: Photosynthesis makes an estimated 160 billion metric tons of carbohydrate per year (a metric ton is 1,000 kg, about 1.1 tons). That's organic matter equivalent in mass to a stack of about 60 trillion copies of this textbook—17 stacks of books reaching from Earth to the sun! No other chemical process on the planet can match the output of photosynthesis. And no process is more important than photosynthesis to the welfare of life on Earth.

MEDIA Go to the Study Area at **www.masteringbio.com** for BioFlix 3-D Animations, MP3 Tutors, Videos, Practice Tests, an eBook, and more.

SUMMARY OF KEY CONCEPTS

CONCEPT 10.1

Photosynthesis converts light energy to the chemical energy of food (pp. 186–189)

▶ **Chloroplasts: The Sites of Photosynthesis in Plants** In autotrophic eukaryotes, photosynthesis occurs in chloroplasts, organelles containing thylakoids. Stacks of thylakoids form grana.

▶ **Tracking Atoms Through Photosynthesis:** *Scientific Inquiry* Photosynthesis is summarized as

$$6 CO_2 + 12 H_2O + \text{Light energy} \rightarrow C_6H_{12}O_6 + 6 O_2 + 6 H_2O$$

Chloroplasts split water into hydrogen and oxygen, incorporating the electrons of hydrogen into sugar molecules. Photosynthesis is a redox process: H_2O is oxidized, CO_2 is reduced.

▶ **The Two Stages of Photosynthesis:** *A Preview* The light reactions in the thylakoid membranes split water, releasing O_2, producing ATP, and forming NADPH. The Calvin cycle in the stroma forms sugar from CO_2, using ATP for energy and NADPH for reducing power.

MEDIA
BioFlix 3-D Animation Photosynthesis
MP3 Tutor Photosynthesis
Activity The Sites of Photosynthesis
Activity Overview of Photosynthesis

CONCEPT 10.2

The light reactions convert solar energy to the chemical energy of ATP and NADPH (pp. 190–198)

▶ **The Nature of Sunlight** Light is a form of electromagnetic energy. The colors we see as visible light include those wavelengths that drive photosynthesis.

▶ **Photosynthetic Pigments: The Light Receptors** A pigment absorbs visible light of specific wavelengths. Chlorophyll *a* is the main photosynthetic pigment in plants. Other accessory pigments absorb different wavelengths of light and pass the energy on to chlorophyll *a*.

▶ **Excitation of Chlorophyll by Light** A pigment goes from a ground state to an excited state when a photon boosts one of its electrons to a higher-energy orbital. This excited state is unstable. Electrons from isolated pigments tend to fall back to the ground state, giving off heat and/or light.

▶ **A Photosystem: A Reaction-Center Complex Associated with Light-Harvesting Complexes** A photosystem is composed of a reaction-center complex surrounded by light-harvesting complexes that funnel the energy of photons to the reaction-center complex. When a special pair of reaction-center chlorophyll *a* molecules absorbs energy, one of its electrons is boosted to a higher energy level and transferred to the primary electron acceptor. Photosystem II contains P680 chlorophyll *a* molecules in the reaction-center complex; photosystem I contains P700 molecules.

▶ **Linear Electron Flow** The flow of electrons during the light reactions produces NADPH, ATP, and oxygen:

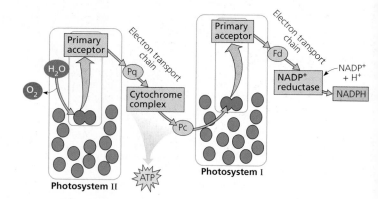

▶ **Cyclic Electron Flow** Cyclic electron flow employs only photosystem I, producing ATP but no NADPH or O_2.

▶ **A Comparison of Chemiosmosis in Chloroplasts and Mitochondria** In both organelles, redox reactions of electron transport chains generate an H^+ gradient across a membrane. ATP synthase uses this proton-motive force to make ATP.

MEDIA
Activity Light Energy and Pigments
Investigation How Does Paper Chromatography Separate Plant Pigments?
Activity The Light Reactions

CONCEPT 10.3

The Calvin cycle uses ATP and NADPH to convert CO_2 to sugar (pp. 198–199)

▶ The Calvin cycle occurs in the stroma, using electrons from NADPH and energy from ATP. One molecule of G3P exits the cycle per three CO_2 molecules fixed and is converted to glucose and other organic molecules.

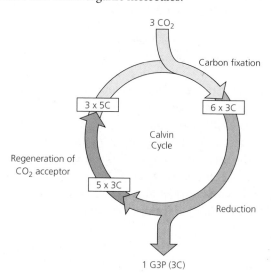

MEDIA
Activity The Calvin Cycle
Investigation How Is the Rate of Photosynthesis Measured?
Biology Labs On-Line LeafLab

CONCEPT 10.4

Alternative mechanisms of carbon fixation have evolved in hot, arid climates (pp. 200–202)

▶ **Photorespiration: An Evolutionary Relic?** On dry, hot days, C_3 plants close their stomata, conserving water. Oxygen from the light reactions builds up. In photorespiration, O_2 substitutes for CO_2 in the active site of rubisco. This process consumes organic fuel and releases CO_2 without producing ATP or carbohydrate.

▶ **C_4 Plants** C_4 plants minimize the cost of photorespiration by incorporating CO_2 into four-carbon compounds in mesophyll cells. These compounds are exported to bundle-sheath cells, where they release carbon dioxide for use in the Calvin cycle.

▶ **CAM Plants** CAM plants open their stomata at night, incorporating CO_2 into organic acids, which are stored in mesophyll cells. During the day, the stomata close, and the CO_2 is released from the organic acids for use in the Calvin cycle.

> **MEDIA**
> **Activity** Photosynthesis in Dry Climates

▶ **The Importance of Photosynthesis:** *A Review* Organic compounds produced by photosynthesis provide the energy and building material for ecosystems.

TESTING YOUR KNOWLEDGE

SELF-QUIZ

1. The light reactions of photosynthesis supply the Calvin cycle with
   a. light energy.
   b. CO_2 and ATP.
   c. H_2O and NADPH.
   d. ATP and NADPH.
   e. sugar and O_2.

2. Which of the following sequences correctly represents the flow of electrons during photosynthesis?
   a. NADPH → O_2 → CO_2
   b. H_2O → NADPH → Calvin cycle
   c. NADPH → chlorophyll → Calvin cycle
   d. H_2O → photosystem I → photosystem II
   e. NADPH → electron transport chain → O_2

3. In *mechanism*, photophosphorylation is most similar to
   a. substrate-level phosphorylation in glycolysis.
   b. oxidative phosphorylation in cellular respiration.
   c. the Calvin cycle.
   d. carbon fixation.
   e. reduction of $NADP^+$.

4. How is photosynthesis similar in C_4 plants and CAM plants?
   a. In both cases, only photosystem I is used.
   b. Both types of plants make sugar without the Calvin cycle.
   c. In both cases, rubisco is not used to fix carbon initially.
   d. Both types of plants make most of their sugar in the dark.
   e. In both cases, thylakoids are not involved in photosynthesis.

5. Which process is most directly driven by light energy?
   a. creation of a pH gradient by pumping protons across the thylakoid membrane
   b. carbon fixation in the stroma
   c. reduction of $NADP^+$ molecules
   d. removal of electrons from chlorophyll molecules
   e. ATP synthesis

6. Which of the following statements is a correct distinction between autotrophs and heterotrophs?
   a. Only heterotrophs require chemical compounds from the environment.
   b. Cellular respiration is unique to heterotrophs.
   c. Only heterotrophs have mitochondria.
   d. Autotrophs, but not heterotrophs, can nourish themselves beginning with CO_2 and other nutrients that are inorganic.
   e. Only heterotrophs require oxygen.

7. Which of the following does *not* occur during the Calvin cycle?
   a. carbon fixation
   b. oxidation of NADPH
   c. release of oxygen
   d. regeneration of the CO_2 acceptor
   e. consumption of ATP

For Self-Quiz answers, see Appendix A.

> **MEDIA** Visit the Study Area at **www.masteringbio.com** for a Practice Test.

EVOLUTION CONNECTION

8. Photorespiration can decrease soybeans' photosynthetic output by about 50%. Would you expect this figure to be higher or lower in wild relatives of soybeans? Why?

SCIENTIFIC INQUIRY

9. **DRAW IT** The following diagram represents an experiment with isolated chloroplasts. The chloroplasts were first made acidic by soaking them in a solution at pH 4. After the thylakoid space reached pH 4, the chloroplasts were transferred to a basic solution at pH 8. The chloroplasts then made ATP in the dark.

Draw an enlargement of part of the thylakoid membrane in the beaker with the solution at pH 8. Draw ATP synthase. Label the areas of high H^+ concentration and low H^+ concentration. Show the direction protons flow through the enzyme, and show the reaction where ATP is synthesized. Would ATP end up in the thylakoid or outside of it? Explain why the chloroplasts in the experiment were able to make ATP in the dark.

SCIENCE, TECHNOLOGY, AND SOCIETY

10. Scientific evidence indicates that the CO_2 added to the air by the burning of wood and fossil fuels is contributing to "global warming," a rise in global temperature. Tropical rain forests are estimated to be responsible for more than 20% of global photosynthesis, yet their consumption of large amounts of CO_2 is thought to make little or no *net* contribution to reduction of global warming. Why might this be? (*Hint:* What happens to the food produced by a rain forest tree when it is eaten by animals or the tree dies?)

Cell Communication

11

KEY CONCEPTS

11.1 External signals are converted to responses within the cell

11.2 Reception: A signaling molecule binds to a receptor protein, causing it to change shape

11.3 Transduction: Cascades of molecular interactions relay signals from receptors to target molecules in the cell

11.4 Response: Cell signaling leads to regulation of transcription or cytoplasmic activities

11.5 Apoptosis (programmed cell death) integrates multiple cell-signaling pathways

OVERVIEW

The Cellular Internet

A hiker slips and falls down a steep ravine, injuring her leg in the fall. Tragedy is averted when she is able to pull out a cell phone and call for help. Cell phones, the Internet, e-mail, instant messaging—no one would deny the importance of communication in our lives. The role of communication in life at the cellular level is equally critical. Cell-to-cell communication is absolutely essential for multicellular organisms such as humans and oak trees. The trillions of cells in a multicellular organism must communicate with each other to coordinate their activities in a way that enables the organism to develop from a fertilized egg, then survive and reproduce in turn. Communication between cells is also important for many unicellular organisms. Networks of communication between cells can be even more complicated than the World Wide Web.

In studying how cells signal to each other and how they interpret the signals they receive, biologists have discovered some universal mechanisms of cellular regulation, additional evidence for the evolutionary relatedness of all life. The same small set of cell-signaling mechanisms shows up again and again in many

lines of biological research—from embryonic development to hormone action to cancer. In one example, a common cell-to-cell signaling pathway leads to dilation of blood vessels. Once the signal subsides, the response is shut down by the enzyme shown in purple in **Figure 11.1**. Also shown is a multicolored molecule that blocks the action of this enzyme and keeps blood vessels dilated. Enzyme-inhibiting compounds like this one are often prescribed for treatment of medical conditions. The action of the multicolored compound, known as Viagra, will be discussed later in the chapter. The signals received by cells, whether originating from other cells or from changes in the physical environment, take various forms, including light and touch. However, cells most often communicate with each other by chemical signals. In this chapter, we focus on the main mechanisms by which cells receive, process, and respond to chemical signals sent from other cells. At the end, we will take a look at *apoptosis*, a type of programmed cell death that integrates input from multiple signaling pathways.

CONCEPT **11.1**

External signals are converted to responses within the cell

What does a "talking" cell say to a "listening" cell, and how does the latter cell respond to the message? Let's approach these questions by first looking at communication among microorganisms, for modern microbes are a window on the role of cell signaling in the evolution of life on Earth.

Evolution of Cell Signaling

One topic of cell "conversation" is sex—at least for the yeast *Saccharomyces cerevisiae*, which people have used for millennia to make bread, wine, and beer. Researchers have learned that cells of this yeast identify their mates by chemical signaling. There are two sexes, or mating types, called **a** and **α** (**Figure 11.2**). Cells of mating type **a** secrete a signaling molecule called **a** factor, which can bind to specific receptor proteins on nearby **α** cells. At the same time, **α** cells secrete **α** factor, which binds to receptors on **a** cells. Without actually entering the cells, the two mating factors cause the cells to grow toward each other and also bring about other cellular changes. The result is the fusion, or mating, of two cells of opposite type. The new **a/α** cell contains all the genes of both original cells, a combination of genetic resources that provides advantages to the cell's descendants, which arise by subsequent cell divisions.

How is the mating signal at the yeast cell surface changed, or *transduced*, into a form that brings about the cellular response of mating? The process by which a signal on a cell's surface is converted to a specific cellular response is a series of steps called a **signal transduction pathway**. Many such pathways have been extensively studied in both yeast and animal cells. Amazingly, the molecular details of signal transduction in yeast and mammals are strikingly similar, even though the last common ancestor of these two groups of organisms lived over a billion years ago. These similarities—

and others more recently uncovered between signaling systems in bacteria and plants—suggest that early versions of the cell-signaling mechanisms used today evolved well before the first multicellular creatures appeared on Earth.

Scientists think that signaling mechanisms first evolved in ancient prokaryotes and single-celled eukaryotes and then were adopted for new uses by their multicellular descendants. Meanwhile, cell signaling has remained important in the microbial world. Cells of many bacterial species secrete small molecules that can be detected by other bacterial cells. The concentration of such signaling molecules allows bacteria to sense the local density of bacterial cells, a phenomenon called *quorum sensing*. Furthermore, signaling among members of a bacterial population can lead to coordination of their activities. In response to the signal, bacterial cells are able to come together and form *biofilms*, aggregations of bacteria that often form recognizable structures containing regions of specialized function. **Figure 11.3** shows an aggregation response characteristic of one type of bacterium.

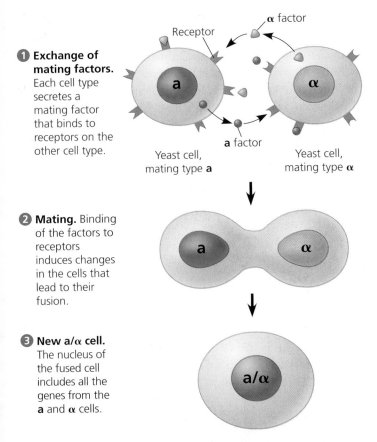

▲ **Figure 11.2 Communication between mating yeast cells.** *Saccharomyces cerevisiae* cells use chemical signaling to identify cells of opposite mating type and initiate the mating process. The two mating types and their corresponding chemical signaling molecules, or mating factors, are called **a** and **α**.

▲ **Figure 11.3 Communication among bacteria.** Soil-dwelling bacteria called myxobacteria ("slime bacteria") use chemical signals to share information about nutrient availability. When food is scarce, starving cells secrete a molecule that reaches neighboring cells and stimulates them to aggregate. The cells form a structure, called a fruiting body, that produces thick-walled spores capable of surviving until the environment improves. The bacteria shown here are *Myxococcus xanthus* (steps 1–3, SEMs; lower photo, LM).

Local and Long-Distance Signaling

Like yeast cells, cells in a multicellular organism usually communicate via chemical messengers targeted for cells that may or may not be immediately adjacent. As we saw in Chapters 6 and 7, cells may communicate by direct contact (Figure 11.4). Both animals

(a) **Cell junctions.** Both animals and plants have cell junctions that allow molecules to pass readily between adjacent cells without crossing plasma membranes.

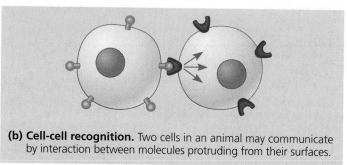

(b) **Cell-cell recognition.** Two cells in an animal may communicate by interaction between molecules protruding from their surfaces.

▲ Figure 11.4 **Communication by direct contact between cells.**

and plants have cell junctions that, where present, directly connect the cytoplasms of adjacent cells (Figure 11.4a). In these cases, signaling substances dissolved in the cytosol can pass freely between adjacent cells. Moreover, animal cells may communicate via direct contact between membrane-bound cell-surface molecules, which occurs during a process called cell-cell recognition (Figure 11.4b). This sort of signaling is important in such processes as embryonic development and the immune response.

In many other cases, messenger molecules are secreted by the signaling cell. Some of these travel only short distances; such **local regulators** influence cells in the vicinity. One class of local regulators in animals, *growth factors*, consists of compounds that stimulate nearby target cells to grow and divide. Numerous cells can simultaneously receive and respond to the molecules of growth factor produced by a single cell in their vicinity. This type of local signaling in animals is called *paracrine signaling* (Figure 11.5a).

Another, more specialized type of local signaling called *synaptic signaling* occurs in the animal nervous system (Figure 11.5b). An electrical signal along a nerve cell triggers the secretion of a chemical signal carried by neurotransmitter molecules. These diffuse across the synapse, the narrow space between the nerve cell and its target cell (often another nerve cell). The neurotransmitter stimulates the target cell.

Local signaling in plants is not as well understood. Because of their cell walls, plants use mechanisms somewhat different from those operating locally in animals.

Both animals and plants use chemicals called **hormones** for long-distance signaling. In hormonal signaling in animals, also known as endocrine signaling, specialized cells release

Local signaling

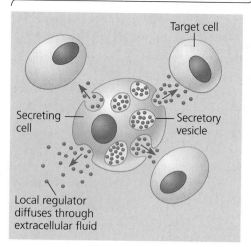

(a) **Paracrine signaling.** A secreting cell acts on nearby target cells by discharging molecules of a local regulator (a growth factor, for example) into the extracellular fluid.

(b) **Synaptic signaling.** A nerve cell releases neurotransmitter molecules into a synapse, stimulating the target cell.

▲ Figure 11.5 **Local and long-distance cell communication in animals.** In both local and long-distance signaling, only specific target cells recognize and respond to a given signaling molecule.

Long-distance signaling

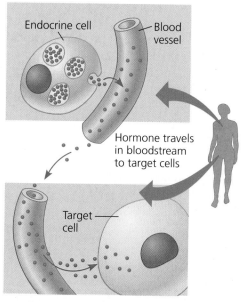

(c) **Hormonal signaling.** Specialized endocrine cells secrete hormones into body fluids, often the blood. Hormones may reach virtually all body cells.

hormone molecules, which travel via the circulatory system to target cells in other parts of the body (Figure 11.5c). Plant hormones (often called *plant growth regulators*) sometimes travel in vessels but more often reach their targets by moving through cells or by diffusing through the air as a gas (see Chapter 39). Hormones vary widely in molecular size and type, as do local regulators. For instance, the plant hormone ethylene, a gas that promotes fruit ripening and helps regulate growth, is a hydrocarbon of only six atoms (C_2H_4), small enough to pass through cell walls. In contrast, the mammalian hormone insulin, which regulates sugar levels in the blood, is a protein with thousands of atoms.

The transmission of a signal through the nervous system can also be considered an example of long-distance signaling. An electrical signal travels the length of a nerve cell and is then converted back to a chemical signal when a signaling molecule is released and crosses the synapse to another nerve cell. Here it is converted back to an electrical signal. In this way, a nerve signal can travel along a series of nerve cells. Because some nerve cells are quite long, the nerve signal can quickly travel great distances—from your brain to your big toe, for example. This type of long-distance signaling will be covered in detail in Chapter 48.

What happens when a cell encounters a signaling molecule? The molecule must be recognized by a specific receptor molecule, and the information it carries, the signal, must be changed into another form—transduced—inside the cell before the cell can respond. The remainder of the chapter discusses this process, primarily as it occurs in animal cells.

The Three Stages of Cell Signaling: *A Preview*

Our current understanding of how chemical messengers act via signal transduction pathways had its origins in the pioneering work of Earl W. Sutherland, whose research led to a Nobel Prize in 1971. Sutherland and his colleagues at Vanderbilt University were investigating how the animal hormone epinephrine stimulates the breakdown of the storage polysaccha-

ride glycogen within liver cells and skeletal muscle cells. Glycogen breakdown releases the sugar glucose-1-phosphate, which the cell converts to glucose-6-phosphate. The cell (a liver cell, for example) can then use this compound, an early intermediate in glycolysis, for energy production. Alternatively, the compound can be stripped of phosphate and released from the liver cell into the blood as glucose, which can fuel cells throughout the body. Thus, one effect of epinephrine, which is secreted from the adrenal gland during times of physical or mental stress, is the mobilization of fuel reserves.

Sutherland's research team discovered that epinephrine stimulates glycogen breakdown by somehow activating a cytosolic enzyme, glycogen phosphorylase. However, when epinephrine was added to a test-tube mixture containing the enzyme and its substrate, glycogen, no breakdown occurred. Epinephrine could activate glycogen phosphorylase only when the hormone was added to a solution containing *intact* cells. This result told Sutherland two things. First, epinephrine does not interact directly with the enzyme responsible for glycogen breakdown; an intermediate step or series of steps must be occurring inside the cell. Second, the plasma membrane is somehow involved in transmitting the epinephrine signal.

Sutherland's early work suggested that the process going on at the receiving end of a cellular conversation can be dissected into three stages: reception, transduction, and response (Figure 11.6):

❶ **Reception.** Reception is the target cell's detection of a signaling molecule coming from outside the cell. A chemical signal is "detected" when the signaling molecule binds to a receptor protein located at the cell's surface or inside the cell.

❷ **Transduction.** The binding of the signaling molecule changes the receptor protein in some way, initiating the process of transduction. The transduction stage converts the signal to a form that can bring about a specific

▶ **Figure 11.6 Overview of cell signaling.** From the perspective of the cell receiving the message, cell signaling can be divided into three stages: signal reception, signal transduction, and cellular response. When reception occurs at the plasma membrane, as shown here, the transduction stage is usually a pathway of several steps, with each relay molecule in the pathway bringing about a change in the next molecule. The final molecule in the pathway triggers the cell's response. The three stages are explained in more detail in the text.

? *How does the epinephrine in Sutherland's experiment fit into this diagram of cell signaling?*

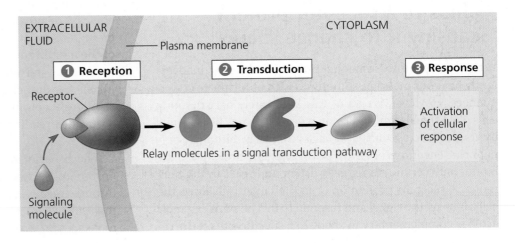

cellular response. In Sutherland's system, the binding of epinephrine to a receptor protein in a liver cell's plasma membrane leads to activation of glycogen phosphorylase. Transduction sometimes occurs in a single step but more often requires a sequence of changes in a series of different molecules—a *signal transduction pathway*. The molecules in the pathway are often called relay molecules.

❸ **Response.** In the third stage of cell signaling, the transduced signal finally triggers a specific cellular response. The response may be almost any imaginable cellular activity—such as catalysis by an enzyme (for example, glycogen phosphorylase), rearrangement of the cytoskeleton, or activation of specific genes in the nucleus. The cell-signaling process helps ensure that crucial activities like these occur in the right cells, at the right time, and in proper coordination with the other cells of the organism. We'll now explore the mechanisms of cell signaling in more detail.

CONCEPT CHECK **11.1**

1. Explain how signaling is involved in ensuring that yeast cells only fuse with cells of the opposite mating type.
2. Explain how nerve cells provide examples of both local and long-distance signaling.
3. When epinephrine is mixed with glycogen phosphorylase and glycogen in a test tube, is glucose-1-phosphate generated? Why or why not?
4. **WHAT IF?** In liver cells, glycogen phosphorylase acts in which of the three stages of the signaling pathway associated with an epinephrine-initiated signal?

For suggested answers, see Appendix A.

CONCEPT **11.2**
Reception: A signaling molecule binds to a receptor protein, causing it to change shape

When we speak to someone, others nearby may inadvertently hear our message, sometimes with unfortunate consequences. However, errors of this kind rarely occur among cells. The signals emitted by an **a** yeast cell are "heard" only by its prospective mates, **α** cells. Similarly, although epinephrine encounters many types of cells as it circulates in the blood, only certain target cells detect and react to the hormone. A receptor protein on or in the target cell allows the cell to "hear" the signal and respond to it. The signaling molecule is complementary in shape to a specific site on the re-

ceptor and attaches there, like a key in a lock or a substrate in the catalytic site of an enzyme. The signaling molecule behaves as a **ligand**, the term for a molecule that specifically binds to another molecule, often a larger one. Ligand binding generally causes a receptor protein to undergo a change in shape. For many receptors, this shape change directly activates the receptor, enabling it to interact with other cellular molecules. For other kinds of receptors, the immediate effect of ligand binding is to cause the aggregation of two or more receptor molecules, which leads to further molecular events inside the cell.

In a general way, ligand binding is similar to the binding of an allosteric regulator to an enzyme, causing a shape change that either promotes or inhibits enzyme activity. In the case of signal transduction, binding of the ligand alters the ability of the receptor to transmit the signal.

Most signal receptors are plasma membrane proteins. Their ligands are water-soluble and generally too large to pass freely through the plasma membrane. Other signal receptors, however, are located inside the cell. We discuss both of these next.

Receptors in the Plasma Membrane

Most water-soluble signaling molecules bind to specific sites on receptor proteins embedded in the cell's plasma membrane. Such a receptor transmits information from the extracellular environment to the inside of the cell by changing shape or aggregating when a specific ligand binds to it. We can see how membrane receptors work by looking at three major types: G protein-coupled receptors, receptor tyrosine kinases, and ion channel receptors. These receptors are discussed and illustrated in **Figure 11.7**, on the next three pages; study this figure before going on.

Intracellular Receptors

Intracellular receptor proteins are found in either the cytoplasm or nucleus of target cells. To reach such a receptor, a chemical messenger passes through the target cell's plasma membrane. A number of important signaling molecules can do this because they are either hydrophobic enough or small enough to cross the phospholipid interior of the membrane. Such hydrophobic chemical messengers include the steroid hormones and thyroid hormones of animals. Another chemical signaling molecule with an intracellular receptor is nitric oxide (NO), a gas; its very small molecules readily pass between the membrane phospholipids.

The behavior of testosterone is representative of steroid hormones. Secreted by cells of the testis, the hormone travels through the blood and enters cells all over the body. In the cytoplasm of target cells, the only cells that contain receptor molecules for testosterone, the hormone binds to the receptor

Exploring Membrane Receptors

G Protein-Coupled Receptors

Signaling-molecule binding site

Segment that interacts with G proteins

G protein-coupled receptor

A **G protein-coupled receptor** is a plasma membrane receptor that works with the help of a **G protein**, a protein that binds the energy-rich molecule GTP. Many different signaling molecules, including yeast mating factors, epinephrine and many other hormones, and neurotransmitters, use G protein-coupled receptors. These receptors vary in the binding sites for both their signaling molecules (also called their ligands) and for different G proteins inside the cell. Nevertheless, G protein-coupled receptor proteins are all remarkably similar in structure. They each have seven α helices spanning the membrane, as shown above.

A large family of eukaryotic receptor proteins has this secondary structure, where the single polypeptide, represented here as a ribbon, has seven transmembrane α helices, represented as cylinders and depicted in a row for clarity. Specific loops between the helices form binding sites for signaling and G-protein molecules.

G protein-coupled receptor systems are extremely widespread and diverse in their functions, including roles in embryonic development and sensory reception. In humans, for example, both vision and smell depend on such proteins. Similarities in structure among G proteins and G protein-coupled receptors in diverse organisms suggest that G proteins and associated receptors evolved very early.

G-protein systems are involved in many human diseases, including bacterial infections. The bacteria that cause cholera, pertussis (whooping cough), and botulism, among others, make their victims ill by producing toxins that interfere with G-protein function. Pharmacologists now realize that up to 60% of all medicines used today exert their effects by influencing G-protein pathways.

1 Loosely attached to the cytoplasmic side of the membrane, the G protein functions as a molecular switch that is either on or off, depending on which of two guanine nucleotides is attached, GDP or GTP—hence the term *G protein*. (GTP, or guanosine triphosphate, is similar to ATP.) When GDP is bound to the G protein, as shown above, the G protein is inactive. The receptor and G protein work together with another protein, usually an enzyme.

2 When the appropriate signaling molecule binds to the extracellular side of the receptor, the receptor is activated and changes shape. Its cytoplasmic side then binds an inactive G protein, causing a GTP to displace the GDP. This activates the G protein.

3 The activated G protein dissociates from the receptor, diffuses along the membrane, and then binds to an enzyme, altering the enzyme's shape and activity. When the enzyme is activated, it can trigger the next step in a pathway leading to a cellular response.

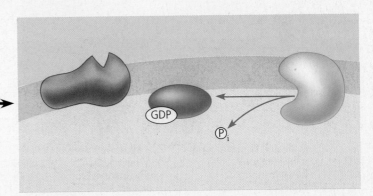

4 The changes in the enzyme and G protein are only temporary because the G protein also functions as a GTPase enzyme—in other words, it then hydrolyzes its bound GTP to GDP. Now inactive again, the G protein leaves the enzyme, which returns to its original state. The G protein is now available for reuse. The GTPase function of the G protein allows the pathway to shut down rapidly when the signaling molecule is no longer present.

Continued on next page

Exploring Membrane Receptors

Receptor Tyrosine Kinases

Receptor tyrosine kinases belong to a major class of plasma membrane receptors characterized by having enzymatic activity. A *kinase* is an enzyme that catalyzes the transfer of phosphate groups. The part of the receptor protein extending into the cytoplasm functions as a tyrosine kinase, an enzyme that catalyzes the transfer of a phosphate group from ATP to the amino acid tyrosine on a substrate protein. Thus, receptor tyrosine kinases are membrane receptors that attach phosphates to tyrosines.

One receptor tyrosine kinase complex may activate ten or more different transduction pathways and cellular responses. Often, more than one signal transduction pathway can be triggered at once, helping the cell regulate and coordinate many aspects of cell growth and cell reproduction. The ability of a single ligand-binding event to trigger so many pathways is a key difference between receptor tyrosine kinases and G protein-coupled receptors. Abnormal receptor tyrosine kinases that function even in the absence of signaling molecules may contribute to some kinds of cancer.

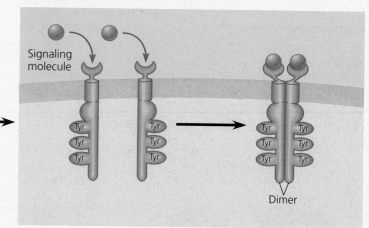

1 Many receptor tyrosine kinases have the structure depicted schematically here. Before the signaling molecule binds, the receptors exist as individual polypeptides. Notice that each has an extracellular ligand-binding site, an α helix spanning the membrane, and an intracellular tail containing multiple tyrosines.

2 The binding of a signaling molecule (such as a growth factor) causes two receptor polypeptides to associate closely with each other, forming a dimer (dimerization).

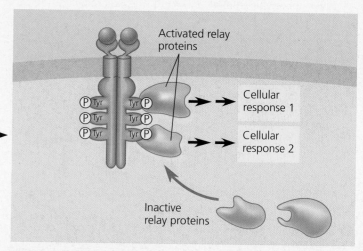

3 Dimerization activates the tyrosine kinase region of each polypeptide; each tyrosine kinase adds a phosphate from an ATP molecule to a tyrosine on the tail of the other polypeptide.

4 Now that the receptor protein is fully activated, it is recognized by specific relay proteins inside the cell. Each such protein binds to a specific phosphorylated tyrosine, undergoing a resulting structural change that activates the bound protein. Each activated protein triggers a transduction pathway, leading to a cellular response.

Ion Channel Receptors

A **ligand-gated ion channel** is a type of membrane receptor containing a region that can act as a "gate" when the receptor changes shape. When a signaling molecule binds as a ligand to the receptor protein, the gate opens or closes, allowing or blocking the flow of specific ions, such as Na^+ or Ca^{2+}, through a channel in the receptor. Like the other receptors we have discussed, these proteins bind the ligand at a specific site on their extracellular sides.

1 Here we show a ligand-gated ion channel receptor in which the gate remains closed until a ligand binds to the receptor.

Signaling molecule (ligand) Gate closed Ions

Ligand-gated ion channel receptor Plasma membrane

2 When the ligand binds to the receptor and the gate opens, specific ions can flow through the channel and rapidly change the concentration of that particular ion inside the cell. This change may directly affect the activity of the cell in some way.

Gate open Cellular response

3 When the ligand dissociates from this receptor, the gate closes and ions no longer enter the cell.

Gate closed

Ligand-gated ion channels are very important in the nervous system. For example, the neurotransmitter molecules released at a synapse between two nerve cells (see Figure 11.5b) bind as ligands to ion channels on the receiving cell, causing the channels to open. Ions flow in (or, in some cases, out), triggering an electrical signal that propagates down the length of the receiving cell. Some gated ion channels are controlled by electrical signals instead of ligands; these *voltage-gated ion channels* are also crucial to the functioning of the nervous system, as we will discuss in Chapter 48.

protein, activating it **(Figure 11.8)**. With the hormone attached, the active form of the receptor protein then enters the nucleus and turns on specific genes that control male sex characteristics.

How does the activated hormone-receptor complex turn on genes? Recall that the genes in a cell's DNA function by being transcribed and processed into messenger RNA (mRNA), which leaves the nucleus and is translated into a specific protein by ribosomes in the cytoplasm (see Figure 5.26). Special proteins called *transcription factors* control which genes are turned on—that is, which genes are transcribed into mRNA—in a particular cell at a particular time. The testosterone receptor, when activated, acts as a transcription factor that turns on specific genes.

By acting as a transcription factor, the testosterone receptor itself carries out the complete transduction of the signal. Most other intracellular receptors function in the same way, although many of them are already in the nucleus before the signaling molecule reaches them (an example is the thyroid hormone receptor). Interestingly, many of these intracellular receptor proteins are structurally similar, suggesting an evolutionary

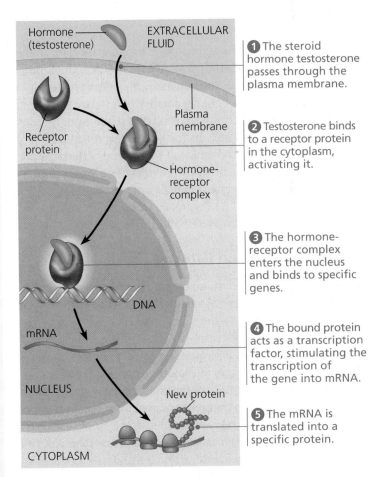

Hormone (testosterone) EXTRACELLULAR FLUID

1 The steroid hormone testosterone passes through the plasma membrane.

Receptor protein

Plasma membrane

2 Testosterone binds to a receptor protein in the cytoplasm, activating it.

Hormone-receptor complex

3 The hormone-receptor complex enters the nucleus and binds to specific genes.

DNA

mRNA

4 The bound protein acts as a transcription factor, stimulating the transcription of the gene into mRNA.

NUCLEUS

New protein

5 The mRNA is translated into a specific protein.

CYTOPLASM

▲ **Figure 11.8 Steroid hormone interacting with an intracellular receptor.**

? *Why is a cell-surface receptor protein not required for this steroid hormone to enter the cell?*

kinship. We will look more closely at hormones with intracellular receptors in Chapter 45.

CONCEPT 11.3
Transduction: Cascades of molecular interactions relay signals from receptors to target molecules in the cell

When receptors for signaling molecules are plasma membrane proteins, like most of those we have discussed, the transduction stage of cell signaling is usually a multistep pathway. Steps often include activation of proteins by addition or removal of phosphate groups, or release of other small molecules or ions that act as messengers. One benefit of multiple steps is the possibility of greatly amplifying a signal. If some of the molecules in a pathway transmit the signal to numerous molecules at the next step in the series, the result can be a large number of activated molecules at the end of the pathway. Moreover, multistep pathways provide more opportunities for coordination and regulation than simpler systems do. This allows fine-tuning of the response, in both unicellular and multicellular organisms, as we'll discuss later in the chapter.

Signal Transduction Pathways

The binding of a specific signaling molecule to a receptor in the plasma membrane triggers the first step in the chain of molecular interactions—the signal transduction pathway—that leads to a particular response within the cell. Like falling dominoes, the signal-activated receptor activates another molecule, which activates yet another molecule, and so on, until the protein that produces the final cellular response is activated. The molecules that relay a signal from receptor to response, which we call relay molecules in this book, are often proteins. The interaction of proteins is a major theme of cell signaling. Indeed, protein interaction is a unifying theme of all regulation at the cellular level.

Keep in mind that the original signaling molecule is not physically passed along a signaling pathway; in most cases, it never even enters the cell. When we say that the signal is re-layed along a pathway, we mean that certain information is passed on. At each step, the signal is transduced into a different form, commonly a shape change in a protein. Very often, the shape change is brought about by phosphorylation.

Protein Phosphorylation and Dephosphorylation

Previous chapters introduced the concept of activating a protein by adding one or more phosphate groups to it (see Figure 8.11a). In Figure 11.7, we have already seen how phosphorylation is involved in the activation of receptor tyrosine kinases. In fact, the phosphorylation and dephosphorylation of proteins is a widespread cellular mechanism for regulating protein activity. The general name for an enzyme that transfers phosphate groups from ATP to a protein is **protein kinase**. Recall that a receptor tyrosine kinase phosphorylates tyrosines on the other receptor tyrosine kinase in a dimer. Most cytoplasmic protein kinases, however, act on proteins different from themselves. Another distinction is that most cytoplasmic protein kinases phosphorylate either the amino acid serine or threonine, rather than tyrosine. Such serine/threonine kinases are widely involved in signaling pathways in animals, plants, and fungi.

Many of the relay molecules in signal transduction pathways are protein kinases, and they often act on other protein kinases in the pathway. **Figure 11.9** depicts a hypothetical pathway containing three different protein kinases that create a "phosphorylation cascade." The sequence shown is similar to many known pathways, including those triggered in yeast by mating factors and in animal cells by many growth factors. The signal is transmitted by a cascade of protein phosphorylations, each bringing with it a shape change. Each such shape change results from the interaction of the newly added phosphate groups with charged or polar amino acids (see Figure 5.17). The addition of phosphate groups often changes a protein from an inactive form to an active form (although in other cases phosphorylation *decreases* the activity of the protein).

The importance of protein kinases can hardly be overstated. About 2% of our own genes are thought to code for protein kinases. A single cell may have hundreds of different kinds, each specific for a different substrate protein. Together, they probably regulate a large proportion of the thousands of proteins in a cell. Among these are most of the proteins that, in turn, regulate cell reproduction. Abnormal activity of such a kinase can cause abnormal cell growth and contribute to the development of cancer.

Equally important in the phosphorylation cascade are the **protein phosphatases**, enzymes that can rapidly remove phosphate groups from proteins, a process called dephosphorylation. By dephosphorylating and thus inactivating protein kinases, phosphatases provide the mechanism for turning off the signal transduction pathway when the initial signal is no

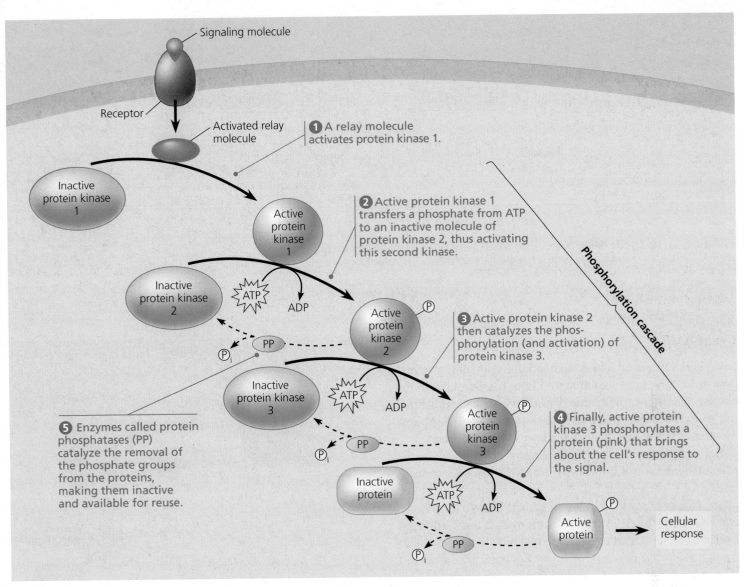

▲ Figure 11.9 A phosphorylation cascade. In a phosphorylation cascade, a series of different molecules in a pathway are phosphorylated in turn, each molecule adding a phosphate group to the next one in line. In this example, phosphorylation activates each molecule, and dephosphorylation returns it to its inactive form. The active and inactive forms of each protein are represented by different shapes to remind you that activation is usually associated with a change in molecular shape.

The figure contains the following labels:

Signaling molecule

Receptor

Activated relay molecule

Inactive protein kinase 1

Active protein kinase 1

1 A relay molecule activates protein kinase 1.

2 Active protein kinase 1 transfers a phosphate from ATP to an inactive molecule of protein kinase 2, thus activating this second kinase.

Inactive protein kinase 2

ATP

ADP

Active protein kinase 2

3 Active protein kinase 2 then catalyzes the phosphorylation (and activation) of protein kinase 3.

Phosphorylation cascade

Inactive protein kinase 3

ATP

ADP

Active protein kinase 3

PP

P_i

5 Enzymes called protein phosphatases (PP) catalyze the removal of the phosphate groups from the proteins, making them inactive and available for reuse.

4 Finally, active protein kinase 3 phosphorylates a protein (pink) that brings about the cell's response to the signal.

Inactive protein

ATP

ADP

Active protein

Cellular response

Which protein is responsible for activation of protein kinase 3?

longer present. Phosphatases also make the protein kinases available for reuse, enabling the cell to respond again to an extracellular signal. At any given moment, the activity of a protein regulated by phosphorylation depends on the balance in the cell between active kinase molecules and active phosphatase molecules. The phosphorylation/dephosphorylation system acts as a molecular switch in the cell, turning activities on or off as required.

Small Molecules and Ions as Second Messengers

Not all components of signal transduction pathways are proteins. Many signaling pathways also involve small, nonprotein,

water-soluble molecules or ions called **second messengers**. (The extracellular signaling molecule that binds to the membrane receptor is a pathway's "first messenger.") Because second messengers are both small and water-soluble, they can readily spread throughout the cell by diffusion. For example, as we'll see shortly, it is a second messenger called cyclic AMP that carries the signal initiated by epinephrine from the plasma membrane of a liver or muscle cell into the cell's interior, where it brings about glycogen breakdown. Second messengers participate in pathways initiated by both G protein-coupled receptors and receptor tyrosine kinases. The two most widely used second messengers are cyclic AMP and calcium ions, Ca^{2+}. A large variety of relay proteins are sensitive to the cytosolic concentration of one or the other of these second messengers.

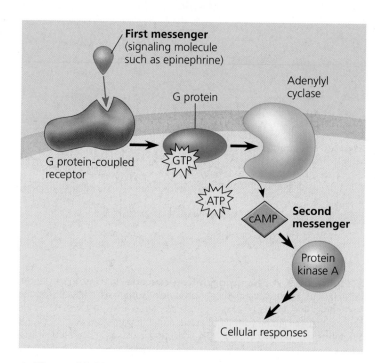

▲ **Figure 11.10 Cyclic AMP.** The second messenger cyclic AMP (cAMP) is made from ATP by adenylyl cyclase, an enzyme embedded in the plasma membrane. Cyclic AMP is inactivated by phosphodiesterase, an enzyme that converts it to AMP.

WHAT IF? *What would happen if a molecule that inactivated phosphodiesterase were introduced into the cell?*

Cyclic AMP

Once Earl Sutherland had established that epinephrine somehow causes glycogen breakdown without passing through the plasma membrane, the search began for what he later named the *second messenger* that transmits the signal from the plasma membrane to the metabolic machinery in the cytoplasm.

Sutherland found that the binding of epinephrine to the plasma membrane of a liver cell elevates the cytosolic concentration of a compound called cyclic adenosine monophosphate, abbreviated **cyclic AMP** or **cAMP** (Figure 11.10). An enzyme embedded in the plasma membrane, **adenylyl cyclase**, converts ATP to cAMP in response to an extracellular signal—in this case, epinephrine. But epinephrine doesn't stimulate adenylyl cyclase directly. When epinephrine outside the cell binds to a specific receptor protein, the protein activates adenylyl cyclase, which in turn can catalyze the synthesis of many molecules of cAMP. In this way, the normal cellular concentration of cAMP can be boosted 20-fold in a matter of seconds. The cAMP broadcasts the signal to the cytoplasm. It does not persist for long in the absence of the hormone because another enzyme, called phosphodiesterase, converts cAMP to AMP. Another surge of epinephrine is needed to boost the cytosolic concentration of cAMP again.

Subsequent research has revealed that epinephrine is only one of many hormones and other signaling molecules that trigger the formation of cAMP. It has also brought to light the other components of cAMP pathways, including G proteins, G protein-coupled receptors, and protein kinases (Figure 11.11). The immediate effect of cAMP is usually the activation of a serine/threonine kinase called *protein kinase A.* The activated kinase then phosphorylates various other proteins, depending on the cell type. (The complete pathway for epinephrine's stimulation of glycogen breakdown is shown later, in Figure 11.15.)

▲ **Figure 11.11 cAMP as a second messenger in a G-protein-signaling pathway.** The first messenger activates a G protein-coupled receptor, which activates a specific G protein. In turn, the G protein activates adenylyl cyclase, which catalyzes the conversion of ATP to cAMP. The cAMP then acts as a second messenger and activates another protein, usually protein kinase A, leading to cellular responses.

Further regulation of cell metabolism is provided by other G-protein systems that *inhibit* adenylyl cyclase. In these systems, a different signaling molecule activates a different receptor, which activates an *inhibitory* G protein.

Now that we know about the role of cAMP in G-protein-signaling pathways, we can explain in molecular detail how certain microbes cause disease. Consider cholera, a disease that is frequently epidemic in places where the water supply is contaminated with human feces. People acquire the cholera bacterium, *Vibrio cholerae*, by drinking contaminated water. The bacteria colonize the lining of the small intestine and produce a toxin. The cholera toxin is an enzyme that chemically modifies a G protein involved in regulating salt and water secretion. Because the modified G protein is unable to hydrolyze GTP to GDP, it remains stuck in its active form, continuously stimulating adenylyl cyclase to make cAMP. The resulting high concentration of cAMP causes the intestinal cells to secrete large amounts of salts, with water following by osmosis, into the intestines. An infected person quickly develops profuse diarrhea and if left untreated can soon die from the loss of water and salts.

Our understanding of signaling pathways involving cyclic AMP or related messengers has allowed us to develop treatments for certain conditions in humans. In one pathway *cyclic GMP*, or *cGMP*, acts as a signaling molecule whose effects include relaxation of smooth muscle cells in artery walls. A compound that inhibits the hydrolysis of cGMP to GMP, thus prolonging the signal, was originally prescribed for chest pains because it increased blood flow to the heart muscle. Under the trade name Viagra (see Figure 11.1), this compound is now widely used as a treatment for erectile dysfunction in human males. Because Viagra leads to dilation of blood vessels, it also allows increased blood flow to the penis, optimizing physiological conditions for penile erections. The similarities between external reproductive structures in males and females (see Chapter 46) have motivated medical researchers to initiate clinical studies exploring whether Viagra might also be used to treat sexual dysfunction in females; these studies are currently under way.

Calcium Ions and Inositol Trisphosphate (IP₃)

Many signaling molecules in animals, including neurotransmitters, growth factors, and some hormones, induce responses in their target cells via signal transduction pathways that increase the cytosolic concentration of calcium ions (Ca^{2+}). Calcium is even more widely used than cAMP as a second messenger. Increasing the cytosolic concentration of Ca^{2+} causes many responses in animal cells, including muscle cell contraction, secretion of certain substances, and cell division. In plant cells, a wide range of hormonal and environmental stimuli can cause brief increases in cytosolic Ca^{2+} concentration, triggering various signaling pathways, such as the pathway for greening in response to light (see Figure 39.4). Cells use Ca^{2+} as a second messenger in both G-protein and receptor tyrosine kinase pathways.

Although cells always contain some Ca^{2+}, this ion can function as a second messenger because its concentration in the cytosol is normally much lower than the concentration outside the cell (**Figure 11.12**). In fact, the level of Ca^{2+} in the blood and extracellular fluid of an animal often exceeds that in the cytosol by more than 10,000 times. Calcium ions are actively transported out of the cell and are actively imported from the cytosol into the endoplasmic reticulum (and, under some conditions, into mitochondria and chloroplasts) by various protein pumps (see Figure 11.12). As a result, the calcium concentration in the ER is usually much higher than that in the cytosol. Because the cytosolic calcium level is low, a small change in absolute numbers of ions represents a relatively large percentage change in calcium concentration.

In response to a signal relayed by a signal transduction pathway, the cytosolic calcium level may rise, usually by a mechanism that releases Ca^{2+} from the cell's ER. The pathways leading to calcium release involve still other second messengers, **inositol trisphosphate (IP₃)** and **diacylglycerol (DAG)**. These two messengers are produced by cleavage of a certain kind of phospholipid in the plasma membrane.

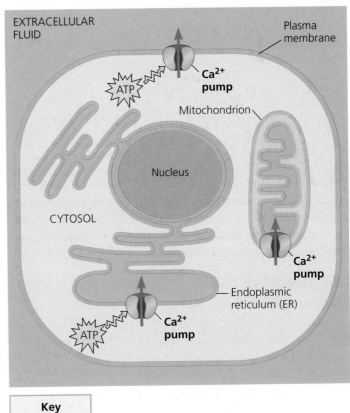

Key

High [Ca^{2+}]
Low [Ca^{2+}]

▲ Figure 11.12 **The maintenance of calcium ion concentrations in an animal cell.** The Ca^{2+} concentration in the cytosol is usually much lower (light blue) than that in the extracellular fluid and ER (darker blue). Protein pumps in the plasma membrane and the ER membrane, driven by ATP, move Ca^{2+} from the cytosol into the extracellular fluid and into the lumen of the ER. Mitochondrial pumps, driven by chemiosmosis (see Chapter 9), move Ca^{2+} into mitochondria when the calcium level in the cytosol rises significantly.

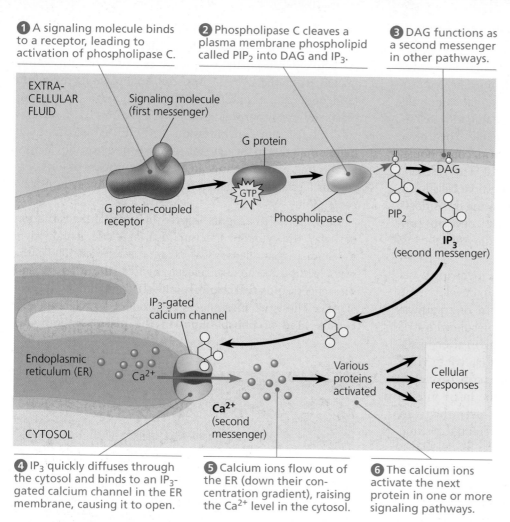

① A signaling molecule binds to a receptor, leading to activation of phospholipase C.

② Phospholipase C cleaves a plasma membrane phospholipid called PIP_2 into DAG and IP_3.

③ DAG functions as a second messenger in other pathways.

◀ **Figure 11.13 Calcium and IP_3 in signaling pathways.** Calcium ions (Ca^{2+}) and inositol trisphosphate (IP_3) function as second messengers in many signal transduction pathways. In this figure, the process is initiated by the binding of a signaling molecule to a G protein-coupled receptor. A receptor tyrosine kinase could also initiate this pathway by activating phospholipase C.

EXTRA-CELLULAR FLUID

Signaling molecule (first messenger)

G protein

G protein-coupled receptor

GTP

Phospholipase C

PIP_2

DAG

IP_3 (second messenger)

IP_3-gated calcium channel

Endoplasmic reticulum (ER)

Ca^{2+}

Ca^{2+} (second messenger)

Various proteins activated

Cellular responses

CYTOSOL

④ IP_3 quickly diffuses through the cytosol and binds to an IP_3-gated calcium channel in the ER membrane, causing it to open.

⑤ Calcium ions flow out of the ER (down their concentration gradient), raising the Ca^{2+} level in the cytosol.

⑥ The calcium ions activate the next protein in one or more signaling pathways.

Figure 11.13 shows how this occurs and how IP_3 stimulates the release of calcium from the ER. Because IP_3 acts before calcium in these pathways, calcium could be considered a "*third* messenger." However, scientists use the term *second messenger* for all small, nonprotein components of signal transduction pathways.

CONCEPT CHECK 11.3

1. What is a protein kinase, and what is its role in a signal transduction pathway?
2. When a signal transduction pathway involves a phosphorylation cascade, how does the cell's response get turned off?
3. What is the actual "signal" that is being transduced in any signal transduction pathway, such as those shown in Figures 11.6 and 11.9? In other words, in what way is information being passed from the exterior to the interior of the cell?
4. **WHAT IF?** Upon activation of phospholipase C by ligand binding to a receptor, what effect does the IP_3-gated calcium channel have on Ca^{2+} concentration in the cytosol?

For suggested answers, see Appendix A.

CONCEPT 11.4

Response: Cell signaling leads to regulation of transcription or cytoplasmic activities

We now take a closer look at the cell's subsequent response to an extracellular signal—what some researchers call the "output response." What is the nature of the final step in a signaling pathway?

Nuclear and Cytoplasmic Responses

Ultimately, a signal transduction pathway leads to the regulation of one or more cellular activities. The response at the end of the pathway may occur in the nucleus of the cell or in the cytoplasm.

Many signaling pathways ultimately regulate protein synthesis, usually by turning specific genes on or off in the nucleus. Like an activated steroid receptor (see Figure 11.8), the final activated molecule in a signaling pathway may function as a transcription factor. **Figure 11.14** shows an example in which a signaling pathway activates a transcription factor

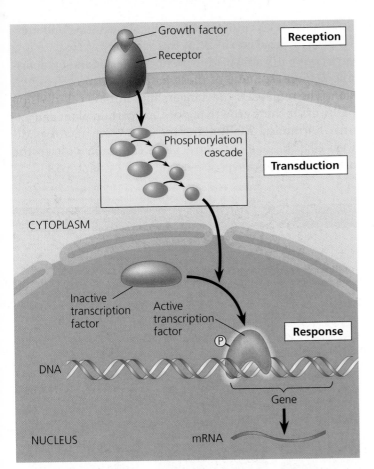

▲ **Figure 11.14 Nuclear responses to a signal: the activation of a specific gene by a growth factor.** This diagram is a simplified representation of a typical signaling pathway that leads to the regulation of gene activity in the cell nucleus. The initial signaling molecule, a local regulator called a growth factor, triggers a phosphorylation cascade. (The ATP molecules that serve as sources of phosphate are not shown.) Once phosphorylated, the last kinase in the sequence enters the nucleus and there activates a gene-regulating protein, a transcription factor. This protein stimulates a specific gene so that an mRNA is synthesized, which then directs the synthesis of a particular protein in the cytoplasm.

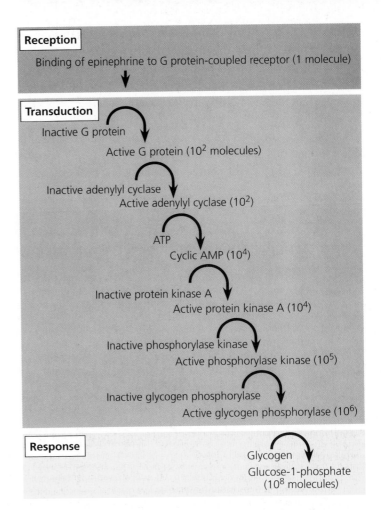

▲ **Figure 11.15 Cytoplasmic response to a signal: the stimulation of glycogen breakdown by epinephrine.** In this signaling system, the hormone epinephrine acts through a G protein-coupled receptor to activate a succession of relay molecules, including cAMP and two protein kinases (see also Figure 11.11). The final protein to be activated is the enzyme glycogen phosphorylase, which uses inorganic phosphate to release glucose monomers from glycogen in the form of glucose-1-phosphate molecules. This pathway amplifies the hormonal signal, because one receptor protein can activate about 100 molecules of G protein, and each enzyme in the pathway, once activated, can act on many molecules of its substrate, the next molecule in the cascade. The number of activated molecules given for each step is approximate.

that turns a gene on: The response to the growth factor signal is the synthesis of mRNA, which will be translated in the cytoplasm into a specific protein. In other cases, the transcription factor might regulate a gene by turning it off. Often a transcription factor regulates several different genes.

Sometimes a signaling pathway may regulate the *activity* of proteins rather than their *synthesis*, directly affecting proteins that function outside the nucleus. For example, a signal may cause the opening or closing of an ion channel in the plasma membrane or a change in cell metabolism. As we have discussed already, the response of liver cells to signaling by the hormone epinephrine helps regulate cellular energy metabolism by affecting the activity of an enzyme. The final step in the signaling pathway that begins with epinephrine binding activates the enzyme that catalyzes the breakdown of glycogen. **Figure 11.15** shows the complete pathway leading to the release of glucose-1-phosphate molecules from glycogen. Note that as each molecule is activated, the response is amplified, as we will discuss later.

In addition to the regulation of enzymes, signaling events may also affect other cellular attributes, such as overall cell shape. An example of this regulation can be found in the activities leading to the mating of yeast cells (see Figure 11.2). Yeast cells are not motile; their mating process depends on the growth of localized projections in one cell toward a cell of the opposite mating type. As shown in **Figure 11.16**, binding of the mating factor causes this directional growth. When the mating factor binds, it activates signaling-pathway kinases that affect the orientation of growth of cytoskeletal microfilaments. Because activation of signaling kinases is coupled in this way to cytoskeletal dynamics, cell projections emerge from regions of the plasma membrane exposed to the highest concentration of the mating factor. As a result, these projections are oriented toward the cell of the opposite mating type, which is the source of the signaling molecule.

The signal receptors, relay molecules, and second messengers introduced so far in this chapter participate in a variety of pathways, leading to both nuclear and cytoplasmic responses. Some of these pathways lead to cell division. The molecular messengers that initiate cell-division pathways include growth factors and certain plant and animal hormones. Malfunctioning of growth factor pathways like the one in Figure 11.14 can contribute to the development of cancer, as we will see in Chapter 18.

▼ **Figure 11.16** **Inquiry**

How do signals induce directional cell growth in yeast?

EXPERIMENT   When a yeast cell binds mating factor molecules from a cell of the opposite mating type, a signaling pathway causes it to grow a projection toward the potential mate. The cell with the projection is called a "shmoo" because it resembles a 1950s cartoon character by that name. Dina Matheos and colleagues in Mark Rose's lab at Princeton University sought to determine how mating factor signaling is linked to this asymmetrical growth. Previous work had shown that activation of one of the kinases in the signaling cascade (Fus3) caused it to move to the membrane near where the factor bound. Preliminary experiments by these researchers identified formin, a protein that directs the construction of microfilaments, as a phosphorylation target of Fus3 kinase. To examine the role of Fus3 and formin in shmoo formation, the researchers generated two mutant yeast strains: one that no longer had the kinase (this strain is called ΔFus3) and one that lacked the formin (Δformin). To observe the effects of these mutations on cell growth induced by the mating factor, the cell walls of each strain were first stained with a green fluorescent dye. These green-stained cells were then exposed to mating factor and stained with a red fluorescent dye that labeled new cell wall growth. Images taken of the cells after the staining procedure were then compared with a similarly treated strain that expressed Fus3 and formin (the wild type).

RESULTS   The cells of the wild-type strain showed shmoo projections, whose walls were stained red, while the rest of their cell walls were green, indicating asymmetrical growth. Cells of both the ΔFus3 and Δformin strains showed no shmoo formation, and their cell walls were stained almost uniformly yellow. This color resulted from merged green and red stains, indicating symmetrical growth, characteristic of cells not exposed to mating factor.

Wild-type (shmoos)   ΔFus3   Δformin

CONCLUSION   The similar defect (lack of ability to form shmoos) in strains lacking either Fus3 or formin suggests that both proteins are required for shmoo formation. These results led the investigators to propose the model shown here for the induction of directed asymmetrical growth in the receiving cell toward the cell of the opposite mating type.

❶ Mating factor activates receptor.

Mating factor — G protein-coupled receptor

❷ G protein binds GTP and becomes activated.

Phosphorylation cascade

❸ Phosphorylation cascade activates Fus3, which moves to plasma membrane.

❹ Fus3 phosphorylates formin, activating it.

❺ Formin initiates growth of microfilaments that form the shmoo projections.

Shmoo projection forming

Formin

Actin subunit

Microfilament

SOURCE   D. Matheos et al., Pheromone-induced polarization is dependent on the Fus3p MAPK acting through the formin Bni1p, *Journal of Cell Biology* 165:99–109 (2004).

WHAT IF?   Based on these results and the proposed model from this work, what would happen to a cell if its Fus3 kinase were not able to associate with the membrane upon activation?

Fine-Tuning of the Response

Regardless of whether the response occurs in the nucleus or in the cytoplasm, it is fine-tuned at multiple points. As mentioned earlier, signaling pathways with numerous steps between a signaling event at the cell surface and the cell's response have two important benefits: They amplify the signal (and thus the response), and they provide different points at which a cell's response can be regulated. This allows coordination of signaling pathways and also contributes to the specificity of the response. The overall efficiency of the response is also enhanced by scaffolding proteins. Finally, a crucial point in fine-tuning the response is the termination of the signal.

Signal Amplification

Elaborate enzyme cascades amplify the cell's response to a signal. At each catalytic step in the cascade, the number of activated products is much greater than in the preceding step. For example, in the epinephrine-triggered pathway in Figure 11.15, each adenylyl cyclase molecule catalyzes the formation of many cAMP molecules, each molecule of protein kinase A phosphorylates many molecules of the next kinase in the pathway, and so on. The amplification effect stems from the fact that these proteins persist in the active form long enough to process numerous molecules of substrate before they become inactive again. As a result of the signal's amplification, a small number of epinephrine molecules binding to receptors on the surface of a liver cell or muscle cell can lead to the release of hundreds of millions of glucose molecules from glycogen.

The Specificity of Cell Signaling and Coordination of the Response

Consider two different cells in your body—a liver cell and a heart muscle cell, for example. Both are in contact with your bloodstream and are therefore constantly exposed to many different hormone molecules, as well as to local regulators secreted by nearby cells. Yet the liver cell responds to some signals but ignores others, and the same is true for the heart cell. And some kinds of signals trigger responses in both cells—but different responses. For instance, epinephrine stimulates the liver cell to break down glycogen, but the main response of the heart cell to epinephrine is contraction, leading to a more rapid heartbeat. How do we account for this difference?

The explanation for the specificity exhibited in cellular responses to signals is the same as the basic explanation for virtually all differences between cells: *Different kinds of cells have different collections of proteins* (**Figure 11.17**). (This is because different kinds of cells turn on different sets of genes.) The response of a particular cell to a signal depends on its particular collection of signal receptor proteins, relay proteins, and proteins needed to carry out the response. A liver cell, for example, is poised to respond appropriately to epinephrine by having the proteins listed in Figure 11.15 as well as those needed to manufacture glycogen.

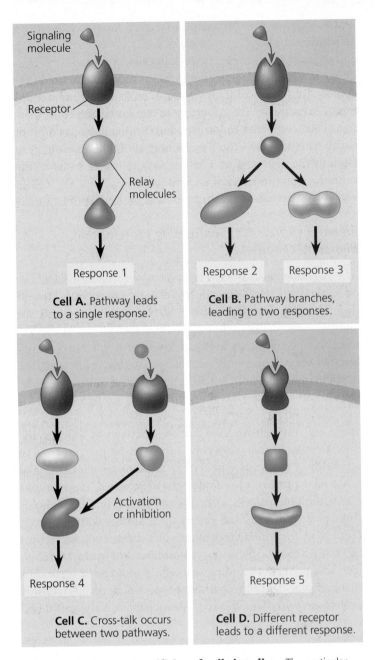

▲ **Figure 11.17 The specificity of cell signaling.** The particular proteins a cell possesses determine what signaling molecules it responds to and the nature of the response. The four cells in these diagrams respond to the same signaling molecule (red) in different ways because each has a different set of proteins (purple and teal shapes). Note, however, that the same kinds of molecules can participate in more than one pathway.

Cell A. Pathway leads to a single response.

Cell B. Pathway branches, leading to two responses.

Cell C. Cross-talk occurs between two pathways.

Cell D. Different receptor leads to a different response.

Thus, two cells that respond differently to the same signal differ in one or more of the proteins that handle and respond to the signal. Notice in Figure 11.17 that different pathways may have some molecules in common. For example, cells A, B, and C all use the same receptor protein for the red signaling molecule; differences in other proteins account for their differing responses. In cell D, a different receptor protein is used for the same signaling molecule, leading to yet another response. In cell B, a pathway that is triggered by a single kind of signal diverges to produce two responses; such branched pathways often involve receptor tyrosine kinases (which can activate multiple relay proteins) or second messengers (which can regulate numerous proteins). In cell C, two pathways triggered by separate signals converge to modulate a single response. Branching of pathways and "cross-talk" (interaction) between pathways are important in regulating and coordinating a cell's responses to information coming in from different sources in the body. (You'll learn more about this coordination later, in the next section.) Moreover, the use of some of the same proteins in more than one pathway allows the cell to economize on the number of different proteins it must make.

Signaling Efficiency: Scaffolding Proteins and Signaling Complexes

The signaling pathways in Figure 11.17 (as well as some of the other pathway depictions in this chapter) are greatly simplified. The diagrams show only a few relay molecules and, for clarity's sake, display these molecules spread out in the cytosol. If this were true in the cell, signaling pathways would operate very inefficiently because most relay molecules are proteins, and proteins are too large to diffuse quickly through the viscous cytosol. How does a particular protein kinase, for instance, find its substrate?

Recent research suggests that the efficiency of signal transduction may in many cases be increased by the presence of **scaffolding proteins**, large relay proteins to which several other relay proteins are simultaneously attached. For example, one scaffolding protein isolated from mouse brain cells holds three protein kinases and carries these kinases with it when it binds to an appropriately activated membrane receptor; it thus facilitates a specific phosphorylation cascade (**Figure 11.18**). In fact, researchers are finding scaffolding proteins in brain cells that *permanently* hold together networks of signaling-pathway proteins at synapses. This hardwiring enhances the speed and accuracy of signal transfer between cells, because the rate of protein-protein interaction is not limited by diffusion.

When signaling pathways were first discovered, they were thought to be linear, independent pathways. Our understanding of the processes of cellular communication has benefited from the realization that things are not that simple. In fact, as seen in Figure 11.17, some proteins may participate in more than one pathway, either in different cell types or in the same cell at different times or under different conditions. This view underscores the importance of permanent or transient protein complexes in the functioning of a cell.

The importance of the relay proteins that serve as points of branching or intersection in signaling pathways is highlighted by the problems arising when these proteins are defective or missing. For instance, in an inherited disorder called Wiskott-Aldrich syndrome (WAS), the absence of a single relay protein leads to such diverse effects as abnormal bleeding, eczema, and a predisposition to infections and leukemia. These symptoms are thought to arise primarily from the absence of the protein in cells of the immune system. By studying normal cells, scientists found that the WAS protein is located just beneath the cell surface. The protein interacts both with microfilaments of the cytoskeleton and with several different components of signaling pathways that relay information from the cell surface, including pathways regulating immune cell proliferation. This multifunctional relay protein is thus both a branch point and an important intersection point in a complex signal transduction network that controls immune cell behavior. When the WAS protein is absent, the cytoskeleton is not properly organized and signaling pathways are disrupted, leading to the WAS symptoms.

Termination of the Signal

To keep Figure 11.17 simple, we did not indicate the *inactivation* mechanisms that are an essential aspect of cell signaling. For a cell of a multicellular organism to remain alert and capable of responding to incoming signals, each molecular change in its signaling pathways must last only a short time. As we saw in the cholera example, if a signaling pathway component becomes locked into one state, whether active or inactive, the consequences for the organism can be dire.

Thus, a key to a cell's continuing receptiveness to regulation by signaling is the reversibility of the changes that signals produce. The binding of signaling molecules to receptors is reversible; the lower the concentration of signaling molecules is, the fewer will be bound at any given moment. When signaling molecules leave the receptor, the receptor reverts to its inactive form. Then, by a variety of means, the relay molecules return to their inactive forms:

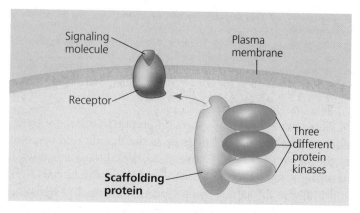

▲ **Figure 11.18 A scaffolding protein.** The scaffolding protein shown here (pink) simultaneously binds to a specific activated membrane receptor and three different protein kinases. This physical arrangement facilitates signal transduction by these molecules.

The GTPase activity intrinsic to a G protein hydrolyzes its bound GTP; the enzyme phosphodiesterase converts cAMP to AMP; protein phosphatases inactivate phosphorylated kinases and other proteins; and so forth. As a result, the cell is soon ready to respond to a fresh signal.

In this section, we explored the complexity of signaling initiation and termination in a single pathway, and we saw the potential for pathways to intersect with each other. In the next section, we'll consider an important network of interacting pathways in the cell.

CONCEPT CHECK 11.4

1. How can a target cell's response to a hormone be amplified more than a millionfold?
2. **WHAT IF?** If two cells have different scaffolding proteins, explain how they could behave differently in response to the same signaling molecule.

For suggested answers, see Appendix A.

CONCEPT 11.5
Apoptosis (programmed cell death) integrates multiple cell-signaling pathways

One of the most elaborate networks of signaling pathways in the cell seems to ask and answer the basic question posed by Hamlet: To be or not to be? Cells that are infected or damaged or that have simply reached the end of their functional life span often enter a program of controlled cell suicide called **apoptosis** (from the Greek, meaning "falling off," and used in a classic Greek poem to refer to leaves falling from a tree). During this process, cellular agents chop up the DNA and fragment the organelles and other cytoplasmic components. The cell shrinks and becomes lobed (called "blebbing") **(Figure 11.19)**, and the cell's parts are packaged up in vesicles that are engulfed and digested by specialized scavenger cells, leaving no trace. Apoptosis protects neighboring cells from damage that they would otherwise suffer if a dying cell merely leaked out all its contents, including its many digestive and other enzymes.

Apoptosis in the Soil Worm *Caenorhabditis elegans*

Embryonic development is a period during which apoptosis is widespread and plays a crucial role. The molecular mechanisms underlying apoptosis were worked out in detail by researchers studying embryonic development of a small soil worm, a nematode called *Caenorhabditis elegans*. Because the adult worm has only about a thousand cells, the researchers were able to work out the entire ancestry of each cell. The timely suicide of cells occurs exactly 131 times during normal development of *C. elegans*, at precisely the same points in the cell lineage of each worm. In worms and other species, apoptosis is triggered by signals that activate a cascade of "suicide" proteins in the cells destined to die.

Genetic research on *C. elegans* has revealed two key apoptosis genes, called *ced-3* and *ced-4* (*ced* stands for "cell death"), which encode proteins essential for apoptosis. (The proteins are called Ced-3 and Ced-4, respectively.) These and most other proteins involved in apoptosis are continually present in cells, but in inactive form; thus, protein activity is regulated rather than protein synthesis (by way of gene activity).

▶ **Figure 11.19 Apoptosis of a human white blood cell.** We can compare a normal white blood cell (left) with a white blood cell undergoing apoptosis (right). The apoptotic cell is shrinking and forming lobes ("blebs"), which eventually are shed as membrane-bounded cell fragments (colorized SEMs).

2 µm

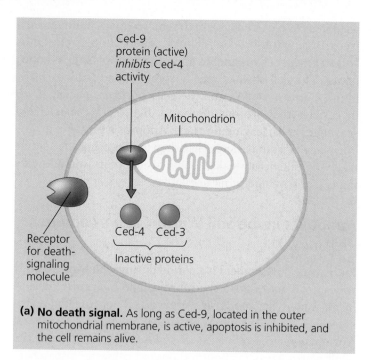

(a) No death signal. As long as Ced-9, located in the outer mitochondrial membrane, is active, apoptosis is inhibited, and the cell remains alive.

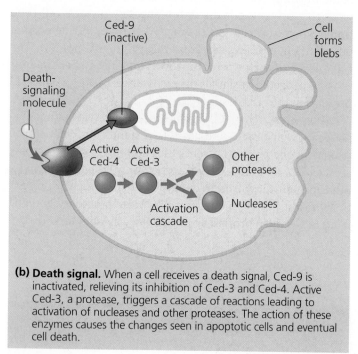

(b) Death signal. When a cell receives a death signal, Ced-9 is inactivated, relieving its inhibition of Ced-3 and Ced-4. Active Ced-3, a protease, triggers a cascade of reactions leading to activation of nucleases and other proteases. The action of these enzymes causes the changes seen in apoptotic cells and eventual cell death.

▲ **Figure 11.20 Molecular basis of apoptosis in *C. elegans.*** Three proteins, Ced-3, Ced-4, and Ced-9, are critical to apoptosis and its regulation in the nematode. Apoptosis is more complicated in mammals but involves proteins similar to those in the nematode.

In *C. elegans*, a protein in the outer mitochondrial membrane, called Ced-9 (the product of the *ced-9* gene), serves as a master regulator of apoptosis, acting as a brake in the absence of a signal promoting apoptosis **(Figure 11.20)**. When a death signal is received by the cell, it overrides the brake, and the apoptotic pathway activates proteases and nucleases, enzymes that cut up the proteins and DNA of the cell. The main pro-

teases of apoptosis are called *caspases*; in the nematode, the chief caspase is Ced-3.

Apoptotic Pathways and the Signals That Trigger Them

In humans and other mammals, several different pathways, involving about 15 different caspases, can carry out apoptosis. The pathway that is used depends on the type of cell and on the particular signal that triggers apoptosis. One major pathway involves mitochondrial proteins. Apoptotic proteins can form molecular pores in the mitochondrial outer membrane, causing it to leak and release proteins that promote apoptosis. Surprisingly, these include cytochrome *c*, which functions in mitochondrial electron transport in healthy cells (see Figure 9.16) but acts as a cell death factor when released from mitochondria. The process of mitochondrial apoptosis in mammals uses proteins similar to the nematode proteins Ced-3, Ced-4, and Ced-9.

At key points in the apoptotic program, proteins integrate signals from several different sources and can send a cell down an apoptotic pathway. Often, the signal originates outside the cell, like the death-signaling molecule depicted in Figure 11.20, which presumably was released by a neighboring cell. When a death-signaling ligand occupies a cell-surface receptor, this binding leads to activation of caspases and other enzymes that carry out apoptosis, without involving the mitochondrial pathway. Two other types of alarm signals originate from *inside* the cell. One comes from the nucleus, generated when the DNA has suffered irreparable damage, and a second comes from the endoplasmic reticulum when excessive protein misfolding occurs. Mammalian cells make life-or-death "decisions" by somehow integrating the death signals and life signals they receive from these external and internal sources.

A built-in cell suicide mechanism is essential to development and maintenance in all animals. The similarities between apoptosis genes in nematodes and mammals, as well as the observation that apoptosis occurs in multicellular fungi and even in single-celled yeasts, indicate that the basic mechanism evolved early in animal evolution. In vertebrates, apoptosis is essential for normal development of the nervous system, for normal operation of the immune system, and for normal morphogenesis of hands and feet in humans and paws in other mammals **(Figure 11.21)**. A lower level of apoptosis in developing limbs accounts for the webbed feet of ducks and other water birds, in contrast to chickens and other land birds with nonwebbed feet. In the case of humans, the failure of appropriate apoptosis can result in webbed fingers and toes.

Significant evidence points to the involvement of apoptosis in certain degenerative diseases of the nervous system, such as Parkinson's disease and Alzheimer's disease. Also, cancer can result from a failure of cell suicide; some cases of human melanoma, for example, have been linked to faulty forms of

Interdigital tissue

1 mm

▲ **Figure 11.21 Effect of apoptosis during paw development in the mouse.** In mice, humans, and other mammals, as well as in land birds, the embryonic region that develops into feet or hands initially has a

solid, platelike structure. Apoptosis eliminates the cells in the interdigital regions, thus forming the digits. The embryonic mouse paws shown in these fluorescence light micrographs are stained so that cells undergoing apoptosis

appear bright yellow. Apoptosis of cells begins at the margin of each interdigital region (left), peaks as the tissue in these regions is reduced (middle), and is no longer visible when the interdigital tissue has been eliminated (right).

the human version of the *C. elegans* Ced-4 protein. It is not surprising, therefore, that the signaling pathways feeding into apoptosis are quite elaborate. After all, the life-or-death question is the most fundamental one imaginable for a cell.

This chapter has introduced you to many of the general mechanisms of cell communication, such as ligand binding, protein-protein interactions and shape changes, cascades of interactions, and protein phosphorylation. As you continue through the text, you will encounter numerous examples of cell signaling.

CONCEPT CHECK 11.5

1. Give an example of apoptosis during embryonic development, and explain its function in the developing embryo.
2. **WHAT IF?** What type of protein defects could result in apoptosis occurring when it should not? What type could result in apoptosis not occurring when it should?

For suggested answers, see Appendix A.

Chapter 11 Review

MEDIA Go to the Study Area at **www.masteringbio.com** for BioFlix 3-D Animations, MP3 Tutors, Videos, Practice Tests, an eBook, and more.

SUMMARY OF KEY CONCEPTS

CONCEPT 11.1

External signals are converted to responses within the cell (pp. 206–210)

▶ **Evolution of Cell Signaling** Signaling in microbes has much in common with processes in multicellular organisms, suggesting an early origin of signaling mechanisms. Bacterial cells can sense the local density of bacterial cells (quorum sensing) by binding molecules secreted by other cells. In some cases, such signals lead to aggregation of these cells into biofilms.

▶ **Local and Long-Distance Signaling** In local signaling, animal cells may communicate by direct contact or by secreting local regulators, such as growth factors or neurotransmitters. For signaling over long distances, both animals and plants use hormones; animals also signal along nerve cells.

▶ **The Three Stages of Cell Signaling:** *A Preview* Earl Sutherland discovered how the hormone epinephrine acts on cells, shown here as an example of a cell-signaling pathway:

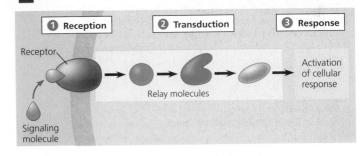

① Reception ② Transduction ③ Response

Receptor

Signaling molecule

Relay molecules

Activation of cellular response

As discussed in Sections 11.2 and 11.3, the signal is transmitted by successive shape changes in the receptor and relay molecules.

MEDIA
Investigation How Do Cells Communicate with Each Other?
Activity Overview of Cell Signaling

CONCEPT 11.2

Reception: A signaling molecule binds to a receptor protein, causing it to change shape (pp. 210–214)

▶ The binding between signaling molecule (ligand) and receptor is highly specific. A shape change in a receptor is often the initial transduction of the signal.

▶ **Receptors in the Plasma Membrane** A G protein-coupled receptor is a membrane receptor that works with the help of a cytoplasmic G protein. Ligand binding activates the receptor, which then activates a specific G protein, which activates yet another protein, thus propagating the signal along a signal transduction pathway.

Receptor tyrosine kinases react to the binding of signaling molecules by forming dimers and then adding phosphate groups to tyrosines on the cytoplasmic part of the other subunit of the dimer. Relay proteins in the cell can then be activated by binding to different phosphorylated tyrosines, allowing this receptor to trigger several pathways at once.

Specific signaling molecules cause ligand-gated ion channels in a membrane to open or close, regulating the flow of specific ions.

▶ **Intracellular Receptors** Intracellular receptors are cytoplasmic or nuclear proteins. Signaling molecules that are small or hydrophobic and can readily cross the plasma membrane use these receptors.

MEDIA

Activity Reception

CONCEPT 11.3

Transduction: Cascades of molecular interactions relay signals from receptors to target molecules in the cell (pp. 214–218)

▶ **Signal Transduction Pathways** At each step in a pathway, the signal is transduced into a different form, commonly a shape change in a protein.

▶ **Protein Phosphorylation and Dephosphorylation** Many signal transduction pathways include phosphorylation cascades, in which a series of protein kinases each add a phosphate group to the next one in line, activating it. Phosphatase enzymes soon remove the phosphates.

▶ **Small Molecules and Ions as Second Messengers** Second messengers, such as cyclic AMP (cAMP) and Ca^{2+}, diffuse readily through the cytosol and thus help broadcast signals quickly. Many G proteins activate adenylyl cyclase, which makes cAMP from ATP. Cells use Ca^{2+} as a second messenger in both G-protein and tyrosine kinase pathways. The tyrosine kinase pathways can also involve two other second messengers, DAG and IP_3. IP_3 can trigger a subsequent increase in Ca^{2+} levels.

MEDIA

Activity Signal Transduction Pathways

CONCEPT 11.4

Response: Cell signaling leads to regulation of transcription or cytoplasmic activities (pp. 218–223)

▶ **Nuclear and Cytoplasmic Responses** Some pathways regulate genes by activating transcription factors, proteins that turn specific genes on or off. In the cytoplasm, signaling pathways regulate, for example, enzyme activity and cytoskeleton rearrangement, which can lead to cell shape changes.

▶ **Fine-Tuning of the Response** Each catalytic protein in a signaling pathway amplifies the signal by activating multiple copies of the next component of the pathway; for long pathways, the total amplification may be a millionfold or more. The particular combination of proteins in a cell gives the cell great specificity in both the signals it detects and the re-

sponses it carries out. Scaffolding proteins can increase signal transduction efficiency. Pathway branching and cross-talk further help the cell coordinate incoming signals. Signal response is terminated quickly by the reversal of ligand binding.

MEDIA

Activity Cellular Responses
Activity Build a Signaling Pathway

CONCEPT 11.5

Apoptosis (programmed cell death) integrates multiple cell-signaling pathways (pp. 223–225)

▶ Apoptosis is a type of programmed cell death in which cell components are disposed of in an orderly fashion, without damage to neighboring cells.

▶ **Apoptosis in the Soil Worm *Caenorhabditis elegans*** Apoptosis occurs at defined times during embryonic development of *C. elegans*. A protein (Ced-9) in the mitochondrial membrane acts as a brake; when released by a death signal, it allows activation of caspases that carry out apoptosis.

▶ **Apoptotic Pathways and the Signals That Trigger Them** Several apoptotic pathways exist in the cells of humans and other mammals, and these pathways may be triggered in different ways. A major pathway involves pore formation in the outer mitochondrial membrane, which leads to release of factors that activate caspases. Signals can originate from outside or inside the cell.

TESTING YOUR KNOWLEDGE

SELF-QUIZ

1. Phosphorylation cascades involving a series of protein kinases are useful for cellular signal transduction because
   a. they are species specific.
   b. they always lead to the same cellular response.
   c. they amplify the original signal manyfold.
   d. they counter the harmful effects of phosphatases.
   e. the number of molecules used is small and fixed.

2. Binding of a signaling molecule to which type of receptor leads directly to a change in the distribution of ions on opposite sides of the membrane?
   a. receptor tyrosine kinase
   b. G protein-coupled receptor
   c. phosphorylated receptor tyrosine kinase dimer
   d. ligand-gated ion channel
   e. intracellular receptor

3. The activation of receptor tyrosine kinases is characterized by
   a. dimerization and phosphorylation.
   b. IP_3 binding.
   c. a phosphorylation cascade.
   d. GTP hydrolysis.
   e. channel protein shape change.

4. Which observation suggested to Sutherland the involvement of a second messenger in epinephrine's effect on liver cells?
   a. Enzymatic activity was proportional to the amount of calcium added to a cell-free extract.
   b. Receptor studies indicated that epinephrine was a ligand.

c. Glycogen breakdown was observed only when epinephrine was administered to intact cells.

d. Glycogen breakdown was observed when epinephrine and glycogen phosphorylase were combined.

e. Epinephrine was known to have different effects on different types of cells.

5. Protein phosphorylation is commonly involved with all of the following *except*

a. regulation of transcription by extracellular signaling molecules.

b. enzyme activation.

c. activation of G protein-coupled receptors.

d. activation of receptor tyrosine kinases.

e. activation of protein kinase molecules.

6. Lipid-soluble signaling molecules, such as testosterone, cross the membranes of all cells but affect only target cells because

a. only target cells retain the appropriate DNA segments.

b. intracellular receptors are present only in target cells.

c. most cells lack the Y chromosome required.

d. only target cells possess the cytosolic enzymes that transduce the testosterone.

e. only in target cells is testosterone able to initiate the phosphorylation cascade leading to activated transcription factor.

7. Consider this pathway: epinephrine → G protein-coupled receptor → G protein → adenylyl cyclase → cAMP. Identify the second messenger.

a. cAMP

b. G protein

c. GTP

d. adenylyl cyclase

e. G protein-coupled receptor

8. Apoptosis involves all but the following:

a. fragmentation of the DNA

b. cell-signaling pathways

c. activation of cellular enzymes

d. lysis of the cell

e. digestion of cellular contents by scavenger cells

9. **DRAW IT** Draw the following apoptotic pathway, which operates in human immune cells. A death signal is received when a molecule called Fas binds its cell-surface receptor. The binding of many Fas molecules to receptors causes receptor clustering. The intracellular regions of the receptors, when together, bind adapter proteins. These in turn bind to inactive forms of caspase-8, which become activated and activate caspase-3, in turn. Once activated, caspase-3 initiates apoptosis.

For Self-Quiz answers, see Appendix A.

MEDIA Visit the Study Area at **www.masteringbio.com** for a Practice Test.

EVOLUTION CONNECTION

10. What evolutionary mechanisms might account for the origin and persistence of cell-to-cell signaling systems in unicellular prokaryotes?

SCIENTIFIC INQUIRY

11. Epinephrine initiates a signal transduction pathway that involves production of cyclic AMP (cAMP) and leads to the breakdown of glycogen to glucose, a major energy source for cells. But glycogen breakdown is actually only part of a "fight-or-flight response" that epinephrine brings about; the overall effect on the body includes increased heart rate and alertness, as well as a burst of energy. Given that caffeine blocks the activity of cAMP phosphodiesterase, propose a mechanism by which caffeine ingestion leads to heightened alertness and sleeplessness.

Biological Inquiry: A Workbook of Investigative Cases Explore cell signaling processes in the hedgehog signaling pathway with the case "Shh: Silencing the Hedgehog Pathway."

SCIENCE, TECHNOLOGY, AND SOCIETY

12. The aging process is thought to be initiated at the cellular level. Among the changes that can occur after a certain number of cell divisions is the loss of a cell's ability to respond to growth factors and other chemical signals. Much research into aging is aimed at understanding such losses, with the ultimate goal of significantly extending the human life span. Not everyone, however, agrees that this is a desirable goal. If life expectancy were greatly increased, what might be the social and ecological consequences? How might we cope with them?

The Cell Cycle 12

12.1 Cell division results in genetically identical daughter cells

12.2 The mitotic phase alternates with interphase in the cell cycle

12.3 The eukaryotic cell cycle is regulated by a molecular control system

OVERVIEW
The Key Roles of Cell Division

The ability of organisms to reproduce their own kind is the one characteristic that best distinguishes living things from nonliving matter. This unique capacity to procreate, like all biological functions, has a cellular basis. Rudolf Virchow, a German physician, put it this way in 1855: "Where a cell exists, there must have been a preexisting cell, just as the animal arises only from an animal and the plant only from a plant." He summarized this concept with the Latin axiom *"Omnis cellula e cellula,"* meaning "Every cell from a

▲ **Figure 12.1 How do a cell's chromosomes change during cell division?**

cell." The continuity of life is based on the reproduction of cells, or **cell division**. The series of fluorescence micrographs in **Figure 12.1** follows an animal cell's chromosomes, from lower left to lower right, as one cell divides into two.

Cell division plays several important roles in the life of an organism. When a unicellular organism, such as an amoeba, divides and forms duplicate offspring, the division of one cell reproduces an entire organism **(Figure 12.2a)**. Cell division on a larger scale can produce progeny from some multicellular organisms (such as plants that grow from cuttings). Cell division also enables sexually reproducing organisms to develop from a single cell—the fertilized egg, or zygote **(Figure 12.2b)**. And after an organism is fully grown, cell division continues to function in renewal and repair, replacing cells that die from normal wear and tear or accidents. For example, dividing cells in your bone marrow continuously make new blood cells **(Figure 12.2c)**.

The cell division process is an integral part of the **cell cycle**, the life of a cell from the time it is first formed from a dividing parent cell until its own division into two cells. Passing identical genetic material to cellular offspring is a crucial function of cell

(a) Reproduction. An amoeba, a single-celled eukaryote, is dividing into two cells. Each new cell will be an individual organism (LM).

(b) Growth and development. This micrograph shows a sand dollar embryo shortly after the fertilized egg divided, forming two cells (LM).

(c) Tissue renewal. These dividing bone marrow cells (arrow) will give rise to new blood cells (LM).

▲ **Figure 12.2 The functions of cell division.**

division. In this chapter, you will learn how cell division distributes identical genetic material to daughter cells.* After studying the cellular mechanics of cell division in eukaryotes and bacteria, you will learn about the molecular control system that regulates progress through the eukaryotic cell cycle and what happens when the control system malfunctions. Because cell cycle regulation, or a lack thereof, plays a major role in cancer development, this aspect of cell biology is an active area of research.

Cell division results in genetically identical daughter cells

The reproduction of an ensemble as complex as a cell cannot occur by a mere pinching in half; a cell is not like a soap bubble that simply enlarges and splits in two. Most cell division involves the distribution of identical genetic material—DNA—to two daughter cells. (The special type of cell division that produces sperm and eggs results in daughter cells that are *not* genetically identical.) What is most remarkable about cell division is the fidelity with which the DNA is passed along from one generation of cells to the next. A dividing cell duplicates its DNA, allocates the two copies to opposite ends of the cell, and only then splits into daughter cells.

Cellular Organization of the Genetic Material

A cell's endowment of DNA, its genetic information, is called its **genome**. Although a prokaryotic genome is often a single long DNA molecule, eukaryotic genomes usually consist of a number of DNA molecules. The overall length of DNA in a eukaryotic cell is enormous. A typical human cell, for example, has about 2 m of DNA—a length about 250,000 times greater than the cell's diameter. Yet before the cell can divide to form genetically identical daughter cells, all of this DNA must be copied and then the two copies separated so that each daughter cell ends up with a complete genome.

The replication and distribution of so much DNA is manageable because the DNA molecules are packaged into **chromosomes**, so named because they take up certain dyes used in microscopy (from the Greek *chroma*, color, and *soma*, body) (**Figure 12.3**). Every eukaryotic species has a characteristic number of chromosomes in each cell nucleus. For example, the nuclei of human **somatic cells** (all body cells except the reproductive cells) each contain 46 chromosomes made up of two sets of 23, one set inherited from each parent. Reproductive cells, or **gametes**—sperm and eggs—have half as many chromosomes as somatic cells, or one set of 23 chromo-

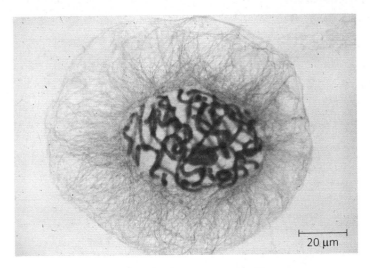

▲ **Figure 12.3 Eukaryotic chromosomes.** Chromosomes (stained purple) are visible within the nucleus of this cell from an African blood lily. The thinner red threads in the surrounding cytoplasm are the cytoskeleton. The cell is preparing to divide (LM).

somes in humans. The number of chromosomes in somatic cells varies widely among species: 18 in cabbage plants, 56 in elephants, 90 in hedgehogs, and 148 in one species of alga.

Eukaryotic chromosomes are made of **chromatin**, a complex of DNA and associated protein molecules. Each single chromosome contains one very long, linear DNA molecule that carries several hundred to a few thousand genes, the units that specify an organism's inherited traits. The associated proteins maintain the structure of the chromosome and help control the activity of the genes.

Distribution of Chromosomes During Eukaryotic Cell Division

When a cell is not dividing, and even as it duplicates its DNA in preparation for cell division, each chromosome is in the form of a long, thin chromatin fiber. After DNA duplication, however, the chromosomes condense: Each chromatin fiber becomes densely coiled and folded, making the chromosomes much shorter and so thick that we can see them with a light microscope.

Each duplicated chromosome has two **sister chromatids**. The two chromatids, each containing an identical DNA molecule, are initially attached all along their lengths by adhesive protein complexes called *cohesins*; this attachment is known as *sister chromatid cohesion*. In its condensed form, the duplicated chromosome has a narrow "waist" at the **centromere**, a specialized region where the two chromatids are most closely attached. The part of a chromatid on either side of the centromere is referred to as an *arm* of the chromatid. Later in the cell division process, the two sister chromatids of each duplicated chromosome separate and move into two new nuclei, one forming at each end of the cell. Once the sister chromatids separate, they are considered individual chromosomes. Thus, each new nucleus receives a collection of chromosomes identical to that of

---

* Although the terms *daughter cells* and *sister chromatids* (a term you will encounter later in the chapter) are traditional and will be used throughout this book, the structures they refer to have no gender.

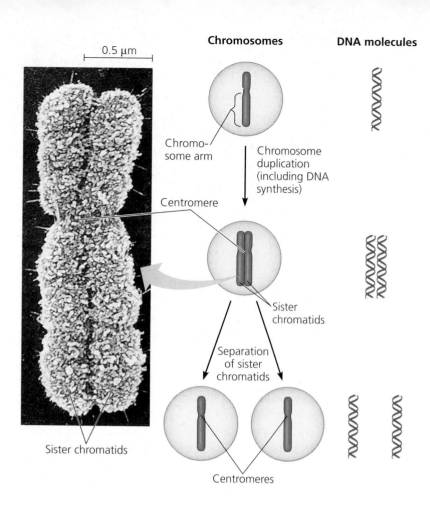

0.5 μm

Chromosomes   **DNA molecules**

Chromosome arm

Chromosome duplication (including DNA synthesis)

Centromere

Sister chromatids

Separation of sister chromatids

Sister chromatids

Centromeres

◀ **Figure 12.4 Chromosome duplication and distribution during cell division.** A eukaryotic cell preparing to divide duplicates each of its chromosomes. Next to each chromosome drawing is a simplified double helix representing each DNA molecule. (In an actual chromosome, each DNA molecule would be tightly folded and coiled, complexed with proteins.) The micrograph shows a highly condensed duplicated human chromosome (SEM). The sister chromatids of each duplicated chromosome are distributed to two daughter cells during cell division. (Chromosomes normally exist in the highly condensed state shown here only during the process of cell division; the chromosomes in the top and bottom cells are shown in condensed form for illustration purposes only.)

? *Circle one chromatid in the chromosome in the micrograph. How many arms does the chromosome have?*

❶ A eukaryotic cell has multiple chromosomes, one of which is represented here. Before duplication, each chromosome has a single DNA molecule.

❷ Once replicated, a chromosome consists of two sister chromatids connected along their entire lengths by sister chromatid cohesion. Each chromatid contains a copy of the DNA molecule.

❸ Mechanical processes separate the sister chromatids into two chromosomes and distribute them to two daughter cells.

the parent cell **(Figure 12.4)**. **Mitosis**, the division of the nucleus, is usually followed immediately by **cytokinesis**, the division of the cytoplasm. Where there was one cell, there are now two, each the genetic equivalent of the parent cell.

What happens to the chromosome number as we follow the human life cycle through the generations? You inherited 46 chromosomes, one set of 23 from each parent. They were combined in the nucleus of a single cell when a sperm from your father united with an egg from your mother, forming a fertilized egg, or zygote. Mitosis and cytokinesis produced the 200 trillion somatic cells that now make up your body, and the same processes continue to generate new cells to replace dead and damaged ones. In contrast, you produce gametes—eggs or sperm—by a variation of cell division called **meiosis**, which yields nonidentical daughter cells that have only one set of chromosomes, thus half as many chromosomes as the parent cell. Meiosis occurs only in your gonads (ovaries or testes). In each generation of humans, meiosis reduces the chromosome number from 46 (two sets of chromosomes) to 23 (one set). Fertilization fuses two gametes together and returns the chromosome number to 46, and mitosis conserves that number in every somatic cell nucleus of the new individual. In Chapter 13, we will examine the role of meiosis in reproduction and inheritance in more detail. In the remainder of this chapter, we focus on mitosis and the rest of the cell cycle in eukaryotes.

CONCEPT CHECK 12.1

1. Starting with a fertilized egg (zygote), a series of five cell divisions would produce an early embryo with how many cells?
2. How many chromatids are in a duplicated chromosome?
3. **WHAT IF?** A chicken has 78 chromosomes in its somatic cells. How many chromosomes did the chicken inherit from each parent? How many chromosomes are in each of the chicken's gametes? How many chromosomes will be in each somatic cell of the chicken's offspring?

For suggested answers, see Appendix A.

CONCEPT 12.2

The mitotic phase alternates with interphase in the cell cycle

In 1882, a German anatomist named Walther Flemming developed dyes that allowed him to observe, for the first time, the behavior of chromosomes during mitosis and cytokinesis. (In fact, Flemming coined the terms *mitosis* and *chromatin*.) During the period between one cell division and the next, it appeared to Flemming that the cell was simply growing larger. But we now know that many critical events occur during this stage in the life of a cell.

Phases of the Cell Cycle

Mitosis is just one part of the cell cycle (**Figure 12.5**). In fact, the **mitotic (M) phase**, which includes both mitosis and cytokinesis, is usually the shortest part of the cell cycle. Mitotic cell division alternates with a much longer stage called **interphase**, which often accounts for about 90% of the cycle. It is during interphase that the cell grows and copies its chromosomes in preparation for cell division. Interphase can be divided into subphases: the G_1 **phase** ("first gap"), the **S phase** ("synthesis"), and the G_2 **phase** ("second gap"). During all three subphases, the cell grows by producing proteins and cytoplasmic organelles such as mitochondria and endoplasmic reticulum. However, chromosomes are duplicated only during the S phase (we will discuss synthesis of DNA in Chapter 16). Thus, a cell grows (G_1), continues to grow as it copies its chromosomes (S), grows more as it completes preparations for cell division (G_2), and divides (M). The daughter cells may then repeat the cycle.

A particular human cell might undergo one division in 24 hours. Of this time, the M phase would occupy less than 1 hour, while the S phase might occupy about 10–12 hours, or about half the cycle. The rest of the time would be apportioned between the G_1 and G_2 phases. The G_2 phase usually takes 4–6 hours; in our example, G_1 would occupy about 5–6 hours. G_1 is the most variable in length in different types of cells.

Mitosis is conventionally broken down into five stages: **prophase, prometaphase, metaphase, anaphase,** and **telophase.** Overlapping with the latter stages of mitosis, cytokinesis completes the mitotic phase. **Figure 12.6**, on the next two pages, describes these stages in an animal cell. Be sure to study this figure thoroughly before progressing to the next two sections, which examine mitosis and cytokinesis more closely.

The Mitotic Spindle: *A Closer Look*

Many of the events of mitosis depend on the **mitotic spindle**, which begins to form in the cytoplasm during prophase. This structure consists of fibers made of microtubules and associated proteins. While the mitotic spindle assembles, the other microtubules of the cytoskeleton partially disassemble, probably providing the material used to construct the spindle. The spindle microtubules elongate (polymerize) by incorporating more subunits of the protein tubulin and shorten (depolymerize) by losing subunits (see Table 6.1).

In animal cells, the assembly of spindle microtubules starts at the **centrosome**, a subcellular region containing material that functions throughout the cell cycle to organize the cell's microtubules (it is also called the *microtubule-organizing center*). A pair of centrioles is located at the center of the centrosome, but they are not essential for cell division: If the centrioles are destroyed with a laser microbeam, a spindle nevertheless forms during mitosis. In fact, centrioles are not even present in plant cells, which do form mitotic spindles.

During interphase in animal cells, the single centrosome replicates, forming two centrosomes, which remain together near the nucleus. The two centrosomes move apart during prophase and prometaphase of mitosis as spindle microtubules grow out from them. By the end of prometaphase, the two centrosomes, one at each pole of the spindle, are at opposite ends of the cell. An **aster**, a radial array of short microtubules, extends from each centrosome. The spindle includes the centrosomes, the spindle microtubules, and the asters.

Each of the two sister chromatids of a replicated chromosome has a **kinetochore**, a structure of proteins associated with specific sections of chromosomal DNA at the centromere. The chromosome's two kinetochores face in opposite directions. During prometaphase, some of the spindle microtubules attach to the kinetochores; these are called kinetochore microtubules. (The number of microtubules attached to a kinetochore varies among species, from one microtubule in yeast cells to 40 or so in some mammalian cells.) When one of a chromosome's kinetochores is "captured" by microtubules, the chromosome begins to move toward the pole from which those microtubules extend. However, this movement is checked as soon as microtubules from the opposite pole attach to the other kinetochore. What happens next is like a tug-of-war that ends in a draw. The chromosome moves first in one direction, then the other, back and forth, finally settling midway between the two ends of the cell. At metaphase, the centromeres of all the duplicated chromosomes are on a plane midway between the spindle's two poles. This imaginary plane is called the **metaphase plate** of the cell

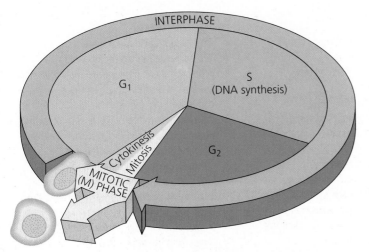

▲ **Figure 12.5 The cell cycle.** In a dividing cell, the mitotic (M) phase alternates with interphase, a growth period. The first part of interphase (G_1) is followed by the S phase, when the chromosomes replicate; G_2 is the last part of interphase. In the M phase, mitosis divides the nucleus and distributes its chromosomes to the daughter nuclei, and cytokinesis divides the cytoplasm, producing two daughter cells. The relative durations of G_1, S, and G_2 may vary.

Exploring The Mitotic Division of an Animal Cell

G₂ of Interphase

Prophase

Prometaphase

Centrosomes (with centriole pairs)

Chromatin (duplicated)

Nucleolus

Nuclear envelope

Plasma membrane

Early mitotic spindle

Aster

Centromere

Chromosome, consisting of two sister chromatids

Fragments of nuclear envelope

Nonkinetochore microtubules

Kinetochore

Kinetochore microtubule

G₂ of Interphase

- A nuclear envelope bounds the nucleus.
- The nucleus contains one or more nucleoli (singular, *nucleolus*).
- Two centrosomes have formed by replication of a single centrosome.
- In animal cells, each centrosome features two centrioles.
- Chromosomes, duplicated during S phase, cannot be seen individually because they have not yet condensed.

The light micrographs show dividing lung cells from a newt, which has 22 chromosomes in its somatic cells (chromosomes appear blue, microtubules green, and intermediate filaments red). For simplicity, the drawings show only six chromosomes.

Prophase

- The chromatin fibers become more tightly coiled, condensing into discrete chromosomes observable with a light microscope.
- The nucleoli disappear.
- Each duplicated chromosome appears as two identical sister chromatids joined together at their centromeres and all along their arms by cohesins (sister chromatid cohesion).
- The mitotic spindle (named for its shape) begins to form. It is composed of the centrosomes and the microtubules that extend from them. The radial arrays of shorter microtubules that extend from the centrosomes are called asters ("stars").
- The centrosomes move away from each other, apparently propelled by the lengthening microtubules between them.

Prometaphase

- The nuclear envelope fragments.
- The microtubules extending from each centrosome can now invade the nuclear area.
- The chromosomes have become even more condensed.
- Each of the two chromatids of each chromosome now has a kinetochore, a specialized protein structure located at the centromere.
- Some of the microtubules attach to the kinetochores, becoming "kinetochore microtubules"; these jerk the chromosomes back and forth.
- Nonkinetochore microtubules interact with those from the opposite pole of the spindle.

? *How many molecules of DNA are in the prometaphase drawing? How many molecules per chromosome? How many double helices are there per chromosome? Per chromatid?*

Metaphase

Anaphase

Telophase and Cytokinesis

Metaphase plate

Spindle

Centrosome at one spindle pole

Daughter chromosomes

Cleavage furrow

Nucleolus forming

Nuclear envelope forming

Metaphase

- Metaphase is the longest stage of mitosis, often lasting about 20 minutes.
- The centrosomes are now at opposite poles of the cell.
- The chromosomes convene on the metaphase plate, an imaginary plane that is equidistant between the spindle's two poles. The chromosomes' centromeres lie on the metaphase plate.
- For each chromosome, the kinetochores of the sister chromatids are attached to kinetochore microtubules coming from opposite poles.

MEDIA

BioFlix Visit the Study Area at **www.masteringbio.com** for the BioFlix 3-D Animation on Mitosis.

Anaphase

- Anaphase is the shortest stage of mitosis, often lasting only a few minutes.
- Anaphase begins when the cohesin proteins are cleaved. This allows the two sister chromatids of each pair to part suddenly. Each chromatid thus becomes a full-fledged chromosome.
- The two liberated daughter chromosomes begin moving toward opposite ends of the cell as their kinetochore microtubules shorten. Because these microtubules are attached at the centromere region, the chromosomes move centromere first (at about 1 µm/min).
- The cell elongates as the nonkinetochore microtubules lengthen.
- By the end of anaphase, the two ends of the cell have equivalent—and complete—collections of chromosomes.

Telophase

- Two daughter nuclei form in the cell.
- Nuclear envelopes arise from the fragments of the parent cell's nuclear envelope and other portions of the endomembrane system.
- Nucleoli reappear.
- The chromosomes become less condensed.
- Mitosis, the division of one nucleus into two genetically identical nuclei, is now complete.

Cytokinesis

- The division of the cytoplasm is usually well under way by late telophase, so the two daughter cells appear shortly after the end of mitosis.
- In animal cells, cytokinesis involves the formation of a cleavage furrow, which pinches the cell in two.

(Figure 12.7). Meanwhile, microtubules that do not attach to kinetochores have been elongating, and by metaphase they overlap and interact with other nonkinetochore microtubules from the opposite pole of the spindle. (These are sometimes called "polar" microtubules.) By metaphase, the microtubules of the asters have also grown and are in contact with the plasma membrane. The spindle is now complete.

Let's now see how the structure of the completed spindle correlates with its function during anaphase. Anaphase commences suddenly when the cohesins holding together the sister chromatids of each chromosome are cleaved by enzymes. Once the chromatids become separate, full-fledged chromosomes, they move toward opposite ends of the cell.

How do the kinetochore microtubules function in this poleward movement of chromosomes? Apparently, two mechanisms are in play, both involving motor proteins. (To review how motor proteins move an object along a microtubule, see Figure 6.21.) A clever experiment carried out in Gary Borisy's lab at the University of Wisconsin in 1987 suggested that motor proteins on the kinetochores "walk" the chromosomes along the microtubules, which depolymerize at their kinetochore ends after the motor proteins have passed (Figure 12.8). (This is referred to as the "Pacman" mechanism because of its resemblance to the arcade game character that moves by eating all the dots in its path.) However, other researchers, working with different cell types or cells from other species, have shown that chromosomes are "reeled in" by motor proteins at the spindle poles and that the microtubules depolymerize after they pass by these motor proteins. The general consensus now is that the relative contributions of these two mechanisms vary among cell types.

What is the function of the *non*kinetochore microtubules? In a dividing animal cell, these microtubules are responsible for elongating the whole cell during anaphase. Nonkinetochore microtubules from opposite poles overlap each other extensively during metaphase (see Figure 12.7). During anaphase, the region of overlap is reduced as motor proteins attached to the microtubules walk them away from one another, using energy from ATP. As the microtubules push apart from each other, their spindle poles are pushed apart, elongating the cell. At the same time, the microtubules lengthen somewhat by the addition of tubulin subunits to their overlapping ends. As a result, the microtubules continue to overlap.

At the end of anaphase, duplicate groups of chromosomes have arrived at opposite ends of the elongated parent cell. Nuclei re-form during telophase. Cytokinesis generally begins during anaphase or telophase, and the spindle eventually disassembles.

Cytokinesis: *A Closer Look*

In animal cells, cytokinesis occurs by a process known as **cleavage**. The first sign of cleavage is the appearance of a **cleavage furrow**, a shallow groove in the cell surface near the old metaphase plate (Figure 12.9a). On the cytoplasmic side of the furrow is a contractile ring of actin microfilaments associated with molecules of the protein myosin. (Actin and myosin are also responsible for muscle contraction and many other kinds of cell movement.) The actin microfilaments interact with the myosin molecules, causing the ring to contract. The contraction of the dividing cell's ring of microfilaments is like the pulling of drawstrings. The cleavage furrow deepens

▲ **Figure 12.7 The mitotic spindle at metaphase.** The kinetochores of each chromosome's two sister chromatids face in opposite directions. Here, each kinetochore is attached to a *cluster* of kinetochore microtubules extending from the nearest centrosome. Nonkinetochore microtubules overlap at the metaphase plate (TEMs).
DRAW IT *On the lower micrograph, draw a line indicating the metaphase plate. Circle an aster. Draw arrows indicating the directions of chromosome movement once anaphase begins.*

▼ Figure 12.8 Inquiry

At which end do kinetochore microtubules shorten during anaphase?

EXPERIMENT Gary Borisy and colleagues wanted to determine whether kinetochore microtubules depolymerize at the kinetochore end or the pole end as chromosomes move toward the poles during mitosis. First, they labeled the microtubules of a pig kidney cell in early anaphase with a yellow fluorescent dye.

Then they marked a region of the kinetochore microtubules between one spindle pole and the chromosomes by using a laser to eliminate the fluorescence from that region. (The microtubules remained intact.) As anaphase proceeded, they monitored the changes in microtubule length on either side of the mark.

RESULTS As the chromosomes moved poleward, the microtubule segments on the kinetochore side of the mark shortened, while those on the spindle pole side stayed the same length.

CONCLUSION During anaphase in this cell type, chromosome movement is correlated with kinetochore microtubules shortening at their kinetochore ends and not at their spindle pole ends. This experiment supports the hypothesis that during anaphase, a chromosome is walked along a microtubule as the microtubule depolymerizes at its kinetochore end, releasing tubulin subunits.

SOURCE G. J. Gorbsky, P. J. Sammak, and G. G. Borisy, Chromosomes move poleward in anaphase along stationary microtubules that coordinately disassemble from their kinetochore ends, *Journal of Cell Biology* 104:9–18 (1987).

WHAT IF? If this experiment had been done on a cell type in which "reeling in" at the poles was the main cause of chromosome movement, how would the mark have moved relative to the poles? How would the microtubule lengths have changed?

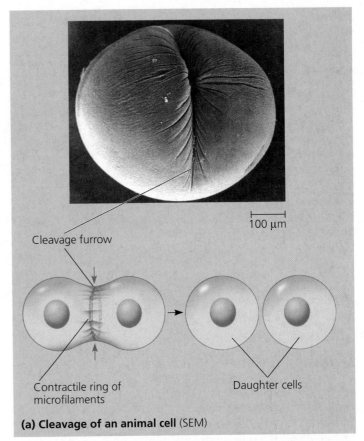

(a) Cleavage of an animal cell (SEM)

(b) Cell plate formation in a plant cell (TEM)

▲ **Figure 12.9 Cytokinesis in animal and plant cells.**

Nucleus
Nucleolus
Chromatin condensing
Chromosomes
Cell plate
10 μm

❶ **Prophase.** The chromatin is condensing and the nucleolus is beginning to disappear. Although not yet visible in the micrograph, the mitotic spindle is starting to form.

❷ **Prometaphase.** Discrete chromosomes are now visible; each consists of two aligned, identical sister chromatids. Later in prometaphase, the nuclear envelope will fragment.

❸ **Metaphase.** The spindle is complete, and the chromosomes, attached to microtubules at their kinetochores, are all at the metaphase plate.

❹ **Anaphase.** The chromatids of each chromosome have separated, and the daughter chromosomes are moving to the ends of the cell as their kinetochore microtubules shorten.

❺ **Telophase.** Daughter nuclei are forming. Meanwhile, cytokinesis has started: The cell plate, which will divide the cytoplasm in two, is growing toward the perimeter of the parent cell.

▲ **Figure 12.10 Mitosis in a plant cell.** These light micrographs show mitosis in cells of an onion root.

until the parent cell is pinched in two, producing two completely separated cells, each with its own nucleus and share of cytosol, organelles, and other subcellular structures.

Cytokinesis in plant cells, which have cell walls, is markedly different. There is no cleavage furrow. Instead, during telophase, vesicles derived from the Golgi apparatus move along microtubules to the middle of the cell, where they coalesce, producing a **cell plate** (**Figure 12.9b**). Cell wall materials carried in the vesicles collect in the cell plate as it grows. The cell plate enlarges until its surrounding membrane fuses with the plasma membrane along the perimeter of the cell. Two daughter cells result, each with its own plasma membrane. Meanwhile, a new cell wall arising from the contents of the cell plate has formed between the daughter cells.

Figure 12.10 is a series of micrographs of a dividing plant cell. Examining this figure will help you review mitosis and cytokinesis.

Binary Fission

The asexual reproduction of single-celled eukaryotes, such as the amoeba in Figure 12.2a, includes mitosis and occurs by a type of cell division called **binary fission**, meaning "division in half." Prokaryotes (bacteria and archaea) also reproduce by binary fission, but the prokaryotic process does not involve mitosis. In bacteria, most genes are carried on a single *bacterial chromosome* that consists of a circular DNA molecule and associated proteins. Although bacteria are smaller and simpler than eukaryotic cells, the challenge of replicating their genomes in an orderly fashion and distributing the copies equally to two daughter cells is still formidable. The chromosome of the bacterium

Escherichia coli, for example, when it is fully stretched out, is about 500 times as long as the cell. For such a long chromosome to fit within the cell requires that it be highly coiled and folded.

In *E. coli*, the process of cell division is initiated when the DNA of the bacterial chromosome begins to replicate at a specific place on the chromosome called the **origin of replication**, producing two origins. As the chromosome continues to replicate, one origin moves rapidly toward the opposite end of the cell (**Figure 12.11**). While the chromosome is replicating, the cell elongates. When replication is complete and the bacterium has reached about twice its initial size, its plasma membrane grows inward, dividing the parent *E. coli* cell into two daughter cells. Each cell inherits a complete genome.

Using the techniques of modern DNA technology to tag the origins of replication with molecules that glow green in fluorescence microscopy (see Figure 6.3), researchers have directly observed the movement of bacterial chromosomes. This movement is reminiscent of the poleward movements of the centromere regions of eukaryotic chromosomes during anaphase of mitosis, but bacteria don't have visible mitotic spindles or even microtubules. In most bacterial species studied, the two origins of replication end up at opposite ends of the cell or in some other very specific location, possibly anchored there by one or more proteins. How bacterial chromosomes move and how their specific location is established and maintained are still not fully understood. However, several proteins have been identified that play important roles: One resembling eukaryotic actin may function in bacterial chromosome movement during cell division, and another that is related to tubulin may help separate the two bacterial daughter cells.

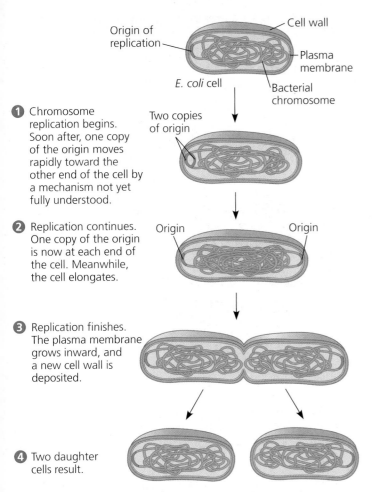

① **Chromosome replication begins.** Soon after, one copy of the origin moves rapidly toward the other end of the cell by a mechanism not yet fully understood.

② **Replication continues.** One copy of the origin is now at each end of the cell. Meanwhile, the cell elongates.

③ **Replication finishes.** The plasma membrane grows inward, and a new cell wall is deposited.

④ **Two daughter cells result.**

▲ **Figure 12.11 Bacterial cell division by binary fission.** The example shown here is the bacterium *E. coli*, which has a single, circular chromosome.

The Evolution of Mitosis

How did mitosis evolve? Given that prokaryotes preceded eukaryotes on Earth by more than a billion years, we might hypothesize that mitosis had its origins in simpler prokaryotic mechanisms of cell reproduction. The fact that some of the proteins involved in bacterial binary fission are related to eukaryotic proteins that function in mitosis supports that hypothesis.

As eukaryotes evolved, along with their larger genomes and nuclear envelopes, the ancestral process of binary fission, seen today in bacteria, somehow gave rise to mitosis. **Figure 12.12** traces a hypothesis for the stepwise evolution of mitosis. Possible intermediate stages are represented by two unusual types of nuclear division found today in certain unicellular eukaryotes. These two examples of nuclear division are thought to be cases where ancestral mechanisms have remained relatively unchanged over evolutionary time. In both types, the nuclear envelope remains intact. In dinoflagellates, replicated chromosomes are attached to the nuclear envelope and separate as the nucleus elongates prior to dividing. In diatoms and yeasts, a spindle *within* the nucleus separates the chromosomes. In most eukaryotic cells, the nuclear envelope breaks down and a spindle separates the chromosomes.

(a) Bacteria. During binary fission in bacteria, the origins of the daughter chromosomes move to opposite ends of the cell. The mechanism is not fully understood, but proteins may anchor the daughter chromosomes to specific sites on the plasma membrane.

(b) Dinoflagellates. In unicellular protists called dinoflagellates, the chromosomes attach to the nuclear envelope, which remains intact during cell division. Microtubules pass through the nucleus inside cytoplasmic tunnels, reinforcing the spatial orientation of the nucleus, which then divides in a process reminiscent of bacterial binary fission.

(c) Diatoms and yeasts. In two other groups of unicellular protists, diatoms and yeasts, the nuclear envelope also remains intact during cell division. But in these organisms, the microtubules form a spindle *within* the nucleus. Microtubules separate the chromosomes, and the nucleus splits into two daughter nuclei.

(d) Most eukaryotes. In most other eukaryotes, including plants and animals, the spindle forms outside the nucleus, and the nuclear envelope breaks down during mitosis. Microtubules separate the chromosomes, and the nuclear envelope then re-forms.

▲ **Figure 12.12 A hypothetical sequence for the evolution of mitosis.** Some unicellular eukaryotes existing today have mechanisms of cell division that appear to be intermediate between the binary fission of bacteria (a) and mitosis as it occurs in most other eukaryotes (d). Except for (a), these schematic diagrams do not show cell walls.

1. How many chromosomes are shown in the diagram in Figure 12.7? How many chromatids are shown?
2. Compare cytokinesis in animal cells and plant cells.
3. What is a function of nonkinetochore microtubules?
4. Identify three similarities between bacterial chromosomes and eukaryotic chromosomes, considering both structure and behavior during cell division.
5. Compare the roles of tubulin and actin during eukaryotic cell division with the roles of tubulin-like and actin-like proteins during bacterial binary fission.
6. **WHAT IF?** During which stages of the cell cycle does a chromosome consist of two identical chromatids?

For suggested answers, see Appendix A.

CONCEPT **12.3**
The eukaryotic cell cycle is regulated by a molecular control system

The timing and rate of cell division in different parts of a plant or animal are crucial to normal growth, development, and maintenance. The frequency of cell division varies with the type of cell. For example, human skin cells divide frequently throughout life, whereas liver cells maintain the ability to divide but keep it in reserve until an appropriate need arises—say, to repair a wound. Some of the most specialized cells, such as fully formed nerve cells and muscle cells, do not divide at all in a mature human. These cell cycle differences result from regulation at the molecular level. The mechanisms of this regulation are of intense interest, not only for understanding the life cycles of normal cells but also for understanding how cancer cells manage to escape the usual controls.

Evidence for Cytoplasmic Signals

What controls the cell cycle? As Paul Nurse mentions in the interview opening this unit, one reasonable hypothesis might be that each event in the cell cycle merely leads to the next, as in a simple metabolic pathway. According to this hypothesis, the replication of chromosomes in the S phase, for example, might cause cell growth during the G_2 phase, which might in turn lead inevitably to the onset of mitosis. However, this hypothesis, which proposes a pathway that is not subject to either internal or external regulation, turns out to be incorrect.

In the early 1970s, a variety of experiments led to an alternative hypothesis: that the cell cycle is driven by specific signaling molecules present in the cytoplasm. Some of the first strong evidence for this hypothesis came from experiments with mammalian cells grown in culture. In these experiments,

▼ **Figure 12.13** Inquiry

Do molecular signals in the cytoplasm regulate the cell cycle?

EXPERIMENT   Researchers at the University of Colorado wondered whether a cell's progression through the cell cycle is controlled by cytoplasmic molecules. To investigate this, they induced cultured mammalian cells at different phases of the cell cycle to fuse. Two such experiments are shown here.

RESULTS

When a cell in the S phase was fused with a cell in G_1, the G_1 nucleus immediately entered the S phase—DNA was synthesized.

When a cell in the M phase was fused with a cell in G_1, the G_1 nucleus immediately began mitosis—a spindle formed and chromatin condensed, even though the chromosome had not been duplicated.

CONCLUSION   The results of fusing a G_1 cell with a cell in the S or M phase of the cell cycle suggest that molecules present in the cytoplasm during the S or M phase control the progression to those phases.

SOURCE   R. T. Johnson and P. N. Rao, Mammalian cell fusion: Induction of premature chromosome condensation in interphase nuclei, *Nature* 226:717–722 (1970).

WHAT IF?   If the progression of phases did not depend on cytoplasmic molecules and each phase began when the previous one was complete, how would the results have differed?

two cells in different phases of the cell cycle were fused to form a single cell with two nuclei. If one of the original cells was in the S phase and the other was in G_1, the G_1 nucleus immediately entered the S phase, as though stimulated by chemicals present in the cytoplasm of the first cell. Similarly, if a cell undergoing mitosis (M phase) was fused with another cell in any stage of its cell cycle, even G_1, the second nucleus immediately entered mitosis, with condensation of the chromatin and formation of a mitotic spindle (**Figure 12.13**).

The Cell Cycle Control System

The experiment shown in Figure 12.13 and other experiments on animal cells and yeasts demonstrated that the sequential events of the cell cycle are directed by a distinct **cell cycle control system,** a cyclically operating set of molecules in the cell that both triggers and coordinates key events in the cell cycle. The cell cycle control system has been compared to the control device of an automatic washing machine **(Figure 12.14).** Like the washer's timing device, the cell cycle control system proceeds on its own, according to a built-in clock. However, just as a washer's cycle is subject to both internal control (such as the sensor that detects when the tub is filled with water) and external adjustment (such as activation of the start mechanism), the cell cycle is regulated at certain checkpoints by both internal and external signals.

A **checkpoint** in the cell cycle is a control point where stop and go-ahead signals can regulate the cycle. (The signals are transmitted within the cell by the kinds of signal transduction pathways discussed in Chapter 11.) Animal cells generally have built-in stop signals that halt the cell cycle at checkpoints until overridden by go-ahead signals. Many signals registered at checkpoints come from cellular surveillance mechanisms inside the cell; the signals report whether crucial cellular processes that should have occurred by that point have in fact been completed correctly and thus whether or not the cell cycle should proceed. Checkpoints also register signals from outside the cell, as we will discuss later. Three major checkpoints are found in the G_1, G_2, and M phases (see Figure 12.14).

For many cells, the G_1 checkpoint—dubbed the "restriction point" in mammalian cells—seems to be the most important. If a cell receives a go-ahead signal at the G_1 checkpoint, it will usually complete the G_1, S, G_2, and M phases and divide. If it does not receive a go-ahead signal at that point, it will exit the cycle, switching into a nondividing state called the **G_0 phase**

(a) If a cell receives a go-ahead signal at the G_1 checkpoint, the cell continues on in the cell cycle.

(b) If a cell does not receive a go-ahead signal at the G_1 checkpoint, the cell exits the cell cycle and goes into G_0, a nondividing state.

▲ **Figure 12.15 The G₁ checkpoint.**

WHAT IF? *What might be the result if the cell ignored the checkpoint and progressed through the cell cycle?*

(Figure 12.15). Most cells of the human body are actually in the G_0 phase. As mentioned earlier, mature nerve cells and muscle cells never divide. Other cells, such as liver cells, can be "called back" from the G_0 phase to the cell cycle by external cues, such as growth factors released during injury.

To understand how cell cycle checkpoints work, we first need to see what kinds of molecules make up the cell cycle control system (the molecular basis for the cell cycle clock) and how a cell progresses through the cycle. Then we will consider the internal and external checkpoint signals that can make the clock pause or continue.

The Cell Cycle Clock: Cyclins and Cyclin-Dependent Kinases

Rhythmic fluctuations in the abundance and activity of cell cycle control molecules pace the sequential events of the cell cycle. These regulatory molecules are mainly proteins of two types: protein kinases and cyclins. Protein kinases are enzymes that activate or inactivate other proteins by phosphorylating them (see Chapter 11). Particular protein kinases give the go-ahead signals at the G_1 and G_2 checkpoints. **Figure 12.16,** on the next page, describes an experiment from Paul Nurse's laboratory that demonstrates the crucial function of the protein kinase Cdc2 in triggering mitosis at the G_2 checkpoint in one type of yeast. Studies by other researchers have shown that this enzyme plays the same role in sea star eggs and cultured human cells, suggesting that the function of this protein has been conserved during the evolution of eukaryotes and is likely the same in many species.

Many of the kinases that drive the cell cycle are actually present at a constant concentration in the growing cell, but much of the time they are in an inactive form. To be active, such a kinase must be attached to a **cyclin,** a protein that gets its name from its cyclically fluctuating concentration in the cell. Because of this requirement, these kinases are called **cyclin-dependent kinases,** or **Cdks.** The activity of a Cdk

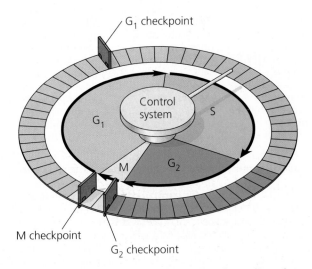

▲ **Figure 12.14 Mechanical analogy for the cell cycle control system.** In this diagram of the cell cycle, the flat "stepping stones" around the perimeter represent sequential events. Like the control device of an automatic washer, the cell cycle control system proceeds on its own, driven by a built-in clock. However, the system is subject to internal and external regulation at various checkpoints, of which three are shown (red).

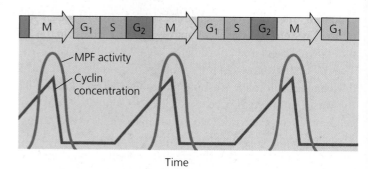

▼ Figure 12.16 Inquiry

How does the activity of a protein kinase essential for mitosis vary during the cell cycle?

EXPERIMENT   Working with the fission yeast *Schizosaccharomyces pombe*, Paul Nurse and colleagues identified a gene, *cdc2*, whose normal functioning is necessary for cell division. They first showed that its product was a protein kinase (see the Unit Two interview, pp. 92–93). As part of a large study on how the *cdc2* protein kinase is regulated during the cell cycle, they measured its activity as the cell cycle progressed. In a culture of yeast cells synchronized so that they divided simultaneously, the researchers removed samples at intervals over a period of time sufficient for two cycles of cell division.

They submitted each sample to two kinds of analysis: (1) microscopic examination to determine the percentage of cells dividing (as shown by the presence of the cell plate formed during yeast cytokinesis) and (2) measurement of kinase activity in an extract of the cells (as indicated by phosphorylation of a standard protein). Control experiments established that the kinase activity they measured was due primarily to the *cdc2* protein kinase. In this way, they were able to see if an increase in enzymatic activity correlated with cell division.

RESULTS   The activity of the *cdc2* protein kinase varied during the cell cycle in a periodic way, rising to a peak just before mitosis and then falling.

CONCLUSION   The correlation between enzyme activity and the onset of mitosis, combined with evidence from other experiments that mitosis does not occur in the absence of *cdc2* kinase activity, supports the hypothesis that the *cdc2* kinase plays an essential role in triggering mitosis.

SOURCE   S. Moreno, J. Hayles, and P. Nurse, Regulation of p34^{cdc2} protein kinase during mitosis, *Cell* 58:361–372 (1989).

WHAT IF?   What results would you expect—for both kinase activity and percentage of cells dividing—if the cells tested were mutants completely deficient in the *cdc2* protein kinase?

---

rises and falls with changes in the concentration of its cyclin partner. **Figure 12.17a** shows the fluctuating activity of **MPF**, the cyclin-Cdk complex that was discovered first (in frog eggs). Note that the peaks of MPF activity correspond to the peaks of cyclin concentration. The cyclin level rises during the S and G$_2$ phases and then falls abruptly during M phase. (The red curve in Figure 12.16 shows the cyclic activity of the MPF in fission yeast.)

The initials MPF stand for "maturation-promoting factor," but we can think of MPF as "M-phase-promoting factor" be-

(a) Fluctuation of MPF activity and cyclin concentration during the cell cycle

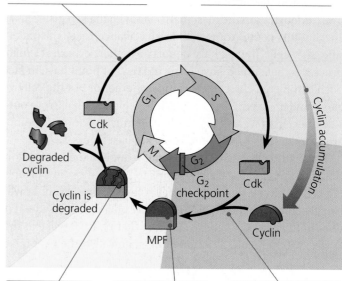

❺ During G$_1$, conditions in the cell favor degradation of cyclin, and the Cdk component of MPF is recycled.

❶ Synthesis of cyclin begins in late S phase and continues through G$_2$. Because cyclin is protected from degradation during this stage, it accumulates.

❹ During anaphase, the cyclin component of MPF is degraded, terminating the M phase. The cell enters the G$_1$ phase.

❸ MPF promotes mitosis by phosphorylating various proteins. MPF's activity peaks during metaphase.

❷ Accumulated cyclin molecules combine with recycled Cdk molecules, producing enough molecules of MPF for the cell to pass the G$_2$ checkpoint and initiate the events of mitosis.

(b) Molecular mechanisms that help regulate the cell cycle

▲ Figure 12.17 **Molecular control of the cell cycle at the G$_2$ checkpoint.** The steps of the cell cycle are timed by rhythmic fluctuations in the activity of cyclin-dependent kinases (Cdks). Here we focus on a cyclin-Cdk complex in animal cells called MPF, which acts at the G$_2$ checkpoint as a go-ahead signal, triggering the events of mitosis. (The Cdk of MPF is the same as the *cdc2* protein kinase of fission yeast featured in Figure 12.16.)

cause it triggers the cell's passage past the G$_2$ checkpoint into M phase **(Figure 12.17b)**. When cyclins that accumulate during G$_2$ associate with Cdk molecules, the resulting MPF complex phosphorylates a variety of proteins, initiating mitosis.

MPF acts both directly as a kinase and indirectly by activating other kinases. For example, MPF causes phosphorylation of various proteins of the nuclear lamina (see Figure 6.10), which promotes fragmentation of the nuclear envelope during prometaphase of mitosis. There is also evidence that MPF contributes to molecular events required for chromosome condensation and spindle formation during prophase.

During anaphase, MPF helps switch itself off by initiating a process that leads to the destruction of its own cyclin. The noncyclin part of MPF, the Cdk, persists in the cell in inactive form until it associates with new cyclin molecules synthesized during the S and G_2 phases of the next round of the cycle.

What controls cell behavior at the G_1 checkpoint? Animal cells appear to have at least three Cdk proteins and several different cyclins that operate at this checkpoint. The fluctuating activities of different cyclin-Cdk complexes are of major importance in controlling all the stages of the cell cycle.

Stop and Go Signs: Internal and External Signals at the Checkpoints

Research scientists are currently working out the pathways that link signals originating inside and outside the cell with the responses by cyclin-dependent kinases and other proteins. An example of an internal signal occurs at the M phase checkpoint. Anaphase, the separation of sister chromatids, does not begin until all the chromosomes are properly attached to the spindle at the metaphase plate. Researchers have learned that as long as some kinetochores are unattached to spindle microtubules, the sister chromatids remain together, delaying anaphase. Only when the kinetochores of all the chromosomes are attached to the spindle does the appropriate regulatory protein become activated. (In this case, the regulatory protein is not a Cdk.) Once activated, the protein sets off a chain of molecular events that ultimately results in the enzymatic cleavage of cohesins, allowing the sister chromatids to separate. This mechanism ensures that daughter cells do not end up with missing or extra chromosomes.

Studies using animal cells in culture have led to the identification of many external factors, both chemical and physical, that can influence cell division. For example, cells fail to divide if an essential nutrient is lacking in the culture medium. (This is analogous to trying to run an automatic washing machine without the water supply hooked up.) And even if all other conditions are favorable, most types of mammalian cells divide in culture only if the growth medium includes specific growth factors. As mentioned in Chapter 11, a **growth factor** is a protein released by certain cells that stimulates other cells to divide. Researchers have discovered more than 50 growth factors. Different cell types respond specifically to different growth factors or combinations of growth factors.

Consider, for example, *platelet-derived growth factor* (*PDGF*), which is made by blood cell fragments called platelets.

1. A sample of human connective tissue is cut up into small pieces.

Scalpels

Petri plate

2. Enzymes are used to digest the extracellular matrix in the tissue pieces, resulting in a suspension of free fibroblasts.

3. Cells are transferred to sterile culture vessels containing a basic growth medium consisting of glucose, amino acids, salts, and antibiotics (as a precaution against bacterial growth). PDGF is added to half the vessels. The culture vessels are incubated at 37°C.

Without PDGF

In the basic growth medium without PDGF (the control), the cells fail to divide.

With PDGF

In the basic growth medium plus PDGF, the cells proliferate. The SEM shows cultured fibroblasts.

10 μm

▲ Figure 12.18 **The effect of a growth factor on cell division.** As this experiment shows, adding platelet-derived growth factor (PDGF) to human fibroblasts in culture causes the cells to proliferate.

? *PDGF is known to signal cells by binding to a cell-surface receptor that is a receptor tyrosine kinase. If you added a chemical that prevented phosphorylation of this receptor, how would the results differ?*

The experiment illustrated in **Figure 12.18** demonstrates that PDGF is required for the division of fibroblasts in culture. Fibroblasts, a type of connective tissue cell, have PDGF receptors on their plasma membranes. The binding of PDGF molecules to these receptors (which are receptor tyrosine kinases; see Chapter 11) triggers a signal transduction pathway that allows the cells to pass the G_1 checkpoint and divide. PDGF stimulates fibroblast division not only in the artificial conditions of cell culture, but in an animal's body as well. When an injury occurs, platelets release PDGF in the vicinity. The resulting proliferation of fibroblasts helps heal the wound.

The effect of an external physical factor on cell division is clearly seen in **density-dependent inhibition**, a phenomenon in which crowded cells stop dividing **(Figure 12.19a)**. As first observed many years ago, cultured cells normally divide until they form a single layer of cells on the inner surface of the culture container, at which point the cells stop dividing. If some cells are removed, those bordering the open space begin dividing again and continue until the vacancy is filled. Recent studies have revealed that the binding of a cell-surface protein to its counterpart on an adjoining cell sends a growth-inhibiting signal to both cells, preventing them from moving forward in the cell cycle, even in the presence of growth factors.

Most animal cells also exhibit **anchorage dependence** (see Figure 12.19a). To divide, they must be attached to a substratum, such as the inside of a culture jar or the extracellular matrix of a tissue. Experiments suggest that like cell density, anchorage is signaled to the cell cycle control system via pathways involving plasma membrane proteins and elements of the cytoskeleton linked to them.

Density-dependent inhibition and anchorage dependence appear to function in the body's tissues as well as in cell culture, checking the growth of cells at some optimal density and location. Cancer cells, which we discuss next, exhibit neither density-dependent inhibition nor anchorage dependence **(Figure 12.19b)**.

Loss of Cell Cycle Controls in Cancer Cells

Cancer cells do not heed the normal signals that regulate the cell cycle. They divide excessively and invade other tissues. If unchecked, they can kill the organism.

In addition to their lack of density-dependent inhibition and anchorage dependence, cancer cells do not stop dividing when growth factors are depleted. A logical hypothesis is that cancer cells do not need growth factors in their culture medium to grow and divide. They may make a required growth factor themselves, or they may have an abnormality in the signaling pathway that conveys the growth factor's signal to the cell cycle control system even in the absence of that factor. Another possibility is an abnormal cell cycle control system. In fact, as you will learn in Chapter 18, these are all conditions that may lead to cancer.

There are other important differences between normal cells and cancer cells that reflect derangements of the cell cycle. If and when they stop dividing, cancer cells do so at random points in the cycle, rather than at the normal checkpoints. Moreover, can-

(a) **Normal mammalian cells.** Contact with neighboring cells and the availability of nutrients, growth factors, and a substratum for attachment limit cell density to a single layer.

(b) **Cancer cells.** Cancer cells usually continue to divide well beyond a single layer, forming a clump of overlapping cells. They do not exhibit anchorage dependence or density-dependent inhibition.

▲ Figure 12.19 **Density-dependent inhibition and anchorage dependence of cell division.** Individual cells are shown disproportionately large in the drawings.

cer cells can go on dividing indefinitely in culture if they are given a continual supply of nutrients; in essence, they are "immortal." A striking example is a cell line that has been reproducing in culture since 1951. Cells of this line are called HeLa cells because their original source was a tumor removed from a woman named Henrietta Lacks. By contrast, nearly all normal mammalian cells growing in culture divide only about 20 to 50 times before they stop dividing, age, and die. (We'll see a possible reason for this phenomenon when we discuss chromosome replication in Chapter 16.)

The abnormal behavior of cancer cells can be catastrophic when it occurs in the body. The problem begins when a single cell in a tissue undergoes **transformation**, the process that converts a normal cell to a cancer cell. The body's immune system normally recognizes a transformed cell as an insurgent and destroys it. However, if the cell evades destruction, it may proliferate and form a tumor, a mass of abnormal cells within otherwise normal tissue. If the abnormal cells remain at the original site, the lump is called a **benign tumor**. Most benign tumors do not cause serious problems and can be completely removed by surgery. In contrast, a **malignant tumor** becomes invasive enough to impair the functions of one or more organs (Figure 12.20). An individual with a malignant tumor is said to have cancer.

The cells of malignant tumors are abnormal in many ways besides their excessive proliferation. They may have unusual numbers of chromosomes (whether this is a cause or an effect of transformation is a current topic of debate). Their metabolism may be disabled, and they may cease to function in any constructive way. Abnormal changes on the cell surface cause cancer cells to lose attachments to neighboring cells and the extracellular matrix, which allows them to spread into nearby tissues. Cancer cells may also secrete signal molecules that cause blood vessels to grow toward the tumor. A few tumor cells may separate from the original tumor, enter blood vessels and lymph vessels, and travel to other parts of the body. There, they may proliferate and form a new tumor. This spread of cancer cells to locations distant from their original site is called **metastasis** (see Figure 12.20).

A tumor that appears to be localized may be treated with high-energy radiation, which damages DNA in cancer cells much more than it does in normal cells, apparently because the majority of cancer cells have lost the ability to repair such damage. To treat known or suspected metastatic tumors, chemotherapy is used, in which drugs that are toxic to actively dividing cells are administered through the circulatory system. As you might expect, chemotherapeutic drugs interfere with specific steps in the cell cycle. For example, the drug Taxol freezes the mitotic spindle by preventing microtubule depolymerization, which stops actively dividing cells from proceeding past metaphase. The side effects of chemotherapy are due to the drugs' effects on normal cells that divide often. For example, nausea results from chemotherapy's effects on intestinal cells, hair loss from effects on hair follicle cells, and susceptibility to infection from effects on immune system cells.

Researchers are beginning to understand how a normal cell is transformed into a cancer cell. You will learn more about the molecular biology of cancer in Chapter 18. Though the causes of cancer are diverse, cellular transformation always involves the alteration of genes that somehow influence the cell cycle control system. Our knowledge of how changes in the genome lead to the various abnormalities of cancer cells remains rudimentary, however.

Perhaps the reason we have so many unanswered questions about cancer cells is that there is still so much to learn about how normal cells function. The cell, life's basic unit of structure and function, holds enough secrets to engage researchers well into the future.

CONCEPT CHECK 12.3

1. In Figure 12.13, why do the nuclei resulting from experiment 2 contain different amounts of DNA?
2. What is the go-ahead signal for a cell to pass the G_2 phase checkpoint and enter mitosis? (See Figure 12.17.)
3. What phase are most of your body cells in?
4. Compare and contrast a benign tumor and a malignant tumor.
5. **WHAT IF?** What would happen if you performed the experiment in Figure 12.18 with cancer cells?

For suggested answers, see Appendix A.

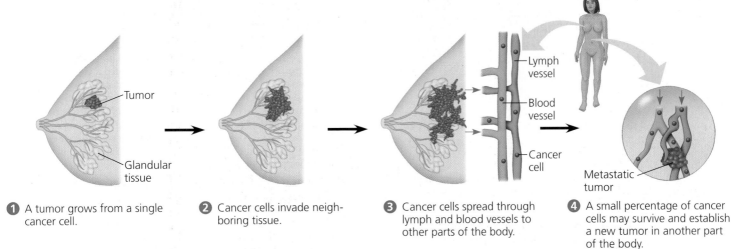

① A tumor grows from a single cancer cell.

② Cancer cells invade neighboring tissue.

③ Cancer cells spread through lymph and blood vessels to other parts of the body.

④ A small percentage of cancer cells may survive and establish a new tumor in another part of the body.

▲ **Figure 12.20 The growth and metastasis of a malignant breast tumor.** The cells of malignant (cancerous) tumors grow in an uncontrolled way and can spread to neighboring tissues and, via lymph and blood vessels, to other parts of the body. The spread of cancer cells beyond their original site is called metastasis.

MEDIA Go to the Study Area at **www.masteringbio.com** for BioFlix 3-D Animations, MP3 Tutors, Videos, Practice Tests, an eBook, and more.

SUMMARY OF KEY CONCEPTS

▶ Unicellular organisms reproduce by cell division; multicellular organisms depend on cell division for their development from a fertilized egg and for growth and repair.

MEDIA

Activity Roles of Cell Division

CONCEPT 12.1

Cell division results in genetically identical daughter cells (pp. 229–230)

▶ Cells duplicate their genetic material before they divide, ensuring that each daughter cell receives an exact copy of the genetic material, DNA.

▶ **Cellular Organization of the Genetic Material** DNA is partitioned among chromosomes. Eukaryotic chromosomes consist of chromatin, a complex of DNA and protein that condenses during mitosis. In animals, gametes have one set of chromosomes and somatic cells have two sets.

▶ **Distribution of Chromosomes During Eukaryotic Cell Division** In preparation for cell division, chromosomes replicate, each one then consisting of two identical sister chromatids joined along their lengths by sister chromatid cohesion. When this cohesion is broken, the chromatids separate during cell division, becoming the chromosomes of the new daughter cells. Eukaryotic cell division consists of mitosis (division of the nucleus) and cytokinesis (division of the cytoplasm).

CONCEPT 12.2

The mitotic phase alternates with interphase in the cell cycle (pp. 230–238)

▶ **Phases of the Cell Cycle** Between divisions, cells are in interphase: the G_1, S, and G_2 phases. The cell grows throughout interphase, but DNA is replicated only during the synthesis (S) phase. Mitosis and cytokinesis make up the mitotic (M) phase of the cell cycle.

▶ **The Mitotic Spindle: *A Closer Look*** The mitotic spindle is an apparatus of microtubules that controls chromosome movement during mitosis. In animal cells, the spindle arises from the centrosomes and includes spindle microtubules and asters. Some spindle microtubules attach to the kinetochores of chromosomes and move the chromosomes to the metaphase plate. In anaphase, sister chromatids separate, and motor proteins move them along the kinetochore microtubules toward opposite ends of the cell. Meanwhile, motor proteins push nonkinetochore microtubules from opposite poles away from each other, elongating the cell. In telophase, genetically identical daughter nuclei form at opposite ends of the cell.

▶ **Cytokinesis: *A Closer Look*** Mitosis is usually followed by cytokinesis. Animal cells carry out cytokinesis by cleavage, and plant cells form a cell plate.

▶ **Binary Fission** During binary fission in bacteria, the chromosome replicates and the two daughter chromosomes actively move apart. The specific proteins involved in this movement are a subject of current research.

▶ **The Evolution of Mitosis** Since prokaryotes preceded eukaryotes by more than a billion years, it is likely that mitosis evolved from prokaryotic cell division. Certain protists exhibit types of cell division that seem intermediate between bacterial binary fission and the process of mitosis carried out by most eukaryotic cells.

MEDIA

BioFlix 3-D Animation Mitosis
MP3 Tutor Mitosis
Activity The Cell Cycle
Activity Mitosis and Cytokinesis Animation
Activity Mitosis and Cytokinesis Video
Investigation How Much Time Do Cells Spend in Each Phase of Mitosis?

CONCEPT 12.3

The eukaryotic cell cycle is regulated by a molecular control system (pp. 238–243)

▶ **Evidence for Cytoplasmic Signals** Molecules present in the cytoplasm regulate progress through the cell cycle.

▶ **The Cell Cycle Control System** Cyclic changes in regulatory proteins work as a cell cycle clock. The clock has specific checkpoints where the cell cycle stops until a go-ahead signal is received. The key molecules are cyclins and cyclin-dependent kinases (Cdks). Cell culture has enabled researchers to study the molecular details of cell division. Both internal signals and external signals control the cell cycle checkpoints via signal transduction pathways. Most cells exhibit density-dependent inhibition of cell division as well as anchorage dependence.

▶ **Loss of Cell Cycle Controls in Cancer Cells** Cancer cells elude normal regulation and divide out of control, forming tumors. Malignant tumors invade surrounding tissues and can metastasize, exporting cancer cells to other parts of the body, where they may form secondary tumors.

MEDIA

Activity Causes of Cancer

SELF-QUIZ

1. Through a microscope, you can see a cell plate beginning to develop across the middle of a cell and nuclei re-forming on either side of the cell plate. This cell is most likely
   a. an animal cell in the process of cytokinesis.
   b. a plant cell in the process of cytokinesis.
   c. an animal cell in the S phase of the cell cycle.
   d. a bacterial cell dividing.
   e. a plant cell in metaphase.

2. Vinblastine is a standard chemotherapeutic drug used to treat cancer. Because it interferes with the assembly of microtubules, its effectiveness must be related to
   a. disruption of mitotic spindle formation.
   b. inhibition of regulatory protein phosphorylation.
   c. suppression of cyclin production.
   d. myosin denaturation and inhibition of cleavage furrow formation.
   e. inhibition of DNA synthesis.

3. A particular cell has half as much DNA as some other cells in a mitotically active tissue. The cell in question is most likely in
   a. G_1.   d. metaphase.
   b. G_2.   e. anaphase.
   c. prophase.

4. One difference between cancer cells and normal cells is that cancer cells
   a. are unable to synthesize DNA.
   b. are arrested at the S phase of the cell cycle.
   c. continue to divide even when they are tightly packed together.
   d. cannot function properly because they are affected by density-dependent inhibition.
   e. are always in the M phase of the cell cycle.

5. The decline of MPF activity at the end of mitosis is due to
   a. the destruction of the protein kinase Cdk.
   b. decreased synthesis of cyclin.
   c. the degradation of cyclin.
   d. synthesis of DNA.
   e. an increase in the cell's volume-to-genome ratio.

6. The drug cytochalasin B blocks the function of actin. Which of the following aspects of the cell cycle would be most disrupted by cytochalasin B?
   a. spindle formation
   b. spindle attachment to kinetochores
   c. DNA synthesis
   d. cell elongation during anaphase
   e. cleavage furrow formation

7. In the cells of some organisms, mitosis occurs without cytokinesis. This will result in
   a. cells with more than one nucleus.
   b. cells that are unusually small.
   c. cells lacking nuclei.
   d. destruction of chromosomes.
   e. cell cycles lacking an S phase.

8. Which of the following does *not* occur during mitosis?
   a. condensation of the chromosomes
   b. replication of the DNA
   c. separation of sister chromatids
   d. spindle formation
   e. separation of the spindle poles

9. In the light micrograph below of dividing cells near the tip of an onion root, identify a cell in each of the following stages: prophase, prometaphase, metaphase, anaphase, and telophase. Describe the major events occurring at each stage.

10. **DRAW IT** Draw one eukaryotic chromosome as it would appear during interphase, during each of the stages of mitosis, and during cytokinesis. Also draw and label the nuclear envelope and any microtubules attached to the chromosome(s).

For Self-Quiz answers, see Appendix A.

MEDIA Visit the Study Area at **www.masteringbio.com** for a Practice Test.

EVOLUTION CONNECTION

11. The result of mitosis is that the daughter cells end up with the same number of chromosomes that the parent cell had. Another way to maintain the number of chromosomes would be to carry out cell division first and then duplicate the chromosomes in each daughter cell. Do you think this would be an equally good way of organizing the cell cycle? Why do you suppose that evolution has not led to this alternative?

SCIENTIFIC INQUIRY

12. Although both ends of a microtubule can gain or lose subunits, one end (called the plus end) polymerizes and depolymerizes at a higher rate than the other end (the minus end). For spindle microtubules, the plus ends are in the center of the spindle, and the minus ends are at the poles. Motor proteins that move on microtubules specialize in walking either toward the plus end or toward the minus end; the two types are called plus end–directed and minus end–directed motor proteins, respectively. Given what you know about chromosome movement and spindle changes during anaphase, predict which type of motor proteins would be present on (a) kinetochore microtubules and (b) nonkinetochore microtubules.

UNIT 3

Genetics

AN INTERVIEW WITH
Terry L. Orr-Weaver

How the daughter cells resulting from cell division end up with equal numbers of chromosomes is the focus of much of Terry Orr-Weaver's research; she also studies how cells control the DNA replication that precedes cell division. Her research group has identified a number of proteins involved in these processes. A professor of biology at MIT and the first woman to become a member of the Whitehead Institute for Biomedical Research, Dr. Orr-Weaver has an undergraduate degree in chemistry from UC San Diego and a Ph.D. in biological chemistry from Harvard. She is a member of the U.S. National Academy of Sciences and a past president of the Genetics Society of America.

After receiving your Ph.D., you switched from using single-celled yeast as your model organism to the multicelled fruit fly *Drosophila melanogaster*. Why?

I was excited by the possibility of working at the interface of two fields. At that time, the cell cycle field was exploding from work with single cells—mainly yeasts and mammalian cells grown in culture—and biochemical experiments using extracts. Meanwhile, developmental biology was entering a new era with the discovery of pattern formation genes. I realized there was a key question at the interface of these two fields that was being ignored: If an organism starts as a single cell and ends up as a multicellular entity, how are pattern and cell divisions coordinated? And I realized there had to be intrinsic regulation from the cell cycle components but also extrinsic developmental control feeding into that. This was clearly going to be an important area of study.

In choosing a multicellular model organism, why use *Drosophila*?

A lot of fundamental discoveries in biology have been made with fruit flies. For example, it was research with *Drosophila* that established in 1916 that chromosomes were the physical basis of inheritance, the structures that carried the genes. Decades later, the master regulatory genes that set up the animal body plan in embryonic development were discovered in *Drosophila*. These genes determine, for example, where the fly's head is and where its legs are. Then, to the amazement of biologists, it turned out that exactly the same genes control how the human body plan is set up! So *Drosophila* has a really rich heritage. When I started working on *Drosophila*, it had a 70-year-long history of use in genetics, providing an incredible array of knowledge and methods.

How do geneticists approach biological questions?

Geneticists want to discover the genes that are involved in a biological process and then figure out what the genes do. First, you decide what process you're interested in—in our case, how chromosomes get partitioned during cell division. Next, you figure out what you would see if you had a mutant in which that process was perturbed—how would you recognize it? Then you generate mutations, usually with the help of high-energy radiation or a chemical, hoping that one or more of the resulting mutants are affected in the process of interest. What you're doing by making a mutation is generating a disease state in your organism. When you've found a mutant you're interested in, you can find out what gene has been made defective, and you know that that gene has to play an important role in the process you're interested in.

Now that we have the genome sequences of many organisms, including the fruit fly and the human, you might think that all their genes are known—so what's to discover? But it turned out that we didn't know the functions of many of the genes that showed up in genome sequences. Even in an organism as simple and well-studied as yeast, at the publication of the genome sequence we didn't know what 70% of the genes did. And we still don't have a clue about half of the human genes. So having genome sequences provides a foundation, but we must still find out what all the genes do, and we geneticists feel the best way to go about this is to use genetics.

A big and useful surprise in this gene-discovery enterprise has been how many genes have been "conserved" through evolutionary history and are still very similar in organisms as distantly related as fruit flies and humans. It's very hard to figure out directly what human genes do. But when we discover a new gene in *Drosophila*, invariably it turns out that there's a similar gene in humans that does the same thing. So *Drosophila* turns out to be an even better model organism than we had guessed.

Besides genetics, what other approaches and methods do you use?

A combination of genetics, biochemistry, and cell biology turns out to be incredibly powerful for our research. For instance, with the microscope, a tool of cell biology, we can literally watch the chromosomes as they undergo mitosis or meiosis. If we have a mutation causing a defect in one of those processes, we can look directly at how the chromosomes behave in mutant cells. And in our research on DNA replication, we can look directly at proteins that attach to the DNA during DNA replication. In this lab, we try to do things as directly as possible!

Here's an example from our work on DNA replication in *Drosophila*. Using a genetic approach, we discovered a mutant that couldn't carry out DNA replication—although such a mutant can live and grow for a while by using proteins its mother stockpiled in the egg. It looked like the gene affected might code for a really important protein. But we wanted to find out if it was a protein that played a *direct* role in DNA replication, and we couldn't tell that from the genetics alone. However, by labeling the normal version of the protein with a fluorescent tag, we could use the microscope to see where the protein was located in cells, and we saw that the protein got on the DNA right at a place where DNA synthesis starts. That established that this protein was directly involved.

How is meiosis different from mitosis?

Let me first review mitosis. After a cell duplicates its DNA, mitosis ensures that each duplicated chromosome gets partitioned to the

246

daughter cells so that you end up with two cells that have exactly the same DNA content and chromosome number. That's what happens in normal cell division.

But what about making a sperm or an egg? In fertilization, a sperm and egg are going to fuse and give rise to a new progeny. If the organism is diploid—that is, has two similar copies of each chromosome, as flies and humans do—and the progeny is going to be diploid, then you've got to make sperm and eggs that have only one copy of each chromosome, so that when those sperm and egg come together you restore the right chromosome number. And to produce sperm and eggs with only half the diploid chromosome number, you need a special kind of cell division—meiosis. There has to be a way to bring together the two similar copies of each chromosome and then pull them apart, with each going to a different daughter cell. In meiosis, there is an extra round of chromosome partitioning where what we call the homologous pairs of chromosomes—the chromosome that initially came from dad and the similar chromosome that came from mom—get separated from each other. To sum up, in mitosis you're separating identical copies of each chromosome, whereas in meiosis you have an extra round of division stuck in there, where the copy of each chromosome from dad and the copy from mom get separated from each other.

What important questions about meiosis still need to be answered?

What we don't understand at all is how the chromosomes of a homologous pair find each other. That pairing is unique to meiosis; it doesn't happen in mitosis. The two strands of the DNA don't come apart, so although the homologous chromosomes have very similar DNA sequences, it's not base-pairing that brings the homologous chromosomes together. Given the relatively gigantic volume of the nucleus and the huge mass of chromatin in a eukaryotic cell, how do the right chromosomes find each other? That's the number one mystery about meiosis. And I would say the second big mystery is why humans are so unbelievably bad at carrying out meiosis.

What makes you say that? Are we worse than fruit flies?

We're about a thousand times worse. Here are some amazing statistics: Twenty percent of recognized pregnancies end in spontaneous miscarriage, and out of those at least half are due to a mistake during meiosis. And for every pregnancy that proceeds far enough to be recognized, there have been many that ended without being recognized. So about 10–20% of the time meiosis doesn't work properly in humans. In fruit flies, meiosis seems to occur inaccurately only 0.01–0.05% of the time. Even mice, which are mammals like ourselves, do much better than humans. So I would call this the second big mystery regarding meiosis: Why are humans so bad at it?

Tell us more about what happens when meiosis doesn't work correctly.

Most of the time the result is early death of the embryo. In humans, if any chromosome other than X or Y is present in only one copy or more than two copies, the embryo dies very early. The only exceptions are for chromosomes number 13, 18, and 21: When one of these is present in three copies, the embyo usually dies at an early stage, but it may survive. Even in the case of Down syndrome, a relatively common condition where a person has three copies of chromosome 21, only a minority of fetuses survive to term. And when the individual does survive, there are serious effects.

In fact, errors in meiosis are the leading cause of mental retardation in the United States. Some scientists argue that, in evolutionary terms, the human species is able to cope with such a high rate of meiotic errors because most of the pregnancies are lost very early.

What do you like best about research?

What's so great about research is that you get to unwrap presents all the time! When you find an interesting mutant, it's like a beautifully wrapped present. And then you unwrap it, and it can be a big surprise to learn which gene is affected and what its protein product is. Sometimes you unwrap it and it's beautiful and satisfying and completely makes sense; other times you don't at first understand what the gift is, and then you have to figure that out. I want to tell students how wonderful it is getting these presents to unwrap. But they also need to realize that it might take three years to get the ribbon and all the tape off. It can take some real patience to unwrap the present!

In your view, how important is it for scientists to reach out beyond the scientific community?

I think scientists do have an obligation to educate the public. It's especially critical for people to understand the importance of basic research and the study of model organisms. Because if we shortchange basic research, in the long run we won't be able to benefit from medical applications. The reason we've done so well in this country is our willingness to invest in basic research science.

The challenge is figuring out how to convey a message like this in an era of soundbites. The media and the public want to hear that a piece of research is directly going to cure a disease. So how can we get a message across that requires an explanation more complex than a catchphrase? There are many stories we can tell where discoveries in basic research have led to very important applications, but these stories take at least a couple of paragraphs to communicate. Also, there's a real need for scientists to try to build a bridge between science and the public.

It's especially important to educate our representatives in government. A coalition of several biology societies, including the Genetics Society of America, has a Joint Steering Committee for Public Policy, which has been terrific in educating members of Congress and their staffs. They bring in scientists to explain their research and why investing in research is important. Maybe that's a good starting point.

When you find an interesting mutant, it's like a beautifully wrapped present . . . and it can be a big surprise . . .

Inquiry in Action

Learn about an experiment by Terry Orr-Weaver in Inquiry Figure 16.22 on page 322.

Jane Reece and Terry Orr-Weaver

Meiosis and Sexual Life Cycles

13

▲ **Figure 13.1 What accounts for family resemblance?**

OVERVIEW

Variations on a Theme

Most people who send out birth announcements mention the sex of the baby, but they don't feel the need to specify that their offspring is a human being! One of the characteristics of life is the ability of organisms to reproduce their own kind—elephants produce little elephants, and oak trees generate oak saplings. Exceptions to this rule show up only as sensational but highly suspect stories in tabloid newspapers.

Another rule often taken for granted is that offspring resemble their parents more than they do unrelated individuals. If you examine the family members shown in **Figure 13.1**—Sissy Spacek and Jack Fisk with daughters Madison and Schuyler Fisk—you can pick out some similar features among them. The transmission of traits from one generation to the next is called inheritance, or **heredity** (from the Latin *heres*, heir). However, sons and daughters are not identical copies of either parent or of their siblings. Along with inherited similarity, there is also **variation**. Farmers have exploited the principles of heredity and variation for thousands of years, breeding plants and animals for desired traits. But what are the biological mechanisms leading to the hereditary similarity and variation that we call a "family resemblance"? This question eluded biologists until the development of genetics in the 20th century.

Genetics is the scientific study of heredity and hereditary variation. In this unit, you will learn about genetics at multiple levels, from organisms to cells to molecules. On the practical side, you will see how genetics continues to revolutionize medicine and agriculture, and you will be asked to consider some social and ethical questions raised by our ability to manipulate DNA, the genetic material. At the end of the unit, you will be able to stand back and consider the whole genome, an organism's entire complement of DNA. The rapid accumulation of the genome sequences of many species, including our own, has taught us a great deal about evolution on the molecular level—in other words, evolution of the genome itself. In fact, genetic methods and discoveries are catalyzing progress in all areas of biology, from cell biology to physiology, developmental biology, behavior, and even ecology.

We begin our study of genetics in this chapter by examining how chromosomes pass from parents to offspring in sexually reproducing organisms. The processes of meiosis (a special type of cell division) and fertilization (the fusion of sperm and egg) maintain a species' chromosome count during the sexual life cycle. We will describe the cellular mechanics of meiosis and how this process differs from mitosis. Finally, we will consider how both meiosis and fertilization contribute to genetic variation, such as the variation obvious in the family shown in Figure 13.1.

CONCEPT 13.1
Offspring acquire genes from parents by inheriting chromosomes

Family friends may tell you that you have your mother's freckles or your father's eyes. However, parents do not, in any literal sense, give their children freckles, eyes, hair, or any other traits. What, then, *is* actually inherited?

Inheritance of Genes

Parents endow their offspring with coded information in the form of hereditary units called **genes**. The genes we inherit from our mothers and fathers are our genetic link to our parents, and they account for family resemblances such as shared eye color or freckles. Our genes program the specific traits that emerge as we develop from fertilized eggs into adults.

The genetic program is written in the language of DNA, the polymer of four different nucleotides you learned about in Chapters 1 and 5. Inherited information is passed on in the form of each gene's specific sequence of DNA nucleotides, much as printed information is communicated in the form of meaningful sequences of letters. In both cases, the language is symbolic. Just as your brain translates the word *apple* into a mental image of the fruit, cells translate genes into freckles and other features. Most genes program cells to synthesize specific enzymes and other proteins, whose cumulative action produces an organism's inherited traits. The programming of these traits in the form of DNA is one of the unifying themes of biology.

The transmission of hereditary traits has its molecular basis in the precise replication of DNA, which produces copies of genes that can be passed along from parents to offspring. In animals and plants, reproductive cells called **gametes** are the vehicles that transmit genes from one generation to the next. During fertilization, male and female gametes (sperm and eggs) unite, thereby passing on genes of both parents to their offspring.

Except for small amounts of DNA in mitochondria and chloroplasts, the DNA of a eukaryotic cell is packaged into chromosomes within the nucleus. Every living species has a characteristic number of chromosomes. For example, humans have 46 chromosomes in almost all of their cells. Each chromosome consists of a single long DNA molecule elaborately coiled in association with various proteins. One chromosome includes several hundred to a few thousand genes, each of which is a specific sequence of nucleotides within the DNA molecule. A gene's specific location along the length of a chromosome is called the gene's **locus** (from the Latin, meaning "place"; plural, *loci*). Our genetic endowment consists of the genes carried on the chromosomes we inherited from our parents.

Comparison of Asexual and Sexual Reproduction

Only organisms that reproduce asexually produce offspring that are exact copies of themselves. In **asexual reproduction**, a single individual is the sole parent and passes copies of all its genes to its offspring. For example, single-celled eukaryotic organisms can reproduce asexually by mitotic cell division, in which DNA is copied and allocated equally to two daughter cells. The genomes of the offspring are virtually exact copies of the parent's genome. Some multicellular organisms are also

(a) Hydra **(b) Redwoods**

▲ **Figure 13.2 Asexual reproduction in two multicellular organisms. (a)** This relatively simple animal, a hydra, reproduces by budding. The bud, a localized mass of mitotically dividing cells, develops into a small hydra, which detaches from the parent (LM). **(b)** Each tree in this circle of redwoods grew from a single parent tree, whose stump is in the center of the circle.

capable of reproducing asexually **(Figure 13.2)**. Because the cells of the offspring are derived by mitosis in the parent, the "chip off the old block" is usually genetically identical to its parent. An individual that reproduces asexually gives rise to a **clone**, a group of genetically identical individuals. Genetic differences occasionally arise in asexually reproducing organisms as a result of changes in the DNA called mutations, which we will discuss in Chapter 17.

In **sexual reproduction**, two parents give rise to offspring that have unique combinations of genes inherited from the two parents. In contrast to a clone, offspring of sexual reproduction vary genetically from their siblings and both parents: They are variations on a common theme of family resemblance, not exact replicas. Genetic variation like that shown in Figure 13.1 is an important consequence of sexual reproduction. What mechanisms generate this genetic variation? The key is the behavior of chromosomes during the sexual life cycle.

CONCEPT CHECK 13.1

1. How are the traits of parents (such as hair color) transmitted to their offspring?
2. Explain how asexually reproducing organisms produce offspring that are genetically identical to each other and to their parents.
3. **WHAT IF?** A horticulturalist breeds orchids, trying to obtain a plant with a unique combination of desirable traits. After many years, she finally succeeds. To produce more plants like this one, should she breed it or clone it? Why?

For suggested answers, see Appendix A.

CONCEPT 13.2

Fertilization and meiosis alternate in sexual life cycles

A **life cycle** is the generation-to-generation sequence of stages in the reproductive history of an organism, from conception to production of its own offspring. In this section, we use humans as an example to track the behavior of chromosomes through sexual life cycles. We begin by considering the chromosome count in human somatic cells and gametes; we will then explore how the behavior of chromosomes relates to the human life cycle and other types of sexual life cycles.

Sets of Chromosomes in Human Cells

In humans, each **somatic cell**—any cell other than those involved in gamete formation—has 46 chromosomes. During mitosis, the chromosomes become condensed enough to be visible in a light microscope. Because chromosomes differ in size, in the positions of their centromeres, and in the pattern of colored bands produced by certain stains, they can be distinguished from one another by microscopic examination when sufficiently condensed.

Careful examination of a micrograph of the 46 human chromosomes from a single cell in mitosis reveals that there are two chromosomes of each of 23 types. This becomes clear when images of the chromosomes are arranged in pairs, starting with the longest chromosomes. The resulting ordered display is called a **karyotype (Figure 13.3)**. The two chromosomes composing a pair have the same length, centromere position, and staining pattern: These are called **homologous chromosomes**, or homologs. Both chromosomes of each pair carry genes controlling the same inherited characters. For example, if a gene for eye color is situated at a particular locus on a certain chromosome, then the homolog of that chromosome will also have a gene specifying eye color at the equivalent locus.

The two distinct chromosomes referred to as X and Y are an important exception to the general pattern of homologous chromosomes in human somatic cells. Human females have a homologous pair of X chromosomes (XX), but males have one X and one Y chromosome (XY). Only small parts of the X and Y are homologous. Most of the genes carried on the X chromosome do not have counterparts on the tiny Y, and the Y chromosome has genes lacking on the X. Because they determine an individual's sex, the X and Y chromosomes are called **sex chromosomes**. The other chromosomes are called **autosomes**.

The occurrence of homologous pairs of chromosomes in each human somatic cell is a consequence of our sexual origins. We inherit one chromosome of each pair from each parent. Thus, the 46 chromosomes in our somatic cells are actually two sets of 23 chromosomes—a maternal set (from our mother)

▼ **Figure 13.3** **Research Method**

Preparing a karyotype

APPLICATION A karyotype is a display of condensed chromosomes arranged in pairs. Karyotyping can be used to screen for abnormal numbers of chromosomes or defective chromosomes associated with certain congenital disorders, such as Down syndrome.

TECHNIQUE Karyotypes are prepared from isolated somatic cells, which are treated with a drug to stimulate mitosis and then grown in culture for several days. Cells arrested in metaphase are stained and then viewed with a microscope equipped with a digital camera. A photograph of the chromosomes is displayed on a computer monitor, and the images of the chromosomes are arranged into pairs according to size and shape.

Pair of homologous replicated chromosomes

Centromere

5 µm

Sister chromatids

Metaphase chromosome

RESULTS This karyotype shows the chromosomes from a normal human male. The size of the chromosome, position of the centromere, and pattern of stained bands help identify specific chromosomes. Although difficult to discern in the karyotype, each metaphase chromosome consists of two closely attached sister chromatids (see the diagram of a pair of homologous replicated chromosomes).

and a paternal set (from our father). The number of chromosomes in a single set is represented by *n*. Any cell with two chromosome sets is called a **diploid cell** and has a diploid number of chromosomes, abbreviated $2n$. For humans, the diploid number is 46 ($2n = 46$), the number of chromosomes in our somatic cells. In a cell in which DNA synthesis has occurred, all the chromosomes are replicated, and therefore each consists of two identical sister chromatids, associated closely at the centromere and along the arms. **Figure 13.4** helps clarify the various terms that we use in describing replicated chromosomes in a diploid cell. Study this figure so that you understand the differences between homologous chromosomes, sister chromatids, nonsister chromatids, and chromosome sets.

Unlike somatic cells, gametes (sperm and eggs) contain a single chromosome set. Such cells are called **haploid cells**, and each has a haploid number of chromosomes (*n*). For humans, the haploid number is 23 ($n = 23$). The set of 23 consists of the 22 autosomes plus a single sex chromosome. An unfertilized egg contains an X chromosome, but a sperm may contain an X or a Y chromosome.

Note that each sexually reproducing species has a characteristic diploid number and haploid number. For example, the fruit fly, *Drosophila melanogaster*, has a diploid number of 8 and a haploid number of 4, while dogs have a diploid number of 78 and a haploid number of 39.

Now that you have learned the concepts of diploid and haploid numbers of chromosomes, let's consider chromosome behavior during sexual life cycles. We'll use the human life cycle as an example.

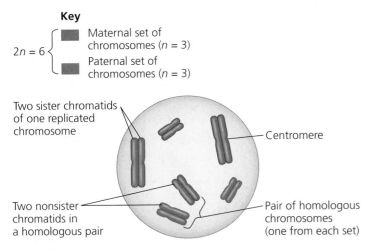

▲ **Figure 13.4 Describing chromosomes.** A cell with a diploid number of 6 ($2n = 6$) is depicted here following chromosome replication and condensation. Each of the six replicated chromosomes consists of two sister chromatids associated closely along their lengths. Each homologous pair is composed of one chromosome from the maternal set (red) and one from the paternal set (blue). Each set is made up of three chromosomes in this example. Nonsister chromatids are any two chromatids in a pair of homologous chromosomes that are not sister chromatids.

? *What is the haploid number of this cell? Is a "set" of chromosomes haploid or diploid?*

Behavior of Chromosome Sets in the Human Life Cycle

The human life cycle begins when a haploid sperm from the father fuses with a haploid egg from the mother. This union of gametes, culminating in fusion of their nuclei, is called **fertilization**. The resulting fertilized egg, or **zygote**, is diploid because it contains two haploid sets of chromosomes bearing genes representing the maternal and paternal family lines. As a human develops into a sexually mature adult, mitosis of the zygote and its descendants generates all the somatic cells of the body. Both chromosome sets in the zygote and all the genes they carry are passed with precision to the somatic cells.

The only cells of the human body not produced by mitosis are the gametes, which develop from specialized cells called *germ cells* in the gonads—ovaries in females and testes in males **(Figure 13.5)**. Imagine what would happen if human gametes were made by mitosis: They would be diploid like the somatic cells. At the next round of fertilization, when two gametes fused, the normal chromosome number of 46 would double to 92, and each subsequent generation would double the

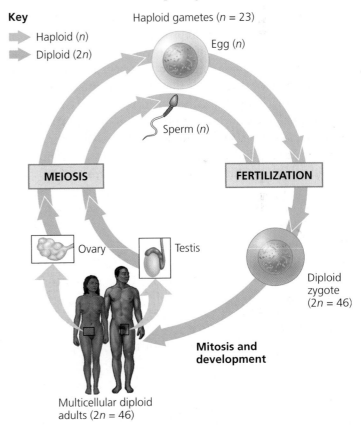

▲ **Figure 13.5 The human life cycle.** In each generation, the number of chromosome sets doubles at fertilization, but is halved during meiosis. For humans, the number of chromosomes in a haploid cell is 23, consisting of one set ($n = 23$); the number of chromosomes in the diploid zygote and all somatic cells arising from it is 46, consisting of two sets ($2n = 46$).

This figure introduces a color code that will be used for other life cycles later in this book. The teal arrows highlight haploid stages of a life cycle, and the beige arrows highlight diploid stages.

number of chromosomes yet again. This does not happen, however, because in sexually reproducing organisms, the gametes are formed by a modified type of cell division called **meiosis**. This type of cell division reduces the number of sets of chromosomes from two to one in the gametes, counterbalancing the doubling that occurs at fertilization. In animals, meiosis occurs only in the ovaries or testes. As a result of meiosis, each human sperm and egg is haploid ($n = 23$). Fertilization restores the diploid condition by combining two haploid sets of chromosomes, and the human life cycle is repeated, generation after generation (see Figure 13.5). You will learn more about the production of sperm and eggs in Chapter 46.

In general, the steps of the human life cycle are typical of many sexually reproducing animals. Indeed, the processes of fertilization and meiosis are the unique trademarks of sexual reproduction, in plants as well as animals. Fertilization and meiosis alternate in sexual life cycles, maintaining a constant number of chromosomes in each species from one generation to the next.

The Variety of Sexual Life Cycles

Although the alternation of meiosis and fertilization is common to all organisms that reproduce sexually, the timing of these two events in the life cycle varies, depending on the species. These variations can be grouped into three main types of life cycles. In the type that occurs in humans and most other animals, gametes are the only haploid cells. Meiosis occurs in germ cells during the production of gametes, which undergo no further cell division prior to fertilization. After fertilization, the diploid zygote divides by mitosis, producing a multicellular organism that is diploid **(Figure 13.6a)**.

Plants and some species of algae exhibit a second type of life cycle called **alternation of generations**. This type includes both diploid and haploid stages that are multicellular. The multicellular diploid stage is called the **sporophyte**. Meiosis in the sporophyte produces haploid cells called **spores**. Unlike a gamete, a haploid spore doesn't fuse with another cell but divides mitotically, generating a multicellular haploid stage called the **gametophyte**. Cells of the gametophyte give rise to gametes by mitosis. Fusion of two haploid gametes at fertilization results in a diploid zygote, which develops into the next sporophyte generation. Therefore, in this type of life cycle, the sporophyte generation produces a gametophyte as its offspring, and the gametophyte generation produces the next sporophyte generation **(Figure 13.6b)**. Clearly, the term *alternation of generations* is a fitting name for this type of life cycle.

A third type of life cycle occurs in most fungi and some protists, including some algae. After gametes fuse and form a diploid zygote, meiosis occurs without a multicellular diploid offspring developing. Meiosis produces not gametes but haploid cells that then divide by mitosis and give rise to either unicellular descendants or a haploid multicellular adult organism. Subsequently, the haploid organism carries out further mitoses, producing the cells that develop into gametes. The only diploid stage found in these species is the single-celled zygote **(Figure 13.6c)**.

Note that *either* haploid or diploid cells can divide by mitosis, depending on the type of life cycle. Only diploid cells, however, can undergo meiosis because haploid cells have a single set of chromosomes that cannot be further reduced. Though the three types of sexual life cycles differ in the timing of meiosis and fertilization, they share a fundamental result: genetic

Key

➡ Haploid (n)
➡ Diploid ($2n$)

(a) Animals

(b) Plants and some algae

(c) Most fungi and some protists

▲ **Figure 13.6 Three types of sexual life cycles.** The common feature of all three cycles is the alternation of meiosis and fertilization, key events that contribute to genetic variation among offspring. The cycles differ in the timing of these two key events.

variation among offspring. A closer look at meiosis will reveal the sources of this variation.

CONCEPT 13.3
Meiosis reduces the number of chromosome sets from diploid to haploid

Many of the steps of meiosis closely resemble corresponding steps in mitosis. Meiosis, like mitosis, is preceded by the replication of chromosomes. However, this single replication is followed by not one but two consecutive cell divisions, called **meiosis I** and **meiosis II**. These two divisions result in four daughter cells (rather than the two daughter cells of mitosis), each with only half as many chromosomes as the parent cell.

The Stages of Meiosis

The overview of meiosis in **Figure 13.7** shows that both members of a single homologous pair of chromosomes in a diploid cell are replicated and that the copies are then sorted into four haploid daughter cells. Recall that sister chromatids are two copies of *one* chromosome, closely associated all along their lengths; this association is called *sister chromatid cohesion*. Together, the sister chromatids make up one replicated chromosome (see Figure 13.4). In contrast, the two chromosomes of a homologous pair are individual chromosomes that were inherited from different parents. Homologs appear alike in the microscope, but they may have different versions of genes, called *alleles*, at corresponding loci (for example, an allele for freckles on one chromosome and an allele for the absence of freckles at the same locus on the homolog). Homologs are not associated with each other except during meiosis, as you will soon see.

▲ **Figure 13.7 Overview of meiosis: how meiosis reduces chromosome number.** After the chromosomes replicate in interphase, the diploid cell divides *twice*, yielding four haploid daughter cells. This overview tracks just one pair of homologous chromosomes, which for the sake of simplicity are drawn in the condensed state throughout (they would not normally be condensed during interphase). The red chromosome was inherited from the female parent, the blue chromosome from the male parent.

DRAW IT *Redraw the cells in this figure using a simple DNA double helix to represent each DNA molecule.*

Figure 13.8, on the next two pages, describes in detail the stages of the two divisions of meiosis for an animal cell whose diploid number is 6. Meiosis halves the total number of chromosomes in a very specific way, reducing the number of sets from two to one, with each daughter cell receiving one set of chromosomes. Study Figure 13.8 thoroughly before going on.

▼ Figure 13.8

Exploring The Meiotic Division of an Animal Cell

Prophase I	Metaphase I	Anaphase I	Telophase I and Cytokinesis

Centrosome (with centriole pair)

Sister chromatids

Chiasmata

Spindle

Homologous chromosomes

Fragments of nuclear envelope

Replicated homologous chromosomes (red and blue) pair and exchange segments; $2n = 6$ in this example

Centromere (with kinetochore)

Metaphase plate

Microtubule attached to kinetochore

Chromosomes line up by homologous pairs

Sister chromatids remain attached

Homologous chromosomes separate

Each pair of homologous chromosomes separates

Cleavage furrow

Two haploid cells form; each chromosome still consists of two sister chromatids

Prophase I
- Chromosomes begin to condense, and homologs loosely pair along their lengths, aligned gene by gene.
- Crossing over (the exchange of corresponding segments of DNA molecules by nonsister chromatids) is completed while homologs are in *synapsis*, held tightly together by proteins along their lengths (before the stage shown).
- Synapsis ends in mid-prophase, and the chromosomes in each pair move apart slightly, as shown above.
- Each homologous pair has one or more chiasmata, points where crossing over has occurred and the homologs are still associated due to cohesion between sister chromatids (*sister chromatid cohesion*).

- Centrosome movement, spindle formation, and nuclear envelope breakdown occur as in mitosis.
- In late prophase I (after the stage shown), microtubules from one pole or the other attach to the two kinetochores, protein structures at the centromeres of the two homologs. The homologous pairs then move toward the metaphase plate.

Metaphase I
- Pairs of homologous chromosomes are now arranged on the metaphase plate, with one chromosome in each pair facing each pole.
- Both chromatids of one homolog are attached to kinetochore microtubules from one pole; those of the other homolog are attached to microtubules from the opposite pole.

Anaphase I
- Breakdown of proteins responsible for sister chromatid cohesion along chromatid arms allows homologs to separate.
- The homologs move toward opposite poles, guided by the spindle apparatus.
- Sister chromatid cohesion persists at the centromere, causing chromatids to move as a unit toward the same pole.

Telophase I and Cytokinesis
- At the beginning of telophase I, each half of the cell has a complete haploid set of replicated chromosomes. Each chromosome is composed of two sister chromatids; one or both chromatids include regions of nonsister chromatid DNA.
- Cytokinesis (division of the cytoplasm) usually occurs simultaneously with telophase I, forming two haploid daughter cells.
- In animal cells, a cleavage furrow forms. (In plant cells, a cell plate forms.)
- In some species, chromosomes decondense and the nuclear envelope re-forms.
- No replication occurs between meiosis I and meiosis II.

| Prophase II | Metaphase II | Anaphase II | Telophase II and Cytokinesis |

During another round of cell division, the sister chromatids finally separate; four haploid daughter cells result, containing unreplicated chromosomes

Sister chromatids separate

Haploid daughter cells forming

Prophase II
- A spindle apparatus forms.
- In late prophase II (not shown here), chromosomes, each still composed of two chromatids associated at the centromere, move toward the metaphase II plate.

Metaphase II
- The chromosomes are positioned on the metaphase plate as in mitosis.
- Because of crossing over in meiosis I, the two sister chromatids of each chromosome are *not* genetically identical.
- The kinetochores of sister chromatids are attached to microtubules extending from opposite poles.

Anaphase II
- Breakdown of proteins holding the sister chromatids together at the centromere allows the chromatids to separate. The chromatids move toward opposite poles as individual chromosomes.

Telophase II and Cytokinesis
- Nuclei form, the chromosomes begin decondensing, and cytokinesis occurs.
- The meiotic division of one parent cell produces four daughter cells, each with a haploid set of (unreplicated) chromosomes.
- Each of the four daughter cells is genetically distinct from the other daughter cells and from the parent cell.

MEDIA *BioFlix* Visit the Study Area at www.masteringbio.com for the BioFlix 3-D Animation on Meiosis.

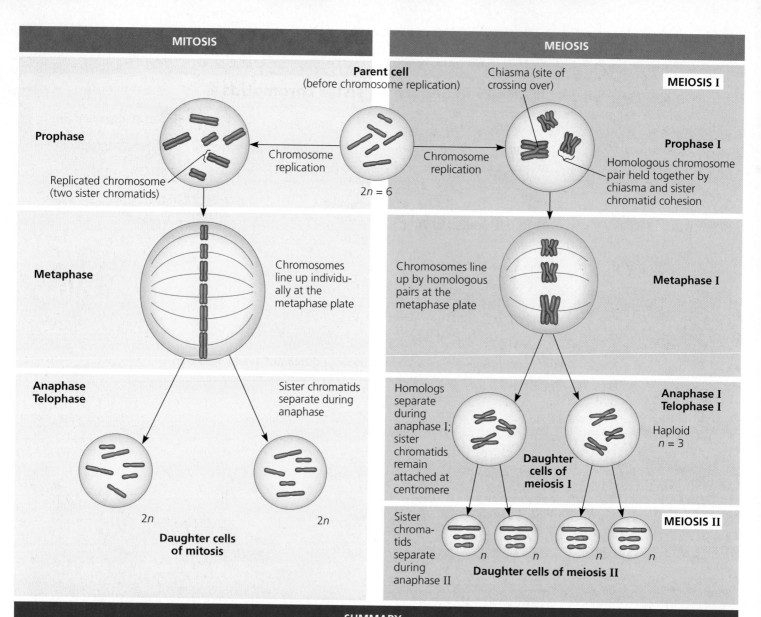

	MITOSIS		MEIOSIS	

Parent cell (before chromosome replication)

Chiasma (site of crossing over)

MEIOSIS I

Prophase — Replicated chromosome (two sister chromatids) — Chromosome replication — 2n = 6 — Chromosome replication — **Prophase I** — Homologous chromosome pair held together by chiasma and sister chromatid cohesion

Metaphase — Chromosomes line up individually at the metaphase plate — Chromosomes line up by homologous pairs at the metaphase plate — **Metaphase I**

Anaphase Telophase — Sister chromatids separate during anaphase — Homologs separate during anaphase I; sister chromatids remain attached at centromere — **Daughter cells of meiosis I** — **Anaphase I Telophase I** — Haploid n = 3

2n — 2n — **Daughter cells of mitosis**

Sister chromatids separate during anaphase II — **Daughter cells of meiosis II** — n — n — n — n — MEIOSIS II

	SUMMARY		
Property	**Mitosis**	**Meiosis**	
DNA replication	Occurs during interphase before mitosis begins	Occurs during interphase before meiosis I begins	
Number of divisions	One, including prophase, metaphase, anaphase, and telophase	Two, each including prophase, metaphase, anaphase, and telophase	
Synapsis of homologous chromosomes	Does not occur	Occurs during prophase I along with crossing over between nonsister chromatids; resulting chiasmata hold pairs together due to sister chromatid cohesion	
Number of daughter cells and genetic composition	Two, each diploid (2n) and genetically identical to the parent cell	Four, each haploid (n), containing half as many chromosomes as the parent cell; genetically different from the parent cell and from each other	
Role in the animal body	Enables multicellular adult to arise from zygote; produces cells for growth, repair, and, in some species, asexual reproduction	Produces gametes; reduces number of chromosomes by half and introduces genetic variability among the gametes	

▲ **Figure 13.9 A comparison of mitosis and meiosis in diploid cells.**

DRAW IT *Could any other combinations of chromosomes be generated during meiosis II from the specific cells shown in telophase I? Explain. (Hint: Draw the cells as they would appear in metaphase II.)*

A Comparison of Mitosis and Meiosis

Figure 13.9 summarizes the key differences between meiosis and mitosis in diploid cells. Basically, meiosis reduces the number of chromosome sets from two (diploid) to one (haploid), whereas mitosis conserves the number of chromosome sets. Therefore, meiosis produces cells that differ genetically from their parent cell and from each other, whereas mitosis produces daughter cells that are genetically identical to their parent cell and to each other.

Three events unique to meiosis occur during meiosis I:

1. **Synapsis and crossing over.** During prophase I, replicated homologs pair up and become physically connected along their lengths by a zipper-like protein structure, the *synaptonemal complex*; this process is called **synapsis**. Genetic rearrangement between nonsister chromatids, known as **crossing over**, is completed during this stage. Following disassembly of the synaptonemal complex in late prophase, the two homologs pull apart slightly but remain connected by at least one X-shaped region called a **chiasma** (plural, *chiasmata*). A chiasma is the physical manifestation of crossing over; it appears as a cross because sister chromatid cohesion still holds the two original sister chromatids together, even in regions where one of them is now part of the other homolog. Synapsis and crossing over normally do not occur during mitosis.

2. **Homologs on the metaphase plate.** At metaphase I of meiosis, chromosomes are positioned on the metaphase plate as pairs of homologs, rather than individual chromosomes, as in metaphase of mitosis.

3. **Separation of homologs.** At anaphase I of meiosis, the replicated chromosomes of each homologous pair move toward opposite poles, but the sister chromatids of each replicated chromosome remain attached. In anaphase of mitosis, by contrast, sister chromatids separate.

How do sister chromatids stay together through meiosis I but separate from each other in meiosis II and mitosis? Sister chromatids are attached along their lengths by protein complexes called *cohesins*. In mitosis, this attachment lasts until the end of metaphase, when enzymes cleave the cohesins, freeing the sister chromatids to move to opposite poles of the cell. In meiosis, sister chromatid cohesion is released in two steps. In metaphase I, homologs are held together by cohesion between sister chromatid arms in regions where DNA has been exchanged. At anaphase I, cohesins are cleaved along the arms, allowing homologs to separate. At anaphase II, cohesins are cleaved at the centromeres, allowing chromatids to separate.

Figure 13.10 shows one of a series of experiments carried out by Yoshinori Watanabe and colleagues at the University of Tokyo. They knew that similar proteins were present in cohesin complexes during mitosis and meiosis, and they wondered what was responsible for preventing cohesin cleavage at the centromere while it was occurring along sister chromatid

---

▼ **Figure 13.10** **Inquiry**

What prevents the separation of sister chromatids at anaphase I of meiosis?

EXPERIMENT Yoshinori Watanabe and colleagues knew that during anaphase I, the protein shugoshin is present only around centromeres. They wondered whether it protects cohesins there from degradation in meiosis I, ensuring that chromatids stay together while homologs separate. To test this hypothesis, they used a species of yeast in which meiosis produces haploid spores lined up in a specific order inside a spore case. To follow the movement of chromosomes, they fluorescently labeled a region near the centromere of both chromatids in one homolog, leaving the other homolog unlabeled. They then disabled the gene coding for shugoshin and compared this yeast strain (shugoshin$^-$) with normal yeast cells (shugoshin$^+$). The researchers expected that the two labeled chromosomes arising from the labeled chromatids in normal cells would end up in separate spores at one end of the spore case. They further predicted that if shugoshin does protect cohesins from cleavage at the centromere at anaphase I, then the labeled chromosomes in shugoshin$^-$ cells would separate randomly in meiosis II, sometimes ending up in the same spore.

RESULTS In shugoshin$^+$ cells, the two labeled chromosomes ended up in different spores in almost all cases. In shugoshin$^-$ cells, they were in the same spore in about half the cases.

CONCLUSION The researchers concluded that shugoshin protects cohesins at the centromere at anaphase I, thus maintaining the attachment between sister chromatids and ensuring that they separate properly during meiosis II.

SOURCE T. S. Kitajima, S. A. Kawashima, and Y. Watanabe, The conserved kinetochore protein shugoshin protects centromeric cohesion during meiosis, *Nature* 427:510–517 (2004).

WHAT IF? Draw a graph showing what you expect happened to the chromatids of the *unlabeled* chromosome in both strains of cells.

arms at the end of metaphase I. They found a protein they named shugoshin (Japanese for "guardian spirit") that protects cohesins from cleavage at the centromere during meiosis I. Shugoshin is similar to a fruit fly protein identified 10 years earlier by Terry Orr-Weaver, this unit's interviewee.

Meiosis I is called the *reductional division* because it halves the number of chromosome sets per cell—a reduction from two sets (the diploid state) to one set (the haploid state). During the second meiotic division, meiosis II (sometimes called the *equational division*), the sister chromatids separate, producing haploid daughter cells. The mechanism for separating sister chromatids is virtually identical in meiosis II and mitosis. The molecular basis of chromosome behavior during meiosis continues to be a focus of intense research interest.

CONCEPT CHECK 13.3

1. How are the chromosomes in a cell at metaphase of mitosis similar to and different from the chromosomes in a cell at metaphase of meiosis II?
2. **WHAT IF?** Given that the synaptonemal complex disappears by the end of prophase, how would the two homologs be associated if crossing over did not occur? What effect might this ultimately have on gamete formation?

For suggested answers, see Appendix A.

CONCEPT 13.4

Genetic variation produced in sexual life cycles contributes to evolution

How do we account for the genetic variation illustrated in Figure 13.1? As you will learn in more detail in later chapters, mutations are the original source of genetic diversity. These changes in an organism's DNA create the different versions of genes known as *alleles*. Once these differences arise, reshuffling of the alleles during sexual reproduction produces the variation that results in each member of a species having its own unique combination of traits.

Origins of Genetic Variation Among Offspring

In species that reproduce sexually, the behavior of chromosomes during meiosis and fertilization is responsible for most of the variation that arises each generation. Let's examine three mechanisms that contribute to the genetic variation arising from sexual reproduction: independent assortment of chromosomes, crossing over, and random fertilization.

Independent Assortment of Chromosomes

One aspect of sexual reproduction that generates genetic variation is the random orientation of homologous pairs of chromosomes at metaphase of meiosis I. At metaphase I, the homologous pairs, each consisting of one maternal and one paternal chromosome, are situated on the metaphase plate. (Note that the terms *maternal* and *paternal* refer, respectively, to the mother and father of the individual whose cells are undergoing meiosis.) Each pair may orient with either its maternal or paternal homolog closer to a given pole—its orientation is as random as the flip of a coin. Thus, there is a 50% chance that a particular daughter cell of meiosis I will get the maternal chromosome of a certain homologous pair and a 50% chance that it will get the paternal chromosome.

Because each homologous pair of chromosomes is positioned independently of the other pairs at metaphase I, the first meiotic division results in each pair sorting its maternal and paternal homologs into daughter cells independently of every other pair. This is called *independent assortment*. Each daughter cell represents one outcome of all possible combinations of maternal and paternal chromosomes. As shown in **Figure 13.11**, the number of combinations possible for daughter cells formed by meiosis of a diploid cell with two homologous pairs of chromosomes is four (two possible arrangements for the first pair times two possible arrangements for the second pair). Note that only two of the four

▶ **Figure 13.11 The independent assortment of homologous chromosomes in meiosis.**

Possibility 1 — Possibility 2
Two equally probable arrangements of chromosomes at metaphase I
Metaphase II
Daughter cells
Combination 1 — Combination 2 — Combination 3 — Combination 4

combinations of daughter cells shown in the figure would result from meiosis of a *single* diploid cell, because a single parent cell would have one or the other possible chromosomal arrangement at metaphase I, but not both. However, the population of daughter cells resulting from meiosis of a large number of diploid cells contains all four types in approximately equal numbers. In the case of $n = 3$, eight combinations of chromosomes are possible for daughter cells. More generally, the number of possible combinations when chromosomes sort independently during meiosis is 2^n, where n is the haploid number of the organism.

In the case of humans ($n = 23$), the number of possible combinations of maternal and paternal chromosomes in the resulting gametes is 2^{23}, or about 8.4 million. Each gamete that you produce in your lifetime contains one of roughly 8.4 million possible combinations of chromosomes.

Crossing Over

As a consequence of the independent assortment of chromosomes during meiosis, each of us produces a collection of gametes differing greatly in their combinations of the chromosomes we inherited from our two parents. Figure 13.11 suggests that each individual chromosome in a gamete is exclusively maternal or paternal in origin. In fact, this is *not* the case, because crossing over produces **recombinant chromosomes**, individual chromosomes that carry genes (DNA) derived from two different parents **(Figure 13.12)**. In meiosis in humans, an average of one to three crossover events occur per chromosome pair, depending on the size of the chromosomes and the position of their centromeres.

Crossing over begins very early in prophase I, as homologous chromosomes pair loosely along their lengths. Each gene on one homolog is aligned precisely with the corresponding gene on the other homolog. In a single crossover event, specific proteins orchestrate an exchange of corresponding segments of two *nonsister* chromatids—one maternal and one paternal chromatid of a homologous pair. In this way, crossing over produces chromosomes with new combinations of maternal and paternal alleles (see Figure 13.12).

In humans and most other organisms studied so far, crossing over also plays an essential role in the lining up of homologous chromosomes during metaphase I. As seen in Figure 13.8, a chiasma forms as the result of a crossover occurring while sister chromatid cohesion is present along the arms. Chiasmata hold homologs together as the spindle forms for the first meiotic division. During anaphase I, the release of cohesion along sister chromatid arms allows homologs to separate. During anaphase II, the release of sister chromatid cohesion at the centromeres allows the sister chromatids to separate.

At metaphase II, chromosomes that contain one or more recombinant chromatids can be oriented in two alternative, nonequivalent ways with respect to other chromosomes, because their sister chromatids are no longer identical. The different possible arrangements of nonidentical sister chromatids dur-

ing meiosis II further increases the number of genetic types of daughter cells that can result from meiosis.

You will learn more about crossing over in Chapter 15. The important point for now is that crossing over, by combining DNA inherited from two parents into a single chromosome, is an important source of genetic variation in sexual life cycles.

Random Fertilization

The random nature of fertilization adds to the genetic variation arising from meiosis. In humans, each male and female gamete represents one of about 8.4 million (2^{23}) possible chromosome combinations due to independent assortment. The fusion of a male gamete with a female gamete during fertilization will produce a zygote with any of about 70 trillion ($2^{23} \times 2^{23}$) diploid combinations. If we factor in the variation brought about by crossing over, the number of possibilities is truly astronomical. It may sound trite, but you really *are* unique.

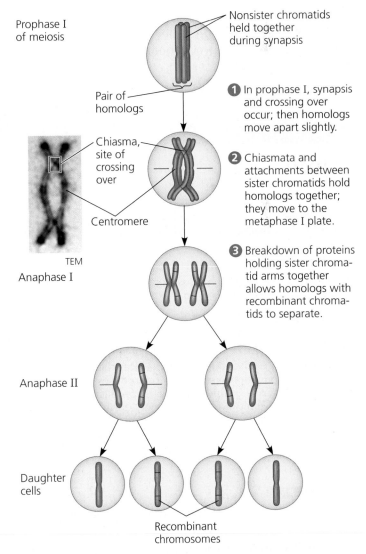

Prophase I of meiosis

Nonsister chromatids held together during synapsis

Pair of homologs

❶ In prophase I, synapsis and crossing over occur; then homologs move apart slightly.

Chiasma, site of crossing over

Centromere

❷ Chiasmata and attachments between sister chromatids hold homologs together; they move to the metaphase I plate.

TEM

Anaphase I

❸ Breakdown of proteins holding sister chromatid arms together allows homologs with recombinant chromatids to separate.

Anaphase II

Daughter cells

Recombinant chromosomes

▲ Figure 13.12 **The results of crossing over during meiosis.**

The Evolutionary Significance of Genetic Variation Within Populations

Now that you've learned how new combinations of genes arise among offspring in a sexually reproducing population, let's see how the genetic variation in a population relates to evolution. Darwin recognized that a population evolves through the differential reproductive success of its variant members. On average, those individuals best suited to the local environment leave the most offspring, thus transmitting their genes. This natural selection results in the accumulation of those genetic variations favored by the environment. As the environment changes, the population may survive if, in each generation, at least some of its members can cope effectively with the new conditions. Different combinations of alleles may work better than those that previously prevailed. Mutations are the original source of different alleles, which are then mixed and matched during meiosis. In this chapter, we have seen how sexual reproduction greatly increases the genetic variation present in a population. In fact, the ability of sexual reproduction to generate genetic variation is one of the most commonly proposed explanations for the persistence of sexual reproduction.

Although Darwin realized that heritable variation is what makes evolution possible, he could not explain why offspring resemble—but are not identical to—their parents. Ironically, Gregor Mendel, a contemporary of Darwin, published a theory of inheritance that helps explain genetic variation, but his discoveries had no impact on biologists until 1900, more than 15 years after Darwin (1809–1882) and Mendel (1822–1884) had died. In the next chapter, you will learn how Mendel discovered the basic rules governing the inheritance of specific traits.

CONCEPT CHECK 13.4

1. What is the original source of all the different alleles of a gene?
2. The diploid number for fruit flies is 8, while that for grasshoppers is 46. If no crossing over took place, would the genetic variation among offspring from a given pair of parents be greater in fruit flies or grasshoppers? Explain.
3. **WHAT IF?** Under what circumstances would crossing over during meiosis *not* contribute to genetic variation among daughter cells?

For suggested answers, see Appendix A.

Chapter 13 Review

 MEDIA Go to the Study Area at **www.masteringbio.com** for BioFlix 3-D Animations, MP3 Tutors, Videos, Practice Tests, an eBook, and more.

SUMMARY OF KEY CONCEPTS

CONCEPT 13.1

Offspring acquire genes from parents by inheriting chromosomes (pp. 248–249)

▶ **Inheritance of Genes** Each gene in an organism's DNA exists at a specific locus on a certain chromosome. We inherit one set of chromosomes from our mother and one set from our father.

▶ **Comparison of Asexual and Sexual Reproduction** In asexual reproduction, a single parent produces genetically identical offspring by mitosis. Sexual reproduction combines sets of genes from two different parents, forming genetically diverse offspring.

MEDIA

Activity Asexual and Sexual Life Cycles

CONCEPT 13.2

Fertilization and meiosis alternate in sexual life cycles (pp. 250–253)

▶ **Sets of Chromosomes in Human Cells** Normal human somatic cells are diploid. They have 46 chromosomes made up

of two sets of 23—one set from each parent. In human diploid cells, there are 22 homologous pairs of autosomes, each with a maternal and a paternal homolog. The 23rd pair, the sex chromosomes, determines whether the person is female (XX) or male (XY).

▶ **Behavior of Chromosome Sets in the Human Life Cycle** At sexual maturity, ovaries and testes (the gonads) produce haploid gametes by meiosis, each gamete containing a single set of 23 chromosomes ($n = 23$). During fertilization, an egg and sperm unite, forming a diploid ($2n = 46$) single-celled zygote, which develops into a multicellular organism by mitosis.

▶ **The Variety of Sexual Life Cycles** Sexual life cycles differ in the timing of meiosis relative to fertilization and in the point(s) of the cycle at which a multicellular organism is produced by mitosis.

CONCEPT 13.3

Meiosis reduces the number of chromosome sets from diploid to haploid (pp. 253–258)

▶ **The Stages of Meiosis** The two cell divisions of meiosis produce four haploid daughter cells. The number of chromosome sets is reduced from two (diploid) to one (haploid) during meiosis I, the reductional division.

▶ **A Comparison of Mitosis and Meiosis** Meiosis is distinguished from mitosis by three events of meiosis I, as shown on the next page:

Prophase I: Each homologous pair undergoes synapsis and crossing over between nonsister chromatids.

Metaphase I: Chromosomes line up as homologous pairs on the metaphase plate.

Anaphase I: Homologs separate from each other; sister chromatids remain joined at the centromere.

Meiosis II separates the sister chromatids.

MEDIA

BioFlix 3-D Animation Meiosis
MP3 Tutor Meiosis
MP3 Tutor Mitosis-Meiosis Comparison
Activity Meiosis Animation

CONCEPT 13.4

Genetic variation produced in sexual life cycles contributes to evolution (pp. 258–260)

▶ **Origins of Genetic Variation Among Offspring** Three events in sexual reproduction contribute to genetic variation in a population: independent assortment of chromosomes during meiosis, crossing over during meiosis I, and random fertilization of egg cells by sperm. Due to sister chromatid cohesion, crossing over leads to chiasmata, which hold homologs together until anaphase I.

▶ **The Evolutionary Significance of Genetic Variation Within Populations** Genetic variation is the raw material for evolution by natural selection. Mutations are the original source of this variation; the production of new combinations of variant genes in sexual reproduction generates additional genetic diversity.

MEDIA

Activity Origins of Genetic Variation
Investigation How Can the Frequency of Crossing Over Be Estimated?

TESTING YOUR KNOWLEDGE

SELF-QUIZ

1. A human cell containing 22 autosomes and a Y chromosome is
   a. a sperm.
   b. an egg.
   c. a zygote.
   d. a somatic cell of a male.
   e. a somatic cell of a female.

2. Which life cycle stage is found in plants but not animals?
   a. gamete
   b. zygote
   c. multicellular diploid
   d. multicellular haploid
   e. unicellular diploid

3. Homologous chromosomes move toward opposite poles of a dividing cell during
   a. mitosis.
   b. meiosis I.
   c. meiosis II.
   d. fertilization.
   e. binary fission.

4. Meiosis II is similar to mitosis in that
   a. sister chromatids separate during anaphase.
   b. DNA replicates before the division.

c. the daughter cells are diploid.
d. homologous chromosomes synapse.
e. the chromosome number is reduced.

5. If the DNA content of a diploid cell in the G_1 phase of the cell cycle is x, then the DNA content of the same cell at metaphase of meiosis I would be
   a. $0.25x$. b. $0.5x$. c. x. d. $2x$. e. $4x$.

6. If we continued to follow the cell lineage from question 5, then the DNA content of a single cell at metaphase of meiosis II would be
   a. $0.25x$. b. $0.5x$. c. x. d. $2x$. e. $4x$.

7. How many different combinations of maternal and paternal chromosomes can be packaged in gametes made by an organism with a diploid number of 8 ($2n = 8$)?
   a. 2 b. 4 c. 8 d. 16 e. 32

Use the diagram of a cell below to answer questions 8–10.

8. How can you tell this cell is undergoing meiosis, not mitosis?

9. Identify the stage of meiosis shown.

10. **DRAW IT** Copy the drawing to a separate sheet of paper and label appropriate structures with these terms, drawing lines or brackets as needed: chromosome (label as replicated or unreplicated), centromere, kinetochore, sister chromatids, nonsister chromatids, homologous pair, homologs, chiasma, sister chromatid cohesion. Describe the makeup of a haploid set and a diploid set.

For Self-Quiz answers, see Appendix A.

MEDIA Visit the Study Area at **www.masteringbio.com** for a Practice Test.

EVOLUTION CONNECTION

11. Many species can reproduce either asexually or sexually. What might be the evolutionary significance of the switch from asexual to sexual reproduction that occurs in some organisms when the environment becomes unfavorable?

SCIENTIFIC INQUIRY

12. The diagram accompanying questions 8–10 represents a meiotic cell in a certain individual. A previous study has shown that the freckles gene is located at the locus marked F, and the hair color gene is located at the locus marked H, both on the long chromosome. The individual from whom this cell was taken has inherited different alleles for each gene ("freckles" and "black hair" from one parent, and "no freckles" and "blond hair" from the other). Predict allele combinations in the gametes resulting from this meiotic event. (It will help if you draw out the rest of meiosis, labeling alleles by name.) List other possible combinations of these alleles in this individual's gametes.

Mendel and the Gene Idea

14

▲ **Figure 14.1 What principles of inheritance did Gregor Mendel discover by breeding garden pea plants?**

OVERVIEW

Drawing from the Deck of Genes

If you happened to see a woman with bright purple hair walking down the street, you would probably conclude that she hadn't inherited her striking hair color from either parent. Consciously or not, you have transformed a lifetime of observations of hair color and other features into a list of possible variations that occur naturally among people. Eyes of brown, blue, green, or gray; hair of black, brown, blond, or red—these are just a few examples of heritable variations that we may observe among individuals in a population. What are the genetic principles that account for the transmission of such traits from parents to offspring in humans and other organisms?

The explanation of heredity most widely in favor during the 1800s was the "blending" hypothesis, the idea that genetic material contributed by the two parents mixes in a manner analogous to the way blue and yellow paints blend to make green. This hypothesis predicts that over many generations, a freely mating population will give rise to a uniform population of individuals. However, our everyday observations and the results of breeding experiments with animals and plants contradict that prediction. The blending hypothesis also fails to explain other phenomena of inheritance, such as traits reappearing after skipping a generation.

An alternative to the blending model is a "particulate" hypothesis of inheritance: the gene idea. According to this model, parents pass on discrete heritable units—genes—that retain their separate identities in offspring. An organism's collection of genes is more like a deck of cards than a pail of paint. Like playing cards, genes can be shuffled and passed along, generation after generation, in undiluted form.

Modern genetics had its genesis in an abbey garden, where a monk named Gregor Mendel documented a particulate mechanism for inheritance. **Figure 14.1** shows Mendel (back row, holding a sprig of fuchsia) with his fellow monks. Mendel developed his theory of inheritance several decades before chromosomes were observed in the microscope and the significance of their behavior was understood. In this chapter, we will step into Mendel's garden to re-create his experiments and explain how he arrived at his theory of inheritance. We will also explore inheritance patterns more complex than those observed by Mendel in garden peas. Finally, we will see how the Mendelian model applies to the inheritance of human variations, including hereditary disorders such as sickle-cell disease.

CONCEPT 14.1

Mendel used the scientific approach to identify two laws of inheritance

Mendel discovered the basic principles of heredity by breeding garden peas in carefully planned experiments. As we retrace his work, you will recognize the key elements of the scientific process that were introduced in Chapter 1.

Mendel's Experimental, Quantitative Approach

Mendel grew up on his parents' small farm in a region of Austria that is now part of the Czech Republic. In this agricultural area, Mendel and the other children received agricultural training in school along with their basic education. As an adolescent, Mendel overcame financial hardship and illness to excel in high school and, later, at the Olmutz Philosophical Institute.

In 1843, at the age of 21, Mendel entered an Augustinian monastery, a reasonable choice at that time for someone who valued the life of the mind. He considered becoming a teacher but failed the necessary examination. In 1851, he left the monastery to pursue two years of study in physics and chemistry at the University of Vienna. These were very important years for Mendel's development as a scientist, in large part due to the strong influence of two professors. One was the physicist Christian Doppler, who encouraged his students to learn science through experimentation and trained Mendel to use mathematics to help explain natural phenomena. The other was a botanist named Franz Unger, who aroused Mendel's interest in the causes of variation in plants. The instruction Mendel received from these two mentors later played a critical role in his experiments with garden peas.

After attending the university, Mendel returned to the monastery and was assigned to teach at a local school, where several other instructors were enthusiastic about scientific research. In addition, his fellow monks shared a long-standing fascination with the breeding of plants. The monastery therefore provided fertile soil in more ways than one for Mendel's scientific endeavors. Around 1857, Mendel began breeding garden peas in the abbey garden to study inheritance. Although the question of heredity had long been a focus of curiosity at the monastery, Mendel's fresh approach allowed him to deduce principles that had remained elusive to others.

One reason Mendel probably chose to work with peas is that they are available in many varieties. For example, one variety has purple flowers, while another variety has white flowers. A heritable feature that varies among individuals, such as flower color, is called a **character**. Each variant for a character, such as purple or white color for flowers, is termed a **trait**.*

Other advantages of using peas are their short generation time and the large number of offspring from each mating. Furthermore, Mendel could strictly control mating between plants. The reproductive organs of a pea plant are in its flowers, and each pea flower has both pollen-producing organs (stamens) and an egg-bearing organ (carpel). In nature, pea plants usually self-fertilize: Pollen grains from the stamens land on the carpel of the same flower, and sperm released from the pollen grains fertilize eggs present in the carpel. To achieve cross-pollination (fertilization between different plants), Mendel removed the immature stamens of a plant before they produced pollen and then dusted pollen from another plant onto the altered flowers (**Figure 14.2**). Each resulting zygote then developed into a plant embryo encased in a seed (pea).

* Some geneticists use the terms *character* and *trait* synonymously, but in this book we distinguish between them.

Whether forcing self-pollination or executing artificial cross-pollination, Mendel could always be sure of the parentage of new seeds.

Mendel chose to track only those characters that varied between two distinct alternatives. For example, his plants had either purple flowers or white flowers; there was nothing intermediate between these two varieties. Had Mendel focused instead on characters that varied in a continuum among individuals—seed weight, for example—he would not have discovered the particulate nature of inheritance. (You'll learn why later.)

Mendel also made sure that he started his experiments with varieties that, over many generations of self-pollination,

▼ Figure 14.2 **Research Method**

Crossing Pea Plants

APPLICATION   By crossing (mating) two true-breeding varieties of an organism, scientists can study patterns of inheritance. In this example, Mendel crossed pea plants that varied in flower color.

TECHNIQUE

① Removed stamens from purple flower

② Transferred sperm-bearing pollen from stamens of white flower to egg-bearing carpel of purple flower

Parental generation (P)

Carpel

Stamens

③ Pollinated carpel matured into pod

④ Planted seeds from pod

RESULTS   When pollen from a white flower was transferred to a purple flower, the first-generation hybrids all had purple flowers. The result was the same for the reciprocal cross, which involved the transfer of pollen from purple flowers to white flowers.

First filial generation offspring (F_1)

⑤ Examined offspring: all purple flowers

had produced only the same variety as the parent plant. Such plants are said to be **true-breeding**. For example, a plant with purple flowers is true-breeding if the seeds produced by self-pollination in successive generations all give rise to plants that also have purple flowers.

In a typical breeding experiment, Mendel cross-pollinated two contrasting, true-breeding pea varieties—for example, purple-flowered plants and white-flowered plants (see Figure 14.2). This mating, or *crossing*, of two true-breeding varieties is called **hybridization**. The true-breeding parents are referred to as the **P generation** (parental generation), and their hybrid offspring are the **F_1 generation** (first filial generation, the word *filial* from the Latin word for "son"). Allowing these F_1 hybrids to self-pollinate produces an **F_2 generation** (second filial generation). Mendel usually followed traits for at least the P, F_1, and F_2 generations. Had Mendel stopped his experiments with the F_1 generation, the basic patterns of inheritance would have escaped him.

Mendel was a thorough and enthusiastic researcher. In a letter dated 1867, he wrote, "In 1859 I obtained a very fertile descendant with large, tasty seeds from a first generation hybrid. Since in the following year, its progeny retained the desirable characteristics and were uniform, the variety was cultivated in our vegetable garden, and many plants were raised every year up to 1865." Mendel's quantitative analysis of the F_2 plants from thousands of genetic crosses like these allowed him to deduce two fundamental principles of heredity, which he called the law of segregation and the law of independent assortment. A rigorous experimentalist, Mendel put these principles to the test again and again by crossing and self-fertilizing F_2 and later-generation pea plants, as well as by carrying out similar experiments on other plants, such as beans.

The Law of Segregation

If the blending model of inheritance were correct, the F_1 hybrids from a cross between purple-flowered and white-flowered pea plants would have pale purple flowers, a trait intermediate between those of the P generation. Notice in Figure 14.2 that the experiment produced a very different result: All the F_1 offspring had flowers just as purple as the purple-flowered parents. What happened to the white-flowered plants' genetic contribution to the hybrids? If it were lost, then the F_1 plants could produce only purple-flowered offspring in the F_2 generation. But when Mendel allowed the F_1 plants to self-pollinate and planted their seeds, the white-flower trait reappeared in the F_2 generation.

Mendel used very large sample sizes and kept accurate records of his results: 705 of the F_2 plants had purple flowers, and 224 had white flowers. These data fit a ratio of approximately three purple to one white (**Figure 14.3**). Mendel reasoned that the heritable factor for white flowers did not disappear in the F_1 plants, but was somehow hidden or masked when the purple-flower factor was present. In Mendel's termi-

nology, purple flower color is a *dominant* trait and white flower color is a *recessive* trait. The reappearance of white-flowered plants in the F_2 generation was evidence that the heritable factor causing white flowers had not been diluted or destroyed by coexisting with the purple-flower factor in the F_1 hybrids.

Mendel observed the same pattern of inheritance in six other characters, each represented by two distinctly different

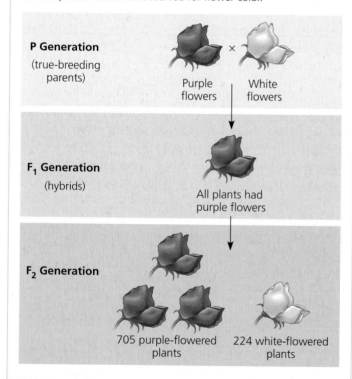

▼ **Figure 14.3** **Inquiry**

When F_1 hybrid pea plants are allowed to self-pollinate, which traits appear in the F_2 generation?

EXPERIMENT Around 1860, in a monastery garden in Brünn, Austria, Gregor Mendel used the character of flower color in pea plants to follow traits through two generations. He crossed true-breeding purple-flowered plants and white-flowered plants (crosses are symbolized by ×). The resulting F_1 hybrids were allowed to self-pollinate or were cross-pollinated with other F_1 hybrids. The F_2 generation plants were then observed for flower color.

P Generation (true-breeding parents)

Purple flowers   White flowers

F_1 Generation (hybrids)

All plants had purple flowers

F_2 Generation

705 purple-flowered plants   224 white-flowered plants

RESULTS Both purple-flowered and white-flowered plants appeared in the F_2 generation, in a ratio of approximately 3:1.

CONCLUSION The "heritable factor" for the recessive trait (white flowers) had not been destroyed or deleted in the F_1 generation, but merely masked by the presence of the factor for purple flowers, which is the dominant trait.

SOURCE G. Mendel, Experiments in plant hybridization, *Proceedings of the Natural History Society of Brünn* 4:3–47 (1866).

WHAT IF? If you mated two purple-flowered plants from the P generation, what ratio of traits would you expect to observe in the offspring? Explain.

traits (Table 14.1). For example, when Mendel crossed a true-breeding variety that produced smooth, round pea seeds with one that produced wrinkled seeds, all the F$_1$ hybrids produced round seeds; this is the dominant trait for seed shape. In the F$_2$ generation, 75% of the seeds were round and 25% were wrinkled—a 3:1 ratio, as in Figure 14.3. Now let's see how Mendel deduced the law of segregation from his experimental results. In the discussion that follows, we will use modern terms instead of some of the terms used by Mendel. (For example, we'll use "gene" instead of Mendel's "heritable factor.")

Mendel's Model

Mendel developed a model to explain the 3:1 inheritance pattern that he consistently observed among the F$_2$ offspring in his pea experiments. We describe four related concepts making up this model, the fourth of which is the law of segregation.

First, *alternative versions of genes account for variations in inherited characters.* The gene for flower color in pea plants, for example, exists in two versions, one for purple flowers and the other for white flowers. These alternative versions of a gene are called **alleles (Figure 14.4).** Today, we can relate this concept to chromosomes and DNA. As noted in Chapter 13, each gene is a sequence of nucleotides at a specific place, or locus, along a particular chromosome. The DNA at that locus, however, can vary slightly in its nucleotide sequence and hence in its information content. The purple-flower allele and the white-flower allele are two DNA variations possible at the flower-color locus on one of a pea plant's chromosomes.

Second, *for each character, an organism inherits two alleles, one from each parent.* Remarkably, Mendel made this deduction without knowing about the role of chromosomes. Recall from Chapter 13 that each somatic cell in a diploid organism has two sets of chromosomes, one set inherited from each parent. Thus, a genetic locus is actually represented twice in a diploid cell, once on each homolog of a specific pair of chromosomes. The two alleles at a particular locus may be identical, as in the true-breeding plants of Mendel's P generation. Or the alleles may differ, as in the F$_1$ hybrids (see Figure 14.4).

Table 14.1 The Results of Mendel's F$_1$ Crosses for Seven Characters in Pea Plants

Character	Dominant Trait	x	Recessive Trait	F$_2$ Generation Dominant:Recessive	Ratio
Flower color	Purple	×	White	705:224	3.15:1
Flower position	Axial	×	Terminal	651:207	3.14:1
Seed color	Yellow	×	Green	6,022:2,001	3.01:1
Seed shape	Round	×	Wrinkled	5,474:1,850	2.96:1
Pod shape	Inflated	×	Constricted	882:299	2.95:1
Pod color	Green	×	Yellow	428:152	2.82:1
Stem length	Tall	×	Dwarf	787:277	2.84:1

▲ Figure 14.4 **Alleles, alternative versions of a gene.** A somatic cell has two copies of each chromosome (forming a homologous pair) and thus two alleles of each gene, which may be identical or different. This figure depicts a homologous pair of chromosomes in an F$_1$ hybrid pea plant. The chromosome with an allele for purple flowers was inherited from one parent, and that with an allele for white flowers from the other parent.

Third, *if the two alleles at a locus differ, then one, the* **dominant allele**, *determines the organism's appearance; the other, the* **recessive allele**, *has no noticeable effect on the organism's appearance.* Accordingly, Mendel's F_1 plants had purple flowers because the allele for that trait is dominant and the allele for white flowers is recessive.

The fourth and final part of Mendel's model, the **law of segregation**, states that *the two alleles for a heritable character segregate (separate) during gamete formation and end up in different gametes.* Thus, an egg or a sperm gets only one of the two alleles that are present in the somatic cells of the organism making the gamete. In terms of chromosomes, this segregation corresponds to the distribution of the two members of a homologous pair of chromosomes to different gametes in meiosis (see Figure 13.7). Note that if an organism has identical alleles for a particular character—that is, the organism is true-breeding for that character—then that allele is present in all gametes. But if different alleles are present, as in the F_1 hybrids, then 50% of the gametes receive the dominant allele and 50% receive the recessive allele.

Does Mendel's segregation model account for the 3:1 ratio he observed in the F_2 generation of his numerous crosses? For the flower-color character, the model predicts that the two different alleles present in an F_1 individual will segregate into gametes such that half the gametes will have the purple-flower allele and half will have the white-flower allele. During self-pollination, gametes of each class unite randomly. An egg with a purple-flower allele has an equal chance of being fertilized by a sperm with a purple-flower allele or one with a white-flower allele. Since the same is true for an egg with a white-flower allele, there are four equally likely combinations of sperm and egg. **Figure 14.5** illustrates these combinations using a **Punnett square**, a handy diagrammatic device for predicting the allele composition of offspring from a cross between individuals of known genetic makeup. Notice that we use a capital letter to symbolize a dominant allele and a lowercase letter for a recessive allele. In our example, P is the purple-flower allele, and p is the white-flower allele; the gene itself may be referred to as the P/p gene.

In the F_2 offspring, what color will the flowers be? One-fourth of the plants have inherited two purple-flower alleles; clearly, these plants will have purple flowers. One-half of the F_2 offspring have inherited one purple-flower allele and one white-flower allele; these plants will also have purple flowers, the dominant trait. Finally, one-fourth of the F_2 plants have inherited two white-flower alleles and will express the recessive trait. Thus, Mendel's model accounts for the 3:1 ratio of traits that he observed in the F_2 generation.

Useful Genetic Vocabulary

An organism that has a pair of identical alleles for a character is said to be **homozygous** for the gene controlling that character. In the parental generation in Figure 14.5, the purple pea plant is homozygous for the dominant allele (PP), while the white plant is homozygous for the recessive allele (pp). Homozygous plants "breed true" because all of their gametes contain the same allele—either P or p in this example. If we

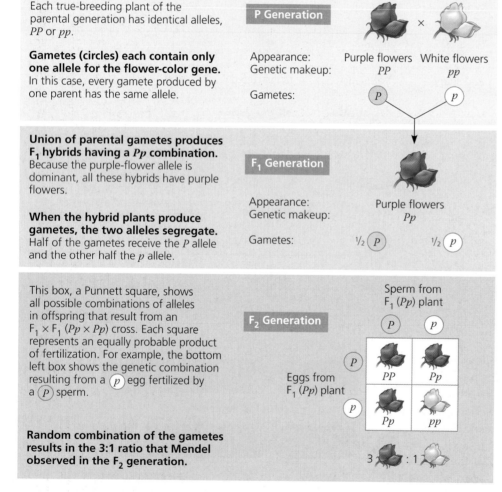

Each true-breeding plant of the parental generation has identical alleles, *PP* or *pp*.

Gametes (circles) each contain only one allele for the flower-color gene. In this case, every gamete produced by one parent has the same allele.

Union of parental gametes produces F_1 hybrids having a *Pp* combination. Because the purple-flower allele is dominant, all these hybrids have purple flowers.

When the hybrid plants produce gametes, the two alleles segregate. Half of the gametes receive the *P* allele and the other half the *p* allele.

This box, a Punnett square, shows all possible combinations of alleles in offspring that result from an $F_1 \times F_1$ (*Pp* × *Pp*) cross. Each square represents an equally probable product of fertilization. For example, the bottom left box shows the genetic combination resulting from a (*p*) egg fertilized by a (*P*) sperm.

Random combination of the gametes results in the 3:1 ratio that Mendel observed in the F_2 generation.

P Generation
Appearance: Purple flowers   White flowers
Genetic makeup: *PP*   *pp*
Gametes: (*P*)   (*p*)

F_1 Generation
Appearance: Purple flowers
Genetic makeup: *Pp*
Gametes: ½ (*P*)   ½ (*p*)

F_2 Generation
Sperm from F_1 (*Pp*) plant
Eggs from F_1 (*Pp*) plant

	P	*p*
P	*PP*	*Pp*
p	*Pp*	*pp*

3 : 1

▲ **Figure 14.5 Mendel's law of segregation.** This diagram shows the genetic makeup of the generations in Figure 14.3. It illustrates Mendel's model for inheritance of the alleles of a single gene. Each plant has two alleles for the gene controlling flower color, one allele inherited from each parent. To construct a Punnett square that predicts the F_2 generation offspring, we list all the possible gametes from one parent (here, the F_1 female) along the left side of the square and all the possible gametes from the other parent (here, the F_1 male) along the top. The boxes represent the offspring resulting from all the possible unions of male and female gametes.

Phenotype		Genotype	

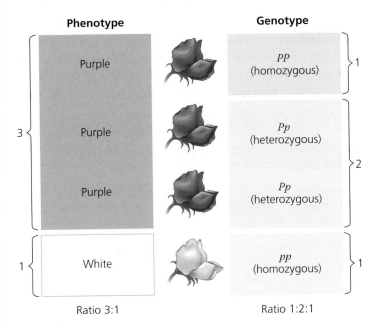

Purple — PP (homozygous) — 1

Purple — Pp (heterozygous)

Purple — Pp (heterozygous) — 2

{ 3

White — pp (homozygous) — 1

{ 1

Ratio 3:1   Ratio 1:2:1

▲ **Figure 14.6 Phenotype versus genotype.** Grouping F₂ offspring from a cross for flower color according to phenotype results in the typical 3:1 phenotypic ratio. In terms of genotype, however, there are actually two categories of purple-flowered plants, *PP* (homozygous) and *Pp* (heterozygous), giving a 1:2:1 genotypic ratio.

cross dominant homozygotes with recessive homozygotes, every offspring will have two different alleles—*Pp* in the case of the F₁ hybrids of our flower-color experiment (see Figure 14.5). An organism that has two different alleles for a gene is said to be **heterozygous** for that gene. Unlike homozygotes, heterozygotes are not true-breeding because they produce gametes with different alleles; for example, *P-* and *p*-containing gametes are both produced by the F₁ hybrids of Figure 14.5. As a result, self-pollination of those F₁ hybrids produces both purple-flowered and white-flowered offspring.

Because of the different effects of dominant and recessive alleles, an organism's traits do not always reveal its genetic composition. Therefore, we distinguish between an organism's appearance or observable traits, called its **phenotype**, and its genetic makeup, its **genotype**. In the case of flower color in pea plants, *PP* and *Pp* plants have the same phenotype (purple) but different genotypes. **Figure 14.6** reviews these terms. Note that "phenotype" refers to physiological traits as well as traits that relate directly to appearance. For example, there is a pea variety that lacks the normal ability to self-pollinate. This physiological variation (non-self-pollination) is a phenotypic trait.

The Testcross

Suppose we have a "mystery" pea plant that has purple flowers. We cannot tell from its flower color if this plant is homozygous (*PP*) or heterozygous (*Pp*) because both genotypes result in the same purple phenotype. To determine the genotype, we can cross this plant with a white-flowered plant (*pp*), which will

▼ **Figure 14.7 Research Method**

The Testcross

APPLICATION   An organism that exhibits a dominant trait, such as purple flowers in pea plants, can be either homozygous for the dominant allele or heterozygous. To determine the organism's genotype, geneticists can perform a testcross.

TECHNIQUE   In a testcross, the individual with the unknown genotype is crossed with a homozygous individual expressing the recessive trait (white flowers in this example), and Punnett squares are used to predict the possible outcomes.

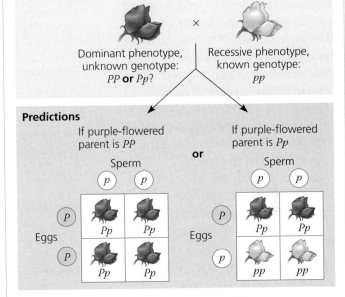

Dominant phenotype, unknown genotype: *PP* or *Pp*?   ×   Recessive phenotype, known genotype: *pp*

Predictions

If purple-flowered parent is *PP*   **or**   If purple-flowered parent is *Pp*

Sperm   Sperm

p   *p*   *p*   *p*

Eggs   *P* | *Pp* | *Pp*   Eggs   *P* | *Pp* | *Pp*
       P | *Pp* | *Pp*   *p* | *pp* | *pp*

RESULTS   Matching the results to either prediction identifies the unknown parental genotype (either *PP* or *Pp* in this example). In this testcross, we transferred pollen from a white-flowered plant to the carpels of a purple-flowered plant; the opposite (reciprocal) cross would have led to the same results.

All offspring purple   **or**   ½ offspring purple and ½ offspring white

make only gametes with the recessive allele (*p*). The allele in the gamete contributed by the mystery plant will therefore determine the appearance of the offspring **(Figure 14.7)**. If all the offspring of the cross have purple flowers, then the purple-flowered mystery plant must be homozygous for the dominant allele, because a *PP* × *pp* cross produces all *Pp* offspring. But if both the purple and the white phenotypes appear among the offspring, then the purple-flowered parent must be heterozygous. The offspring of a *Pp* × *pp* cross will have a 1:1 phenotypic ratio. Breeding an organism of unknown genotype with a recessive homozygote is called a **testcross** because it can reveal the genotype of that organism. The testcross was devised by Mendel and continues to be an important tool of geneticists.

The Law of Independent Assortment

Mendel derived the law of segregation from experiments in which he followed only a *single* character, such as flower color. All the F_1 progeny produced in his crosses of true-breeding parents were **monohybrids**, meaning that they were heterozygous for one character. We refer to a cross between such heterozygotes as a *monohybrid cross.*

Mendel identified his second law of inheritance by following *two* characters at the same time, such as seed color and seed shape. Seeds (peas) may be either yellow or green. They also may be either round (smooth) or wrinkled. From single-character crosses, Mendel knew that the allele for yellow seeds is dominant (Y) and the allele for green seeds is recessive (y). For the seed-shape character, the allele for round is dominant (R), and the allele for wrinkled is recessive (r).

Imagine crossing two true-breeding pea varieties that differ in *both* of these characters—a cross between a plant with yellow-round seeds ($YYRR$) and a plant with green-wrinkled seeds ($yyrr$). The F_1 plants will be **dihybrids**, individuals heterozygous for two characters ($YyRr$). But are these two characters transmitted from parents to offspring as a package? That is, will the Y and R alleles always stay together, generation after generation? Or are seed color and seed shape inherited independently? Figure 14.8 illustrates how a *dihybrid cross*, a cross between F_1 dihybrids, can determine which of these two hypotheses is correct.

The F_1 plants, of genotype $YyRr$, exhibit both dominant phenotypes, yellow seeds with round shapes, no matter which hypothesis is correct. The key step in the experiment is to see what happens when F_1 plants self-pollinate and produce F_2 offspring. If the hybrids must transmit their alleles in the same combinations in which the alleles were inherited from the P generation, then the F_1 hybrids will produce only two classes of gametes: YR and yr. This "dependent assortment" hypothesis predicts that the phenotypic ratio of the F_2 generation will be 3:1, just as in a monohybrid cross (Figure 14.8, left side).

The alternative hypothesis is that the two pairs of alleles segregate independently of each other. In other words, genes are packaged into gametes in all possible allelic combinations, as long as each gamete has one allele for each gene. In our example, an F_1 plant will produce four classes of gametes in equal quantities: YR,

Do the alleles for one character assort into gametes dependently or independently of the alleles for a different character?

EXPERIMENT   Gregor Mendel followed the characters of seed color and seed shape through the F_2 generation. He crossed a true-breeding plant with yellow-round seeds with a true-breeding plant with green-wrinkled seeds, producing dihybrid F_1 plants. Self-pollination of the F_1 dihybrids produced the F_2 generation. The two hypotheses (dependent and independent assortment) predict different phenotypic ratios.

RESULTS

315 ⬤   108 ⬤   101 🟫   32 🟫   Phenotypic ratio approximately 9:3:3:1

CONCLUSION   Only the hypothesis of independent assortment predicts the appearance of two of the observed phenotypes: green-round seeds and yellow-wrinkled seeds (see the right-hand Punnett square). The alleles for seed color and seed shape sort into gametes independently of each other.

SOURCE   G. Mendel, Experiments in plant hybridization, *Proceedings of the Natural History Society of Brünn* 4:3–47 (1866).

WHAT IF?   Suppose Mendel had transferred pollen from an F_1 plant to the carpel of a plant that was homozygous recessive for both genes. Set up the cross and draw Punnett squares that predict the offspring for both hypotheses. Would this cross have supported the hypothesis of independent assortment equally well?

Yr, yR, and *yr.* If sperm of the four classes fertilize eggs of the four classes, there will be 16 (4 × 4) equally probable ways in which the alleles can combine in the F₂ generation, as shown in Figure 14.8, right side. These combinations make up four phenotypic categories with a ratio of 9:3:3:1 (nine yellow-round to three green-round to three yellow-wrinkled to one green-wrinkled). When Mendel did the experiment and classified the F₂ offspring, his results were close to the predicted 9:3:3:1 phenotypic ratio, supporting the hypothesis that the alleles for one gene—controlling seed color or seed shape, in this example—are sorted into gametes independently of the alleles of other genes.

Mendel tested his seven pea characters in various dihybrid combinations and always observed a 9:3:3:1 phenotypic ratio in the F₂ generation. However, notice in Figure 14.8 that there is a 3:1 phenotypic ratio for each of the two characters if you consider them separately: three yellow to one green, and three round to one wrinkled. As far as a single character is concerned, the alleles segregate as if this were a monohybrid cross. The results of Mendel's dihybrid experiments are the basis for what we now call the **law of independent assortment**, which states that *each pair of alleles segregates independently of each other pair of alleles during gamete formation.*

Strictly speaking, this law applies only to genes (allele pairs) located on different chromosomes—that is, on chromosomes that are not homologous. Genes located near each other on the same chromosome tend to be inherited together and have more complex inheritance patterns than predicted by the law of independent assortment (see Chapter 15). All the pea characters Mendel chose for analysis were controlled by genes on different chromosomes (or behaved as though they were); this situation greatly simplified interpretation of his multicharacter pea crosses. All the examples we consider in the rest of this chapter involve genes located on different chromosomes.

The laws of probability govern Mendelian inheritance

Mendel's laws of segregation and independent assortment reflect the same rules of probability that apply to tossing coins, rolling dice, and drawing cards from a deck. The probability scale ranges from 0 to 1. An event that is certain to occur has a probability of 1, while an event that is certain *not* to occur has a probability of 0. With a coin that has heads on both sides, the probability of tossing heads is 1, and the probability of tossing tails is 0. With a normal coin, the chance of tossing heads is ½, and the chance of tossing tails is ½. The probability of drawing the ace of spades from a 52-card deck is ¹⁄₅₂. The probabilities of all possible outcomes for an event must add up to 1. With a deck of cards, the chance of picking a card other than the ace of spades is ⁵¹⁄₅₂.

Tossing a coin illustrates an important lesson about probability. For every toss, the probability of heads is ½. The outcome of any particular toss is unaffected by what has happened on previous trials. We refer to phenomena such as coin tosses as independent events. Each toss of a coin, whether done sequentially with one coin or simultaneously with many, is independent of every other toss. And like two separate coin tosses, the alleles of one gene segregate into gametes independently of another gene's alleles (the law of independent assortment). Two basic rules of probability can help us predict the outcome of the fusion of such gametes in simple monohybrid crosses and more complicated crosses.

The Multiplication and Addition Rules Applied to Monohybrid Crosses

How do we determine the probability that two or more independent events will occur together in some specific combination? For example, what is the chance that two coins tossed simultaneously will both land heads up? The *multiplication rule* states that to determine this probability, we multiply the probability of one event (one coin coming up heads) by the probability of the other event (the other coin coming up heads). By the multiplication rule, then, the probability that both coins will land heads up is ½ × ½ = ¼.

We can apply the same reasoning to an F₁ monohybrid cross. With seed shape in pea plants as the heritable character, the genotype of F₁ plants is *Rr*. Segregation in a heterozygous plant is like flipping a coin: Each egg produced has a ½ chance of carrying the dominant allele (*R*) and a ½ chance of carrying the recessive allele (*r*). The same odds apply to each sperm cell produced. For a particular F₂ plant to have wrinkled seeds, the recessive trait, both the egg and the sperm that come together must carry the *r* allele. The probability that two *r* alleles will be present in gametes at fertilization is found by multiplying ½ (the

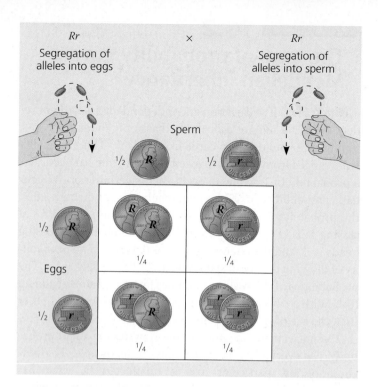

▲ Figure 14.9 Segregation of alleles and fertilization as chance events. When a heterozygote (*Rr*) forms gametes, whether a particular gamete ends up with an *R* or an *r* is like the toss of a coin. We can determine the probability for any genotype among the offspring of two heterozygotes by multiplying together the individual probabilities of an egg and sperm having a particular allele (*R* or *r* in this example).

probability that the egg will have an *r*) × ½ (the probability that the sperm will have an *r*). Thus, the multiplication rule tells us that the probability of an F_2 plant with wrinkled seeds (*rr*) is ¼ **(Figure 14.9)**. Likewise, the probability of an F_2 plant carrying both dominant alleles for seed shape (*RR*) is ¼.

To figure out the probability that an F_2 plant from a monohybrid cross will be heterozygous rather than homozygous, we need to invoke a second rule. Notice in Figure 14.9 that the dominant allele can come from the egg and the recessive allele from the sperm, or vice versa. That is, F_1 gametes can combine to produce *Rr* offspring in two independent and mutually exclusive ways: For any particular heterozygous F_2 plant, the dominant allele can come from the egg *or* the sperm, but not from both. According to the *addition rule*, the probability that any one of two or more mutually exclusive events will occur is calculated by adding their individual probabilities. As we have just seen, the multiplication rule gives us the individual probabilities that we will now add together. The probability for one possible way of obtaining an F_2 heterozygote—the dominant allele from the egg and the recessive allele from the sperm—is ¼. The probability for the other possible way—the recessive allele from the egg and the dominant allele from the sperm—is also ¼ (see Figure 14.9). Using the rule of addition, then, we can calculate the probability of an F_2 heterozygote as ¼ + ¼ = ½.

Solving Complex Genetics Problems with the Rules of Probability

We can also apply the rules of probability to predict the outcome of crosses involving multiple characters. Recall that each allelic pair segregates independently during gamete formation (the law of independent assortment). Thus, a dihybrid or other multicharacter cross is equivalent to two or more independent monohybrid crosses occurring simultaneously. By applying what we have learned about monohybrid crosses, we can determine the probability of specific genotypes occurring in the F_2 generation without having to construct unwieldy Punnett squares.

Consider the dihybrid cross between *YyRr* heterozygotes shown in Figure 14.8. We will focus first on the seed-color character. For a monohybrid cross of *Yy* plants, the probabilities of the offspring genotypes are ¼ for *YY*, ½ for *Yy*, and ¼ for *yy*. The same probabilities apply to the offspring genotypes for seed shape: ¼ *RR*, ½ *Rr*, and ¼ *rr*. Knowing these probabilities, we can simply use the multiplication rule to determine the probability of each of the genotypes in the F_2 generation. For example, the probability of an F_2 plant having the *YYRR* genotype is ¼ (*YY*) × ¼ (*RR*) = ¹⁄₁₆. This corresponds to the upper left box in the larger Punnett square in Figure 14.8. To give another example, the probability of an F_2 plant with the *YyRR* genotype is ½ (*Yy*) × ¼ (*RR*) = ⅛. If you look closely at the larger Punnett square in Figure 14.8, you will see that 2 of the 16 boxes (⅛) correspond to the *YyRR* genotype.

Now let's see how we can combine the multiplication and addition rules to solve even more complex problems in Mendelian genetics. For instance, imagine a cross of two pea varieties in which we track the inheritance of three characters. Suppose we cross a trihybrid with purple flowers and yellow, round seeds (heterozygous for all three genes) with a plant with purple flowers and green, wrinkled seeds (heterozygous for flower color but homozygous recessive for the other two characters). Using Mendelian symbols, our cross is *PpYyRr* × *Ppyyrr*. What fraction of offspring from this cross would be predicted to exhibit the recessive phenotypes for *at least two* of the three characters?

To answer this question, we can start by listing all genotypes that fulfill this condition: *ppyyRr*, *ppYyrr*, *Ppyyrr*, *PPyyrr*, and *ppyyrr*. (Because the condition is *at least two* recessive traits, it includes the last genotype, which produces all three recessive traits.) Next, we calculate the probability for each of these genotypes resulting from our *PpYyRr* × *Ppyyrr* cross by multiplying together the individual probabilities for the allele pairs, just as we did in our dihybrid example. Note that in a cross involving heterozygous and homozygous allele pairs (for example, *Yy* × *yy*), the probability of heterozygous offspring is ½ and the probability of homozygous offspring is ½. Finally, we use the addition rule to add the probabilities for all the different genotypes that fulfill the condition of at least two recessive traits, as shown below.

$ppyyRr$	¼ (probability of pp) × ½ (yy) × ½ (Rr) =	¹⁄₁₆
$ppYyrr$	¼ × ½ × ½	= ¹⁄₁₆
$Ppyyrr$	½ × ½ × ½	= ²⁄₁₆
$PPyyrr$	¼ × ½ × ½	= ¹⁄₁₆
$ppyyrr$	¼ × ½ × ½	= ¹⁄₁₆
Chance of *at least two* recessive traits		= ⁶⁄₁₆ or ³⁄₈

With practice, you'll be able to solve genetics problems faster by using the rules of probability than by filling in Punnett squares.

We cannot predict with certainty the exact numbers of progeny of different genotypes resulting from a genetic cross. But the rules of probability give us the *chance* of various outcomes. Usually, the larger the sample size, the closer the results will conform to our predictions. The reason Mendel counted so many offspring from his crosses is that he understood this statistical feature of inheritance and had a keen sense of the rules of chance.

CONCEPT CHECK 14.2

1. For any gene with a dominant allele C and recessive allele c, what proportions of the offspring from a $CC \times Cc$ cross are expected to be homozygous dominant, homozygous recessive, and heterozygous?

2. An organism with the genotype $BbDD$ is mated to one with the genotype $BBDd$. Assuming independent assortment of these two genes, write the genotypes of all possible offspring from this cross and use the rules of probability to calculate the chance of each genotype occurring.

3. **WHAT IF?** Three characters (flower color, seed color, and pod shape) are considered in a cross between two pea plants ($PpYyIi \times ppYyii$). What fraction of offspring would be predicted to be homozygous recessive for at least two of the three characters?

For suggested answers, see Appendix A.

CONCEPT 14.3

Inheritance patterns are often more complex than predicted by simple Mendelian genetics

In the 20th century, geneticists extended Mendelian principles not only to diverse organisms, but also to patterns of inheritance more complex than those described by Mendel. For the work that led to his two laws of inheritance, Mendel chose pea plant characters that turn out to have a relatively simple genetic basis: Each character is determined by one gene, for which there are only two

alleles, one completely dominant and the other completely recessive.* But these conditions are not met by all heritable characters, and the relationship between genotype and phenotype is rarely so simple. Mendel himself realized that he could not explain the more complicated patterns he observed in crosses involving other pea characters or other plant species. This does not diminish the utility of Mendelian genetics (also called Mendelism), however, because the basic principles of segregation and independent assortment apply even to more complex patterns of inheritance. In this section, we will extend Mendelian genetics to hereditary patterns that were not reported by Mendel.

Extending Mendelian Genetics for a Single Gene

The inheritance of characters determined by a single gene deviates from simple Mendelian patterns when alleles are not completely dominant or recessive, when a particular gene has more than two alleles, or when a single gene produces multiple phenotypes. We will describe examples of each of these situations in this section.

Degrees of Dominance

Alleles can show different degrees of dominance and recessiveness in relation to each other. In Mendel's classic pea crosses, the F_1 offspring always looked like one of the two parental varieties because one allele in a pair showed **complete dominance** over the other. In such situations, the phenotypes of the heterozygote and the dominant homozygote are indistinguishable.

For some genes, however, neither allele is completely dominant, and the F_1 hybrids have a phenotype somewhere between those of the two parental varieties. This phenomenon, called **incomplete dominance**, is seen when red snapdragons are crossed with white snapdragons: All the F_1 hybrids have pink flowers, as shown in **Figure 14.10** on the next page. This third phenotype results from flowers of the heterozygotes having less red pigment than the red homozygotes (unlike the situation in Mendel's pea plants, where the Pp heterozygotes make enough pigment for the flowers to be a purple color indistinguishable from that of PP plants).

At first glance, incomplete dominance of either allele seems to provide evidence for the blending hypothesis of inheritance, which would predict that the red or white trait could never be retrieved from the pink hybrids. In fact, interbreeding F_1 hybrids produces F_2 offspring with a phenotypic ratio of one red to two pink to one white. (Because heterozygotes have a separate phenotype, the genotypic and phenotypic ratios for the F_2 generation are the same, 1:2:1.) The segregation of the red-flower and white-flower alleles in the

---

* There is one exception: Geneticists have found that Mendel's pod-shape character is actually determined by two genes.

▲ **Figure 14.10 Incomplete dominance in snapdragon color.** When red snapdragons are crossed with white ones, the F₁ hybrids have pink flowers. Segregation of alleles into gametes of the F₁ plants results in an F₂ generation with a 1:2:1 ratio for both genotype and phenotype. The letter *C* with a superscript indicates an allele for flower color: C^R for red and C^W for white.

? *Suppose a classmate argues that this figure supports the blending hypothesis for inheritance. What might your classmate say, and how would you respond?*

gametes produced by the pink-flowered plants confirms that the alleles for flower color are heritable factors that maintain their identity in the hybrids; that is, inheritance is particulate.

Another variation on dominance relationships between alleles is called **codominance**; in this variation, the two alleles both affect the phenotype in separate, distinguishable ways. For example, the human MN blood group is determined by codominant alleles for two specific molecules located on the surface of red blood cells, the M and N molecules. A single gene locus, at which two allelic variations are possible, determines the phenotype of this blood group. Individuals homozygous for the *M* allele (*MM*) have red blood cells with only M molecules; individuals homozygous for the *N* allele (*NN*) have red blood cells with only N molecules. But *both* M and N molecules are present on the red blood cells of individuals heterozygous for the *M* and *N* alleles (*MN*). Note that the MN phenotype is *not* intermediate between the M and N phenotypes, which distinguishes codominance from incomplete

dominance. Rather, *both* M and N phenotypes are exhibited by heterozygotes, since both molecules are present.

The Relationship Between Dominance and Phenotype

We've now seen that the relative effects of two alleles range from complete dominance of one allele, through incomplete dominance of either allele, to codominance of both alleles. It is important to understand that an allele is not termed *dominant* because it somehow subdues a recessive allele. Recall that alleles are simply variations in a gene's nucleotide sequence. When a dominant allele coexists with a recessive allele in a heterozygote, they do not actually interact at all. It is in the pathway from genotype to phenotype that dominance and recessiveness come into play.

To illustrate the relationship between dominance and phenotype, we can use one of the characters Mendel studied—round versus wrinkled pea seed shape. The dominant allele (round) codes for an enzyme that helps convert an unbranched form of starch to a branched form in the seed. The recessive allele (wrinkled) codes for a defective form of this enzyme, leading to an accumulation of unbranched starch, which causes excess water to enter the seed by osmosis. Later, when the seed dries, it wrinkles. If a dominant allele is present, no excess water enters the seed and it does not wrinkle when it dries. One dominant allele results in enough of the enzyme to synthesize adequate amounts of branched starch, which means dominant homozygotes and heterozygotes have the same phenotype: round seeds.

A closer look at the relationship between dominance and phenotype reveals an intriguing fact: For any character, the observed dominant/recessive relationship of alleles depends on the level at which we examine phenotype. **Tay-Sachs disease**, an inherited disorder in humans, provides an example. The brain cells of a child with Tay-Sachs disease cannot metabolize certain lipids because a crucial enzyme does not work properly. As these lipids accumulate in brain cells, the child begins to suffer seizures, blindness, and degeneration of motor and mental performance and dies within a few years.

Only children who inherit two copies of the Tay-Sachs allele (homozygotes) have the disease. Thus, at the *organismal* level, the Tay-Sachs allele qualifies as recessive. However, the activity level of the lipid-metabolizing enzyme in heterozygotes is intermediate between that in individuals homozygous for the normal allele and that in individuals with Tay-Sachs disease. The intermediate phenotype observed at the *biochemical* level is characteristic of incomplete dominance of either allele. Fortunately, the heterozygote condition does not lead to disease symptoms, apparently because half the normal enzyme activity is sufficient to prevent lipid accumulation in the brain. Extending our analysis to yet another level, we find that heterozygous individuals produce equal numbers of normal and dysfunctional enzyme molecules. Thus, at the *molecular* level, the normal allele and the Tay-Sachs allele are codominant. As you can see, whether alleles appear to be completely dominant, incompletely dominant, or codominant depends on the level at which the phenotype is analyzed.

Frequency of Dominant Alleles Although you might assume that the dominant allele for a particular character would be more common in a population than the recessive allele for that character, this is not necessarily the case. For example, about one baby out of 400 in the United States is born with extra fingers or toes, a condition known as polydactyly. Some cases of polydactyly are caused by the presence of a dominant allele. The low frequency of polydactyly indicates that the recessive allele, which results in five digits per appendage, is far more prevalent than the dominant allele in the population. In Chapter 23, you will learn how the relative frequencies of alleles in a population are affected by natural selection.

Multiple Alleles

Only two alleles exist for the pea characters that Mendel studied, but most genes exist in more than two allelic forms. The ABO blood groups in humans, for instance, are determined by three alleles of a single gene: I^A, I^B, and i. A person's blood group (phenotype) may be one of four types: A, B, AB, or O. These letters refer to two carbohydrates—A and B—that may be found on the surface of red blood cells. A person's blood cells may have carbohydrate A (type A blood), carbohydrate B (type B), both (type AB), or neither (type O), as shown schematically in **Figure 14.11**. Matching compatible blood groups is critical for safe blood transfusions (see Chapter 43).

Pleiotropy

So far, we have treated Mendelian inheritance as though each gene affects only one phenotypic character. Most genes, however, have multiple phenotypic effects, a property called **pleiotropy** (from the Greek *pleion*, more). In humans, for example, pleiotropic alleles are responsible for the multiple symptoms associated with certain hereditary diseases, such as cystic fibrosis and sickle-cell disease, discussed later in this chapter. In the garden pea, the gene that determines flower color also affects the color of the coating on the outer surface of the seed, which can be gray or white. Given the intricate molecular and cellular interactions responsible for an organism's development and physiology, it isn't surprising that a single gene can affect a number of characteristics in an organism.

Extending Mendelian Genetics for Two or More Genes

Dominance relationships, multiple alleles, and pleiotropy all have to do with the effects of the alleles of a single gene. We now consider two situations in which two or more genes are involved in determining a particular phenotype.

Epistasis

In **epistasis** (from the Greek for "standing upon"), a gene at one locus alters the phenotypic expression of a gene at a second lo-

(a) The three alleles for the ABO blood groups and their associated carbohydrates. Each allele codes for an enzyme that may add a specific carbohydrate (designated by the superscript on the allele and shown as a triangle or circle) to the red blood cell.

(b) Blood group genotypes and phenotypes. There are six possible genotypes, resulting in four different phenotypes.

▲ **Figure 14.11 Multiple alleles for the ABO blood groups.** The four blood groups result from different combinations of three alleles.
? *Based on the surface carbohydrate phenotype in (b), what are the dominance relationships among the alleles?*

cus. An example will help clarify this concept. In mice and many other mammals, black coat color is dominant to brown. Let's designate B and b as the two alleles for this character. For a mouse to have brown fur, its genotype must be bb. But there is more to the story. A second gene determines whether or not pigment will be deposited in the hair. The dominant allele, symbolized by C (for color), results in the deposition of either black or brown pigment, depending on the genotype at the first locus. But if the mouse is homozygous recessive for the second locus (cc), then the coat is white (albino), regardless of the genotype at the black/brown locus. In this case, the gene for pigment deposition (C/c) is said to be epistatic to the gene that codes for black or brown pigment (B/b).

What happens if we mate black mice that are heterozygous for both genes ($BbCc$)? Although the two genes affect the same phenotypic character (coat color), they follow the law of independent assortment. Thus, our breeding experiment represents an F_1 dihybrid cross, like those that produced a 9:3:3:1

▲ **Figure 14.12 An example of epistasis.** This Punnett square illustrates the genotypes and phenotypes predicted for offspring of matings between two black mice of genotype *BbCc*. The *C/c* gene, which is epistatic to the *B/b* gene coding for hair pigment, controls whether or not pigment of any color will be deposited in the hair.

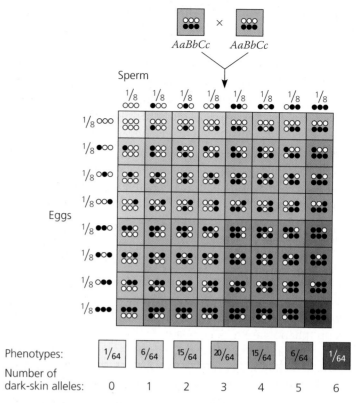

▲ **Figure 14.13 A simplified model for polygenic inheritance of skin color.** According to this model, three separately inherited genes affect the darkness of skin. The heterozygous individuals (*AaBbCc*) represented by the two rectangles at the top of this figure each carry three dark-skin alleles (black circles, which represent *A*, *B*, or *C*) and three light-skin alleles (white circles, which represent *a*, *b*, or *c*). The Punnett square shows all the possible genetic combinations in gametes and in offspring of a large number of hypothetical matings between these heterozygotes. The results are summarized by the phenotypic ratios under the Punnett square.

DRAW IT *Make a bar graph of the results, with skin color (number of dark-skin alleles) along the x-axis and fraction of offspring along the y-axis. Draw a rough curve corresponding to the results and discuss what it shows about the relative proportions of different phenotypes among the offspring.*

ratio in Mendel's experiments. We can use a Punnett square to represent the genotypes of the F$_2$ offspring (**Figure 14.12**). As a result of epistasis, the phenotypic ratio among the F$_2$ offspring is 9 black to 3 brown to 4 white. Other types of epistatic interactions produce different ratios, but all are modified versions of 9:3:3:1.

Polygenic Inheritance

Mendel studied characters that could be classified on an either-or basis, such as purple versus white flower color. But for many characters, such as human skin color and height, an either-or classification is impossible because the characters vary in the population along a continuum (in gradations). These are called **quantitative characters**. Quantitative variation usually indicates **polygenic inheritance**, an additive effect of two or more genes on a single phenotypic character (the converse of pleiotropy, where a single gene affects several phenotypic characters).

There is evidence, for instance, that skin pigmentation in humans is controlled by at least three separately inherited genes (probably more, but we will simplify). Let's consider three genes, with a dark-skin allele for each gene (*A*, *B*, or *C*) contributing one "unit" of darkness to the phenotype and be-

ing incompletely dominant to the other allele (*a*, *b*, or *c*). An *AABBCC* person would be very dark, while an *aabbcc* individual would be very light. An *AaBbCc* person would have skin of an intermediate shade. Because the alleles have a cumulative effect, the genotypes *AaBbCc* and *AABbcc* would make the same genetic contribution (three units) to skin darkness. The Punnett square in **Figure 14.13** shows all possible genotypes of offspring from a mating between individuals heterozygous for all three genes. As indicated by the row of squares below the Punnett square, there are seven skin-color phenotypes that could result from this mating. Environmental factors, such as exposure to the sun, also affect the skin-color phenotype.

Nature and Nurture: The Environmental Impact on Phenotype

Another departure from simple Mendelian genetics arises when the phenotype for a character depends on environment

▲ **Figure 14.14 The effect of environment on phenotype.**
The outcome of a genotype lies within its norm of reaction, a phenotypic range that depends on the environment in which the genotype is expressed. For example, hydrangea flowers of the same genetic variety range in color from blue-violet to pink, with the shade and intensity of color depending on the acidity and aluminum content of the soil.

as well as genotype. A single tree, locked into its inherited genotype, has leaves that vary in size, shape, and greenness, depending on exposure to wind and sun. For humans, nutrition influences height, exercise alters build, sun-tanning darkens the skin, and experience improves performance on intelligence tests. Even identical twins, who are genetic equals, accumulate phenotypic differences as a result of their unique experiences.

Whether human characteristics are more influenced by genes or the environment—nature or nurture—is a very old and hotly contested debate that we will not attempt to settle here. We can say, however, that a genotype generally is not associated with a rigidly defined phenotype, but rather with a range of phenotypic possibilities due to environmental influences. This phenotypic range is called the **norm of reaction** for a genotype (**Figure 14.14**). For some characters, such as the ABO blood group system, the norm of reaction has no breadth whatsoever; that is, a given genotype mandates a very specific phenotype. Other characteristics, such as a person's blood count of red and white cells, vary quite a bit, depending on such factors as the altitude, the customary level of physical activity, and the presence of infectious agents.

Generally, norms of reaction are broadest for polygenic characters. Environment contributes to the quantitative nature of these characters, as we have seen in the continuous variation of skin color. Geneticists refer to such characters as **multifactorial**, meaning that many factors, both genetic and environmental, collectively influence phenotype.

Integrating a Mendelian View of Heredity and Variation

Over the past several pages, we have broadened our view of Mendelian inheritance by exploring degrees of dominance as well as multiple alleles, pleiotropy, epistasis, polygenic inheritance, and the phenotypic impact of the environment. How

can we integrate these refinements into a comprehensive theory of Mendelian genetics? The key is to make the transition from the reductionist emphasis on single genes and phenotypic characters to the emergent properties of the organism as a whole, one of the themes of this book.

The term *phenotype* can refer not only to specific characters, such as flower color and blood group, but also to an organism in its entirety—*all* aspects of its physical appearance, internal anatomy, physiology, and behavior. Similarly, the term *genotype* can refer to an organism's entire genetic makeup, not just its alleles for a single genetic locus. In most cases, a gene's impact on phenotype is affected by other genes and by the environment. In this integrated view of heredity and variation, an organism's phenotype reflects its overall genotype and unique environmental history.

Considering all that can occur in the pathway from genotype to phenotype, it is indeed impressive that Mendel could uncover the fundamental principles governing the transmission of individual genes from parents to offspring. Mendel's two laws, segregation and independent assortment, explain heritable variations in terms of alternative forms of genes (hereditary "particles," now known as the alleles of genes) that are passed along, generation after generation, according to simple rules of probability. This theory of inheritance is equally valid for peas, flies, fishes, birds, and human beings—indeed for any organism with a sexual life cycle. Furthermore, by extending the principles of segregation and independent assortment to help explain such hereditary patterns as epistasis and quantitative characters, we begin to see how broadly Mendelism applies. From Mendel's abbey garden came a theory of particulate inheritance that anchors modern genetics. In the last section of this chapter, we will apply Mendelian genetics to human inheritance, with emphasis on the transmission of hereditary diseases.

CONCEPT CHECK 14.3

1. *Incomplete dominance* and *epistasis* are both terms that define genetic relationships. What is the most basic distinction between these terms?
2. If a man with type AB blood marries a woman with type O blood, what blood types would you expect in their children?
3. **WHAT IF?** A rooster with gray feathers is mated with a hen of the same phenotype. Among their offspring, 15 chicks are gray, 6 are black, and 8 are white. What is the simplest explanation for the inheritance of these colors in chickens? What phenotypes would you expect in the offspring of a cross between a gray rooster and a black hen?

For suggested answers, see Appendix A.

Many human traits follow Mendelian patterns of inheritance

Whereas peas are convenient subjects for genetic research, humans are not. The human generation span is about 20 years, and human parents produce relatively few offspring compared to peas and most other species. Even more important, no one would consider it ethical to ask pairs of humans to breed so that the phenotypes of their offspring could be analyzed! In spite of these constraints, the study of human genetics continues to advance, spurred on by the desire to understand our own inheritance. New techniques in molecular biology have led to many breakthrough discoveries, as we will see in Chapter 20, but basic Mendelism endures as the foundation of human genetics.

Pedigree Analysis

Unable to manipulate the mating patterns of people, geneticists must analyze the results of matings that have already occurred. They do so by collecting information about a family's history for a particular trait and assembling this information into a family tree describing the traits of parents and children across the generations—the family **pedigree**.

Figure 14.15a shows a three-generation pedigree that traces the occurrence of a pointed contour of the hairline on the forehead. This trait, called a widow's peak, is due to a dominant allele, *W*. Because the widow's-peak allele is dominant, all individuals who lack a widow's peak must be homozygous recessive (*ww*). The two grandparents with widow's peaks must have the *Ww* genotype, since some of their offspring are homozygous recessive. The offspring in the second generation who *do* have widow's peaks must also be heterozygous, because they are the products of *Ww* × *ww* matings. The third generation in this pedigree consists of two sisters. The one who has a widow's peak could be either homozygous (*WW*) or heterozygous (*Ww*), given what we know about the genotypes of her parents (both *Ww*).

Figure 14.15b is a pedigree of the same family, but this time we focus on a recessive trait, attached earlobes. We'll use *f* for the recessive allele and *F* for the dominant allele, which results in free earlobes. As you work your way through the pedigree, notice once again that you can apply what you have learned about Mendelian inheritance to understand the genotypes shown for the family members.

An important application of a pedigree is to help us calculate the probability that a child will have a particular genotype and phenotype. Suppose that the couple represented in the second generation of Figure 14.15 decides to have one more child. What is the probability that the child will have a widow's

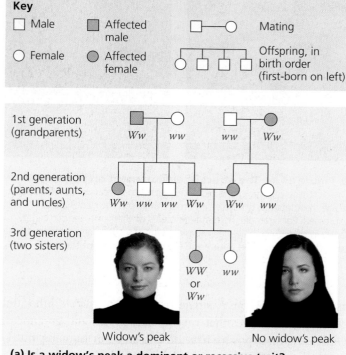

(a) Is a widow's peak a dominant or recessive trait?
Tips for pedigree analysis: Notice in the third generation that the second-born daughter lacks a widow's peak, although both of her parents had the trait. Such a pattern of inheritance supports the hypothesis that the trait is due to a dominant allele. If the trait were due to a *recessive* allele, and both parents had the recessive phenotype, then *all* of their offspring would also have the recessive phenotype.

(b) Is an attached earlobe a dominant or recessive trait?
Tips for pedigree analysis: Notice that the first-born daughter in the third generation has attached earlobes, although both of her parents lack that trait (they have free earlobes). Such a pattern is easily explained if the attached-lobe phenotype is due to a recessive allele. If it were due to a *dominant* allele, then at least one parent would also have had the trait.

▲ **Figure 14.15 Pedigree analysis.** Each of these pedigrees traces a trait through three generations of the same family. The two traits have different inheritance patterns, as seen by analysis of the pedigrees.

peak? This is equivalent to a Mendelian F_1 monohybrid cross ($Ww \times Ww$), and thus the probability that a child will inherit a dominant allele and have a widow's peak is $\frac{3}{4}$ ($\frac{1}{4}$ WW + $\frac{1}{2}$ Ww). What is the probability that the child will have attached earlobes? Again, we can treat this as a monohybrid cross ($Ff \times Ff$), but this time we want to know the chance that the offspring will be homozygous recessive (ff). That probability is $\frac{1}{4}$. Finally, what is the chance that the child will have a widow's peak *and* attached earlobes? Assuming that the genes for these two characters are on different chromosomes, the two pairs of alleles will assort independently in this dihybrid cross ($WwFf \times WwFf$). Thus, we can use the multiplication rule: $\frac{3}{4}$ (chance of widow's peak) $\times$ $\frac{1}{4}$ (chance of attached earlobes) = $\frac{3}{16}$ (chance of widow's peak and attached earlobes).

Pedigrees are a more serious matter when the alleles in question cause disabling or deadly diseases instead of innocuous human variations such as hairline or earlobe configuration. However, for disorders inherited as simple Mendelian traits, the same techniques of pedigree analysis apply.

Recessively Inherited Disorders

Thousands of genetic disorders are known to be inherited as simple recessive traits. These disorders range in severity from relatively mild, such as albinism (lack of pigmentation, which results in susceptibility to skin cancers and vision problems), to life-threatening, such as cystic fibrosis.

The Behavior of Recessive Alleles

How can we account for the behavior of alleles that cause recessively inherited disorders? Recall that genes code for proteins of specific function. An allele that causes a genetic disorder (let's call it allele *a*) codes either for a malfunctioning protein or for no protein at all. In the case of disorders classified as recessive, heterozygotes (Aa) are normal in phenotype because one copy of the normal allele (A) produces a sufficient amount of the specific protein. Thus, a recessively inherited disorder shows up only in the homozygous individuals (aa) who inherit one recessive allele from each parent. Although phenotypically normal with regard to the disorder, heterozygotes may transmit the recessive allele to their offspring and thus are called **carriers**. **Figure 14.16** illustrates these ideas using albinism as an example.

Most people who have recessive disorders are born to parents who are carriers of the disorder but themselves have a normal phenotype, as is the case shown in the Punnett square in Figure 14.16. A mating between two carriers corresponds to a Mendelian F_1 monohybrid cross, so the predicted genotypic ratio for the offspring is 1 AA : 2 Aa : 1 aa. Thus, each child has a $\frac{1}{4}$ chance of inheriting a double dose of the recessive allele; in the case of albinism, such a child will be albino. From the genotypic ratio, we also can see that out of three offspring with the *normal* phenotype (one AA plus two Aa), two are pre-

dicted to be heterozygous carriers, a $\frac{2}{3}$ chance. Recessive homozygotes could also result from $Aa \times aa$ and $aa \times aa$ matings, but if the disorder is lethal before reproductive age or results in sterility (neither of which is true for albinism), no aa individuals will reproduce. Even if recessive homozygotes are able to reproduce, such individuals will still account for a much smaller percentage of the population than heterozygous carriers (for reasons we will examine in Chapter 23).

In general, genetic disorders are not evenly distributed among all groups of people. For example, the incidence of Tay-Sachs disease, which we described earlier in this chapter, is disproportionately high among Ashkenazic Jews, Jewish people whose ancestors lived in central Europe. In that population, Tay-Sachs disease occurs in one out of 3,600 births, an incidence about 100 times greater than that among non-Jews or Mediterranean (Sephardic) Jews. This uneven distribution results from the different genetic histories of the world's peoples during less technological times, when populations were more geographically (and hence genetically) isolated.

When a disease-causing recessive allele is rare, it is relatively unlikely that two carriers of the same harmful allele will meet and mate. However, if the man and woman are close relatives (for example, siblings or first cousins), the probability of passing on recessive traits increases greatly. These are called consanguineous ("same blood") matings, and they are indicated in pedigrees by double lines. Because people with recent common ancestors are more likely to carry the same recessive alleles than are unrelated people, it is more likely that a mating of close relatives will produce offspring homozygous for recessive traits—including harmful ones. Such effects can be observed in many types of domesticated and zoo animals that have become inbred.

There is debate among geneticists about the extent to which human consanguinity increases the risk of inherited

▲ **Figure 14.16 Albinism: a recessive trait.** One of the two sisters shown here has normal coloration; the other is albino. Most recessive homozygotes are born to parents who are carriers of the disorder but themselves have a normal phenotype, the case shown in the Punnett square.

? *What is the probability that the sister with normal coloration is a carrier of the albinism allele?*

diseases. Many deleterious alleles have such severe effects that a homozygous embryo spontaneously aborts long before birth. Still, most societies and cultures have laws or taboos forbidding marriages between close relatives. These rules may have evolved out of empirical observation that in most populations, stillbirths and birth defects are more common when parents are closely related. Social and economic factors have also influenced the development of customs and laws against consanguineous marriages.

Cystic Fibrosis

The most common lethal genetic disease in the United States is **cystic fibrosis**, which strikes one out of every 2,500 people of European descent, though it is much rarer in other groups. Among people of European descent, one out of 25 (4%) are carriers of the cystic fibrosis allele. The normal allele for this gene codes for a membrane protein that functions in the transport of chloride ions between certain cells and the extracellular fluid. These chloride transport channels are defective or absent in the plasma membranes of children who inherit two recessive alleles for cystic fibrosis. The result is an abnormally high concentration of extracellular chloride, which causes the mucus that coats certain cells to become thicker and stickier than normal. The mucus builds up in the pancreas, lungs, digestive tract, and other organs, leading to multiple (pleiotropic) effects, including poor absorption of nutrients from the intestines, chronic bronchitis, and recurrent bacterial infections. Recent research indicates that the high concentration of extracellular chloride also contributes to infection by disabling a natural antibiotic made by some body cells. When immune cells come to the rescue, their remains add to the mucus, creating a vicious cycle.

If untreated, most children with cystic fibrosis die before their 5th birthday. But daily doses of antibiotics to prevent infection, gentle pounding on the chest to clear mucus from clogged airways, and other preventive treatments can prolong life. In the United States, more than half of those with cystic fibrosis now survive into their late 20s or even 30s and beyond.

Sickle-Cell Disease

The most common inherited disorder among people of African descent is **sickle-cell disease**, which affects one out of 400 African-Americans. Sickle-cell disease is caused by the substitution of a single amino acid in the hemoglobin protein of red blood cells. When the oxygen content of an affected individual's blood is low (at high altitudes or under physical stress, for instance), the sickle-cell hemoglobin molecules aggregate into long rods that deform the red cells into a sickle shape (see Figure 5.22). Sickled cells may clump and clog small blood vessels, often leading to other symptoms throughout the body, including physical weakness, pain, organ damage,

and even paralysis. The multiple effects of a double dose of the sickle-cell allele are another example of pleiotropy. Regular blood transfusions can ward off brain damage in children with sickle-cell disease, and new drugs can help prevent or treat other problems, but there is no cure.

Although two sickle-cell alleles are necessary for an individual to manifest full-blown sickle-cell disease, the presence of one sickle-cell allele can affect the phenotype. Thus, at the organismal level, the normal allele is incompletely dominant to the sickle-cell allele. Heterozygotes, said to have *sickle-cell trait*, are usually healthy, but they may suffer some sickle-cell symptoms during prolonged periods of reduced blood oxygen content. At the molecular level, the two alleles are codominant; both normal and abnormal (sickle-cell) hemoglobins are made in heterozygotes.

About one out of ten African-Americans have sickle-cell trait, an unusually high frequency of heterozygotes for an allele with severe detrimental effects in homozygotes. One explanation for this is that a single copy of the sickle-cell allele reduces the frequency and severity of malaria attacks, especially among young children. The malaria parasite spends part of its life cycle in red blood cells (see Figure 28.10), and the presence of even heterozygous amounts of sickle-cell hemoglobin results in lower parasite densities and hence reduced malaria symptoms. Thus, in tropical Africa, where infection with the malaria parasite is common, the sickle-cell allele is both boon and bane. The relatively high frequency of African-Americans with sickle-cell trait is a vestige of their African roots.

Dominantly Inherited Disorders

Although many harmful alleles are recessive, a number of human disorders are due to dominant alleles. One example is *achondroplasia*, a form of dwarfism that occurs in one of every 25,000 people. Heterozygous individuals have the dwarf phenotype **(Figure 14.17)**. Therefore, all people who are not achondroplastic dwarfs—99.99% of the population—are homozygous for the recessive allele. Like the presence of extra fingers or toes mentioned earlier, achondroplasia is a trait for which the recessive allele is much more prevalent than the corresponding dominant allele.

Dominant alleles that cause a lethal disease are much less common than recessive alleles that do so. All lethal alleles arise by mutations (changes to the DNA) in cells that produce sperm or eggs; presumably, such mutations occur equally often whether the mutant allele is dominant or recessive. However, if a lethal dominant allele causes the death of offspring before they mature and can reproduce, the allele will not be passed on to future generations. (In contrast, a lethal recessive allele can be perpetuated from generation to generation by heterozygous carriers who have normal phenotypes, since only homozygous recessive offspring will have the lethal disease.)

▲ **Figure 14.17 Achondroplasia: a dominant trait.** The late actor David Rappaport had achondroplasia, a form of dwarfism caused by a dominant allele (D). The allele might have arisen as a mutation in the egg or sperm of a parent or could have been inherited from an affected parent, as shown for an affected father in the Punnett square.

Huntington's Disease

A lethal dominant allele can escape elimination if it causes death only after an individual who carries the allele has reached a relatively advanced age. By the time the symptoms become evident, the individual may have already transmitted the lethal allele to his or her children. For example, **Huntington's disease**, a degenerative disease of the nervous system, is caused by a lethal dominant allele that has no obvious phenotypic effect until the individual is about 35 to 45 years old. Once the deterioration of the nervous system begins, it is irreversible and inevitably fatal. Any child born to a parent who has the allele for Huntington's disease has a 50% chance of inheriting the allele and the disorder (see the Punnett square in Figure 14.17). In the United States, this devastating disease afflicts about one in 10,000 people.

Until relatively recently, the onset of symptoms was the only way to know if a person had inherited the Huntington's allele. This is no longer the case. By analyzing DNA samples from a large family with a high incidence of the disorder, geneticists tracked the Huntington's allele to a locus near the tip of chromosome 4, and the gene has now been sequenced. This information led to development of a test that can detect the presence of the Huntington's allele in an individual's genome. (The methods that make such tests possible are discussed in Chapter 20.) The availability of this test poses an agonizing dilemma for those with a family history of Huntington's disease, such as relatives of the folk singer Woody Guthrie, who died of the disease. Does a person currently in good health benefit by finding out whether he or she has inherited a fatal and not yet curable disease? Some individuals may want to be tested for the disease before planning a family, whereas others may decide it would be too stressful to find out. Clearly, this is a personal decision.

Multifactorial Disorders

The hereditary diseases we have discussed so far are sometimes described as simple Mendelian disorders because they result from abnormality of one or both alleles at a single genetic locus. Many more people are susceptible to diseases that have a multifactorial basis—a genetic component plus a significant environmental influence. Heart disease, diabetes, cancer, alcoholism, certain mental illnesses such as schizophrenia and bipolar disorder, and many other diseases are multifactorial. In many cases, the hereditary component is polygenic. For example, many genes affect cardiovascular health, making some of us more prone than others to heart attacks and strokes. No matter what our genotype, however, our lifestyle has a tremendous effect on phenotype for cardiovascular health and other multifactorial characters. Exercise, a healthful diet, abstinence from smoking, and an ability to handle stressful situations all reduce our risk of heart disease and some types of cancer.

At present, so little is understood about the genetic contributions to most multifactorial diseases that the best public health strategy is to educate people about the importance of environmental factors and to promote healthful behavior.

Genetic Testing and Counseling

A preventive approach to simple Mendelian disorders is possible when the risk of a particular genetic disorder can be assessed before a child is conceived or during the early stages of the pregnancy. Many hospitals have genetic counselors who can provide information to prospective parents concerned about a family history for a specific disease.

Counseling Based on Mendelian Genetics and Probability Rules

Consider the case of a hypothetical couple, John and Carol. Both had a brother who died from the same recessively inherited lethal disease. Before conceiving their first child, John and Carol seek genetic counseling to determine the risk of having a child with the disease. From the information about their brothers, we know that both parents of John and both parents of Carol must have been carriers of the recessive allele. Thus, John and Carol are both products of $Aa \times Aa$ crosses, where a symbolizes the allele that causes this particular disease. We also know that John and Carol are not homozygous recessive (aa), because they do not have the disease. Therefore, their genotypes are either AA or Aa.

Given a genotypic ratio of 1 AA : 2 Aa : 1 aa for offspring of an $Aa \times Aa$ cross, John and Carol each have a ⅔ chance of being carriers (Aa). According to the rule of multiplication, the overall probability of their firstborn having the disorder is $\frac{2}{3}$ (the chance that John is a carrier) times $\frac{2}{3}$ (the chance that Carol is a carrier) times $\frac{1}{4}$ (the chance of two carriers having a child with the disease), which equals $\frac{1}{9}$. Suppose that Carol and John decide to have a child—after all, there is an $\frac{8}{9}$ chance that their baby will not have the disorder. If, despite these odds, their child is born with the disease, then we would know that *both* John and Carol are, in fact, carriers (*Aa* genotype). If both John and Carol are carriers, there is a $\frac{1}{4}$ chance that any subsequent child this couple has will have the disease.

When we use Mendel's laws to predict possible outcomes of matings, it is important to remember that each child represents an independent event in the sense that its genotype is unaffected by the genotypes of older siblings. Suppose that John and Carol have three more children, and *all three* have the hypothetical hereditary disease. There is only one chance in 64 ($\frac{1}{4} \times \frac{1}{4} \times \frac{1}{4}$) that such an outcome will occur. Despite this run of misfortune, the chance that still another child of this couple will have the disease remains $\frac{1}{4}$.

Tests for Identifying Carriers

Because most children with recessive disorders are born to parents with normal phenotypes, the key to accurately assessing the genetic risk for a particular disease is determining whether the prospective parents are heterozygous carriers of the recessive allele. For an increasing number of heritable disorders, tests are available that can distinguish individuals of normal phenotype who are dominant homozygotes from those who are heterozygotes. There are now tests that can identify carriers of the alleles for Tay-Sachs disease, sickle-cell disease, and the most common form of cystic fibrosis.

These tests for identifying carriers enable people with family histories of genetic disorders to make informed decisions about having children. But these new methods for genetic screening pose potential problems. If confidentiality is breached, will carriers be stigmatized? Will they be denied health or life insurance, even though they themselves are healthy? Will misinformed employers equate "carrier" with disease? And will sufficient genetic counseling be available to help a large number of individuals understand their test results? Advances in biotechnology offer possibilities for reducing human suffering, but not before key ethical issues are resolved.

Fetal Testing

Suppose a couple learns that they are both carriers of the Tay-Sachs allele, but they decide to have a child anyway. Tests performed in conjunction with a technique known as **amniocentesis** can determine, beginning at the 14th–16th week of pregnancy, whether the developing fetus has Tay-Sachs disease **(Figure 14.18a)**. To perform this procedure, a physician inserts a needle into the uterus and extracts about 10 mL of amniotic fluid, the liquid that bathes the fetus. Some genetic disorders can be detected from the presence of certain chemicals in the amniotic fluid itself. Tests for other disorders, including Tay-Sachs disease, are performed on cells cultured in the laboratory, descendants of the fetal cells sloughed off into the amniotic fluid. These cultured cells can also be used for karyotyping to identify certain chromosomal defects (see Figure 13.3).

In an alternative technique called **chorionic villus sampling (CVS)**, a physician inserts a narrow tube through the cervix into the uterus and suctions out a tiny sample of tissue from the placenta, the organ that transmits nutrients and fetal wastes between the fetus and the mother **(Figure 14.18b)**. The cells of the chorionic villi of the placenta, the portion sampled, are derived from the fetus and have the same genotype as the new individual. These cells are proliferating rapidly enough to allow karyotyping to be carried out immediately. This rapid analysis is an advantage over amniocentesis, in which the cells must be cultured for several weeks before karyotyping. Another advantage of CVS is that it can be performed as early as the 8th–10th week of pregnancy. However, CVS is not suitable for tests requiring amniotic fluid. Recently, medical scientists have developed methods for isolating fetal cells that have escaped into the mother's blood. Although very few in number, these cells can be cultured and then tested.

Imaging techniques allow a physician to examine a fetus directly for major anatomical abnormalities. In the *ultrasound* technique, sound waves are used to produce an image of the fetus by a simple noninvasive procedure. In *fetoscopy*, a needle-thin tube containing a viewing scope and fiber optics (to transmit light) is inserted into the uterus.

Ultrasound has no known risk to either mother or fetus, while the other procedures can cause complications in a small percentage of cases. Previously, amniocentesis or CVS for diagnostic testing was generally offered only to women over age 35, due to their increased risk of bearing a child with Down syndrome. In 2007, however, reassessment of the risks and possible benefits led to a change in the recommended practice, and now such testing is offered to all pregnant women. If the fetal tests reveal a serious disorder, the parents face the difficult choice of terminating the pregnancy or preparing to care for a child with a genetic disorder.

Newborn Screening

Some genetic disorders can be detected at birth by simple tests that are now routinely performed in most hospitals in the United States. One common screening program is for phenylketonuria (PKU), a recessively inherited disorder that occurs in about one out of every 10,000 to 15,000 births in the United States. Children with this disease cannot properly metabolize the amino acid phenylalanine. This compound and its by-product, phenylpyruvate, can accumulate to toxic levels in the blood, causing mental retardation. However, if the deficiency is detected in the newborn, a special diet low in phenylalanine will usually allow normal development and prevent retardation. Unfortunately, very few other genetic disorders are treatable at the present time.

Screening of newborns and fetuses for serious inherited diseases, tests for identifying carriers, and genetic counseling all rely on the Mendelian model of inheritance. We owe the "gene idea"—the concept of particulate heritable factors transmitted according to simple rules of chance—to the elegant quantitative experiments of Gregor Mendel. The importance of his discoveries was overlooked by most biologists until early in the 20th century, several decades after his findings were reported. In the next chapter, you will learn how Mendel's laws have their physical basis in the behavior of chromosomes during sexual life cycles and how the synthesis of Mendelism and a chromosome theory of inheritance catalyzed progress in genetics.

CONCEPT CHECK 14.4

1. Beth and Tom each have a sibling with cystic fibrosis, but neither Beth nor Tom nor any of their parents have the disease. Calculate the probability that if this couple has a child, the child will have cystic fibrosis. What would be the probability if a test revealed that Tom is a carrier but Beth is not?
2. Joan was born with six toes on each foot, a dominant trait called polydactyly. Two of her five siblings and her mother, but not her father, also have extra digits. What is Joan's genotype for the number-of-digits character? Explain your answer. Use *D* and *d* to symbolize the alleles for this character.
3. **WHAT IF?** What would you suspect if Peter was born with polydactyly, but neither of his biological parents had extra digits?

For suggested answers, see Appendix A.

(a) Amniocentesis

❶ A sample of amniotic fluid can be taken starting at the 14th to 16th week of pregnancy.

❷ Biochemical tests can be performed immediately on the amniotic fluid or later on the cultured cells.

❸ Fetal cells must be cultured for several weeks to obtain sufficient numbers for karyotyping.

Amniotic fluid withdrawn

Fetus
Placenta
Uterus Cervix

Centrifugation

Fluid
Fetal cells

Several hours

Several weeks

Several weeks

Biochemical tests

Karyotyping

(b) Chorionic villus sampling (CVS)

❶ A sample of chorionic villus tissue can be taken as early as the 8th to 10th week of pregnancy.

Fetus

Suction tube inserted through cervix

Placenta Chorionic villi

Several hours

Fetal cells

❷ Karyotyping and biochemical tests can be performed on the fetal cells immediately, providing results within a day or so.

Several hours

▲ **Figure 14.18 Testing a fetus for genetic disorders.** Biochemical tests may detect substances associated with particular disorders. Karyotyping shows whether the chromosomes of the fetus are normal in number and appearance.

Chapter **14** Review

MEDIA Go to the Study Area at **www.masteringbio.com** for BioFlix 3-D animations, MP3 Tutors, Videos, Practice Tests, an eBook, and more.

SUMMARY OF KEY CONCEPTS

CONCEPT **14.1**

Mendel used the scientific approach to identify two laws of inheritance (pp. 262–269)

▶ **Mendel's Experimental, Quantitative Approach** In the 1860s, Gregor Mendel formulated a theory of inheritance based on experiments with garden peas, proposing that parents pass on to their offspring discrete genes that retain their identity through generations.

▶ **The Law of Segregation** Genes have alternative forms, or alleles. In a diploid organism, the two alleles of a gene segregate (separate) during gamete formation; each sperm or egg carries only one allele of each pair. This law explains the 3:1 ratio of F_2 phenotypes observed when monohybrids self-pollinate. Each organism inherits one allele for each gene from each parent. In heterozygotes, the two alleles are different, and expression of one (the dominant allele) masks the phenotypic effect of the other (the recessive allele). Homozygotes have identical alleles of a given gene and are true-breeding.

▶ **The Law of Independent Assortment** Each pair of alleles (for one gene) segregates into gametes independently of the pair of alleles for any other gene. In a cross between dihybrids (individuals heterozygous for two genes), the offspring have four phenotypes in a 9:3:3:1 ratio.

> **MEDIA**
>
> **MP3 Tutor** Chromosomal Basis of Inheritance
> **Activity** Monohybrid Cross
> **Activity** Dihybrid Cross
> **Biology Labs On-Line** PedigreeLab
> **Biology Labs On-Line** FlyLab

CONCEPT **14.2**

The laws of probability govern Mendelian inheritance (pp. 269–271)

▶ **The Multiplication and Addition Rules Applied to Monohybrid Crosses** The multiplication rule states that the probability of a compound event is equal to the product of the individual probabilities of the independent single events. The addition rule states that the probability of an event that can occur in two or more independent, mutually exclusive ways is the sum of the individual probabilities.

▶ **Solving Complex Genetics Problems with the Rules of Probability** A dihybrid or other multicharacter cross is equivalent to two or more independent monohybrid crosses occurring simultaneously. In calculating the chances of the various offspring genotypes from such crosses, each character first is considered separately and then the individual probabilities are multiplied.

MEDIA
Activity Gregor's Garden

CONCEPT **14.3**

Inheritance patterns are often more complex than predicted by simple Mendelian genetics (pp. 271–275)

▶ **Extending Mendelian Genetics for a Single Gene**

Degree of dominance	Description	Example
Complete dominance of one allele	Heterozygous phenotype same as that of homozygous dominant	PP Pp
Incomplete dominance of either allele	Heterozygous phenotype intermediate between the two homozygous phenotypes	$C^R C^R$ $C^R C^W$ $C^W C^W$
Codominance	Heterozygotes: Both phenotypes expressed	$I^A I^B$
Multiple alleles	In the whole population, some genes have more than two alleles	ABO blood group alleles I^A, I^B, i
Pleiotropy	One gene is able to affect multiple phenotypic characters	Sickle-cell disease

▶ **Extending Mendelian Genetics for Two or More Genes**

Relationship among genes	Description	Example
Epistasis	One gene affects the expression of another	$BbCc$ × $BbCc$ 9 : 3 : 4
Polygenic inheritance	A single phenotypic character is affected by two or more genes	$AaBbCc$ × $AaBbCc$

▶ **Nature and Nurture: The Environmental Impact on Phenotype** The expression of a genotype can be affected by environmental influences. The phenotypic range of a particular genotype is called its norm of reaction. Polygenic characters that are also influenced by the environment are called multifactorial characters.

▶ **Integrating a Mendelian View of Heredity and Variation** An organism's overall phenotype, including its physical appearance, internal anatomy, physiology, and behavior, reflects its overall genotype and unique environmental history. Even in more complex inheritance patterns, Mendel's fundamental laws of segregation and independent assortment still apply.

Activity Incomplete Dominance

CONCEPT **14.4**

Many human traits follow Mendelian patterns of inheritance (pp. 276–281)

▶ **Pedigree Analysis** Family pedigrees can be used to deduce the possible genotypes of individuals and make predictions about future offspring. Predictions are usually statistical probabilities rather than certainties.

▶ **Recessively Inherited Disorders** Many genetic disorders are inherited as simple recessive traits. Most affected (ho-

mozygous recessive) individuals are children of phenotypically normal, heterozygous carriers.

▶ **Dominantly Inherited Disorders** Lethal dominant alleles are eliminated from the population if affected people die before reproducing. Nonlethal dominant alleles and lethal ones that strike relatively late in life are inherited in a Mendelian way.

▶ **Multifactorial Disorders** Many human diseases have both genetic and environmental components and do not follow simple Mendelian inheritance patterns.

▶ **Genetic Testing and Counseling** Using family histories, genetic counselors help couples determine the odds that their children will have genetic disorders. Amniocentesis and chorionic villus sampling can indicate whether a suspected genetic disorder is present in a fetus. Other genetic tests can be performed after birth.

Investigation How Do You Diagnose a Genetic Disorder?

TESTING YOUR KNOWLEDGE

TIPS FOR GENETICS PROBLEMS

1. Write down symbols for the alleles. (These may be given in the problem.) When represented by single letters, the dominant allele is uppercase and the recessive is lowercase.

2. Write down the possible genotypes, as determined by the phenotype.
   a. If the phenotype is that of the dominant trait (for example, purple flowers), then the genotype is either homozygous dominant or heterozygous (*PP* or *Pp*, in this example).
   b. If the phenotype is that of the recessive trait, the genotype must be homozygous recessive (for example, *pp*).
   c. If the problem says "true-breeding," the genotype is homozygous.

3. Determine what the problem is asking for. If asked to do a cross, write it out in the form [Genotype] × [Genotype], using the alleles you've decided on.

4. To figure out the outcome of a cross, set up a Punnett square.
   a. Put the gametes of one parent at the top and those of the other on the left. To determine the allele(s) in each gamete for a given genotype, set up a systematic way to list all the possibilities. (Remember, each gamete has one allele of each gene.) Note that there are 2^n possible types of gametes, where *n* is the number of gene loci that are heterozygous. For example, an individual with genotype *AaBbCc* would produce $2^3 = 8$ types of gametes. Write the genotypes of the gametes in circles above the columns and to the left of the rows.
   b. Fill in the Punnett square as if each possible sperm were fertilizing each possible egg, making all of the possible offspring. In a cross of *AaBbCc* × *AaBbCc*, for example, the Punnett square would have 8 columns and 8 rows, so there are 64 different offspring; you would know the genotype of each and thus the phenotype. Count genotypes and phenotypes to obtain the genotypic and phenotypic ratios.

5. You can use the rules of probability if the Punnett square would be too big. (For example, see Genetics Problem 4.) You can consider each gene separately (see pp. 270–271).

6. If, instead, the problem gives you the phenotypic ratios of offspring, but not the genotypes of the parents in a given cross, the phenotypes can help you deduce the parents' unknown genotypes.
   a. For example, if ½ the offspring have the recessive phenotype and ½ the dominant, you know that the cross was between a heterozygote and a homozygous recessive.
   b. If the ratio is 3:1, the cross was between two heterozygotes.
   c. If two genes are involved and you see a 9:3:3:1 ratio in the offspring, you know that each parent is heterozygous for both genes. Caution: Don't assume that the reported numbers will exactly equal the predicted ratios. For example, if there are 13 offspring with the dominant trait and 11 with the recessive, assume that the ratio is one dominant to one recessive.

7. For pedigree problems, use the tips in Figure 14.15 and below to determine what kind of trait is involved.
   a. If parents without the trait have offspring with the trait, the trait must be recessive and the parents both carriers.
   b. If the trait is seen in every generation, it is most likely dominant (see the next possibility, though).
   c. If both parents have the trait, then in order for it to be recessive, all offspring must show the trait.
   d. To determine the likely genotype of a certain individual in a pedigree, first label the genotypes of all the family members you can. Even if some of the genotypes are incomplete, label what you do know. For example, if an individual has the dominant phenotype, the genotype must be *AA* or *Aa*; you can write this as *A_*. Try different possibilities to see which fits the results. Use the rules of probability to calculate the probability of each possible genotype being the correct one.

GENETICS PROBLEMS

1. Match each term on the left with a statement on the right.

Term	Statement
__ Gene	a. Has no effect on phenotype in a heterozygote
__ Allele	
__ Character	b. A variant for a character
__ Trait	c. Having two identical alleles for a gene
__ Dominant allele	d. A cross between individuals heterozygous for a single character
__ Recessive allele	
__ Genotype	e. An alternative version of a gene
__ Phenotype	f. Having two different alleles for a gene
__ Homozygous	g. A heritable feature that varies among individuals
__ Heterozygous	
__ Testcross	h. An organism's appearance or observable traits
__ Monohybrid cross	
	i. A cross between an individual with an unknown genotype and a homozygous recessive individual
	j. Determines phenotype in a heterozygote
	k. The genetic makeup of an individual
	l. A heritable unit that determines a character; can exist in different forms

2. **DRAW IT** Two pea plants heterozygous for the characters of pod color and pod shape are crossed. Draw a Punnett square to determine the phenotypic ratios of the offspring.

3. In some plants, a true-breeding, red-flowered strain gives all pink flowers when crossed with a white-flowered strain: $C^R C^R$ (red) $\times$ $C^W C^W$ (white) $\rightarrow$ $C^R C^W$ (pink). If flower position (axial or terminal) is inherited as it is in peas (see Table 14.1), what will be the ratios of genotypes and phenotypes of the F_1 generation resulting from the following cross: axial-red (true-breeding) $\times$ terminal-white? What will be the ratios in the F_2 generation?

4. Flower position, stem length, and seed shape were three characters that Mendel studied. Each is controlled by an independently assorting gene and has dominant and recessive expression as follows:

Character	Dominant	Recessive
Flower position	Axial (A)	Terminal (a)
Stem length	Tall (T)	Dwarf (t)
Seed shape	Round (R)	Wrinkled (r)

   If a plant that is heterozygous for all three characters is allowed to self-fertilize, what proportion of the offspring would you expect to be as follows? (*Note:* Use the rules of probability instead of a huge Punnett square.)
   a. homozygous for the three dominant traits
   b. homozygous for the three recessive traits
   c. heterozygous for all three characters
   d. homozygous for axial and tall, heterozygous for seed shape

5. A black guinea pig crossed with an albino guinea pig produces 12 black offspring. When the albino is crossed with a second black one, 7 blacks and 5 albinos are obtained. What is the best

6. In sesame plants, the one-pod condition (P) is dominant to the three-pod condition (p), and normal leaf (L) is dominant to wrinkled leaf (l). Pod type and leaf type are inherited independently. Determine the genotypes for the two parents for all possible matings producing the following offspring:
   a. 318 one-pod, normal leaf and 98 one-pod, wrinkled leaf
   b. 323 three-pod, normal leaf and 106 three-pod, wrinkled leaf
   c. 401 one-pod, normal leaf
   d. 150 one-pod, normal leaf, 147 one-pod, wrinkled leaf, 51 three-pod, normal leaf, and 48 three-pod, wrinkled leaf
   e. 223 one-pod, normal leaf, 72 one-pod, wrinkled leaf, 76 three-pod, normal leaf, and 27 three-pod, wrinkled leaf

7. A man with type A blood marries a woman with type B blood. Their child has type O blood. What are the genotypes of these individuals? What other genotypes, and in what frequencies, would you expect in offspring from this marriage?

8. Phenylketonuria (PKU) is an inherited disease caused by a recessive allele. If a woman and her husband, who are both carriers, have three children, what is the probability of each of the following?
   a. All three children are of normal phenotype.
   b. One or more of the three children have the disease.
   c. All three children have the disease.
   d. At least one child is phenotypically normal.
   (*Note:* Remember that the probabilities of all possible outcomes always add up to 1.)

9. The genotype of F_1 individuals in a tetrahybrid cross is *AaBbCcDd*. Assuming independent assortment of these four genes, what are the probabilities that F_2 offspring will have the following genotypes?
   a. *aabbccdd*
   b. *AaBbCcDd*
   c. *AABBCCDD*
   d. *AaBBccDd*
   e. *AaBBCCdd*

10. What is the probability that each of the following pairs of parents will produce the indicated offspring? (Assume independent assortment of all gene pairs.)
    a. *AABBCC* $\times$ *aabbcc* $\rightarrow$ *AaBbCc*
    b. *AABbCc* $\times$ *AaBbCc* $\rightarrow$ *AAbbCC*
    c. *AaBbCc* $\times$ *AaBbCc* $\rightarrow$ *AaBbCc*
    d. *aaBbCC* $\times$ *AABbcc* $\rightarrow$ *AaBbCc*

11. Karen and Steve each have a sibling with sickle-cell disease. Neither Karen nor Steve nor any of their parents have the disease, and none of them have been tested to see if they have the sickle-cell trait. Based on this incomplete information, calculate the probability that if this couple has a child, the child will have sickle-cell disease.

12. In 1981, a stray black cat with unusual rounded, curled-back ears was adopted by a family in California. Hundreds of descendants of the cat have since been born, and cat fanciers

hope to develop the curl cat into a show breed. Suppose you owned the first curl cat and wanted to develop a true-breeding variety. How would you determine whether the curl allele is dominant or recessive? How would you obtain true-breeding curl cats? How could you be sure they are true-breeding?

13. Imagine that a newly discovered, recessively inherited disease is expressed only in individuals with type O blood, although the disease and blood group are independently inherited. A normal man with type A blood and a normal woman with type B blood have already had one child with the disease. The woman is now pregnant for a second time. What is the probability that the second child will also have the disease? Assume that both parents are heterozygous for the gene that causes the disease.

14. In tigers, a recessive allele causes an absence of fur pigmentation (a white tiger) and a cross-eyed condition. If two phenotypically normal tigers that are heterozygous at this locus are mated, what percentage of their offspring will be cross-eyed? What percentage of cross-eyed tigers will be white?

15. In maize (corn) plants, a dominant allele *I* inhibits kernel color, while the recessive allele *i* permits color when homozygous. At a different locus, the dominant allele *P* causes purple kernel color, while the homozygous recessive genotype *pp* causes red kernels. If plants heterozygous at both loci are crossed, what will be the phenotypic ratio of the offspring?

16. The pedigree below traces the inheritance of alkaptonuria, a biochemical disorder. Affected individuals, indicated here by the colored circles and squares, are unable to metabolize a substance called alkapton, which colors the urine and stains body tissues. Does alkaptonuria appear to be caused by a dominant allele or by a recessive allele? Fill in the genotypes of the individuals whose genotypes can be deduced. What genotypes are possible for each of the other individuals?

17. A man has six fingers on each hand and six toes on each foot. His wife and their daughter have the normal number of digits. Extra digits is a dominant trait. What fraction of this couple's children would be expected to have extra digits?

18. Imagine that you are a genetic counselor, and a couple planning to start a family comes to you for information. Charles was married once before, and he and his first wife had a child with cystic fibrosis. The brother of his current wife, Elaine, died of cystic fibrosis. What is the probability that Charles and Elaine will have a baby with cystic fibrosis? (Neither Charles nor Elaine has cystic fibrosis.)

19. In mice, black color (*B*) is dominant to white (*b*). At a different locus, a dominant allele (*A*) produces a band of yellow just below the tip of each hair in mice with black fur. This gives a frosted appearance known as agouti. Expression of the recessive allele (*a*) results in a solid coat color. If mice that are heterozygous at both loci are crossed, what is the expected phenotypic ratio of their offspring?

For Genetics Problems answers, see Appendix A.

MEDIA Visit the Study Area at **www.masteringbio.com** for a Practice Test.

EVOLUTION CONNECTION

20. Over the past half century, there has been a trend in the United States and other developed countries for people to marry and start families later in life than did their parents and grandparents. What effects might this trend have on the incidence (frequency) of late-acting dominant lethal alleles in the population?

SCIENTIFIC INQUIRY

21. You are handed a mystery pea plant with tall stems and axial flowers and asked to determine its genotype as quickly as possible. You know that the allele for tall stems (*T*) is dominant to that for dwarf stems (*t*) and that the allele for axial flowers (*A*) is dominant to that for terminal flowers (*a*).
   a. What are *all* the possible genotypes for your mystery plant?
   b. Describe the *one* cross you would do, out in your garden, to determine the exact genotype of your mystery plant.
   c. While waiting for the results of your cross, you predict the results for each possible genotype listed in part a. How do you do this? Why is this not called "performing a cross"?
   d. Explain how the results of your cross and your predictions will help you learn the genotype of your mystery plant.

SCIENCE, TECHNOLOGY, AND SOCIETY

22. Imagine that one of your parents had Huntington's disease. What is the probability that you, too, will someday manifest the disease? There is no cure for Huntington's. Would you want to be tested for the Huntington's allele? Why or why not?

The Chromosomal Basis of Inheritance

15

OVERVIEW

Locating Genes Along Chromosomes

Gregor Mendel's "hereditary factors" were purely an abstract concept when he proposed their existence in 1860. At that time, no cellular structures were known that could house these imaginary units. Even after chromosomes were first observed, many biologists remained skeptical about Mendel's laws of segregation and independent assortment until there was sufficient evidence that these principles of heredity had a physical basis in chromosomal behavior.

Today, we can show that genes—Mendel's "factors"—are located along chromosomes. We can see the location of a particular gene by tagging chromosomes with a fluorescent dye that highlights that gene. For example, the yellow dots in **Figure 15.1** mark the locus of a specific gene on a homologous pair of human chromosomes. (Because the chromosomes in this light micrograph have already replicated, we see two dots per chromosome, one on each sister chromatid.) In this chapter, which integrates and extends what you learned in the past two chapters, we describe the chromosomal basis for the transmission of genes from parents to offspring, along with some important exceptions to the standard mode of inheritance.

CONCEPT 15.1

Mendelian inheritance has its physical basis in the behavior of chromosomes

Using improved techniques of microscopy, cytologists worked out the process of mitosis in 1875 and meiosis in the 1890s. Cytology and genetics converged when biologists began to see parallels between the behavior of chromosomes and the behavior of Mendel's proposed hereditary factors during sexual life cycles: Chromosomes and genes are both present in pairs in diploid cells; homologous chromosomes separate and alleles segregate during the process of meiosis; and fertilization restores the paired condition for both chromosomes and genes. Around 1902, Walter S. Sutton, Theodor Boveri, and others independently noted these parallels, and the **chromosome theory of inheritance** began to take form. According to this theory, Mendelian genes have specific loci (positions) along chromosomes, and it is the chromosomes that undergo segregation and independent assortment.

Figure 15.2 shows that the behavior of homologous chromosomes during meiosis can account for the segregation of the alleles at each genetic locus to different gametes. The figure also shows that the behavior of nonhomologous chromosomes can account for the independent assortment of the alleles for two or more genes located on different chromosomes. By carefully studying this figure, which traces the same dihybrid pea cross you learned about in Figure 14.8, you can see how the behavior of chromosomes during meiosis in the F_1 generation and subsequent random fertilization give rise to the F_2 phenotypic ratio observed by Mendel.

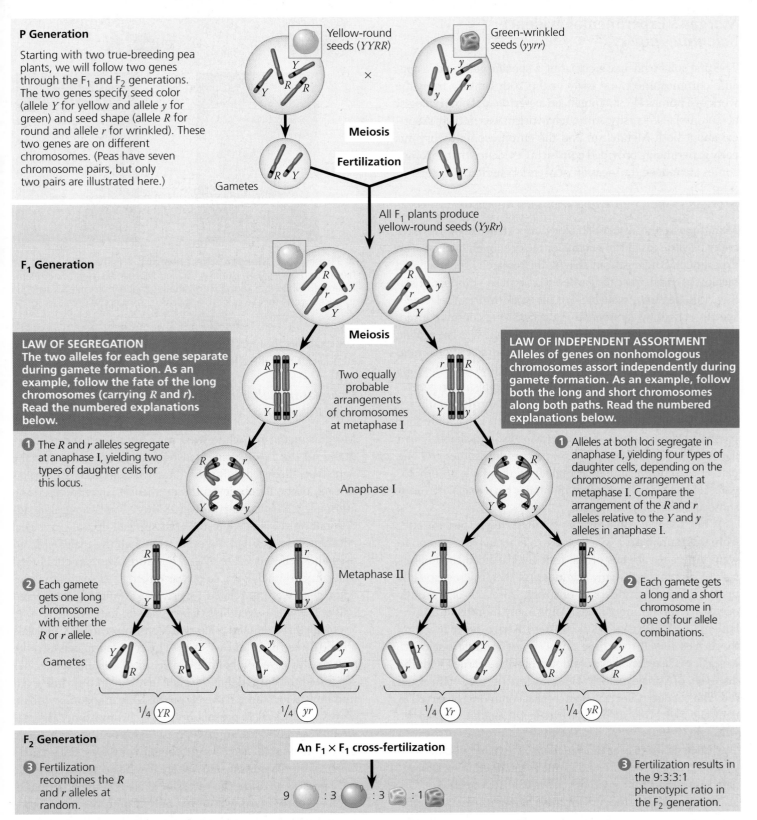

P Generation

Starting with two true-breeding pea plants, we will follow two genes through the F_1 and F_2 generations. The two genes specify seed color (allele *Y* for yellow and allele *y* for green) and seed shape (allele *R* for round and allele *r* for wrinkled). These two genes are on different chromosomes. (Peas have seven chromosome pairs, but only two pairs are illustrated here.)

Yellow-round seeds (*YYRR*)

Green-wrinkled seeds (*yyrr*)

Meiosis

Fertilization

Gametes

All F_1 plants produce yellow-round seeds (*YyRr*)

F_1 Generation

LAW OF SEGREGATION
The two alleles for each gene separate during gamete formation. As an example, follow the fate of the long chromosomes (carrying *R* and *r*). Read the numbered explanations below.

Meiosis

Two equally probable arrangements of chromosomes at metaphase I

LAW OF INDEPENDENT ASSORTMENT
Alleles of genes on nonhomologous chromosomes assort independently during gamete formation. As an example, follow both the long and short chromosomes along both paths. Read the numbered explanations below.

❶ The *R* and *r* alleles segregate at anaphase I, yielding two types of daughter cells for this locus.

Anaphase I

❶ Alleles at both loci segregate in anaphase I, yielding four types of daughter cells, depending on the chromosome arrangement at metaphase I. Compare the arrangement of the *R* and *r* alleles relative to the *Y* and *y* alleles in anaphase I.

Metaphase II

❷ Each gamete gets one long chromosome with either the *R* or *r* allele.

Gametes

❷ Each gamete gets a long and a short chromosome in one of four allele combinations.

¼ (YR)   ¼ (yr)   ¼ (Yr)   ¼ (yR)

F_2 Generation

❸ Fertilization recombines the *R* and *r* alleles at random.

An $F_1 \times F_1$ cross-fertilization

9   :3   :3   :1

❸ Fertilization results in the 9:3:3:1 phenotypic ratio in the F_2 generation.

▲ **Figure 15.2 The chromosomal basis of Mendel's laws.** Here we correlate the results of one of Mendel's dihybrid crosses (see Figure 14.8) with the behavior of chromosomes during meiosis (see Figure 13.8). The arrangement of chromosomes at metaphase I of meiosis and their movement during anaphase I account for the segregation and independent assortment of the alleles for seed color and shape. Each cell that undergoes meiosis in an F_1 plant produces two kinds of gametes. If we count the results for all cells, however, each F_1 plant produces equal numbers of all four kinds of gametes because the alternative chromosome arrangements at metaphase I are equally likely.

? *If you crossed an F_1 plant with a plant that was homozygous recessive for both genes (yyrr), how would the phenotypic ratio of the offspring compare with the 9:3:3:1 ratio seen here?*

Morgan's Experimental Evidence: Scientific Inquiry

The first solid evidence associating a specific gene with a specific chromosome came early in the 20th century from the work of Thomas Hunt Morgan, an experimental embryologist at Columbia University. Although Morgan was initially skeptical about both Mendelism and the chromosome theory, his early experiments provided convincing evidence that chromosomes are indeed the location of Mendel's heritable factors.

Morgan's Choice of Experimental Organism

Many times in the history of biology, important discoveries have come to those insightful enough or lucky enough to choose an experimental organism suitable for the research problem being tackled. Mendel chose the garden pea because a number of distinct varieties were available. For his work, Morgan selected a species of fruit fly, *Drosophila melanogaster*, a common insect that feeds on the fungi growing on fruit. Fruit flies are prolific breeders; a single mating will produce hundreds of offspring, and a new generation can be bred every two weeks. Morgan's laboratory began using this convenient organism for genetic studies in 1907 and soon became known as "the fly room."

Another advantage of the fruit fly is that it has only four pairs of chromosomes, which are easily distinguishable with a light microscope. There are three pairs of autosomes and one pair of sex chromosomes. Female fruit flies have a homologous pair of X chromosomes, and males have one X chromosome and one Y chromosome.

While Mendel could readily obtain different pea varieties from seed suppliers, Morgan was probably the first person to want different varieties of the fruit fly. He faced the tedious task of carrying out many matings and then microscopically inspecting large numbers of offspring in search of naturally occurring variant individuals. After many months of this, he lamented, "Two years' work wasted. I have been breeding those flies for all that time and I've got nothing out of it." Morgan persisted, however, and was finally rewarded with the discovery of a single male fly with white eyes instead of the usual red. The phenotype for a character most commonly observed in natural populations, such as red eyes in *Drosophila*, is called the **wild type** (**Figure 15.3**). Traits that are alternatives to the wild type, such as white eyes in *Drosophila*, are called *mutant phenotypes* because they are due to alleles assumed to have originated as changes, or mutations, in the wild-type allele.

Morgan and his students invented a notation for symbolizing alleles in *Drosophila* that is still widely used for fruit flies. For a given character in flies, the gene takes its symbol from the first mutant (non–wild type) discovered. Thus, the allele for white eyes in *Drosophila* is symbolized by *w*. A superscript + identifies the allele for the wild-type trait—w^+ for the allele for red eyes, for example. Over the years, a variety of gene notation systems have been developed for different organisms.

▲ **Figure 15.3 Morgan's first mutant.** Wild-type *Drosophila* flies have red eyes (left). Among his flies, Morgan discovered a mutant male with white eyes (right). This variation made it possible for Morgan to trace a gene for eye color to a specific chromosome (LMs).

For example, human genes are usually written in all capitals, such as *HD* for the allele for Huntington's disease.

Correlating Behavior of a Gene's Alleles with Behavior of a Chromosome Pair

Morgan mated his white-eyed male fly with a red-eyed female. All the F_1 offspring had red eyes, suggesting that the wild-type allele is dominant. When Morgan bred the F_1 flies to each other, he observed the classical 3:1 phenotypic ratio among the F_2 offspring. However, there was a surprising additional result: The white-eye trait showed up only in males. All the F_2 females had red eyes, while half the males had red eyes and half had white eyes. Therefore, Morgan concluded that somehow a fly's eye color was linked to its sex. (If the eye-color gene were unrelated to sex, one would have expected half of the white-eyed flies to be male and half female.)

Recall that a female fly has two X chromosomes (XX), while a male fly has an X and a Y (XY). The correlation between the trait of white eye color and the male sex of the affected F_2 flies suggested to Morgan that the gene involved in his white-eyed mutant was located exclusively on the X chromosome, with no corresponding allele present on the Y chromosome. His reasoning can be followed in **Figure 15.4**. For a male, a single copy of the mutant allele would confer white eyes; since a male has only one X chromosome, there can be no wild-type allele (w^+) present to offset the recessive allele. On the other hand, a female could have white eyes only if both her X chromosomes carried the recessive mutant allele (w). This was impossible for the F_2 females in Morgan's experiment because all the F_1 fathers had red eyes.

Morgan's finding of the correlation between a particular trait and an individual's sex provided support for the chromosome theory of inheritance: namely, that a specific gene is carried on a specific chromosome (in this case, an eye-color gene

In a cross between a wild-type female fruit fly and a mutant white-eyed male, what color eyes will the F₁ and F₂ offspring have?

EXPERIMENT   Thomas Hunt Morgan wanted to analyze the behavior of two alleles of a fruit fly eye-color gene. In crosses similar to those done by Mendel with pea plants, Morgan and his colleagues mated a wild-type (red-eyed) female with a mutant white-eyed male.

Morgan then bred an F₁ red-eyed female to an F₁ red-eyed male to produce the F₂ generation.

RESULTS   The F₂ generation showed a typical Mendelian ratio of 3 red-eyed flies : 1 white-eyed fly. However, no females displayed the white-eye trait; all white-eyed flies were males.

CONCLUSION   All F₁ offspring had red eyes, so the mutant white-eye trait (*w*) must be recessive to the wild-type red-eye trait (*w⁺*). Since the recessive trait—white eyes—was expressed only in males in the F₂ generation, Morgan deduced that this eye-color gene is located on the X chromosome and that there is no corresponding locus on the Y chromosome.

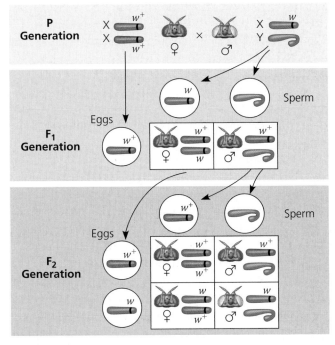

SOURCE   T. H. Morgan, Sex-limited inheritance in *Drosophila*, *Science* 32:120–122 (1910).

WHAT IF?   Suppose this eye-color gene were located on an autosome. Predict the phenotypes (including gender) of the F₂ flies in this hypothetical cross. (*Hint:* Draw a Punnett square.)

---

on the X chromosome). In addition, Morgan's work indicated that genes located on a sex chromosome exhibit unique inheritance patterns, which we will discuss in the next section. Recognizing the importance of Morgan's early work, many bright students were attracted to his fly room.

CONCEPT CHECK   15.1

1. Which one of Mendel's laws relates to the inheritance of alleles for a single character? Which law relates to the inheritance of alleles for two characters in a dihybrid cross?
2. What is the physical basis of Mendel's laws?
3. **WHAT IF?**   Propose a possible reason that the first naturally occurring mutant fruit fly Morgan saw involved a gene on a sex chromosome.

For suggested answers, see Appendix A.

CONCEPT   15.2
Sex-linked genes exhibit unique patterns of inheritance

As you just learned, Morgan's discovery of a trait (white eyes) that correlated with the sex of flies was a key episode in the development of the chromosome theory of inheritance. Because the identity of the sex chromosomes in an individual could be inferred by observing the sex of the fly, the behavior of the two members of the pair of sex chromosomes could be correlated with the behavior of the two alleles of the eye-color gene. In this section, we consider the role of sex chromosomes in inheritance in more detail. We begin by reviewing the chromosomal basis of sex determination in humans and some other animals.

The Chromosomal Basis of Sex

Whether we are male or female is one of our more obvious phenotypic characters. Although the anatomical and physiological differences between women and men are numerous, the chromosomal basis for determining sex is rather simple. In humans and other mammals, there are two varieties of sex chromosomes, designated X and Y. The Y chromosome is much smaller than the X chromosome (**Figure 15.5**). A person who inherits two X chromosomes, one from each parent, usually develops as a female. A male develops from a zygote containing one X chromosome and one Y chromosome

▲ **Figure 15.5** **Human sex chromosomes.**

(Figure 15.6a). Short segments at either end of the Y chromosome are the only regions that are homologous with corresponding regions of the X. These homologous regions allow the X and Y chromosomes in males to pair and behave like homologous chromosomes during meiosis in the testes.

(a) The X-Y system. In mammals, the sex of an offspring depends on whether the sperm cell contains an X chromosome or a Y.

(b) The X-0 system. In grasshoppers, cockroaches, and some other insects, there is only one type of sex chromosome, the X. Females are XX; males have only one sex chromosome (X0). Sex of the offspring is determined by whether the sperm cell contains an X chromosome or no sex chromosome.

(c) The Z-W system. In birds, some fishes, and some insects, the sex chromosomes present in the egg (not the sperm) determine the sex of offspring. The sex chromosomes are designated Z and W. Females are ZW and males are ZZ.

(d) The haplo-diploid system. There are no sex chromosomes in most species of bees and ants. Females develop from fertilized eggs and are thus diploid. Males develop from unfertilized eggs and are haploid; they have no fathers.

▲ **Figure 15.6 Some chromosomal systems of sex determination.** Numerals indicate the number of autosomes in the species pictured. In *Drosophila*, males are XY, but sex depends on the ratio between the number of X chromosomes and the number of autosome sets, not simply on the presence of a Y chromosome.

In both testes and ovaries, the two sex chromosomes segregate during meiosis, and each gamete receives one. Each egg contains one X chromosome. In contrast, sperm fall into two categories: Half the sperm cells a male produces contain an X chromosome, and half contain a Y chromosome. We can trace the sex of each offspring to the moment of conception: If a sperm cell bearing an X chromosome happens to fertilize an egg, the zygote is XX, a female; if a sperm cell containing a Y chromosome fertilizes an egg, the zygote is XY, a male (see Figure 15.6a). Thus, sex determination is a matter of chance—a fifty-fifty chance. Besides the mammalian X-Y system, three other chromosomal systems for determining sex are shown in **Figure 15.6b–d**.

In humans, the anatomical signs of sex begin to emerge when the embryo is about 2 months old. Before then, the rudiments of the gonads are generic—they can develop into either testes or ovaries, depending on whether or not a Y chromosome is present. In 1990, a British research team identified a gene on the Y chromosome required for the development of testes. They named the gene *SRY*, for *s*ex-determining *r*egion of *Y*. In the absence of *SRY*, the gonads develop into ovaries. The biochemical, physiological, and anatomical features that distinguish males and females are complex, and many genes are involved in their development. In fact, *SRY* codes for a protein that regulates other genes.

Researchers have sequenced the human Y chromosome and have identified 78 genes, which code for about 25 proteins (some genes are duplicates). About half of these genes are expressed only in the testis, and some are required for normal testicular functioning. In their absence, an XY individual is male but does not produce normal sperm.

Inheritance of Sex-Linked Genes

In addition to their role as carriers of genes that determine sex, the sex chromosomes, especially X chromosomes, have genes for many characters unrelated to sex. A gene located on either sex chromosome is called a **sex-linked gene**, although in humans the term has historically referred specifically to a gene on the X chromosome. Sex-linked genes in humans follow the same pattern of inheritance that Morgan observed for the eye-color locus he studied in *Drosophila* (see Figure 15.4). Fathers pass sex-linked alleles to all of their daughters but to none of their sons. In contrast, mothers can pass sex-linked alleles to both sons and daughters, as shown in **Figure 15.7**.

If a sex-linked trait is due to a recessive allele, a female will express the phenotype only if she is a homozygote. Because males have only one locus, the terms *homozygous* and *heterozygous* lack meaning for describing their sex-linked genes; the term *hemizygous* is used in such cases. Any male receiving the recessive allele from his mother will express the trait. For this reason, far more males than females have sex-linked recessive disorders. However, even though the chance of a female inheriting a double dose of the mutant allele is much less

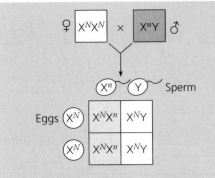

(a) A color-blind father will transmit the mutant allele to all daughters but to no sons. When the mother is a dominant homozygote, the daughters will have the normal phenotype but will be carriers of the mutation.

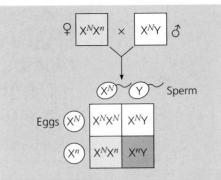

(b) If a carrier mates with a male who has normal color vision, there is a 50% chance that each daughter will be a carrier like her mother and a 50% chance that each son will have the disorder.

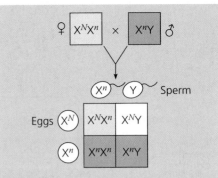

(c) If a carrier mates with a color-blind male, there is a 50% chance that each child born to them will have the disorder, regardless of sex. Daughters who have normal color vision will be carriers, whereas males who have normal color vision will be free of the recessive allele.

▲ **Figure 15.7 The transmission of sex-linked recessive traits.** In this diagram, color blindness is used as an example. The superscript N represents the dominant allele for normal color vision carried on the X chromosome, and the superscript n represents the recessive allele, which has a mutation causing color blindness. White boxes indicate unaffected individuals, light orange boxes indicate carriers, and dark orange boxes indicate color-blind individuals.

? *If a color-blind woman married a man who had normal color vision, what would be the probable phenotypes of their children?*

than the probability of a male inheriting a single dose, there *are* females with sex-linked disorders. For instance, color blindness is a mild disorder inherited as a sex-linked trait. A color-blind daughter may be born to a color-blind father whose mate is a carrier (see Figure 15.7c). Because the sex-linked allele for color blindness is relatively rare, though, the probability that such a man and woman will mate is low.

A number of human sex-linked disorders are much more serious than color blindness. An example is **Duchenne muscular dystrophy**, which affects about one out of every 3,500 males born in the United States. The disease is characterized by a progressive weakening of the muscles and loss of coordination. Affected individuals rarely live past their early 20s. Researchers have traced the disorder to the absence of a key muscle protein called dystrophin and have mapped the gene for this protein to a specific locus on the X chromosome.

Hemophilia is a sex-linked recessive disorder defined by the absence of one or more of the proteins required for blood clotting. When a person with hemophilia is injured, bleeding is prolonged because a firm clot is slow to form. Small cuts in the skin are usually not a problem, but bleeding in the muscles or joints can be painful and can lead to serious damage. Today, people with hemophilia are treated as needed with intravenous injections of the missing protein.

X Inactivation in Female Mammals

Since female mammals, including humans, inherit two X chromosomes, you may wonder whether females make twice as much of the proteins encoded by genes on the X chromosome, compared to the amounts in males. In fact, one X chromosome in each cell in females becomes almost completely inactivated during embryonic development. As a result, the cells of females and males have the same effective dose (one copy) of these genes. The inactive X in each cell of a female condenses into a compact object called a **Barr body**, which lies along the inside of the nuclear envelope. Most of the genes of the X chromosome that forms the Barr body are not expressed. In the ovaries, Barr-body chromosomes are reactivated in the cells that give rise to eggs, so every female gamete has an active X.

British geneticist Mary Lyon demonstrated that selection of which X chromosome will form the Barr body occurs randomly and independently in each embryonic cell present at the time of X inactivation. As a consequence, females consist of a *mosaic* of two types of cells: those with the active X derived from the father and those with the active X derived from the mother. After an X chromosome is inactivated in a particular cell, all mitotic descendants of that cell have the same inactive X. Thus, if a female is heterozygous for a sex-linked trait, about half her cells will express one allele, while the others will express the alternate allele. **Figure 15.8**, on the next page, shows how this mosaicism results in the mottled coloration of a tortoiseshell cat. In humans, mosaicism can be observed in a recessive X-linked mutation that prevents the development of sweat glands. A woman who is heterozygous for this trait has patches of normal skin and patches of skin lacking sweat glands.

Inactivation of an X chromosome involves modification of the DNA, including attachment of methyl groups ($-CH_3$) to one of the nitrogenous bases of DNA nucleotides. (The regulatory role of DNA methylation is discussed further in Chapter 18.) Researchers also have discovered an X chromosome gene called *XIST* (for *X-i*nactive *s*pecific *t*ranscript) that is active

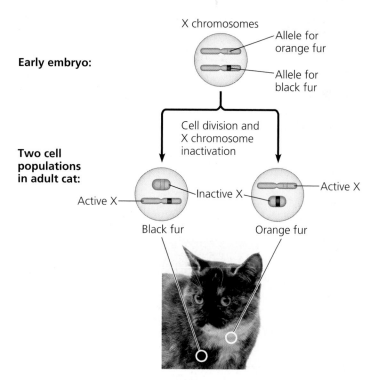

Early embryo:

X chromosomes — Allele for orange fur

Allele for black fur

Cell division and X chromosome inactivation

Two cell populations in adult cat:

Active X — Inactive X — Active X

Black fur   Orange fur

▲ **Figure 15.8 X inactivation and the tortoiseshell cat.** The tortoiseshell gene is on the X chromosome, and the tortoiseshell phenotype requires the presence of two different alleles, one for orange fur and one for black fur. Normally, only females can have both alleles, because only they have two X chromosomes. If a female is heterozygous for the tortoiseshell gene, she is tortoiseshell. Orange patches are formed by populations of cells in which the X chromosome with the orange allele is active; black patches have cells in which the X chromosome with the black allele is active. ("Calico" cats also have white areas, which are determined by yet another gene.)

only on the Barr-body chromosome. Multiple copies of the RNA product of this gene apparently attach to the X chromosome on which they are made, eventually almost covering it. Interaction of this RNA with the chromosome seems to initiate X inactivation, and regulation of this process by other genes is currently an active area of research.

CONCEPT 15.3

Linked genes tend to be inherited together because they are located near each other on the same chromosome

The number of genes in a cell is far greater than the number of chromosomes; in fact, each chromosome has hundreds or thousands of genes. (Only 78 genes have been identified so far on the Y chromosome, but more may be found as methods for analyzing genetic sequences become more refined.) Genes located on the same chromosome that tend to be inherited together in genetic crosses are said to be **linked genes**. (Note the distinction between the terms *sex-linked gene*, referring to a single gene on a sex chromosome, and *linked genes*, referring to two or more genes on the same chromosome that tend to be inherited together.) When geneticists follow linked genes in breeding experiments, the results deviate from those expected from Mendel's law of independent assortment.

How Linkage Affects Inheritance

To see how linkage between genes affects the inheritance of two different characters, let's examine another of Morgan's *Drosophila* experiments. In this case, the characters are body color and wing size, each with two different phenotypes. Wild-type flies have gray bodies and normal-sized wings. In addition to these flies, Morgan had doubly mutant flies with black bodies and wings much smaller than normal, called vestigial wings. The mutant alleles are recessive to the wild-type alleles, and neither gene is on a sex chromosome. In his investigation of these two genes, Morgan carried out the crosses shown in **Figure 15.9**.

In these crosses, Morgan observed a much higher proportion of parental phenotypes than would be expected if the two genes assorted independently. Based on these results, he concluded that body color and wing size are usually inherited together in specific combinations (the parental combinations) because the genes for these characters are on the same chromosome:

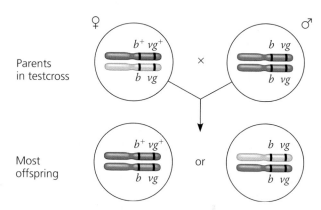

Parents in testcross

Most offspring

How does linkage between two genes affect inheritance of characters?

EXPERIMENT Morgan wanted to know whether the genes for body color and wing size were on the same chromosome, and if so, how this affected their inheritance. The alleles for body color are b^+ (gray) and b (black), and those for wing size are vg^+ (normal) and vg (vestigial).

Morgan first mated true-breeding wild-type flies with black, vestigial-winged flies to produce heterozygous F_1 dihybrids ($b^+ b$ $vg^+ vg$), all of which are wild-type in appearance.

He then mated wild-type F_1 dihybrid females with black, vestigial-winged males.

The male's sperm contributes only recessive alleles, so the phenotype of the offspring reflects the genotype of the female's eggs.

Note: Although only females (with pointed abdomen) are shown, half the offspring in each class would be male (with rounded abdomen).

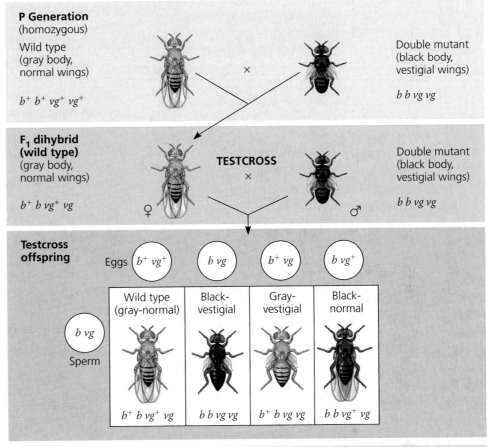

PREDICTED RATIOS

If genes are located on different chromosomes:	1	:	1	:	1	:	1
If genes are located on the same chromosome *and* parental alleles are always inherited together:	1	:	1	:	0	:	0
RESULTS	965	:	944	:	206	:	185

CONCLUSION Since most offspring had a parental phenotype, Morgan concluded that the genes for body color and wing size are located on the same chromosome. However, the production of a relatively small number of offspring with nonparental phenotypes indicated that some mechanism occasionally breaks the linkage between specific alleles of genes on the same chromosome.

SOURCE T. H. Morgan, The explanation of a new sex ratio in *Drosophila*, *Science* 36:718–720 (1912).

WHAT IF? If the parental flies had been true-breeding for gray body with vestigial wings and black body with normal wings, which phenotypic class(es) would be largest among the testcross offspring?

However, as Figure 15.9 shows, both of the nonparental phenotypes were also produced in Morgan's experiments, suggesting that the body-color and wing-size genes are only partially linked genetically. To understand this conclusion, we need to further explore **genetic recombination**, the production of offspring with combinations of traits that differ from those found in either parent.

Genetic Recombination and Linkage

In Chapter 13, you learned that meiosis and random fertilization generate genetic variation among offspring of sexually reproducing organisms. Here we will examine the chromosomal basis of recombination in relation to the genetic findings of Mendel and Morgan.

Recombination of Unlinked Genes: Independent Assortment of Chromosomes

Mendel learned from crosses in which he followed two characters that some offspring have combinations of traits that do not match those of either parent. For example, we can represent the cross between a pea plant with yellow-round seeds that is heterozygous for both seed color and seed shape (*YyRr*) and a plant with green-wrinkled seeds (homozygous for both recessive alleles, *yyrr*) by the following Punnett square

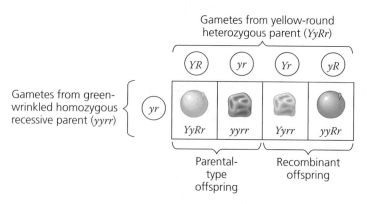

Notice in this Punnett square that one-half of the offspring are expected to inherit a phenotype that matches one of the parental phenotypes. These offspring are called **parental types**. But two nonparental phenotypes are also found among the offspring. Because these offspring have new combinations of seed shape and color, they are called **recombinant types**, or **recombinants** for short. When 50% of all offspring are recombinants, as in this example, geneticists say that there is a 50% frequency of recombination. The predicted phenotypic ratios among the offspring are similar to what Mendel actually found in *YyRr × yyrr* crosses (a type of testcross).

A 50% frequency of recombination in such testcrosses is observed for any two genes that are located on different chromosomes and are thus unlinked. The physical basis of recombination between unlinked genes is the random orientation of homologous chromosomes at metaphase I of meiosis, which leads to the independent assortment of the two unlinked genes (see Figure 13.11 and the question in the Figure 15.2 legend).

Recombination of Linked Genes: Crossing Over

Now let's return to Morgan's fly room to see how we can explain the results of the *Drosophila* testcross illustrated in Figure 15.9. Recall that most of the offspring from the testcross for body color and wing size had parental phenotypes. That suggested that the two genes were on the same chromosome, since the occurrence of parental types with a frequency greater than 50% indicates that the genes are linked. About 17% of offspring, however, were recombinants.

Faced with these results, Morgan proposed that some process must occasionally break the physical connection between specific alleles of genes on the same chromosome. Sub-

sequent experiments demonstrated that this process, now called **crossing over**, accounts for the recombination of linked genes. In crossing over, which occurs while replicated homologous chromosomes are paired during prophase of meiosis I, a set of proteins orchestrates an exchange of corresponding segments of one maternal and one paternal chromatid (see Figure 13.12). In effect, end portions of two nonsister chromatids trade places each time a crossover occurs.

The recombinant chromosomes resulting from crossing over may bring alleles together in new combinations, and the subsequent events of meiosis distribute the recombinant chromosomes to gametes. **Figure 15.10** shows how crossing over in a dihybrid female fly resulted in recombinant eggs and ultimately recombinant offspring in Morgan's testcross. Most of the eggs had a chromosome with either the $b^+ \, vg^+$ or $b \, vg$ parental genotype for body color and wing size, but some eggs had a recombinant chromosome ($b^+ \, vg$ or $b \, vg^+$). Fertilization of these various classes of eggs by homozygous recessive sperm ($b \, vg$) produced an offspring population in which 17% exhibited a nonparental, recombinant phenotype. As we discuss next, the percentage of recombinant offspring, the *recombination frequency*, is related to the distance between linked genes.

Mapping the Distance Between Genes Using Recombination Data: *Scientific Inquiry*

The discovery of linked genes and recombination due to crossing over led one of Morgan's students, Alfred H. Sturtevant, to a method for constructing a **genetic map**, an ordered list of the genetic loci along a particular chromosome.

Sturtevant hypothesized that recombination frequencies calculated from experiments like the one in Figures 15.9 and 15.10 depend on the distances between genes on a chromosome. He assumed that crossing over is a random event, with the chance of crossing over approximately equal at all points along a chromosome. Based on these assumptions, Sturtevant predicted that *the farther apart two genes are, the higher the probability that a crossover will occur between them and therefore the higher the recombination frequency.* His reasoning was simple: The greater the distance between two genes, the more points there are between them where crossing over can occur. Using recombination data from various fruit fly crosses, Sturtevant proceeded to assign relative positions to genes on the same chromosomes—that is, to *map* genes.

A genetic map based on recombination frequencies is called a **linkage map**. **Figure 15.11**, on page 296, shows Sturtevant's linkage map of three genes: the body-color (*b*) and wing-size (*vg*) genes depicted in Figure 15.10 and a third gene, called cinnabar (*cn*). Cinnabar is one of many *Drosophila* genes affecting eye color. Cinnabar eyes, a mutant phenotype, are a brighter red than the wild-type color. The recombination frequency between *cn* and *b* is 9%; that between *cn* and *vg*,

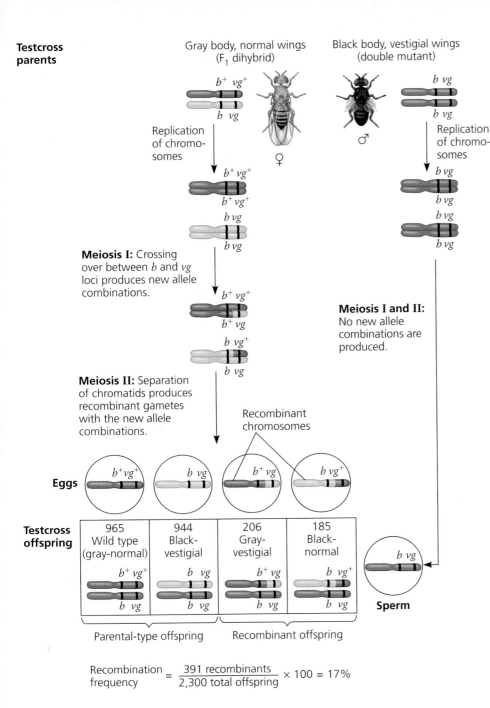

Testcross parents

Gray body, normal wings
(F_1 dihybrid)

b^+ vg^+
b vg

Black body, vestigial wings
(double mutant)

b vg
b vg

♀ ♂

Replication of chromosomes

b^+ vg^+
b^+ vg^+
b vg
b vg

Replication of chromosomes

b vg
b vg
b vg
b vg

Meiosis I: Crossing over between b and vg loci produces new allele combinations.

b^+ vg^+
b^+ vg
b vg^+
b vg

Meiosis I and II: No new allele combinations are produced.

Meiosis II: Separation of chromatids produces recombinant gametes with the new allele combinations.

Recombinant chromosomes

Eggs

b^+vg^+ | b vg | b^+vg | b vg^+

Testcross offspring

965 Wild type (gray-normal)	944 Black-vestigial	206 Gray-vestigial	185 Black-normal
b^+ vg^+	b vg	b^+ vg	b vg^+
b vg	b vg	b vg	b vg

Sperm
b vg

Parental-type offspring   Recombinant offspring

Recombination frequency $= \dfrac{391 \text{ recombinants}}{2{,}300 \text{ total offspring}} \times 100 = 17\%$

▲ **Figure 15.10 Chromosomal basis for recombination of linked genes.** In these diagrams re-creating the testcross in Figure 15.9, we track chromosomes as well as genes. The maternal chromosomes are color-coded red and pink to distinguish one homolog from the other before any meiotic crossing over has taken place. Because crossing over between the b and vg loci occurs in some, but not all, egg-producing cells, more eggs with parental-type chromosomes than with recombinant ones are produced in the mating females. Fertilization of the eggs by sperm of genotype b vg gives rise to some recombinant offspring. The recombination frequency is the percentage of recombinant flies in the total pool of offspring.

DRAW IT *Suppose, as in the question at the bottom of Figure 15.9, that the parental flies were true-breeding for gray body with vestigial wings and black body with normal wings. Draw the chromosomes in each of the four possible kinds of eggs from an F_1 female, and label each chromosome as "parental" or "recombinant."*

9.5%; and that between b and vg, 17%. In other words, crossovers between cn and b and between cn and vg are about half as frequent as crossovers between b and vg. Only a map that locates cn about midway between b and vg is consistent with these data, as you can prove to yourself by drawing alternative maps. Sturtevant expressed the distances between genes in **map units**, defining one map unit as equivalent to a 1% recombination frequency. Today, map units are often called *centimorgans* in honor of Morgan.

In practice, the interpretation of recombination data is more complicated than this example suggests. For example, some genes on a chromosome are so far from each other that a crossover between them is virtually certain. The observed fre-

quency of recombination in crosses involving two such genes can have a maximum value of 50%, a result indistinguishable from that for genes on different chromosomes. In this case, the physical connection between genes on the same chromosome is not reflected in the results of genetic crosses. Despite being on the same chromosome and thus being *physically linked*, the genes are *genetically unlinked*; alleles of such genes assort independently, as if they were on different chromosomes. In fact, several of the genes for pea characters that Mendel studied are now known to be on the same chromosome, but the distance between them is so great that linkage is not observed in genetic crosses. Consequently, they behaved as if they were on different chromosomes in Mendel's experiments. Genes located far

▼ Figure 15.11 Research Method

Constructing a Linkage Map

APPLICATION A linkage map shows the relative locations of genes along a chromosome.

TECHNIQUE A linkage map is based on the assumption that the probability of a crossover between two genetic loci is proportional to the distance separating the loci. The recombination frequencies used to construct a linkage map for a particular chromosome are obtained from experimental crosses, such as the cross depicted in Figures 15.9 and 15.10. The distances between genes are expressed as map units (centimorgans), with one map unit equivalent to a 1% recombination frequency. Genes are arranged on the chromosome in the order that best fits the data.

RESULTS In this example, the observed recombination frequencies between three *Drosophila* gene pairs (*b–cn* 9%, *cn–vg* 9.5%, and *b–vg* 17%) best fit a linear order in which *cn* is positioned about halfway between the other two genes:

The *b–vg* recombination frequency (17%) is slightly less than the sum of the *b–cn* and *cn–vg* frequencies (9 + 9.5 = 18.5%) because of the few times that a crossover occurs between *b* and *cn* and an additional crossover occurs between *cn* and *vg*. The second crossover would "cancel out" the first, reducing the observed *b–vg* recombination frequency while contributing to the frequency between each of the closer pairs of genes. The value of 18.5% (18.5 map units) is closer to the actual distance between the genes, so a geneticist would add the smaller distances in constructing a map.

apart on a chromosome are mapped by adding the recombination frequencies from crosses involving a set of closer pairs of genes lying between the two distant genes.

Using recombination data, Sturtevant and his colleagues were able to map numerous *Drosophila* genes in linear arrays. They found that the genes clustered into four groups of linked genes. Because light microscopy had revealed four pairs of chromosomes in *Drosophila* cells, the linkage map thus provided additional evidence that genes are located on chromosomes. Each chromosome has a linear array of specific genes, each with its own locus (**Figure 15.12**).

Because a linkage map is based only on recombination frequencies, it gives only an approximate picture of a chromosome. The frequency of crossing over is not actually uniform over the length of a chromosome, as Sturtevant assumed, and therefore map units do not correspond to actual physical distances (in nanometers, for instance). A linkage map does portray the order of genes along a chromosome, but it does not accurately portray the precise locations of those genes. Other methods enable geneticists to construct **cytogenetic maps** of chromosomes, which

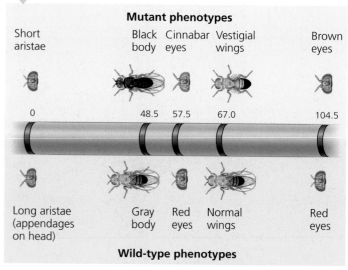

▲ **Figure 15.12 A partial genetic (linkage) map of a *Drosophila* chromosome.** This simplified map shows just a few of the genes that have been mapped on *Drosophila* chromosome II. The number at each gene locus indicates the number of map units between that locus and the locus for arista length (left). Notice that more than one gene can affect a given phenotypic characteristic, such as eye color. Also, note that in contrast to the homologous autosomes (II–IV), the X and Y sex chromosomes (I) have distinct shapes.

locate genes with respect to chromosomal features, such as stained bands, that can be seen in the microscope. The ultimate maps, which we will discuss in Chapter 21, show the physical distances between gene loci in DNA nucleotides. Comparing a linkage map with such a physical map or with a cytogenetic map of the same chromosome, we find that the linear order of genes is identical in all the maps, but the spacing between genes is not.

CONCEPT CHECK 15.3

1. When two genes are located on the same chromosome, what is the physical basis for the production of recombinant offspring in a testcross between a dihybrid parent and a double-mutant (recessive) parent?
2. For each type of offspring of the testcross in Figure 15.9, explain the relationship between its phenotype and the alleles contributed by the female parent.
3. **WHAT IF?** Genes *A*, *B*, and *C* are located on the same chromosome. Testcrosses show that the recombination frequency between *A* and *B* is 28% and between *A* and *C* is 12%. Can you determine the linear order of these genes? Explain.

For suggested answers, see Appendix A.

CONCEPT 15.4

Alterations of chromosome number or structure cause some genetic disorders

As you have learned so far in this chapter, the phenotype of an organism can be affected by small-scale changes involving individual genes. Random mutations are the source of all new alleles, which can lead to new phenotypic traits.

Large-scale chromosomal changes can also affect an organism's phenotype. Physical and chemical disturbances, as well as errors during meiosis, can damage chromosomes in major ways or alter their number in a cell. Large-scale chromosomal alterations often lead to spontaneous abortion (miscarriage) of a fetus, and individuals born with these types of genetic defects commonly exhibit various developmental disorders. In plants, such genetic defects may be tolerated to a greater extent than in animals.

Abnormal Chromosome Number

Ideally, the meiotic spindle distributes chromosomes to daughter cells without error. But there is an occasional mishap, called a **nondisjunction**, in which the members of a pair of homologous chromosomes do not move apart properly during meiosis I or sister chromatids fail to separate during meiosis II (**Figure 15.13**). In these cases, one gamete receives two of the same type of chromosome and

another gamete receives no copy. The other chromosomes are usually distributed normally.

If either of the aberrant gametes unites with a normal one at fertilization, the zygote will also have an abnormal number of a chromosome, a condition known as **aneuploidy**. (Aneuploidy may involve more than one chromosome.) Fertilization involving a gamete that has no copy of a particular chromosome will lead to a missing chromosome in the zygote (so that the cell has $2n - 1$ chromosomes); the aneuploid zygote is said to be **monosomic** for that chromosome. If a chromosome is present in triplicate in the zygote (so that the cell has $2n + 1$ chromosomes), the aneuploid cell is **trisomic** for that chromosome. Mitosis will subsequently transmit the anomaly to all embryonic cells. If the organism survives, it usually has a set of traits caused by the abnormal dose of the genes associated with the extra or missing chromosome. Down syndrome is an example of trisomy in humans that will be discussed later. Nondisjunction can also occur during mitosis. If such an error takes place early in embryonic development, then the aneuploid condition is passed along by mitosis to a large number of cells and is likely to have a substantial effect on the organism.

Some organisms have more than two complete chromosome sets in all somatic cells. The general term for this chromosomal alteration is **polyploidy**; the specific terms *triploidy* ($3n$) and *tetraploidy* ($4n$) indicate three or four chromosomal sets, respectively. One way a triploid cell may arise is by the fertilization of an abnormal diploid egg produced by nondisjunction of all its chromosomes. Tetraploidy could result from the failure of a $2n$ zygote to divide after replicating its chromosomes. Subsequent normal mitotic divisions would then produce a $4n$ embryo.

Polyploidy is fairly common in the plant kingdom. As we will see in Chapter 24, the spontaneous origin of polyploid individuals plays an important role in the evolution of plants. Many of the plant species we eat are polyploid; for example, bananas are triploid and wheat is hexaploid ($6n$). In the animal kingdom, polyploid species are much less common, although they are known to occur among fishes and amphibians. Researchers in Chile were the first to identify a polyploid mammal, a rodent whose cells are tetraploid (**Figure 15.14**, on the next page); a closely related species also appears to be tetraploid. In general, polyploids are more nearly normal in appearance than aneuploids. One extra (or missing) chromosome apparently disrupts genetic balance more than does an entire extra set of chromosomes.

Meiosis I

Meiosis II

Nondisjunction

Nondisjunction

Gametes

$n + 1$ $\quad$ $n + 1$ $\quad$ $n - 1$ $\quad$ $n - 1$ $\qquad$ $n + 1$ $\quad$ $n - 1$ $\quad$ n $\quad$ n

Number of chromosomes

(a) Nondisjunction of homologous chromosomes in meiosis I

(b) Nondisjunction of sister chromatids in meiosis II

▲ **Figure 15.13 Meiotic nondisjunction.** Gametes with an abnormal chromosome number can arise by nondisjunction in either meiosis I or meiosis II.

▲ **Figure 15.14 A tetraploid mammal.** The somatic cells of this burrowing rodent, *Tympanoctomys barrerae*, have about twice as many chromosomes as those of closely related species. Interestingly, its sperm's head is unusually large, presumably a necessity for holding all that genetic material. Scientists think that this tetraploid species may have arisen when an ancestor doubled its chromosome number, presumably by errors in mitosis or meiosis within the animal's reproductive organs.

Alterations of Chromosome Structure

Errors in meiosis or damaging agents such as radiation can cause breakage of a chromosome, which can lead to four types of changes in chromosome structure (**Figure 15.15**). A **deletion** occurs when a chromosomal fragment is lost. The affected chromosome is then missing certain genes. (If the centromere is deleted, the entire chromosome will be lost.) The "deleted" fragment may become attached as an extra segment to a sister chromatid, producing a **duplication**. Alterna-

tively, a detached fragment could attach to a nonsister chromatid of a homologous chromosome. In that case, though, the "duplicated" segments might not be identical because the homologs could carry different alleles of certain genes. A chromosomal fragment may also reattach to the original chromosome but in the reverse orientation, producing an **inversion**. A fourth possible result of chromosomal breakage is for the fragment to join a nonhomologous chromosome, a rearrangement called a **translocation**.

Deletions and duplications are especially likely to occur during meiosis. In crossing over, nonsister chromatids sometimes exchange unequal-sized segments of DNA, so that one partner gives up more genes than it receives. The products of such a *nonreciprocal* crossover are one chromosome with a deletion and one chromosome with a duplication.

A diploid embryo that is homozygous for a large deletion (or has a single X chromosome with a large deletion, in a male) is usually missing a number of essential genes, a condition that is ordinarily lethal. Duplications and translocations also tend to be harmful. In reciprocal translocations, in which segments are exchanged between nonhomologous chromosomes, and in inversions, the balance of genes is not abnormal—all genes are present in their normal doses. Nevertheless, translocations and inversions can alter phenotype because a gene's expression can be influenced by its location among neighboring genes; such events sometimes have devastating effects.

(a) A **deletion** removes a chromosomal segment.

(b) A **duplication** repeats a segment.

(c) An **inversion** reverses a segment within a chromosome.

(d) A **translocation** moves a segment from one chromosome to a nonhomologous chromosome. In a reciprocal translocation, the most common type, nonhomologous chromosomes exchange fragments. In a nonreciprocal translocation, which is less common, a chromosome transfers a fragment without receiving a fragment in return.

▲ **Figure 15.15 Alterations of chromosome structure.** Vertical arrows indicate breakage points. Dark purple highlights the chromosomal parts affected by the rearrangements.

Human Disorders Due to Chromosomal Alterations

Alterations of chromosome number and structure are associated with a number of serious human disorders. As described earlier, nondisjunction in meiosis results in aneuploidy in gametes and any resulting zygotes. Although the frequency of aneuploid zygotes may be quite high in humans, most of these chromosomal alterations are so disastrous to development that the embryos are spontaneously aborted long before birth. However, some types of aneuploidy appear to upset the genetic balance less than others, with the result that individuals with certain aneuploid conditions can survive to birth and beyond. These individuals have a set of traits—a *syndrome*—characteristic of the type of aneuploidy. Genetic disorders caused by aneuploidy can be diagnosed before birth by fetal testing (see Figure 14.18).

Down Syndrome (Trisomy 21)

One aneuploid condition, **Down syndrome**, affects approximately one out of every 700 children born in the United States **(Figure 15.16)**. Down syndrome is usually the result of an extra chromosome 21, so that each body cell has a total of 47 chromosomes. Because the cells are trisomic for chromosome 21, Down syndrome is often called *trisomy 21*. Down syndrome includes characteristic facial features, short stature, heart defects, susceptibility to respiratory infection, and mental retardation. Furthermore, individuals with Down syndrome are prone to developing leukemia and Alzheimer's disease. Although people with Down syndrome, on average,

▲ **Figure 15.16 Down syndrome.** The child exhibits the facial features characteristic of Down syndrome. The karyotype shows trisomy 21, the most common cause of this disorder.

have a life span shorter than normal, some live to middle age or beyond. Most are sexually underdeveloped and sterile.

The frequency of Down syndrome increases with the age of the mother. While the disorder occurs in just 0.04% of children born to women under age 30, the risk climbs to 0.92% for mothers at age 40 and is even higher for older mothers. The correlation of Down syndrome with maternal age has not yet been explained. Most cases result from nondisjunction during meiosis I, and some research points to an age-dependent abnormality in a meiosis checkpoint that normally delays anaphase until all the kinetochores are attached to the spindle (like the M phase checkpoint of the mitotic cell cycle; see Chapter 12). Trisomies of some other chromosomes also increase in incidence with maternal age, although infants with other autosomal trisomies rarely survive for long. Prenatal screening for trisomies in the embryo is now offered to all pregnant women since the possible benefits outweigh any risks.

Aneuploidy of Sex Chromosomes

Nondisjunction of sex chromosomes produces a variety of aneuploid conditions. Most of these conditions appear to upset genetic balance less than aneuploid conditions involving autosomes. This may be because the Y chromosome carries relatively few genes and because extra copies of the X chromosome become inactivated as Barr bodies in somatic cells.

An extra X chromosome in a male, producing XXY, occurs approximately once in every 2,000 live births. People with this disorder, called *Klinefelter syndrome*, have male sex organs, but the testes are abnormally small and the man is sterile. Even though the extra X is inactivated, some breast enlargement and other female body characteristics are common. Affected individuals may have subnormal intelligence. Males with an extra Y chromosome (XYY) do not exhibit any well-defined syndrome, but they tend to be somewhat taller than average.

Females with trisomy X (XXX), which occurs once in approximately 1,000 live births, are healthy and cannot be distinguished from XX females except by karyotype. Monosomy X, called *Turner syndrome*, occurs about once in every 5,000 births and is the only known viable monosomy in humans. Although these X0 individuals are phenotypically female, they are sterile because their sex organs do not mature. When provided with estrogen replacement therapy, girls with Turner syndrome do develop secondary sex characteristics. Most have normal intelligence.

Disorders Caused by Structurally Altered Chromosomes

Many deletions in human chromosomes, even in a heterozygous state, cause severe problems. One such syndrome, known as *cri du chat* ("cry of the cat"), results from a specific deletion in chromosome 5. A child born with this deletion is mentally retarded, has a small head with unusual facial features, and has a cry that sounds like the mewing of a distressed cat. Such individuals usually die in infancy or early childhood.

Chromosomal translocations have been implicated in certain cancers, including *chronic myelogenous leukemia* (*CML*). This disease occurs when a reciprocal translocation happens during mitosis of cells that will become white blood cells. In these cells, the exchange of a large portion of chromosome 22 with a small fragment from a tip of chromosome 9 produces a much shortened, easily recognized chromosome 22, called the *Philadelphia chromosome* (**Figure 15.17**). We will discuss how such an exchange can cause cancer in Chapter 18.

▲ **Figure 15.17 Translocation associated with chronic myelogenous leukemia (CML).** The cancerous cells in nearly all CML patients contain an abnormally short chromosome 22, the so-called Philadelphia chromosome, and an abnormally long chromosome 9. These altered chromosomes result from the translocation shown here, which presumably occurred in a single white blood cell precursor undergoing mitosis and was then passed along to all descendant cells.

CONCEPT CHECK **15.4**

1. More common than completely polyploid animals are mosaic polyploids, animals that are diploid except for patches of polyploid cells. How might a mosaic tetraploid—an animal with some cells containing four sets of chromosomes—arise?
2. About 5% of individuals with Down syndrome have a chromosomal translocation in which a third copy of chromosome 21 is attached to chromosome 14. If this translocation occurred in a parent's gonad, how could it lead to Down syndrome in a child?
3. **WHAT IF?** The ABO blood type locus has been mapped on chromosome 9. A father who has type AB blood and a mother who has type O blood have a child with trisomy 9 and type A blood. Using this information, can you tell in which parent the nondisjunction occurred? Explain your answer.

For suggested answers, see Appendix A.

CONCEPT **15.5**
Some inheritance patterns are exceptions to the standard chromosome theory

In the previous section, you learned about deviations from the usual patterns of chromosomal inheritance due to abnormal events in meiosis and mitosis. We conclude this chapter by describing two normally occurring exceptions to Mendelian genetics, one involving genes located in the nucleus and the other involving genes located outside the nucleus. In both cases, the sex of the parent contributing an allele is a factor in the pattern of inheritance.

Genomic Imprinting

Throughout our discussions of Mendelian genetics and the chromosomal basis of inheritance, we have assumed that a given allele will have the same effect whether it was inherited from the mother or the father. This is probably a safe assumption most of the time. For example, when Mendel crossed purple-flowered pea plants with white-flowered pea plants, he observed the same results regardless of whether the purple-flowered parent supplied the eggs or the sperm. In recent years, however, geneticists have identified two to three dozen traits in mammals that depend on which parent passed along the alleles for those traits. Such variation in phenotype depending on whether an allele is inherited from the male or female parent is called **genomic imprinting**. (Note that this phenomenon is different from sex linkage; most imprinted genes are on autosomes.)

Genomic imprinting occurs during the formation of gametes and results in the silencing of one allele of certain genes. Because these genes are imprinted differently in sperm and eggs, a zygote expresses only one allele of an imprinted gene, either the allele inherited from the female parent or the allele inherited from the male parent. The imprints are transmitted to all the body cells during development, so either the maternal or paternal allele of a given imprinted gene is expressed in every cell of that organism. In each generation, the old imprints are "erased" in gamete-producing cells, and the chromosomes of the developing gametes are newly imprinted according to the sex of the individual forming the gametes. In a given species, the imprinted genes are always imprinted in the same way. For instance, a gene imprinted for maternal allele expression is always imprinted for maternal allele expression, generation after generation.

Consider, for example, the mouse gene for insulin-like growth factor 2 (*Igf2*), one of the first imprinted genes to be identified. Although this growth factor is required for normal prenatal growth, only the paternal allele is expressed (**Figure 15.18a**). Evidence that the *Igf2* gene is imprinted initially came from crosses between wild-type mice and dwarf mice homozygous for a recessive mutation in the *Igf2* gene. The phenotypes of heterozygous offspring (which had one normal allele and one

(a) Homozygote. A mouse homozygous for the wild-type *Igf2* allele is normal sized. Only the paternal allele of this gene is expressed.

(b) Heterozygotes. Matings between wild-type mice and those homozygous for the recessive mutant *Igf2* allele produce heterozygous offspring. The mutant phenotype is seen only when the father contributed the mutant allele because the maternal allele is not expressed.

▲ **Figure 15.18 Genomic imprinting of the mouse *Igf2* gene.**

mutant) differed, depending on whether the mutant allele came from the mother or the father **(Figure 15.18b)**.

What exactly is a genomic imprint? In many cases, it seems to consist of methyl (—CH₃) groups that are added to cytosine nucleotides of one of the alleles. Such methylation may directly silence the allele, an effect consistent with evidence that heavily methylated genes are usually inactive (see Chapter 18). However, for a few genes, methylation has been shown to *activate* expression of the allele. This is the case for the *Igf2* gene: Methylation of certain cytosines on the paternal chromosome leads to expression of the paternal *Igf2* allele.

Genomic imprinting is thought to affect only a small fraction of the genes in mammalian genomes, but most of the known imprinted genes are critical for embryonic development. In experiments with mice, for example, embryos engineered to inherit both copies of certain chromosomes from the same parent usually die before birth, whether that parent is male or female. In 2004, however, scientists in Japan combined the genetic material from two eggs in a zygote while allowing

expression of the *Igf2* gene from only one of the egg nuclei. The zygote developed into an apparently healthy mouse, shown in the photograph at the right. Apparently, normal development requires that embryonic cells have exactly one active copy—not zero, not two—of certain genes. The association of aberrant imprinting with abnormal development and certain cancers has stimulated numerous studies of how different genes are imprinted.

Inheritance of Organelle Genes

Although our focus in this chapter has been on the chromosomal basis of inheritance, we end with an important amendment: Not all of a eukaryotic cell's genes are located on nuclear chromosomes, or even in the nucleus. Some genes are located in organelles in the cytoplasm; because they are outside the nucleus, these genes are sometimes called *extranuclear genes* or *cytoplasmic genes*. Mitochondria, as well as chloroplasts and other plant plastids, contain small circular DNA molecules that carry a number of genes. These organelles reproduce themselves and transmit their genes to daughter organelles. Organelle genes are not distributed to offspring according to the same rules that direct the distribution of nuclear chromosomes during meiosis, so they do not display Mendelian inheritance.

The first hint that extranuclear genes exist came from studies by the German scientist Karl Correns on the inheritance of yellow or white patches on the leaves of an otherwise green plant. In 1909, he observed that the coloration of the offspring was determined only by the maternal parent (the source of eggs) and not by the paternal parent (the source of sperm). Subsequent research showed that such coloration patterns, or variegation, are due to mutations in plastid genes that control pigmentation **(Figure 15.19)**. In most plants, a zygote receives all its plastids from the cytoplasm of the egg and none from the sperm, which contributes little more than a haploid set of chromosomes. As the zygote develops, plastids containing

▶ **Figure 15.19 Variegated leaves from *Croton dioicus*.** Variegated (striped or spotted) leaves result from mutations in pigment genes located in plastids, which generally are inherited from the maternal parent.

wild-type or mutant pigment genes are distributed randomly to daughter cells. The pattern of leaf coloration exhibited by a plant depends on the ratio of wild-type to mutant plastids in its various tissues.

Similar maternal inheritance is also the rule for mitochondrial genes in most animals and plants, because almost all the mitochondria passed on to a zygote come from the cytoplasm of the egg. The products of most mitochondrial genes help make up the protein complexes of the electron transport chain and ATP synthase (see Chapter 9). Defects in one or more of these proteins, therefore, reduce the amount of ATP the cell can make and have been shown to cause a number of rare human disorders. Because the parts of the body most susceptible to energy deprivation are the nervous system and the muscles, most mitochondrial diseases primarily affect these systems. For example, *mitochondrial myopathy* causes weakness, intolerance of exercise, and muscle deterioration. Another mitochondrial disorder is *Leber's hereditary optic neuropathy*, which can produce sudden blindness in people as young as their 20s or 30s. The four mutations found thus far to cause this disorder affect oxidative phosphorylation during cellular respiration, a crucial function for the cell.

In addition to the rare diseases clearly caused by defects in mitochondrial DNA, mitochondrial mutations inherited from a person's mother may contribute to at least some cases of diabetes and heart disease, as well as to other disorders that commonly debilitate the elderly, such as Alzheimer's disease. In the course of a lifetime, new mutations gradually accumulate in our mitochondrial DNA, and some researchers think that these mutations play a role in the normal aging process.

Wherever genes are located in the cell—in the nucleus or in cytoplasmic organelles—their inheritance depends on the precise replication of DNA, the genetic material. In the next chapter, you will learn how this molecular reproduction occurs.

CONCEPT CHECK 15.5

1. Gene dosage, the number of active copies of a gene, is important to proper development. Identify and describe two processes that establish the proper dosage of certain genes.

2. Reciprocal crosses between two primrose varieties, A and B, produced the following results: A female × B male ⟶ offspring with all green (nonvariegated) leaves. B female × A male ⟶ offspring with spotted (variegated) leaves. Explain these results.

3. **WHAT IF?** Mitochondrial genes are critical to the energy metabolism of cells, but mitochondrial disorders caused by mutations in these genes are generally not lethal. Why not?

For suggested answers, see Appendix A.

Chapter 15 Review

 MEDIA Go to the Study Area at **www.masteringbio.com** for BioFlix 3-D Animations, MP3 Tutors, Videos, Practice Tests, an eBook, and more.

SUMMARY OF KEY CONCEPTS

CONCEPT 15.1

Mendelian inheritance has its physical basis in the behavior of chromosomes (pp. 286–289)

► The behavior of chromosomes during meiosis accounts for Mendel's laws of segregation and independent assortment.

► **Morgan's Experimental Evidence:** *Scientific Inquiry* Morgan's discovery that transmission of the X chromosome in *Drosophila* correlates with inheritance of an eye-color trait was the first solid evidence indicating that a specific gene is associated with a specific chromosome.

> **MEDIA**

MP3 Tutor Chromosomal Basis of Inheritance

CONCEPT 15.2

Sex-linked genes exhibit unique patterns of inheritance (pp. 289–292)

► **The Chromosomal Basis of Sex** Sex is an inherited phenotypic character usually determined by which sex chromosomes are present. Humans and other mammals have an X-Y system in which sex is determined by whether a Y chromosome is present. Other systems are found in birds, fishes, and insects.

► **Inheritance of Sex-Linked Genes** The sex chromosomes carry genes for some traits that are unrelated to sex characteristics. For instance, recessive alleles causing color blindness are carried on the X chromosome. Fathers transmit this and other sex-linked alleles to all daughters but to no sons. Any male who inherits such an allele from his mother will express the trait.

► **X Inactivation in Female Mammals** In mammalian females, one of the two X chromosomes in each cell is randomly inactivated during early embryonic development. If a female is heterozygous for a particular gene located on the X chromosome, she will be mosaic for that character, with about half her cells expressing the maternal allele and about half expressing the paternal allele.

> **MEDIA**

Activity Sex-Linked Genes
Investigation What Can Fruit Flies Reveal About Inheritance?

CONCEPT 15.3

Linked genes tend to be inherited together because they are located near each other on the same chromosome (pp. 292–296)

► **How Linkage Affects Inheritance**

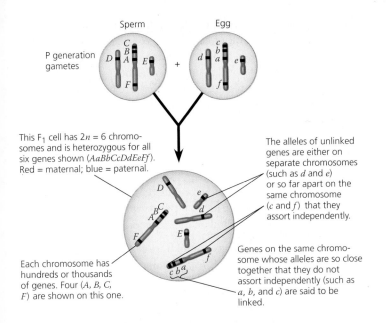

Sperm   Egg

P generation
gametes

This F₁ cell has $2n = 6$ chromosomes and is heterozygous for all six genes shown ($AaBbCcDdEeFf$). Red = maternal; blue = paternal.

The alleles of unlinked genes are either on separate chromosomes (such as d and e) or so far apart on the same chromosome (c and f) that they assort independently.

Each chromosome has hundreds or thousands of genes. Four (A, B, C, F) are shown on this one.

Genes on the same chromosome whose alleles are so close together that they do not assort independently (such as a, b, and c) are said to be linked.

▶ **Genetic Recombination and Linkage** Recombinant offspring exhibit new combinations of traits inherited from two parents. Because of the independent assortment of chromosomes, unlinked genes exhibit a 50% frequency of recombination in the gametes. For linked genes, crossing over between nonsister chromatids during meiosis I accounts for the observed recombinants, always less than 50% of the total.

▶ **Mapping the Distance Between Genes Using Recombination Data: *Scientific Inquiry*** The order of genes on a chromosome and the relative distances between them can be deduced from recombination frequencies observed in genetic crosses. The farther apart genes are, the more likely their allele combinations will be recombined during crossing over.

CONCEPT 15.4

Alterations of chromosome number or structure cause some genetic disorders (pp. 297–300)

▶ **Abnormal Chromosome Number** Aneuploidy can result from nondisjunction during meiosis. When a normal gamete unites with one containing two copies or no copies of a particular chromosome, the resulting zygote and its descendant cells either have one extra copy of that chromosome (trisomy, $2n + 1$) or are missing a copy (monosomy, $2n - 1$). Polyploidy (more than two complete sets of chromosomes) can result from complete nondisjunction during gamete formation.

▶ **Alterations of Chromosome Structure** Chromosome breakage can result in deletions, inversions, duplications, and translocations.

▶ **Human Disorders Due to Chromosomal Alterations** Changes in the number of chromosomes per cell or in the structure of individual chromosomes can affect phenotype. Such alterations cause Down syndrome (usually due to trisomy of chromosome 21), certain cancers associated with chromosomal translocations, and various other human disorders.

CONCEPT 15.5

Some inheritance patterns are exceptions to the standard chromosome theory (pp. 300–302)

▶ **Genomic Imprinting** In mammals, the phenotypic effects of certain genes depend on which allele is inherited from each parent. Imprints are formed during gamete production, with the result that one allele (either maternal or paternal) is not expressed in offspring.

▶ **Inheritance of Organelle Genes** The inheritance of traits controlled by the genes present in mitochondria and plastids depends solely on the maternal parent because the zygote's cytoplasm comes from the egg. Some diseases affecting the nervous and muscular systems are caused by defects in mitochondrial genes that prevent cells from making enough ATP.

TESTING YOUR KNOWLEDGE

GENETICS PROBLEMS

1. A man with hemophilia (a recessive, sex-linked condition) has a daughter of normal phenotype. She marries a man who is normal for the trait. What is the probability that a daughter of this mating will be a hemophiliac? That a son will be a hemophiliac? If the couple has four sons, what is the probability that all four will be born with hemophilia?

2. Pseudohypertrophic muscular dystrophy is an inherited disorder that causes gradual deterioration of the muscles. It is seen almost exclusively in boys born to apparently normal parents and usually results in death in the early teens. Is this disorder caused by a dominant or a recessive allele? Is its inheritance sex-linked or autosomal? How do you know? Explain why this disorder is almost never seen in girls.

3. Red-green color blindness is caused by a sex-linked recessive allele. A color-blind man marries a woman with normal vision whose father was color-blind. What is the probability that they will have a color-blind daughter? What is the probability that their first son will be color-blind? (Note the different wording in the two questions.)

4. A wild-type fruit fly (heterozygous for gray body color and normal wings) is mated with a black fly with vestigial wings. The offspring have the following phenotypic distribution: wild type, 778; black-vestigial, 785; black-normal, 158; gray-vestigial, 162. What is the recombination frequency between these genes for body color and wing size?

5. In another cross, a wild-type fruit fly (heterozygous for gray body color and red eyes) is mated with a black fruit fly with purple eyes. The offspring are as follows: wild type, 721; black-purple, 751; gray-purple, 49; black-red, 45. What is the recombination frequency between these genes for body color and eye color? Using information from problem 4, what fruit flies (genotypes and phenotypes) would you mate to determine the sequence of the body-color, wing-size, and eye-color genes on the chromosome?

6. **DRAW IT** A fruit fly that is true-breeding for gray body with vestigial wings ($b^+ b^+ vg\ vg$) is mated with one that is true-breeding for black body with normal wings ($b\ b\ vg^+\ vg^+$).

    a. Draw the chromosomes for the P generation flies, using red for the gray fly and pink for the black one. Show the position of each allele.

    b. Draw the chromosomes and label the alleles of an F_1 fly.

    c. Suppose an F_1 female is testcrossed. Draw the chromosomes of the resulting offspring in a Punnett square.

    d. Knowing that the distance between these two genes is 17 map units, predict the phenotypic ratios of these offspring.

7. What pattern of inheritance would lead a geneticist to suspect that an inherited disorder of cell metabolism is due to a defective mitochondrial gene?

8. Women born with an extra X chromosome (XXX) are healthy and phenotypically indistinguishable from normal XX women. What is a likely explanation for this finding? How could you test this explanation?

9. Determine the sequence of genes along a chromosome based on the following recombination frequencies: *A–B*, 8 map units; *A–C*, 28 map units; *A–D*, 25 map units; *B–C*, 20 map units; *B–D*, 33 map units.

10. Assume that genes *A* and *B* are linked and are 50 map units apart. An animal heterozygous at both loci is crossed with one that is homozygous recessive at both loci. What percentage of the offspring will show phenotypes resulting from crossovers? If you did not know that genes *A* and *B* were linked, how would you interpret the results of this cross?

11. A space probe discovers a planet inhabited by creatures that reproduce with the same hereditary patterns seen in humans. Three phenotypic characters are height (*T* = tall, *t* = dwarf), head appendages (*A* = antennae, *a* = no antennae), and nose morphology (*S* = upturned snout, *s* = downturned snout). Since the creatures are not "intelligent," Earth scientists are able to do some controlled breeding experiments using various heterozygotes in testcrosses. For tall heterozygotes with antennae, the offspring are: tall-antennae, 46; dwarf-antennae, 7; dwarf-no antennae, 42; tall-no antennae, 5. For heterozygotes with antennae and an upturned snout, the offspring are: antennae-upturned snout, 47; antennae-downturned snout, 2; no antennae-downturned snout, 48; no antennae-upturned snout, 3. Calculate the recombination frequencies for both experiments.

12. Using the information from problem 11, scientists do a further testcross using a heterozygote for height and nose morphology. The offspring are: tall-upturned snout, 40; dwarf-upturned snout, 9; dwarf-downturned snout, 42; tall-downturned snout, 9. Calculate the recombination frequency from these data; then use your answer from problem 11 to determine the correct sequence of the three linked genes.

13. Two genes of a flower, one controlling blue (*B*) versus white (*b*) petals and the other controlling round (*R*) versus oval (*r*) stamens, are linked and are 10 map units apart. You cross a homozygous blue-oval plant with a homozygous white-round plant. The resulting F_1 progeny are crossed with homozygous white-oval plants, and 1,000 F_2 progeny are obtained. How many F_2 plants of each of the four phenotypes do you expect?

14. You design *Drosophila* crosses to provide recombination data for gene *a*, which is located on the chromosome shown in Figure 15.12. Gene *a* has recombination frequencies of 14% with the vestigial-wing locus and 26% with the brown-eye locus. Where is *a* located on the chromosome?

15. Banana plants, which are triploid, are seedless and therefore sterile. Propose a possible explanation.

For Genetics Problems answers, see Appendix A.

MEDIA Visit the Study Area at **www.masteringbio.com** for a Practice Test.

EVOLUTION CONNECTION

16. You have seen that crossing over, or recombination, is thought to be evolutionarily advantageous because it continually shuffles genetic alleles into novel combinations, allowing evolutionary processes to occur. Until recently, it was thought that the genes on the Y chromosome might degenerate because they lack homologous genes on the X chromosome with which to recombine. However, when the Y chromosome was sequenced, eight large regions were found to be internally homologous to each other, and quite a few of the 78 genes represent duplicates. (Y chromosome researcher David Page has called it a "hall of mirrors.") What might be a benefit of these regions?

SCIENTIFIC INQUIRY

17. Butterflies have an X-Y sex determination system that is different from that of flies or humans. Female butterflies may be either XY or XO, while butterflies with two or more X chromosomes are males. This photograph shows a tiger swallowtail *gynandromorph*, an individual that is half male (left side) and half female (right side). Given that the first division of the zygote divides the embryo into the future right and left halves of the butterfly, propose a hypothesis that explains how nondisjunction during the first mitosis might have produced this unusual-looking butterfly.

The Molecular Basis of Inheritance

16

▲ Figure 16.1 **How was the structure of DNA determined?**

KEY CONCEPTS

16.1 DNA is the genetic material
16.2 Many proteins work together in DNA replication and repair
16.3 A chromosome consists of a DNA molecule packed together with proteins

OVERVIEW

Life's Operating Instructions

In April 1953, James Watson and Francis Crick shook the scientific world with an elegant double-helical model for the structure of deoxyribonucleic acid, or DNA. **Figure 16.1** shows Watson (left) and Crick admiring their DNA model, which they built from tin and wire. Over the past 50 years, their model has evolved from a novel proposition to an icon of modern biology. DNA, the substance of inheritance, is the most celebrated molecule of our time. Mendel's heritable factors and Morgan's genes on chromosomes are, in fact, composed of DNA. Chemically speaking, your genetic endowment is the DNA contained in the 46 chromosomes you inherited from your parents and in the mitochondria passed along by your mother.

Of all nature's molecules, nucleic acids are unique in their ability to direct their own replication from monomers. Indeed, the resemblance of offspring to their parents has its basis in the precise replication of DNA and its transmission from one generation to the next. Hereditary information is encoded in the chemical language of DNA and reproduced in all the cells of your body. It is this DNA program that directs the development of your biochemical, anatomical, physiological, and, to some extent, behavioral traits. In this chapter, you will learn how biologists deduced that DNA is the genetic material and how Watson and Crick discovered its structure. You will also see how DNA is replicated—the molecular basis of inheritance—and how cells repair their DNA. Finally, you will explore how a molecule of DNA is packed together with proteins in a chromosome.

CONCEPT 16.1
DNA is the genetic material

Today, even schoolchildren have heard of DNA, and scientists routinely manipulate DNA in the laboratory, often to change the heritable traits of cells in their experiments. Early in the 20th century, however, the identification of the molecules of inheritance loomed as a major challenge to biologists.

The Search for the Genetic Material: *Scientific Inquiry*

Once T. H. Morgan's group showed that genes are located along chromosomes (described in Chapter 15), the two chemical components of chromosomes—DNA and protein—became the candidates for the genetic material. Until the 1940s, the case for proteins seemed stronger, especially since biochemists had identified them as a class of macromolecules with great heterogeneity and specificity of function, essential requirements for the hereditary material. Moreover, little was known about nucleic acids, whose physical and chemical properties seemed far too uniform to account for the multitude of specific inherited traits exhibited by every organism. This view gradually changed as experiments with microorganisms yielded unexpected results. As with the work of Mendel and Morgan, a key factor in determining the identity of the genetic material was the choice of appropriate experimental organisms. The role of DNA in heredity was first worked out by studying bacteria and the viruses that infect them, which are far simpler than pea plants, fruit flies, or humans. In this section, we will trace the search for the genetic material in some detail as a case study in scientific inquiry.

Evidence That DNA Can Transform Bacteria

We can trace the discovery of the genetic role of DNA back to 1928. While attempting to develop a vaccine against pneumonia, a British medical officer named Frederick Griffith studied *Streptococcus pneumoniae*, a bacterium that causes pneumonia in mammals. Griffith had two strains (varieties) of the bacterium, one pathogenic (disease-causing) and one nonpathogenic (harmless). He was surprised to find that when he killed

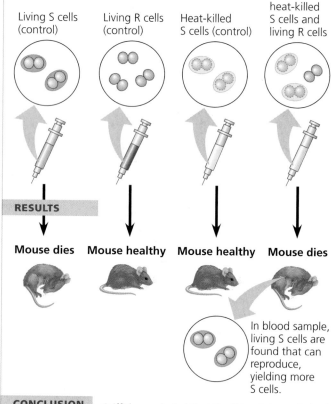

▼ Figure 16.2 **Inquiry**

Can a genetic trait be transferred between different bacterial strains?

EXPERIMENT Frederick Griffith studied two strains of the bacterium *Streptococcus pneumoniae*. Bacteria of the S (smooth) strain can cause pneumonia in mice; they are pathogenic because they have a capsule that protects them from an animal's defense system. Bacteria of the R (rough) strain lack a capsule and are nonpathogenic. To test for the trait of pathogenicity, Griffith injected mice with the two strains as shown below:

Living S cells (control)
Living R cells (control)
Heat-killed S cells (control)
Mixture of heat-killed S cells and living R cells

RESULTS

Mouse dies   Mouse healthy   Mouse healthy   Mouse dies

In blood sample, living S cells are found that can reproduce, yielding more S cells.

CONCLUSION Griffith concluded that the living R bacteria had been transformed into pathogenic S bacteria by an unknown, heritable substance from the dead S cells that allowed the R cells to make capsules.

SOURCE F. Griffith, The significance of pneumococcal types, *Journal of Hygiene* 27:113–159 (1928).

WHAT IF? How did this experiment rule out the possibility that the R cells could have simply used the capsules of the dead S cells to become pathogenic?

the pathogenic bacteria with heat and then mixed the cell remains with living bacteria of the nonpathogenic strain, some of the living cells became pathogenic **(Figure 16.2)**. Furthermore, this newly acquired trait of pathogenicity was inherited by all the descendants of the transformed bacteria. Clearly, some chemical component of the dead pathogenic cells caused this heritable change, although the identity of the substance was not known. Griffith called the phenomenon **transformation**, now defined as a change in genotype and phenotype due to the assimilation of external DNA by a cell. (This use of the word *transformation* should not be confused with the conversion of a normal animal cell to a cancerous one, discussed in Chapter 12.)

Griffith's work set the stage for a 14-year search by American bacteriologist Oswald Avery for the identity of the transforming substance. Avery focused on the three main candidates: DNA, RNA (the other nucleic acid), and protein. Avery broke open the heat-killed pathogenic bacteria and extracted the cellular contents. In separate samples, he used specific treatments that inactivated each of the three types of molecules. He then tested each treated sample for its ability to transform live nonpathogenic bacteria. Only when DNA was allowed to remain active did transformation occur. In 1944, Avery and his colleagues Maclyn McCarty and Colin MacLeod announced that the transforming agent was DNA. Their discovery was greeted with interest but considerable skepticism, in part because of the lingering belief that proteins were better candidates to be the genetic material. Moreover, many biologists were not convinced that the genes of bacteria would be similar in composition and function to those of more complex organisms. But the major reason for the continued doubt was that so little was known about DNA.

Evidence That Viral DNA Can Program Cells

Additional evidence for DNA as the genetic material came from studies of viruses that infect bacteria **(Figure 16.3)**. These

▲ **Figure 16.3 Viruses infecting a bacterial cell.** T2 and related phages attach to the host cell and inject their genetic material through the plasma membrane, while the head and tail parts remain on the outer bacterial surface (colorized TEM).

viruses are called **bacteriophages** (meaning "bacteria-eaters"), or just **phages**. Viruses are much simpler than cells. A virus is little more than DNA (or sometimes RNA) enclosed by a protective coat, which is often simply protein. To reproduce, a virus must infect a cell and take over the cell's metabolic machinery.

Phages have been widely used as tools by researchers in molecular genetics. In 1952, Alfred Hershey and Martha Chase performed experiments showing that DNA is the genetic material of a phage known as T2. This is one of many phages that infect *Escherichia coli* (*E. coli*), a bacterium that normally lives in the intestines of mammals. At that time, biologists already knew that T2, like many other phages, was composed almost entirely of DNA and protein. They also knew that the T2 phage could quickly turn an *E. coli* cell into a T2-producing factory that released many copies when the cell ruptured. Somehow, T2 could reprogram its host cell to produce viruses. But which viral component—protein or DNA—was responsible?

Hershey and Chase answered this question by devising an experiment showing that only one of the two components of T2 actually enters the *E. coli* cell during infection (**Figure 16.4**). In

▼ Figure 16.4 **Inquiry**

Is protein or DNA the genetic material of phage T2?

EXPERIMENT   Alfred Hershey and Martha Chase used radioactive sulfur and phosphorus to trace the fates of protein and DNA, respectively, of T2 phages that infected bacterial cells. They wanted to see which of these molecules entered and could reprogram the cells to make more phages.

① Mixed radioactively labeled phages with bacteria. The phages infected the bacterial cells.

② Agitated the mixture in a blender to free phage parts outside the bacteria from the cells.

③ Centrifuged the mixture so that bacteria formed a pellet at the bottom of the test tube; free phages and phage parts, which are lighter, remained suspended in the liquid.

④ Measured the radioactivity in the pellet and the liquid.

Batch 1: Phages were grown with radioactive sulfur (^{35}S), which was incorporated into phage protein (pink).

Batch 2: Phages were grown with radioactive phosphorus (^{32}P), which was incorporated into phage DNA (blue).

RESULTS   When proteins were labeled (batch 1), radioactivity remained outside the cells; but when DNA was labeled (batch 2), radioactivity was found inside the cells. Bacterial cells with radioactive phage DNA released new phages with some radioactive phosphorus.

CONCLUSION   Phage DNA entered bacterial cells, but phage proteins did not. Hershey and Chase concluded that DNA, not protein, functions as the genetic material of phage T2.

SOURCE   A. D. Hershey and M. Chase, Independent functions of viral protein and nucleic acid in growth of bacteriophage, *Journal of General Physiology* 36:39–56 (1952).

WHAT IF?   How would the results have differed if proteins carried the genetic information?

their experiment, they used a radioactive isotope of sulfur to tag protein in one batch of T2 and a radioactive isotope of phosphorus to tag DNA in a second batch. Because protein, but not DNA, contains sulfur, radioactive sulfur atoms were incorporated only into the protein of the phage. In a similar way, the atoms of radioactive phosphorus labeled only the DNA, not the protein, because nearly all the phage's phosphorus is in its DNA. In the experiment, separate samples of nonradioactive *E. coli* cells were allowed to be infected by the protein-labeled and DNA-labeled batches of T2. The researchers then tested the two samples shortly after the onset of infection to see which type of molecule—protein or DNA—had entered the bacterial cells and would therefore be capable of reprogramming them.

Hershey and Chase found that the phage DNA entered the host cells but the phage protein did not. Moreover, when these bacteria were returned to a culture medium, the infection ran its course, and the *E. coli* released phages that contained some radioactive phosphorus, further showing that the DNA inside the cell played an ongoing role during the infection process.

Hershey and Chase concluded that the DNA injected by the phage must be the molecule carrying the genetic information that makes the cells produce new viral DNA and proteins. The Hershey-Chase experiment was a landmark study because it provided powerful evidence that nucleic acids, rather than proteins, are the hereditary material, at least for viruses.

Additional Evidence That DNA Is the Genetic Material

Further evidence that DNA is the genetic material came from the laboratory of biochemist Erwin Chargaff. It was already known that DNA is a polymer of nucleotides, each consisting of three components: a nitrogenous (nitrogen-containing) base, a pentose sugar called deoxyribose, and a phosphate group **(Figure 16.5)**. The base can be adenine (A), thymine (T), guanine (G), or cytosine (C). Chargaff analyzed the base composition of DNA from a number of different organisms. In 1950, he reported that the base composition of DNA varies from one species to another. For example, 30.3% of human DNA nucleotides have the base A, whereas DNA from the bacterium *E. coli* has only 26.0% A. This evidence of molecular diversity among species, which had been presumed absent from DNA, made DNA a more credible candidate for the genetic material.

Chargaff also noticed a peculiar regularity in the ratios of nucleotide bases within a single species. In the DNA of each species he studied, the number of adenines approximately equaled the number of thymines, and the number of guanines approximately equaled the number of cytosines. In human DNA, for example, the four bases are present in these percentages: A = 30.3% and T = 30.3%; G = 19.5% and C = 19.9%. The equivalences for any given species between the number of A and T bases and the number of G and C bases became known as *Chargaff's rules*. The basis for these rules remained unexplained until the discovery of the double helix.

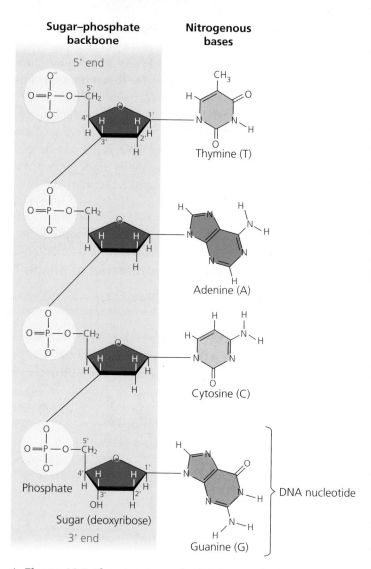

▲ Figure 16.5 **The structure of a DNA strand.** Each nucleotide monomer consists of a nitrogenous base (T, A, C, or G), the sugar deoxyribose (blue), and a phosphate group (yellow). The phosphate of one nucleotide is attached to the sugar of the next, resulting in a "backbone" of alternating phosphates and sugars from which the bases project. The polynucleotide strand has directionality, from the 5′ end (with the phosphate group) to the 3′ end (with the —OH group). 5′ and 3′ refer to the numbers assigned to the carbons in the sugar ring.

Building a Structural Model of DNA: *Scientific Inquiry*

Once most biologists were convinced that DNA was the genetic material, the challenge was to determine how the structure of DNA could account for its role in inheritance. By the early 1950s, the arrangement of covalent bonds in a nucleic acid polymer was well established (see Figure 16.5), and researchers focused on discovering the three-dimensional structure of DNA. Among the scientists working on the problem were Linus Pauling, at the California Institute of Technology, and Maurice Wilkins and Rosalind Franklin, at King's College in London. First to come up with the correct answer, however, were two scientists who were relatively unknown at the time—the American James Watson and the Englishman Francis Crick.

The brief but celebrated partnership that solved the puzzle of DNA structure began soon after Watson journeyed to Cambridge University, where Crick was studying protein structure with a technique called X-ray crystallography (see Figure 5.25). While visiting the laboratory of Maurice Wilkins, Watson saw an X-ray diffraction image of DNA produced by Wilkins's accomplished colleague Rosalind Franklin (**Figure 16.6a**). Images produced by X-ray crystallography are not actually pictures of molecules. The spots and smudges in **Figure 16.6b** were produced by X-rays that were diffracted (deflected) as they passed through aligned fibers of purified DNA. Crystallographers use mathematical equations to translate such patterns into information about the three-dimensional shapes of molecules, and Watson was familiar with the types of patterns that helical molecules produce. A careful study of Franklin's X-ray diffraction photo of DNA not only told him that DNA was helical in shape, but also enabled him to approximate the width of the helix and the spacing of the nitrogenous bases along it. The width of the helix suggested that it was made up of two strands, contrary to a three-stranded model that Linus Pauling had proposed a short time earlier. The presence of two strands accounts for the now-familiar term **double helix** (**Figure 16.7**).

Watson and Crick began building models of a double helix that would conform to the X-ray measurements and what was

(a) Rosalind Franklin

(b) Franklin's X-ray diffraction photograph of DNA

▲ **Figure 16.6 Rosalind Franklin and her X-ray diffraction photo of DNA.** Franklin, a very accomplished X-ray crystallographer, conducted critical experiments resulting in the photograph that allowed Watson and Crick to deduce the double-helical structure of DNA. Franklin died of cancer in 1958, when she was only 38. Her colleague Maurice Wilkins received the Nobel Prize in 1962 along with Watson and Crick.

then known about the chemistry of DNA. Having also read an unpublished annual report summarizing Franklin's work, they knew she had concluded that the sugar-phosphate backbones were on the outside of the double helix. This arrangement was appealing because it put the relatively hydrophobic nitrogenous

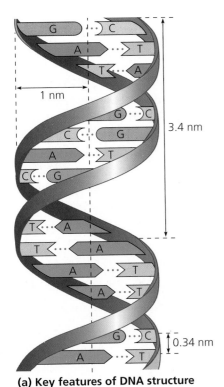

(a) Key features of DNA structure

(b) Partial chemical structure

(c) Space-filling model

▲ **Figure 16.7 The double helix. (a)** The "ribbons" in this diagram represent the sugar-phosphate backbones of the two DNA strands. The helix is "right-handed," curving up to the right. The two strands are held together by hydrogen bonds (dotted lines) between the nitrogenous bases, which are paired in the interior of the double helix. **(b)** For clarity, the two DNA strands are shown untwisted in this partial chemical structure. Strong covalent bonds link the units of each strand, while weaker hydrogen bonds hold one strand to the other. Notice that the strands are antiparallel, meaning that they are oriented in opposite directions. **(c)** The tight stacking of the base pairs is clear in this computer model. Van der Waals attractions between the stacked pairs play a major role in holding the molecule together (see Chapter 2).

bases in the molecule's interior and thus away from the surrounding aqueous solution. Watson constructed a model with the nitrogenous bases facing the interior of the double helix. In this model, the two sugar-phosphate backbones are antiparallel—that is, their subunits run in opposite directions to each other (see Figure 16.7). You can imagine the overall arrangement as a rope ladder with rigid rungs. The side ropes are the equivalent of the sugar-phosphate backbones, and the rungs represent pairs of nitrogenous bases. Now imagine holding one end of the ladder and twisting the other end, forming a spiral. Franklin's X-ray data indicated that the helix makes one full turn every 3.4 nm along its length. With the bases stacked just 0.34 nm apart, there are ten layers of base pairs, or rungs of the ladder, in each full turn of the helix.

The nitrogenous bases of the double helix are paired in specific combinations: adenine (A) with thymine (T), and guanine (G) with cytosine (C). It was mainly by trial and error that Watson and Crick arrived at this key feature of DNA. At first, Watson imagined that the bases paired like with like—for example, A with A and C with C. But this model did not fit the X-ray data, which suggested that the double helix had a uniform diameter. Why is this requirement inconsistent with like-with-like pairing of bases? Adenine and guanine are purines, nitrogenous bases with two organic rings. In contrast, cytosine and thymine belong to the family of nitrogenous bases known as pyrimidines, which have a single ring. Thus, purines (A and G) are about twice as wide as pyrimidines (C and T). A purine-purine pair is too wide and a pyrimidine-pyrimidine pair too narrow to account for the 2-nm diameter of the double helix. Always pairing a purine with a pyrimidine, however, results in a uniform diameter:

Purine + purine: too wide

Pyrimidine + pyrimidine: too narrow

Purine + pyrimidine: width consistent with X-ray data

Watson and Crick reasoned that there must be additional specificity of pairing dictated by the structure of the bases. Each base has chemical side groups that can form hydrogen bonds with its appropriate partner: Adenine can form two hydrogen bonds with thymine and only thymine; guanine forms three hydrogen bonds with cytosine and only cytosine. In shorthand, A pairs with T, and G pairs with C (Figure 16.8).

The Watson-Crick model explained the basis for Chargaff's rules. Wherever one strand of a DNA molecule has an A, the partner strand has a T. And a G in one strand is always paired with a C in the complementary strand. Therefore, in the DNA of any organism, the amount of adenine equals the amount of thymine,

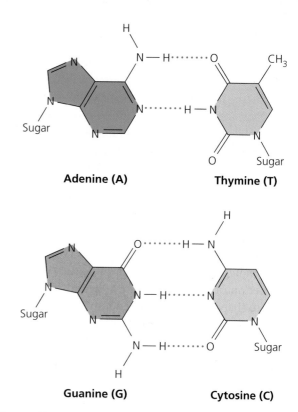

▲ Figure 16.8 **Base pairing in DNA.** The pairs of nitrogenous bases in a DNA double helix are held together by hydrogen bonds, shown here as pink dotted lines.

and the amount of guanine equals the amount of cytosine. Although the base-pairing rules dictate the combinations of nitrogenous bases that form the "rungs" of the double helix, they do not restrict the sequence of nucleotides *along* each DNA strand. The linear sequence of the four bases can be varied in countless ways, and each gene has a unique order, or base sequence.

In April 1953, Watson and Crick surprised the scientific world with a succinct, one-page paper in the British journal *Nature.* The paper reported their molecular model for DNA: the double helix, which has since become the symbol of molecular biology. The beauty of the model was that the structure of DNA suggested the basic mechanism of its replication.

CONCEPT CHECK **16.1**

1. A fly has the following percentages of nucleotides in its DNA: 27.3% A, 27.6% T, 22.5% G, and 22.5% C. How do these numbers demonstrate Chargaff's rules?
2. How did Watson and Crick's model explain the basis for Chargaff's rules?
3. **WHAT IF?** If transformation had not occurred in Griffith's experiment, how would the results have differed? Explain.

For suggested answers, see Appendix A.

* J. D. Watson and F. H. C. Crick, Molecular structure of nucleic acids: a structure for deoxyribose nucleic acids, *Nature* 171:737–738 (1953).

Many proteins work together in DNA replication and repair

The relationship between structure and function is manifest in the double helix. The idea that there is specific pairing of nitrogenous bases in DNA was the flash of inspiration that led Watson and Crick to the correct double helix. At the same time, they saw the functional significance of the base-pairing rules. They ended their classic paper with this wry statement: "It has not escaped our notice that the specific pairing we have postulated immediately suggests a possible copying mechanism for the genetic material." In this section, you will learn about the basic principle of DNA replication, as well as some important details of the process.

The Basic Principle: Base Pairing to a Template Strand

In a second paper, Watson and Crick stated their hypothesis for how DNA replicates:

> Now our model for deoxyribonucleic acid is, in effect, a pair of templates, each of which is complementary to the other. We imagine that prior to duplication the hydrogen bonds are broken, and the two chains unwind and separate. Each chain then acts as a template for the formation onto itself of a new companion chain, so that eventually we shall have two pairs of chains, where we only had one before. Moreover, the sequence of the pairs of bases will have been duplicated exactly.*

---

* F. H. C. Crick and J. D. Watson, The complementary structure of deoxyribonucleic acid, *Proceedings of the Royal Society of London A* 223:80 (1954).

Figure 16.9 illustrates Watson and Crick's basic idea. To make it easier to follow, we show only a short section of double helix in untwisted form. Notice that if you cover one of the two DNA strands of Figure 16.9a, you can still determine its linear sequence of bases by referring to the uncovered strand and applying the base-pairing rules. The two strands are complementary; each stores the information necessary to reconstruct the other. When a cell copies a DNA molecule, each strand serves as a template for ordering nucleotides into a new, complementary strand. Nucleotides line up along the template strand according to the base-pairing rules and are linked to form the new strands. Where there was one double-stranded DNA molecule at the beginning of the process, there are soon two, each an exact replica of the "parent" molecule. The copying mechanism is analogous to using a photographic negative to make a positive image, which can in turn be used to make another negative, and so on.

This model of DNA replication remained untested for several years following publication of the DNA structure. The requisite experiments were simple in concept but difficult to perform. Watson and Crick's model predicts that when a double helix replicates, each of the two daughter molecules will have one old strand, derived from the parent molecule, and one newly made strand. This **semiconservative model** can be distinguished from a conservative model of replication, in which the two parent strands somehow come back together after the process (that is, the parent molecule is conserved). In yet a third model, called the dispersive model, all four strands of DNA following replication have a mixture of old and new DNA (**Figure 16.10**, on the next page). Although mechanisms for conservative or dispersive DNA replication are not easy to devise, these models remained possibilities until they could be ruled out. After two years of preliminary work in the late

(a) The parent molecule has two complementary strands of DNA. Each base is paired by hydrogen bonding with its specific partner, A with T and G with C.

(b) The first step in replication is separation of the two DNA strands. Each parental strand can now serve as a template that determines the order of nucleotides along a new, complementary strand.

(c) The complementary nucleotides line up and are connected to form the sugar-phosphate backbones of the new strands. Each "daughter" DNA molecule consists of one parental strand (dark blue) and one new strand (light blue).

▲ **Figure 16.9 A model for DNA replication: the basic concept.** In this simplified illustration, a short segment of DNA has been untwisted into a structure that resembles a ladder. The rails of the ladder are the sugar-phosphate backbones of the two DNA strands; the rungs are the pairs of nitrogenous bases. Simple shapes symbolize the four kinds of bases. Dark blue represents DNA strands present in the parent molecule; light blue represents newly synthesized DNA.

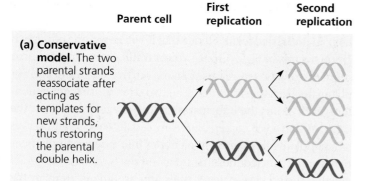

(a) Conservative model. The two parental strands reassociate after acting as templates for new strands, thus restoring the parental double helix.

(b) Semiconservative model. The two strands of the parental molecule separate, and each functions as a template for synthesis of a new, complementary strand.

(c) Dispersive model. Each strand of *both* daughter molecules contains a mixture of old and newly synthesized DNA.

▲ **Figure 16.10** **Three alternative models of DNA replication.** Each short segment of double helix symbolizes the DNA within a cell. Beginning with a parent cell, we follow the DNA for two generations of cells—two rounds of DNA replication. Newly made DNA is light blue.

1950s, Matthew Meselson and Franklin Stahl devised a clever experiment that distinguished between the three models. Their experiment supported the semiconservative model of DNA replication, as predicted by Watson and Crick, and is widely acknowledged among biologists to be a classic example of elegant experimental design (**Figure 16.11**).

The basic principle of DNA replication is conceptually simple. However, the actual process involves some complicated biochemical gymnastics, as we will now see.

DNA Replication: *A Closer Look*

The bacterium *E. coli* has a single chromosome of about 4.6 million nucleotide pairs. In a favorable environment, an *E. coli* cell

---

Inquiry

Does DNA replication follow the conservative, semiconservative, or dispersive model?

EXPERIMENT   At the California Institute of Technology, Matthew Meselson and Franklin Stahl cultured *E. coli* for several generations in a medium containing nucleotide precursors labeled with a heavy isotope of nitrogen, ^{15}N. The scientists then transferred the bacteria to a medium with only ^{14}N, a lighter isotope. Two DNA samples were taken from this flask, one at 20 minutes and one at 40 minutes, after the first and second replications, respectively. Meselson and Stahl could distinguish DNA of different densities by centrifuging DNA extracted from the bacteria.

❶ Bacteria cultured in medium containing ^{15}N

❷ Bacteria transferred to medium containing ^{14}N

RESULTS

❸ DNA sample centrifuged after 20 min (after first replication)

❹ DNA sample centrifuged after 40 min (after second replication)

Less dense

More dense

CONCLUSION   Meselson and Stahl compared their results to those predicted by each of the three models in Figure 16.10, as shown below. The first replication in the ^{14}N medium produced a band of hybrid (^{15}N-^{14}N) DNA. This result eliminated the conservative model. The second replication produced both light and hybrid DNA, a result that refuted the dispersive model and supported the semiconservative model. They therefore concluded that DNA replication is semiconservative.

	First replication	Second replication
Conservative model		
Semiconservative model		
Dispersive model		

SOURCE   M. Meselson and F. W. Stahl, The replication of DNA in *Escherichia coli, Proceedings of the National Academy of Sciences USA* 44:671–682 (1958).

Inquiry in Action   Read and analyze the original paper in *Inquiry in Action: Interpreting Scientific Papers.*

WHAT IF?   If Meselson and Stahl had first grown the cells in ^{14}N-containing medium and then moved them into ^{15}N-containing medium before taking samples, what would have been the result?

---

can copy all this DNA and divide to form two genetically identical daughter cells in less than an hour. Each of *your* cells has 46 DNA molecules in its nucleus, one long double-helical molecule per chromosome. In all, that represents about 6 billion base pairs, or over a thousand times more DNA than is found in a bacterial cell. If we were to print the one-letter symbols for these bases (A, G, C, and T) the size of the letters you are now reading, the 6 billion base pairs of information in a diploid human cell would fill about 1,200 books as thick as this text. Yet it takes a cell just a few hours to copy all of this DNA. This replication of an enormous amount of genetic information is achieved with very few errors—only about one per 10 billion nucleotides. The copying of DNA is remarkable in its speed and accuracy.

More than a dozen enzymes and other proteins participate in DNA replication. Much more is known about how this "replication machine" works in bacteria (such as *E. coli*) than in eukaryotes, and we will describe the basic steps of the process for *E. coli*, except where otherwise noted. What scientists have learned about eukaryotic DNA replication suggests, however, that most of the process is fundamentally similar for prokaryotes and eukaryotes.

Getting Started

The replication of a DNA molecule begins at special sites called **origins of replication**, short stretches of DNA having a specific sequence of nucleotides. The *E. coli* chromosome, like many other bacterial chromosomes, is circular and has a single origin. Proteins that initiate DNA replication recognize this sequence and attach to the DNA, separating the two strands and opening up a replication "bubble." Replication of DNA then proceeds in both directions until the entire molecule is copied **(Figure 16.12a)**. In

(a) In the circular chromosome of *E. coli* and many other bacteria, only one origin of replication is present. The parental strands separate at the origin, forming a replication bubble with two forks. Replication proceeds in both directions until the forks meet on the other side, resulting in two daughter DNA molecules. The TEM shows a bacterial chromosome with a replication bubble.

(b) In each linear chromosome of eukaryotes, DNA replication begins when replication bubbles form at many sites along the giant DNA molecule. The bubbles expand as replication proceeds in both directions. Eventually, the bubbles fuse and synthesis of the daughter strands is complete. The TEM shows three replication bubbles along the DNA of a cultured Chinese hamster cell.

▲ **Figure 16.12 Origins of replication in *E. coli* and eukaryotes.** The red arrows indicate the movement of the replication forks and thus the overall directions of DNA replication within each bubble.

DRAW IT *In the TEM in (b), add arrows for the third bubble.*

contrast to a bacterial chromosome, a eukaryotic chromosome may have hundreds or even a few thousand replication origins. Multiple replication bubbles form and eventually fuse, thus speeding up the copying of the very long DNA molecules **(Figure 16.12b)**. As in bacteria, eukaryotic DNA replication proceeds in both directions from each origin.

At each end of a replication bubble is a **replication fork**, a Y-shaped region where the parental strands of DNA are being unwound. Several kinds of proteins participate in the unwinding **(Figure 16.13)**. **Helicases** are enzymes that untwist the double helix at the replication forks, separating the two parental strands and making them available as template strands. After parental strand separation, **single-strand binding proteins** bind to the unpaired DNA strands, stabilizing them. The untwisting of the double helix causes tighter twisting and strain ahead of the replication fork. **Topoisomerase** helps relieve this strain by breaking, swiveling, and rejoining DNA strands.

The unwound sections of parental DNA strands are now available to serve as templates for the synthesis of new complementary DNA strands. However, the enzymes that synthesize DNA cannot *initiate* the synthesis of a polynucleotide; they can only add nucleotides to the end of an already existing chain that is base-paired with the template strand. The initial nucleotide chain that is produced during DNA synthesis is actually a short stretch of RNA, not DNA. This RNA chain is called a **primer** and is synthesized by the enzyme **primase** (see Figure 16.13). Primase starts an RNA chain from a single RNA nucleotide, adding RNA nucleotides one at a time, using the parental DNA strand as a template. The completed primer, generally 5 to 10 nucleotides long, is thus base-paired to the template strand. The new DNA strand will start from the 3′ end of the RNA primer.

Synthesizing a New DNA Strand

Enzymes called **DNA polymerases** catalyze the synthesis of new DNA by adding nucleotides to a preexisting chain. In *E. coli*, there are several different DNA polymerases, but two appear to play the major roles in DNA replication: DNA polymerase III and DNA polymerase I. The situation in eukaryotes is more complicated, with at least 11 different DNA polymerases discovered so far; however, the general principles are the same.

Most DNA polymerases require a primer and a DNA template strand, along which complementary DNA nucleotides line up. In *E. coli*, DNA polymerase III (abbreviated DNA pol III) adds a DNA nucleotide to the RNA primer and then continues adding DNA nucleotides, complementary to the parental DNA template strand, to the growing end of the new DNA strand. The rate of elongation is about 500 nucleotides per second in bacteria and 50 per second in human cells.

Each nucleotide added to a growing DNA strand comes from a nucleoside triphosphate, which is a nucleoside (a sugar and a base) with three phosphate groups. You have already encountered such a molecule—ATP (adenosine triphosphate; see Figure 8.8). The only difference between the ATP of energy metabolism and dATP, the nucleoside triphosphate that supplies an adenine nucleotide to DNA, is the sugar component, which is deoxyribose in the building block of DNA, but ribose in ATP. Like ATP, the nucleoside triphosphates used for DNA synthesis are chemically reactive, partly because their triphosphate tails have an unstable cluster of negative charge. As each monomer joins the growing end of a DNA strand, two phosphate groups are lost as a molecule of pyrophosphate ⓟ—ⓟᵢ. Subsequent hydrolysis of the pyrophosphate to two molecules of inorganic phosphate ⓟᵢ is a coupled exergonic reaction that helps drive the polymerization reaction **(Figure 16.14)**.

▶ **Figure 16.13 Some of the proteins involved in the initiation of DNA replication.** The same proteins function at both replication forks in a replication bubble. For simplicity, only one fork is shown.

Single-strand binding proteins stabilize the unwound parental strands.

Primase synthesizes RNA primers, using the parental DNA as a template.

Topoisomerase breaks, swivels, and rejoins the parental DNA ahead of the replication fork, relieving the strain caused by unwinding.

RNA primer

Helicase unwinds and separates the parental DNA strands.

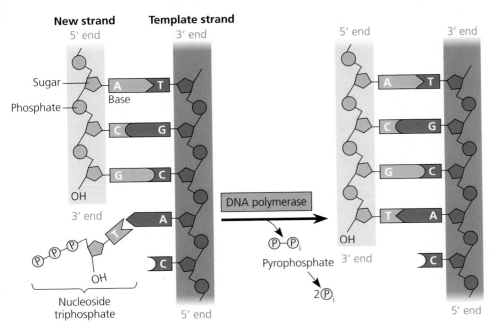

New strand   Template strand
5′ end   3′ end

Sugar

Phosphate

Base

OH

3′ end

P P P

OH

Nucleoside
triphosphate

5′ end

DNA polymerase

P—Pᵢ

Pyrophosphate

2 Pᵢ

5′ end   3′ end

OH

3′ end

5′ end

◄ **Figure 16.14 Incorporation of a nucleotide into a DNA strand.** DNA polymerase catalyzes the addition of a nucleoside triphosphate to the 3′ end of a growing DNA strand, with the release of two phosphates.

? *Use this diagram to explain what we mean when we say that each DNA strand has directionality.*

Antiparallel Elongation

As we have noted previously, the two ends of a DNA strand are different, giving each strand directionality, like a one-way street (see Figure 16.5). In addition, the two strands of DNA in a double helix are antiparallel, meaning that they are oriented in opposite directions to each other, like a divided highway (see Figure 16.14). Clearly, the two new strands formed during DNA replication must also be antiparallel to their template strands.

How does the antiparallel arrangement of the double helix affect replication? Because of their structure, DNA polymerases can add nucleotides only to the free 3′ end of a primer or growing DNA strand, never to the 5′ end (see Figure 16.14). Thus, a new DNA strand can elongate only in the 5′→3′ direction. With this in mind, let's examine a replication fork **(Figure 16.15)**. Along one template strand, DNA polymerase III can synthesize a complementary strand continuously by elongating the new DNA in the mandatory 5′→3′ direction. DNA pol III simply nestles in the replication fork on that template strand and continuously adds nucleotides to the new complementary strand as the fork progresses. The DNA strand made by this mechanism is called the **leading strand**. Only one primer is required for DNA pol III to synthesize the leading strand (see Figure 16.15).

To elongate the other new strand of DNA in the mandatory 5′→3′ direction, DNA pol III must work along the other template strand in the direction *away from* the replication fork. The DNA strand elongating in this direction is called the **lagging strand**.* In contrast to the leading strand, which elongates continuously,

---

* Synthesis of the leading strand and synthesis of the lagging strand occur concurrently and at the same rate. The lagging strand is so named because its synthesis is delayed slightly relative to synthesis of the leading strand; each new fragment of the lagging strand cannot be started until enough template has been exposed at the replication fork.

Overview

Origin of replication

Leading strand   Lagging strand

Primer

Lagging strand   Overall directions   Leading strand
                  of replication

❶ After RNA primer is made, DNA pol III starts to synthesize the leading strand.

Origin of replication

3′
5′

RNA primer

"Sliding clamp"

Parental DNA

5′
3′

5′

DNA pol III

5′
3′

3′
5′

❷ The leading strand is elongated continuously in the 5′→ 3′ direction as the fork progresses.

5′

▲ **Figure 16.15 Synthesis of the leading strand during DNA replication.** This diagram focuses on the left replication fork shown in the overview box. DNA polymerase III (DNA pol III), shaped like a cupped hand, is closely associated with a protein called the "sliding clamp" that encircles the newly synthesized double helix like a doughnut. The sliding clamp moves DNA pol III along the DNA template strand.

Overview

Leading strand

Origin of replication

Lagging strand

Lagging strand

② ①

Leading strand

Overall directions of replication

1 Primase joins RNA nucleotides into a primer.

3′ 5′

Template strand

5′ 3′

2 DNA pol III adds DNA nucleotides to the primer, forming Okazaki fragment 1.

3′

RNA primer ①

5′ 3′ 5′

3 After reaching the next RNA primer to the right, DNA pol III detaches.

3′

Okazaki fragment ①

3′ 5′

5′

4 After fragment 2 is primed, DNA pol III adds DNA nucleotides until it reaches the fragment 1 primer and detaches.

5′ 3′

② ①

3′ 5′

5 DNA pol I replaces the RNA with DNA, adding to the 3′ end of fragment 2.

5′ 3′

② ①

3′ 5′

6 DNA ligase forms a bond between the newest DNA and the DNA of fragment 1.

7 The lagging strand in this region is now complete.

5′ 3′

② ①

3′ 5′

Overall direction of replication

▲ **Figure 16.16 Synthesis of the lagging strand.**

the lagging strand is synthesized discontinuously, as a series of segments. These segments of the lagging strand are called **Okazaki fragments**, after the Japanese scientist who discovered them. The fragments are about 1,000 to 2,000 nucleotides long in *E. coli* and 100 to 200 nucleotides long in eukaryotes.

Figure 16.16 illustrates the steps in the synthesis of the lagging strand. Whereas only one primer is required on the leading strand, each Okazaki fragment on the lagging strand must be primed separately. Another DNA polymerase, DNA polymerase I (DNA pol I), replaces the RNA nucleotides of the primers with DNA versions, adding them one by one onto the 3′ end of the adjacent Okazaki fragment (fragment 2 in Figure 16.16). But DNA pol I cannot join the final nucleotide of this replacement DNA segment to the first DNA nucleotide of the Okazaki fragment whose primer was just replaced (fragment 1 in Figure 16.16). Another enzyme, **DNA ligase**, accomplishes this task, joining the sugar-phosphate backbones of all the Okazaki fragments into a continuous DNA strand.

Figure 16.17 and **Table 16.1**, on the next page, summarize DNA replication. Study them carefully before proceeding.

The DNA Replication Complex

It is traditional—and convenient—to represent DNA polymerase molecules as locomotives moving along a DNA "railroad track," but such a model is inaccurate in two important ways. First, the various proteins that participate in DNA replication actually form a single large complex, a "DNA replication machine." Many protein-protein interactions facilitate the efficiency of this complex. For example, by interacting with other proteins at the fork, primase apparently acts as a molecular brake, slowing progress of the replication fork and coordinating the rate of replication on the leading and lagging strands. Second, the DNA replication complex does not move along the DNA; rather, the DNA moves through the complex during the replication process. In eukaryotic cells, multiple copies of the complex, perhaps grouped into "factories," may be anchored to the nuclear matrix, a framework of fibers extending through the interior of the nucleus. Recent studies support a model in which two DNA polymerase molecules, one on each template strand, "reel in" the parental DNA and extrude newly made daughter DNA molecules. Additional evidence suggests that the lagging strand is looped back through the complex, so that when a DNA polymerase completes synthesis of an Okazaki fragment and dissociates, it doesn't have far to travel to reach the primer for the next fragment, near the replication fork. This looping of the lagging strand enables more Okazaki fragments to be synthesized in less time.

Proofreading and Repairing DNA

We cannot attribute the accuracy of DNA replication solely to the specificity of base pairing. Although errors in the completed DNA molecule amount to only one in 10 billion nucleotides, initial pairing errors between incoming nucleotides and those in

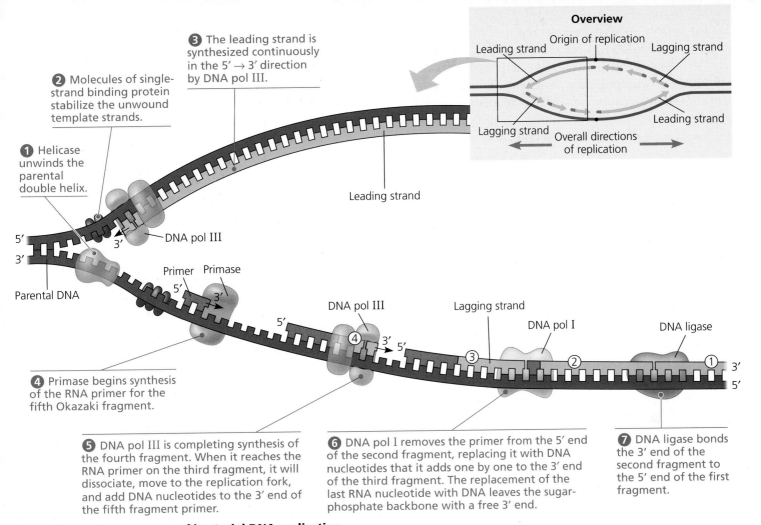

Overview

Leading strand · Origin of replication · Lagging strand
Lagging strand · Leading strand
Overall directions of replication

❶ Helicase unwinds the parental double helix.

❷ Molecules of single-strand binding protein stabilize the unwound template strands.

❸ The leading strand is synthesized continuously in the 5′ → 3′ direction by DNA pol III.

5′
3′

Parental DNA

DNA pol III

Primer · Primase

5′ · 3′

5′

Leading strand

DNA pol III

4 · 3′ · 5′

Lagging strand

DNA pol I

3 · 2 · DNA ligase

1 · 3′
5′

❹ Primase begins synthesis of the RNA primer for the fifth Okazaki fragment.

❺ DNA pol III is completing synthesis of the fourth fragment. When it reaches the RNA primer on the third fragment, it will dissociate, move to the replication fork, and add DNA nucleotides to the 3′ end of the fifth fragment primer.

❻ DNA pol I removes the primer from the 5′ end of the second fragment, replacing it with DNA nucleotides that it adds one by one to the 3′ end of the third fragment. The replacement of the last RNA nucleotide with DNA leaves the sugar-phosphate backbone with a free 3′ end.

❼ DNA ligase bonds the 3′ end of the second fragment to the 5′ end of the first fragment.

▲ **Figure 16.17 A summary of bacterial DNA replication.**
The detailed diagram shows one replication fork, but as indicated in the overview (upper right), replication usually occurs simultaneously at two forks, one at either end of a replication bubble. Viewing each daughter strand in its entirety in the overview, you can see that half of it is made continuously as the leading strand, while the other half (on the other side of the origin) is synthesized in fragments as the lagging strand.

the template strand are 100,000 times more common—an error rate of one in 100,000 nucleotides. During DNA replication, DNA polymerases proofread each nucleotide against its template as soon as it is added to the growing strand. Upon finding an incorrectly paired nucleotide, the polymerase removes the nucleotide and then resumes synthesis. (This action is similar to fixing a word processing error by using the "delete" key and then entering the correct letter.)

Mismatched nucleotides sometimes evade proofreading by a DNA polymerase. In **mismatch repair**, enzymes remove and replace incorrectly paired nucleotides that have resulted from replication errors. Researchers spotlighted the importance of such enzymes when they found that a hereditary defect in one of them is associated with a form of colon cancer. Apparently, this defect allows cancer-causing errors to accumulate in the DNA at a faster rate than normal.

Incorrectly paired or altered nucleotides can also arise after replication. In fact, maintenance of the genetic information

Table 16.1 Bacterial DNA Replication Proteins and Their Functions	
Protein	**Function**
Helicase	Unwinds parental double helix at replication forks
Single-strand binding protein	Binds to and stabilizes single-stranded DNA until it can be used as a template
Topoisomerase	Relieves "overwinding" strain ahead of replication forks by breaking, swiveling, and rejoining DNA strands
Primase	Synthesizes an RNA primer at 5′ end of leading strand and of each Okazaki fragment of lagging strand
DNA pol III	Using parental DNA as a template, synthesizes new DNA strand by covalently adding nucleotides to the 3′ end of a pre-existing DNA strand or RNA primer
DNA pol I	Removes RNA nucleotides of primer from 5′ end and replaces them with DNA nucleotides
DNA ligase	Joins 3′ end of DNA that replaces primer to rest of leading strand and joins Okazaki fragments of lagging strand

encoded in DNA requires frequent repair of various kinds of damage to existing DNA. DNA molecules are constantly subjected to potentially harmful chemical and physical agents, as we'll discuss in Chapter 17. Reactive chemicals (in the environment and occurring naturally in cells), radioactive emissions, X-rays, ultraviolet light, and certain molecules in cigarette smoke can change nucleotides in ways that affect encoded genetic information. In addition, DNA bases often undergo spontaneous chemical changes under normal cellular conditions. However, these changes in DNA are usually corrected before they become mutations perpetuated through successive replications. Each cell continuously monitors and repairs its genetic material. Because repair of damaged DNA is so important to the survival of an organism, it is no surprise that many different DNA repair enzymes have evolved. Almost 100 are known in *E. coli*, and about 130 have been identified so far in humans.

Most cellular systems for repairing incorrectly paired nucleotides, whether they are due to DNA damage or to replication errors, use a mechanism that takes advantage of the base-paired structure of DNA. Often, a segment of the strand containing the damage is cut out (excised) by a DNA-cutting enzyme—a **nuclease**—and the resulting gap is then filled in with nucleotides, using the undamaged strand as a template. The enzymes involved in filling the gap are a DNA polymerase and DNA ligase. One such DNA repair system is called **nucleotide excision repair** (Figure 16.18).

An important function of the DNA repair enzymes in our skin cells is to repair genetic damage caused by the ultraviolet rays of sunlight. One type of damage, shown in Figure 16.18, is the covalent linking of thymine bases that are adjacent on a DNA strand. Such *thymine dimers* cause the DNA to buckle and interfere with DNA replication. The importance of repairing this kind of damage is underscored by the disorder xeroderma pigmentosum, which in most cases is caused by an inherited defect in a nucleotide excision repair enzyme. Individuals with this disorder are hypersensitive to sunlight; mutations in their skin cells caused by ultraviolet light are left uncorrected and cause skin cancer.

Replicating the Ends of DNA Molecules

In spite of the impressive capabilities of DNA polymerases, there is a small portion of the cell's DNA that DNA polymerases can neither replicate nor repair. For linear DNA, such as the DNA of eukaryotic chromosomes, the fact that a DNA polymerase can add nucleotides only to the 3′ end of a preexisting polynucleotide leads to an apparent problem. The usual replication machinery provides no way to complete the 5′ ends of daughter DNA strands. Even if an Okazaki fragment can be started with an RNA primer bound to the very end of the template strand, once that primer is removed, it cannot be replaced with DNA because there is no 3′ end available for nucleotide addition (Figure 16.19). As a

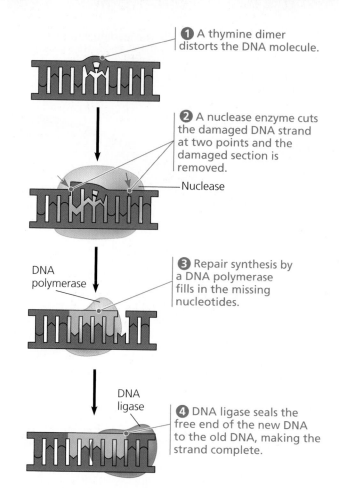

1 A thymine dimer distorts the DNA molecule.

2 A nuclease enzyme cuts the damaged DNA strand at two points and the damaged section is removed.

Nuclease

DNA polymerase

3 Repair synthesis by a DNA polymerase fills in the missing nucleotides.

DNA ligase

4 DNA ligase seals the free end of the new DNA to the old DNA, making the strand complete.

▲ **Figure 16.18 Nucleotide excision repair of DNA damage.** A team of enzymes detects and repairs damaged DNA. This figure shows DNA containing a thymine dimer, a type of damage often caused by ultraviolet radiation. A nuclease enzyme cuts out the damaged region of DNA, and a DNA polymerase (in bacteria, DNA pol I) replaces it with nucleotides complementary to the undamaged strand. DNA ligase completes the process by closing the remaining break in the sugar-phosphate backbone.

result, repeated rounds of replication produce shorter and shorter DNA molecules with uneven ("staggered") ends.

The shortening of DNA does not occur in most prokaryotes because their DNA is circular and therefore has no ends. But what protects the genes of eukaryotes from being eroded away during successive rounds of DNA replication? It turns out that eukaryotic chromosomal DNA molecules have special nucleotide sequences called **telomeres** at their ends (Figure 16.20). Telomeres do not contain genes; instead, the DNA typically consists of multiple repetitions of one short nucleotide sequence. In each human telomere, for example, the six-nucleotide sequence TTAGGG is repeated between 100 and 1,000 times. Telomeric DNA protects the organism's genes. In addition, specific proteins associated with telomeric DNA prevent the staggered ends of the daughter molecule from activating the cell's systems for monitoring DNA damage. (Staggered ends of a DNA molecule, which often result from double-strand breaks, can trig-

▲ **Figure 16.20 Telomeres.** Eukaryotes have repetitive, noncoding sequences called telomeres at the ends of their DNA. Telomeres are stained orange in these mouse chromosomes (LM).

▲ **Figure 16.19 Shortening of the ends of linear DNA molecules.** Here we follow the end of one strand of a DNA molecule through two rounds of replication. After the first round, the new lagging strand is shorter than its template. After a second round, both the leading and lagging strands have become shorter than the original parental DNA. Although not shown here, the other ends of these DNA molecules also become shorter.

ger signal transduction pathways leading to cell cycle arrest or cell death.)

Telomeres do not prevent the shortening of DNA molecules due to successive rounds of replication; they just postpone the erosion of genes near the ends of DNA molecules. As shown in Figure 16.19, telomeres become shorter during every round of replication. As we would expect, telomeric DNA does tend to be shorter in dividing somatic cells of older individuals and in cultured cells that have divided many times. It has been proposed that shortening of telomeres is somehow connected to the aging process of certain tissues and even to aging of the organism as a whole.

But what about the cells whose genomes must persist unchanged from an organism to its offspring over many generations? If the chromosomes of germ cells (which give rise to gametes) became shorter in every cell cycle, essential genes would eventually be missing from the gametes they produce. However, this does not occur: An enzyme called **telomerase** catalyzes the lengthening of telomeres in eukaryotic germ cells, thus restoring their original length and compensating for the shortening that occurs during DNA replication. Telomerase is not active in most human somatic cells, but its activity in germ cells results in telomeres of maximum length in the zygote.

Normal shortening of telomeres may protect organisms from cancer by limiting the number of divisions that somatic cells can undergo. Cells from large tumors often have unusually short telomeres, as one would expect for cells that have undergone many cell divisions. Further shortening would presumably lead to self-destruction of the tumor cells. Intriguingly, researchers have found telomerase activity in cancerous somatic cells, suggesting that its ability to stabilize telomere length may allow these cancer cells to persist. Many cancer cells do seem capable of unlimited cell division, as do immortal strains of cultured cells (see Chapter 12). If telomerase is indeed an important factor in many cancers, it may provide a useful target for both cancer diagnosis and chemotherapy.

Thus far in this chapter, you have learned about the structure and replication of a DNA molecule. In the next section, we'll examine how DNA is packaged into chromosomes, the structures that carry the genetic information.

CONCEPT CHECK 16.2

1. What role does complementary base pairing play in the replication of DNA?
2. Identify two major functions of DNA pol III in DNA replication.
3. **WHAT IF?** If the DNA pol I in a given cell were nonfunctional, how would that affect the synthesis of a *leading* strand? In the overview box in Figure 16.17, point out where DNA pol I would normally function on the top leading strand.

For suggested answers, see Appendix A.

A chromosome consists of a DNA molecule packed together with proteins

The main component of the genome in most bacteria is one double-stranded, circular DNA molecule that is associated with a small amount of protein. Although we refer to this structure as the *bacterial chromosome*, it is very different from a eukaryotic chromosome, which consists of one linear DNA molecule associated with a large amount of protein. In *E. coli*, the chromosomal DNA consists of about 4.6 million nucleotide pairs, representing about 4,400 genes. This is 100 times more DNA than is found in a typical virus, but only about one-thousandth as much DNA as in a human somatic cell. Still, it is a lot of DNA to be packaged in such a small container.

Stretched out, the DNA of an *E. coli* cell would measure about a millimeter in length, 500 times longer than the cell.

▼ **Figure 16.21**

Exploring Chromatin Packing in a Eukaryotic Chromosome

This series of diagrams and transmission electron micrographs depicts a current model for the progressive levels of DNA coiling and folding. The illustration zooms out from a single molecule of DNA to a metaphase chromosome, which is large enough to be seen with a light microscope.

Nucleosome (10 nm in diameter)

H1

Histone tail

Histones

DNA double helix (2 nm in diameter)

1 DNA, the double helix

Shown here is a ribbon model of DNA, with each ribbon representing one of the sugar-phosphate backbones. As you will recall from Figure 16.7, the phosphate groups along the backbone contribute a negative charge along the outside of each strand. The TEM shows a molecule of naked DNA; the double helix alone is 2 nm across.

2 Histones

Proteins called histones are responsible for the first level of DNA packing in chromatin. Although each histone is small—containing about 100 amino acids—the total mass of histone in chromatin approximately equals the mass of DNA. More than a fifth of a histone's amino acids are positively charged (lysine or arginine) and bind tightly to the negatively charged DNA.

Four types of histones are most common in chromatin: H2A, H2B, H3, and H4. The histones are very similar among eukaryotes; for example, all but two of the amino acids in cow H4 are identical to those in pea H4. The apparent conservation of histone genes during evolution probably reflects the pivotal role of histones in organizing DNA within cells.

The four main types of histones are critical to the next level of DNA packing. (A fifth type of histone, called H1, is involved in a further stage of packing.)

3 Nucleosomes, or "beads on a string" (10-nm fiber)

In electron micrographs, unfolded chromatin is 10 nm in diameter (the *10-nm fiber*). Such chromatin resembles beads on a string (see the TEM). Each "bead" is a *nucleosome*, the basic unit of DNA packing; the "string" between beads is called *linker DNA*.

A nucleosome consists of DNA wound twice around a protein core composed of two molecules each of the four main histone types. The amino end (N-terminus) of each histone (the *histone tail*) extends outward from the nucleosome.

In the cell cycle, the histones leave the DNA only briefly during DNA replication. Generally, they do the same during gene expression, another process that requires access to the DNA by the cell's molecular machinery. Chapter 18 will discuss some recent findings about the role of histone tails and nucleosomes in the regulation of gene expression.

Within a bacterium, however, certain proteins cause the chromosome to coil and "supercoil," densely packing it so that it fills only part of the cell. Unlike the nucleus of a eukaryotic cell, this dense region of DNA in a bacterium, called the **nucleoid**, is not bounded by membrane (see Figure 6.6).

Eukaryotic chromosomes each contain a single linear DNA double helix that, in humans, averages about 1.5×10^8 nucleotide pairs. This is an enormous amount of DNA relative to a chromosome's condensed length. If completely stretched out, such a DNA molecule would be about 4 cm long, thousands of times the diameter of a cell nucleus—and that's not even considering the DNA of the other 45 human chromosomes!

In the cell, eukaryotic DNA is precisely combined with a large amount of protein. Together, this complex of DNA and protein, called **chromatin**, fits into the nucleus through an elaborate, multilevel system of DNA packing. Our current view of the successive levels of DNA packing in a chromosome is outlined in **Figure 16.21**. Study this figure carefully before reading further.

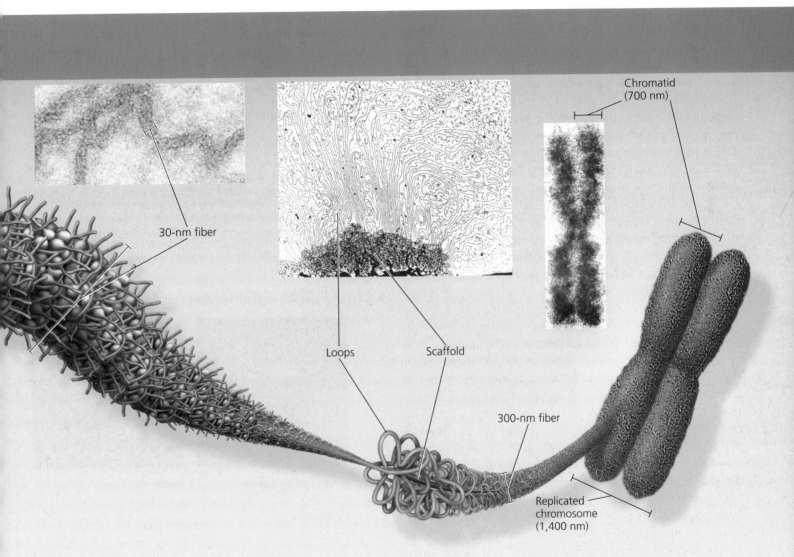

30-nm fiber

Chromatid (700 nm)

Loops

Scaffold

300-nm fiber

Replicated chromosome (1,400 nm)

4 30-nm fiber

The next level of packing is due to interactions between the histone tails of one nucleosome and the linker DNA and nucleosomes on either side. A fifth histone, H1, is involved at this level. These interactions cause the extended 10-nm fiber to coil or fold, forming a chromatin fiber roughly 30 nm in thickness, the *30-nm fiber*. Although the 30-nm fiber is quite prevalent in the interphase nucleus, the packing arrangement of nucleosomes in this form of chromatin is still a matter of some debate.

5 Looped domains (300-nm fiber)

The 30-nm fiber, in turn, forms loops called *looped domains* attached to a chromosome scaffold made of proteins, thus making up a *300-nm fiber*. The scaffold is rich in one type of topoisomerase, and H1 molecules also appear to be present.

6 Metaphase chromosome

In a mitotic chromosome, the looped domains themselves coil and fold in a manner not yet fully understood, further compacting all the chromatin to produce the characteristic metaphase chromosome shown in the micrograph above. The width of one chromatid is 700 nm. Particular genes always end up located at the same places in metaphase chromosomes, indicating that the packing steps are highly specific and precise.

Chromatin undergoes striking changes in its degree of packing during the course of the cell cycle (see Figure 12.6). In interphase cells stained for light microscopy, the chromatin usually appears as a diffuse mass within the nucleus, suggesting that the chromatin is highly extended. As a cell prepares for mitosis, its chromatin coils and folds up (condenses), eventually forming a characteristic number of short, thick metaphase chromosomes that are distinguishable from each other with the light microscope.

Though interphase chromatin is generally much less condensed than the chromatin of mitotic chromosomes, it shows several of the same levels of higher-order packing. Some of the chromatin comprising a chromosome seems to be present as a 10-nm fiber, but much is compacted into a 30-nm fiber, which in some regions is further folded into looped domains. Although an interphase chromosome lacks an obvious scaffold, its looped domains appear to be attached to the nuclear lamina, on the inside of the nuclear envelope, and perhaps also to fibers of the nuclear matrix. These attachments may help organize regions of chromatin where genes are active. The chromatin of each chromosome occupies a specific restricted area within the interphase nucleus, and the chromatin fibers of different chromosomes do not become entangled.

Even during interphase, the centromeres and telomeres of chromosomes, as well as other chromosomal regions in some cells, exist in a highly condensed state similar to that seen in a metaphase chromosome. This type of interphase chromatin, visible as irregular clumps with a light microscope, is called **heterochromatin**, to distinguish it from the less compacted, more dispersed **euchromatin** ("true chromatin"). Because of its compaction, heterochromatin DNA is largely inaccessible to the machinery in the cell responsible for expressing (making use of) the genetic information coded in the DNA. In contrast, the looser packing of euchromatin makes its DNA accessible to this machinery, so the genes present in euchromatin can be expressed.

The chromosome is a dynamic structure that is condensed, loosened, modified, and remodeled as necessary for various cell processes, including mitosis, meiosis, and gene activity. The pathways regulating these transformations are currently a focus of intense study by researchers. It has become clear that histones are not simply inert spools around which the DNA is wrapped. Instead, they can undergo chemical modifications that result in changes in chromatin organization. Terry Orr-Weaver, the scientist interviewed at the beginning of this unit (pp. 246–247), has long been interested in the molecular mechanisms of chromosome dynamics during mitosis and meiosis. Using a genetic approach in *Drosophila*, she and her colleagues showed that phosphorylation of a specific amino acid on a histone tail plays a crucial role in chromosome behavior during prophase I of meiosis (**Figure 16.22**).

▼ Figure 16.22 **Inquiry**

What role does histone phosphorylation play in chromosome behavior during meiosis?

EXPERIMENT Terry Orr-Weaver and colleagues at the Massachusetts Institute of Technology mutagenized fruit flies and looked for mutations that caused sterility, reasoning that such mutations might be found in genes coding for proteins that play important roles during meiosis. They found a mutation in the *nhk-1* gene that caused sterility in *Drosophila* females. They knew that the gene product, nucleosomal histone kinase-1, or NHK-1, is an enzyme that phosphorylates a specific amino acid on the tail of histone H2A. They hypothesized that sterility is caused by unsuccessful meiosis due to abnormal chromosome behavior when this enzyme does not function properly.

To test this hypothesis, they observed chromosome behavior closely during meiosis in ovarian cells of normal and mutant flies. In one experiment, they used a red fluorescent dye to mark the location of DNA and a green fluorescent dye to mark the location of the protein *condensin*, which normally coats the chromosomes at the end of prophase I and helps them condense.

RESULTS At the end of prophase I in ovarian cells of normal flies, condensin and DNA were both localized to a very small region in the nucleus (below left; the yellow color is the result of green and red dyes located together). However, in mutant flies, condensin was spread diffusely throughout the nucleus while the DNA was restricted to the periphery of the nucleus (below right; the red of the DNA is very faint). This result suggested that condensin does not coat the chromosomes in the cells of mutant flies and that, consequently, the chromosomes don't condense.

Condensin and DNA (yellow) — Outline of nucleus — Condensin (green) — DNA (red at periphery)

Normal cell nucleus   **Mutant cell nucleus**

CONCLUSION Because this process and others during meiosis are not completed successfully when the histone kinase NHK-1 does not function properly, the researchers concluded that a specific phosphorylation of histone H2A is necessary for normal chromosome behavior during meiosis.

SOURCE I. Ivanovska, T. Khandan, T. Ito, and T. L. Orr-Weaver, A histone code in meiosis: the histone kinase, NHK-1, is required for proper chromosomal architecture in *Drosophila* oocytes, *Genes and Development* 19:2571–2582 (2005).

WHAT IF? Suppose a researcher discovered a mutant fly in which the histone H2A tail was missing the specific amino acid usually phosphorylated by the histone kinase NHK-1. How would this mutation likely affect chromosome behavior during meiosis in ovarian cells?

Phosphorylation and other chemical modifications of histones also have multiple effects on gene activity, as you will see in Chapter 18.

In this chapter, you have learned how DNA molecules are arranged in chromosomes and how DNA replication provides the copies of genes that parents pass to offspring. However, it is not enough that genes be copied and transmitted; the information they carry must be used by the cell. In other words, genes must also be "expressed." In the next chapter, we will examine how the cell translates genetic information encoded in DNA.

Chapter 16 Review

SUMMARY OF KEY CONCEPTS

CONCEPT 16.1
DNA is the genetic material (pp. 305–310)

▶ **The Search for the Genetic Material: *Scientific Inquiry***
Experiments with bacteria and with phages provided the first strong evidence that the genetic material is DNA.

▶ **Building a Structural Model of DNA: *Scientific Inquiry***
Watson and Crick deduced that DNA is a double helix. Two antiparallel sugar-phosphate chains wind around the outside of the molecule; the nitrogenous bases project into the interior, where they hydrogen-bond in specific pairs, A with T, G with C.

Sugar-phosphate backbone
Nitrogenous bases
Hydrogen bond

CONCEPT 16.2
Many proteins work together in DNA replication and repair (pp. 311–319)

▶ **The Basic Principle: Base Pairing to a Template Strand**
The Meselson-Stahl experiment showed that DNA replication is semiconservative: The parent molecule unwinds, and each strand then serves as a template for the synthesis of a new strand according to base-pairing rules.

▶ **DNA Replication: *A Closer Look***

DNA pol III synthesizes leading strand continuously

Parental DNA

DNA pol III starts DNA synthesis at 3' end of primer, continues in 5' → 3' direction

Lagging strand synthesized in short Okazaki fragments, later joined by DNA ligase

Primase synthesizes a short RNA primer

▶ **Proofreading and Repairing DNA** DNA polymerases proofread new DNA, replacing incorrect nucleotides. In mismatch repair, enzymes correct errors that persist. Nucleotide excision repair is a general process by which enzymes cut out and replace damaged stretches of DNA.

▶ **Replicating the Ends of DNA Molecules** The ends of eukaryotic chromosomal DNA get shorter with each round of replication. The presence of telomeres, repetitive sequences at the ends of linear DNA molecules, postpones the erosion of genes. Telomerase catalyzes the lengthening of telomeres in germ cells.

CONCEPT 16.3
A chromosome consists of a DNA molecule packed together with proteins (pp. 320–323)

▶ The bacterial chromosome is usually a circular DNA molecule with some associated proteins. Eukaryotic chromatin making up a chromosome is composed mostly of DNA, histones, and other proteins. The histones bind to each other and to the DNA to form nucleosomes, the most basic units of DNA packing. Histone tails extend outward from each bead-like nucleosome core. Additional folding leads ultimately to the highly condensed chromatin of the metaphase chromosome. In interphase cells, most chromatin is less compacted (euchromatin), but some remains highly condensed (heterochromatin). Histone modifications may influence the state of chromatin condensation.

MEDIA

Activity DNA Packing

TESTING YOUR KNOWLEDGE

SELF-QUIZ

1. In his work with pneumonia-causing bacteria and mice, Griffith found that
   a. the protein coat from pathogenic cells was able to transform nonpathogenic cells.
   b. heat-killed pathogenic cells caused pneumonia.
   c. some substance from pathogenic cells was transferred to nonpathogenic cells, making them pathogenic.
   d. the polysaccharide coat of bacteria caused pneumonia.
   e. bacteriophages injected DNA into bacteria.

2. *E. coli* cells grown on ^{15}N medium are transferred to ^{14}N medium and allowed to grow for two more generations (two rounds of DNA replication). DNA extracted from these cells is centrifuged. What density distribution of DNA would you expect in this experiment?
   a. one high-density and one low-density band
   b. one intermediate-density band
   c. one high-density and one intermediate-density band
   d. one low-density and one intermediate-density band
   e. one low-density band

3. A biochemist isolates and purifies molecules needed for DNA replication. When she adds some DNA, replication occurs, but each DNA molecule consists of a normal strand paired with numerous segments of DNA a few hundred nucleotides long. What has she probably left out of the mixture?
   a. DNA polymerase   d. Okazaki fragments
   b. DNA ligase   e. primase
   c. nucleotides

4. What is the basis for the difference in how the leading and lagging strands of DNA molecules are synthesized?
   a. The origins of replication occur only at the 5′ end.
   b. Helicases and single-strand binding proteins work at the 5′ end.
   c. DNA polymerase can join new nucleotides only to the 3′ end of a growing strand.
   d. DNA ligase works only in the 3′→5′ direction.
   e. Polymerase can work on only one strand at a time.

5. In analyzing the number of different bases in a DNA sample, which result would be consistent with the base-pairing rules?
   a. A = G   d. A = C
   b. A + G = C + T   e. G = T
   c. A + T = G + T

6. The elongation of the leading strand during DNA synthesis
   a. progresses away from the replication fork.
   b. occurs in the 3′→5′ direction.
   c. produces Okazaki fragments.
   d. depends on the action of DNA polymerase.
   e. does not require a template strand.

7. The spontaneous loss of amino groups from adenine results in hypoxanthine, an uncommon base, opposite thymine in DNA. What combination of molecules could repair such damage?
   a. nuclease, DNA polymerase, DNA ligase
   b. telomerase, primase, DNA polymerase
   c. telomerase, helicase, single-strand binding protein
   d. DNA ligase, replication fork proteins, adenylyl cyclase
   e. nuclease, telomerase, primase

8. In a nucleosome, the DNA is wrapped around
   a. polymerase molecules.   d. a thymine dimer.
   b. ribosomes.   e. satellite DNA.
   c. histones.

For Self-Quiz answers, see Appendix A.

MEDIA Visit the Study Area at **www.masteringbio.com** for a Practice Test.

EVOLUTION CONNECTION

9. Some bacteria may be able to respond to environmental stress by increasing the rate at which mutations occur during cell division. How might this be accomplished? Might there be an evolutionary advantage of this ability? Explain.

SCIENTIFIC INQUIRY

10. **DRAW IT** Model building can be an important part of the scientific process. The illustration above is a computer-generated model of a DNA replication complex. The parental and newly synthesized DNA strands are color-coded differently, as are each of the following three proteins: DNA pol III, the sliding clamp, and single-strand binding protein. Use what you've learned in this chapter to clarify this model by labeling each DNA strand and each protein and showing the overall direction of DNA replication.

From Gene to Protein

17

▲ **Figure 17.1** **How does a single faulty gene result in the dramatic appearance of an albino deer?**

OVERVIEW

The Flow of Genetic Information

In 2006, a young albino deer seen frolicking with several brown deer in the mountains of eastern Germany elicited a public outcry (**Figure 17.1**). A local hunting organization said the albino deer suffered from a "genetic disorder" and should be shot. Some people felt the deer should merely be prevented from mating with other deer in order to safeguard the gene pool of the population. Others favored relocating the albino deer to a nature reserve because they worried that it might be more noticeable to predators if left in the wild. A German rock star even held a benefit concert to raise funds for the relocation. What led to the striking phenotype of this deer, the cause of this lively debate?

You learned in Chapter 14 that inherited traits are determined by genes and that the trait of albinism is caused by a recessive allele of a pigmentation gene. The information content of genes is in the form of specific sequences of nucleotides along strands of DNA, the genetic material. But how does this information determine an organism's traits? Put another way, what does a gene actually say? And how is its

message translated by cells into a specific trait, such as brown hair, type A blood, or, in the case of an albino deer, a total lack of pigment? The albino deer has a faulty version of a key protein, an enzyme required for pigment synthesis, and this protein is faulty because the gene that codes for it contains incorrect information.

This example illustrates the main point of this chapter: The DNA inherited by an organism leads to specific traits by dictating the synthesis of proteins and of RNA molecules involved in protein synthesis. In other words, proteins are the link between genotype and phenotype. **Gene expression** is the process by which DNA directs the synthesis of proteins (or, in some cases, just RNAs). The expression of genes that code for proteins includes two stages: transcription and translation. This chapter describes the flow of information from gene to protein in detail and explains how genetic mutations affect organisms through their proteins. Gene expression involves similar processes in all three domains of life. Understanding these processes will allow us to revisit the concept of the gene in more detail at the end of the chapter.

CONCEPT 17.1

Genes specify proteins via transcription and translation

Before going into the details of how genes direct protein synthesis, let's step back and examine how the fundamental relationship between genes and proteins was discovered.

Evidence from the Study of Metabolic Defects

In 1909, British physician Archibald Garrod was the first to suggest that genes dictate phenotypes through enzymes that catalyze specific chemical reactions in the cell. Garrod postulated that the symptoms of an inherited disease reflect a person's inability to make a particular enzyme. He referred to such diseases as "inborn errors of metabolism." Garrod gave as one example the hereditary condition called alkaptonuria, in which the urine is black because it contains the chemical alkapton, which darkens upon exposure to air. Garrod reasoned that most people have an enzyme that metabolizes alkapton, whereas people with alkaptonuria have inherited an inability to make that enzyme.

Garrod may have been the first person to recognize that Mendel's principles of heredity apply to humans as well as peas. Garrod's realization was ahead of its time, but research conducted several decades later supported his hypothesis that a gene dictates the production of a specific enzyme. Biochemists accumulated much evidence that cells synthesize and degrade most organic molecules via metabolic pathways, in which each chemical reaction in a sequence is catalyzed by a specific enzyme (see p. 142). Such metabolic pathways lead, for instance, to the synthesis of the pigments that give fruit flies (*Drosophila*) their eye color (see Figure 15.3). In the 1930s, George Beadle and Boris Ephrussi speculated that in *Drosophila*, each of the various mutations affecting eye color blocks pigment synthesis at a specific step by preventing production of the enzyme that catalyzes that step. However, neither the chemical reactions nor the enzymes that catalyze them were known at the time.

Nutritional Mutants in Neurospora: Scientific Inquiry

A breakthrough in demonstrating the relationship between genes and enzymes came a few years later, when Beadle and Edward Tatum began working with a bread mold, *Neurospora crassa*. Using a treatment shown in the 1920s to cause genetic changes, they bombarded *Neurospora* with X-rays and then looked among the survivors for mutants that differed in their nutritional needs from the wild-type mold. Wild-type *Neurospora* has modest food requirements. It can survive in the laboratory on a moist support medium called agar, mixed only with inorganic salts, glucose, and the vitamin biotin. From this *minimal medium*, the mold cells use their metabolic pathways to produce all the other molecules they need. Beadle and Tatum identified mutants that could not survive on minimal medium, apparently because they were unable to synthesize certain essential molecules from the minimal ingredients. To ensure survival of these nutritional mutants, Beadle and Tatum allowed them to grow on a *complete growth medium*, which consisted of minimal medium supplemented with all 20 amino acids and a few other nutrients. The complete growth medium could support any mutant that couldn't synthesize one of the supplements.

To characterize the metabolic defect in each nutritional mutant, Beadle and Tatum took samples from the mutant growing on complete medium and distributed them to a number of different vials. Each vial contained minimal medium plus a single additional nutrient. The particular supplement that allowed growth indicated the metabolic defect. For example, if the only supplemented vial that supported growth of the mutant was the one fortified with the amino acid arginine, the researchers could conclude that the mutant was defective in the biochemical pathway that wild-type cells use to synthesize arginine.

Beadle and Tatum went on to pin down each mutant's defect more specifically. **Figure 17.2** shows how they used additional tests to distinguish among three classes of arginine-requiring mutants. Mutants in each class required a different set of compounds along the arginine-synthesizing pathway, which has three steps. Based on their results, the researchers reasoned that each class must be blocked at a different step in this pathway because mutants in that class lacked the enzyme that catalyzes the blocked step.

Because each mutant was defective in a single gene, Beadle and Tatum's results provided strong support for the *one gene–one enzyme hypothesis*, as they dubbed it, which states that the function of a gene is to dictate the production of a specific enzyme. Further support for this hypothesis came from experiments that identified the specific enzymes lacking in the mutants. Beadle and Tatum shared a Nobel Prize in 1958 for "their discovery that genes act by regulating definite chemical events" (in the words of the Nobel committee).

The Products of Gene Expression: A Developing Story

As researchers learned more about proteins, they made revisions to the one gene–one enzyme hypothesis. First of all, not all proteins are enzymes. Keratin, the structural protein of animal hair, and the hormone insulin are two examples of nonenzyme proteins. Because proteins that are not enzymes are nevertheless gene products, molecular biologists began to think in terms of one gene–one protein. However, many proteins are constructed from two or more different polypeptide chains, and each polypeptide is specified by its own gene. For example, hemoglobin, the oxygen-transporting protein of vertebrate red blood cells, is built from two kinds of polypeptides, and thus two genes code for this protein (see Figure 5.21). Beadle and Tatum's idea was therefore restated as the *one gene–one polypeptide hypothesis*. Even this description is not entirely accurate, though. First, many eukaryotic genes can code for a set of closely related polypeptides in a process called alternative splicing, which you will learn about later in this chapter. Second, quite a few genes code for RNA molecules that have important functions in cells even though they are never translated into protein. For now, we will focus on genes that do code for polypeptides. (Note that it is common to refer to these gene products as proteins, rather than more precisely as polypeptides—a practice you will encounter in this book.)

▼ Figure 17.2 Inquiry

Do individual genes specify the enzymes that function in a biochemical pathway?

EXPERIMENT   Working with the mold *Neurospora crassa*, George Beadle and Edward Tatum, then at Stanford University, isolated mutants that required arginine in their growth medium. The researchers showed that these mutants fell into three classes, each defective in a different gene. From other considerations, they suspected that the metabolic pathway of arginine biosynthesis involved a precursor nutrient and the intermediate molecules ornithine and citrulline. Their most famous experiment, shown here, tested both their one gene–one enzyme hypothesis and their postulated arginine-synthesizing pathway. In this experiment, they grew their three classes of mutants under the four different conditions shown in the Results section below. They included minimal medium (MM) as a control because they knew that wild-type cells could grow on MM but mutant cells could not. (See test tubes on the right.)

RESULTS   The wild-type strain was capable of growth under all experimental conditions, requiring only the minimal medium. The three classes of mutants each had a specific set of growth requirements. For example, class II mutants could not grow when ornithine alone was added but could grow when either citrulline or arginine was added.

CONCLUSION   From the growth requirements of the mutants, Beadle and Tatum deduced that each class of mutant was unable to carry out one step in the pathway for synthesizing arginine, presumably because it lacked the necessary enzyme. Because each of their mutants was mutated in a single gene, they concluded that each mutated gene must normally dictate the production of one enzyme. Their results supported the one gene–one enzyme hypothesis and also confirmed the arginine pathway. (Notice in the Results that a mutant can grow only if supplied with a compound made *after* the defective step, because this bypasses the defect.)

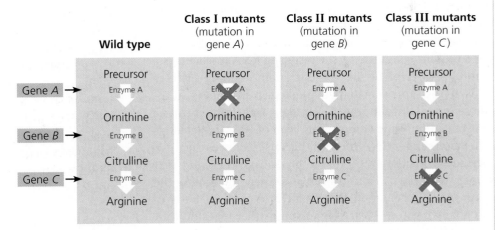

SOURCE   G. W. Beadle and E. L. Tatum, Genetic control of biochemical reactions in *Neurospora*, *Proceedings of the National Academy of Sciences* 27:499–506 (1941).

WHAT IF?   Suppose the experiment had shown that class I mutants could grow only in MM supplemented by ornithine or arginine and that class II mutants could grow in MM supplemented by citrulline, ornithine, or arginine. What conclusions would Beadle and Tatum have drawn from those results regarding the biochemical pathway and the defect in class I and class II mutants?

Basic Principles of Transcription and Translation

Genes provide the instructions for making specific proteins. But a gene does not build a protein directly. The bridge between DNA and protein synthesis is the nucleic acid RNA. You learned in Chapter 5 that RNA is chemically similar to DNA, except that it contains ribose instead of deoxyribose as its sugar and has the nitrogenous base uracil rather than thymine (see Figure 5.27). Thus, each nucleotide along a DNA strand has A, G, C, or T as its base, and each nucleotide along an RNA strand has A, G, C, or U as its base. An RNA molecule usually consists of a single strand.

It is customary to describe the flow of information from gene to protein in linguistic terms because both nucleic acids and proteins are polymers with specific sequences of monomers that convey information, much as specific sequences of letters communicate information in a language like English. In DNA or RNA, the monomers are the four types of nucleotides, which differ in their nitrogenous bases. Genes are typically hundreds or thousands of nucleotides long, each gene having a specific sequence of bases. Each polypeptide of a protein also has monomers arranged in a particular linear order (the protein's primary structure), but its monomers are amino acids. Thus, nucleic acids and proteins contain information written in two different chemical languages. Getting from DNA to protein requires two major stages: transcription and translation.

Transcription is the synthesis of RNA under the direction of DNA. Both nucleic acids use the same language, and the information is simply transcribed, or copied, from one molecule to the other. Just as a DNA strand provides a template for the synthesis of a new complementary strand during DNA replication, it also can serve as a template for assembling a complementary sequence of RNA nucleotides. For a protein-coding gene, the resulting RNA molecule is a faithful transcript of the gene's protein-building instructions, in the same way that your college transcript is an accurate record of your grades, and like a transcript, it can be sent out in multiple copies. This type of RNA molecule is called **messenger RNA (mRNA)** because it carries a genetic message from the DNA to the protein-synthesizing machinery of the cell. (Transcription is the general term for the synthesis of *any* kind of RNA on a DNA template. Later in this chapter, you will learn about some other types of RNA produced by transcription.)

Translation is the synthesis of a polypeptide, which occurs under the direction of mRNA. During this stage, there is a change in language: The cell must translate the base sequence of an mRNA molecule into the amino acid sequence of a polypeptide. The sites of translation are **ribosomes**, complex particles that facilitate the orderly linking of amino acids into polypeptide chains.

Transcription and translation occur in all organisms. Recall from Chapter 1 that there are three domains of life: Bacteria, Archaea, and Eukarya. Organisms in the first two domains are grouped as prokaryotes because their cells lack a membrane-bounded nucleus—a defining feature of eukaryotic cells. Most studies of transcription and translation have been done on bacteria and eukaryotes, which are therefore our main focus in this chapter. Although our understanding of these processes in archaea lags behind, in the last section we will discuss a few aspects of archaeal gene expression.

The basic mechanics of transcription and translation are similar for bacteria and eukaryotes, but there is an important difference in the flow of genetic information within the cells. Because bacteria do not have nuclei, their DNA is not segregated from ribosomes and the other protein-synthesizing equipment (Figure 17.3a). As you will see later, this lack of segregation allows translation of an mRNA to begin while its transcription is still in progress. In a eukaryotic cell, by contrast, the nuclear envelope separates transcription from translation in space and time (Figure 17.3b). Transcription occurs in the nucleus, and mRNA is transported to the cytoplasm, where translation occurs. But before they can leave the nucleus, eukaryotic RNA transcripts from protein-coding genes are modified in various ways to produce the final, functional mRNA. The transcription of a protein-coding eukaryotic gene results in *pre-mRNA*, and further processing yields the finished mRNA. The initial RNA transcript from any gene, including those coding for RNA that is not translated into protein, is more generally called a **primary transcript**.

Let's summarize: Genes program protein synthesis via genetic messages in the form of messenger RNA. Put another way, cells are governed by a molecular chain of command with a directional flow of genetic information: DNA → RNA → protein. This concept was dubbed the *central dogma* by Francis Crick in 1956. How has the concept held up over time? In the 1970s, scientists were surprised to discover that some RNA molecules can act as templates for DNA, a process you'll read about in Chapter 19. However, this rare exception does not invalidate the idea that, in general, genetic information flows from DNA to RNA to protein. In the next section, we discuss how the instructions for assembling amino acids into a specific order are encoded in nucleic acids.

The Genetic Code

When biologists began to suspect that the instructions for protein synthesis were encoded in DNA, they recognized a problem: There are only four nucleotide bases to specify 20 amino acids. Thus, the genetic code cannot be a language like Chinese, where each written symbol corresponds to a word. How many bases, then, correspond to an amino acid?

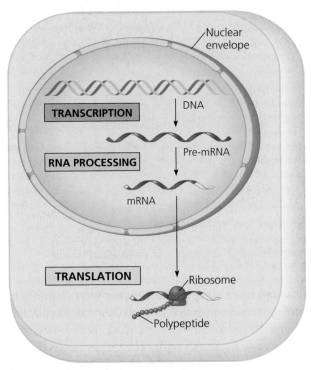

(a) **Bacterial cell.** In a bacterial cell, which lacks a nucleus, mRNA produced by transcription is immediately translated without additional processing.

(b) **Eukaryotic cell.** The nucleus provides a separate compartment for transcription. The original RNA transcript, called pre-mRNA, is processed in various ways before leaving the nucleus as mRNA.

▲ **Figure 17.3 Overview: the roles of transcription and translation in the flow of genetic information.** In a cell, inherited information flows from DNA to RNA to protein. The two main stages of information flow are transcription and translation. A miniature version of part (a) or (b) accompanies several figures later in the chapter as an orientation diagram to help you see where a particular figure fits into the overall scheme.

Codons: Triplets of Bases

If each nucleotide base were translated into an amino acid, only 4 of the 20 amino acids could be specified. Would a language of two-letter code words suffice? The two-base sequence AG, for example, could specify one amino acid, and GT could specify another. Since there are four possible bases

in each position, this would give us 16 (that is, 4^2) possible arrangements—still not enough to code for all 20 amino acids.

Triplets of nucleotide bases are the smallest units of uniform length that can code for all the amino acids. If each arrangement of three consecutive bases specifies an amino acid, there can be 64 (that is, 4^3) possible code words—more than enough to specify all the amino acids. Experiments have verified that the flow of information from gene to protein is based on a **triplet code**: The genetic instructions for a polypeptide chain are written in the DNA as a series of nonoverlapping, three-nucleotide words. For example, the base triplet AGT at a particular position along a DNA strand results in the placement of the amino acid serine at the corresponding position of the polypeptide being produced.

During transcription, the gene determines the sequence of bases along the length of an mRNA molecule (**Figure 17.4**). For each gene, only one of the two DNA strands is transcribed. This strand is called the **template strand** because it provides the pattern, or template, for the sequence of nucleotides in an RNA transcript. A given DNA strand is the template strand for some genes along a DNA molecule, while for other genes the complementary strand functions as the template. Note that

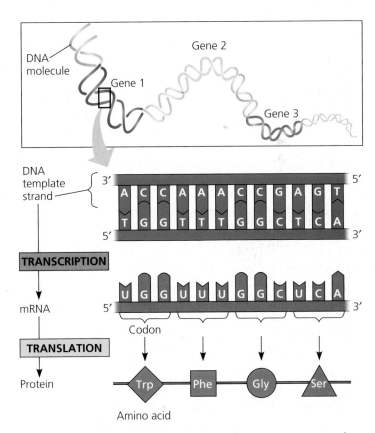

▲ **Figure 17.4 The triplet code.** For each gene, one DNA strand functions as a template for transcription. The base-pairing rules for DNA synthesis also guide transcription, but uracil (U) takes the place of thymine (T) in RNA. During translation, the mRNA is read as a sequence of base triplets, called codons. Each codon specifies an amino acid to be added to the growing polypeptide chain. The mRNA is read in the 5' → 3' direction.

for a particular gene, the same strand is used as the template every time it is transcribed.

An mRNA molecule is complementary rather than identical to its DNA template because RNA bases are assembled on the template according to base-pairing rules. The pairs are similar to those that form during DNA replication, except that U, the RNA substitute for T, pairs with A and the mRNA nucleotides contain ribose instead of deoxyribose. Like a new strand of DNA, the RNA molecule is synthesized in an antiparallel direction to the template strand of DNA. (To review what is meant by "antiparallel" and the 5′ and 3′ ends of a nucleic acid chain, see Figure 16.7.) For example, the base triplet ACC along the DNA (written as 3′-ACC-5′) provides a template for 5′-UGG-3′ in the mRNA molecule. The mRNA base triplets are called **codons**, and they are customarily written in the 5′ → 3′ direction. In our example, UGG is the codon for the amino acid tryptophan (abbreviated Trp). The term *codon* is also used for the DNA base triplets along the *nontemplate* strand. These codons are complementary to the template strand and thus identical in sequence to the mRNA except that they have T instead of U. (For this reason, the nontemplate DNA strand is sometimes called the "coding strand.")

During translation, the sequence of codons along an mRNA molecule is decoded, or translated, into a sequence of amino acids making up a polypeptide chain. The codons are read by the translation machinery in the 5′ → 3′ direction along the mRNA. Each codon specifies which one of the 20 amino acids will be incorporated at the corresponding position along a polypeptide. Because codons are base triplets, the number of nucleotides making up a genetic message must be three times the number of amino acids in the protein product. For example, it takes 300 nucleotides along an mRNA strand to code for the amino acids in a polypeptide that is 100 amino acids long.

Cracking the Code

Molecular biologists cracked the code of life in the early 1960s when a series of elegant experiments disclosed the amino acid translations of each of the RNA codons. The first codon was deciphered in 1961 by Marshall Nirenberg, of the National Institutes of Health, and his colleagues. Nirenberg synthesized an artificial mRNA by linking identical RNA nucleotides containing uracil as their base. No matter where this message started or stopped, it could contain only one codon in repetition: UUU. Nirenberg added this "poly-U" to a test-tube mixture containing amino acids, ribosomes, and the other components required for protein synthesis. His artificial system translated the poly-U into a polypeptide containing many units of the amino acid phenylalanine (Phe), strung together as a long polyphenylalanine chain. Thus, Nirenberg determined that the mRNA codon UUU specifies the amino acid phenylalanine. Soon, the amino acids specified by the codons AAA, GGG, and CCC were also determined.

▲ **Figure 17.5 The dictionary of the genetic code.** The three bases of an mRNA codon are designated here as the first, second, and third bases, reading in the 5′ → 3′ direction along the mRNA. (Practice using this dictionary by finding the codons in Figure 17.4.) The codon AUG not only stands for the amino acid methionine (Met) but also functions as a "start" signal for ribosomes to begin translating the mRNA at that point. Three of the 64 codons function as "stop" signals, marking the end of a genetic message. See Figure 5.17 for a list of the three-letter abbreviations for all the amino acids.

Although more elaborate techniques were required to decode mixed triplets such as AUA and CGA, all 64 codons were deciphered by the mid-1960s. As **Figure 17.5** shows, 61 of the 64 triplets code for amino acids. The three codons that do not designate amino acids are "stop" signals, or termination codons, marking the end of translation. Notice that the codon AUG has a dual function: It codes for the amino acid methionine (Met) and also functions as a "start" signal, or initiation codon. Genetic messages begin with the mRNA codon AUG, which signals the protein-synthesizing machinery to begin translating the mRNA at that location. (Because AUG also stands for methionine, polypeptide chains begin with methionine when they are synthesized. However, an enzyme may subsequently remove this starter amino acid from the chain.)

Notice in Figure 17.5 that there is redundancy in the genetic code, but no ambiguity. For example, although codons GAA and GAG both specify glutamic acid (redundancy), neither of them ever specifies any other amino acid (no ambiguity). The redundancy in the code is not altogether random. In many cases, codons that are synonyms for a particular amino acid differ only in the third base of the triplet. We will consider a possible benefit of this redundancy later in the chapter.

Our ability to extract the intended message from a written language depends on reading the symbols in the correct groupings—that is, in the correct **reading frame**. Consider this statement: "The red dog ate the bug." Group the letters incorrectly by starting at the wrong point, and the result will probably be gibberish: for example, "her edd oga tet heb ug." The reading frame is also important in the molecular language of cells. The short stretch of polypeptide shown in Figure 17.4, for instance, will be made correctly only if the mRNA nucleotides are read from left to right ($5' \rightarrow 3'$) in the groups of three shown in the figure: UGG UUU GGC UCA. Although a genetic message is written with no spaces between the codons, the cell's protein-synthesizing machinery reads the message as a series of nonoverlapping three-letter words. The message is *not* read as a series of overlapping words—UGGUUU, and so on—which would convey a very different message.

Evolution of the Genetic Code

The genetic code is nearly universal, shared by organisms from the simplest bacteria to the most complex plants and animals. The RNA codon CCG, for instance, is translated as the amino acid proline in all organisms whose genetic code has been examined. In laboratory experiments, genes can be transcribed and translated after being transplanted from one species to another, sometimes with quite striking results, as shown in **Figure 17.6**! Bacteria can be programmed by the insertion of human genes to synthesize certain human proteins for medical use, such as insulin. Such applications have produced many exciting developments in the area of biotechnology (see Chapter 20).

Exceptions to the universality of the genetic code include translation systems in which a few codons differ from the standard ones. Slight variations in the genetic code exist in certain unicellular eukaryotes and in the organelle genes of some species. There are also exceptions in which stop codons can be translated into one of two amino acids not found in most organisms. Although one of these amino acids (pyrrolysine) has been detected thus far only in archaea, the other (selenocysteine) is a component of some bacterial proteins and even some human enzymes. Despite these exceptions, the evolutionary significance of the code's *near* universality is clear. A language shared by all living things must have been operating very early in the history of life—early enough to be present in the common ancestor of all present-day organisms. A shared genetic vocabulary is a reminder of the kinship that bonds all life on Earth.

CONCEPT 17.2

Transcription is the DNA-directed synthesis of RNA: *a closer look*

Now that we have considered the linguistic logic and evolutionary significance of the genetic code, we are ready to reexamine transcription, the first stage of gene expression, in more detail.

Molecular Components of Transcription

Messenger RNA, the carrier of information from DNA to the cell's protein-synthesizing machinery, is transcribed from the template strand of a gene. An enzyme called an **RNA polymerase** pries the two strands of DNA apart and joins the RNA nucleotides as they base-pair along the DNA

(a) Tobacco plant expressing a firefly gene. The yellow glow is produced by a chemical reaction catalyzed by the protein product of the firefly gene.

(b) Pig expressing a jellyfish gene. Researchers injected the gene for a fluorescent protein into fertilized pig eggs. One of the eggs developed into this fluorescent pig.

▲ **Figure 17.6 Expression of genes from different species.** Because diverse forms of life share a common genetic code, one species can be programmed to produce proteins characteristic of a second species by introducing DNA from the second species into the first.

template **(Figure 17.7)**. Like the DNA polymerases that function in DNA replication, RNA polymerases can assemble a polynucleotide only in its 5′ → 3′ direction. Unlike DNA polymerases, however, RNA polymerases are able to start a chain from scratch; they don't need a primer.

Specific sequences of nucleotides along the DNA mark where transcription of a gene begins and ends. The DNA sequence where RNA polymerase attaches and initiates transcription is known as the **promoter**; in bacteria, the sequence that signals the end of transcription is called the **terminator**. (The termination mechanism is different in eukaryotes; we'll describe it later.) Molecular biologists refer to the direction of transcription as "downstream" and the other direction as "upstream." These terms are also used to describe the positions of nucleotide sequences within the DNA or RNA. Thus, the pro-

moter sequence in DNA is said to be upstream from the terminator. The stretch of DNA that is transcribed into an RNA molecule is called a **transcription unit**.

Bacteria have a single type of RNA polymerase that synthesizes not only mRNA but also other types of RNA that function in protein synthesis, such as ribosomal RNA. In contrast, eukaryotes have at least three types of RNA polymerase in their nuclei. The one used for mRNA synthesis is called RNA polymerase II. The other RNA polymerases transcribe RNA molecules that are not translated into protein. In the discussion of transcription that follows, we start with the features of mRNA synthesis common to both bacteria and eukaryotes and then describe some key differences.

Synthesis of an RNA Transcript

The three stages of transcription, as shown in Figure 17.7 and described next, are initiation, elongation, and termination of the RNA chain. Study Figure 17.7 to familiarize yourself with the stages and the terms used to describe them.

RNA Polymerase Binding and Initiation of Transcription

The promoter of a gene includes within it the transcription start point (the nucleotide where RNA synthesis actually begins) and typically extends several dozen nucleotide pairs

Promoter · Transcription unit

5′ 3′ — DNA — 3′ 5′

Start point
RNA polymerase

1 Initiation. After RNA polymerase binds to the promoter, the DNA strands unwind, and the polymerase initiates RNA synthesis at the start point on the template strand.

Unwound DNA · RNA transcript · Template strand of DNA

2 Elongation. The polymerase moves downstream, unwinding the DNA and elongating the RNA transcript 5′ → 3′. In the wake of transcription, the DNA strands re-form a double helix.

Rewound DNA
RNA transcript

3 Termination. Eventually, the RNA transcript is released, and the polymerase detaches from the DNA.

Completed RNA transcript

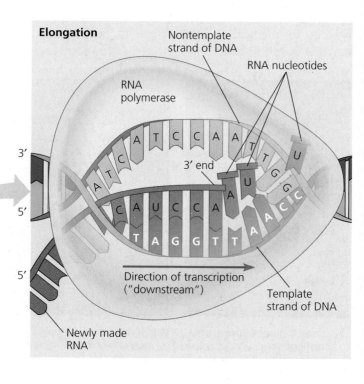

Elongation · Nontemplate strand of DNA · RNA polymerase · RNA nucleotides · 3′ end · Direction of transcription ("downstream") · Template strand of DNA · Newly made RNA

▲ **Figure 17.7 The stages of transcription: initiation, elongation, and termination.** This general depiction of transcription applies to both bacteria and eukaryotes, but the details of termination differ, as described in the text. Also, in a bacterium, the RNA transcript is immediately usable as mRNA; in a eukaryote, the RNA transcript must first undergo processing.

upstream from the start point. In addition to serving as a binding site for RNA polymerase and determining where transcription starts, the promoter determines which of the two strands of the DNA helix is used as the template.

Certain sections of a promoter are especially important for binding RNA polymerase. In bacteria, the RNA polymerase itself specifically recognizes and binds to the promoter. In eukaryotes, a collection of proteins called **transcription factors** mediate the binding of RNA polymerase and the initiation of transcription. Recall from Chapter 16 that the DNA of a eukaryotic chromosome is complexed with histones and other proteins in the form of chromatin. The roles of these proteins in making the DNA accessible to transcription factors will be discussed in Chapter 18. Only after certain transcription factors are attached to the promoter does RNA polymerase II bind to it. The whole complex of transcription factors and RNA polymerase II bound to the promoter is called a **transcription initiation complex**. **Figure 17.8** shows the role of transcription factors and a crucial promoter DNA sequence called a **TATA box** in forming the initiation complex at a eukaryotic promoter.

The interaction between eukaryotic RNA polymerase II and transcription factors is an example of the importance of protein-protein interactions in controlling eukaryotic transcription. Once the polymerase is firmly attached to the promoter DNA, the two DNA strands unwind there, and the enzyme starts transcribing the template strand.

Elongation of the RNA Strand

As RNA polymerase moves along the DNA, it continues to untwist the double helix, exposing about 10 to 20 DNA bases at a time for pairing with RNA nucleotides (see Figure 17.7). The enzyme adds nucleotides to the 3′ end of the growing RNA molecule as it continues along the double helix. In the wake of this advancing wave of RNA synthesis, the new RNA molecule peels away from its DNA template and the DNA double helix re-forms. Transcription progresses at a rate of about 40 nucleotides per second in eukaryotes.

A single gene can be transcribed simultaneously by several molecules of RNA polymerase following each other like trucks in a convoy. A growing strand of RNA trails off from each polymerase, with the length of each new strand reflecting how far along the template the enzyme has traveled from the start point (see the mRNA molecules in Figure 17.24). The congregation of many polymerase molecules simultaneously transcribing a single gene increases the amount of mRNA transcribed from it, which helps the cell make the encoded protein in large amounts.

Termination of Transcription

The mechanism of termination differs between bacteria and eukaryotes. In bacteria, transcription proceeds through a terminator sequence in the DNA. The transcribed terminator

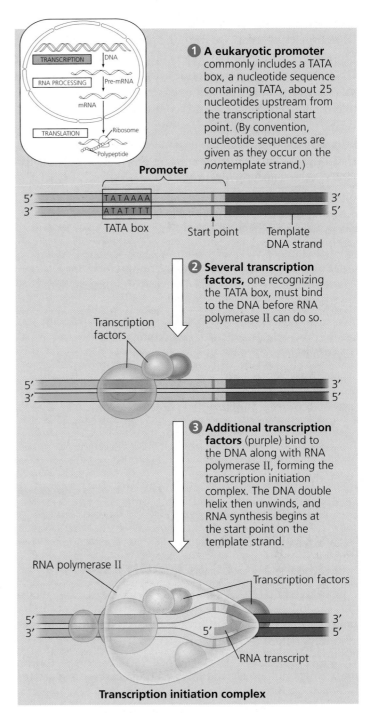

1 **A eukaryotic promoter** commonly includes a TATA box, a nucleotide sequence containing TATA, about 25 nucleotides upstream from the transcriptional start point. (By convention, nucleotide sequences are given as they occur on the *non*template strand.)

2 **Several transcription factors,** one recognizing the TATA box, must bind to the DNA before RNA polymerase II can do so.

3 **Additional transcription factors** (purple) bind to the DNA along with RNA polymerase II, forming the transcription initiation complex. The DNA double helix then unwinds, and RNA synthesis begins at the start point on the template strand.

▲ **Figure 17.8 The initiation of transcription at a eukaryotic promoter.** In eukaryotic cells, proteins called transcription factors mediate the initiation of transcription by RNA polymerase II.

? *Explain how the interaction of RNA polymerase with the promoter would differ if the figure showed transcription initiation for bacteria.*

(an RNA sequence) functions as the termination signal, causing the polymerase to detach from the DNA and release the transcript, which is available for immediate use as mRNA. In eukaryotes, RNA polymerase II transcribes a sequence on the DNA called the polyadenylation signal sequence, which codes for a polyadenylation signal (AAUAAA) in the pre-mRNA. Then, at a point about 10 to 35 nucleotides downstream from the AAUAAA signal, proteins associated with the growing RNA transcript cut it free from the polymerase, releasing the pre-mRNA. However, the polymerase continues transcribing DNA for hundreds of nucleotides past the site where the pre-mRNA was released. Recent research on yeast cells suggests that the RNA produced by this continued transcription is digested by an enzyme that moves along the RNA. The data support the idea that when the enzyme reaches the polymerase, transcription is terminated and the polymerase falls off the DNA. Meanwhile, the pre-mRNA undergoes processing, the topic of the next section.

CONCEPT CHECK **17.2**

1. Compare DNA polymerase and RNA polymerase in terms of how they function, the requirement for a template and primer, the direction of synthesis, and the type of nucleotides used.
2. What is a promoter, and is it located at the upstream or downstream end of a transcription unit?
3. What makes RNA polymerase start transcribing a gene at the right place on the DNA in a bacterial cell? In a eukaryotic cell?
4. **WHAT IF?** Suppose X-rays caused a sequence change in the TATA box of a particular gene's promoter. How would that affect transcription of the gene? (See Figure 17.8.)

For suggested answers, see Appendix A.

CONCEPT **17.3**
Eukaryotic cells modify RNA after transcription

Enzymes in the eukaryotic nucleus modify pre-mRNA in specific ways before the genetic messages are dispatched to the cytoplasm. During this **RNA processing**, both ends of the primary transcript are altered. Also, in most cases, certain inte-

rior sections of the RNA molecule are cut out and the remaining parts spliced together. These modifications produce an mRNA molecule ready for translation.

Alteration of mRNA Ends

Each end of a pre-mRNA molecule is modified in a particular way **(Figure 17.9)**. The 5′ end is synthesized first; it receives a **5′ cap**, a modified form of a guanine (G) nucleotide added onto the 5′ end after transcription of the first 20 to 40 nucleotides. The 3′ end of the pre-mRNA molecule is also modified before the mRNA exits the nucleus. Recall that the pre-mRNA is released soon after the polyadenylation signal, AAUAAA, is transcribed. At the 3′ end, an enzyme adds 50 to 250 more adenine (A) nucleotides, forming a **poly-A tail**. The 5′ cap and poly-A tail share several important functions. First, they seem to facilitate the export of the mature mRNA from the nucleus. Second, they help protect the mRNA from degradation by hydrolytic enzymes. And third, they help ribosomes attach to the 5′ end of the mRNA once the mRNA reaches the cytoplasm. Figure 17.9 shows a diagram of a eukaryotic mRNA molecule with cap and tail. The figure also shows the untranslated regions (UTRs) at the 5′ and 3′ ends of the mRNA (referred to as the 5′ UTR and 3′ UTR). The UTRs are parts of the mRNA that will not be translated into protein, but they have other functions, such as ribosome binding.

Split Genes and RNA Splicing

A remarkable stage of RNA processing in the eukaryotic nucleus is the removal of large portions of the RNA molecule that is initially synthesized—a cut-and-paste job called **RNA splicing**, similar to editing a video **(Figure 17.10)**. The average length of a transcription unit along a human DNA molecule is about 27,000 base pairs, so the primary RNA transcript is also that long. However, it takes only 1,200 nucleotides in RNA to code for the average-sized protein of 400 amino acids. (Remember, each amino acid is encoded by a *triplet* of nucleotides.) This means that most eukaryotic genes and their RNA transcripts have long noncoding stretches of nucleotides, regions that are not

▲ **Figure 17.9 RNA processing: addition of the 5′ cap and poly-A tail.** Enzymes modify the two ends of a eukaryotic pre-mRNA molecule. The modified ends may promote the export of mRNA from the nucleus, and they help protect the mRNA from degradation. When the mRNA reaches the cytoplasm, the modified ends, in conjunction with certain cytoplasmic proteins, facilitate ribosome attachment. The 5′ cap and poly-A tail are not translated into protein, nor are the regions called the 5′ untranslated region (5′ UTR) and 3′ untranslated region (3′ UTR).

Pre-mRNA
5′ Cap | Exon | Intron | Exon | Intron | Exon | 3′ Poly-A tail
5′   Exon   Intron   Exon   Intron   Exon   3′
1   30   31   104   105   146

Coding segment

Introns cut out and exons spliced together

mRNA
5′ Cap   Poly-A tail
  1   146
5′ UTR   3′ UTR

▲ **Figure 17.10 RNA processing: RNA splicing.** The RNA molecule shown here codes for β-globin, one of the polypeptides of hemoglobin. The numbers under the RNA refer to codons; β-globin is 146 amino acids long. The β-globin gene and its pre-mRNA transcript have three exons, corresponding to sequences that will leave the nucleus as mRNA. (The 5′ UTR and 3′ UTR are parts of exons because they are included in the mRNA; however, they do not code for protein.) During RNA processing, the introns are cut out and the exons spliced together. In many genes, the introns are much larger relative to the exons than they are in the β-globin gene. (The pre-mRNA is not drawn to scale.)

translated. Even more surprising is that most of these noncoding sequences are interspersed between coding segments of the gene and thus between coding segments of the pre-mRNA. In other words, the sequence of DNA nucleotides that codes for a eukaryotic polypeptide is usually not continuous; it is split into segments. The noncoding segments of nucleic acid that lie between coding regions are called intervening sequences, or **introns**. The other regions are called **exons**, because they are eventually expressed, usually by being translated into amino acid sequences. (Exceptions include the UTRs of the exons at the ends of the RNA, which make up part of the mRNA but are not translated into protein. Because of these exceptions, you may find it helpful to think of exons as sequences of RNA that *exit* the nucleus.) The terms *intron* and *exon* are used for both RNA sequences and the DNA sequences that encode them.

In making a primary transcript from a gene, RNA polymerase II transcribes both introns and exons from the DNA, but the mRNA molecule that enters the cytoplasm is an abridged version. The introns are cut out from the molecule and the exons joined together, forming an mRNA molecule with a continuous coding sequence. This is the process of RNA splicing.

How is pre-mRNA splicing carried out? Researchers have learned that the signal for RNA splicing is a short nucleotide sequence at each end of an intron. Particles called *small nuclear ribonucleoproteins*, abbreviated *snRNPs* (pronounced "snurps"), recognize these splice sites. As the name implies, snRNPs are located in the cell nucleus and are composed of RNA and protein molecules. The RNA in a snRNP particle is called a *small nuclear RNA (snRNA)*; each molecule is about 150 nucleotides long. Several different snRNPs join with additional proteins to form an even larger assembly called a **spliceosome**, which is almost as big as a ribosome. The spliceosome interacts with certain sites along an intron, releasing the intron and joining together the two exons that flanked the intron **(Figure 17.11)**. There is strong evidence that snRNAs catalyze these processes, as well as participating in spliceosome assembly and splice site recognition.

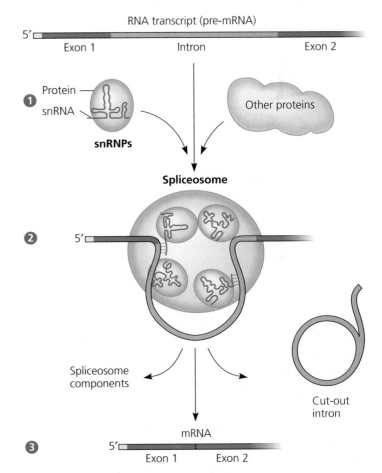

▲ **Figure 17.11 The roles of snRNPs and spliceosomes in pre-mRNA splicing.** The diagram shows only a portion of the pre-mRNA transcript; additional introns and exons lie downstream from the ones pictured here. ❶ Small nuclear ribonucleoproteins (snRNPs) and other proteins form a molecular complex called a spliceosome on a pre-mRNA molecule containing exons and introns. ❷ Within the spliceosome, snRNA base-pairs with nucleotides at specific sites along the intron. ❸ The spliceosome cuts the pre-mRNA, releasing the intron, and at the same time splices the exons together. The spliceosome then comes apart, releasing mRNA, which now contains only exons.

Ribozymes

The idea of a catalytic role for snRNA arose from the discovery of **ribozymes**, RNA molecules that function as enzymes. In some organisms, RNA splicing can occur without proteins or even additional RNA molecules: The intron RNA functions as a ribozyme and catalyzes its own excision! For example, in the ciliate protist *Tetrahymena*, self-splicing occurs in the production of ribosomal RNA (rRNA), a component of the organism's ribosomes. The pre-rRNA actually removes its own introns. The discovery of ribozymes rendered obsolete the idea that all biological catalysts are proteins.

Three properties of RNA enable some RNA molecules to function as enzymes. First, because RNA is single-stranded, a region of an RNA molecule may base-pair with a complementary region elsewhere in the same molecule, which gives the molecule a particular three-dimensional structure. A specific structure is essential to the catalytic function of ribozymes, just as it is for enzymatic proteins. Second, like certain amino acids in an enzymatic protein, some of the bases in RNA contain functional groups that may participate in catalysis. Third, the ability of RNA to hydrogen-bond with other nucleic acid molecules (either RNA or DNA) adds specificity to its catalytic activity. For example, complementary base pairing between the RNA of the spliceosome and the RNA of a primary RNA transcript precisely locates the region where the ribozyme catalyzes splicing. Later in this chapter, you will see how these properties of RNA also allow it to perform important noncatalytic roles in the cell, such as recognition of the three-nucleotide codons on mRNA.

The Functional and Evolutionary Importance of Introns

What could be the biological functions of introns and RNA splicing? While specific functions may not have been identified for most introns, at least some contain sequences that regulate gene activity. And the splicing process itself is necessary for the passage of mRNA from the nucleus to the cytoplasm.

One consequence of the presence of introns in genes is that a single gene can encode more than one kind of polypeptide. Many genes are known to give rise to two or more different polypeptides, depending on which segments are treated as exons during RNA processing; this is called **alternative RNA splicing** (see Figure 18.11). For example, sex differences in fruit flies are largely due to differences in how males and females splice the RNA transcribed from certain genes. Results from the Human Genome Project (discussed in Chapter 21) suggest that alternative RNA splicing is one reason humans can get along with a relatively small number of genes—about one and a half times as many as a fruit fly. Because of alternative splicing, the number of different protein products an organism produces can be much greater than its number of genes.

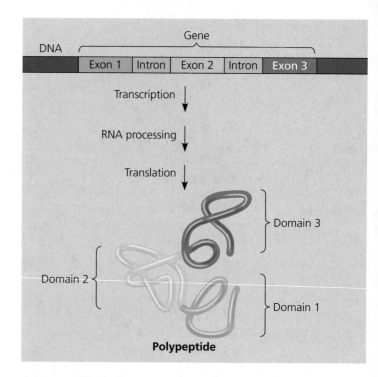

▲ **Figure 17.12 Correspondence between exons and protein domains.**

Proteins often have a modular architecture consisting of discrete structural and functional regions called **domains**. One domain of an enzymatic protein, for instance, might include the active site, while another might attach the protein to a cellular membrane. In quite a few cases, different exons code for the different domains of a protein (**Figure 17.12**).

The presence of introns in a gene may facilitate the evolution of new and potentially useful proteins as a result of a process known as *exon shuffling*. Introns increase the probability of potentially beneficial crossing over between the exons of alleles—simply by providing more terrain for crossovers without interrupting coding sequences. We can also imagine the occasional mixing and matching of exons between completely different (nonallelic) genes. Exon shuffling of either sort could lead to new proteins with novel combinations of functions. While most of the shuffling would result in nonbeneficial changes, occasionally a beneficial variant might arise.

CONCEPT CHECK 17.3

1. How does alteration of the 5′ and 3′ ends of pre-mRNA affect the mRNA that exits the nucleus?
2. How is RNA splicing similar to editing a video?
3. **WHAT IF?** In nematode worms, a gene that codes for an ATPase has two alternatives for exon 4 and three alternatives for exon 7. How many different forms of the protein could be made from this gene?

For suggested answers, see Appendix A.

Translation is the RNA-directed synthesis of a polypeptide: *a closer look*

We will now examine in greater detail how genetic information flows from mRNA to protein—the process of translation. As we did for transcription, we'll concentrate on the basic steps of translation that occur in both bacteria and eukaryotes, while pointing out key differences.

Molecular Components of Translation

In the process of translation, a cell interprets a genetic message and builds a polypeptide accordingly. The message is a series of codons along an mRNA molecule, and the interpreter is called **transfer RNA (tRNA)**. The function of tRNA is to transfer amino acids from the cytoplasmic pool of amino acids to a ribosome. A cell keeps its cytoplasm stocked with all 20 amino acids, either by synthesizing them from other compounds or by taking them up from the surrounding solution. The ribosome adds each amino acid brought to it by tRNA to the growing end of a polypeptide chain **(Figure 17.13)**.

Molecules of tRNA are not all identical. The key to translating a genetic message into a specific amino acid sequence is that each type of tRNA molecule translates a particular mRNA codon into a particular amino acid. As a tRNA molecule arrives at a ribosome, it bears a specific amino acid at one end. At the other end of the tRNA is a nucleotide triplet called an **anticodon**, which base-pairs with a complementary codon on mRNA. For example, consider the mRNA codon UUU, which is translated as the amino acid phenylalanine. The tRNA that base-pairs with this codon by hydrogen bonding has AAA as its anticodon and carries phenylalanine at its other end (see the middle tRNA on the ribosome in Figure 17.13). As an mRNA molecule is moved through a ribosome, phenylalanine will be added to the polypeptide chain whenever the codon UUU is presented for translation. Codon by codon, the genetic message is translated as tRNAs deposit amino acids in the order prescribed, and the ribosome joins the amino acids into a chain. The tRNA molecule is a translator because it can read a nucleic acid word (the mRNA codon) and interpret it as a protein word (the amino acid).

Translation is simple in principle but complex in its biochemistry and mechanics, especially in the eukaryotic cell. In dissecting translation, we'll concentrate on the slightly less complicated version of the process that occurs in bacteria. Let's first look at the major components in this cellular process. Then we will see how they act together to make a polypeptide.

▲ **Figure 17.13 Translation: the basic concept.** As a molecule of mRNA is moved through a ribosome, codons are translated into amino acids, one by one. The interpreters are tRNA molecules, each type with a specific anticodon at one end and a corresponding amino acid at the other end. A tRNA adds its amino acid cargo to a growing polypeptide chain when the anticodon hydrogen-bonds to a complementary codon on the mRNA. The figures that follow show some of the details of translation in a bacterial cell.

MEDIA ***BioFlix*** Visit **www.campbellbiology.com** for the BioFlix 3-D Animation on Protein Synthesis.

The Structure and Function of Transfer RNA

Like mRNA and other types of cellular RNA, transfer RNA molecules are transcribed from DNA templates. In a eukaryotic cell, tRNA, like mRNA, is made in the nucleus and must travel from the nucleus to the cytoplasm, where translation occurs. In both bacterial and eukaryotic cells, each tRNA molecule is used repeatedly, picking up its designated amino acid in the cytosol, depositing this cargo onto a polypeptide chain at the ribosome, and then leaving the ribosome, ready to pick up another amino acid.

A tRNA molecule consists of a single RNA strand that is only about 80 nucleotides long (compared to hundreds of nucleotides for most mRNA molecules). Because of the presence of complementary stretches of bases that can hydrogen-bond to each other, this single strand can fold back upon itself and form a molecule with a three-dimensional structure. Flattened into one plane to reveal this base pairing, a tRNA molecule

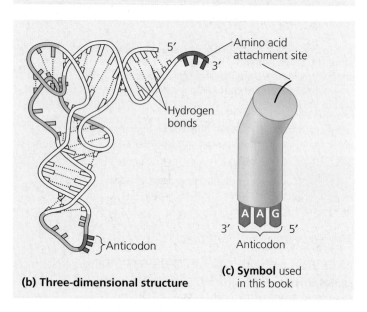

(a) Two-dimensional structure. The four base-paired regions and three loops are characteristic of all tRNAs, as is the base sequence of the amino acid attachment site at the 3' end. The anticodon triplet is unique to each tRNA type, as are some sequences in the other two loops. (The asterisks mark bases that have been chemically modified, a characteristic of tRNA.)

(b) Three-dimensional structure

(c) Symbol used in this book

▲ **Figure 17.14 The structure of transfer RNA (tRNA).** Anticodons are conventionally written 3' → 5' to align properly with codons written 5' → 3' (see Figure 17.13). For base pairing, RNA strands must be antiparallel, like DNA. For example, anticodon 3'-AAG-5' pairs with mRNA codon 5'-UUC-3'.

looks like a cloverleaf **(Figure 17.14a)**. The tRNA actually twists and folds into a compact three-dimensional structure that is roughly L-shaped **(Figure 17.14b)**. The loop extending from one end of the L includes the anticodon, the particular base triplet that base-pairs to a specific mRNA codon. From the other end of the L-shaped tRNA molecule protrudes its 3'

Computer model

1 Active site binds the amino acid and ATP.

2 ATP loses two P groups and joins amino acid as AMP.

3 Appropriate tRNA covalently bonds to amino acid, displacing AMP.

4 The tRNA charged with amino acid is released by the enzyme.

▲ **Figure 17.15 An aminoacyl-tRNA synthetase joining a specific amino acid to a tRNA.** Linkage of the tRNA and amino acid is an endergonic process that occurs at the expense of ATP. The ATP loses two phosphate groups, becoming AMP (adenosine monophosphate).

end, which is the attachment site for an amino acid. Thus, the structure of a tRNA molecule fits its function.

The accurate translation of a genetic message requires two processes that involve molecular recognition. First, a tRNA that binds to an mRNA codon specifying a particular amino acid must carry that amino acid, and no other, to the ribosome. The correct matching up of tRNA and amino acid is carried out by a family of related enzymes called **aminoacyl-tRNA synthetases** **(Figure 17.15)**. The active site of each type of aminoacyl-tRNA synthetase fits only a specific combination of amino acid and tRNA. There are 20 different synthetases, one for each amino acid; each synthetase is able to bind all the different tRNAs that code for its particular amino acid. The synthetase catalyzes the covalent attachment of the amino acid to its tRNA in a process driven by the hydrolysis of ATP. The resulting aminoacyl tRNA, also called a charged tRNA, is released from the enzyme and is then available to deliver its amino acid to a growing polypeptide chain on a ribosome.

The second recognition process involves matching up the tRNA anticodon with the appropriate mRNA codon. If one tRNA variety existed for each mRNA codon that specifies an amino acid, there would be 61 tRNAs (see Figure 17.5). In fact, there are only about 45, signifying that some tRNAs must be able to bind to more than one codon. Such versatility is possible because the rules for base pairing between the third base of a codon and the corresponding base of a tRNA anticodon are relaxed compared to those at other codon positions. For example, the base U at the 5′ end of a tRNA anticodon can pair with either A or G in the third position (at the 3′ end) of an mRNA codon. The flexible base pairing at this codon position is called **wobble**. Wobble explains why the synonymous codons for a given amino acid can differ in their third base, but usually not in their other bases. For example, a tRNA with the anticodon 3′-UCU-5′ can base-pair with either the mRNA codon 5′-AGA-3′ or 5′-AGG-3′, both of which code for arginine (see Figure 17.5).

Ribosomes

Ribosomes facilitate the specific coupling of tRNA anticodons with mRNA codons during protein synthesis. A ribosome is made up of two subunits, called the large and small subunits **(Figure 17.16)**. The ribosomal subunits are constructed of proteins and RNA molecules named **ribosomal RNAs**, or **rRNAs**. In eukaryotes, the subunits are made in the nucleolus. Ribosomal RNA genes on the chromosomal DNA are transcribed, and the RNA is processed and assembled with proteins imported from the cytoplasm. The resulting ribosomal subunits are then exported via nuclear pores to the cytoplasm. In both bacteria and eukaryotes, large and small subunits join to form a functional ribosome only when they attach to an mRNA molecule. About two-thirds of the mass of a ribosome consists of rRNAs, either three molecules (in bacteria) or four (in eukaryotes). Because most cells contain thousands of ribosomes, rRNA is the most abundant type of cellular RNA.

Although the ribosomes of bacteria and eukaryotes are very similar in structure and function, those of eukaryotes are slightly larger and differ somewhat from bacterial ribosomes in their molecular composition. The differences are medically significant. Certain antibiotic drugs can inactivate bacterial ribosomes without inhibiting the ability of eukaryotic ribosomes to make proteins. These drugs, including tetracycline and streptomycin, are used to combat bacterial infections.

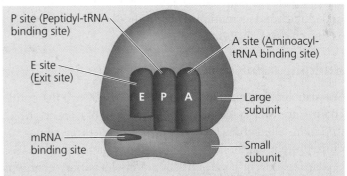

(a) Computer model of functioning ribosome. This is a model of a bacterial ribosome, showing its overall shape. The eukaryotic ribosome is roughly similar. A ribosomal subunit is an aggregate of ribosomal RNA molecules and proteins.

(b) Schematic model showing binding sites. A ribosome has an mRNA binding site and three tRNA binding sites, known as the A, P, and E sites. This schematic ribosome will appear in later diagrams.

(c) Schematic model with mRNA and tRNA. A tRNA fits into a binding site when its anticodon base-pairs with an mRNA codon. The P site holds the tRNA attached to the growing polypeptide. The A site holds the tRNA carrying the next amino acid to be added to the polypeptide chain. Discharged tRNA leaves from the E site.

▲ **Figure 17.16 The anatomy of a functioning ribosome.**

The structure of a ribosome reflects its function of bringing mRNA together with tRNAs carrying amino acids. In addition to a binding site for mRNA, each ribosome has three binding sites for tRNA (see Figure 17.16). The **P site** (peptidyl-tRNA site) holds the tRNA carrying the growing polypeptide chain, while the **A site** (aminoacyl-tRNA site) holds the tRNA carrying the next amino acid to be added to the chain. Discharged tRNAs leave the ribosome from the **E site** (exit site). The ribosome holds the tRNA and mRNA in close proximity and positions the new amino acid for addition to the carboxyl end of the growing polypeptide. It then catalyzes the formation of the peptide bond. As the polypeptide becomes longer, it passes through an *exit tunnel* in the ribosome's large subunit. When the polypeptide is complete, it is released to the cytosol through the exit tunnel.

Recent research strongly supports the hypothesis that rRNA, not protein, is primarily responsible for both the structure and the function of the ribosome. The proteins, which are largely on the exterior, support the shape changes of the rRNA molecules as they carry out catalysis during translation. Ribosomal RNA is the main constituent of the interface between the two subunits and of the A and P sites, and it is the catalyst of peptide bond formation. Thus, a ribosome can be regarded as one colossal ribozyme!

Building a Polypeptide

We can divide translation, the synthesis of a polypeptide chain, into three stages (analogous to those of transcription): initiation, elongation, and termination. All three stages require protein "factors" that aid in the translation process. For certain aspects of chain initiation and elongation, energy is also required. It is provided by the hydrolysis of GTP (guanosine triphosphate), a molecule closely related to ATP.

Ribosome Association and Initiation of Translation

The initiation stage of translation brings together mRNA, a tRNA bearing the first amino acid of the polypeptide, and the two subunits of a ribosome (**Figure 17.17**). First, a small ribosomal subunit binds to both mRNA and a specific initiator tRNA, which carries the amino acid methionine. In bacteria, the small subunit can bind these two in either order; it binds the mRNA at a specific RNA sequence, just upstream of the start codon, AUG. In eukaryotes, the small subunit, with the initiator tRNA already bound, binds to the 5' cap of the mRNA and then moves, or *scans*, downstream along the mRNA until it reaches the start codon, and the initiator tRNA hydrogen-bonds to it. In either case, the start codon signals the start of translation; this is important because it establishes the codon reading frame for the mRNA.

The union of mRNA, initiator tRNA, and a small ribosomal subunit is followed by the attachment of a large ribosomal subunit, completing the *translation initiation complex*. Proteins called *initiation factors* are required to bring all these components together. The cell also expends energy in the form of a GTP molecule to form the initiation complex. At the completion of the initiation process, the initiator tRNA sits in the P site of the ribosome, and the vacant A site is ready for the next aminoacyl tRNA. Note that a polypeptide is always synthesized in one direction, from the initial methionine at the amino end, also called the N-terminus, toward the final amino acid at the carboxyl end, also called the C-terminus (see Figure 5.18).

▶ **Figure 17.17 The initiation of translation.**

❶ A small ribosomal subunit binds to a molecule of mRNA. In a bacterial cell, the mRNA binding site on this subunit recognizes a specific nucleotide sequence on the mRNA just upstream of the start codon. An initiator tRNA, with the anticodon UAC, base-pairs with the start codon, AUG. This tRNA carries the amino acid methionine (Met).

❷ The arrival of a large ribosomal subunit completes the initiation complex. Proteins called initiation factors (not shown) are required to bring all the translation components together. GTP provides the energy for the assembly. The initiator tRNA is in the P site; the A site is available to the tRNA bearing the next amino acid.

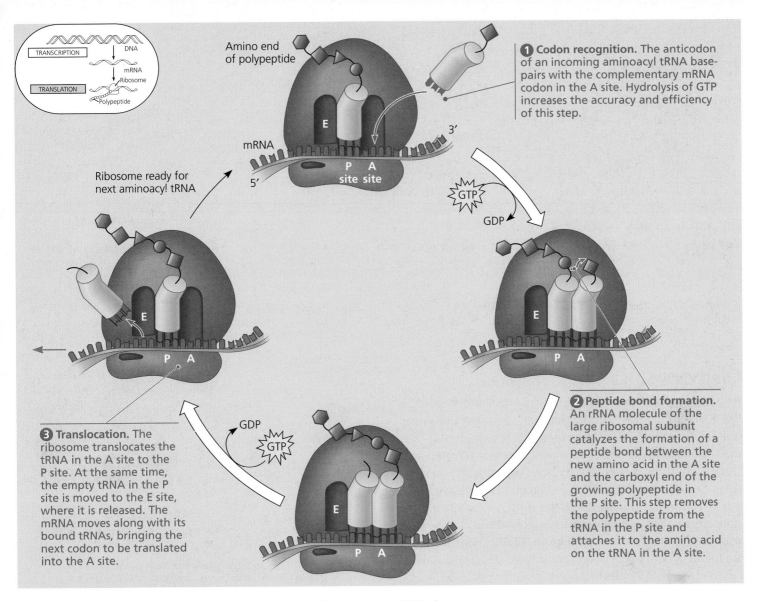

Amino end of polypeptide

① **Codon recognition.** The anticodon of an incoming aminoacyl tRNA base-pairs with the complementary mRNA codon in the A site. Hydrolysis of GTP increases the accuracy and efficiency of this step.

mRNA

E P A
   site site

GTP → GDP

Ribosome ready for next aminoacyl tRNA

E P A

② **Peptide bond formation.** An rRNA molecule of the large ribosomal subunit catalyzes the formation of a peptide bond between the new amino acid in the A site and the carboxyl end of the growing polypeptide in the P site. This step removes the polypeptide from the tRNA in the P site and attaches it to the amino acid on the tRNA in the A site.

③ **Translocation.** The ribosome translocates the tRNA in the A site to the P site. At the same time, the empty tRNA in the P site is moved to the E site, where it is released. The mRNA moves along with its bound tRNAs, bringing the next codon to be translated into the A site.

GDP ← GTP

E P A

▲ **Figure 17.18 The elongation cycle of translation.** The hydrolysis of GTP plays an important role in the elongation process. Not shown are the proteins called elongation factors.

Elongation of the Polypeptide Chain

In the elongation stage of translation, amino acids are added one by one to the preceding amino acid. Each addition involves the participation of several proteins called *elongation factors* and occurs in a three-step cycle described in **Figure 17.18**. Energy expenditure occurs in the first and third steps. Codon recognition requires hydrolysis of one molecule of GTP, which increases the accuracy and efficiency of this step. One more GTP is hydrolyzed to provide energy for the translocation step.

The mRNA is moved through the ribosome in one direction only, 5′ end first; this is equivalent to the ribosome moving 5′ → 3′ on the mRNA. The important point is that the ribosome and the mRNA move relative to each other, unidirectionally, codon by codon. The elongation cycle takes less than a tenth of a second in bacteria and is repeated as each amino acid is added to the chain until the polypeptide is completed.

Termination of Translation

The final stage of translation is termination (**Figure 17.19**, on the next page). Elongation continues until a stop codon in the mRNA reaches the A site of the ribosome. The base triplets UAG, UAA, and UGA do not code for amino acids but instead act as signals to stop translation. A protein called a *release factor* binds directly to the stop codon in the A site. The release factor causes the addition of a water molecule instead of an amino acid to the polypeptide chain. This reaction breaks (hydrolyzes) the bond between the completed polypeptide and the tRNA in the P site, releasing the polypeptide through the exit tunnel of the ribosome's large subunit (see Figure 17.16a). The remainder of the translation assembly then comes apart in a multistep process, aided by other protein factors. Breakdown of the translation assembly requires the hydrolysis of two more GTP molecules.

Release factor

Stop codon (UAG, UAA, or UGA)

1 When a ribosome reaches a stop codon on mRNA, the A site of the ribosome accepts a release factor," a protein shaped like a tRNA, instead of an aminoacyl tRNA.

Free polypeptide

2 The release factor promotes hydrolysis of the bond between the tRNA in the P site and the last amino acid of the polypeptide, thus freeing the polypeptide from the ribosome.

3 The two ribosomal subunits and the other components of the assembly dissociate.

▲ **Figure 17.19 The termination of translation.** Like elongation, termination requires GTP hydrolysis as well as additional protein factors, which are not shown here.

Polyribosomes

A single ribosome can make an average-sized polypeptide in less than a minute. Typically, however, multiple ribosomes translate an mRNA at the same time; that is, a single mRNA is used to make many copies of a polypeptide simultaneously. Once a ribosome moves past the start codon, a second ribosome can attach to the mRNA, eventually resulting in a number of ribosomes trailing along the mRNA. Such strings of ribosomes, called **polyribosomes** (or **polysomes**), can be seen with an electron microscope **(Figure 17.20)**. Polyribosomes are found in both bacterial and eukaryotic cells. They enable a cell to make many copies of a polypeptide very quickly.

Completing and Targeting the Functional Protein

The process of translation is often not sufficient to make a functional protein. In this section, you will learn about modifications that polypeptide chains undergo after the translation process as well as some of the mechanisms used to target completed proteins to specific sites in the cell.

Protein Folding and Post-Translational Modifications

During its synthesis, a polypeptide chain begins to coil and fold spontaneously as a consequence of its amino acid sequence (primary structure), forming a protein with a specific shape: a three-dimensional molecule with secondary and tertiary structure (see Figure 5.21). Thus, a gene determines primary structure, and primary structure in turn determines shape. In many cases, a chaperone protein (chaperonin) helps the polypeptide fold correctly (see Figure 5.24).

Additional steps—*post-translational modifications*—may be required before the protein can begin doing its particular job

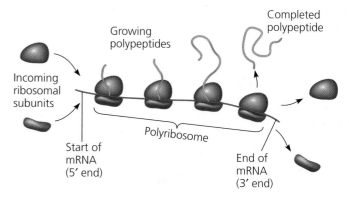

Incoming ribosomal subunits

Growing polypeptides

Completed polypeptide

Start of mRNA (5′ end)

Polyribosome

End of mRNA (3′ end)

(a) An mRNA molecule is generally translated simultaneously by several ribosomes in clusters called polyribosomes.

Ribosomes

mRNA

0.1 μm

(b) This micrograph shows a large polyribosome in a bacterial cell (TEM).

▲ **Figure 17.20 Polyribosomes.**

in the cell. Certain amino acids may be chemically modified by the attachment of sugars, lipids, phosphate groups, or other additions. Enzymes may remove one or more amino acids from the leading (amino) end of the polypeptide chain. In some cases, a polypeptide chain may be enzymatically cleaved into two or more pieces. For example, the protein insulin is first synthesized as a single polypeptide chain but becomes active only after an enzyme cuts out a central part of the chain, leaving a protein made up of two polypeptide chains connected by disulfide bridges. In other cases, two or more polypeptides that are synthesized separately may come together, becoming the subunits of a protein that has quaternary structure. A familiar example is hemoglobin (see Figure 5.21).

Targeting Polypeptides to Specific Locations

In electron micrographs of eukaryotic cells active in protein synthesis, two populations of ribosomes (and polyribosomes) are evident: free and bound (see Figure 6.11). Free ribosomes are suspended in the cytosol and mostly synthesize proteins that stay in the cytosol and function there. In contrast, bound ribosomes are attached to the cytosolic side of the endoplasmic reticulum (ER) or to the nuclear envelope. Bound ribosomes make proteins of the endomembrane system (the nuclear envelope, ER, Golgi apparatus, lysosomes, vacuoles, and plasma membrane) as well as proteins secreted from the cell, such as insulin. The ribosomes themselves are identical and can switch their status from free to bound.

What determines whether a ribosome will be free in the cytosol or bound to rough ER at any given time? Polypeptide synthesis always begins in the cytosol, when a free ribosome starts to translate an mRNA molecule. There the process continues to completion—*unless* the growing polypeptide itself cues the ribosome to attach to the ER. The polypeptides of proteins destined for the endomembrane system or for secretion are marked by a **signal peptide**, which targets the protein to the ER (**Figure 17.21**). The signal peptide, a sequence of about 20 amino acids at or near the leading (amino) end of the polypeptide, is recognized as it emerges from the ribosome by a protein-RNA complex called a **signal-recognition particle (SRP)**. This particle functions as an adapter that brings the ribosome to a receptor protein built into the ER membrane. This receptor is part of a multiprotein translocation complex. Polypeptide synthesis continues there, and the growing polypeptide snakes across the membrane into the ER lumen via a protein pore. The signal peptide is usually removed by an enzyme. The rest of the completed polypeptide, if it is to be secreted from the cell, is released into solution within the ER lumen (as in Figure 17.21). Alternatively, if the polypeptide is to be a membrane protein, it remains partially embedded in the ER membrane.

1 Polypeptide synthesis begins on a free ribosome in the cytosol.

2 An SRP binds to the signal peptide, halting synthesis momentarily.

3 The SRP binds to a receptor protein in the ER membrane. This receptor is part of a protein complex (a translocation complex) that has a membrane pore and a signal-cleaving enzyme.

4 The SRP leaves, and polypeptide synthesis resumes, with simultaneous translocation across the membrane. (The signal peptide stays attached to the translocation complex.)

5 The signal-cleaving enzyme cuts off the signal peptide.

6 The rest of the completed polypeptide leaves the ribosome and folds into its final conformation.

▲ **Figure 17.21 The signal mechanism for targeting proteins to the ER.** A polypeptide destined for the endomembrane system or for secretion from the cell begins with a signal peptide, a series of amino acids that targets it for the ER. This figure shows the synthesis of a secretory protein and its simultaneous import into the ER. In the ER and then in the Golgi, the protein will be processed further. Finally, a transport vesicle will convey it to the plasma membrane for release from the cell (see Figure 7.10).

Other kinds of signal peptides are used to target polypeptides to mitochondria, chloroplasts, the interior of the nucleus, and other organelles that are not part of the endomembrane system. The critical difference in these cases is that translation is completed in the cytosol before the polypeptide is imported into the organelle. The mechanisms of translocation also vary, but in all cases studied to date, the "zip codes" that address proteins for secretion or to cellular locations are signal peptides of some sort. Bacteria also employ signal peptides to target proteins for secretion.

CONCEPT CHECK 17.4

1. What two processes ensure that the correct amino acid is added to a growing polypeptide chain?
2. Describe how the formation of polyribosomes can benefit the cell.
3. Describe how a polypeptide to be secreted is transported to the endomembrane system.
4. **WHAT IF?** Discuss the ways in which rRNA structure likely contributes to ribosomal function.

For suggested answers, see Appendix A.

CONCEPT 17.5
Point mutations can affect protein structure and function

Now that you have explored the process of gene expression, you are ready to understand the effects of changes to the genetic information of a cell (or virus). These changes, called **mutations**, are responsible for the huge diversity of genes found among organisms because mutations are the ultimate source of new genes. In Figure 15.15, we considered large-scale mutations, chromosomal rearrangements that affect long segments of DNA. Here we examine **point mutations**, chemical changes in a single base pair of a gene.

If a point mutation occurs in a gamete or in a cell that gives rise to gametes, it may be transmitted to offspring and to a succession of future generations. If the mutation has an adverse effect on the phenotype of an organism, the mutant condition is referred to as a genetic disorder or hereditary disease. For example, we can trace the genetic basis of sickle-cell disease to the mutation of a single base pair in the gene that encodes the β-globin polypeptide of hemoglobin. The change of a single nucleotide in the DNA's template strand leads to the production of an abnormal protein (**Figure 17.22**; also see Figure 5.22). In individuals who are homozygous for the mutant allele, the sickling of red blood cells caused by the altered hemoglobin produces the multiple symptoms associated with sickle-cell disease (see Chapter 14). Another example is a heart condition responsible for some incidents of sudden death in young athletes, called familial cardiomyopathy. Point mutations in several genes have been identified, each of which can lead to this disorder.

Types of Point Mutations

Point mutations within a gene can be divided into two general categories: base-pair substitutions and base-pair insertions or deletions. Let's now consider how these mutations affect proteins.

Substitutions

A **base-pair substitution** is the replacement of one nucleotide and its partner with another pair of nucleotides (**Figure 17.23a**). Some substitutions are called *silent mutations* because, owing to the redundancy of the genetic code, they have no effect on the encoded protein. In other words, a change in a base pair may transform one codon into another that is translated into the same amino acid. For example, if 3'-CCG-5' on the template strand mutated to 3'-CCA-5', the mRNA codon that used to be GGC would become GGU, but a glycine would still be inserted at the proper location in the protein (see Figure 17.5). Substitutions that change one amino acid to another one are called **missense mutations**. Such a mutation may have little effect on the protein: The new amino acid may have properties similar to those of the amino acid it replaces, or it may be in a region of the protein where the exact sequence of amino acids is not essential to the protein's function.

▲ **Figure 17.22 The molecular basis of sickle-cell disease: a point mutation.** The allele that causes sickle-cell disease differs from the wild-type (normal) allele by a single DNA base pair.

(a) Base-pair substitution

(b) Base-pair insertion or deletion

▲ **Figure 17.23 Types of point mutations.** Mutations are changes in DNA that result in changes in the mRNA.

However, the base-pair substitutions of greatest interest are those that cause a major change in a protein. The alteration of a single amino acid in a crucial area of a protein—such as in the part of hemoglobin shown in Figure 17.22 or in the active site of an enzyme—will significantly alter protein activity. Occasionally, such a mutation leads to an improved protein or one with novel capabilities, but much more often such mutations are detrimental, leading to a useless or less active protein that impairs cellular function.

Substitution mutations are usually missense mutations; that is, the altered codon still codes for an amino acid and thus makes sense, although not necessarily the *right* sense.

But a point mutation can also change a codon for an amino acid into a stop codon. This is called a **nonsense mutation**, and it causes translation to be terminated prematurely; the resulting polypeptide will be shorter than the polypeptide encoded by the normal gene. Nearly all nonsense mutations lead to nonfunctional proteins.

Insertions and Deletions

Insertions and **deletions** are additions or losses of nucleotide pairs in a gene **(Figure 17.23b)**. These mutations have a disastrous effect on the resulting protein more often than substitutions do. Insertion or deletion of nucleotides may alter the reading frame of the genetic message, the triplet grouping of bases on the mRNA that is read during translation. Such a mutation, called a **frameshift mutation**, will occur whenever the number of nucleotides inserted or deleted is not a multiple of three. All the nucleotides that are downstream of the deletion or insertion will be improperly grouped into codons, and the result will be extensive missense, usually ending sooner or later in nonsense and premature termination. Unless the frameshift is very near the end of the gene, the protein is almost certain to be nonfunctional.

Mutagens

Mutations can arise in a number of ways. Errors during DNA replication or recombination can lead to base-pair substitutions, insertions, or deletions, as well as to mutations affecting longer stretches of DNA. If an incorrect base is added to a growing chain during replication, for example, that base will then be mismatched with the base on the other strand. In many cases, the error will be corrected by systems you learned about in Chapter 16. Otherwise, the incorrect base will be used as a template in the next round of replication, resulting in a mutation. Such mutations are called *spontaneous mutations*. It is difficult to calculate the rate at which such mutations occur. Rough estimates have been made of the rate of mutation during DNA replication for both *E. coli* and eukaryotes, and the numbers are similar: About one nucleotide in every 10^{10} is altered, and the change is passed on to the next generation of cells.

A number of physical and chemical agents, called **mutagens**, interact with DNA in ways that cause mutations. In the 1920s, Hermann Muller discovered that X-rays caused genetic changes in fruit flies, and he used X-rays to make *Drosophila* mutants for his genetic studies. But he also recognized an alarming implication of his discovery: X-rays and other forms of high-energy radiation pose hazards to the genetic material of people as well as laboratory organisms. Mutagenic radiation, a physical mutagen, includes ultraviolet (UV) light, which can cause disruptive thymine dimers in DNA (see Figure 16.18).

Chemical mutagens fall into several categories. Base analogs are chemicals that are similar to normal DNA bases but that pair incorrectly during DNA replication. Some other chemical mutagens interfere with correct DNA replication by inserting themselves into the DNA and distorting the double helix. Still other mutagens cause chemical changes in bases that change their pairing properties.

Researchers have developed various methods to test the mutagenic activity of chemicals. A major application of these tests is the preliminary screening of chemicals to identify those that may cause cancer. This approach makes sense because most carcinogens (cancer-causing chemicals) are mutagenic, and conversely, most mutagens are carcinogenic.

1. What happens when one nucleotide pair is lost from the middle of the coding sequence of a gene?
2. **WHAT IF?** A gene whose template strand contains the sequence 3′-TACTTGTCCGATATC-5′ is mutated to 3′-TACTTGTCCAATATC-5′. For both normal and mutant genes, draw the double-stranded DNA, the resulting mRNA, and the amino acid sequence each encodes. What is the effect of the mutation on the amino acid sequence?

For suggested answers, see Appendix A.

CONCEPT **17.6**

While gene expression differs among the domains of life, the concept of a gene is universal

Although bacteria and eukaryotes carry out transcription and translation in very similar ways, we have noted certain differences in cellular machinery and in details of the processes in these two domains. The division of organisms into three domains was established about 40 years ago, when archaea were recognized as distinct from bacteria. Like bacteria, archaea are prokaryotes. However, archaea share many aspects of the mechanisms of gene expression with eukaryotes, as well as a few with bacteria.

Comparing Gene Expression in Bacteria, Archaea, and Eukarya

Recent advances in molecular biology have enabled researchers to determine the complete nucleotide sequences of hundreds of genomes, including many genomes from each domain. This wealth of data allows us to compare gene and protein sequences across domains. Foremost among genes of interest are those that encode components of such fundamental biological processes as transcription and translation.

Bacterial and eukaryotic RNA polymerases differ significantly from each other. In contrast, the single RNA polymerase of archaea resembles the three eukaryotic RNA polymerases, and archaea and eukaryotes use a complex set of transcription factors, unlike bacteria. Transcription is terminated differently in bacteria and eukaryotes. Here again, the little that is known about archaeal transcription termination suggests it may be more like the eukaryotic process.

As far as translation is concerned, bacterial and eukaryotic ribosomes are slightly different. Archaeal ribosomes are the same size as bacterial ribosomes, but their sensitivity to chemical inhibitors most closely matches that of eukaryotic ribosomes. We mentioned earlier that initiation of translation is slightly different in bacteria and eukaryotes. In this respect, the archaeal process is more like that of bacteria.

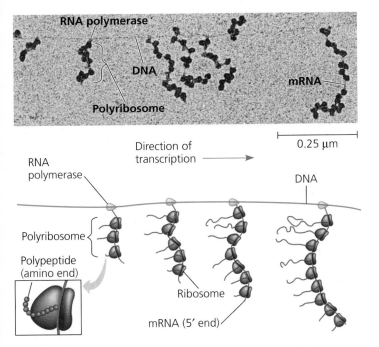

Direction of transcription →

0.25 μm

RNA polymerase

DNA

Polyribosome

Polypeptide (amino end)

Ribosome

mRNA (5′ end)

▲ **Figure 17.24 Coupled transcription and translation in bacteria.** In bacterial cells, the translation of mRNA can begin as soon as the leading (5′) end of the mRNA molecule peels away from the DNA template. The micrograph (TEM) shows a strand of *E. coli* DNA being transcribed by RNA polymerase molecules. Attached to each RNA polymerase molecule is a growing strand of mRNA, which is already being translated by ribosomes. The newly synthesized polypeptides are not visible in the micrograph but are shown in the diagram.

? *Which one of the mRNA molecules started transcription first? On that mRNA, which ribosome started translating first?*

The most important differences between bacteria and eukaryotes with regard to gene expression arise from the bacterial cell's relative absence of compartmental organization. Like a one-room workshop, a bacterial cell ensures a streamlined operation. In the absence of a nucleus, it can simultaneously transcribe and translate the same gene **(Figure 17.24)**, and the newly made protein can quickly diffuse to its site of function. Little is currently known about whether the processes of transcription and translation are coupled like this in archaeal cells, but most researchers suspect that they are, since archaea lack a nuclear envelope. In contrast, the eukaryotic cell's nuclear envelope segregates transcription from translation and provides a compartment for extensive RNA processing. This processing stage includes additional steps whose regulation can help coordinate the eukaryotic cell's elaborate activities (see Chapter 18). Finally, eukaryotic cells have complicated mechanisms for targeting proteins to the appropriate cellular compartment (organelle).

Learning more about the proteins and RNAs involved in archaeal transcription and translation will tell us much about the evolution of these processes in all three domains. In spite of the differences in gene expression cataloged here, however, the idea of the gene itself is a unifying concept among all forms of life.

What Is a Gene? *Revisiting the Question*

Our definition of a gene has evolved over the past few chapters, as it has through the history of genetics. We began with the Mendelian concept of a gene as a discrete unit of inheritance that affects a phenotypic character (Chapter 14). We saw that Morgan and his colleagues assigned such genes to specific loci on chromosomes (Chapter 15). We went on to view a gene as a region of specific nucleotide sequence along the length of a DNA molecule in a chromosome (Chapter 16). Finally, in this chapter, we have considered a functional definition of a gene as a DNA sequence that codes for a specific polypeptide chain. (**Figure 17.25**, on the next page, summarizes the path from gene to polypeptide in a eukaryotic cell.) All these definitions are useful, depending on the context in which genes are being studied.

Clearly, the statement that a gene codes for a polypeptide is too simple. Most eukaryotic genes contain noncoding segments (introns), so large portions of these genes have no corresponding segments in polypeptides. Molecular biologists also often include promoters and certain other regulatory regions of DNA within the boundaries of a gene. These DNA sequences are not transcribed, but they can be considered part of the functional gene because they must be present for transcription to occur. Our molecular definition of a gene must also be broad enough to include the DNA that is transcribed into rRNA, tRNA, and other RNAs that are not translated. These genes have no polypeptide products but play crucial roles in the cell. Thus, we arrive at the following definition: *A gene is a region of DNA that can be expressed to produce a final functional product that is either a polypeptide or an RNA molecule.*

When considering phenotypes, however, it is often useful to start by focusing on genes that code for polypeptides. In this chapter, you have learned in molecular terms how a typical gene is expressed—by transcription into RNA and then translation into a polypeptide that forms a protein of specific structure and function. Proteins, in turn, bring about an organism's observable phenotype.

A given type of cell expresses only a subset of its genes. This is an essential feature in multicellular organisms: You'd be in trouble if the lens cells in your eyes started expressing the genes for hair proteins, which are normally expressed only in hair follicle cells! Gene expression is precisely regulated. We'll explore gene regulation in the next chapter, beginning with the simpler case of bacteria and continuing with eukaryotes.

CONCEPT CHECK 17.6

1. Would the coupling of processes shown in Figure 17.24 be found in a eukaryotic cell? Explain.

2. **WHAT IF?** In eukaryotic cells, mRNAs have been found to have a circular arrangement in which the poly-A tail is held by proteins near the 5′ end cap. How might this increase translation efficiency?

For suggested answers, see Appendix A.

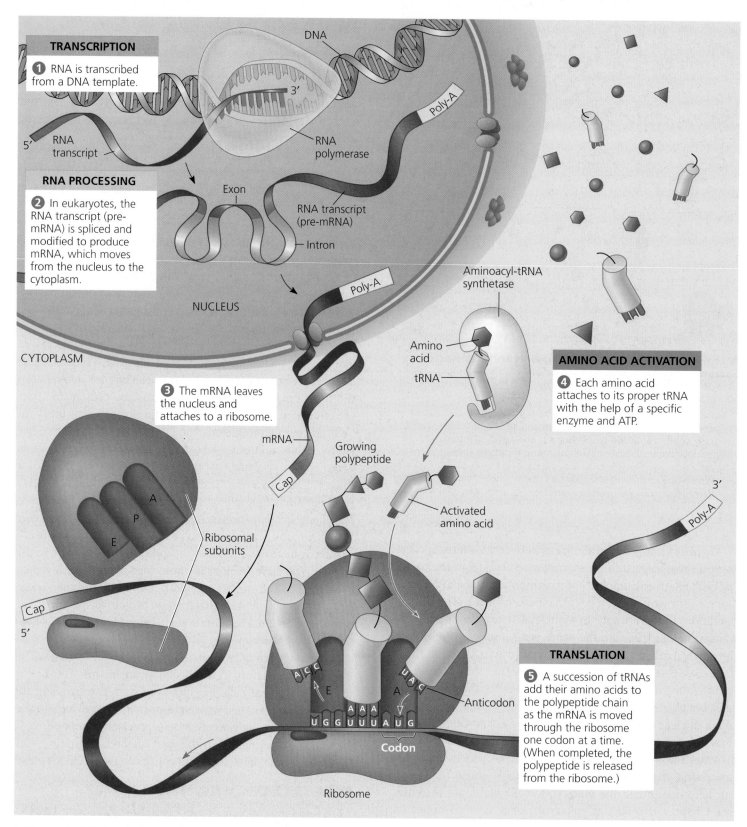

TRANSCRIPTION

❶ RNA is transcribed from a DNA template.

DNA

RNA polymerase

RNA transcript

RNA PROCESSING

❷ In eukaryotes, the RNA transcript (pre-mRNA) is spliced and modified to produce mRNA, which moves from the nucleus to the cytoplasm.

Exon

Intron

RNA transcript (pre-mRNA)

Poly-A

NUCLEUS

CYTOPLASM

Poly-A

❸ The mRNA leaves the nucleus and attaches to a ribosome.

mRNA

Cap

Aminoacyl-tRNA synthetase

Amino acid

tRNA

AMINO ACID ACTIVATION

❹ Each amino acid attaches to its proper tRNA with the help of a specific enzyme and ATP.

Growing polypeptide

Activated amino acid

Ribosomal subunits

Cap

5′

A

P

E

Anticodon

TRANSLATION

❺ A succession of tRNAs add their amino acids to the polypeptide chain as the mRNA is moved through the ribosome one codon at a time. (When completed, the polypeptide is released from the ribosome.)

E

A

A C C

U A C

A A A

U G G U U U A U G

Codon

Poly-A

3′

Ribosome

▲ **Figure 17.25 A summary of transcription and translation in a eukaryotic cell.** This diagram shows the path from one gene to one polypeptide. Keep in mind that each gene in the DNA can be transcribed repeatedly into many identical RNA molecules and that each mRNA can be translated repeatedly to yield many identical polypeptide molecules. (Also, remember that the final products of some genes are not polypeptides but RNA molecules, including tRNA and rRNA.) In general, the steps of transcription and translation are similar in bacterial, archaeal, and eukaryotic cells. The major difference is the occurrence of RNA processing in the eukaryotic nucleus. Other significant differences are found in the initiation stages of both transcription and translation and in the termination of transcription.

SUMMARY OF KEY CONCEPTS

CONCEPT 17.1
Genes specify proteins via transcription and translation (pp. 325–331)

▶ **Evidence from the Study of Metabolic Defects** DNA controls metabolism by directing cells to make specific enzymes and other proteins. Beadle and Tatum's experiments with mutant strains of *Neurospora* supported the one gene–one enzyme hypothesis. Genes code for polypeptide chains or for RNA molecules.

▶ **Basic Principles of Transcription and Translation** Transcription is the nucleotide-to-nucleotide transfer of information from DNA to RNA, while translation is the informational transfer from nucleotide sequence in RNA to amino acid sequence in a polypeptide.

▶ **The Genetic Code** Genetic information is encoded as a sequence of nonoverlapping base triplets, or codons. A codon in messenger RNA (mRNA) either is translated into an amino acid (61 of the 64 codons) or serves as a stop signal (3 codons). Codons must be read in the correct reading frame.

MEDIA
Investigation How Is a Metabolic Pathway Analyzed?
MP3 Tutor DNA to RNA to Protein
Activity Overview of Protein Synthesis

CONCEPT 17.2
Transcription is the DNA-directed synthesis of RNA: *a closer look* (pp. 331–334)

▶ **Molecular Components of Transcription** RNA synthesis is catalyzed by RNA polymerase. It follows the same base-pairing rules as DNA replication, except that in RNA, uracil substitutes for thymine.

Transcription unit

Promoter

5′
3′

5′

3′
5′

Template strand of DNA

RNA polymerase

RNA transcript

▶ **Synthesis of an RNA Transcript** The three stages of transcription are initiation, elongation, and termination. Promoters signal the initiation of RNA synthesis. Transcription factors help eukaryotic RNA polymerase recognize promoter sequences. The mechanisms of termination are different in bacteria and eukaryotes.

MEDIA
Activity Transcription

CONCEPT 17.3
Eukaryotic cells modify RNA after transcription (pp. 334–336)

▶ **Alteration of mRNA Ends** Eukaryotic mRNA molecules are processed before leaving the nucleus by modification of their ends and by RNA splicing. The 5′ end receives a modified nucleotide cap, and the 3′ end a poly-A tail.

Pre-mRNA

Cap

Poly-A tail

mRNA

▶ **Split Genes and RNA Splicing** Most eukaryotic genes have introns interspersed among the coding regions, the exons. In RNA splicing, introns are removed and exons joined. RNA splicing is typically carried out by spliceosomes, but in some cases, RNA alone catalyzes its own splicing. The catalytic ability of some RNA molecules, called ribozymes, derives from the inherent properties of RNA. The presence of introns allows for alternative RNA splicing.

MEDIA
Activity RNA Processing

CONCEPT 17.4
Translation is the RNA-directed synthesis of a polypeptide: *a closer look* (pp. 337–344)

▶ **Molecular Components of Translation** A cell translates an mRNA message into protein using transfer RNAs (tRNAs). After binding specific amino acids, tRNAs line up via their anticodons at complementary codons on mRNA. Ribosomes help facilitate this coupling with binding sites for mRNA and tRNA.

▶ **Building a Polypeptide** Ribosomes coordinate the three stages of translation: initiation, elongation, and termination. The formation of peptide bonds between amino acids is catalyzed by rRNA. A number of ribosomes can translate a single mRNA molecule simultaneously, forming a polyribosome.

mRNA   Ribosome

Polypeptide

▶ **Completing and Targeting the Functional Protein** After translation, modifications to proteins can affect their three-dimensional shape. Free ribosomes in the cytosol initiate synthesis of all proteins, but proteins destined for the endomembrane system or for secretion are transported into the ER. Such proteins have a signal peptide to which a signal-recognition particle (SRP) binds, enabling the translating ribosome to bind to the ER.

MEDIA
BioFlix 3-D Animation Protein Synthesis
Activity Translation
Biology Labs On-Line TranslationLab

CONCEPT 17.5
Point mutations can affect protein structure and function (pp. 344–346)

▶ **Types of Point Mutations** A point mutation is a change in one DNA base pair, which may lead to production of a nonfunctional protein. Base-pair substitutions can cause missense or nonsense mutations. Base-pair insertions or deletions may produce frameshift mutations.

▶ **Mutagens** Spontaneous mutations can occur during DNA replication, recombination, or repair. Chemical and physical mutagens cause DNA damage that can alter genes.

While gene expression differs among the domains of life, the concept of a gene is universal (pp. 346–348)

▶ **Comparing Gene Expression in Bacteria, Archaea, and Eukarya** Because bacterial cells lack a nuclear envelope, translation can begin while transcription is still in progress. Archaeal cells show similarities to both eukaryotic and bacterial cells in their processes of gene expression. In a eukaryotic cell, the nuclear envelope separates transcription from translation, and extensive RNA processing occurs in the nucleus.

▶ **What Is a Gene?** *Revisiting the Question* A gene is a region of DNA whose final functional product is either a polypeptide or an RNA molecule.

TESTING YOUR KNOWLEDGE

SELF-QUIZ

1. In eukaryotic cells, transcription cannot begin until
   a. the two DNA strands have completely separated and exposed the promoter.
   b. several transcription factors have bound to the promoter.
   c. the 5′ caps are removed from the mRNA.
   d. the DNA introns are removed from the template.
   e. DNA nucleases have isolated the transcription unit.

2. Which of the following is *not* true of a codon?
   a. It consists of three nucleotides.
   b. It may code for the same amino acid as another codon.
   c. It never codes for more than one amino acid.
   d. It extends from one end of a tRNA molecule.
   e. It is the basic unit of the genetic code.

3. The anticodon of a particular tRNA molecule is
   a. complementary to the corresponding mRNA codon.
   b. complementary to the corresponding triplet in rRNA.
   c. the part of tRNA that bonds to a specific amino acid.
   d. changeable, depending on the amino acid that attaches to the tRNA.
   e. catalytic, making the tRNA a ribozyme.

4. Which of the following is *not* true of RNA processing?
   a. Exons are cut out before mRNA leaves the nucleus.
   b. Nucleotides may be added at both ends of the RNA.
   c. Ribozymes may function in RNA splicing.
   d. RNA splicing can be catalyzed by spliceosomes.
   e. A primary transcript is often much longer than the final RNA molecule that leaves the nucleus.

5. Using Figure 17.5, identify a 5′ → 3′ sequence of nucleotides in the DNA template strand for an mRNA coding for the polypeptide sequence Phe-Pro-Lys.

   a. 5′-UUUGGGAAA-3′   d. 5′-CTTCGGGAA-3′
   b. 5′-GAACCCCTT-3′   e. 5′-AAACCCUUU-3′
   c. 5′-AAAACCTTT-3′

6. Which of the following mutations would be *most* likely to have a harmful effect on an organism?
   a. a base-pair substitution
   b. a deletion of three nucleotides near the middle of a gene
   c. a single nucleotide deletion in the middle of an intron
   d. a single nucleotide deletion near the end of the coding sequence
   e. a single nucleotide insertion downstream of, and close to, the start of the coding sequence

7. Which component is *not* directly involved in translation?
   a. mRNA   d. ribosomes
   b. DNA   e. GTP
   c. tRNA

8. **DRAW IT** Review the roles of RNA by filling in the following table:

Type of RNA	Functions
Messenger RNA (mRNA)	
Transfer RNA (tRNA)	
	Plays catalytic (ribozyme) roles and structural roles in ribosomes
Primary transcript	
Small nuclear RNA (snRNA)	

For Self-Quiz answers, see Appendix A.

MEDIA Visit the Study Area at **www.masteringbio.com** for a Practice Test.

EVOLUTION CONNECTION

9. The genetic code (see Figure 17.5) is rich with evolutionary implications. For instance, notice that the 20 amino acids are not randomly scattered; most amino acids are coded for by a similar set of codons. What evolutionary explanations can be given for this pattern? (*Hint:* There is one explanation relating to historical ancestry, and some less obvious ones of a "form-fits-function" type.)

SCIENTIFIC INQUIRY

10. Knowing that the genetic code is almost universal, a scientist uses molecular biological methods to insert the human β-globin gene (shown in Figure 17.10) into bacterial cells, hoping the cells will express it and synthesize functional β-globin protein. Instead, the protein produced is nonfunctional and is found to contain many fewer amino acids than does β-globin made by a eukaryotic cell. Explain why.

    Biological Inquiry: A Workbook of Investigative Cases Explore translation and use of sequence data in testing hypotheses with the case "The Doctor's Dilemma."

Regulation of Gene Expression

18

▲ **Figure 18.1 What regulates the precise pattern of expression of different genes?**

OVERVIEW

Conducting the Genetic Orchestra

An oboe squawks loudly, several violins squeak shrilly, and a tuba adds its rumble to the noisy chaos. Then the conductor's baton rises, pauses, and begins a series of elaborate movements, directing specific instruments to join in and others to raise or lower their volume at exact moments. Properly balanced and timed, discordant sounds are thus transformed into a beautiful symphony that enraptures the audience.

In a similar way, cells intricately and precisely regulate their gene expression. Both prokaryotes and eukaryotes must alter their patterns of gene expression in response to changes in environmental conditions. Multicellular eukaryotes must also develop and maintain multiple cell types. Each cell type contains the same genome but expresses a different subset of genes, a significant challenge in gene regulation.

An adult fruit fly, for example, develops from a single fertilized egg, passing through a wormlike stage called a larva. At every stage, gene expression is carefully regulated, ensuring that the right genes are expressed only at the correct time and place. In the larva, the adult wing forms in a disk-shaped pocket of several thousand cells, shown in **Figure 18.1**. The tissue in this image has been treated to reveal the mRNA for three genes—labeled red, blue, and green—using techniques covered in Chapter 20. (Red and green together appear yellow.) The intricate pattern of expression for each gene is the same from larva to larva at this stage, and it provides a graphic display of the precision of gene regulation. But what is the molecular basis for this pattern? Why is one particular gene expressed only in the few hundred cells that appear blue in this image and not in the other cells?

In this chapter, we first explore how bacteria regulate expression of their genes in response to different environmental conditions. We then examine how eukaryotes regulate gene expression to maintain different cell types. Gene expression in eukaryotes, as in bacteria, is often regulated at the stage of transcription, but control at other levels of gene expression is also important. In recent years, researchers have been surprised to discover the many roles played by RNA molecules in regulating eukaryotic gene expression, a topic we cover next. Putting together these aspects of gene regulation, we then consider how a carefully orchestrated program of gene regulation can allow a single cell—the fertilized egg—to become a fully functioning organism made up of many different cell types. Finally, we investigate how disruptions in gene regulation can lead to cancer. Orchestrating proper gene expression by all cells is crucial to the functions of life.

CONCEPT 18.1

Bacteria often respond to environmental change by regulating transcription

Bacterial cells that can conserve resources and energy have a selective advantage over cells that are unable to do so. Thus,

351

natural selection has favored bacteria that express only the genes whose products are needed by the cell.

Consider, for instance, an individual *E. coli* cell living in the erratic environment of a human colon, dependent for its nutrients on the whimsical eating habits of its host. If the environment is lacking in the amino acid tryptophan, which the bacterium needs to survive, the cell responds by activating a metabolic pathway that makes tryptophan from another compound. Later, if the human host eats a tryptophan-rich meal, the bacterial cell stops producing tryptophan, thus saving itself from squandering its resources to produce a substance that is available from the surrounding solution in prefabricated form. This is just one example of how bacteria tune their metabolism to changing environments.

Metabolic control occurs on two levels, as shown for the synthesis of tryptophan in **Figure 18.2**. First, cells can adjust the activity of enzymes already present. This is a fairly fast response, which relies on the sensitivity of many enzymes to chemical cues that increase or decrease their catalytic activity (see Chapter 8). The activity of the first enzyme in the tryptophan synthesis pathway is inhibited by the pathway's end product (Figure 18.2a). Thus, if tryptophan accumulates in a cell, it shuts down the synthesis of more tryptophan by in-

hibiting enzyme activity. Such *feedback inhibition*, typical of anabolic (biosynthetic) pathways, allows a cell to adapt to short-term fluctuations in the supply of a substance it needs.

Second, cells can adjust the production level of certain enzymes; that is, they can regulate the expression of the genes encoding the enzymes. If, in our example, the environment provides all the tryptophan the cell needs, the cell stops making the enzymes that catalyze the synthesis of tryptophan (Figure 18.2b). In this case, the control of enzyme production occurs at the level of transcription, the synthesis of messenger RNA coding for these enzymes. More generally, many genes of the bacterial genome are switched on or off by changes in the metabolic status of the cell. The basic mechanism for this control of gene expression in bacteria, described as the *operon model*, was discovered in 1961 by François Jacob and Jacques Monod at the Pasteur Institute in Paris. Let's see what an operon is and how it works, using the control of tryptophan synthesis as our first example.

Operons: The Basic Concept

E. coli synthesizes the amino acid tryptophan from a precursor molecule in the multistep pathway shown in Figure 18.2. Each reaction in the pathway is catalyzed by a specific enzyme, and the five genes that code for the subunits of these enzymes are clustered together on the bacterial chromosome. A single promoter serves all five genes, which together constitute a transcription unit. (Recall from Chapter 17 that a promoter is a site where RNA polymerase can bind to DNA and begin transcription.) Thus, transcription gives rise to one long mRNA molecule that codes for the five polypeptides making up the enzymes in the tryptophan pathway. The cell can translate this one mRNA into five separate polypeptides because the mRNA is punctuated with start and stop codons that signal where the coding sequence for each polypeptide begins and ends.

A key advantage of grouping genes of related function into one transcription unit is that a single on-off "switch" can control the whole cluster of functionally related genes; in other words, these genes are under *coordinate control*. When an *E. coli* cell must make tryptophan for itself because the nutrient medium lacks this amino acid, all the enzymes for the metabolic pathway are synthesized at one time. The switch is a segment of DNA called an **operator**. Both its location and name suit its function: Positioned within the promoter or, in some cases, between the promoter and the enzyme-coding genes, the operator controls the access of RNA polymerase to the genes. All together, the operator, the promoter, and the genes they control—the entire stretch of DNA required for enzyme production for the tryptophan pathway—constitute an **operon**. The *trp* operon (*trp* for tryptophan) is one of many operons in the *E. coli* genome **(Figure 18.3)**.

If the operator is the switch for controlling transcription, how does this switch work? By itself, the *trp* operon is turned on; that

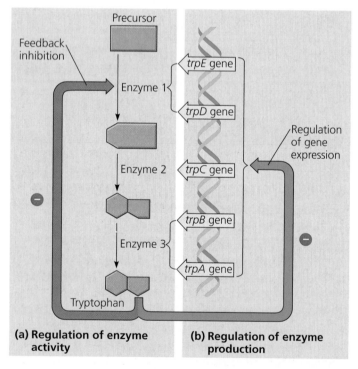

▲ **Figure 18.2 Regulation of a metabolic pathway.** In the pathway for tryptophan synthesis, an abundance of tryptophan can both **(a)** inhibit the activity of the first enzyme in the pathway (feedback inhibition), a rapid response, and **(b)** repress expression of the genes encoding all subunits of the enzymes in the pathway, a longer-term response. Genes *trpE* and *trpD* encode the two subunits of enzyme 1, and genes *trpB* and *trpA* encode the two subunits of enzyme 3. (The genes were named before the order in which they functioned in the pathway was determined.) The ⊖ symbol stands for inhibition.

(a) Tryptophan absent, repressor inactive, operon on. RNA polymerase attaches to the DNA at the promoter and transcribes the operon's genes.

(b) Tryptophan present, repressor active, operon off. As tryptophan accumulates, it inhibits its own production by activating the repressor protein, which binds to the operator, blocking transcription.

▲ **Figure 18.3 The *trp* operon in *E. coli*: regulated synthesis of repressible enzymes.** Tryptophan is an amino acid produced by an anabolic pathway catalyzed by repressible enzymes. **(a)** The five genes encoding the polypeptide subunits of the enzymes in this pathway (see Figure 18.2) are grouped, along with a promoter, into the *trp* operon. The *trp* operator (the repressor-binding site) is located within the *trp* promoter (the RNA polymerase-binding site). **(b)** Accumulation of tryptophan, the end product of the pathway, represses transcription of the *trp* operon, thus blocking synthesis of all the enzymes in the pathway.

? *Describe what happens to the* trp *operon as the cell uses up its store of tryptophan.*

is, RNA polymerase can bind to the promoter and transcribe the genes of the operon. The operon can be switched off by a protein called the *trp* **repressor**. The repressor binds to the operator and blocks attachment of RNA polymerase to the promoter, preventing transcription of the genes. A repressor protein is specific for the operator of a particular operon. For example, the repressor that switches off the *trp* operon by binding to the *trp* operator has no effect on other operons in the *E. coli* genome.

The *trp* repressor is the product of a **regulatory gene** called *trpR*, which is located some distance from the operon it controls and has its own promoter. Regulatory genes are expressed continuously, although at a low rate, and a few *trp* repressor molecules are always present in *E. coli* cells. Why, then, is the *trp* operon not switched off permanently? First, the binding of repressors to operators is reversible. An operator vacillates between two states: one without the repressor bound and one with the repressor bound. The relative duration of each state depends on the number of active repressor molecules around. Second, the *trp* repressor, like most regulatory proteins, is an allosteric protein, with two alternative

shapes, active and inactive (see Figure 8.20). The *trp* repressor is synthesized in an inactive form with little affinity for the *trp* operator. Only if tryptophan binds to the *trp* repressor at an allosteric site does the repressor protein change to the active form that can attach to the operator, turning the operon off.

Tryptophan functions in this system as a **corepressor**, a small molecule that cooperates with a repressor protein to switch an operon off. As tryptophan accumulates, more tryptophan molecules associate with *trp* repressor molecules, which can then bind to the *trp* operator and shut down production of the tryptophan pathway enzymes. If the cell's tryptophan level drops, transcription of the operon's genes resumes. This is one example of how gene expression can respond to changes in the cell's internal and external environment.

Repressible and Inducible Operons: Two Types of Negative Gene Regulation

The *trp* operon is said to be a *repressible operon* because its transcription is usually on but can be inhibited (repressed) when a specific small molecule (in this case, tryptophan) binds allosterically to a regulatory protein. In contrast, an *inducible operon* is usually off but can be stimulated (induced) when a specific small molecule interacts with a regulatory protein. The classic example of an inducible operon is the *lac* operon (*lac* for lactose), which was the subject of Jacob and Monod's pioneering research.

The disaccharide lactose (milk sugar) is available to *E. coli* in the human colon if the host drinks milk. Lactose metabolism begins with hydrolysis of the disaccharide into its component monosaccharides, glucose and galactose, a reaction catalyzed by the enzyme β-galactosidase. Only a few molecules of this enzyme are present in an *E. coli* cell growing in the absence of lactose. If lactose is added to the bacterium's environment, however, the number of β-galactosidase molecules in the cell increases a thousandfold within about 15 minutes.

The gene for β-galactosidase is part of the *lac* operon, which includes two other genes coding for enzymes that function in lactose utilization. The entire transcription unit is un-

der the command of a single operator and promoter. The regulatory gene, *lacI*, located outside the operon, codes for an allosteric repressor protein that can switch off the *lac* operon by binding to the operator. So far, this sounds just like regulation of the *trp* operon, but there is one important difference. Recall that the *trp* repressor is inactive by itself and requires tryptophan as a corepressor in order to bind to the operator. The *lac* repressor, in contrast, is active by itself, binding to the operator and switching the *lac* operon off. In this case, a specific small molecule, called an **inducer**, *inactivates* the repressor.

For the *lac* operon, the inducer is allolactose, an isomer of lactose formed in small amounts from lactose that enters the cell. In the absence of lactose (and hence allolactose), the *lac* repressor is in its active configuration, and the genes of the *lac* operon are silenced **(Figure 18.4a)**. If lactose is added to the cell's surroundings, allolactose binds to the *lac* repressor and alters its conformation, nullifying the repressor's ability to attach to the operator. Without bound repressor, the *lac*

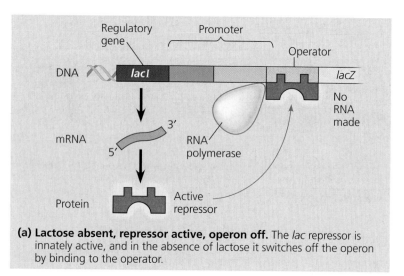

▼ Figure 18.4 **The *lac* operon in *E.coli*: regulated synthesis of inducible enzymes.** *E. coli* uses three enzymes to take up and metabolize lactose. The genes for these three enzymes are clustered in the *lac* operon. One gene, *lacZ*, codes for ß-galactosidase, which hydrolyzes lactose to glucose and galactose. The second gene, *lacY*, codes for a permease, the membrane protein that transports lactose into the cell. The third gene, *lacA*, codes for an enzyme called transacetylase, whose function in lactose metabolism is still unclear. The gene for the *lac* repressor, *lacI*, happens to be adjacent to the *lac* operon, an unusual situation. The function of the darker green region at the upstream (left) end of the promoter is revealed in Figure 18.5.

(a) Lactose absent, repressor active, operon off. The *lac* repressor is innately active, and in the absence of lactose it switches off the operon by binding to the operator.

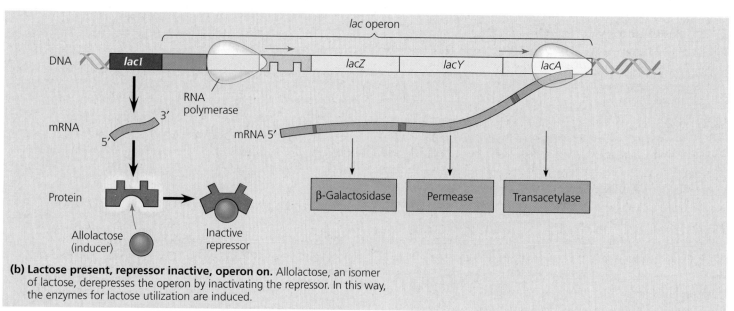

(b) Lactose present, repressor inactive, operon on. Allolactose, an isomer of lactose, derepresses the operon by inactivating the repressor. In this way, the enzymes for lactose utilization are induced.

operon is transcribed into mRNA for the lactose-utilizing enzymes (Figure 18.4b).

In the context of gene regulation, the enzymes of the lactose pathway are referred to as *inducible enzymes* because their synthesis is induced by a chemical signal (allolactose, in this case). Analogously, the enzymes for tryptophan synthesis are said to be repressible. *Repressible enzymes* generally function in anabolic pathways, which synthesize essential end products from raw materials (precursors). By suspending production of an end product when it is already present in sufficient quantity, the cell can allocate its organic precursors and energy for other uses. In contrast, inducible enzymes usually function in catabolic pathways, which break down a nutrient to simpler molecules. By producing the appropriate enzymes only when the nutrient is available, the cell avoids wasting energy and precursors making proteins that are not needed.

Regulation of both the *trp* and *lac* operons involves the *negative* control of genes, because the operons are switched off by the active form of the repressor protein. It may be easier to see this for the *trp* operon, but it is also true for the *lac* operon. Allolactose induces enzyme synthesis not by acting directly on the genome, but by freeing the *lac* operon from the negative effect of the repressor. Gene regulation is said to be *positive* only when a regulatory protein interacts directly with the genome to switch transcription on. Let's look at an example of positive control of genes, again involving the *lac* operon.

Positive Gene Regulation

When glucose and lactose are both present in its environment, *E. coli* preferentially uses glucose. The enzymes for glucose breakdown in glycolysis (see Figure 9.9) are continually present. Only when lactose is present *and* glucose is in short supply does *E. coli* use lactose as an energy source, and only then does it synthesize appreciable quantities of the enzymes for lactose breakdown.

How does the *E. coli* cell sense the glucose concentration and relay this information to the genome? Again, the mechanism depends on the interaction of an allosteric regulatory protein with a small organic molecule, in this case **cyclic AMP (cAMP)**, which accumulates when glucose is scarce (see Figure 11.10 for the structure of cAMP). The regulatory protein, called *catabolite activator protein (CAP)*, is an **activator**, a protein that binds to DNA and stimulates transcription of a gene. When cAMP binds to this regulatory protein, CAP assumes its active shape and can attach to a specific site at the upstream end of the *lac* promoter (Figure 18.5a). This attachment increases the affinity of RNA polymerase for the promoter, which is actually rather low even when no repressor is bound to the operator. By facilitating the binding of RNA polymerase to the promoter and thereby increasing the rate of transcription, the attachment of CAP to the promoter directly stimulates gene expression. Therefore, this mechanism qualifies as positive regulation.

If the amount of glucose in the cell increases, the cAMP concentration falls, and without cAMP, CAP detaches from the operon. Because CAP is inactive, RNA polymerase binds less efficiently to the promoter, and transcription of the *lac* operon proceeds at only a low level, even in the presence of lactose (Figure 18.5b). Thus, the *lac* operon is under dual control: negative control by the *lac* repressor and positive control by CAP. The state of the *lac* repressor (with or without bound allolactose) determines whether or not transcription of the *lac* operon's genes occurs at all; the state of CAP (with or without bound cAMP) controls the *rate* of transcription if the operon is repressor-free. It is as though the operon has both an on-off switch and a volume control.

(a) **Lactose present, glucose scarce (cAMP level high): abundant *lac* mRNA synthesized.** If glucose is scarce, the high level of cAMP activates CAP, and the *lac* operon produces large amounts of mRNA coding for the enzymes in the lactose pathway.

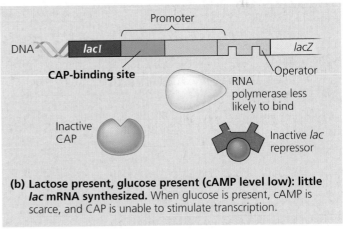

(b) **Lactose present, glucose present (cAMP level low): little *lac* mRNA synthesized.** When glucose is present, cAMP is scarce, and CAP is unable to stimulate transcription.

▲ **Figure 18.5 Positive control of the *lac* operon by catabolite activator protein (CAP).** RNA polymerase has high affinity for the *lac* promoter only when catabolite activator protein (CAP) is bound to a DNA site at the upstream end of the promoter. CAP attaches to its DNA site only when associated with cyclic AMP (cAMP), whose concentration in the cell rises when the glucose concentration falls. Thus, when glucose is present, even if lactose also is available, the cell preferentially catabolizes glucose and makes very little of the lactose-utilizing enzymes.

In addition to the *lac* operon, CAP helps regulate other operons that encode enzymes used in catabolic pathways. All told, it may affect the expression of more than 100 genes in *E. coli*. When glucose is plentiful and CAP is inactive, the synthesis of enzymes that catabolize compounds other than glucose generally slows down. The ability to catabolize other compounds, such as lactose, enables a cell deprived of glucose to survive. The compounds present in the cell at the moment determine which operons are switched on—the result of simple interactions of activator and repressor proteins with the promoters of the genes in question.

CONCEPT 18.2
Eukaryotic gene expression can be regulated at any stage

All organisms, whether prokaryotes or eukaryotes, must regulate which genes are expressed at any given time. Both unicellular organisms and the cells of multicellular organisms must continually turn genes on and off in response to signals from their external and internal environments. Regulation of gene expression is also essential for cell specialization in multicellular organisms, which are made up of different types of cells, each with a distinct role. To perform its role, each cell type must maintain a specific program of gene expression in which certain genes are expressed and others are not.

Differential Gene Expression

A typical human cell probably expresses about 20% of its genes at any given time. Highly differentiated cells, such as muscle or nerve cells, express an even smaller fraction of their genes. Almost all the cells in an organism contain an identical genome. (Cells of the immune system are one exception. During their differentiation, rearrangement of the immunoglobulin genes results in a change in the genome, as you will see in

Chapter 43.) However, the subset of genes expressed in the cells of each type is unique, allowing these cells to carry out their specific function. The differences between cell types, therefore, are due not to different genes being present, but to **differential gene expression**, the expression of different genes by cells with the same genome.

The genomes of eukaryotes may contain tens of thousands of genes, but for quite a few species, only a small amount of the DNA—about 1.5% in humans—codes for protein. The rest of the DNA either codes for RNA products, such as tRNAs, or isn't transcribed at all. The transcription factors of a cell must locate the right genes at the right time, a task on a par with finding a needle in a haystack. When gene expression goes awry, serious imbalances and diseases, including cancer, can arise.

Figure 18.6 summarizes the entire process of gene expression in a eukaryotic cell, highlighting key stages in the expression of a protein-coding gene. Each stage depicted in Figure 18.6 is a potential control point at which gene expression can be turned on or off, accelerated, or slowed down.

Only 40 years ago, an understanding of the mechanisms that control gene expression in eukaryotes seemed almost hopelessly out of reach. Since then, new research methods, notably advances in DNA technology (see Chapter 20), have enabled molecular biologists to uncover many of the details of eukaryotic gene regulation. In all organisms, a common control point for gene expression is at transcription; regulation at this stage is often in response to signals coming from outside the cell, such as hormones or other signaling molecules. For that reason, the term *gene expression* is often equated with transcription for both bacteria and eukaryotes. While this is most often the case for bacteria, the greater complexity of eukaryotic cell structure and function provides opportunities for regulating gene expression at many additional stages (see Figure 18.6). In the remainder of this section, we'll examine some of the important control points of eukaryotic gene expression more closely.

Regulation of Chromatin Structure

Recall that the DNA of eukaryotic cells is packaged with proteins in an elaborate complex known as chromatin, the basic unit of which is the nucleosome (see Figure 16.21). The structural organization of chromatin not only packs a cell's DNA into a compact form that fits inside the nucleus but also helps regulate gene expression in several ways. The location of a gene's promoter relative to nucleosomes and to the sites where the DNA attaches to the chromosome scaffold or nuclear lamina can affect whether the gene is transcribed. In addition, genes within heterochromatin, which is highly condensed, are usually not expressed. The repressive effect of heterochromatin has been seen in experiments in which a transcriptionally active gene was inserted into a region of heterochromatin in yeast cells; the inserted gene was no longer expressed. Lastly, as revealed in a flurry of recent research, certain chemical modifications to the histones and DNA

▲ **Figure 18.6 Stages in gene expression that can be regulated in eukaryotic cells.** In this diagram, the colored boxes indicate the processes most often regulated; each color indicates the type of molecule that is affected (blue = DNA, orange = RNA, purple = protein). The nuclear envelope separating transcription from translation in eukaryotic cells offers an opportunity for post-transcriptional control in the form of RNA processing that is absent in prokaryotes. In addition, eukaryotes have a greater variety of control mechanisms operating before transcription and after translation. The expression of any given gene, however, does not necessarily involve every stage shown; for example, not every polypeptide is cleaved.

of chromatin can influence both chromatin structure and gene expression. Here we examine the effects of these modifications, which are catalyzed by specific enzymes.

Histone Modifications

There is mounting evidence that chemical modifications to histones, the proteins around which the DNA is wrapped in nucleosomes, play a direct role in the regulation of gene transcription. The N-terminus of each histone molecule in a nucleosome protrudes outward from the nucleosome (**Figure 18.7a**). These

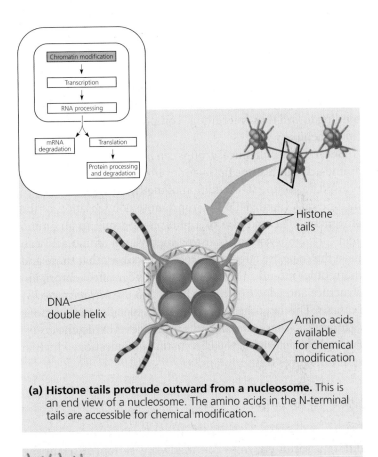

(a) Histone tails protrude outward from a nucleosome. This is an end view of a nucleosome. The amino acids in the N-terminal tails are accessible for chemical modification.

(b) Acetylation of histone tails promotes loose chromatin structure that permits transcription. A region of chromatin in which nucleosomes are unacetylated forms a compact structure (left) in which the DNA is not transcribed. When nucleosomes are highly acetylated (right), the chromatin becomes less compact, and the DNA is accessible for transcription.

▲ **Figure 18.7 A simple model of histone tails and the effect of histone acetylation.** In addition to acetylation, histones can undergo several other types of modifications that also help determine the chromatin configuration in a region.

histone tails are accessible to various modifying enzymes, which catalyze the addition or removal of specific chemical groups.

In **histone acetylation,** acetyl groups ($—COCH_3$) are attached to lysines in histone tails; deacetylation is the removal of acetyl groups. When the lysines are acetylated, their positive charges are neutralized and the histone tails no longer bind to neighboring nucleosomes (**Figure 18.7b**). Recall that such binding promotes the folding of chromatin into a more compact structure; when this binding does not occur, chromatin has a looser structure. As a result, transcription proteins have easier access to genes in an acetylated region. Researchers have shown that some enzymes that acetylate or deacetylate histones are closely associated with or even components of the transcription factors that bind to promoters (see Figure 17.8). These observations suggest that histone acetylation enzymes may promote the initiation of transcription not only by remodeling chromatin structure, but also by binding to and thus "recruiting" components of the transcription machinery.

Several other chemical groups can be reversibly attached to amino acids in histone tails—for example, methyl groups and phosphate groups. The addition of methyl groups ($—CH_3$) to histone tails (methylation) can promote condensation of the chromatin. The addition of a phosphate group to an amino acid (phosphorylation) next to a methylated amino acid can have the opposite effect. The recent discovery that these and many other modifications to histone tails can affect chromatin structure and gene expression has led to the *histone code hypothesis.* This hypothesis proposes that specific combinations of modifications, rather than the overall level of histone acetylation, help determine the chromatin configuration, which in turn influences transcription.

DNA Methylation

While some enzymes methylate the tails of histone proteins, a different set of enzymes can methylate certain bases in the DNA itself. In fact, the DNA of most plants, animals, and fungi has methylated bases, usually cytosine. Inactive DNA, such as that of inactivated mammalian X chromosomes (see Figure 15.8), is generally more methylated than DNA that is actively transcribed, although there are exceptions.

Comparison of the same genes in different tissues shows that the genes are usually more heavily methylated in cells in which they are not expressed. Removal of the extra methyl groups can turn on some of these genes. Moreover, researchers have discovered proteins that bind to methylated DNA and recruit histone deacetylation enzymes. Thus, a dual mechanism, involving both DNA methylation and histone deacetylation, can repress transcription.

At least in some species, DNA methylation seems to be essential for the long-term inactivation of genes that occurs during normal cell differentiation in the embryo. For instance, experiments have shown that deficient DNA methylation due to lack of a methylating enzyme leads to abnormal embryonic development in organisms as different as mice and *Arabidopsis* (a plant). Once methylated, genes usually stay that way through successive cell divisions in a given individual. At DNA sites where one strand is already methylated, methylation enzymes correctly methylate the daughter strand after each round of DNA replication. Methylation patterns are thus passed on, and cells forming specialized tissues keep a chemical record of what occurred during embryonic development. A methylation pattern maintained in this way also accounts for **genomic imprinting** in mammals, where methylation permanently regulates expression of either the maternal or paternal allele of particular genes at the start of development (see Chapter 15).

Epigenetic Inheritance

The chromatin modifications that we have just discussed do not entail a change in the DNA sequence, yet they may be passed along to future generations of cells. Inheritance of traits transmitted by mechanisms not directly involving the nucleotide sequence is called **epigenetic inheritance.** Whereas mutations in the DNA are permanent changes, modifications to the chromatin can be reversed, by processes that are not yet fully understood. The molecular systems for chromatin modification may well interact with each other in a regulated way. In *Drosophila,* for example, experiments have suggested that a particular histone-modifying enzyme recruits a DNA methylation enzyme to one region and that the two enzymes collaborate to silence a particular set of genes.

Researchers are amassing more and more evidence for the importance of epigenetic information in the regulation of gene expression. Epigenetic variations might help explain why one identical twin acquires a genetically based disease, such as schizophrenia, but the other does not, despite their identical genomes. Alterations in normal patterns of DNA methylation are seen in some cancers, where they are associated with inappropriate gene expression. Evidently, enzymes that modify chromatin structure are integral parts of the eukaryotic cell's machinery for regulating transcription.

Regulation of Transcription Initiation

Chromatin-modifying enzymes provide initial control of gene expression by making a region of DNA either more or less able to bind the transcription machinery. Once the chromatin of a gene is optimally modified for expression, the initiation of transcription is the next major step at which gene expression is regulated. As in bacteria, the regulation of transcription initiation in eukaryotes involves proteins that bind to DNA and either facilitate or inhibit binding of RNA polymerase. The process is more complicated in eukaryotes, however. Before looking at how eukaryotic cells control their transcription,

Organization of a Typical Eukaryotic Gene

A eukaryotic gene and the DNA elements (segments) that control it are typically organized as shown in **Figure 18.8**, which extends what you learned about eukaryotic genes in Chapter 17. Recall that a cluster of proteins called a *transcription initiation complex* assembles on the promoter sequence at the "upstream" end of the gene. One of these proteins, RNA polymerase II, then proceeds to transcribe the gene, synthesizing a primary RNA transcript (pre-mRNA). RNA processing includes enzymatic addition of a 5′ cap and a poly-A tail, as well as splicing out of introns, to yield a mature mRNA. Associated with most eukaryotic genes are multiple **control elements**, segments of noncoding DNA that help regulate transcription by binding certain proteins. These control elements and the proteins they bind are critical to the precise regulation of gene expression seen in different cell types.

The Roles of Transcription Factors

To initiate transcription, eukaryotic RNA polymerase requires the assistance of proteins called transcription factors. Some transcription factors, such as those illustrated in Figure 17.8,

are essential for the transcription of *all* protein-coding genes; therefore, they are often called *general transcription factors*. Only a few general transcription factors independently bind a DNA sequence, such as the TATA box within the promoter; the others primarily bind proteins, including each other and RNA polymerase II. Protein-protein interactions are crucial to the initiation of eukaryotic transcription. Only when the complete initiation complex has assembled can the polymerase begin to move along the DNA template strand, producing a complementary strand of RNA.

The interaction of general transcription factors and RNA polymerase II with a promoter usually leads to only a low rate of initiation and production of few RNA transcripts. In eukaryotes, high levels of transcription of particular genes at the appropriate time and place depend on the interaction of control elements with another set of proteins, which can be thought of as *specific transcription factors*.

Enhancers and Specific Transcription Factors As you can see in Figure 18.8, some control elements, named *proximal control elements*, are located close to the promoter. (Although some biologists consider proximal control elements part of the promoter, we do not.) The more distant *distal control elements*, groupings of which are called **enhancers**, may be thousands of nucleotides upstream or downstream of a gene

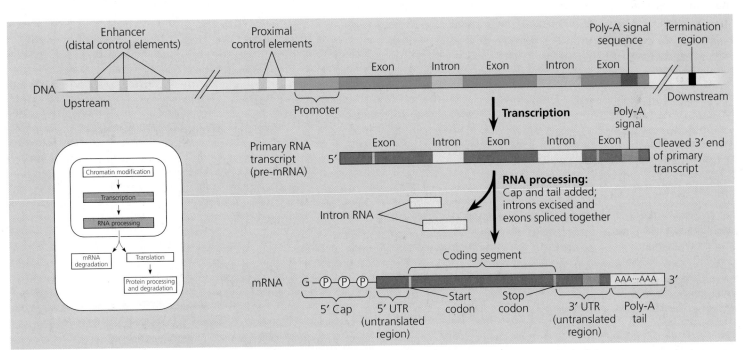

▲ **Figure 18.8 A eukaryotic gene and its transcript.** Each eukaryotic gene has a promoter, a DNA sequence where RNA polymerase binds and starts transcription, proceeding "downstream." A number of control elements (gold) are involved in regulating the initiation of transcription; these are DNA sequences located near (proximal to) or far from (distal to) the promoter. Distal control elements can be grouped together as enhancers, one of which is shown for this gene. A polyadenylation (poly-A) signal sequence in the last exon of the gene is transcribed into an RNA sequence that signals where the transcript is cleaved and the poly-A tail added. Transcription may continue for hundreds of nucleotides beyond the poly-A signal before terminating. RNA processing of the primary transcript into a functional mRNA involves three steps: addition of the 5′ cap, addition of the poly-A tail, and splicing. In the cell, the 5′ cap is added soon after transcription is initiated; splicing and poly-A tail addition may also occur while transcription is still under way (see Figure 17.9).

or even within an intron. A given gene may have multiple enhancers, each active at a different time or in a different cell type or location in the organism. Each enhancer, however, is associated with only that gene and no other.

In eukaryotes, the rate of gene expression can be strongly increased or decreased by the binding of proteins, either activators or repressors, to the control elements of enhancers. **Figure 18.9** shows a current model for how binding of activators to an enhancer located far from the promoter can influence transcription. Protein-mediated bending of the DNA is thought to bring the bound activators in contact with a group of so-called *mediator proteins*, which in turn interact with proteins at the promoter. These multiple protein-protein interactions help assemble and position the initiation complex on the promoter. Support for this

model includes a study showing that the proteins regulating a mouse globin gene contact both the gene's promoter and an enhancer located about 50,000 nucleotides upstream. Clearly, these two regions in the DNA must be brought together in a very specific fashion for this interaction to occur.

Hundreds of transcription activators have been discovered in eukaryotes. Researchers have identified two common structural elements in a large number of activator proteins: a DNA-binding domain—a part of the protein's three-dimensional structure that binds to DNA—and one or more activation domains. Activation domains bind other regulatory proteins or components of the transcription machinery, facilitating a sequence of protein-protein interactions that result in transcription of a given gene.

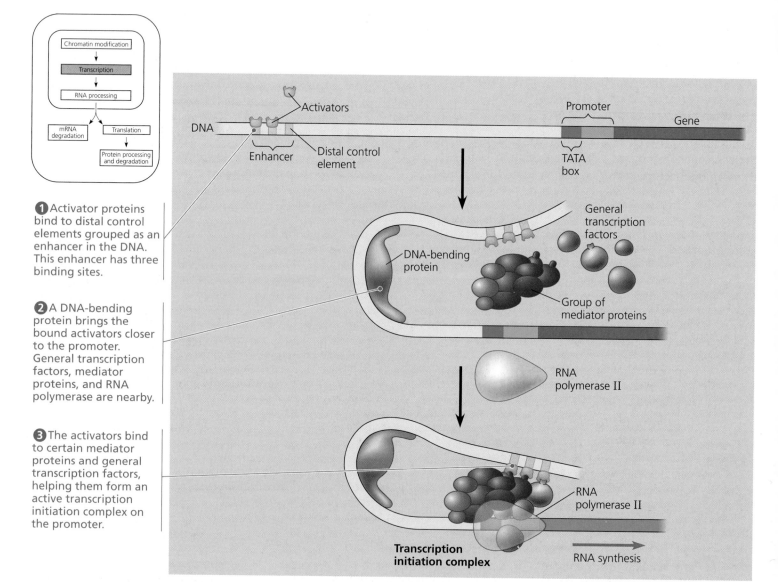

❶ Activator proteins bind to distal control elements grouped as an enhancer in the DNA. This enhancer has three binding sites.

❷ A DNA-bending protein brings the bound activators closer to the promoter. General transcription factors, mediator proteins, and RNA polymerase are nearby.

❸ The activators bind to certain mediator proteins and general transcription factors, helping them form an active transcription initiation complex on the promoter.

▲ **Figure 18.9 A model for the action of enhancers and transcription activators.** Bending of the DNA by a protein enables enhancers to influence a promoter hundreds or even thousands of nucleotides away. Specific transcription factors called activators bind to the enhancer DNA sequences and then to a group of mediator proteins, which in turn bind to general transcription factors, assembling the transcription initiation complex. These protein-protein interactions facilitate the correct positioning of the complex on the promoter and the initiation of RNA synthesis. Only one enhancer (with three orange control elements) is shown here, but a gene may have several enhancers that act at different times or in different cell types.

Specific transcription factors that function as repressors can inhibit gene expression in several different ways. Some repressors bind directly to control element DNA (in enhancers or elsewhere), blocking activator binding or, in some cases, turning off transcription even when activators are bound. Other repressors block the binding of activators to proteins that allow the activators to bind to DNA.

In addition to influencing transcription directly, some activators and repressors act indirectly by affecting chromatin structure. Studies using yeast and mammalian cells show that some activators recruit proteins that acetylate histones near the promoters of specific genes, thus promoting transcription (see Figure 18.7). Similarly, some repressors recruit proteins that deacetylate histones, leading to reduced transcription, a phenomenon referred to as *silencing*. Indeed, recruitment of chromatin-modifying proteins seems to be the most common mechanism of repression in eukaryotes.

Combinatorial Control of Gene Activation In eukaryotes, the precise control of transcription depends largely on the binding of activators to DNA control elements. Considering the great number of genes that must be regulated in a typical animal or plant cell, the number of completely different nucleotide sequences found in control elements is surprisingly small. A dozen or so short nucleotide sequences appear again and again in the control elements for different genes. On average, each enhancer is composed of about ten control elements, each of which can bind only one or two specific transcription factors. The particular *combination* of control elements in an enhancer associated with a gene turns out to be more important than the presence of a single unique control element in regulating transcription of the gene.

Even with only a dozen control element sequences available, a very large number of combinations are possible. A particular combination of control elements will be able to activate transcription only when the appropriate activator proteins are present, which may occur at a precise time during development or in a particular cell type. **Figure 18.10** illustrates how the use of different combinations of just a few control elements can allow differential regulation of transcription in two cell types.

(a) Liver cell. The albumin gene is expressed, and the crystallin gene is not.

(b) Lens cell. The crystallin gene is expressed, and the albumin gene is not.

▲ **Figure 18.10 Cell type–specific transcription.** Both liver cells and lens cells have the genes for making the proteins albumin and crystallin, but only liver cells make albumin (a blood protein) and only lens cells make crystallin (the main protein of lenses). The specific transcription factors made in a cell determine which genes are expressed. In this example, the genes for albumin and crystallin are shown at the top, each with an enhancer made up of three different control elements. Although the enhancers for the two genes share one control element (gray), each enhancer has a unique combination of elements. All the activators required for high-level expression of the albumin gene are present only in liver cells (a), whereas the activators needed for expression of the crystallin gene are present only in lens cells (b). For simplicity, we consider only the role of activators here, although the presence or absence of repressors may also influence transcription in certain cell types.

? *Describe the enhancer for the albumin gene in each cell. How would the nucleotide sequence of this enhancer in the liver cell compare with that in the lens cell?*

Coordinately Controlled Genes in Eukaryotes

How does the eukaryotic cell deal with genes of related function that need to be turned on or off at the same time? Earlier in this chapter, you learned that in bacteria, such coordinately controlled genes are often clustered into an operon, which is regulated by a single promoter and transcribed into a single mRNA molecule. Thus, the genes are expressed together, and the encoded proteins are produced concurrently. Operons that work in this way have not been found in eukaryotic cells, with some exceptions.

Analysis of the genomes of several eukaryotic species has revealed some co-expressed genes that are clustered near one another on the same chromosome. Examples include certain genes in the testis of the fruit fly and muscle-related genes in a small worm called a nematode. But in contrast to the genes of bacterial operons, each gene in such a cluster has its own promoter and is individually transcribed. The coordinate regulation of these clustered genes is thought to involve changes in chromatin structure that make the entire group of genes either available or unavailable for transcription. In other cases, including 15% of nematode genes, several related genes do share a promoter and are transcribed into a single pre-mRNA. Unlike in bacteria, however, the RNA transcript is processed into separate mRNAs. The nematode operons do not appear to be evolutionarily related to bacterial operons.

More commonly, co-expressed eukaryotic genes, such as genes coding for the enzymes of a metabolic pathway, are found scattered over different chromosomes. In these cases, coordinate gene expression seems to depend on the association of a specific combination of control elements with every gene of a dispersed group. The presence of these elements can be compared to the raised flags on a few mailboxes out of many, signaling to the mail carrier to check those boxes. Copies of the activators that recognize the control elements bind to them, promoting simultaneous transcription of the genes, no matter where they are in the genome.

Coordinate control of dispersed genes in a eukaryotic cell often occurs in response to chemical signals from outside the cell. A steroid hormone, for example, enters a cell and binds to a specific intracellular receptor protein, forming a hormone-receptor complex that serves as a transcription activator (see Figure 11.8). Every gene whose transcription is stimulated by a particular steroid hormone, regardless of its chromosomal location, has a control element recognized by that hormone-receptor complex. This is how estrogen activates a group of genes that stimulate cell division in uterine cells, preparing the uterus for pregnancy.

Many signal molecules, such as nonsteroid hormones and growth factors, bind to receptors on a cell's surface and never actually enter the cell. Such molecules can control gene expression indirectly by triggering signal transduction pathways that lead to activation of particular transcription activators or repressors (see Figure 11.14). The principle of coordinate regulation is the same as in the case of steroid hormones: Genes with the same control elements are activated by the same chemical signals. Systems for coordinating gene regulation probably arose early in evolutionary history and evolved by the duplication and distribution of control elements within the genome.

Mechanisms of Post-Transcriptional Regulation

Transcription alone does not constitute gene expression. The expression of a protein-coding gene is ultimately measured by the amount of functional protein a cell makes, and much happens between the synthesis of the RNA transcript and the activity of the protein in the cell. Researchers are discovering more and more regulatory mechanisms that operate at various stages after transcription (see Figure 18.6). These mechanisms allow a cell to fine-tune gene expression rapidly in response to environmental changes without altering its transcription patterns. Here we discuss how cells can regulate gene expression once a gene has been transcribed.

RNA Processing

RNA processing in the nucleus and the export of mature RNA to the cytoplasm provide several opportunities for regulating gene expression that are not available in prokaryotes. One example of regulation at the RNA-processing level is **alternative RNA splicing**, in which different mRNA molecules are produced from the same primary transcript, depending on which RNA segments are treated as exons and which as introns. Regulatory proteins specific to a cell type control intron-exon choices by binding to regulatory sequences within the primary transcript.

A simple example of alternative RNA splicing is shown in **Figure 18.11** for the troponin T gene, which encodes two different (though related) proteins. Other genes offer possibilities for greater numbers of products. For instance, researchers have discovered a fruit fly gene that has enough alternatively spliced exons to generate more than 38,000 different proteins, although only a small number have been found to be synthesized. It is clear that alternative RNA splicing can significantly expand the repertoire of a eukaryotic genome.

mRNA Degradation

The life span of mRNA molecules in the cytoplasm is important in determining the pattern of protein synthesis in a cell. Bacterial mRNA molecules typically are degraded by enzymes within a few minutes of their synthesis. This short life span of mRNAs is one reason bacteria can change their patterns of protein synthesis so quickly in response to environmental changes. In contrast, mRNAs in multicellular eukaryotes typically survive for hours, days, or even weeks. For instance, the mRNAs for the hemoglobin polypeptides

Exons

DNA

Troponin T gene

◀ **Figure 18.11 Alternative RNA splicing of the troponin T gene.** The primary transcript of this gene can be spliced in more than one way, generating different mRNA molecules. Notice that one mRNA molecule has ended up with exon 3 (green) and the other with exon 4 (purple). These two mRNAs are translated into different but related muscle proteins.

Primary RNA transcript

RNA splicing

mRNA   1 2 3 5   or   1 2 4 5

(α-globin and β-globin) in developing red blood cells are unusually stable, and these long-lived mRNAs are translated repeatedly in these cells.

Research on yeast species suggests that a common pathway of mRNA breakdown begins with the enzymatic shortening of the poly-A tail (see Figure 18.8). This helps trigger the action of enzymes that remove the 5′ cap (the two ends of the mRNA may be briefly held together by the proteins involved). Removal of the cap, a critical step, is also regulated by particular nucleotide sequences within the mRNA. Once the cap is removed, nuclease enzymes rapidly chew up the mRNA.

Nucleotide sequences that affect how long an mRNA remains intact are often found in the untranslated region (UTR) at the 3′ end of the molecule (see Figure 18.8). In one experiment, researchers transferred such a sequence from the short-lived mRNA for a growth factor to the 3′ end of a normally stable globin mRNA. The globin mRNA was quickly degraded.

During the past few years, other mechanisms that degrade or block expression of mRNA molecules have come to light. These mechanisms involve an important group of newly discovered RNA molecules that regulate gene expression at several levels, and we will discuss them later in this chapter.

Initiation of Translation

Translation presents another opportunity for regulating gene expression; such regulation occurs most commonly at the initiation stage (see Figure 17.17). The initiation of translation of some mRNAs can be blocked by regulatory proteins that bind to specific sequences or structures within the untranslated region at the 5′ end (5′ UTR) of the mRNA, preventing the attachment of ribosomes. (Recall from Chapter 17 that both the 5′ cap and the poly-A tail of an mRNA molecule are important for ribosome binding.) A different mechanism for blocking translation is seen in a variety of mRNAs present in the eggs of many organisms: Initially, these stored mRNAs lack poly-A tails of sufficient length to allow translation initiation. At the

appropriate time during embryonic development, however, a cytoplasmic enzyme adds more adenine (A) nucleotides, prompting translation to begin.

Alternatively, translation of *all* the mRNAs in a cell may be regulated simultaneously. In a eukaryotic cell, such "global" control usually involves the activation or inactivation of one or more of the protein factors required to initiate translation. This mechanism plays a role in starting translation of mRNAs that are stored in eggs. Just after fertilization, translation is triggered by the sudden activation of translation initiation factors. The response is a burst of synthesis of the proteins encoded by the stored mRNAs. Some plants and algae store mRNAs during periods of darkness; light then triggers the reactivation of the translational apparatus.

Protein Processing and Degradation

The final opportunities for controlling gene expression occur after translation. Often, eukaryotic polypeptides must be processed to yield functional protein molecules. For instance, cleavage of the initial insulin polypeptide (pro-insulin) forms the active hormone. In addition, many proteins undergo chemical modifications that make them functional. Regulatory proteins are commonly activated or inactivated by the reversible addition of phosphate groups, and proteins destined for the surface of animal cells acquire sugars. Cell-surface proteins and many others must also be transported to target destinations in the cell in order to function. Regulation might occur at any of the steps involved in modifying or transporting a protein.

Finally, the length of time each protein functions in the cell is strictly regulated by means of selective degradation. Many proteins, such as the cyclins involved in regulating the cell cycle, must be relatively short-lived if the cell is to function appropriately (see Figure 12.17). To mark a particular protein for destruction, the cell commonly attaches molecules of a small protein called ubiquitin to the protein. Giant protein complexes called **proteasomes** then recognize the ubiquitin-tagged

① Multiple ubiquitin molecules are attached to a protein by enzymes in the cytosol.

② The ubiquitin-tagged protein is recognized by a proteasome, which unfolds the protein and sequesters it within a central cavity.

③ Enzymatic components of the proteasome cut the protein into small peptides, which can be further degraded by other enzymes in the cytosol.

Ubiquitin

Proteasome

Proteasome and ubiquitin to be recycled

Protein to be degraded

Ubiquitinated protein

Protein entering a proteasome

Protein fragments (peptides)

▲ **Figure 18.12 Degradation of a protein by a proteasome.** A proteasome, an enormous protein complex shaped like a trash can, chops up unneeded proteins in the cell. In most cases, the proteins attacked by a proteasome have been tagged with short chains of ubiquitin, a small protein. Steps 1 and 3 require ATP. Eukaryotic proteasomes are as massive as ribosomal subunits and are distributed throughout the cell. Their shape somewhat resembles that of chaperone proteins, which protect protein structure rather than destroy it (see Figure 5.24).

proteins and degrade them **(Figure 18.12)**. The importance of proteasomes is underscored by the finding that mutations making specific cell cycle proteins impervious to proteasome degradation can lead to cancer.

CONCEPT CHECK **18.2**

1. In general, what is the effect of histone acetylation and DNA methylation on gene expression?
2. Compare the roles of general and specific transcription factors in regulating gene expression.
3. Suppose you compared the nucleotide sequences of the distal control elements in the enhancers of three genes that are expressed only in muscle tissue. What would you expect to find? Why?
4. Once mRNA encoding a particular protein reaches the cytoplasm, what are four mechanisms that can regulate the amount of the protein that is active in the cell?
5. **WHAT IF?** Examine Figure 18.10 and suggest a mechanism by which the yellow activator protein comes to be present in the liver cell but not in the lens cell.

For suggested answers, see Appendix A.

CONCEPT **18.3**
Noncoding RNAs play multiple roles in controlling gene expression

Recall that only 1.5% of the human genome—and a similarly small percentage of the genome of many other multicellular

eukaryotes—codes for proteins. Of the remainder, a very small fraction consists of genes for small RNAs, such as ribosomal RNA and transfer RNA. Until recently, most of the rest of the DNA was assumed to be untranscribed. The general idea was that since it didn't code for proteins or the few known types of RNA, such DNA didn't contain meaningful genetic information. However, a flood of recent data has contradicted this idea. For example, a study of two human chromosomes showed that ten times as much of the genome was transcribed as was predicted by the number of protein-coding exons present. Introns accounted for some of this transcribed, nontranslated RNA, but only a small fraction of the total. These and other results suggest that a significant amount of the genome may be transcribed into non-protein-coding RNAs (also called *noncoding RNAs*), including a variety of small RNAs. While many questions about the functions of these RNAs remain unanswered, researchers are uncovering more evidence of their biological roles every day.

Biologists are excited about these recent discoveries, which hint at a large, diverse population of RNA molecules in the cell that play crucial roles in regulating gene expression—and have gone largely unnoticed until now. Clearly, we must revise our long-standing view that because they code for proteins, mRNAs are the most important RNAs functioning in the cell. It's as if we've been so focused on the famous ruler of a country that we've completely overlooked the many advisors and cabinet members working behind the scenes.

Regulation by noncoding RNAs is known to occur at two points in the pathway of gene expression: mRNA translation and chromatin configuration. We will focus on several types of small RNAs that have been extensively studied in the past few years; the importance of these RNAs was recognized when they were the focus of the 2006 Nobel Prize in Physiology or Medicine.

Effects on mRNAs by MicroRNAs and Small Interfering RNAs

Since 1993, a number of research studies have uncovered small single-stranded RNA molecules, called **microRNAs (miRNAs)**, that are capable of binding to complementary sequences in mRNA molecules. The miRNAs are formed from longer RNA precursors that fold back on themselves, forming one or more short double-stranded hairpin structures, each held together by hydrogen bonds (**Figure 18.13**). After each hairpin is cut away from the precursor, it is trimmed by an enzyme (fittingly called Dicer) into a short double-stranded fragment of about 20 nucleotide pairs. One of the two strands is degraded, while the other strand, which is the miRNA, forms a complex with one or more proteins; the miRNA allows the complex to bind to any mRNA molecule with the complementary sequence. The miRNA-protein complex then either degrades the target mRNA or blocks its translation. It has been estimated that expression of up to one-third of all human genes may be regulated by miRNAs, a remarkable figure given that the existence of miRNAs was unknown a mere two decades ago.

A growing understanding of the miRNA pathway provided an explanation for a perplexing observation: Researchers had found that injecting double-stranded RNA molecules into a cell somehow turned off expression of a gene with the same sequence as the RNA. They called this experimental phenomenon **RNA interference (RNAi)**. It was later shown to be due to **small interfering RNAs (siRNAs)**, which are similar in size and function to miRNAs. In fact, subsequent research showed that the same cellular machinery generates miRNAs and siRNAs and that both can associate with the same proteins, producing similar results. The distinction between miRNAs and siRNAs is based on the nature of the precursor molecule for each. While an miRNA is usually formed from a single hairpin in a precursor RNA (see Figure 18.13), siRNAs are formed from much longer double-stranded RNA molecules, each of which gives rise to many siRNAs.

We mentioned that laboratory investigators had injected double-stranded RNAs into cells, and you may wonder whether such molecules are ever found naturally. As you will learn in Chapter 19, some viruses have double-stranded RNA genomes. Because the cellular RNAi pathway can lead to the destruction of

▶ **Figure 18.13 Regulation of gene expression by miRNAs.** RNA transcripts are processed into miRNAs, which prevent expression of mRNAs containing complementary sequences.

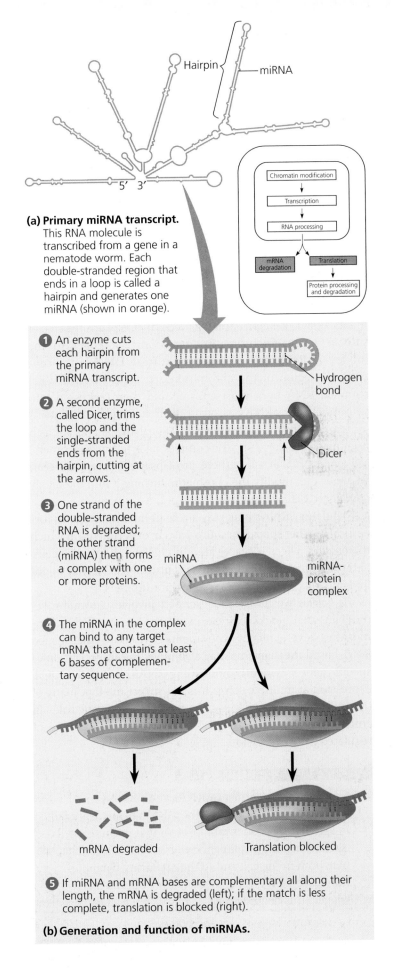

(a) Primary miRNA transcript. This RNA molecule is transcribed from a gene in a nematode worm. Each double-stranded region that ends in a loop is called a hairpin and generates one miRNA (shown in orange).

1. An enzyme cuts each hairpin from the primary miRNA transcript.

2. A second enzyme, called Dicer, trims the loop and the single-stranded ends from the hairpin, cutting at the arrows.

3. One strand of the double-stranded RNA is degraded; the other strand (miRNA) then forms a complex with one or more proteins.

4. The miRNA in the complex can bind to any target mRNA that contains at least 6 bases of complementary sequence.

5. If miRNA and mRNA bases are complementary all along their length, the mRNA is degraded (left); if the match is less complete, translation is blocked (right).

mRNA degraded

Translation blocked

(b) Generation and function of miRNAs.

RNAs with sequences complementary to those found in double-stranded RNAs, this pathway may have evolved as a natural defense against infection by such viruses. However, the fact that the RNAi pathway can also affect the expression of nonviral cellular genes may reflect a different evolutionary origin for the RNAi pathway. Moreover, some species apparently produce their own long double-stranded RNA precursors to small RNAs such as siRNAs. Once produced, these RNAs can interfere with gene expression at stages other than translation, as we'll discuss next.

Chromatin Remodeling and Silencing of Transcription by Small RNAs

In addition to affecting mRNAs, small RNAs can cause remodeling of chromatin structure. In yeast, siRNAs produced by the yeast cells themselves appear to be crucial for the formation of heterochromatin at the centromeres of chromosomes. Experimental results have prompted a model that explains the role of siRNAs in heterochromatin formation. According to the model, an RNA transcript produced from DNA in the centromeric region of the chromosome is copied into double-stranded RNA by a yeast enzyme and then processed into siRNAs. These siRNAs associate with a complex of proteins (different from the one shown in Figure 18.13) and act as a homing device, targeting the complex back to the centromeric sequences of DNA. Once there, proteins in the complex recruit enzymes that modify the chromatin, turning it into the highly condensed heterochromatin found at the centromere.

Regulatory RNAs may play a role in heterochromatin formation in other species besides yeast. In experiments in which the enzyme Dicer is inactivated in chicken and mouse cells, heterochromatin fails to form at centromeres. As you might imagine, this has dire consequences for the cells.

The cases we have just described involve chromatin remodeling that blocks expression of large regions of the chromosome. Several recent experiments have shown that related RNA-based mechanisms may also block the transcription of specific genes. Evidently, noncoding RNAs can regulate gene expression at multiple steps. It is not surprising that many of the miRNAs characterized thus far play important roles in embryonic development—perhaps the ultimate example of regulated gene expression.

CONCEPT CHECK 18.3

1. Compare and contrast miRNAs and siRNAs.
2. **WHAT IF?** Imagine that the mRNA being degraded in Figure 18.13 codes for a protein that promotes cell division in a multicellular organism. What would happen, both in the cell and to the organism, if a mutation disabled the gene encoding the miRNA that triggers this degradation?

For suggested answers, see Appendix A.

A program of differential gene expression leads to the different cell types in a multicellular organism

In the embryonic development of multicellular organisms, a fertilized egg (a zygote) gives rise to cells of many different types, each with a different structure and corresponding function. Typically, cells are organized into tissues, tissues into organs, organs into organ systems, and organ systems into the whole organism. Thus, any developmental program must produce cells of different types that form higher-level structures arranged in a particular way in three dimensions. The processes that occur during development in plants and animals are detailed in Chapters 35 and 47, respectively. In this chapter, we focus instead on the program of regulation of gene expression that orchestrates development, using a few animal species as examples.

A Genetic Program for Embryonic Development

The photos in **Figure 18.14** illustrate the dramatic difference between a zygote and the organism it becomes. This remarkable transformation results from three interrelated processes: cell division, cell differentiation, and morphogenesis. Through a succession of mitotic cell divisions, the zygote gives rise to a large number of cells. Cell division alone, however, would produce only a great ball of identical cells, nothing like a tadpole. During embryonic development, cells not only increase in number, but also undergo **cell differentiation**, the process by which cells become specialized in structure and function. Moreover, the different kinds of cells are not randomly distributed but are organized into tissues and organs in a particular three-dimensional

(a) Fertilized eggs of a frog   **(b) Newly hatched tadpole**

▲ **Figure 18.14 From fertilized egg to animal: What a difference four days makes.** It takes just four days for cell division, differentiation, and morphogenesis to transform each of the fertilized frog eggs shown in (a) into a tadpole like the one in (b).

arrangement. The physical processes that give an organism its shape constitute **morphogenesis**, meaning "creation of form."

All three processes have their basis in cellular behavior. Even morphogenesis, the shaping of the organism, can be traced back to changes in the shape, motility, and other characteristics of the cells that make up various regions of the embryo. As you have seen, the activities of a cell depend on the genes it expresses and the proteins it produces. Almost all cells in an organism have the same genome; therefore, differential gene expression results from the genes being regulated differently in each cell type.

In Figure 18.10, you saw a simplified view of how differential gene expression occurs in two cell types, a liver cell and a lens cell. Each of these fully differentiated cells has a particular mix of specific activators that turn on the collection of genes whose products are required in the cell. The fact that both cells arose through a series of mitoses from a common fertilized egg inevitably leads to a question: How do different sets of activators come to be present in the two cells?

It turns out that materials placed into the egg by the mother set up a sequential program of gene regulation that is carried out as cells divide, and this program makes the cells become different from each other in a coordinated fashion. To understand how this works, we will consider two basic developmental processes: First, we'll explore how cells that arise from early embryonic mitoses develop the differences that start each cell along its own differentiation pathway. Second, we'll see how cellular differentiation leads to one particular cell type, using muscle development as an example.

Cytoplasmic Determinants and Inductive Signals

What generates the first differences among cells in an early embryo? And what controls the differentiation of all the various cell types as development proceeds? By this point in the chapter, you can probably deduce the answer: The specific genes expressed in any particular cell of a developing organism determine its path. Two sources of information, used to varying extents in different species, "tell" a cell which genes to express at any given time during embryonic development.

One important source of information early in development is the egg's cytoplasm, which contains both RNA and proteins encoded by the mother's DNA. The cytoplasm of an unfertilized egg is not homogeneous. Messenger RNA, proteins, other substances, and organelles are distributed unevenly in the unfertilized egg, and this unevenness has a profound impact on the development of the future embryo in many species. Maternal substances in the egg that influence the course of early development are called **cytoplasmic determinants** (Figure 18.15a). After fertilization, early

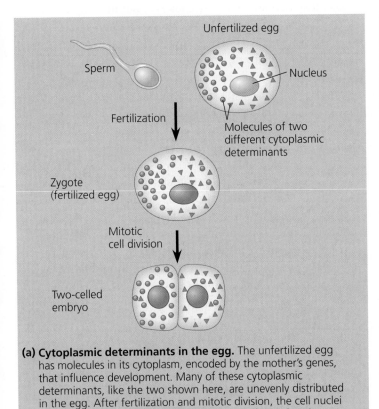

(a) Cytoplasmic determinants in the egg. The unfertilized egg has molecules in its cytoplasm, encoded by the mother's genes, that influence development. Many of these cytoplasmic determinants, like the two shown here, are unevenly distributed in the egg. After fertilization and mitotic division, the cell nuclei of the embryo are exposed to different sets of cytoplasmic determinants and, as a result, express different genes.

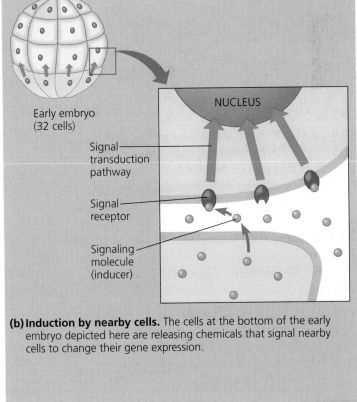

(b) Induction by nearby cells. The cells at the bottom of the early embryo depicted here are releasing chemicals that signal nearby cells to change their gene expression.

▲ **Figure 18.15 Sources of developmental information for the early embryo.**

mitotic divisions distribute the zygote's cytoplasm into separate cells. The nuclei of these cells may thus be exposed to different cytoplasmic determinants, depending on which portions of the zygotic cytoplasm a cell received. The combination of cytoplasmic determinants in a cell helps determine its developmental fate by regulating expression of the cell's genes during the course of cell differentiation.

The other major source of developmental information, which becomes increasingly important as the number of embryonic cells increases, is the environment around a particular cell. Most influential are the signals impinging on an embryonic cell from other embryonic cells in the vicinity, including contact with cell-surface molecules on neighboring cells and the binding of growth factors secreted by neighboring cells. Such signals cause changes in the target cells, a process called **induction** **(Figure 18.15b)**. The molecules conveying these signals within the target cell are cell-surface receptors and other proteins expressed by the embryo's own genes. In general, the signaling molecules send a cell down a specific developmental path by causing changes in its gene expression that eventually result in observable cellular changes. Thus, interactions between embryonic cells help induce differentiation of the many specialized cell types making up a new organism.

Sequential Regulation of Gene Expression During Cellular Differentiation

As the tissues and organs of an embryo develop and their cells differentiate, the cells become noticeably different in structure and function. These observable changes are actually the outcome of a cell's developmental history beginning at the first mitotic division of the zygote, as we have just seen. The earliest changes that set a cell on a path to specialization are subtle ones, showing up only at the molecular level. Before biologists knew much about the molecular changes occurring in embryos, they coined the term **determination** to refer to the events that lead to the observable differentiation of a cell. Once it has undergone determination, an embryonic cell is irreversibly committed to its final fate. If a committed cell is experimentally placed in another location in the embryo, it will still differentiate into the cell type that is its normal fate.

Today we understand determination in terms of molecular changes. The outcome of determination, observable cell differentiation, is marked by the expression of genes for *tissue-specific proteins*. These proteins are found only in a specific cell type and give the cell its characteristic structure and function. The first evidence of differentiation is the appearance of mRNAs for these proteins. Eventually, differentiation is observable with a microscope as changes in cellular structure. On the molecular level, different sets of genes are sequentially expressed in a regulated manner as new cells arise from division of their precursors. A number of the steps in gene ex-

pression may be regulated during differentiation, with transcription among the most important. In the fully differentiated cell, transcription remains the principal regulatory point for maintaining appropriate gene expression.

Differentiated cells are specialists at making tissue-specific proteins. For example, as a result of transcriptional regulation, liver cells specialize in making albumin, and lens cells specialize in making crystallin (see Figure 18.10). Skeletal muscle cells in vertebrates are another instructive example. Each of these cells is a long fiber containing many nuclei within a single plasma membrane. Skeletal muscle cells have high concentrations of muscle-specific versions of the contractile proteins myosin and actin, as well as membrane receptor proteins that detect signals from nerve cells.

Muscle cells develop from embryonic precursor cells that have the potential to develop into a number of cell types, including cartilage cells and fat cells, but particular conditions commit them to becoming muscle cells. Although the committed cells appear unchanged under the microscope, determination has occurred, and they are now *myoblasts*. Eventually, myoblasts start to churn out large amounts of muscle-specific proteins and fuse to form mature, elongated, multinucleate skeletal muscle cells (**Figure 18.16**, left).

Researchers have worked out what happens at the molecular level during muscle cell determination by growing myoblasts in culture and analyzing them using molecular biological techniques you will learn about in Chapter 20. In a series of experiments, they isolated different genes, caused each to be expressed in a separate embryonic precursor cell, and then looked for differentiation into myoblasts and muscle cells. In this way, they identified several so-called "master regulatory genes" whose protein products commit the cells to becoming skeletal muscle. Thus, in the case of muscle cells, the molecular basis of determination is the expression of one or more of these master regulatory genes.

To understand more about how commitment occurs in muscle cell differentiation, let's focus on the master regulatory gene called *myoD* (**Figure 18.16**, right). This gene encodes MyoD protein, a transcription factor that binds to specific control elements in the enhancers of various target genes and stimulates their expression. Some target genes for MyoD encode still other muscle-specific transcription factors. MyoD also stimulates expression of the *myoD* gene itself, thus perpetuating its effect in maintaining the cell's differentiated state. Presumably, all the genes activated by MyoD have enhancer control elements recognized by MyoD and are thus coordinately controlled. Finally, the secondary transcription factors activate the genes for proteins such as myosin and actin that confer the unique properties of skeletal muscle cells.

The MyoD protein deserves its designation as a master regulatory gene. Researchers have shown that it is even capable of changing some kinds of fully differentiated nonmuscle cells, such as fat cells and liver cells, into muscle cells. Why doesn't

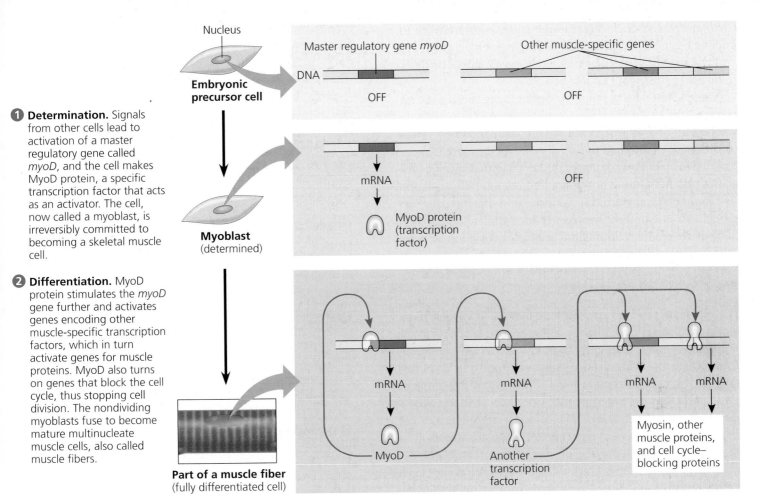

1 Determination. Signals from other cells lead to activation of a master regulatory gene called *myoD*, and the cell makes MyoD protein, a specific transcription factor that acts as an activator. The cell, now called a myoblast, is irreversibly committed to becoming a skeletal muscle cell.

2 Differentiation. MyoD protein stimulates the *myoD* gene further and activates genes encoding other muscle-specific transcription factors, which in turn activate genes for muscle proteins. MyoD also turns on genes that block the cell cycle, thus stopping cell division. The nondividing myoblasts fuse to become mature multinucleate muscle cells, also called muscle fibers.

Nucleus

Embryonic precursor cell

Master regulatory gene *myoD*   Other muscle-specific genes

DNA   OFF   OFF

Myoblast (determined)

mRNA   OFF

MyoD protein (transcription factor)

Part of a muscle fiber (fully differentiated cell)

mRNA   mRNA   mRNA   mRNA

MyoD   Another transcription factor   Myosin, other muscle proteins, and cell cycle–blocking proteins

▲ **Figure 18.16 Determination and differentiation of muscle cells.** Skeletal muscle cells arise from embryonic cells as a result of changes in gene expression. (In this depiction, the process of gene activation is greatly simplified.)

WHAT IF?   *What would happen if a mutation in the* myoD *gene resulted in a MyoD protein that could not activate the* myoD *gene?*

it work on *all* kinds of cells? One likely explanation is that activation of the muscle-specific genes is not solely dependent on MyoD but requires a particular *combination* of regulatory proteins, some of which are lacking in cells that do not respond to MyoD. The determination and differentiation of other kinds of tissues may play out in a similar fashion.

We have now seen how different programs of gene expression that are activated in the fertilized egg can result in differentiated cells and tissues. But for the tissues to function effectively in the organism as a whole, the organism's *body plan*—its overall three-dimensional arrangement—must be established and superimposed on the differentiation process. Next we'll investigate the molecular basis for the establishment of the body plan, using the well-studied *Drosophila* as an example.

Pattern Formation: Setting Up the Body Plan

Cytoplasmic determinants and inductive signals both contribute to the development of a spatial organization in which the tissues and organs of an organism are all in their characteristic places. This process is called **pattern formation**.

Pattern formation in animals begins in the early embryo, when the major axes of an animal are established. Before construction begins on a new building, the locations of the front, back, and sides are determined. In the same way, before the tissues and organs of a bilaterally symmetrical animal appear, the relative positions of the animal's head and tail, right and left sides, and back and front are set up, thus establishing the three major body axes. The molecular cues that control pattern formation, collectively called **positional information**, are provided by cytoplasmic determinants and inductive signals (see Figure 18.15). These cues tell a cell its location relative to the body axes and to neighboring cells and determine how the cell and its progeny will respond to future molecular signals.

During the first half of the 20th century, classical embryologists made detailed anatomical observations of embryonic development in a number of species and performed experiments in which they manipulated embryonic tissues (see

Chapter 47). Although this research laid the groundwork for understanding the mechanisms of development, it did not reveal the specific molecules that guide development or determine how patterns are established.

Then, in the 1940s, scientists began using the genetic approach—the study of mutants—to investigate *Drosophila* development. That approach has had spectacular success. These studies have established that genes control development and have led to an understanding of the key roles that specific molecules play in defining position and directing differentiation. By combining anatomical, genetic, and biochemical approaches to the study of *Drosophila* development, researchers have discovered developmental principles common to many other species, including humans.

The Life Cycle of Drosophila

Fruit flies and other arthropods have a modular construction, an ordered series of segments. These segments make up the body's three major parts: the head, the thorax (the midbody, from which the wings and legs extend), and the abdomen (Figure 18.17a). Like other bilaterally symmetrical animals, *Drosophila* has an anterior-posterior (head-to-tail) axis, a dorsal-ventral (back-to-belly) axis, and a right-left axis. In *Drosophila*, cytoplasmic determinants that are localized in the unfertilized egg provide positional information for the placement of anterior-posterior and dorsal-ventral axes even before fertilization. We'll focus here on the molecules involved in establishing the anterior-posterior axis.

The *Drosophila* egg develops in the female's ovary, surrounded by ovarian cells called nurse cells and follicle cells (Figure 18.17b, top). These support cells supply the egg with nutrients, mRNAs, and other substances needed for development and make the egg shell. After fertilization and laying of the egg, embryonic development results in the formation of a segmented larva, which goes through three larval stages. Then, in a process much like that by which a caterpillar becomes a butterfly, the fly larva forms a cocoon in which it metamorphoses into the adult fly pictured in Figure 18.17a.

Genetic Analysis of Early Development: Scientific Inquiry

Edward B. Lewis was a visionary American biologist who, in the 1940s, first showed the value of the genetic approach to studying embryonic development in *Drosophila*. Lewis studied bizarre mutant flies with developmental defects that led to extra wings or legs in the wrong places (Figure 18.18). He located the mutations on the fly's genetic map, thus connecting the developmental abnormalities to specific genes. This research supplied the first concrete evidence that genes somehow direct the developmental processes studied by embryologists. The genes Lewis discovered, called **homeotic genes**, control pattern formation in the late embryo, larva, and adult.

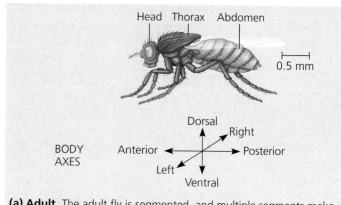

(a) Adult. The adult fly is segmented, and multiple segments make up each of the three main body parts—head, thorax, and abdomen. The body axes are shown by arrows.

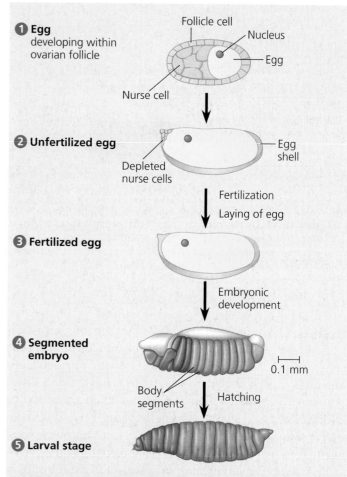

(b) Development from egg to larva. ❶ The yellow egg is surrounded by other cells that form a structure called the follicle within one of the mother's ovaries. ❷ The nurse cells shrink as they supply nutrients and mRNAs to the developing egg, which grows larger. Eventually, the mature egg fills the egg shell that is secreted by the follicle cells. ❸ The egg is fertilized within the mother and then laid. ❹ Embryonic development forms ❺ a larva, which goes through three stages. The third stage forms a cocoon (not shown), within which the larva metamorphoses into the adult shown in (a).

▲ **Figure 18.17 Key developmental events in the life cycle of *Drosophila*.**

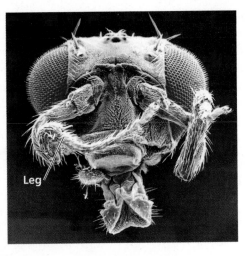

◀ **Figure 18.18 Abnormal pattern formation in _Drosophila_.** Mutations in certain regulatory genes, called homeotic genes, cause a misplacement of structures in an animal. These micrographs contrast the head of a wild-type fly, bearing a pair of small antennae, with that of a homeotic mutant, bearing a pair of legs in place of antennae (SEMs).

Wild type

Mutant

Insight into pattern formation during early embryonic development did not come for another 30 years, when two researchers in Germany, Christiane Nüsslein-Volhard and Eric Wieschaus, set out to identify _all_ the genes that affect segment formation in _Drosophila_. The project was daunting for three reasons. The first was the sheer number of _Drosophila_ genes, now known to total about 13,700. The genes affecting segmentation might be just a few needles in a haystack or might be so numerous and varied that the scientists would be unable to make sense of them. Second, mutations affecting a process as fundamental as segmentation would surely be **embryonic lethals**, mutations with phenotypes causing death at the embryonic or larval stage. Because organisms with embryonic lethal mutations never reproduce, they cannot be bred for study. The researchers dealt with this problem by looking for recessive mutations, which can be propagated in heterozygous flies. Third, cytoplasmic determinants in the egg were known to play a role in axis formation, and therefore the researchers knew they would have to study the mother's genes as well as those of the embryo. It is the mother's genes that we will discuss further as we focus on how the anterior-posterior body axis is set up in the developing egg.

Nüsslein-Volhard and Wieschaus began their search for segmentation genes by exposing flies to a mutagenic chemical that affected the flies' gametes. They mated the mutagenized flies and then scanned their descendants for dead embryos or larvae with abnormal segmentation or other defects. For example, to find genes that might set up the anterior-posterior axis, they looked for embryos or larvae with abnormal ends, such as two heads or two tails, predicting that such abnormalities would arise from mutations in maternal genes required for correctly setting up the offspring's head or tail end.

Using this approach, Nüsslein-Volhard and Wieschaus eventually identified about 1,200 genes essential for pattern formation during embryonic development. Of these, about 120 were essential for normal segmentation. Over several years, the re-searchers were able to group these segmentation genes by general function, to map them, and to clone many of them for further study in the lab. The result was a detailed molecular understanding of the early steps in pattern formation in _Drosophila_.

When the results of Nüsslein-Volhard and Wieschaus were combined with Lewis's earlier work, a coherent picture of _Drosophila_ development emerged. In recognition of their discoveries, the three researchers were awarded a Nobel Prize in 1995.

Let's consider further the genes that Nüsslein-Volhard, Wieschaus, and co-workers found for cytoplasmic determinants deposited in the egg by the mother. These genes set up the initial pattern of the embryo by regulating gene expression in broad regions of the early embryo.

Axis Establishment

As we mentioned earlier, cytoplasmic determinants in the egg are the substances that initially establish the axes of the _Drosophila_ body. These substances are encoded by genes of the mother, fittingly called maternal effect genes. A **maternal effect gene** is a gene that, when mutant in the mother, results in a mutant phenotype in the offspring, regardless of the offspring's own genotype. In fruit fly development, the mRNA or protein products of maternal effect genes are placed in the egg while it is still in the mother's ovary. When the mother has a mutation in such a gene, she makes a defective gene product (or none at all), and her eggs are defective; when these eggs are fertilized, they fail to develop properly.

Because they control the orientation (polarity) of the egg and consequently of the fly, maternal effect genes are also called **egg-polarity genes**. One group of these genes sets up the anterior-posterior axis of the embryo, while a second group establishes the dorsal-ventral axis. Like mutations in segmentation genes, mutations in maternal effect genes are generally embryonic lethals.

Bicoid: A Morphogen Determining Head Structures To see how maternal effect genes determine the body axes of the offspring, we will focus on one such gene, called *bicoid*, a term meaning "two-tailed." An embryo whose mother has a mutant *bicoid* gene lacks the front half of its body and has posterior structures at both ends **(Figure 18.19)**. This phenotype sug-

gested to Nüsslein-Volhard and her colleagues that the product of the mother's *bicoid* gene is essential for setting up the anterior end of the fly and might be concentrated at the future anterior end of the embryo. This hypothesis is a specific example of the *morphogen gradient hypothesis* first proposed by embryologists a century ago; in this hypothesis, gradients of

---

▼ **Figure 18.19** **Inquiry**

Is Bicoid a morphogen that determines the anterior end of a fruit fly?

EXPERIMENT Using a genetic approach to study *Drosophila* development, Christiane Nüsslein-Volhard and colleagues at the European Molecular Biology Laboratory in Heidelberg, Germany, obtained many embryos and larvae with defects in their body patterns, some due to mutations in the mother's genes. One such gene was called *bicoid*, meaning "two-tailed," because its mutation resulted in larvae with two tails and no head. Subsequent studies analyzed expression of the *bicoid* gene.

The researchers hypothesized that *bicoid* normally codes for a morphogen that specifies the head (anterior) end of the embryo. To test this hypothesis, they used molecular techniques to determine where the mRNA and protein encoded by this gene were found in the fertilized egg and early embryo.

Wild-type larva

Mutant larva (*bicoid*)

RESULTS *Bicoid* mRNA (dark blue) was confined to the anterior end of the unfertilized egg. Later in development, Bicoid protein was seen to be concentrated in cells at the anterior end of the embryo.

Bicoid mRNA in mature unfertilized egg

Fertilization, translation of *bicoid* mRNA

Anterior end

Bicoid protein in early embryo

CONCLUSION The results support the hypothesis that Bicoid protein is a morphogen specifying formation of head-specific structures.

Developing egg

Bicoid mRNA in mature unfertilized egg

Bicoid protein in early embryo

SOURCE C. Nüsslein-Volhard et al., Determination of anteroposterior polarity in *Drosophila*, *Science* 238:1675–1681 (1987). W. Driever and C. Nüsslein-Volhard, A gradient of *bicoid* protein in *Drosophila* embryos, *Cell* 54:83–93 (1988). T. Berleth et al., The role of localization of *bicoid* RNA in organizing the anterior pattern of the *Drosophila* embryo, *EMBO Journal* 7:1749–1756 (1988).

WHAT IF? If the hypothesis is correct, predict what would happen if you injected *bicoid* mRNA into the anterior end of an egg from a female mutant for *bicoid*.

substances called **morphogens** establish an embryo's axes and other features of its form.

DNA technology and other modern biochemical methods enabled the researchers to test whether the *bicoid* product is in fact a morphogen that determines the anterior end of the fly. The first question they asked was whether the mRNA and protein products of these genes are located in the egg in a position consistent with the hypothesis. They found that *bicoid* mRNA is highly concentrated at the extreme anterior end of the mature egg, as predicted by the hypothesis (see Figure 18.19). The mRNA is produced in nurse cells, transferred to the egg via cytoplasmic bridges, and anchored to the cytoskeleton at the anterior end of the egg. After the egg is fertilized, the mRNA is translated into protein. The Bicoid protein then diffuses from the anterior end toward the posterior, resulting in a gradient of protein within the early embryo, with the highest concentration at the anterior end. These results are consistent with the hypothesis that Bicoid protein is responsible for specifying the fly's anterior end. To test the hypothesis more specifically, scientists injected pure *bicoid* mRNA into various regions of early embryos. The protein that resulted from its translation caused anterior structures to form at the injection sites.

The *bicoid* research was groundbreaking for several reasons. First, it led to the identification of a specific protein required for some of the earliest steps in pattern formation. It thus helped us understand how different regions of the egg can give rise to cells that go down different developmental pathways. Second, it increased our understanding of the mother's critical role in the initial phases of embryonic development. (As one developmental biologist has put it, "Mom tells Junior which way is up.") Finally, the principle that a gradient of morphogens can determine polarity and position has proved to be a key developmental concept for a number of species, just as early embryologists had thought.

In *Drosophila*, gradients of specific proteins determine the posterior end as well as the anterior and also are responsible for establishing the dorsal-ventral axis. Later, positional information operating on an ever finer scale establishes a specific number of correctly oriented segments and finally triggers the formation of each segment's characteristic structures. When the genes operating in this final step are abnormal, the pattern of the adult is abnormal, as you saw in Figure 18.18.

In this section, we have seen how a carefully orchestrated program of sequential gene regulation controls the transformation of a fertilized egg into a multicellular organism. The program is carefully balanced between turning on the genes for differentiation in the right place and turning off other genes. Even when an organism is fully developed, gene expression is regulated in a similarly fine-tuned manner. In the final section of the chapter, we'll consider how fine this tuning is, by looking at how specific changes in expression of one or a few genes can lead to the development of cancer.

CONCEPT 18.5
Cancer results from genetic changes that affect cell cycle control

In Chapter 12, we considered cancer as a set of diseases in which cells escape from the control mechanisms that normally limit their growth. Now that we have discussed the molecular basis of gene expression and its regulation, we are ready to look at cancer more closely. The gene regulation systems that go wrong during cancer turn out to be the very same systems that play important roles in embryonic development, the immune response, and many other biological processes. Thus, research into the molecular basis of cancer has both benefited from and informed many other fields of biology.

Types of Genes Associated with Cancer

The genes that normally regulate cell growth and division during the cell cycle include genes for growth factors, their receptors, and the intracellular molecules of signaling pathways. (To review the cell cycle, see Chapter 12.) Mutations that alter any of these genes in somatic cells can lead to cancer. The agent of such change can be random spontaneous mutation. However, it is likely that many cancer-causing mutations result from environmental influences, such as chemical carcinogens, X-rays and other high-energy radiation, and certain viruses.

An early breakthrough in understanding cancer came in 1911, when Peyton Rous, an American pathologist, discovered a virus that causes cancer in chickens. Since then, scientists have recognized a number of *tumor viruses* that cause cancer in various animals, including humans (see Table 19.1). The Epstein-Barr virus, which causes infectious mononucleosis, has been linked to several types of cancer, notably Burkitt's lymphoma. Papillomaviruses are associated with cancer of the cervix, and a virus called HTLV-1 causes a type of adult leukemia. Worldwide, viruses seem to play a role in about 15% of the cases of human cancer.

Oncogenes and Proto-Oncogenes

Research on tumor viruses led to the discovery of cancer-causing genes called **oncogenes** (from the Greek *onco*, tumor) in certain retroviruses (see Chapter 19). Subsequently, close counterparts of these oncogenes were found in the genomes of humans and other animals. The normal versions of the cellular genes, called **proto-oncogenes**, code for proteins that stimulate normal cell growth and division.

How might a proto-oncogene—a gene that has an essential function in normal cells—become an oncogene, a cancer-causing gene? In general, an oncogene arises from a genetic change that leads to an increase either in the amount of the proto-oncogene's protein product or in the intrinsic activity of each protein molecule. The genetic changes that convert proto-oncogenes to oncogenes fall into three main categories: movement of DNA within the genome, amplification of a proto-oncogene, and point mutations in a control element or in the proto-oncogene itself **(Figure 18.20)**.

Cancer cells are frequently found to contain chromosomes that have broken and rejoined incorrectly, translocating fragments from one chromosome to another (see Figure 15.15). Now that you have learned how gene expression is regulated, you can understand the possible consequences of such translocations. If a translocated proto-oncogene ends up near an especially active promoter (or other control element), its transcription may increase, making it an oncogene. The second main type of genetic change, amplification, increases the number of copies of the proto-oncogene in the cell. The third

possibility is a point mutation either (1) in the promoter or an enhancer that controls a proto-oncogene, causing an increase in its expression, or (2) in the coding sequence, changing the gene's product to a protein that is more active or more resistant to degradation than the normal protein. All these mechanisms can lead to abnormal stimulation of the cell cycle and put the cell on the path to malignancy.

Tumor-Suppressor Genes

In addition to genes whose products normally promote cell division, cells contain genes whose normal products *inhibit* cell division. Such genes are called **tumor-suppressor genes** because the proteins they encode help prevent uncontrolled cell growth. Any mutation that decreases the normal activity of a tumor-suppressor protein may contribute to the onset of cancer, in effect stimulating growth through the absence of suppression.

The protein products of tumor-suppressor genes have various functions. Some tumor-suppressor proteins normally repair damaged DNA, a function that prevents the cell from accumulating cancer-causing mutations. Other tumor-suppressor proteins control the adhesion of cells to each other or to the extracellular matrix; proper cell anchorage is crucial in normal tissues—and often absent in cancers. Still other tumor-suppressor proteins are components of cell-signaling pathways that inhibit the cell cycle.

Interference with Normal Cell-Signaling Pathways

The proteins encoded by many proto-oncogenes and tumor-suppressor genes are components of cell-signaling pathways **(Figure 18.21)**. Let's take a closer look at how such proteins function in normal cells and what goes wrong with their function in cancer cells. We will focus on the products of two key

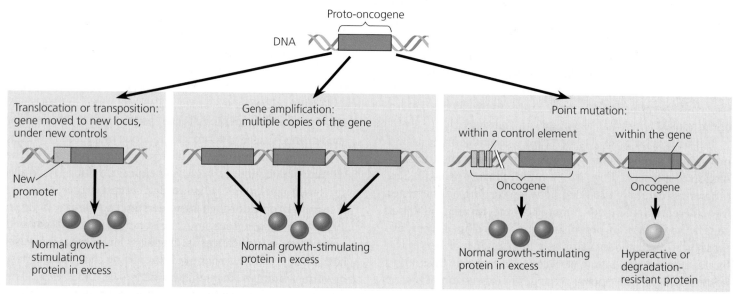

▲ **Figure 18.20 Genetic changes that can turn proto-oncogenes into oncogenes.**

(a) Cell cycle–stimulating pathway.
This pathway is triggered by ① a growth factor that binds to ② its receptor in the plasma membrane. The signal is relayed to ③ a G protein called Ras. Like all G proteins, Ras is active when GTP is bound to it. Ras passes the signal to ④ a series of protein kinases. The last kinase activates ⑤ a transcription activator that turns on one or more genes for proteins that stimulate the cell cycle. If a mutation makes Ras or any other pathway component abnormally active, excessive cell division and cancer may result.

(b) Cell cycle–inhibiting pathway. In this pathway, ① DNA damage is an intracellular signal that is passed via ② protein kinases and leads to activation of ③ p53. Activated p53 promotes transcription of the gene for a protein that inhibits the cell cycle. The resulting suppression of cell division ensures that the damaged DNA is not replicated. Mutations causing deficiencies in any pathway component can contribute to the development of cancer.

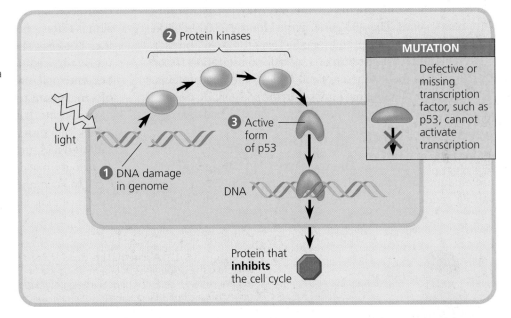

(c) Effects of mutations. Increased cell division, possibly leading to cancer, can result if the cell cycle is overstimulated, as in (a), or not inhibited when it normally would be, as in (b).

▲ **Figure 18.21 Signaling pathways that regulate cell division.** Both stimulatory and inhibitory pathways regulate the cell cycle, commonly by influencing transcription. Cancer can result from aberrations in such pathways, which may be caused by mutations, either spontaneous or environmentally triggered.

? *Looking at the pathway in (b), explain whether a cancer-causing mutation in a tumor-suppressor gene, such as p53, is more likely to be a recessive or a dominant mutation.*

genes, the *ras* proto-oncogene and the *p53* tumor-suppressor gene. Mutations in *ras* occur in about 30% of human cancers, mutations in *p53* in more than 50%.

The Ras protein, encoded by the **ras gene** (named for <u>ra</u>t <u>s</u>arcoma, a connective tissue cancer), is a G protein that relays a signal from a growth factor receptor on the plasma membrane to a cascade of protein kinases (see Chapter 11). The cellular response at the end of the pathway is the synthesis of a protein that stimulates the cell cycle (**Figure 18.21a**). Normally, such a pathway will not operate unless triggered by the appropriate growth factor. But certain mutations in the *ras* gene can lead to production of a hyperactive Ras protein that triggers the kinase cascade even in the absence of growth factor, resulting in increased cell division. In fact, hyperactive versions or excess amounts of any of the pathway's components can have the same outcome: excessive cell division.

Figure 18.21b shows a pathway in which a signal leads to the synthesis of a protein that suppresses the cell cycle. In this case, the signal is damage to the cell's DNA, perhaps as the result of exposure to ultraviolet light. Operation of this signaling pathway blocks the cell cycle until the damage has been repaired. Otherwise, the damage might contribute to tumor formation by causing mutations or chromosomal abnormalities. Thus, the genes for the components of the pathway act as tumor-suppressor genes. The **p53 gene**, named for the 53,000-dalton molecular weight of its protein product, is a tumor-suppressor gene. The protein it encodes is a specific transcription factor that promotes the synthesis of cell cycle–inhibiting proteins. That is why a mutation that knocks out the *p53* gene, like a mutation that leads to a hyperactive Ras protein, can lead to excessive cell growth and cancer (**Figure 18.21c**).

The *p53* gene has been called the "guardian angel of the genome." Once activated, for example by DNA damage, the p53 protein functions as an activator for several genes. Often it activates a gene called *p21*, whose product halts the cell cycle by binding to cyclin-dependent kinases, allowing time for the cell to repair the DNA; the p53 protein can also turn on genes directly involved in DNA repair. When DNA damage is irreparable, p53 activates "suicide" genes, whose protein products cause cell death by apoptosis (see Figure 11.20). Thus, in at least three ways, p53 prevents a cell from passing on mutations due to DNA damage. If mutations do accumulate and the cell survives through many divisions—as is more likely if the *p53* tumor-suppressor gene is defective or missing—cancer may ensue.

The Multistep Model of Cancer Development

More than one somatic mutation is generally needed to produce all the changes characteristic of a full-fledged cancer cell. This may help explain why the incidence of cancer increases greatly with age. If cancer results from an accumulation of mutations and if mutations occur throughout life, then the longer we live, the more likely we are to develop cancer.

The model of a multistep path to cancer is well supported by studies of one of the best-understood types of human cancer, colorectal cancer. About 135,000 new cases of colorectal cancer are diagnosed each year in the United States, and the disease causes 60,000 deaths each year. Like most cancers, colorectal cancer develops gradually (**Figure 18.22**). The first sign is often a polyp, a small, benign growth in the colon lining. The cells of the polyp look normal, although they divide unusually frequently. The tumor grows and may eventually become malignant, invading other tissues. The development of a malignant tumor is paralleled by a gradual accumulation of mutations that convert proto-oncogenes to oncogenes and knock out tumor-suppressor genes. A *ras* oncogene and a mutated *p53* tumor-suppressor gene are often involved.

About a half dozen changes must occur at the DNA level for a cell to become fully cancerous. These usually include the appearance of at least one active oncogene and the mutation or

▼ **Figure 18.22 A multistep model for the development of colorectal cancer.** Affecting the colon and/or rectum, this type of cancer is one of the best understood. Changes in a tumor parallel a series of genetic changes, including mutations affecting several tumor-suppressor genes (such as *p53*) and the *ras* proto-oncogene. Mutations of tumor-suppressor genes often entail loss (deletion) of the gene. *APC* stands for "adenomatous polyposis coli," and *DCC* stands for "deleted in colorectal cancer." Other mutation sequences can also lead to colorectal cancer.

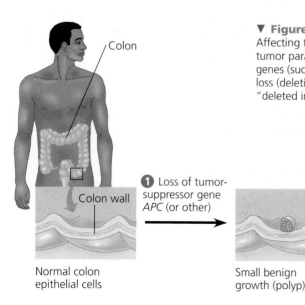

Colon

Colon wall

Normal colon epithelial cells

1 Loss of tumor-suppressor gene *APC* (or other)

Small benign growth (polyp)

2 Activation of *ras* oncogene

3 Loss of tumor-suppressor gene *DCC*

Larger benign growth (adenoma)

4 Loss of tumor-suppressor gene *p53*

5 Additional mutations

Malignant tumor (carcinoma)

loss of several tumor-suppressor genes. Furthermore, since mutant tumor-suppressor alleles are usually recessive, in most cases mutations must knock out *both* alleles in a cell's genome to block tumor suppression. (Most oncogenes, on the other hand, behave as dominant alleles.) In many malignant tumors, the gene for telomerase is activated. This enzyme reverses the shortening of chromosome ends during DNA replication (see Figure 16.19). Production of telomerase in cancer cells removes a natural limit on the number of times the cells can divide.

Inherited Predisposition and Other Factors Contributing to Cancer

The fact that multiple genetic changes are required to produce a cancer cell helps explain the observation that cancers can run in families. An individual inheriting an oncogene or a mutant allele of a tumor-suppressor gene is one step closer to accumulating the necessary mutations for cancer to develop than is an individual without any such mutations.

Geneticists are devoting much effort to identifying inherited cancer alleles so that predisposition to certain cancers can be detected early in life. About 15% of colorectal cancers, for example, involve inherited mutations. Many of these affect the tumor-suppressor gene called *adenomatous polyposis coli*, or *APC* (see Figure 18.22). This gene has multiple functions in the cell, including regulation of cell migration and adhesion. Even in patients with no family history of the disease, the *APC* gene is mutated in 60% of colorectal cancers. In these individuals, new mutations must occur in both *APC* alleles before the gene's function is lost. Since only 15% of colorectal cancers are associated with known inherited mutations, researchers continue in their efforts to identify "markers" that could predict the risk of developing this type of cancer.

There is evidence of a strong inherited predisposition in 5–10% of patients with breast cancer. This is the second most common type of cancer in the United States, striking over 180,000 women (and some men) annually and killing 40,000 each year. Mutations in the *BRCA1* or *BRCA2* gene are found in at least half of inherited breast cancers (Figure 18.23). (*BRCA* stands for *br*east *ca*ncer.) A woman who inherits one mutant *BRCA1* allele has a 60% probability of developing breast cancer before the age of 50, compared with only a 2% probability for an individual homozygous for the normal allele. Both *BRCA1* and *BRCA2* are considered tumor-suppressor genes because their wild-type alleles protect against breast cancer and their mutant alleles are recessive. Apparently, the BRCA1 and BRCA2 proteins both function in the cell's DNA damage repair pathway. More is known about BRCA2, which, in association with another protein, helps to repair breaks that occur in both strands of DNA, crucial for maintaining undamaged DNA in a cell's nucleus.

Because DNA breakage can contribute to cancer, it makes sense that the risk of cancer can be lowered by minimizing exposure to DNA-damaging agents, such as the ultraviolet radia-

▲ Figure 18.23 **Tracking the molecular basis of breast cancer.** In 1990, after 16 years of research, geneticist Mary-Claire King convincingly demonstrated that mutations in one gene—*BRCA1*—are associated with increased susceptibility to breast cancer, a finding that flew in the face of medical opinion at the time. Her lab is currently working to identify the environmental conditions that may affect the timing of cancer development in people who carry mutations in *BRCA1* and another breast cancer gene, *BRCA2*.

tion in sunlight and chemicals found in cigarette smoke. Novel methods for early diagnosis and treatment of specific cancers are being developed that rely on new techniques for analyzing, and perhaps interfering with, gene expression in tumors. Ultimately, such approaches may lower the death rate from cancer.

The study of genes associated with cancer, inherited or not, increases our basic understanding of how disruption of normal gene regulation results in this disease. We've come a long way in our understanding since Peyton Rous's discovery. We now know that viruses can contribute to cancer development in several ways if they integrate their genetic material into the DNA of infected cells. Viral integration may donate an oncogene to the cell, disrupt a tumor-suppressor gene, or convert a proto-oncogene to an oncogene. In addition, some viruses produce proteins that inactivate p53 and other tumor-suppressor proteins, thus making the cell more prone to becoming cancerous. Although viruses are little more than a nucleic acid surrounded by a protective coat, they are powerful biological agents. You'll learn more about how viruses function in the next chapter.

CONCEPT CHECK 18.5

1. Compare the usual functions of proteins encoded by proto-oncogenes with those encoded by tumor-suppressor genes.
2. Under what circumstances is cancer considered to have a hereditary component?
3. **WHAT IF?** Explain how the types of mutations that lead to cancer are different for a proto-oncogene and a tumor-suppressor gene, in terms of the effect of the mutation on the activity of the gene product.

For suggested answers, see Appendix A.

MEDIA Go to the Study Area at **www.masteringbio.com** for BioFlix 3-D Animations, MP3 Tutors, Videos, Practice Tests, an eBook, and more.

SUMMARY OF KEY CONCEPTS

CONCEPT 18.1

Bacteria often respond to environmental change by regulating transcription (pp. 351–356)

▶ **Operons: The Basic Concept** Cells control metabolism by regulating enzyme activity or the expression of genes coding for enzymes. In bacteria, genes are often clustered into operons, with one promoter serving several adjacent genes. An operator site on the DNA switches the operon on or off, resulting in coordinate regulation of the genes.

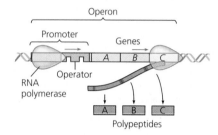

▶ **Repressible and Inducible Operons: Two Types of Negative Gene Regulation** In either type of operon, binding of a specific repressor protein to the operator shuts off transcription. (The repressor is encoded by a separate regulatory gene.) In a repressible operon, the repressor is active when bound to a corepressor, usually the end product of an anabolic pathway.

In an inducible operon, binding of an inducer to an innately active repressor inactivates the repressor and turns on transcription. Inducible enzymes usually function in catabolic pathways.

▶ **Positive Gene Regulation** Some operons are also subject to positive control via a stimulatory activator protein, such as catabolite activator protein (CAP), which promotes transcription when bound to a site within the promoter.

MEDIA

MP3 Tutor Control of Gene Expression
Activity The *lac* Operon in *E. coli*

CONCEPT 18.2

Eukaryotic gene expression can be regulated at any stage (pp. 356–364)

Chromatin modification
• Genes in highly compacted chromatin are generally not transcribed.
• Histone acetylation seems to loosen chromatin structure, enhancing transcription.
• DNA methylation generally reduces transcription.

Transcription
• Regulation of transcription initiation: DNA control elements bind specific transcription factors.

Bending of the DNA enables activators to contact proteins at the promoter, initiating transcription.
• Coordinate regulation:
Enhancer for liver-specific genes   Enhancer for lens-specific genes

RNA processing
• Alternative RNA splicing:
Primary RNA transcript
mRNA ▭ or ▭

Translation
• Initiation of translation can be controlled via regulation of initiation factors.

mRNA degradation
• Each mRNA has a characteristic life span, determined in part by sequences in the 5′ and 3′ UTRs.

Protein processing and degradation
• Protein processing and degradation by proteasomes are subject to regulation.

CONCEPT 18.3

Noncoding RNAs play multiple roles in controlling gene expression (pp. 364–366)

Chromatin modification
• Small RNAs can promote the formation of heterochromatin in certain regions, blocking transcription.

Translation
• miRNA or siRNA can block the translation of specific mRNAs.

mRNA degradation
• miRNA or siRNA can target specific mRNAs for destruction.

Activity Overview: Control of Gene Expression
Activity Control of Transcription
Activity Post-Transcriptional Control Mechanisms
Activity Review: Control of Gene Expression
Investigation How Do You Design a Gene Expression System?

CONCEPT 18.4

A program of differential gene expression leads to the different cell types in a multicellular organism (pp. 366–373)

▶ **A Genetic Program for Embryonic Development**
Embryonic cells undergo differentiation, becoming specialized in structure and function. Morphogenesis encompasses the processes that give shape to the organism and its various parts. Cells differ in structure and function not because they contain different genes but because they express different portions of a common genome.

▶ **Cytoplasmic Determinants and Inductive Signals**
Cytoplasmic determinants in the unfertilized egg regulate the expression of genes in the zygote that affect the developmental fate of embryonic cells. In the process called induction, signaling molecules from embryonic cells cause transcriptional changes in nearby target cells.

▶ **Sequential Regulation of Gene Expression During Cellular Differentiation** Differentiation is heralded by the appearance of tissue-specific proteins, which enable differentiated cells to carry out their specialized roles.

▶ **Pattern Formation: Setting Up the Body Plan** In animals, pattern formation, the development of a spatial organization of tissues and organs, begins in the early embryo. Positional information, the molecular cues that control pattern formation, tell a cell its location relative to the body's axes and to other cells. In *Drosophila*, gradients of morphogens encoded by maternal effect genes determine the body axes. For example, the gradient of Bicoid protein determines the anterior-posterior axis.

MEDIA

Activity Signal Transduction Pathways
Activity Role of *bicoid* Gene in *Drosophila* Development
Investigation How Do *bicoid* Mutations Alter Development?

CONCEPT 18.5

Cancer results from genetic changes that affect cell cycle control (pp. 373–377)

▶ **Types of Genes Associated with Cancer** The products of proto-oncogenes and tumor-suppressor genes control cell division. A DNA change that makes a proto-oncogene excessively active converts it to an oncogene, which may promote excessive cell division and cancer. A tumor-suppressor gene encodes a protein that inhibits abnormal cell division. A mutation in such a gene that reduces the activity of its protein product may also lead to excessive cell division and possibly to cancer.

▶ **Interference with Normal Cell-Signaling Pathways** Many proto-oncogenes and tumor-suppressor genes encode components of growth-stimulating and growth-inhibiting signaling pathways, respectively. A hyperactive version of a protein in a stimulatory pathway, such as Ras (a G protein), functions as an oncogene protein. A defective version of a protein in an inhibitory pathway, such as p53 (a transcription activator), fails to function as a tumor suppressor.

▶ **The Multistep Model of Cancer Development** Normal cells are converted to cancer cells by the accumulation of mutations affecting proto-oncogenes and tumor-suppressor genes.

▶ **Inherited Predisposition and Other Factors Contributing to Cancer** Individuals who inherit a mutant oncogene or tumor-suppressor allele have an increased risk of developing cancer. Certain viruses promote cancer by integration of viral DNA into a cell's genome.

MEDIA

Activity Causes of Cancer

TESTING YOUR KNOWLEDGE

SELF-QUIZ

1. If a particular operon encodes enzymes for making an essential amino acid and is regulated like the *trp* operon, then
   a. the amino acid inactivates the repressor.
   b. the enzymes produced are called inducible enzymes.
   c. the repressor is active in the absence of the amino acid.
   d. the amino acid acts as a corepressor.
   e. the amino acid turns on transcription of the operon.

2. Muscle cells differ from nerve cells mainly because they
   a. express different genes.
   b. contain different genes.
   c. use different genetic codes.
   d. have unique ribosomes.
   e. have different chromosomes.

3. What would occur if the repressor of an inducible operon were mutated so it could not bind the operator?
   a. irreversible binding of the repressor to the promoter
   b. reduced transcription of the operon's genes
   c. buildup of a substrate for the pathway controlled by the operon
   d. continuous transcription of the operon's genes
   e. overproduction of catabolite activator protein (CAP)

4. The functioning of enhancers is an example of
   a. transcriptional control of gene expression.
   b. a post-transcriptional mechanism for editing mRNA.
   c. the stimulation of translation by initiation factors.
   d. post-translational control that activates certain proteins.
   e. a eukaryotic equivalent of prokaryotic promoter functioning.

5. Absence of *bicoid* mRNA from a *Drosophila* egg leads to the absence of anterior larval body parts and mirror-image duplication of posterior parts. This is evidence that the product of the *bicoid* gene
   a. is transcribed in the early embryo.
   b. normally leads to formation of tail structures.
   c. normally leads to formation of head structures.
   d. is a protein present in all head structures.
   e. leads to programmed cell death.

6. Which of the following statements about the DNA in one of your brain cells is true?
   a. Most of the DNA codes for protein.
   b. The majority of genes are likely to be transcribed.
   c. Each gene lies immediately adjacent to an enhancer.
   d. Many genes are grouped into operon-like clusters.
   e. It is the same as the DNA in one of your heart cells.

7. Cell differentiation always involves
   a. the production of tissue-specific proteins, such as muscle actin.
   b. the movement of cells.
   c. the transcription of the *myoD* gene.
   d. the selective loss of certain genes from the genome.
   e. the cell's sensitivity to environmental cues, such as light or heat.

8. Which of the following is an example of post-transcriptional control of gene expression?
   a. the addition of methyl groups to cytosine bases of DNA
   b. the binding of transcription factors to a promoter
   c. the removal of introns and splicing together of exons
   d. gene amplification contributing to cancer
   e. the folding of DNA to form heterochromatin

9. Within a cell, the amount of protein made using a given mRNA molecule depends partly on
   a. the degree of DNA methylation.
   b. the rate at which the mRNA is degraded.
   c. the presence of certain transcription factors.
   d. the number of introns present in the mRNA.
   e. the types of ribosomes present in the cytoplasm.

10. Proto-oncogenes can change into oncogenes that cause cancer. Which of the following best explains the presence of these potential time bombs in eukaryotic cells?
    a. Proto-oncogenes first arose from viral infections.
    b. Proto-oncogenes normally help regulate cell division.
    c. Proto-oncogenes are genetic "junk."
    d. Proto-oncogenes are mutant versions of normal genes.
    e. Cells produce proto-oncogenes as they age.

11. **DRAW IT** The diagram below shows five genes (with their enhancers) from the genome of a certain species. Imagine that orange, blue, green, black, red, and purple activator proteins exist that can bind to the appropriately color-coded control elements in the enhancers of these genes.

a. Draw an X above enhancer elements (of all the genes) that would have activators bound in a cell in which only gene 5 is transcribed. Which colored activators would be present?
b. Draw a dot above all enhancer elements that would have activators bound in a cell in which the green, blue, and orange activators are present. Which gene(s) would be transcribed?
c. Imagine that genes 1, 2, and 4 code for nerve-specific proteins, and genes 3 and 5 are skin specific. Which activators would have to be present in each cell type to ensure transcription of the appropriate genes?

For Self-Quiz answers, see Appendix A.

MEDIA Visit the Study Area at **www.masteringbio.com** for a Practice Test.

EVOLUTION CONNECTION

12. DNA sequences can act as "tape measures of evolution" (see Chapter 5). Scientists analyzing the human genome sequence were surprised to find that some of the regions of the human genome that are most highly conserved (similar to comparable regions in other species) don't code for proteins. Propose a possible explanation for this observation.

SCIENTIFIC INQUIRY

13. Prostate cells usually require testosterone and other androgens to survive. But some prostate cancer cells thrive despite treatments that eliminate androgens. One hypothesis is that estrogen, often considered a female hormone, may be activating genes normally controlled by an androgen in these cancer cells. Describe one or more experiments to test this hypothesis. (See Figure 11.8 to review the action of these steroid hormones.)

Biological Inquiry: A Workbook of Investigative Cases Explore gene regulation by the hedgehog pathway with the case "Shh: Silencing the Hedgehog Pathway."

SCIENCE, TECHNOLOGY, AND SOCIETY

14. Trace amounts of dioxin were present in Agent Orange, a defoliant sprayed on vegetation during the Vietnam War. Animal tests suggest that dioxin can cause birth defects, cancer, liver and thymus damage, and immune system suppression, sometimes leading to death. But the animal tests are equivocal; a hamster is not affected by a dose that can kill a guinea pig. Dioxin acts somewhat like a steroid hormone, entering a cell and binding to a receptor protein that then attaches to the cell's DNA. How might this mechanism help explain the variety of dioxin's effects on different body systems and in different animals? How might you determine whether a type of illness is related to dioxin exposure? How might you determine whether a particular individual became ill as a result of exposure to dioxin? Which would be more difficult to demonstrate? Why?

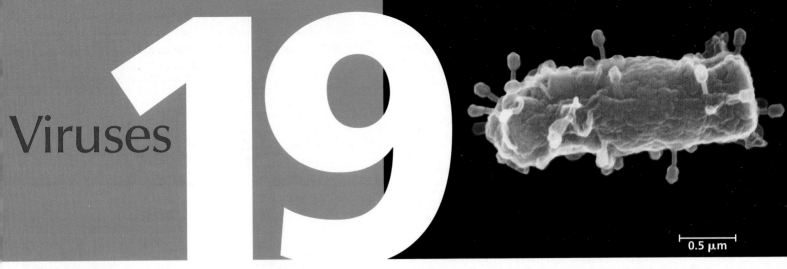

Viruses 19

▲ **Figure 19.1 Are the tiny viruses infecting this *E. coli* cell alive?**

KEY CONCEPTS

19.1 A virus consists of a nucleic acid surrounded by a protein coat

19.2 Viruses reproduce only in host cells

19.3 Viruses, viroids, and prions are formidable pathogens in animals and plants

OVERVIEW

A Borrowed Life

The photo in **Figure 19.1** shows a remarkable event: the attack of a bacterial cell by numerous structures that resemble miniature lollipops. These structures, a type of virus called T4 bacteriophage, are seen infecting the bacterium *Escherichia coli* in this colorized SEM. By injecting its DNA into the cell, the virus sets in motion a genetic takeover of the bacterium, recruiting cellular machinery to mass-produce many new viruses.

Recall that bacteria and other prokaryotes are cells much smaller and more simply organized than those of eukaryotes, such as plants and animals. Viruses are smaller and simpler still. Lacking the structures and metabolic machinery found in cells, most viruses are little more than genes packaged in protein coats.

Are viruses living or nonliving? Early on, they were considered biological chemicals; in fact, the Latin root for the word *virus* means "poison." Because viruses are capable of causing a wide variety of diseases and can be spread between organisms, researchers in the late 1800s saw a parallel with bacteria and proposed that viruses were the simplest of living forms. However, viruses cannot reproduce or carry out metabolic activities outside of a host cell. Most biologists studying viruses today would probably agree that they are not alive but exist in a shady area between life-forms and chemicals. The simple phrase used recently by two researchers describes them aptly enough: Viruses lead "a kind of borrowed life."

To a large extent, molecular biology was born in the laboratories of biologists studying viruses that infect bacteria. Experiments with viruses provided important evidence that genes are made of nucleic acids, and they were critical in working out the molecular mechanisms of the fundamental processes of DNA replication, transcription, and translation.

Beyond their value as experimental systems, viruses have unique genetic mechanisms that are interesting in their own right and that also help us understand how viruses cause disease. In addition, the study of viruses has led to the development of techniques that enable scientists to manipulate genes and transfer them from one organism to another. These techniques play an important role in basic research, biotechnology, and medical applications. For instance, viruses are used as agents of gene transfer in gene therapy (see Chapter 20).

In this chapter, we will explore the biology of viruses. We will begin with the structure of these simplest of all genetic systems and then describe their reproductive cycles. Next, we will discuss the role of viruses as disease-causing agents, or pathogens, and conclude by considering some even simpler infectious agents, viroids and prions.

CONCEPT 19.1

A virus consists of a nucleic acid surrounded by a protein coat

Scientists were able to detect viruses indirectly long before they were actually able to see them. The story of how viruses were discovered begins near the end of the 19th century.

The Discovery of Viruses: *Scientific Inquiry*

Tobacco mosaic disease stunts the growth of tobacco plants and gives their leaves a mottled, or mosaic, coloration. In 1883, Adolf Mayer, a German scientist, discovered that he could transmit the disease from plant to plant by rubbing sap extracted from diseased leaves onto healthy plants. After an unsuccessful search for an infectious microbe in the sap, Mayer suggested that the disease was caused by unusually small bacteria that were invisible under a microscope. This hypothesis was tested a decade later by Dimitri Ivanowsky, a Russian biologist who passed sap from infected tobacco leaves through a filter designed to remove bacteria. After filtration, the sap still produced mosaic disease.

But Ivanowsky clung to the hypothesis that bacteria caused tobacco mosaic disease. Perhaps, he reasoned, the bacteria were small enough to pass through the filter or made a toxin that could do so. The second possibility was ruled out when the Dutch botanist Martinus Beijerinck carried out a classic series of experiments that showed that the infectious agent in the filtered sap could reproduce (Figure 19.2).

In fact, the pathogen reproduced only within the host it infected. In further experiments, Beijerinck showed that unlike bacteria used in the lab at that time, the mysterious agent of mosaic disease could not be cultivated on nutrient media in test tubes or petri dishes. Beijerinck imagined a reproducing particle much smaller and simpler than a bacterium, and he is generally credited with being the first scientist to voice the concept of a virus. His suspicions were confirmed in 1935 when the American scientist Wendell Stanley crystallized the infectious particle, now known as tobacco mosaic virus (TMV). Subsequently, TMV and many other viruses were actually seen with the help of the electron microscope.

Structure of Viruses

The tiniest viruses are only 20 nm in diameter—smaller than a ribosome. Millions could easily fit on a pinhead. Even the largest known virus, which has a diameter of several hundred nanometers, is barely visible in the light microscope. Stanley's discovery that some viruses could be crystallized was exciting and puzzling news. Not even the simplest of cells can aggregate into regular crystals. But if viruses are not cells, then what are they? Examining the structure of viruses more closely reveals that they are infectious particles consisting of nucleic acid enclosed in a protein coat and, in some cases, a membranous envelope.

Viral Genomes

We usually think of genes as being made of double-stranded DNA—the conventional double helix—but many viruses defy this convention. Their genomes may consist of double-stranded DNA, single-stranded DNA, double-stranded RNA, or single-stranded RNA, depending on the kind of virus. A virus is called a DNA virus or an RNA virus, according to the kind of nucleic acid that makes up its genome. In either case, the genome is usually organized as a single linear or circular molecule of nucleic acid, although the genomes of some

▼ Figure 19.2 **Inquiry**

What causes tobacco mosaic disease?

EXPERIMENT   In the late 1800s, Martinus Beijerinck, of the Technical School in Delft, the Netherlands, investigated the properties of the agent that causes tobacco mosaic disease (then called spot disease).

RESULTS   When the filtered sap was rubbed on healthy plants, they became infected. Their sap, when extracted and filtered, could then act as the source of infection for another group of plants. Each successive group of plants developed the disease to the same extent as earlier groups.

❶ Extracted sap from tobacco plant with tobacco mosaic disease

❷ Passed sap through a porcelain filter known to trap bacteria

❸ Rubbed filtered sap on healthy tobacco plants

❹ Healthy plants became infected

CONCLUSION   The infectious agent was apparently not a bacterium because it could pass through a bacterium-trapping filter. The pathogen must have been reproducing in the plants because its ability to cause disease was undiluted after several transfers from plant to plant.

SOURCE   M. J. Beijerinck, Concerning a *contagium vivum fluidum* as cause of the spot disease of tobacco leaves, *Verhandelingen der Koninkyke akademie Wettenschappen te Amsterdam* 65:3–21 (1898). Translation published in English as Phytopathological Classics Number 7 (1942), American Phytopathological Society Press, St. Paul, MN.

WHAT IF?   If Beijerinck had observed that the infection of each group was weaker than that of the previous group and that ultimately the sap could no longer cause disease, what might he have concluded?

viruses consist of multiple molecules of nucleic acid. The smallest viruses known have only four genes in their genome, while the largest have several hundred to a thousand. For comparison, bacterial genomes contain about 200 to a few thousand genes.

Capsids and Envelopes

The protein shell enclosing the viral genome is called a **capsid**. Depending on the type of virus, the capsid may be rod-shaped, polyhedral, or more complex in shape (like T4). Capsids are built from a large number of protein subunits called *capsomeres*, but the number of different *kinds* of proteins in a capsid is usually small. Tobacco mosaic virus has a rigid, rod-shaped capsid made from over a thousand molecules of a single type of protein arranged in a helix; rod-shaped viruses are commonly called *helical viruses* for this reason **(Figure 19.3a)**. Adenoviruses, which infect the respiratory tracts of animals, have 252 identical protein molecules arranged in a polyhedral capsid with 20 triangular facets—an icosahedron; thus, these and other similarly shaped viruses are referred to as *icosahedral viruses* **(Figure 19.3b)**.

Some viruses have accessory structures that help them infect their hosts. For instance, a membranous envelope surrounds the capsids of influenza viruses and many other viruses found in animals **(Figure 19.3c)**. These **viral envelopes**, which are derived from the membranes of the host cell, contain host cell phospholipids and membrane proteins. They also contain proteins and glycoproteins of viral origin. (Glycoproteins are proteins with carbohydrates covalently attached.) Some viruses carry a few viral enzyme molecules within their capsids.

Many of the most complex capsids are found among the viruses that infect bacteria, called **bacteriophages**, or simply **phages**. The first phages studied included seven that infect *E. coli*. These seven phages were named type 1 (T1), type 2 (T2), and so forth, in the order of their discovery. The three T-even phages (T2, T4, and T6) turned out to be very similar in structure. Their capsids have elongated icosahedral heads enclosing their DNA. Attached to the head is a protein tail piece with fibers by which the phages attach to a bacterium **(Figure 19.3d)**. In the next section, we'll examine how these few viral parts function together with cellular components to produce large numbers of viral progeny.

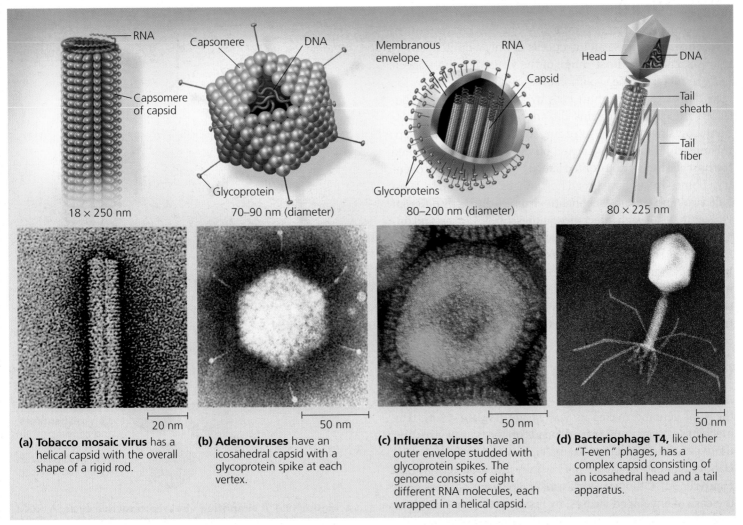

18 × 250 nm   70–90 nm (diameter)   80–200 nm (diameter)   80 × 225 nm

20 nm   50 nm   50 nm   50 nm

(a) Tobacco mosaic virus has a helical capsid with the overall shape of a rigid rod.

(b) Adenoviruses have an icosahedral capsid with a glycoprotein spike at each vertex.

(c) Influenza viruses have an outer envelope studded with glycoprotein spikes. The genome consists of eight different RNA molecules, each wrapped in a helical capsid.

(d) Bacteriophage T4, like other "T-even" phages, has a complex capsid consisting of an icosahedral head and a tail apparatus.

▲ **Figure 19.3 Viral structure.** Viruses are made up of nucleic acid (DNA or RNA) enclosed in a protein coat (the capsid) and sometimes further wrapped in a membranous envelope. The individual protein subunits making up the capsid are called capsomeres. Although diverse in size and shape, viruses have common structural features, most of which appear in the four examples shown here. (All the micrographs are colorized TEMs.)

1. Compare the structures of tobacco mosaic virus (TMV) and influenza virus (see Figure 19.3).
2. **WHAT IF?** In 2005, scientists discovered a virus that could, under certain conditions, develop pointed projections at each end while outside a host cell. How does this observation fit with the characterization of viruses as nonliving?

For suggested answers, see Appendix A.

CONCEPT **19.2**
Viruses reproduce only in host cells

Viruses lack metabolic enzymes and equipment for making proteins, such as ribosomes. They are obligate intracellular parasites; in other words, they can reproduce only within a host cell. It is fair to say that viruses in isolation are merely packaged sets of genes in transit from one host cell to another.

Each type of virus can infect cells of only a limited variety of hosts, called the **host range** of the virus. This host specificity results from the evolution of recognition systems by the virus. Viruses identify host cells by a "lock-and-key" fit between viral surface proteins and specific receptor molecules on the outside of cells. (According to one model, such receptor molecules originally carried out functions that benefited the host cell but were co-opted later by viruses as portals of entry.) Some viruses have broad host ranges. For example, West Nile virus and equine encephalitis virus are distinctly different viruses that can each infect mosquitoes, birds, horses, and humans. Other viruses have host ranges so narrow that they infect only a single species. Measles virus, for instance, can infect only humans. Furthermore, viral infection of multicellular eukaryotes is usually limited to particular tissues. Human cold viruses infect only the cells lining the upper respiratory tract, and the AIDS virus binds to receptors present only on certain types of white blood cells.

General Features of Viral Reproductive Cycles

A viral infection begins when a virus binds to a host cell and the viral genome makes its way inside **(Figure 19.4)**. The mechanism of genome entry depends on the type of virus and the type of host cell. For example, T-even phages use their elaborate tail apparatus to inject DNA into a bacterium (see Figure 19.3d). Other viruses are taken up by endocytosis or, in the case of enveloped viruses, by fusion of the viral envelope with the plasma membrane. Once the viral genome is inside, the proteins it encodes can commandeer the host, reprogramming the cell to copy the viral nucleic acid and manufacture viral proteins. The host provides the nucleotides for

making viral nucleic acids, as well as enzymes, ribosomes, tRNAs, amino acids, ATP, and other components needed for making the viral proteins. Most DNA viruses use the DNA polymerases of the host cell to synthesize new genomes along the templates provided by the viral DNA. In contrast, to replicate their genomes, RNA viruses use virally encoded polymerases that can use RNA as a template. (Uninfected cells generally make no enzymes for carrying out this process.)

After the viral nucleic acid molecules and capsomeres are produced, they spontaneously self-assemble into new viruses. In fact, researchers can separate the RNA and capsomeres of TMV and then reassemble complete viruses simply by mixing the components together under the right conditions. The simplest type of viral reproductive cycle ends with the exit of

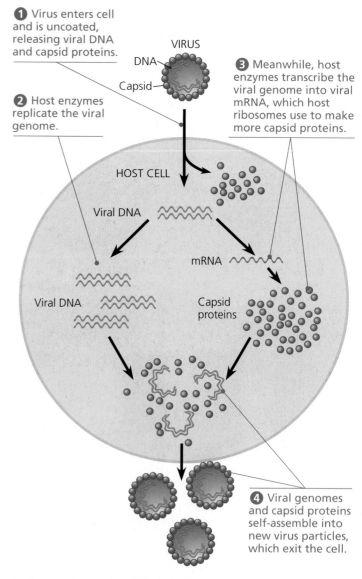

① Virus enters cell and is uncoated, releasing viral DNA and capsid proteins.

② Host enzymes replicate the viral genome.

③ Meanwhile, host enzymes transcribe the viral genome into viral mRNA, which host ribosomes use to make more capsid proteins.

④ Viral genomes and capsid proteins self-assemble into new virus particles, which exit the cell.

VIRUS
DNA
Capsid
HOST CELL
Viral DNA
Viral DNA
mRNA
Capsid proteins

▲ Figure 19.4 **A simplified viral reproductive cycle.** A virus is an obligate intracellular parasite that uses the equipment and small molecules of its host cell to reproduce. In this simplest of viral cycles, the parasite is a DNA virus with a capsid consisting of a single type of protein.
? *Label each of the straight black arrows with one word representing the name of the process that is occurring.*

hundreds or thousands of viruses from the infected host cell, a process that often damages or destroys the cell. Such cellular damage and death, as well as the body's responses to this destruction, cause many of the symptoms associated with viral infections. The viral progeny that exit a cell have the potential to infect additional cells, spreading the viral infection.

There are many variations on the simplified viral reproductive cycle we have traced in this general description. We will now take a closer look at some of these variations in bacterial viruses (phages) and animal viruses; later in the chapter, we will consider plant viruses.

Reproductive Cycles of Phages

Phages are the best understood of all viruses, although some of them are also among the most complex. Research on phages led to the discovery that some double-stranded DNA viruses can reproduce by two alternative mechanisms: the lytic cycle and the lysogenic cycle.

The Lytic Cycle

A phage reproductive cycle that culminates in death of the host cell is known as a **lytic cycle**. The term refers to the last stage of infection, during which the bacterium lyses (breaks open) and releases the phages that were produced within the cell. Each of these phages can then infect a healthy cell, and a few successive lytic cycles can destroy an entire bacterial population in just a few hours. A phage that reproduces only by a lytic cycle is a **virulent phage**. **Figure 19.5** illustrates the major steps in the lytic cycle of T4, a typical virulent phage. The figure and legend describe the process, which you should study before proceeding.

After reading about the lytic cycle, you may wonder why phages haven't exterminated all bacteria. In fact, phage treatments have been used medically in some countries to help control bacterial infections in patients. Solutions containing bacteriophages have also been sprayed on chicken carcasses, significantly reducing bacterial contamination of poultry on the way to the marketplace. Bacteria are not defenseless, however. First, natural selection favors bacterial mutants with receptors that are no longer recognized by a particular type of phage. Second, when phage DNA successfully enters a bacterium, the DNA often is identified as foreign and cut up by cellular enzymes called **restriction enzymes**, which are so named because their activity *restricts* the ability of the phage to infect the bacterium. The bacterial cell's own DNA is methylated in a

▶ **Figure 19.5 The lytic cycle of phage T4, a virulent phage.** Phage T4 has almost 300 genes, which are transcribed and translated using the host cell's machinery. One of the first phage genes translated after the viral DNA enters the host cell codes for an enzyme that degrades the host cell's DNA (step 2); the phage DNA is protected from breakdown because it contains a modified form of cytosine that is not recognized by the enzyme. The entire lytic cycle, from the phage's first contact with the cell surface to cell lysis, takes only 20–30 minutes at 37°C.

Phage assembly

Head   Tail   Tail fibers

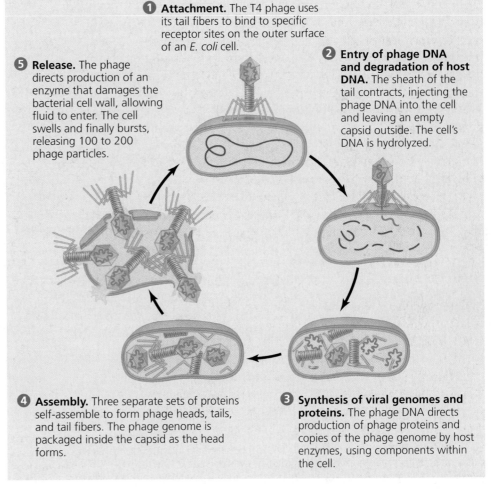

1 **Attachment.** The T4 phage uses its tail fibers to bind to specific receptor sites on the outer surface of an *E. coli* cell.

2 **Entry of phage DNA and degradation of host DNA.** The sheath of the tail contracts, injecting the phage DNA into the cell and leaving an empty capsid outside. The cell's DNA is hydrolyzed.

3 **Synthesis of viral genomes and proteins.** The phage DNA directs production of phage proteins and copies of the phage genome by host enzymes, using components within the cell.

4 **Assembly.** Three separate sets of proteins self-assemble to form phage heads, tails, and tail fibers. The phage genome is packaged inside the capsid as the head forms.

5 **Release.** The phage directs production of an enzyme that damages the bacterial cell wall, allowing fluid to enter. The cell swells and finally bursts, releasing 100 to 200 phage particles.

way that prevents attack by its own restriction enzymes. But just as natural selection favors bacteria with mutant receptors or effective restriction enzymes, it also favors phage mutants that can bind the altered receptors or are resistant to particular restriction enzymes. Thus, the parasite-host relationship is in constant evolutionary flux.

There is yet a third important reason bacteria have been spared from extinction as a result of phage activity. Instead of lysing their host cells, many phages coexist with them in a state called lysogeny, which we'll now discuss.

The Lysogenic Cycle

In contrast to the lytic cycle, which kills the host cell, the **lysogenic cycle** allows replication of the phage genome without destroying the host. Phages capable of using both modes of reproducing within a bacterium are called **temperate phages**. A temperate phage called lambda, written with the Greek letter λ, is widely used in biological research. Phage λ resembles T4, but its tail has only one, short tail fiber.

Infection of an *E. coli* cell by phage λ begins when the phage binds to the surface of the cell and injects its linear DNA genome **(Figure 19.6)**. Within the host, the λ DNA molecule forms a circle. What happens next depends on the reproductive mode: lytic cycle or lysogenic cycle. During a lytic cycle, the viral genes im-

mediately turn the host cell into a λ-producing factory, and the cell soon lyses and releases its viral products. During a lysogenic cycle, however, the λ DNA molecule is incorporated into a specific site on the *E. coli* chromosome by viral proteins that break both circular DNA molecules and join them to each other. When integrated into the bacterial chromosome in this way, the viral DNA is known as a **prophage**. One prophage gene codes for a protein that prevents transcription of most of the other prophage genes. Thus, the phage genome is mostly silent within the bacterium. Every time the *E. coli* cell prepares to divide, it replicates the phage DNA along with its own and passes the copies on to daughter cells. A single infected cell can quickly give rise to a large population of bacteria carrying the virus in prophage form. This mechanism enables viruses to propagate without killing the host cells on which they depend.

The term *lysogenic* implies that prophages are capable of generating active phages that lyse their host cells. This occurs when the λ genome is induced to exit the bacterial chromosome and initiate a lytic cycle. An environmental signal, such as a certain chemical or high-energy radiation, usually triggers the switchover from the lysogenic to the lytic mode.

In addition to the gene for the transcription-preventing protein, a few other prophage genes may be expressed during lysogeny. Expression of these genes may alter the host's phenotype, a phenomenon that can have important medical

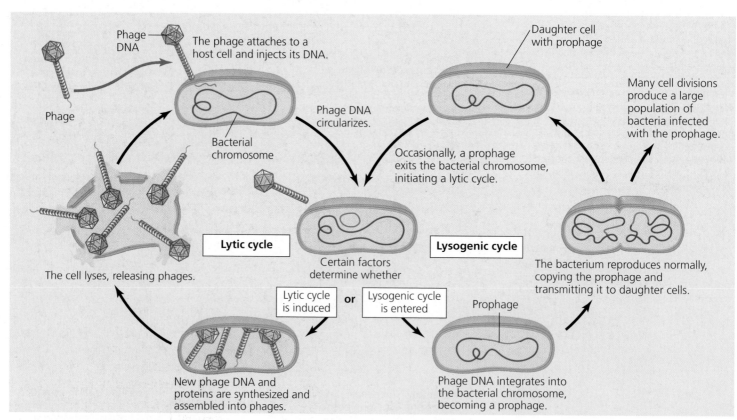

The phage attaches to a host cell and injects its DNA.

Phage DNA

Phage

Bacterial chromosome

Phage DNA circularizes.

Daughter cell with prophage

Many cell divisions produce a large population of bacteria infected with the prophage.

Occasionally, a prophage exits the bacterial chromosome, initiating a lytic cycle.

Lytic cycle

Lysogenic cycle

The bacterium reproduces normally, copying the prophage and transmitting it to daughter cells.

Certain factors determine whether

The cell lyses, releasing phages.

Lytic cycle is induced

or

Lysogenic cycle is entered

Prophage

New phage DNA and proteins are synthesized and assembled into phages.

Phage DNA integrates into the bacterial chromosome, becoming a prophage.

▲ **Figure 19.6 The lytic and lysogenic cycles of phage λ, a temperate phage.** After entering the bacterial cell and circularizing, the λ DNA can immediately initiate the production of a large number of progeny phages (lytic cycle) or integrate into the bacterial chromosome (lysogenic cycle). In most cases, phage λ follows the lytic pathway, which is similar to that detailed in Figure 19.5. However, once a lysogenic cycle begins, the prophage may be carried in the host cell's chromosome for many generations. Phage λ has one main tail fiber, which is short.

Table 19.1 Classes of Animal Viruses

Class/Family	Envelope	Examples/Disease
I. Double-stranded DNA (dsDNA)		
Adenovirus (see Figure 19.3b)	No	Respiratory diseases; tumors
Papovavirus	No	Papillomavirus (warts, cervical cancer); polyomavirus (tumors)
Herpesvirus	Yes	Herpes simplex I and II (cold sores, genital sores); varicella zoster (shingles, chicken pox); Epstein-Barr virus (mononucleosis, Burkitt's lymphoma)
Poxvirus	Yes	Smallpox virus; cowpox virus
II. Single-stranded DNA (ssDNA)		
Parvovirus	No	B19 parvovirus (mild rash)
III. Double-stranded RNA (dsRNA)		
Reovirus	No	Rotavirus (diarrhea); Colorado tick fever virus
IV. Single-stranded RNA (ssRNA); serves as mRNA		
Picornavirus	No	Rhinovirus (common cold); poliovirus, hepatitis A virus, and other enteric (intestinal) viruses
Coronavirus	Yes	Severe acute respiratory syndrome (SARS)
Flavivirus	Yes	Yellow fever virus; West Nile virus; hepatitis C virus
Togavirus	Yes	Rubella virus; equine encephalitis viruses
V. ssRNA; template for mRNA synthesis		
Filovirus	Yes	Ebola virus (hemorrhagic fever)
Orthomyxovirus (see Figures 19.3c and 19.9b)	Yes	Influenza virus
Paramyxovirus	Yes	Measles virus; mumps virus
Rhabdovirus	Yes	Rabies virus
VI. ssRNA; template for DNA synthesis		
Retrovirus (see Figure 19.8)	Yes	HIV, human immunodeficiency virus (AIDS); RNA tumor viruses (leukemia)

significance. For example, the three species of bacteria that cause the human diseases diphtheria, botulism, and scarlet fever would not be so harmful to humans without certain prophage genes that cause the host bacteria to make toxins. And the difference between the *E. coli* strain that resides in our intestines and the O157:H7 strain that has caused several deaths by food poisoning appears to be the presence of prophages in the O157:H7 strain.

Reproductive Cycles of Animal Viruses

Everyone has suffered from viral infections, whether cold sores, influenza, or the common cold. Like all viruses, those that cause illness in humans and other animals can reproduce only inside host cells. Many variations on the basic scheme of viral infection and reproduction are represented among the animal viruses. One key variable is the nature of the viral genome: Is it composed of DNA or RNA? Is it double-stranded or single-stranded? The nature of the genome is the basis for the common classification of viruses shown in **Table 19.1**. Single-stranded RNA viruses are further classified into three classes (IV–VI) according to how the RNA genome functions in a host cell.

Whereas few bacteriophages have an envelope or RNA genome, many animal viruses have both. In fact, nearly all animal viruses with RNA genomes have an envelope, as do some with DNA genomes (see Table 19.1). Rather than consider all the mechanisms of viral infection and reproduction, we will focus on the roles of viral envelopes and on the functioning of RNA as the genetic material of many animal viruses.

Viral Envelopes

An animal virus equipped with an envelope—that is, an outer membrane—uses it to enter the host cell. Protruding from the outer surface of this envelope are viral glycoproteins that bind to specific receptor molecules on the surface of a host cell. **Figure 19.7,** on the next page, outlines the events in the reproductive cycle of an enveloped virus with an RNA genome. The protein parts of envelope glycoproteins are made by ribosomes bound to the endoplasmic reticulum (ER) of the host cell; cellular enzymes in the ER and Golgi apparatus then add the sugars. The resulting viral glycoproteins, embedded in host cell-derived membrane, are transported to the cell surface. In a process much like exocytosis, new viral capsids are wrapped in membrane as they bud from the cell. In other words, the viral envelope is derived from the host cell's plasma membrane, although some of the molecules of this membrane are specified by viral genes. The enveloped viruses are now free to infect other cells. This reproductive cycle does not necessarily kill the host cell, in contrast to the lytic cycles of phages.

Some viruses have envelopes that are not derived from plasma membrane. Herpesviruses, for example, are temporarily cloaked in membrane derived from the nuclear envelope of the host; they then shed this membrane in the cytoplasm and acquire a new envelope made from membrane of the Golgi apparatus. These

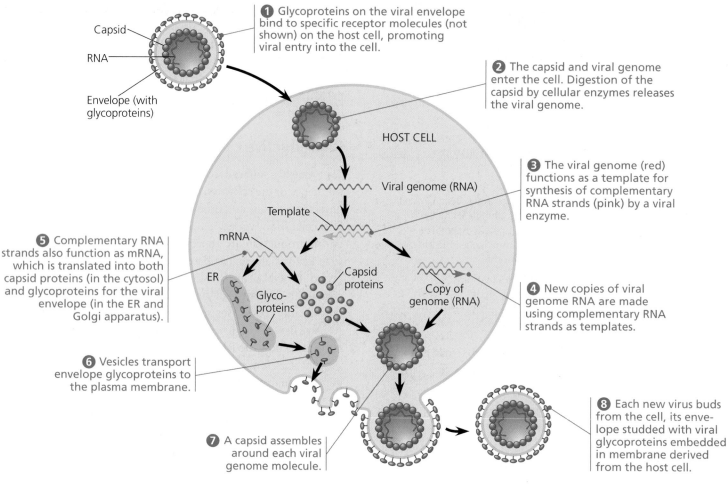

1 Glycoproteins on the viral envelope bind to specific receptor molecules (not shown) on the host cell, promoting viral entry into the cell.

Capsid

RNA

Envelope (with glycoproteins)

2 The capsid and viral genome enter the cell. Digestion of the capsid by cellular enzymes releases the viral genome.

HOST CELL

Viral genome (RNA)

3 The viral genome (red) functions as a template for synthesis of complementary RNA strands (pink) by a viral enzyme.

Template

mRNA

5 Complementary RNA strands also function as mRNA, which is translated into both capsid proteins (in the cytosol) and glycoproteins for the viral envelope (in the ER and Golgi apparatus).

ER

Glyco-proteins

Capsid proteins

Copy of genome (RNA)

4 New copies of viral genome RNA are made using complementary RNA strands as templates.

6 Vesicles transport envelope glycoproteins to the plasma membrane.

8 Each new virus buds from the cell, its envelope studded with viral glycoproteins embedded in membrane derived from the host cell.

7 A capsid assembles around each viral genome molecule.

▲ **Figure 19.7 The reproductive cycle of an enveloped RNA virus.** Shown here is a virus with a single-stranded RNA genome that functions as a template for synthesis of mRNA. Some enveloped viruses enter the host cell by fusion of the envelope with the cell's plasma membrane; others enter by endocytosis. For all enveloped RNA viruses, the formation of new envelopes for progeny viruses occurs by the mechanism depicted in this figure.

? *Name a virus that has infected you and has a reproductive cycle matching this one. (Hint: See Table 19.1.)*

viruses have a double-stranded DNA genome and reproduce within the host cell nucleus, using a combination of viral and cellular enzymes to replicate and transcribe their DNA. In the case of herpesviruses, copies of the viral DNA can remain behind as mini-chromosomes in the nuclei of certain nerve cells. There they remain latent until some sort of physical or emotional stress triggers a new round of active virus production. The infection of other cells by these new viruses causes the blisters characteristic of herpes, such as cold sores or genital sores. Once someone acquires a herpesvirus infection, flare-ups may recur throughout the person's life.

RNA as Viral Genetic Material

Although some phages and most plant viruses are RNA viruses, the broadest variety of RNA genomes is found among the viruses that infect animals. Among the three types of single-stranded RNA genomes found in animal viruses, the genome of class IV viruses can directly serve as mRNA and thus can be translated into viral protein immediately after infection. Figure 19.7 shows a virus of class V, in which the RNA genome serves as a *template* for mRNA synthesis. The RNA genome is transcribed into complementary RNA strands, which function both as mRNA and as templates for the synthesis of additional copies of genomic RNA. All viruses that require RNA → RNA synthesis to make mRNA use a viral enzyme capable of carrying out this process; there are no such enzymes in most cells. The viral enzyme is packaged with the genome inside the viral capsid.

The RNA animal viruses with the most complicated reproductive cycles are the **retroviruses** (class VI). These viruses are equipped with an enzyme called **reverse transcriptase**, which transcribes an RNA template into DNA, providing an RNA → DNA information flow, the opposite of the usual direction. This unusual phenomenon is the source of the name retroviruses (*retro* means "backward"). Of particular medical importance is **HIV (human immunodeficiency virus)**, the retrovirus that causes **AIDS (acquired immunodeficiency syndrome)**. HIV and other retroviruses are enveloped viruses that contain two identical molecules of single-stranded RNA and two molecules of reverse transcriptase.

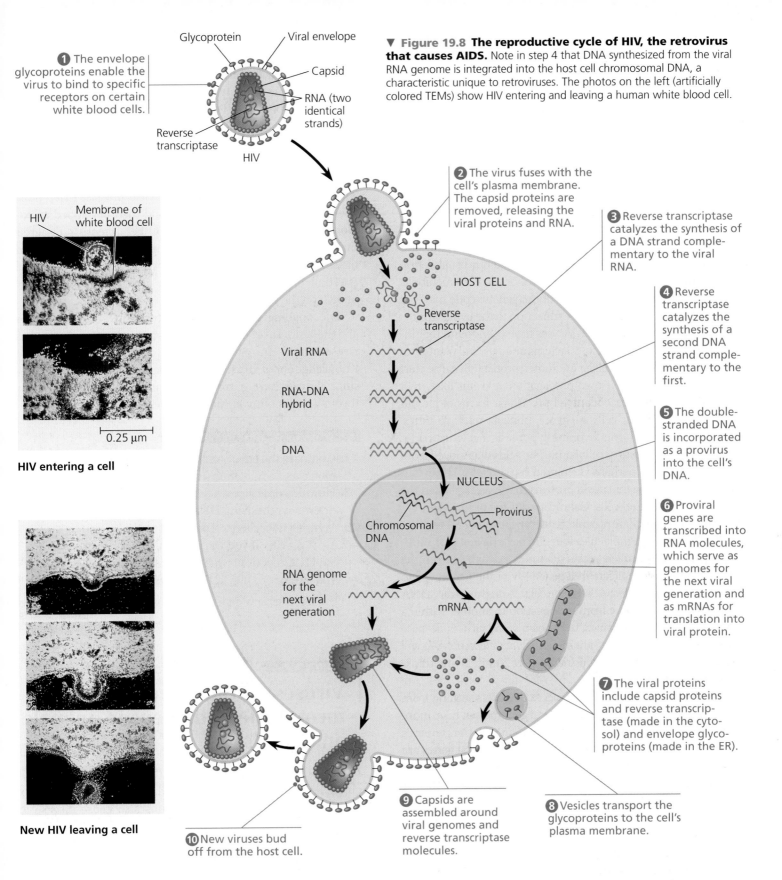

① The envelope glycoproteins enable the virus to bind to specific receptors on certain white blood cells.

Glycoprotein — Viral envelope
Capsid
RNA (two identical strands)
Reverse transcriptase
HIV

▼ **Figure 19.8 The reproductive cycle of HIV, the retrovirus that causes AIDS.** Note in step 4 that DNA synthesized from the viral RNA genome is integrated into the host cell chromosomal DNA, a characteristic unique to retroviruses. The photos on the left (artificially colored TEMs) show HIV entering and leaving a human white blood cell.

HIV
Membrane of white blood cell
0.25 μm

HIV entering a cell

New HIV leaving a cell

② The virus fuses with the cell's plasma membrane. The capsid proteins are removed, releasing the viral proteins and RNA.

③ Reverse transcriptase catalyzes the synthesis of a DNA strand complementary to the viral RNA.

④ Reverse transcriptase catalyzes the synthesis of a second DNA strand complementary to the first.

⑤ The double-stranded DNA is incorporated as a provirus into the cell's DNA.

⑥ Proviral genes are transcribed into RNA molecules, which serve as genomes for the next viral generation and as mRNAs for translation into viral protein.

⑦ The viral proteins include capsid proteins and reverse transcriptase (made in the cytosol) and envelope glycoproteins (made in the ER).

⑧ Vesicles transport the glycoproteins to the cell's plasma membrane.

⑨ Capsids are assembled around viral genomes and reverse transcriptase molecules.

⑩ New viruses bud off from the host cell.

HOST CELL
Reverse transcriptase
Viral RNA
RNA-DNA hybrid
DNA
NUCLEUS
Chromosomal DNA
Provirus
RNA genome for the next viral generation
mRNA

Figure 19.8 traces the HIV reproductive cycle, which is typical of a retrovirus. After HIV enters a host cell, its reverse transcriptase molecules are released into the cytoplasm, where they catalyze synthesis of viral DNA. The newly made viral DNA then enters the cell's nucleus and integrates into the DNA of a chromosome. The integrated viral DNA, called a **provirus**, never leaves the host's genome, remaining a permanent resident of the cell. (Recall that a prophage, in contrast, leaves the host's genome at the start of a lytic cycle.) The host's RNA polymerase transcribes the proviral DNA into RNA molecules, which can function both as mRNA for the synthesis of viral proteins and as genomes for the new viruses that will be assembled and released from the cell. In Chapter 43, we describe how HIV causes the deterioration of the immune system that occurs in AIDS.

Evolution of Viruses

We began this chapter by asking whether or not viruses are alive. Viruses do not really fit our definition of living organisms. An isolated virus is biologically inert, unable to replicate its genes or regenerate its own supply of ATP. Yet it has a genetic program written in the universal language of life. Do we think of viruses as nature's most complex associations of molecules or as the simplest forms of life? Either way, we must bend our usual definitions. Although viruses cannot reproduce or carry out metabolic activities independently, their use of the genetic code makes it hard to deny their evolutionary connection to the living world.

How did viruses originate? Viruses have been found that infect every form of life—not just bacteria, animals, and plants, but also archaea, fungi, and algae and other protists. Because they depend on cells for their own propagation, it seems likely that viruses are not the descendants of precellular forms of life but evolved *after* the first cells appeared, possibly multiple times. Most molecular biologists favor the hypothesis that viruses originated from naked bits of cellular nucleic acids that moved from one cell to another, perhaps via injured cell surfaces. The evolution of genes coding for capsid proteins may have facilitated the infection of uninjured cells. Candidates for the original sources of viral genomes include plasmids and transposons. *Plasmids* are small, circular DNA molecules found in bacteria and in the unicellular eukaryotes called yeasts. Plasmids exist apart from the cell's genome, can replicate independently of the genome, and are occasionally transferred between cells. *Transposons* are DNA segments that can move from one location to another within a cell's genome. Thus, plasmids, transposons, and viruses all share an important feature: They are *mobile genetic elements*. We will discuss plasmids in more detail in Chapters 20 and 27 and transposons in Chapter 21.

Consistent with this vision of pieces of DNA shuttling from cell to cell is the observation that a viral genome can have more in common with the genome of its host than with the genomes of viruses that infect other hosts. Indeed, some viral genes are essentially identical to genes of the host. On the other hand, recent sequencing of many viral genomes has shown that the genetic sequences of some viruses are quite similar to those of seemingly distantly related viruses; for example, some animal viruses share similar sequences with plant viruses. This genetic similarity may reflect the persistence of groups of viral genes that were favored by natural selection during the early evolution of viruses and the eukaryotic cells that served as their hosts.

The debate about the origin of viruses has been reinvigorated recently by reports of mimivirus, the largest virus yet discovered. Mimivirus is a double-stranded DNA virus with an icosa-

hedral capsid that is 400 nm in diameter. (The beginning of its name is short for *mi*micking *mi*crobe because the virus is the size of a small bacterium.) Its genome contains 1.2 million bases (about 100 times as many as the influenza virus genome) and an estimated 1,000 genes. Perhaps the most surprising aspect of mimivirus, however, is that some of the genes appear to code for products previously thought to be hallmarks of cellular genomes. These products include proteins involved in translation, DNA repair, protein folding, and polysaccharide synthesis. The researchers who described mimivirus propose that it most likely evolved *before* the first cells and then developed an exploitative relationship with them. Other scientists disagree, maintaining that the virus evolved more recently than cells and has simply been efficient at scavenging genes from its hosts. The question of whether some viruses deserve their own early branch on the tree of life may not be answered for some time.

The ongoing evolutionary relationship between viruses and the genomes of their host cells is an association that makes viruses very useful experimental systems in molecular biology. Knowledge about viruses also has many practical applications, since viruses have a tremendous impact on all organisms through their ability to cause disease.

CONCEPT CHECK 19.2

1. Compare the effect on the host cell of a lytic (virulent) phage and a lysogenic (temperate) phage.
2. How do some viruses reproduce without possessing or ever synthesizing DNA?
3. Why is HIV called a retrovirus?
4. **WHAT IF?** If you were a researcher trying to combat HIV infection, what molecular processes could you attempt to block? (See Figure 19.8.)

For suggested answers, see Appendix A.

CONCEPT 19.3
Viruses, viroids, and prions are formidable pathogens in animals and plants

Diseases caused by viral infections afflict humans, agricultural crops, and livestock worldwide. Other smaller, less complex entities known as viroids and prions also cause disease in plants and animals, respectively.

Viral Diseases in Animals

A viral infection can produce symptoms by a number of different routes. Viruses may damage or kill cells by causing the release of hydrolytic enzymes from lysosomes. Some viruses cause infected cells to produce toxins that lead to disease symptoms, and some have molecular components that are toxic, such as envelope proteins. How much damage a virus causes depends partly on the ability of the infected tissue to regenerate by cell division. People usually recover completely from colds because the epithelium of the respiratory tract, which the viruses infect, can efficiently repair itself. In contrast, damage inflicted by poliovirus to mature nerve cells is permanent, because these cells do not divide and usually cannot be replaced. Many of the temporary symptoms associated with viral infections, such as fever and aches, actually result from the body's own efforts at defending itself against infection rather than from cell death caused by the virus.

The immune system is a complex and critical part of the body's natural defenses (see Chapter 43). It is also the basis for the major medical tool for preventing viral infections—vaccines. A **vaccine** is a harmless variant or derivative of a pathogen that stimulates the immune system to mount defenses against the harmful pathogen. Smallpox, a viral disease that was at one time a devastating scourge in many parts of the world, was eradicated by a vaccination program carried out by the World Health Organization. The very narrow host range of the smallpox virus—it infects only humans—was a critical factor in the success of this program. Similar worldwide vaccination campaigns are currently under way to eradicate polio and measles. Effective vaccines are also available against rubella, mumps, hepatitis B, and a number of other viral diseases.

Although vaccines can prevent certain viral illnesses, medical technology can do little, at present, to cure most viral infections once they occur. The antibiotics that help us recover from bacterial infections are powerless against viruses. Antibiotics kill bacteria by inhibiting enzymes specific to bacteria but have no effect on eukaryotic or virally encoded enzymes. However, the few enzymes that are encoded by viruses have provided targets for other drugs. Most antiviral drugs resemble nucleosides and as a result interfere with viral nucleic acid synthesis. One such drug is acyclovir, which impedes herpesvirus reproduction by inhibiting the viral polymerase that synthesizes viral DNA. Similarly, azidothymidine (AZT) curbs HIV reproduction by interfering with the synthesis of DNA by reverse transcriptase. In the past two decades, much effort has gone into developing drugs against HIV. Currently, multidrug treatments, sometimes called "cocktails," have been found to be most effective. Such treatments commonly include a combination of two nucleoside mimics and a protease inhibitor, which interferes with an enzyme required for assembly of the viruses.

Emerging Viruses

Viruses that appear suddenly or are new to medical scientists are often referred to as *emerging viruses*. HIV, the AIDS virus, is a classic example: This virus appeared in San Francisco in the early 1980s, seemingly out of nowhere, although later studies uncovered a case in the Belgian Congo that occurred as early as 1959. The deadly Ebola virus, recognized initially in 1976 in central Africa, is one of several emerging viruses that cause *hemorrhagic fever*, an often fatal syndrome (set of symptoms) characterized by fever, vomiting, massive bleeding, and circulatory system collapse. A number of other dangerous emerging viruses cause encephalitis, inflammation of the brain. One example is the West Nile virus, which appeared in North America for the first time in 1999 and has spread to all 48 contiguous states in the United States.

Severe acute respiratory syndrome (*SARS*) first appeared in southern China in November 2002. A global outbreak that occurred during the following eight months infected about 8,000 people and killed more than 700. Researchers quickly identified the infectious agent as a *coronavirus*, a virus with a single-stranded RNA genome (class IV) that had not previously been known to cause disease in humans. Public health workers responded rapidly, isolating patients and quarantining those who had come in contact with them. Because of low infectivity and other characteristics of the SARS virus, this rapid response succeeded in quelling the outbreak before it could infect a much larger population.

How do such viruses burst on the human scene, giving rise to harmful diseases that were previously rare or even unknown? Three processes contribute to the emergence of viral diseases. The first, and perhaps most important, is the mutation of existing viruses. RNA viruses tend to have an unusually high rate of mutation because errors in replicating their RNA genomes are not corrected by proofreading. Some mutations change existing viruses into new genetic varieties (strains) that can cause disease, even in individuals who are immune to the ancestral virus. For instance, general outbreaks of flu, or flu **epidemics**, are caused by new strains of influenza virus genetically different enough from earlier strains that people have little immunity to them.

A second process that can lead to the emergence of viral diseases is the dissemination of a viral disease from a small, isolated human population. For instance, AIDS went unnamed and virtually unnoticed for decades before it began to spread around the world. In this case, technological and social factors, including affordable international travel, blood transfusions, sexual promiscuity, and the abuse of intravenous drugs, allowed a previously rare human disease to become a global scourge.

A third source of new viral diseases in humans is the spread of existing viruses from other animals. Scientists estimate that about three-quarters of new human diseases originate in this way. Animals that harbor and can transmit a particular virus but are generally unaffected by it are said to act as a natural reservoir for that virus. For example, a species of bat has been identified as the likely natural reservoir of the SARS virus. Bats are sold as food in China, and their dried feces are even sold for medicinal uses; either of these practices could provide a route for transmission of the virus to humans.

Flu epidemics provide an instructive example of the effects of viruses moving between species. There are three types of influenza virus: types B and C, which infect only humans and have never caused an epidemic, and type A, which infects a wide range of animals, including birds, pigs, horses, and humans. Influenza A strains have caused three major flu epidemics among humans in the last 100 years. The worst was the "Spanish flu" **pandemic** (a global epidemic) of 1918–1919, which killed about 40 million people, including many World War I soldiers **(Figure 19.9a)**. Evidence points to birds as the source of the 1918 flu pandemic.

A likely scenario for that pandemic and others is that they began when the virus mutated as it passed from one host species to another. When an animal is infected with more than one strain of flu virus, the different strains can undergo genetic recombination if the RNA molecules making up their genomes mix and match during viral assembly. Coupled with mutation, these changes can lead to the emergence of a viral strain that is capable of infecting human cells. Having never

been exposed to that particular strain before, humans will lack immunity, and the recombinant virus has the potential to be highly pathogenic. If such a flu virus recombines with viruses that circulate widely among humans, it may acquire the ability to spread easily from person to person, dramatically increasing the potential for a major human outbreak.

Different strains of influenza A are given standardized names; for example, the strain that caused the 1918 flu is called H1N1. The name identifies which forms of two viral surface proteins are present: hemagglutinin (H) and neuraminidase (N). There are 16 different types of hemagglutinin, a protein that helps the flu virus attach to host cells, and 9 types of neuraminidase, an enzyme that helps release new virus particles from infected cells. Water birds have been found that carry viruses with all possible combinations of H and N.

In 1997, at least 18 people in Hong Kong were infected with an H5N1 virus **(Figure 19.9b)**; six of these people subsequently died. The same strain, previously seen only in wild birds, had killed several thousand chickens earlier that year, presumably passed along from wild birds or other species. A mass culling of all of Hong Kong's 1.5 million domestic birds appeared to stop that outbreak. Beginning in 2002, however, new cases of H5N1 human infection began to crop up around southeast Asia. By 2007, the disease caused by this virus, now called "avian flu," had killed about 160 people. Perhaps even more alarming is the overall mortality rate, which is greater than 50%. More than 100 million birds have either died from the disease or been killed to prevent the spread of infection; efforts are under way to vaccinate birds of several species **(Figure 19.9c)**.

The geographical and host ranges of avian flu virus continue to expand. It has shown up in wild or domestic birds in Africa and Europe, as well as in pigs, tigers, and domestic cats and dogs. The expanding host range provides increasing opportunities for different strains of virus to reassort their genetic material and for new strains to emerge. If the H5N1 avian flu virus evolves so that it can spread easily from person to person, it could bring about a major human outbreak. Human-to-human transmission is strongly suspected in several cases where the disease has clustered in families, but so far the disease has not spread beyond small groups to cause an epidemic. For those studying emerging viruses and their ability to give rise to a human pandemic, avian flu provides a sobering lesson in progress.

As we have seen, emerging viruses are generally not new; rather, they are existing viruses that mutate, disseminate more widely in the current host species, or spread to new host species. Changes in host behavior or environmental changes can increase the viral traffic responsible for emerging diseases. For example, new roads through remote areas can allow viruses to spread between previously isolated human populations. Also, the destruction of forests to expand cropland can bring humans into contact with other animals that may host viruses capable of infecting humans.

(a) The 1918 flu pandemic. Many of those infected were treated in large makeshift hospitals, such as this one.

(b) Influenza A H5N1 virus. Virus particles are seen budding from an infected cell in this colorized TEM.

(c) Vaccinating ducks. Veterinarians administer vaccinations in a region of China reporting cases of avian flu, caused by strain H5N1.

▲ **Figure 19.9 Influenza in humans and other animals.**

Viral Diseases in Plants

More than 2,000 types of viral diseases of plants are known, and together they account for an estimated annual loss of $15 billion worldwide due to their destruction of agricultural and horticultural crops. Common signs of viral infection include bleached or brown spots on leaves and fruits, stunted growth, and damaged flowers or roots, all tending to diminish the yield and quality of crops (Figure 19.10).

Plant viruses have the same basic structure and mode of reproduction as animal viruses. Most plant viruses discovered thus far, including tobacco mosaic virus (TMV), have an RNA genome. Many have a helical capsid, like TMV (see Figure 19.3a); others have an icosahedral capsid.

Viral diseases of plants spread by two major routes. In the first route, called *horizontal transmission*, a plant is infected from an external source of the virus. Because the invading virus must get past the plant's outer protective layer of cells (the epidermis), a plant becomes more susceptible to viral infections if it has been damaged by wind, injury, or herbivores. Herbivores, especially insects, pose a double threat because they can also act as carriers of viruses, transmitting disease from plant to plant. Farmers and gardeners may transmit plant viruses inadvertently on pruning shears and other tools. The other route of viral infection is *vertical transmission*, in which a plant inherits a viral infection from a parent. Vertical transmission can occur in asexual propagation (for example, cuttings) or in sexual reproduction via infected seeds.

Once a virus enters a plant cell and begins reproducing, viral genomes and associated proteins can spread throughout the plant by means of plasmodesmata, the cytoplasmic connections that penetrate the walls between adjacent plant cells (see Figure 6.28). The passage of viral macromolecules from cell to cell is facilitated by virally encoded proteins that cause enlargement of plasmodesmata. Scientists have not yet devised cures for most viral plant diseases. Consequently, their efforts are focused largely on reducing the transmission of such diseases and on breeding resistant varieties of crop plants.

Viroids and Prions: The Simplest Infectious Agents

As small and simple as viruses are, they dwarf another class of pathogens: **viroids**. These are circular RNA molecules, only a few hundred nucleotides long, that infect plants. Viroids do not encode proteins but can replicate in host plant cells, apparently using host cell enzymes. These small RNA molecules seem to cause errors in the regulatory systems that control plant growth, and the typical signs of viroid diseases are abnormal development and stunted growth. One viroid disease, called cadang-cadang, has killed more than 10 million coconut palms in the Philippines.

An important lesson from viroids is that a single molecule can be an infectious agent that spreads a disease. But viroids are nucleic acid, whose ability to be replicated is well known. Even more surprising is the evidence for infectious *proteins*, called **prions**, which appear to cause a number of degenerative brain diseases in various animal species. These diseases include scrapie in sheep; mad cow disease, which has plagued the European beef industry in recent years; and Creutzfeldt-Jakob disease in humans, which has caused the death of some 150 people in Great Britain over the past decade. Prions are most likely transmitted in food, as may occur when people eat prion-laden beef from cattle with mad cow disease. Kuru, another human disease caused by prions, was identified in the early 1900s among the South Fore natives of New Guinea. A kuru epidemic peaked there in the 1960s, puzzling scientists, who at first thought the disease had a genetic basis. Eventually, however, anthropological investigations ferreted out how the disease was spread: ritual cannibalism, a widespread practice among South Fore natives at that time.

Two characteristics of prions are especially alarming. First, prions act very slowly, with an incubation period of at least ten years before symptoms develop. The lengthy incubation period prevents sources of infection from being identified until long after the first cases appear, allowing many more infections to occur. Second, prions are virtually indestructible; they are not destroyed or deactivated by heating to normal cooking temperatures. To date, there is no known cure for

▲ **Figure 19.10 Viral infection of plants.**
Infection with particular viruses causes irregular brown patches on tomatoes (left), black blotching on squash (center), and streaking in tulips due to redistribution of pigment granules (right).

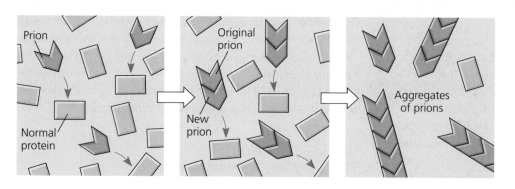

◀ **Figure 19.11 Model for how prions propagate.** Prions are misfolded versions of normal brain proteins. When a prion contacts a normally folded version of the same protein, it may induce the normal protein to assume the abnormal shape. The resulting chain reaction may continue until high levels of prion aggregation cause cellular malfunction and eventual degeneration of the brain.

prion diseases, and the only hope for developing effective treatments lies in understanding the process of infection.

How can a protein, which cannot replicate itself, be a transmissible pathogen? According to the leading model, a prion is a misfolded form of a protein normally present in brain cells. When the prion gets into a cell containing the normal form of the protein, the prion somehow converts normal protein molecules to the misfolded prion versions. Several prions then aggregate into a complex that can convert other normal proteins to prions, which join the chain **(Figure 19.11)**. Prion aggregation interferes with normal cellular functions and causes disease symptoms. This model was greeted with much skepticism when it was first proposed by Stanley Prusiner in the early 1980s, but it is now widely accepted. Prusiner was awarded the Nobel Prize in 1997 for his work on prions.

CONCEPT CHECK 19.3

1. Describe two ways a preexisting virus can become an emerging virus.
2. Contrast horizontal and vertical transmission of viruses in plants.
3. TMV has been isolated from virtually all commercial tobacco products. Why, then, is TMV infection not an additional hazard for smokers?
4. **WHAT IF?** How might the H5N1 avian flu virus have spread from Asia to Africa and Europe? Is it likely that human air travel could have spread this virus? How could you test your hypothesis?

For suggested answers, see Appendix A.

Chapter 19 Review

 MEDIA Go to the Study Area at **www.masteringbio.com** for BioFlix 3-D Animations, MP3 Tutors, Videos, Practice Tests, an eBook, and more.

SUMMARY OF KEY CONCEPTS

CONCEPT 19.1

A virus consists of a nucleic acid surrounded by a protein coat (pp. 381–384)

▶ **The Discovery of Viruses: *Scientific Inquiry*** Researchers discovered viruses in the late 1800s by studying a plant disease, tobacco mosaic disease.

▶ **Structure of Viruses** A virus is a small nucleic acid genome enclosed in a protein capsid and sometimes a membranous envelope containing viral proteins that help viruses enter cells. The genome may be single- or double-stranded DNA or RNA.

CONCEPT 19.2

Viruses reproduce only in host cells (pp. 384–390)

▶ **General Features of Viral Reproductive Cycles** Viruses use enzymes, ribosomes, and small molecules of host cells to synthesize progeny viruses. Each type of virus has a characteristic host range.

▶ **Reproductive Cycles of Phages** Phages (viruses that infect bacteria) can reproduce by two alternative mechanisms: the lytic cycle and the lysogenic cycle.

Lytic cycle
• Virulent or temperate phage
• Destruction of host DNA
• Production of new phages
• Lysis of host cell causes release of progeny phages

Lysogenic cycle
• Temperate phage only
• Genome integrates into bacterial chromosome as prophage, which
(1) is replicated and passed on to daughter cells and
(2) can be induced to leave the chromosome and initiate a lytic cycle

► **Reproductive Cycles of Animal Viruses** Many animal viruses have an envelope. Retroviruses (such as HIV) use the enzyme reverse transcriptase to copy their RNA genome into DNA, which can be integrated into the host genome as a provirus.

► **Evolution of Viruses** Since viruses can reproduce only within cells, they probably evolved after the first cells appeared, perhaps as packaged fragments of cellular nucleic acid. The origin of viruses is still being debated.

MEDIA

Activity Simplified Viral Reproductive Cycle
Activity Phage Lytic Cycle
Activity Phage Lysogenic and Lytic Cycles
Activity Retrovirus (HIV) Reproductive Cycle

CONCEPT 19.3

Viruses, viroids, and prions are formidable pathogens in animals and plants (pp. 390–394)

► **Viral Diseases in Animals** Symptoms may be caused by direct viral harm to cells or by the body's immune response. Vaccines stimulate the immune system to defend the host against specific viruses.

► **Emerging Viruses** Outbreaks of "new" viral diseases in humans are usually caused by existing viruses that expand their host territory. The H5N1 avian flu virus is being closely monitored for its potential to cause a serious flu pandemic.

► **Viral Diseases in Plants** Viruses enter plant cells through damaged cell walls (horizontal transmission) or are inherited from a parent (vertical transmission).

► **Viroids and Prions: The Simplest Infectious Agents** Viroids are naked RNA molecules that infect plants and disrupt their growth. Prions are slow-acting, virtually indestructible infectious proteins that cause brain diseases in mammals.

MEDIA

Investigation What Causes Infections in AIDS Patients?
Investigation Why Do AIDS Rates Differ Across the U.S.?

TESTING YOUR KNOWLEDGE

SELF-QUIZ

1. A bacterium is infected with an experimentally constructed bacteriophage composed of the T2 phage protein coat and T4 phage DNA. The new phages produced would have
   a. T2 protein and T4 DNA.
   b. T2 protein and T2 DNA.
   c. a mixture of the DNA and proteins of both phages.
   d. T4 protein and T4 DNA.
   e. T4 protein and T2 DNA.

2. RNA viruses require their own supply of certain enzymes because
   a. host cells rapidly destroy the viruses.
   b. host cells lack enzymes that can replicate the viral genome.
   c. these enzymes translate viral mRNA into proteins.
   d. these enzymes penetrate host cell membranes.
   e. these enzymes cannot be made in host cells.

3. Which of the following characteristics, structures, or processes is common to both bacteria and viruses?
   a. metabolism
   b. ribosomes

c. genetic material composed of nucleic acid
d. cell division
e. independent existence

4. Emerging viruses arise by
   a. mutation of existing viruses.
   b. the spread of existing viruses to new host species.
   c. the spread of existing viruses more widely within their host species.
   d. all of the above
   e. none of the above

5. To cause a human pandemic, the H5N1 avian flu virus would have to
   a. spread to primates such as chimpanzees.
   b. develop into a virus with a different host range.
   c. become capable of human-to-human transmission.
   d. arise independently in chickens in North and South America.
   e. become much more pathogenic.

6. **DRAW IT** Redraw Figure 19.7 to show the reproductive cycle of a virus with a single-stranded genome that can function as mRNA (a class IV virus).

For Self-Quiz answers, see Appendix A.

MEDIA Visit the Study Area at **www.masteringbio.com** for a Practice Test.

EVOLUTION CONNECTION

7. The success of some viruses lies in their ability to evolve rapidly within the host. Such a virus evades the host's defenses by mutating and producing many altered progeny viruses before the body can mount an attack. Thus, the viruses present late in infection differ from those that initially infected the body. Discuss this as an example of evolution in microcosm. Which viral lineages tend to predominate?

SCIENTIFIC INQUIRY

8. When bacteria infect an animal, the number of bacteria in the body increases in an exponential fashion (graph A). After infection by a virulent animal virus with a lytic reproductive cycle, there is no evidence of infection for a while. Then, the number of viruses rises suddenly and subsequently increases in a series of steps (graph B). Explain the difference in the curves.

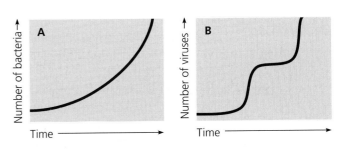

Biological Inquiry: A Workbook of Investigative Cases Explore West Nile virus in the case "The Donor's Dilemma." Explore the immune response to flu pathogens with the case "Pandemic Flu (Past and Possible)."

Biotechnology

▲ Figure 20.1 **How can this array of spots be used to compare normal and cancerous tissues?**

KEY CONCEPTS

20.1 DNA cloning yields multiple copies of a gene or other DNA segment

20.2 DNA technology allows us to study the sequence, expression, and function of a gene

20.3 Cloning organisms may lead to production of stem cells for research and other applications

20.4 The practical applications of DNA technology affect our lives in many ways

OVERVIEW

The DNA Toolbox

In 1995, a major scientific milestone was announced: For the first time, researchers had sequenced the entire genome of a free-living organism, the bacterium *Haemophilus influenzae.* This news electrified the scientific community. Few among them would have dared to dream that a mere 12 years later, genome sequencing would be under way for more than 2,000 species. By 2007, researchers had completely sequenced hundreds of prokaryotic genomes and dozens of eukaryotic ones, including all 3 billion base pairs of the human genome.

Ultimately, these achievements can be attributed to advances in DNA technology—methods of working with and manipulating DNA—that had their roots in the 1970s. A key accomplishment was the invention of techniques for making **recombinant DNA**, DNA molecules formed when segments of DNA from two different sources—often different species—are combined *in vitro* (in a test tube). This advance set the stage for further development of powerful techniques for analyzing genes and gene expression. How scientists prepare recombinant DNA and use DNA technology to answer fundamental biological questions are one focus of this chapter.

Another focus of the chapter is how our lives are affected by **biotechnology**, the manipulation of organisms or their compo-

nents to make useful products. Biotechnology has a long history that includes such early practices as selective breeding of farm animals and using microorganisms to make wine and cheese. Today, biotechnology also encompasses **genetic engineering**, the direct manipulation of genes for practical purposes. Genetic engineering has launched a revolution in biotechnology, greatly expanding the scope of its potential applications. Tools from the DNA toolbox are now applied in ways that were unthinkable only a decade ago, affecting everything from agriculture to criminal law to medical research. For instance, on the DNA microarray in **Figure 20.1**, the colored spots represent the relative level of expression of 2,400 human genes. Using microarray analysis, researchers can quickly compare gene expression in different samples, such as those obtained from normal and cancerous tissues. The knowledge gained from such gene expression studies is making a significant contribution to the study of cancer and other diseases.

In this chapter, we first describe the main techniques for manipulating DNA and analyzing gene expression and function. Next, we explore parallel advances in cloning organisms and producing stem cells, techniques that have both expanded our basic understanding of biology and enhanced our ability to apply this understanding to global problems. Finally, we survey the practical applications of biotechnology and consider some of the social and ethical issues that arise as modern biotechnology becomes more pervasive in our lives.

CONCEPT 20.1

DNA cloning yields multiple copies of a gene or other DNA segment

The molecular biologist studying a particular gene faces a challenge. Naturally occurring DNA molecules are very long, and a single molecule usually carries many genes. Moreover, in many eukaryotic genomes, genes occupy only a small proportion of the chromosomal DNA, the rest being noncoding nucleotide sequences. A single human gene, for example, might constitute only $\frac{1}{100,000}$ of a chromosomal DNA molecule. As a further complication, the distinctions between a gene and the surrounding DNA are subtle, consisting only of differences in nucleotide sequence. To work directly with specific genes, scientists have developed methods for preparing well-defined segments of DNA in multiple identical copies, a process called *DNA cloning*.

DNA Cloning and Its Applications: *A Preview*

Most methods for cloning pieces of DNA in the laboratory share certain general features. One common approach uses bacteria, most often *Escherichia coli*. Recall from Chapter 16 that the *E. coli* chromosome is a large circular molecule of DNA. In addition, *E. coli* and many other bacteria have **plasmids**, small circular DNA molecules that replicate separately from the bacterial chromosome. A plasmid has only a small number of genes; these genes may be useful when the bacterium is in a particular environment but may not be required for survival or reproduction under most conditions.

To clone pieces of DNA in the laboratory, researchers first isolate a plasmid from a bacterial cell and insert DNA from another source ("foreign" DNA) into it **(Figure 20.2)**. The resulting plasmid is now a recombinant DNA molecule, combining DNA from two sources. The plasmid is then returned to a bacterial cell, producing a *recombinant bacterium*. This single cell reproduces through repeated cell divisions to form a clone of cells, a population of genetically identical cells. Because the dividing bacteria replicate the recombinant plasmid and pass it on to their descendants, the foreign DNA and any genes it carries are cloned at the same time. The production of multiple copies of a single gene is called **gene cloning**.

Gene cloning is useful for two basic purposes: to make many copies of a particular gene and to produce a protein product. Researchers can isolate copies

of a cloned gene from bacteria for use in basic research or to endow an organism with a new metabolic capability, such as pest resistance. For example, a resistance gene present in one crop species might be cloned and transferred into plants of another species. Alternatively, a protein with medical uses, such as human growth hormone, can be harvested in large quantities from cultures of bacteria carrying the cloned gene for the protein.

Most protein-coding genes exist in only one copy per haploid genome—roughly one part per million in the case of human DNA—so the ability to prepare large amounts of

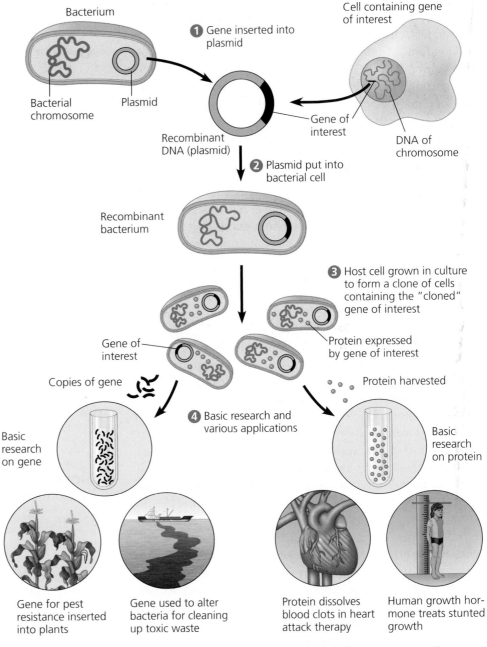

▲ **Figure 20.2 A preview of gene cloning and some uses of cloned genes.** In this simplified diagram of gene cloning, we start with a plasmid isolated from a bacterial cell and a gene of interest from another organism. Only one copy of the plasmid and one copy of the gene of interest are shown at the top of the figure, but the starting materials would include many copies of each.

such rare DNA fragments is crucial for any application involving a single gene. In the rest of this chapter, you will learn more about the techniques outlined in Figure 20.2 and related methods.

Using Restriction Enzymes to Make Recombinant DNA

Gene cloning and genetic engineering rely on the use of enzymes that cut DNA molecules at a limited number of specific locations. These enzymes, called restriction endonucleases, or **restriction enzymes**, were discovered in the late 1960s by researchers studying bacteria. As you learned in Chapter 19, restriction enzymes protect the bacterial cell by cutting up foreign DNA from other organisms or phages.

Hundreds of different restriction enzymes have been identified and isolated. Each restriction enzyme is very specific, recognizing a particular short DNA sequence, or **restriction site**, and cutting both DNA strands at precise points within this restriction site. The DNA of a bacterial cell is protected from the cell's own restriction enzymes by the addition of methyl groups (—CH_3) to adenines or cytosines within the sequences recognized by the enzymes.

The top of **Figure 20.3** illustrates a restriction site recognized by a particular restriction enzyme from *E. coli*. As shown in this example, most restriction sites are symmetrical. That is, the sequence of nucleotides is the same on both strands when read in the $5' \rightarrow 3'$ direction. Most restriction enzymes recognize sequences containing four to eight nucleotides. Because any sequence this short usually occurs (by chance) many times in a long DNA molecule, a restriction enzyme will make many cuts in a DNA molecule, yielding a set of **restriction fragments**. All copies of a particular DNA molecule always yield the same set of restriction fragments when exposed to the same restriction enzyme. In other words, a restriction enzyme cuts a DNA molecule in a reproducible way. (Later you will learn how the different fragments can be separated and distinguished from each other.)

The most useful restriction enzymes cleave the sugar-phosphate backbones in the two DNA strands in a staggered manner, as indicated in Figure 20.3. The resulting double-stranded restriction fragments have at least one single-stranded end, called a **sticky end**. These short extensions can form hydrogen-bonded base pairs with complementary sticky ends on any other DNA molecules cut with the same enzyme. The associations formed in this way are only temporary but can be made permanent by the enzyme **DNA ligase**. As you learned in Chapter 16, this enzyme catalyzes the formation of covalent bonds that close up the sugar-phosphate backbones of DNA strands; for example, it joins Okazaki fragments during replication. You can see at the bottom of Figure 20.3 that the ligase-catalyzed joining of DNA from two different sources produces a stable recombinant DNA molecule.

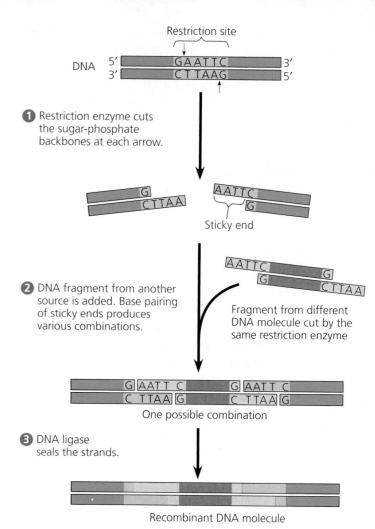

▲ **Figure 20.3 Using a restriction enzyme and DNA ligase to make recombinant DNA.** The restriction enzyme in this example (called *Eco*RI) recognizes a specific six-base-pair sequence, the restriction site, and makes staggered cuts in the sugar-phosphate backbones within this sequence, producing fragments with sticky ends. Any fragments with complementary sticky ends can base-pair, including the two original fragments; if the fragments come from different DNA molecules, the product is recombinant DNA.

DRAW IT *The restriction enzyme* Hind III *recognizes the sequence 5'-AAGCTT-3', cutting between the two 'A's. Draw the double-stranded sequence before and after the enzyme cuts.*

Cloning a Eukaryotic Gene in a Bacterial Plasmid

Now that you've learned about restriction enzymes and DNA ligase, we can take a closer look at how genes are cloned in plasmids. The original plasmid is called a **cloning vector**, defined as a DNA molecule that can carry foreign DNA into a host cell and replicate there. Bacterial plasmids are widely used as cloning vectors for several reasons. They can be easily isolated from bacteria, manipulated to form recombinant plasmids by insertion of foreign DNA *in vitro*, and then reintroduced into bacterial cells. Moreover, recombinant bacterial plasmids (and the foreign DNA they carry) multiply rapidly owing to the high reproductive rate of their host cells.

Producing Clones of Cells Carrying Recombinant Plasmids

Let's say we are researchers interested in studying the β-globin gene in a particular species of hummingbird to see if this oxygen-carrying protein is different from its counterpart in other, less metabolically active species. **Figure 20.4** details one method for cloning hummingbird genes using a bacterial plasmid as the cloning vector.

❶ We begin by isolating hummingbird genomic DNA from hummingbird cells. We also isolate our chosen vector, a particular bacterial plasmid from *E. coli* cells. The plasmid has been engineered to carry two genes that will later prove useful: *amp^R*, which makes *E. coli* cells resistant to the antibiotic ampicillin, and *lacZ*, which encodes an enzyme called β-galactosidase that hydrolyzes the sugar lactose. This enzyme can also hydrolyze a similar synthetic molecule called X-gal to form a blue product. The plasmid contains only one copy of the restriction site recognized by the restriction enzyme used in the next step; that site is within the *lacZ* gene.

❷ Both the plasmid and the hummingbird DNA are cut with the same restriction enzyme, and then ❸ the fragments are mixed together, allowing base pairing between their complementary sticky ends. We then add DNA ligase, which covalently bonds the sugarphosphate backbones of the fragments whose sticky ends have base-paired. Some of the resulting recombinant plasmids contain hummingbird DNA fragments like the three shown in Figure 20.4; one of the three carries the β-globin gene. This step will also generate other products, such as plasmids containing several hummingbird DNA fragments, a combination of two plasmids, or a rejoined, nonrecombinant version of the original plasmid.

❹ The DNA mixture is then added to bacteria that have a mutation in the *lacZ* gene on their own chromosome, making them unable to hydrolyze lactose or X-gal. Under suitable experimental conditions, the cells take up foreign DNA by

---

▼ **Figure 20.4** # Research Method

Cloning Genes in Bacterial Plasmids

APPLICATION　Gene cloning is a process that produces many copies of a gene of interest. These copies can be used in sequencing the gene, in producing its encoded protein, or in basic research or other applications.

TECHNIQUE　In this example, hummingbird genes are inserted into plasmids from *E. coli*. Only three plasmids and three hummingbird DNA fragments are shown, but millions of copies of the plasmid and a mixture of millions of different hummingbird DNA fragments would be present in the samples.

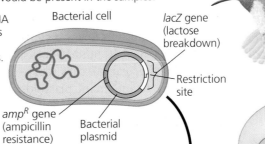

❶ Isolate plasmid DNA from bacterial cells and DNA from hummingbird cells. The hummingbird DNA contains the gene of interest.

❷ Cut both DNA samples with the same restriction enzyme, one that makes a single cut within the *lacZ* gene and many cuts within the hummingbird DNA.

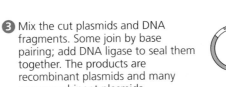

❸ Mix the cut plasmids and DNA fragments. Some join by base pairing; add DNA ligase to seal them together. The products are recombinant plasmids and many nonrecombinant plasmids.

Recombinant plasmids　　Nonrecombinant plasmid

❹ Mix the DNA with bacterial cells that have a mutation in their own *lacZ* gene. Some cells take up a recombinant plasmid or other DNA molecule by transformation.

Bacteria carrying plasmids

❺ Plate the bacteria on agar containing ampicillin and X-gal, a molecule resembling lactose. Incubate until colonies grow.

RESULTS　Only a cell that took up a plasmid, which has the *amp^R* gene, will reproduce and form a colony. Colonies with nonrecombinant plasmids will be blue, because they can hydrolyze X-gal, forming a blue product. Colonies with recombinant plasmids, in which *lacZ* is disrupted, will be white, because they cannot hydrolyze X-gal.

Colony carrying non-recombinant plasmid with intact *lacZ* gene

Colony carrying recombinant plasmid with disrupted *lacZ* gene

One of many bacterial clones

WHAT IF?　*If the medium used in step 5 did not contain ampicillin, what other colonies would grow? What color would they be?*

transformation (see pp. 306 and 561). Some cells acquire a recombinant plasmid carrying a gene, while others may take up a nonrecombinant plasmid, a fragment of noncoding hummingbird DNA, or nothing at all. The *amp^R* and *lacZ* genes on the plasmid can help us sort out these possibilities.

⑤ First, plating out all the bacteria on solid nutrient medium (agar) containing ampicillin allows us to distinguish the cells that have taken up plasmids, whether recombinant or not, from the other cells. Under these conditions, only cells with a plasmid will reproduce because only they have the *amp^R* gene conferring resistance to the ampicillin in the medium. Each reproducing bacterium forms a clone of cells. Once the clone contains between 10^5 and 10^8 cells, it is visible as a mass, or *colony*, on the agar. As cells reproduce, any foreign genes carried by recombinant plasmids are also copied (cloned).

Second, the presence of X-gal in the medium allows us to distinguish colonies with recombinant plasmids from those with nonrecombinant plasmids. Colonies containing nonrecombinant plasmids have the *lacZ* gene intact and will produce functional β-galactosidase. These colonies will be blue because the enzyme hydrolyzes the X-gal in the medium, forming a blue product. In contrast, no functional β-galactosidase is produced in colonies containing recombinant plasmids with foreign DNA inserted into the *lacZ* gene; these colonies will therefore be white.

The procedure to this point will have cloned many different hummingbird DNA fragments, not just the β-globin gene that interests us. In fact, taken together, the white colonies should represent all the DNA sequences from the hummingbird genome, including noncoding regions as well as genes. How do we find the colony (cell clone) carrying the β-globin gene among the many clones carrying other pieces of hummingbird DNA? Before addressing this question, we must consider how the clones are stored.

Storing Cloned Genes in DNA Libraries

The cloning procedure in Figure 20.4, which starts with a mixture of fragments from the entire genome of an organism, is called a "shotgun" approach; no single gene is targeted for cloning. Thousands of different recombinant plasmids are produced in step 3, and a clone of cells carrying each type of plasmid ends up as a white colony in step 5. The complete set of plasmid-containing cell clones, each carrying copies of a particular segment from the initial genome, is referred to as a **genomic library (Figure 20.5a)**. Each "plasmid clone" in the library is like a book containing specific information. Today, scientists often obtain such libraries (or even particular cloned genes) from another researcher, a commercial source, or a sequencing center.

Certain bacteriophages have also been used as cloning vectors for making genomic libraries. Fragments of foreign DNA

(a) Plasmid library. Shown are three of the thousands of "books" in a plasmid library. Each "book" is a clone of bacterial cells, which contain copies of a particular foreign genome fragment (pink, yellow, black segments) in their recombinant plasmids.

(b) Phage library. The same three foreign genome segments are shown in three "books" of a phage library.

(c) A library of bacterial artificial chromosome (BAC) clones. Such libraries are usually stored in a "multiwell" plastic plate; a 384-well plate is shown here. Each clone occupies one well. (The library of an entire genome would require many such plates.) Plasmid libraries can also be stored this way.

▲ **Figure 20.5 Genomic libraries.** A genomic library is a collection of many bacterial or phage clones. Each clone carries copies of a particular DNA segment from a foreign genome, integrated into an appropriate DNA vector, such as a plasmid or a trimmed-down phage genome. In a complete genomic library, the foreign DNA segments cover the entire genome of an organism. Note that the bacterial chromosomes in (a) and (c) are not drawn to scale; they are actually about 1,000 times as large as the vectors.

can be spliced into a trimmed-down version of a phage genome, as into a plasmid, by using a restriction enzyme and DNA ligase. The normal infection process allows production of many new phage particles, each carrying the foreign DNA. An advantage of using phages as vectors is that while a standard plasmid can carry a DNA insert no larger than 12,000 base pairs (12 kb), a phage can carry an insert of about 25 kb. A genomic library made using phages is stored as a collection of phage clones **(Figure 20.5b)**. Because restriction enzymes do not recognize gene boundaries, some genes in either type of genomic library will be cut and divided up among two or more clones.

Another type of vector used in library construction is a **bacterial artificial chromosome (BAC)**. In spite of the name, these are simply large plasmids, trimmed down so they contain just the genes necessary to ensure replication and capable of carrying inserts of 100–300 kb. The very large insert size minimizes the number of clones needed to make up the genomic library, but it also makes them more challenging to work with in the lab. BAC clones are usually stored in multiwelled plastic plates, with one clone per well **(Figure 20.5c)**. This orderly storage of clones, identified by their location in the plate, makes screening for the gene of interest very efficient, as we will see.

Researchers can make another kind of DNA library by starting with mRNA extracted from cells **(Figure 20.6)**. The enzyme reverse transcriptase (obtained from retroviruses) is used *in vitro* to make single-stranded DNA transcripts of the mRNA molecules. Recall that the 3′ end of the mRNA has a stretch of adenine (A) ribonucleotides called a poly-A tail. This feature allows use of a short strand of thymine (dT) deoxyribonucleotides as a primer for the reverse transcriptase. Following enzymatic degradation of the mRNA, a second DNA strand, complementary to the first, is synthesized by DNA polymerase. The resulting double-stranded DNA is called **complementary DNA (cDNA)**. For creating a library, the cDNA is modified by the addition of restriction enzyme recognition sequences at each end. Then the cDNA is inserted into vector DNA in a manner similar to the insertion of genomic DNA fragments. The extracted mRNA is a mixture of all the mRNA molecules in the original cells, transcribed from many different genes. Therefore, the cDNAs that are cloned make up a **cDNA library** containing a collection of genes. However, a cDNA library represents only part of the genome—only the subset of genes that were transcribed in the cells from which the mRNA was isolated.

Genomic and cDNA libraries each have advantages, depending on what is being studied. If you want to clone a gene but don't know what cell type expresses it or cannot obtain enough cells of the appropriate type, a genomic library is almost certain to contain the gene. Also, if you are interested in the regulatory sequences or introns associated with a gene, a genomic library is required because these sequences are absent from the fully processed mRNAs used in making a cDNA library. For this very reason, if you are interested only in the coding sequence of a gene, you can obtain a stripped-down

▲ **Figure 20.6 Making complementary DNA (cDNA) for a eukaryotic gene.** Complementary DNA is DNA made *in vitro* using mRNA as a template for the first strand. Because the mRNA contains only exons, the resulting double-stranded cDNA carries the complete coding sequence of the gene but no introns. Although only one mRNA is shown here, the final collection of cDNAs would reflect all the mRNAs that were present in the cell.

version of the gene from a cDNA library. In our example of the hummingbird β-globin protein, a cDNA library would serve us well. We know which cells express the gene, so we could start making the library by isolating mRNA from hummingbird red blood cells. A cDNA library is also useful for studying the set of genes responsible for the specialized functions of a particular cell type, such as brain or liver cells. Finally, by making cDNA from cells of the same type at different times in the life of an organism, researchers can trace changes in patterns of gene expression during development.

Screening a Library for Clones Carrying a Gene of Interest

Now, returning to the results in Figure 20.4, we're ready to screen all the colonies with recombinant plasmids (the white colonies) for a clone of cells containing the hummingbird β-globin gene. We can detect this gene's DNA by its ability to base-pair with a complementary sequence on another nucleic acid molecule, using **nucleic acid hybridization**. The complementary molecule, a short, single-stranded nucleic acid that can be either RNA or DNA, is called a **nucleic acid probe**. If we know at least part of the nucleotide sequence of the gene of interest (perhaps from knowing the amino acid sequence of the protein it encodes or, as in our case, the gene's nucleotide sequence in a closely related species), we can synthesize a probe complementary to it. For example, if part of the sequence on one strand of the desired gene were

5′ ···GGCTAACTTAGC··· 3′

then we would synthesize this probe:

3′ CCGATTGAATCG 5′

Each probe molecule, which will hydrogen-bond specifically to a complementary sequence in the desired gene, is labeled with a radioactive isotope or a fluorescent tag so we can track it.

Recall that the clones in our hummingbird genomic library have been stored in a multiwell plate (see Figure 20.5c). If we transfer a few cells from each well to a defined location on a membrane made of nylon or nitrocellulose, we can screen a large number of clones simultaneously for the presence of DNA complementary to our DNA probe (Figure 20.7).

Once we've identified the location of a clone carrying the β-globin gene, we can grow some cells from that colony in liquid

---

▼ Figure 20.7 **Research Method**

Detecting a Specific DNA Sequence by Hybridization with a Nucleic Acid Probe

APPLICATION Hybridization with a complementary nucleic acid probe detects a specific DNA sequence within a mixture of DNA molecules. In this example, a collection of bacterial clones from a hummingbird genomic library is screened to identify clones that carry a recombinant plasmid bearing the gene of interest. The library is stored in many multiwell plates, with one clone per well (see Figure 20.5c).

TECHNIQUE Cells from each clone are applied to a special nylon membrane. Each membrane has room for thousands of clones (many more than are shown here) so only a few membranes are needed to hold samples of all the clones in the library. This set of membranes is an *arrayed library* that can be screened for a specific gene using a labeled probe. Here the label is a radioactive nucleotide, but other commonly used labels include enzymes, covalently linked to the probe nucleotides, that can produce either a colored or luminescent product.

Solution in plastic bag contains radioactively labeled probe molecules.

Probe DNA

Gene of interest

Single-stranded DNA from cell

Film

Nylon membrane

Location of DNA with the complementary sequence

Multiwell plates holding library clones

Nylon membrane

1 Plate by plate, cells from each well, representing one clone, are transferred to a defined spot on a special nylon membrane. The nylon membrane is treated to break open the cells and denature their DNA; the resulting single-stranded DNA molecules stick to the membrane.

2 The membrane is then incubated in a solution of radioactive probe molecules complementary to the gene of interest. Because the DNA immobilized on the membrane is single-stranded, the single-stranded probe can base-pair with any complementary DNA on the membrane. Excess DNA is then rinsed off. (One spot with radioactive probe–DNA hybrids is shown here in orange but would not be visible yet.)

3 The membrane is laid under photographic film, allowing any radioactive areas to expose the film (autoradiography). Black spots on the film correspond to the locations on the membrane of DNA that has hybridized to the probe. This location can be traced back to the original well containing the bacterial clone that holds the gene of interest.

RESULTS The location of the black spot on the photographic film identifies the clone containing the gene of interest. By using probes with different nucleotide sequences, researchers can screen the collection of bacterial clones for different genes.

culture in a large tank and then easily isolate many copies of the gene for our studies. We can also use the cloned gene as a probe to identify similar or identical genes in DNA from other sources, such as other species of birds.

Expressing Cloned Eukaryotic Genes

Once a particular gene has been cloned in host cells, its protein product can be produced in large amounts for research purposes or valuable practical applications, which we'll explore in Concept 20.4. Cloned genes can be expressed as protein in either bacterial or eukaryotic cells; each option has advantages and disadvantages.

Bacterial Expression Systems

Getting a cloned eukaryotic gene to function in bacterial host cells can be difficult because certain aspects of gene expression are different in eukaryotes and bacteria. To overcome differences in promoters and other DNA control sequences, scientists usually employ an **expression vector**, a cloning vector that contains a highly active bacterial promoter just upstream of a restriction site where the eukaryotic gene can be inserted in the correct reading frame. The bacterial host cell will recognize the promoter and proceed to express the foreign gene now linked to that promoter. Such expression vectors allow the synthesis of many eukaryotic proteins in bacterial cells.

Another problem with expressing cloned eukaryotic genes in bacteria is the presence of noncoding regions (introns) in most eukaryotic genes. Introns can make a eukaryotic gene very long and unwieldy, and they prevent correct expression of the gene by bacterial cells, which do not have RNA-splicing machinery. This problem can be surmounted by using a cDNA form of the gene, which includes only the exons.

Eukaryotic Cloning and Expression Systems

Molecular biologists can avoid eukaryotic-bacterial incompatibility by using eukaryotic cells such as yeasts, rather than bacteria, as hosts for cloning and/or expressing eukaryotic genes of interest. Yeasts, single-celled fungi, offer two advantages: They are as easy to grow as bacteria, and they have plasmids, a rarity among eukaryotes. Scientists have even constructed recombinant plasmids that combine yeast and bacterial DNA and can replicate in either type of cell. Another useful tool for cloning eukaryotic genes are **yeast artificial chromosomes (YACs)**, which combine the essentials of a eukaryotic chromosome—an origin for DNA replication, a centromere, and two telomeres—with foreign DNA. These chromosome-like vectors behave like ordinary chromosomes during mitosis, cloning the foreign DNA as the yeast cell divides. Because a YAC can carry a much longer DNA segment than can a plasmid vector, a cloned fragment is more likely to contain an entire gene rather than just a portion of it.

Another reason to use eukaryotic host cells for expressing a cloned eukaryotic gene is that many eukaryotic proteins will not function unless they are modified after translation, for example by the addition of carbohydrate or lipid groups. Bacterial cells cannot carry out these modifications, and if the gene product requiring such processing is from a mammal, even yeast cells may not be able to modify the protein correctly. The use of host cells from an animal cell culture may therefore be necessary.

Scientists have developed a variety of methods for introducing recombinant DNA into eukaryotic cells. In **electroporation**, a brief electrical pulse applied to a solution containing cells creates temporary holes in their plasma membranes, through which DNA can enter. (This technique is now commonly used for bacteria as well.) Alternatively, scientists can inject DNA directly into single eukaryotic cells using microscopically thin needles. To get DNA into plant cells, the soil bacterium *Agrobacterium* can be used, as well as other methods you will learn about later. If the introduced DNA is incorporated into a cell's genome by genetic recombination, then it may be expressed by the cell.

Amplifying DNA *in Vitro*: The Polymerase Chain Reaction (PCR)

DNA cloning in cells remains the best method for preparing large quantities of a particular gene or other DNA sequence. However, when the source of DNA is scanty or impure, the **polymerase chain reaction**, or **PCR**, is quicker and more selective. In this technique, any specific target segment within one or many DNA molecules can be quickly amplified (copied many times) in a test tube. With automation, PCR can make billions of copies of a target segment of DNA in a few hours, significantly faster than the days it would take to obtain the same number of copies by screening a DNA library for a clone with the desired gene and letting it replicate within host cells. In fact, PCR is being used increasingly to make enough of a specific DNA fragment to insert it directly into a vector, entirely skipping the steps of making and screening a library. To continue our literary analogy, PCR is like photocopying just one page rather than checking out all the books in a library.

In the PCR procedure, a three-step cycle brings about a chain reaction that produces an exponentially growing population of identical DNA molecules. During each cycle, the reaction mixture is heated to denature (separate) the DNA strands and then cooled to allow annealing (hydrogen bonding) of short, single-stranded DNA primers complementary to sequences on opposite strands at each end of the target sequence; finally, a heat-stable DNA polymerase extends the primers in the $5' \rightarrow 3'$ direction. If a standard DNA polymerase were used, the protein would be denatured along with the DNA during the first heating step and would have to be replaced after each cycle. The key to automating PCR was the discovery of an unusual heat-stable DNA polymerase, first isolated from cells of a bacterial species living in hot springs, that could withstand the heat at the start of each cycle. **Figure 20.8** illustrates the steps in PCR.

Just as impressive as the speed of PCR is its specificity. Only minute amounts of DNA need be present in the starting material, and this DNA can be in a partially degraded state, as long as a few molecules contain the complete target sequence. The key to this high specificity is the primers, which hydrogen-bond *only* to sequences at opposite ends of the target segment. (For high specificity, the primers must be at least 15 or so nucleotides long.) By the end of the third cycle, one-fourth of the molecules are identical to the target segment, with both strands the appropriate length. With each successive cycle, the number of target segment molecules of the correct length doubles, soon greatly outnumbering all other DNA molecules in the reaction.

Despite its speed and specificity, PCR amplification cannot substitute for gene cloning in cells when large amounts of a gene are desired. Occasional errors during PCR replication impose limits on the number of good copies that can be made by this method. When PCR is used to provide the specific DNA fragment for cloning, the resulting clones are sequenced to select clones with error-free inserts.

Devised in 1985, PCR has had a major impact on biological research and biotechnology. PCR has been used to amplify DNA from a wide variety of sources: fragments of ancient DNA from a 40,000-year-old frozen woolly mammoth; DNA from fingerprints or from tiny amounts of blood, tissue, or semen found at crime scenes; DNA from single embryonic cells for rapid prenatal diagnosis of genetic disorders; and DNA of viral genes from cells infected with viruses that are difficult to detect, such as HIV. We'll return to applications of PCR later in the chapter.

▼ **Figure 20.8** **Research Method**

The Polymerase Chain Reaction (PCR)

APPLICATION With PCR, any specific segment—the target sequence—within a DNA sample can be copied many times (amplified), completely *in vitro*.

TECHNIQUE PCR requires double-stranded DNA containing the target sequence, a heat-resistant DNA polymerase, all four nucleotides, and two 15- to 20-nucleotide DNA strands that serve as primers. One primer is complementary to one end of the target sequence on one strand; the second primer is complementary to the other end of the sequence on the other strand.

RESULTS After 3 cycles, one-fourth of the molecules match the target sequence exactly. After 30 cycles, more than 99.99% of the molecules match the target sequence.

CONCEPT **20.2**

DNA technology allows us to study the sequence, expression, and function of a gene

Once DNA cloning has provided us with large quantities of specific DNA segments, we can tackle some interesting questions about a particular gene and its function. For example, does the sequence of the hummingbird β-globin gene suggest a protein structure that can carry oxygen more efficiently than its counterpart in less metabolically active species? Does a particular human gene differ from person to person, and are certain alleles of that gene associated with a hereditary disorder? Where in the body and when is a given gene expressed? And, ultimately, what role does a certain gene play in an organism?

Before we can begin to address such compelling questions, we must consider a few standard laboratory techniques that are used to analyze the DNA of genes.

Gel Electrophoresis and Southern Blotting

Many approaches for studying DNA molecules involve **gel electrophoresis**. This technique uses a gel made of a polymer, such as a polysaccharide. The gel acts as a molecular sieve to separate nucleic acids or proteins on the basis of size, electrical charge, and other physical properties (**Figure 20.9**). Because nucleic acid molecules carry negative charges on their phosphate groups, they all travel toward the positive pole in

▼ **Figure 20.9** **Research Method**

Gel Electrophoresis

APPLICATION Gel electrophoresis is used for separating nucleic acids or proteins that differ in size, electrical charge, or other physical properties. DNA molecules are separated by gel electrophoresis in restriction fragment analysis of both cloned genes (see Figure 20.10) and genomic DNA (see Figure 20.11).

TECHNIQUE Gel electrophoresis separates macromolecules on the basis of their rate of movement through a polymeric gel in an electric field: The distance a DNA molecule travels is inversely proportional to its length. A mixture of DNA molecules, usually fragments produced by restriction enzyme digestion (cutting) or PCR amplification, is separated into bands. Each band contains thousands of molecules of the same length.

1 Each sample, a mixture of DNA molecules, is placed in a separate well near one end of a thin slab of gel. The gel is set into a small plastic support and immersed in an aqueous solution in a tray with electrodes at each end.

Mixture of DNA molecules of different sizes

Power source

Cathode

Anode

Gel

2 When the current is turned on, the negatively charged DNA molecules move toward the positive electrode, with shorter molecules moving faster than longer ones. Bands are shown here in blue, but on an actual gel, the bands would not be visible at this time.

Power source

Longer molecules

Shorter molecules

RESULTS After the current is turned off, a DNA-binding dye is added. This dye fluoresces pink in ultraviolet light, revealing the separated bands to which it binds. In the gel below, the pink bands correspond to DNA fragments of different lengths separated by electrophoresis. If all the samples were initially cut with the same restriction enzyme, then the different band patterns indicate that they came from different sources.

an electric field. As they move, the thicket of polymer fibers impedes longer molecules more than it does shorter ones, separating them by length. Thus, gel electrophoresis separates a mixture of linear DNA molecules into bands, each consisting of DNA molecules of the same length.

One useful application of this technique is *restriction fragment analysis*, which can rapidly provide useful information about DNA sequences. In this type of analysis, the DNA fragments produced by restriction enzyme digestion (cutting) of a DNA molecule are sorted by gel electrophoresis. When the mixture of restriction fragments undergoes electrophoresis, it yields a band pattern characteristic of the starting molecule and the restriction enzyme used. In fact, the relatively small DNA molecules of viruses and plasmids can be identified simply by their restriction fragment patterns. Because DNA can be recovered undamaged from gels, the procedure also provides a way to prepare pure samples of individual fragments—if the bands can be clearly resolved. (Very large DNA molecules, such as those of eukaryotic chromosomes, yield so many fragments that they appear as a smear instead of distinct bands.)

Restriction fragment analysis is also useful for comparing two different DNA molecules—for example, two alleles of a gene. A restriction enzyme recognizes a specific sequence of nucleotides, and a change in even one base pair of that sequence will prevent it from cutting at a particular site. Therefore, if the nucleotide differences between two alleles occur within a restriction site, digestion with the enzyme that recognizes the site will produce a different mixture of fragments from each allele. Each mixture will give its own band pattern in gel electrophoresis. For example, sickle-cell disease is caused by mutation of a single nucleotide located within a restriction sequence in the human β-globin gene (see Figure 17.22 and p. 278). Consequently, restriction fragment analysis by electrophoresis can distinguish the normal and sickle-cell alleles of the β-globin gene, as shown in **Figure 20.10**.

The starting materials in Figure 20.10 are samples of the cloned and purified β-globin alleles. But what can we do if we don't have purified alleles to start with? Suppose we wanted to determine whether a person is a heterozygous carrier of the mutant allele for sickle-cell disease. In this case, we would directly compare the genomic DNA from that person with DNA from both a person who has sickle-cell disease (and is homozygous for the mutant allele) and a person who is homozygous for the normal allele. As we mentioned already, electrophoresis of genomic DNA digested with a restriction enzyme and stained with a DNA-binding dye yields too many bands to distinguish them individually. However, a method called **Southern blotting** (developed by British biochemist Edwin Southern), which combines gel electrophoresis and nucleic acid hybridization, allows us to detect just those bands that include parts of the β-globin gene. The principle is the same as in nucleic acid hybridization for screening bacterial clones (see Figure 20.7). In Southern blotting, the probe is usu-

Normal β-globin allele

←175 bp→←—201 bp—→←——Large fragment——→

DdeI   DdeI   DdeI   DdeI

Sickle-cell mutant β-globin allele

←————376 bp————→←—Large fragment—→

DdeI   DdeI   DdeI

(a) *Dde*I **restriction sites in normal and sickle-cell alleles of β-globin gene.** Shown here are the cloned alleles, separated from the vector DNA but including some DNA next to the coding sequence. The normal allele contains two sites within the coding sequence recognized by the *Dde*I restriction enzyme. The sickle-cell allele lacks one of these sites.

Normal allele   Sickle-cell allele

Large fragment

201 bp
175 bp

376 bp

(b) **Electrophoresis of restriction fragments from normal and sickle-cell alleles.** Samples of each purified allele were cut with the *Dde*I enzyme and then subjected to gel electrophoresis, resulting in three bands for the normal allele and two bands for the sickle-cell allele. (The tiny fragments on the ends of both initial DNA molecules are identical and are not seen here.)

▲ **Figure 20.10 Using restriction fragment analysis to distinguish the normal and sickle-cell alleles of the human β-globin gene. (a)** The sickle-cell mutation destroys one of the *Dde*I restriction sites within the gene. **(b)** As a result, digestion with the *Dde*I enzyme generates different fragments from the normal and sickle-cell alleles.

WHAT IF? *Given recombinant bacterial clones carrying each of these alleles, how would you isolate the DNA of the alleles to provide the pure samples run on the gel in (b)? (Hint: Study Figures 20.4 and 20.9.)*

ally a radioactive single-stranded DNA molecule that is complementary to the gene of interest. **Figure 20.11** outlines the entire procedure and demonstrates how it can differentiate a heterozygote (in this case, for the sickle-cell allele) from an individual homozygous for the normal allele.

The identification of carriers of mutant alleles associated with genetic diseases is only one of the ways Southern blotting has been used. In fact, this technique has been a laboratory workhorse for many years. Recently, however, it has been supplanted by more rapid methods, often involving PCR amplification of the specific parts of genomes that may differ.

▼ Figure 20.11 Research Method

Southern Blotting of DNA Fragments

APPLICATION   Researchers can detect specific nucleotide sequences within a complex DNA sample with this method. In particular, Southern blotting is useful for comparing the restriction fragments produced from different samples of genomic DNA.

TECHNIQUE   In this example, we compare genomic DNA samples from three individuals: a homozygote for the normal β-globin allele (I), a homozygote for the mutant sickle-cell allele (II), and a heterozygote (III). As in Figure 20.7, we show a radioactively labeled probe, but other methods of probe labeling and detection are also used.

1 Preparation of restriction fragments. Each DNA sample is mixed with the same restriction enzyme, in this case *Dde*I. Digestion of each sample yields a mixture of thousands of restriction fragments.

2 Gel electrophoresis. The restriction fragments in each sample are separated by electrophoresis, forming a characteristic pattern of bands. (In reality, there would be many more bands than shown here, and they would be invisible unless stained.)

3 DNA transfer (blotting). With the gel arranged as shown above, capillary action pulls the alkaline solution upward through the gel, transferring the DNA to a nitrocellulose membrane, producing the blot; the DNA is denatured in the process. (Another version of this method uses an electrical current to hasten the DNA transfer.) The single strands of DNA stuck to the nitrocellulose are positioned in bands corresponding to those on the gel.

4 Hybridization with radioactive probe. The nitrocellulose blot is exposed to a solution containing a radioactively labeled probe. In this example, the probe is single-stranded DNA complementary to the β-globin gene. Probe molecules attach by base-pairing to any restriction fragments containing a part of the β-globin gene. (The bands would not be visible yet.)

5 Probe detection. A sheet of photographic film is laid over the blot. The radioactivity in the bound probe exposes the film to form an image corresponding to those bands containing DNA that base-paired with the probe.

RESULTS   Because the band patterns for the three samples are clearly different, this method can be used to identify heterozygous carriers of the sickle-cell allele (III), as well as those with the disease, who have two mutant alleles (II), and unaffected individuals, who have two normal alleles (I). The band patterns for samples I and II resemble those observed for the purified normal and mutant alleles, respectively, seen in Figure 20.10b. The band pattern for the sample from the heterozygote (III) is a combination of the patterns for the two homozygotes (I and II).

Research Method

Dideoxy Chain Termination Method for Sequencing DNA

APPLICATION The sequence of nucleotides in any cloned DNA fragment up to about 800 base pairs in length can be determined rapidly with machines that carry out sequencing reactions and separate the labeled reaction products by length.

TECHNIQUE This method synthesizes a set of DNA strands complementary to the original DNA fragment. Each strand starts with the same primer and ends with a dideoxyribonucleotide (ddNTP), a modified nucleotide. Incorporation of a ddNTP terminates a growing DNA strand because it lacks a 3' —OH group, the site for attachment of the next nucleotide (see Figure 16.14). In the set of strands synthesized, each nucleotide position along the original sequence is represented by strands ending at that point with the complementary ddNTP. Because each type of ddNTP is tagged with a distinct fluorescent label, the identity of the ending nucleotides of the new strands, and ultimately the entire original sequence, can be determined.

1 The fragment of DNA to be sequenced is denatured into single strands and incubated in a test tube with the necessary ingredients for DNA synthesis: a primer designed to base pair with the known 3' end of the template strand, DNA polymerase, the four deoxyribonucleotides, and the four dideoxyribonucleotides, each tagged with a specific fluorescent molecule.

2 Synthesis of each new strand starts at the 3' end of the primer and continues until a dideoxy-ribonucleotide is inserted, at random, instead of the normal equivalent deoxyribonucleotide. This prevents further elongation of the strand. Eventually, a set of labeled strands of various lengths is generated, with the color of the tag representing the last nucleotide in the sequence.

3 The labeled strands in the mixture are separated by passage through a polyacryl-amide gel, with shorter strands moving through faster. For DNA sequencing, the gel is formed in a capillary tube rather than a slab like that shown in Figure 20.9. The small size of the tube allows a fluorescence detector to sense the color of each fluorescent tag as the strands come through. Strands differing in length by as little as one nucleotide can be distinguished from each other.

RESULTS The color of the fluorescent tag on each strand indicates the identity of the nucleotide at its end. The results can be printed out as a spectrogram, and the sequence, which is complementary to the template strand, can then be read from bottom (shortest strand) to top (longest strand). (Notice that the sequence here begins after the primer.)

DNA Sequencing

Once a gene is cloned, its complete nucleotide sequence can be determined. Today, sequencing is automated, carried out by sequencing machines. The automated procedure is based on a technique called the *dideoxyribonucleotide* (or *dideoxy*, for short) *chain termination method*, for reasons you can see in **Figure 20.12**. This method was developed by British biochemist Frederick Sanger, who received the Nobel Prize in 1980 for this accomplishment. (One of only four people to win two Nobel Prizes, Sanger also won one in 1975 for determining the amino acid sequence of insulin.)

Knowing the sequence of a gene allows researchers to compare it directly with genes in other species, where the function of the gene product may be known. If two genes from different species are quite similar in sequence, it is reasonable to suppose that their gene products perform similar functions. In this way, sequence comparisons provide clues to a gene's function, a topic we'll return to shortly. Another set of clues is provided by experimental approaches that analyze when and where a gene is expressed.

Analyzing Gene Expression

Having cloned a given gene, researchers can make labeled nucleic acid probes that will hybridize with mRNAs transcribed from the gene. The probes can provide information about when or where in the organism the gene is transcribed. Transcription levels are commonly used as a measure of gene expression.

Studying the Expression of Single Genes

Suppose we want to find out how the expression of the β-globin gene changes during the embryonic development of the hummingbird. There are at least two ways to do this.

The first is called **Northern blotting** (a play on words based on this method's similarity to Southern blotting). In this method, we carry out gel electrophoresis on samples of mRNA from hummingbird embryos at different stages of development, transfer the samples to a nitrocellulose membrane, and then allow the mRNAs on the membrane to hybridize with a labeled probe recognizing β-globin mRNA. If we expose a film to the membrane, the resulting image will look similar to the Southern blot in Figure 20.11, with one band of a given size showing up in each sample. If the mRNA band is seen at a particular stage, we can hypothesize that the protein functions during events taking place at that stage. Like Southern blotting, Northern blotting has been a mainstay over the years, but it is being supplanted in many labs by other techniques.

A method that is quicker and more sensitive (and therefore becoming more widely used) is the **reverse transcriptase–polymerase chain reaction**, or **RT-PCR (Figure 20.13)**. Analysis of hummingbird β-globin gene expression with RT-PCR be-

RT-PCR Analysis of the Expression of Single Genes

APPLICATION RT-PCR uses the enzyme reverse transcriptase (RT) in combination with PCR and gel electrophoresis. RT-PCR can be used to compare gene expression between samples—for instance, in different embryonic stages, in different tissues, or in the same type of cell under different conditions.

TECHNIQUE In this example, samples containing mRNAs from six embryonic stages of hummingbird were processed as shown below. (The mRNA from only one stage is shown.)

❶ **cDNA synthesis** is carried out by incubating the mRNAs with reverse transcriptase and other necessary components.

❷ **PCR amplification** of the sample is performed using primers specific to the hummingbird β-globin gene.

❸ **Gel electrophoresis** will reveal amplified DNA products only in samples that contained mRNA transcribed from the β-globin gene.

RESULTS The mRNA for this gene first is expressed at stage 2 and continues to be expressed through stage 6. The size of the amplified fragment depends on the distance between the primers that were used.

gins similarly to Northern blotting, with the isolation of mRNAs from different developmental stages of hummingbird embryos. Reverse transcriptase is added next to make cDNA, which then serves as a template for PCR amplification using primers from the β-globin gene. When the products are run on a gel, copies of the amplified region will be observed as bands only in samples that originally contained the β-globin mRNA. In the case of hummingbird β-globin, for instance, we might expect to see a band appear at the stage when red blood cells begin forming, with all subsequent stages showing the same band. RT-PCR can also be carried out with mRNAs collected from different tissues at one time to discover which tissue is producing a specific mRNA.

An alternative way to determine which tissues or cells are expressing certain genes is to track down the location of specific mRNAs using labeled probes in place, or *in situ*, in the in-

▲ **Figure 20.14 Determining where genes are expressed by *in situ* hybridization analysis.** This *Drosophila* embryo was incubated in a solution containing probes for five different mRNAs, each probe labeled with a different fluorescently colored tag. The embryo was then viewed using fluorescence microscopy. Each color marks where a specific gene is expressed as mRNA.

tact organism. This technique, called *in situ* **hybridization**, is most often carried out with probes labeled by attachment of fluorescent dyes (see Chapter 6). Different probes can be labeled with different dyes, sometimes with strikingly beautiful results **(Figure 20.14)**.

Studying the Expression of Interacting Groups of Genes

A major goal of biologists is to learn how genes act together to produce and maintain a functioning organism. Now that the entire genomes of a number of organisms have been sequenced, it is possible to study the expression of large groups of genes—a systems approach. Researchers use genome sequences as probes to investigate which genes are transcribed in different situations, such as in different tissues or at different stages of development. They also look for groups of genes that are expressed in a coordinated manner, with the aim of identifying networks of gene expression across an entire genome.

The basic strategy in such global (genome-wide) expression studies is to isolate the mRNAs made in particular cells, use these molecules as templates for making the corresponding cDNAs by reverse transcription, and then employ nucleic acid hybridization to compare this set of cDNAs with a collection of DNA fragments representing all or part of the genome. The results identify the subset of genes in the genome that are being expressed at a given time or under certain conditions. DNA technology makes such studies possible; with automation, they are easily performed on a large scale. Scientists can now measure the expression of thousands of genes at one time.

Genome-wide expression studies are made possible by **DNA microarray assays**. A DNA microarray consists of tiny amounts of a large number of single-stranded DNA fragments representing different genes fixed to a glass slide in a tightly spaced array, or grid (see Figure 20.1). (The microarray is also called a *DNA chip* by analogy to a computer chip.) Ideally, these fragments represent all the genes of an organism. **Figure 20.15** outlines how the DNA fragments on a microarray are tested for

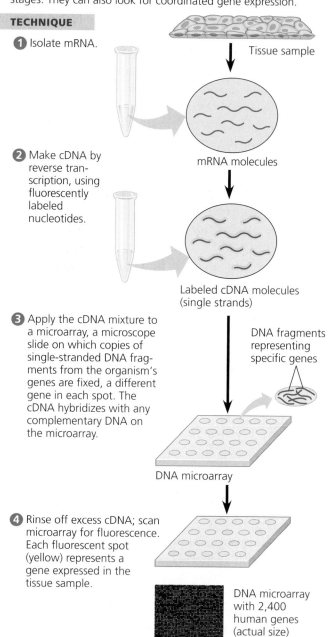

▼ **Figure 20.15 Research Method**

DNA Microarray Assay of Gene Expression Levels

APPLICATION With this method, researchers can test thousands of genes simultaneously to determine which ones are expressed in a particular tissue, under different environmental conditions, in various disease states, or at different developmental stages. They can also look for coordinated gene expression.

TECHNIQUE

1 Isolate mRNA.

Tissue sample

mRNA molecules

2 Make cDNA by reverse transcription, using fluorescently labeled nucleotides.

Labeled cDNA molecules (single strands)

3 Apply the cDNA mixture to a microarray, a microscope slide on which copies of single-stranded DNA fragments from the organism's genes are fixed, a different gene in each spot. The cDNA hybridizes with any complementary DNA on the microarray.

DNA fragments representing specific genes

DNA microarray

4 Rinse off excess cDNA; scan microarray for fluorescence. Each fluorescent spot (yellow) represents a gene expressed in the tissue sample.

DNA microarray with 2,400 human genes (actual size)

RESULTS The intensity of fluorescence at each spot is a measure of the expression in the tissue sample of the gene represented by that spot. Most often, as in the actual microarray above, two different samples are tested together by labeling the cDNAs prepared from each sample with labels of different colors, often green and red. The resulting color at a spot reveals the relative levels of expression of a particular gene in the two samples: Green indicates expression in one sample, red in the other, yellow in both, and black in neither. (See Figure 20.1 for a larger view.)

hybridization with cDNA molecules that have been prepared from the mRNAs in particular cells of interest and labeled with fluorescent dyes.

Using this technique, researchers have performed DNA microarray assays on more than 90% of the genes of the nematode *Caenorhabditis elegans*, during every stage of its life cycle. The results show that expression of nearly 60% of the genes changes dramatically during development and that many genes are expressed in a sex-specific pattern. This study supports the model held by most developmental biologists that embryonic development involves a complex and elaborate program of gene expression, rather than simply the expression of a small number of important genes. This example illustrates the ability of DNA microarrays to reveal general profiles of gene expression over the lifetime of an organism.

In addition to uncovering gene interactions and providing clues to gene function, DNA microarray assays may contribute to a better understanding of diseases and suggest new diagnostic techniques or therapies. For instance, comparing patterns of gene expression in breast cancer tumors and noncancerous breast tissue has already resulted in more informed and effective treatment protocols. Ultimately, information from DNA microarray assays should provide a grander view of how ensembles of genes interact to form an organism and maintain its vital systems.

Determining Gene Function

How do scientists determine the function of a gene identified by the techniques described thus far in the chapter? Perhaps the most common approach is to disable the gene and then observe the consequences in the cell or organism. In one application of this approach, called *in vitro* mutagenesis, specific mutations are introduced into a cloned gene, and then the mutated gene is returned to a cell in such a way that it disables ("knocks out") the normal cellular copies of the same gene. If the introduced mutations alter or destroy the function of the gene product, the phenotype of the mutant cell may help reveal the function of the missing normal protein. Using molecular and genetic techniques worked out in the 1980s, researchers can even generate mice with any given gene disabled, in order to study the role of that gene in development and in the adult. Mario Capecchi, Martin Evans, and Oliver Smithies received the 2007 Nobel Prize in Medicine for first accomplishing this feat. Several projects currently underway aim to disable every one of the over 20,000 genes in the mouse genome. These ambitious efforts will enhance our understanding of mammalian gene function.

A newer method for silencing expression of selected genes exploits the phenomenon of **RNA interference (RNAi)**, described in Chapter 18. This experimental approach uses synthetic double-stranded RNA molecules matching the sequence of a particular gene to trigger breakdown of the gene's messenger RNA or to block its translation. To date, the RNAi technique has been used successfully to reduce ("knock down") the expression of specific genes in mammalian cells, including human cells in culture, and plans are under way to try RNAi for the treatment of certain human disorders, including macular degeneration of the eye. In other organisms, such as the nematode and the fruit fly, RNAi has already proved valuable for analyzing the functions of genes on a large scale. In one study, RNAi was used to prevent expression of 86% of the genes in early nematode embryos, one gene at a time. Analysis of the phenotypes of the worms that developed from these embryos allowed the researchers to classify most of the genes into a small number of groups by function. This type of genome-wide analysis of gene function is sure to become more common as research focuses on the importance of interactions between genes in the system as a whole—the basis of systems biology (see Chapter 1).

The techniques and experimental approaches you have learned about thus far have already taught us a great deal about genes and the functions of their products. This DNA research is now being augmented by the development of powerful techniques for cloning whole multicellular organisms. An aim of this work is to obtain special types of cells, called stem cells, that give rise to all the different kinds of tissues. On a basic level, stem cells would allow scientists to use the DNA methods previously discussed to study the process of cell differentiation. On a more applied level, recombinant DNA techniques could be used to alter stem cells for the treatment of disease. Methods involving the cloning of organisms and production of stem cells are the subject of the next section.

CONCEPT CHECK 20.2

1. Suppose you carried out electrophoresis on a sample of genomic DNA isolated from an individual and treated with a restriction enzyme. After staining the gel with a DNA-binding dye, what would you see? Explain.

2. Describe the roles played by complementary base pairing between nucleic acid strands in each of the following techniques: Southern blotting, DNA sequencing, Northern blotting, RT-PCR, and microarray analysis.

3. **WHAT IF?** Look at the microarray in Figure 20.1, which is a larger version of the one in Figure 20.15. If one sample, labeled with a green fluorescent dye, was from normal tissue, and the other, labeled red, was from cancerous tissue, what does this mean for a spot that is green? Red? Yellow? Black? Based on their expression patterns, which genes would you be interested in examining further if you were studying cancer? Explain.

For suggested answers, see Appendix A.

CONCEPT 20.3

Cloning organisms may lead to production of stem cells for research and other applications

In parallel with advances in DNA technology, scientists have been developing and refining methods for cloning whole multicellular organisms from single cells. In this context, cloning produces one or more organisms genetically identical to the "parent" that donated the single cell. This is often called *organismal cloning* to differentiate it from gene cloning and, more significantly, from cell cloning—the division of an asexually reproducing cell into a collection of genetically identical cells. (The common theme for all types of cloning is that the product is genetically identical to the parent. In fact, the word *clone* comes from the Greek *klon*, meaning "twig.") The current interest in organismal cloning arises primarily from its potential to generate stem cells, which can in turn generate many different tissues.

The cloning of plants and animals was first attempted over 50 years ago in experiments designed to answer basic biological questions. For example, researchers wondered if all the cells of an organism have the same genes (a concept called *genomic equivalence*) or if cells lose genes during the process of differentiation (see Chapter 18). One way to answer this question is to see whether a differentiated cell can generate a whole organism—in other words, whether cloning an organism is possible. Let's discuss these early experiments before we consider more recent progress in organismal cloning and procedures for producing stem cells.

Cloning Plants: Single-Cell Cultures

The successful cloning of whole plants from single differentiated cells was accomplished during the 1950s by F. C. Steward and his students at Cornell University, who worked with carrot plants **(Figure 20.16)**. They found that differentiated cells taken from the root (the carrot) and incubated in culture medium could grow into normal adult plants, each genetically identical to the parent plant. These results showed that differentiation does not necessarily involve irreversible changes in the DNA. In plants, at least, mature cells can "dedifferentiate" and then give rise to all the specialized cell types of the organism. Any cell with this potential is said to be **totipotent**.

Plant cloning is now used extensively in agriculture. For some plants, such as orchids, cloning is the only commercially practical means of reproducing plants. In other cases, cloning has been used to reproduce a plant with valuable characteristics, such as the ability to resist a plant pathogen. In fact, you yourself may be a plant cloner: If you have ever grown a new plant from a cutting, you have practiced cloning!

▼ **Figure 20.16** **Inquiry**

Can a differentiated plant cell develop into a whole plant?

EXPERIMENT   In 1958, F. C. Steward and colleagues at Cornell University tested individual cells from a fully formed carrot for their ability to form a plant.

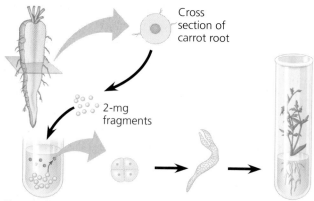

Cross section of carrot root

2-mg fragments

Fragments were cultured in nutrient medium; stirring caused single cells to shear off into the liquid.

Single cells free in suspension began to divide.

Embryonic plant developed from a cultured single cell.

Plantlet was cultured on agar medium. Later it was planted in soil.

RESULTS   A single somatic (nonreproductive) carrot cell developed into a mature carrot plant. The new plant was a genetic duplicate (clone) of the parent plant.

Adult plant

CONCLUSION   At least some differentiated somatic cells in plants are totipotent, able to reverse their differentiation and then give rise to all the cell types in a mature plant.

SOURCE   F. C. Steward et al., Growth and organized development of cultured cells. II. Organization in cultures grown from suspended cells, *American Journal of Botany* 45:705–708 (1958).

WHAT IF?   If each individual cell had developed into only one type of tissue instead of a whole plant, what might the researchers have concluded?

Cloning Animals: Nuclear Transplantation

Differentiated cells from animals generally do not divide in culture, much less develop into the multiple cell types of a new organism. Therefore, early researchers had to use a different approach to the question of whether differentiated animal cells can be totipotent. Their approach was to remove the nucleus of an unfertilized or fertilized egg and replace it with the nucleus of a differentiated cell, a procedure called *nuclear transplantation*. If the nucleus from the differentiated donor cell retains its full genetic capability, then it should be able to direct development of the recipient cell into all the tissues and organs of an organism.

Such experiments were conducted on frogs by Robert Briggs and Thomas King in the 1950s and by John Gurdon in the 1970s. These researchers transplanted a nucleus from an embryonic or tadpole cell into an enucleated (nucleus-lacking) egg of the same species. In Gurdon's experiments, the transplanted nucleus was often able to support normal development of the egg into a tadpole (**Figure 20.17**). However, he found that the potential of a transplanted nucleus to direct normal development was inversely related to the age of the donor: the older the donor nucleus, the lower the percentage of normally developing tadpoles.

From these results, Gurdon concluded that something in the nucleus *does* change as animal cells differentiate. In frogs and most other animals, nuclear potential tends to be restricted more and more as embryonic development and cell differentiation progress.

Reproductive Cloning of Mammals

In addition to cloning frogs, researchers have long been able to clone mammals using nuclei or cells from a variety of early embryos. But it was not known whether a nucleus from a fully differentiated cell could be reprogrammed to succeed in acting as a donor nucleus. In 1997, however, Scottish researchers captured newspaper headlines when they announced the birth of Dolly, a lamb cloned from an adult sheep by nuclear transplantation from a differentiated cell (**Figure 20.18**, on the next page). These researchers achieved the necessary dedifferentiation of donor nuclei by culturing mammary cells in nutrient-poor medium. They then fused these cells with enucleated sheep eggs. The resulting diploid cells divided to form early embryos, which were implanted into surrogate mothers. Out of several hundred implanted embryos, one successfully completed normal development, and Dolly was born.

Later analyses showed that Dolly's chromosomal DNA was indeed identical to that of the nucleus donor. (Her mitochondrial DNA came from the egg donor, as expected.) In 2003, at age 6, Dolly suffered complications from a lung disease usually seen only in much older sheep and was euthanized. Dolly's premature death, as well as her arthritic condition, led to speculation that her cells were in some way not quite as healthy as those of a normal sheep, possibly reflecting incomplete reprogramming of the original transplanted nucleus.

Since 1997, researchers have cloned numerous other mammals, including mice, cats, cows, horses, mules, pigs, and dogs. In most cases, their goal has been the production of new indi-

▼ **Figure 20.17** **Inquiry**

Can the nucleus from a differentiated animal cell direct development of an organism?

EXPERIMENT John Gurdon and colleagues at Oxford University, in England, destroyed the nuclei of frog eggs by exposing the eggs to ultraviolet light. They then transplanted nuclei from cells of frog embryos and tadpoles into the enucleated eggs.

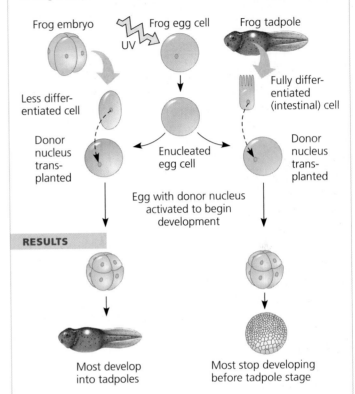

When the transplanted nuclei came from an early embryo, whose cells are relatively undifferentiated, most of the recipient eggs developed into tadpoles. But when the nuclei came from the fully differentiated intestinal cells of a tadpole, fewer than 2% of the eggs developed into normal tadpoles, and most of the embryos stopped developing at a much earlier stage.

CONCLUSION The nucleus from a differentiated frog cell can direct development of a tadpole. However, its ability to do so decreases as the donor cell becomes more differentiated, presumably because of changes in the nucleus.

SOURCE J. B. Gurdon et al., The developmental capacity of nuclei transplanted from keratinized cells of adult frogs, *Journal of Embryology and Experimental Morphology* 34:93–112 (1975).

WHAT IF? If each cell in a four-cell embryo was already so specialized that it was not totipotent, what results would you predict for the experiment on the left side of the figure?

viduals; this is known as *reproductive cloning*. We have already learned a lot from such experiments. For example, cloned animals of the same species do *not* always look or behave identically. In a herd of cows cloned from the same line of cultured cells, certain cows are dominant in behavior and others are

Research Method

Reproductive Cloning of a Mammal by Nuclear Transplantation

APPLICATION This method is used to produce cloned animals whose nuclear genes are identical to those of the animal supplying the nucleus.

TECHNIQUE Shown here is the procedure used to produce Dolly, the first reported case of a mammal cloned using the nucleus of a differentiated cell.

1 Mammary cell donor

2 Egg cell donor

Egg cell from ovary

Nucleus removed

Cultured mammary cells are semistarved, arresting the cell cycle and causing dedifferentiation.

3 Cells fused

Nucleus from mammary cell

4 Grown in culture

Early embryo

5 Implanted in uterus of a third sheep

Surrogate mother

6 Embryonic development

RESULTS

Lamb ("Dolly") genetically identical to mammary cell donor

The genetic makeup of the cloned animal is identical to that of the animal supplying the nucleus but differs from that of the egg donor and surrogate mother. (The latter two are "Scottish black-face" sheep, with dark faces.)

▲ **Figure 20.19 CC, the first cloned cat, and her single parent.** Rainbow (left) donated the nucleus in a cloning procedure that resulted in CC (right). However, the two cats are not identical: Rainbow is a classic calico cat with orange patches on her fur and has a "reserved personality," while CC has a gray and white coat and is more playful.

more submissive. Another example of nonidentity in clones is the first cloned cat, named CC for Carbon Copy **(Figure 20.19)**. She has a calico coat, like her single female parent, but the color and pattern are different because of random X chromosome inactivation, which is a normal occurrence during embryonic development (see Figure 15.8). And identical human twins, which are naturally occurring "clones," are always slightly different. Clearly, environmental influences and random phenomena can play a significant role during development.

The successful cloning of so many mammals has heightened speculation about the cloning of humans. Scientists in several labs around the world have tackled the first steps of this feat. In the most common approach, nuclei from differentiated human cells are transplanted into unfertilized enucleated eggs, and the eggs are stimulated to divide. In 2001, a research group in Massachusetts observed a few early cell divisions in such an experiment. A few years later, South Korean researchers reported cloning embryos to an early stage called the blastocyst stage. This apparent success of human cloning techniques raised unprecedented ethical issues, igniting a heated debate. The later retraction of the Korean report has bought us a little more time to consider such issues.

Problems Associated with Animal Cloning

In most nuclear transplantation studies thus far, only a small percentage of cloned embryos develop normally to birth. And like Dolly, many cloned animals exhibit defects. Cloned mice, for instance, are prone to obesity, pneumonia, liver failure, and premature death. Scientists assert that even cloned animals that appear normal are likely to have subtle defects.

In recent years, we have begun to uncover some reasons for the low efficiency of cloning and the high incidence of abnormalities. In the nuclei of fully differentiated cells, a small subset of genes is turned on and expression of the rest is repressed. This regulation often is the result of epigenetic changes in chromatin, such as acetylation of histones or methylation of DNA (see Figure 18.7). During the nuclear transfer procedure, many of these changes must be reversed in the later-stage nucleus from a donor animal for genes to be expressed or repressed appropriately in early stages of development. Researchers have found that the DNA in embryonic cells from cloned embryos, like that of differentiated cells, often has more methyl groups than does the DNA in equivalent cells from uncloned embryos of the same species. This finding suggests that the reprogramming of donor nuclei requires chromatin restructuring, which occurs incompletely during cloning procedures. Because DNA methylation helps regulate gene expression, misplaced methyl groups in the DNA of donor nuclei may interfere with the pattern of gene expression necessary for normal embryonic development. In fact, the success of a cloning attempt may depend in large part on whether or not the chromatin structure in the donor nucleus can be restored to that of a newly fertilized egg.

Stem Cells of Animals

The major goal of cloning human embryos is not reproduction, but the production of stem cells for treating human diseases. A **stem cell** is a relatively unspecialized cell that can both reproduce itself indefinitely and, under appropriate conditions, differentiate into specialized cells of one or more types. Thus, stem cells are able both to replenish their own population and to generate cells that travel down specific differentiation pathways.

Many early animal embryos contain stem cells capable of giving rise to differentiated embryonic cells of any type. Stem cells can be isolated from early embryos at a stage called the blastula stage or its human equivalent, the blastocyst stage (Figure 20.20). In culture, these *embryonic stem (ES) cells* reproduce indefinitely; and depending on culture conditions, they can be made to differentiate into a variety of specialized cells, including even eggs and sperm.

The adult body also has stem cells, which serve to replace nonreproducing specialized cells as needed. In contrast to ES cells, *adult stem cells* are not able to give rise to all cell types in the organism, though they can generate multiple types. For example, one of the several types of stem cells in bone marrow can generate all the different kinds of blood cells (see Figure 20.20), and another can differentiate into bone, cartilage, fat, muscle, and the linings of blood vessels. To the surprise of many, the adult brain has been found to contain stem cells that continue to produce certain kinds of nerve cells there. And recently, re-

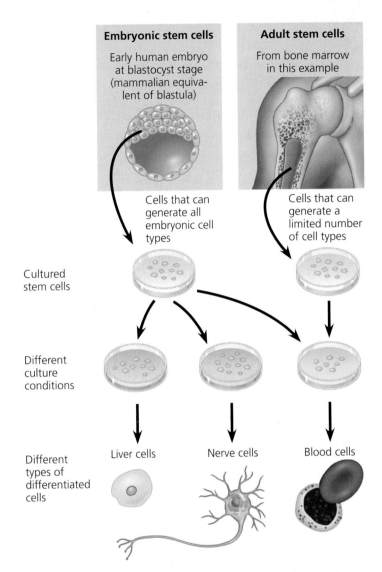

▲ **Figure 20.20 Working with stem cells.** Animal stem cells, which can be isolated from early embryos or adult tissues and grown in culture, are self-perpetuating, relatively undifferentiated cells. Embryonic stem cells are easier to grow than adult stem cells and can theoretically give rise to *all* types of cells in an organism. The range of cell types that can arise from adult stem cells is not yet fully understood.

searchers have reported finding stem cells in skin, hair, eyes, and dental pulp. Although adult animals have only tiny numbers of stem cells, scientists are learning to identify and isolate these cells from various tissues and, in some cases, to grow them in culture. With the right culture conditions (for instance, the addition of specific growth factors), cultured stem cells from adult animals have been made to differentiate into multiple types of specialized cells.

Research with embryonic or adult stem cells is a source of valuable data about differentiation and has enormous potential for medical applications. The ultimate aim is to supply cells for the repair of damaged or diseased organs: for example, insulin-producing pancreatic cells for people with diabetes or certain kinds of brain cells for people with Parkinson's disease or Huntington's disease. Adult stem cells from bone marrow have long been used as a source of immune system cells in patients whose own immune systems are nonfunctional because of genetic disorders or radiation treatments for cancer.

The developmental potential of adult stem cells is limited to certain tissues. ES cells hold more promise than adult stem cells for medical applications because ES cells are **pluripotent**, capable of differentiating into many different cell types. The only way to obtain ES cells thus far, however, has been to harvest them from human embryos, which raises ethical and political issues.

ES cells are currently obtained from embryos donated by patients undergoing infertility treatment or from long-term cell cultures originally established with cells isolated from donated embryos. If scientists are able to clone human embryos to the blastocyst stage, they might be able to use such clones as the source of ES cells in the future. Furthermore, with a donor nucleus from a person with a particular disease, they might be able to produce ES cells for treatment that match the patient and are thus not rejected by his or her immune system. When the main aim of cloning is to produce ES cells to treat disease, the process is called *therapeutic cloning*. Although most people believe that reproductive cloning of humans is unethical, opinions vary about the morality of therapeutic cloning.

Resolving the debate now seems less imperative due to recent reports that ES cells can be acquired by turning back the clock in fully differentiated adult cells. Accomplishing this feat, which posed formidable obstacles, was announced in 2007, first by labs using mouse skin cells and then by others using human skin cells. In all cases, researchers transformed the skin cells into ES cells by using retroviruses to introduce extra cloned copies of four "stem cell" master regulatory genes. All tests carried out so far indicate that the transformed cells, which are known as *induced pluripotent stem (iPS) cells*, can do everything ES cells can do. Fine-tuning of techniques to direct iPS cells to become specific cell types is an area of intense research that has already seen some success. These cell types could eventually provide tailor-made "replacement" cells for patients without using any human eggs or embryos, thus circumventing most ethical objections.

CONCEPT CHECK 20.3

1. If you clone a carrot, will all the progeny plants ("clones") look identical? Why or why not?

2. Based on current knowledge, how would you explain the difference in the percentage of tadpoles that developed from the two kinds of donor nuclei in Figure 20.17?

3. **WHAT IF?** If you were a doctor who wanted to use iPS cells to treat a patient with severe diabetes, what new technique would have to be developed?

For suggested answers, see Appendix A.

CONCEPT 20.4
The practical applications of DNA technology affect our lives in many ways

DNA technology is in the news almost every day. Most often, the topic is a new and promising application in medicine, but this is just one of numerous fields benefiting from DNA technology and genetic engineering.

Medical Applications

One important use of DNA technology is the identification of human genes whose mutation plays a role in genetic diseases. These discoveries may lead to ways of diagnosing, treating, and even preventing such conditions. DNA technology is also contributing to our understanding of "nongenetic" diseases, from arthritis to AIDS, since a person's genes influence susceptibility to these diseases. Furthermore, diseases of all sorts involve changes in gene expression within the affected cells and often within the patient's immune system. By using DNA microarray assays or other techniques to compare gene expression in healthy and diseased tissues, as seen in Figure 20.1, researchers hope to find many of the genes that are turned on or off in particular diseases. These genes and their products are potential targets for prevention or therapy.

Diagnosis of Diseases

A new chapter in the diagnosis of infectious diseases has been opened by DNA technology, in particular the use of PCR and labeled nucleic acid probes to track down pathogens. For example, because the sequence of the RNA genome of HIV is known, RT-PCR can be used to amplify, and thus detect, HIV RNA in blood or tissue samples (see Figure 20.13). RT-PCR is often the best way to detect an otherwise elusive infective agent.

Medical scientists can now diagnose hundreds of human genetic disorders by using PCR with primers that target the genes associated with these disorders. The amplified DNA product is then sequenced to reveal the presence or absence of the disease-causing mutation. Among the genes for human diseases that have been identified are those for sickle-cell disease, hemophilia, cystic fibrosis, Huntington's disease, and Duchenne muscular dystrophy. Individuals afflicted with such diseases can often be identified before the onset of symptoms, even before birth. PCR can also be used to identify symptomless carriers of potentially harmful recessive alleles, essentially replacing Southern blotting for this purpose.

For some genetic disorders, medical scientists can detect an abnormal disease-causing allele by testing for *genetic markers* that are known to be very close (linked) to the allele. A genetic marker is a DNA sequence that varies in a population; in a gene, such sequence variation is the basis of different alleles. Just like coding sequences, noncoding DNA at a specific locus on a chromosome may exhibit small nucleotide differences among individuals. Variations in DNA sequence are called *polymorphisms* (from the Greek for "many forms").

Among the most useful of these genetic markers are single base-pair variations in the genomes of the human population. A single base-pair site where variation is found in at least 1% of the population is called a **single nucleotide polymorphism** (**SNP**, pronounced "snip"). SNPs occur on average about once in 100 to 300 base pairs in the human genome and are found in both coding and noncoding DNA sequences. (About 99% of our genome doesn't code for protein, as you will learn in Chapter 21.)

Some SNPs alter the sequence recognized by a restriction enzyme, as is the case for the single-nucleotide difference between the alleles for normal and sickle-cell β-globin. Such alterations change the lengths of the restriction fragments formed by digestion with that enzyme (see Figure 20.10). This type of sequence change, which can occur in either coding or noncoding regions, is called a **restriction fragment length polymorphism** (**RFLP**, pronounced "Rif-lip"). Scientists figured out how to use Southern blotting to detect RFLPs almost 30 years ago, realizing that RFLPs could serve as useful genetic markers. It is not necessary to actually sequence the DNA of multiple individuals to find SNPs; today they can be detected by very sensitive microarray analysis or by PCR.

But how can RFLPs or other SNPs help us diagnose a genetic disorder? The presence of an abnormal allele can be diagnosed with reasonable accuracy if a closely linked SNP marker has been found (**Figure 20.21**). Alleles for Huntington's disease and a number of other genetic diseases were first detected by means of RFLPs in this indirect way. If the marker and the gene itself are close enough, crossing over between the marker and the gene is very unlikely during gamete formation. Therefore, the marker and gene will almost always be inherited together, even though the marker is not part of the gene. The same principle applies to all kinds of markers.

Human Gene Therapy

Gene therapy—introducing genes into an afflicted individual for therapeutic purposes—holds great potential for treating disorders traceable to a single defective gene. In theory, a normal allele of the defective gene could be inserted into the somatic cells of the tissue affected by the disorder.

For gene therapy of somatic cells to be permanent, the cells that receive the normal allele must be ones that multiply throughout the patient's life. Bone marrow cells, which include the stem cells that give rise to all the cells of the blood and immune system, are prime candidates. **Figure 20.22** outlines one possible procedure for gene therapy of an individual whose bone marrow cells do not produce a vital enzyme because of a single defective gene. One type of severe combined immunodeficiency (SCID) is caused by just this kind of defect. If the treatment is successful, the patient's bone marrow cells will begin producing the missing protein, and the patient will be cured.

▲ **Figure 20.22 Gene therapy using a retroviral vector.** A retrovirus that has been rendered harmless is used as a vector in this procedure, which exploits the ability of a retrovirus to insert a DNA transcript of its RNA genome into the chromosomal DNA of its host cell (see Figure 19.8). If the foreign gene carried by the retroviral vector is expressed, the cell and its descendants will possess the gene product, and the patient may be cured. Cells that reproduce throughout life, such as bone marrow cells, are ideal candidates for gene therapy.

① Insert RNA version of normal allele into retrovirus.

② Let retrovirus infect bone marrow cells that have been removed from the patient and cultured.

③ Viral DNA carrying the normal allele inserts into chromosome.

④ Inject engineered cells into patient.

▲ **Figure 20.21 Single nucleotide polymorphisms (SNPs) as genetic markers for disease-causing alleles.** This diagram depicts homologous segments of DNA from a family in which some members have a genetic disease. In this family, unaffected family members have a T at a particular SNP locus. If a family member has a C at that locus, there is a high probability that the individual has also inherited the disease-causing allele. (Here, only a single strand is shown for each DNA molecule.)

The procedure shown in Figure 20.22 has been used in gene therapy trials for SCID. In a trial begun in France in 2000, ten young children with SCID were treated by the same procedure. Nine of these patients showed significant, definitive improvement after two years, the first indisputable success of gene therapy. However, three of the patients subsequently developed leukemia, a type of blood cell cancer, and one of them died. Researchers discovered that in two cases, the retroviral vector used to carry the normal allele into bone marrow cells had inserted near a gene involved in the proliferation and development of blood cells, which could have led to the leukemia. In a recent experiment on mice, a replacement of the mouse version of the same gene led to a high incidence of lymphoma, also a blood cancer. These results suggest that an unknown function of the gene itself may be responsible.

Gene therapy also raises several other technical questions. For example, how can the activity of the transferred gene be controlled so that cells make appropriate amounts of the gene product at the right time and in the right place? How can we be sure that the insertion of the therapeutic gene does not harm some other necessary cell function? As more is learned about DNA control elements and gene interactions, researchers may be able to answer such questions.

In addition to technical challenges, gene therapy raises ethical questions. Some critics believe that tampering with human genes in any way is immoral. Other observers see no fundamental difference between the transplantation of genes into somatic cells and the transplantation of organs.

Treatment of human germ-line cells in the hope of correcting a defect in future generations raises further ethical issues. Such genetic engineering is routinely done in laboratory mice, and the technical problems relating to similar genetic engineering in humans will eventually be solved. Under what circumstances, if any, should we alter the genomes of human germ lines? Would this inevitably lead to the practice of eugenics, a deliberate effort to control the genetic makeup of human populations? From a biological perspective, the elimination of unwanted alleles from the gene pool could backfire. Genetic variation is a necessary ingredient for the survival of a species as environmental conditions change with time. Alleles that are damaging under some conditions may be advantageous under other conditions (one example is the sickle-cell allele, discussed in Chapter 14). Are we willing to risk making genetic changes that could be detrimental to the survival of our species in the future? We may have to face this question soon.

Pharmaceutical Products

The pharmaceutical industry derives significant benefit from advances in DNA technology and genetic research, applying them to the development of useful drugs to treat diseases. Pharmaceutical products are synthesized using methods of either organic chemistry or biotechnology, depending on the nature of the product.

Synthesis of Small Molecules for Use as Drugs   An exciting recent development has been the synthesis of small molecules that are tailored to combat certain cancers by blocking the function of a protein crucial for the tumor cells' survival. One drug, imatinib (trade name Gleevec), is a small molecule that inhibits a specific receptor tyrosine kinase (see Figure 11.7). The overexpression of this receptor, resulting from a chromosomal translocation, is instrumental in causing chronic myelogenous leukemia (CML; see Figure 15.17). Patients in the early stages of CML who are treated with imatinib have exhibited nearly complete, sustained remission from the cancer. Drugs that work like this have also been used with success to treat a few types of lung and breast cancers. This approach is feasible only for cancers for which the molecular basis is fairly well understood.

Pharmaceutical products that are proteins can be synthesized on a large scale, using cells or whole organisms. Cell cultures are more widely used at present.

Protein Production in Cell Cultures   You learned earlier in the chapter about DNA cloning and gene expression systems for producing large quantities of proteins that are present naturally in only minute amounts. The host cells used in such expression systems can even be engineered to secrete a protein as it is made, thereby simplifying the task of purifying it by traditional biochemical methods.

Among the first pharmaceutical products "manufactured" in this way were human insulin and human growth hormone (HGH). Some 2 million people with diabetes in the United States depend on insulin treatment to control their disease. Human growth hormone has been a boon to children born with a form of dwarfism caused by inadequate amounts of HGH. Another important pharmaceutical product produced by genetic engineering is tissue plasminogen activator (TPA). If administered shortly after a heart attack, TPA helps dissolve blood clots and reduces the risk of subsequent heart attacks.

Cells in culture can also be used to produce vaccines, which stimulate the immune system to defend the body against specific pathogens (see Chapter 43). A pathogen typically has one or more proteins on its surface that trigger an immune response against it. This type of protein, made by recombinant DNA techniques, can function as a vaccine against the pathogen. Alternatively, genetic engineering can be used to modify a pathogen's genome, resulting in a weakened pathogen that can then serve as a "live" vaccine.

Protein Production by "Pharm" Animals and Plants   In some cases, instead of using cell systems *in vitro* to produce large quantities of protein products, pharmaceutical scientists can use whole animals. Their techniques are those we alluded to when we discussed the possibility of genetically engineering human germ-line cells, but they are performed on animals other than humans. Using these methods, scientists can introduce a gene from an animal of one genotype into the genome of another individual, often of a different species. This individual is then called a **transgenic** animal. To do this, they first remove eggs from a female of the recipient species and fertilize them *in vitro*. Meanwhile, they have cloned the desired gene from the donor organism. They then inject the cloned DNA directly into the nuclei of the fertilized eggs. Some of the cells integrate the foreign DNA, the *transgene*, into their genomes and are able to express the foreign gene. The engineered embryos are then surgically implanted in a surrogate mother. If an embryo develops successfully, the result is a transgenic animal, containing a gene from a third "parent," which may be of a different species.

Assuming that the introduced gene encodes a protein desired in large quantities, these transgenic animals can act as pharmaceutical "factories." For example, a transgene for a human blood protein such as antithrombin can be inserted into the genome of a goat in such a way that the transgene's product is secreted in the animal's milk **(Figure 20.23)**. The protein can then be purified from the milk, usually more easily than from a cell culture. Researchers have also engineered transgenic chickens that express large amounts of the transgene's product in eggs. Biotechnology companies consider the characteristics of candidate animals in deciding which to use for engineering. For example, goats reproduce faster than cows, and it is possible to harvest more protein from goat milk than from the milk of other rapidly reproducing mammals, such as rabbits.

Human proteins produced in transgenic farm animals for use in humans may differ in some ways from the naturally produced human proteins, possibly because of subtle differences in protein modification. Therefore, such proteins must be tested very carefully to ensure that they (or contaminants from the farm animals) will not cause allergic reactions or other adverse effects in patients who receive them.

In a novel twist, the pharmaceutical industry is beginning to develop "pharm" plants, analogous to "pharm" animals. Although natural plants have long been sources of drugs, researchers are now creating plants that make human proteins for medical use and viral proteins for use as vaccines. In 2007, the U.S. Food and Drug Administration (FDA) approved a plan to plant over 3,000 acres in Kansas with rice harboring genes for milk proteins. The harvested proteins would be used in rehydration formulas to treat infant diarrhea, a serious problem in developing countries.

Forensic Evidence and Genetic Profiles

In violent crimes, body fluids or small pieces of tissue may be left at the scene or on the clothes or other possessions of the victim or assailant. If enough blood, semen, or tissue is available, forensic laboratories can determine the blood type or tissue type by using antibodies to detect specific cell-surface proteins. However, such tests require fairly fresh samples in relatively large amounts. Also, because many people have the same blood or tissue type, this approach can only exclude a suspect; it cannot provide strong evidence of guilt.

DNA testing, on the other hand, can identify the guilty individual with a high degree of certainty, because the DNA sequence of every person is unique (except for identical twins). Genetic markers that vary in the population can be analyzed for a given person to determine that individual's unique set of genetic markers, or **genetic profile**. (This term is preferred over "DNA fingerprint" by forensic scientists, who want to emphasize the heritable aspect of these markers rather than simply the fact that they produce a pattern on a gel that, like a fingerprint, is visually recognizable.) The FBI started applying DNA technology in forensics in 1988, using RFLP analysis by Southern blotting to detect similarities and differences in DNA samples. This method required much smaller samples of blood or tissue than earlier methods—only about 1,000 cells.

Today, forensic scientists use an even more sensitive method that takes advantage of variations in length of genetic markers called **short tandem repeats (STRs)**. These are tandemly repeated units of 2- to 5-base sequences in specific regions of the genome. The number of repeats present in these regions is highly variable from person to person (polymorphic). For example, one individual may have the sequence ACAT repeated 30 times at one genome locus, whereas another individual may have 18 repeats at this locus. PCR is used to amplify particular STRs, using sets of primers that are labeled with different-colored fluorescent tags; the length of the region, and thus the number of repeats, can then be determined by electrophoresis. Because Southern blotting is not required, this method is quicker than RFLP analysis. And the PCR step allows use of the

▲ **Figure 20.23 Goats as "pharm" animals.** This transgenic goat carries a gene for a human blood protein, antithrombin, which she secretes in her milk. Patients with a rare hereditary disorder in which this protein is lacking suffer from formation of blood clots in their blood vessels. Easily purified from the goat's milk, the protein is currently under evaluation as an anticlotting agent.

method even when the DNA is in poor condition or available only in minute quantities. A tissue sample containing as few as 20 cells can be sufficient for PCR amplification.

In a murder case, for example, this method can be used to compare DNA samples from the suspect, the victim, and a small amount of blood found at the crime scene. The forensic scientist tests only a few selected portions of the DNA—usually 13 STR markers. However, even this small set of markers can provide a forensically useful genetic profile because the probability that two people (who are not identical twins) would have exactly the same set of STR markers is vanishingly small. The Innocence Project, a nonprofit organization dedicated to overturning wrongful convictions, uses STR analysis of archived samples from crime scenes to revisit old cases. As of 2006, 18 innocent people had been released from prison as a result of forensic and legal work by this group **(Figure 20.24)**.

Genetic profiles can also be useful for other purposes. A comparison of the DNA of a mother, her child, and the purported father can conclusively settle a question of paternity. Sometimes paternity is of historical interest: Genetic profiles

provided strong evidence that Thomas Jefferson or one of his close male relatives fathered at least one of the children of his slave Sally Hemings. Genetic profiles can also identify victims of mass casualties. The largest such effort occurred after the attack on the World Trade Center in 2001; more than 10,000 samples of victims' remains were compared with DNA samples from personal items, such as toothbrushes, provided by families. Ultimately, forensic scientists succeeded in identifying almost 3,000 victims using these methods.

Just how reliable is a genetic profile? The greater the number of markers examined in a DNA sample, the more likely it is that the profile is unique to one individual. In forensic cases using STR analysis with 13 markers, the probability of two people having identical DNA profiles is somewhere between one chance in 10 billion and one in several trillion. (For comparison, the world's population in 2007 was about 6.6 billion.) The exact probability depends on the frequency of those markers in the general population. Information on how common various markers are in different ethnic groups is critical because these marker frequencies may vary considerably among ethnic groups and between a particular ethnic group and the population as a whole. With the increasing availability of frequency data, forensic scientists can make extremely accurate statistical calculations. Thus, despite problems that can still arise from insufficient data, human error, or flawed evidence, genetic profiles are now accepted as compelling evidence by legal experts and scientists alike.

Environmental Cleanup

Increasingly, the remarkable ability of certain microorganisms to transform chemicals is being exploited for environmental cleanup. If the growth needs of such microbes make them unsuitable for direct use, scientists can now transfer the genes for their valuable metabolic capabilities into other microorganisms, which can then be used to treat environmental problems. For example, many bacteria can extract heavy metals, such as copper, lead, and nickel, from their environments and incorporate the metals into compounds such as copper sulfate or lead sulfate, which are readily recoverable. Genetically engineered microbes may become important in both mining minerals (especially as ore reserves are depleted) and cleaning up highly toxic mining wastes. Biotechnologists are also trying to engineer microbes that can degrade chlorinated hydrocarbons and other harmful compounds. These microbes could be used in wastewater treatment plants or by manufacturers before the compounds are ever released into the environment.

In a more "old-fashioned" application of biotechnology, *biofuels* from crops such as corn, soybeans, and cassava have been proposed as a supplement or even replacement for fossil fuels. In this case, no genetic engineering is involved. To produce "bioethanol," the starch made naturally by the plants is simply converted to sugar and then fermented by microorganisms; a

(a) In 1984, Earl Washington was convicted and sentenced to death for the 1982 rape and murder of Rebecca Williams. His sentence was commuted to life in prison in 1993 due to new doubts about the evidence. In 2000, STR analysis by forensic scientists associated with The Innocence Project showed conclusively that he was innocent. This photo shows Washington just before his release in 2001, after 17 years in prison.

Source of sample	STR marker 1	STR marker 2	STR marker 3
Semen on victim	17, 19	13, 16	12, 12
Earl Washington	16, 18	14, 15	11, 12
Kenneth Tinsley	17, 19	13, 16	12, 12

(b) In STR analysis, selected STR markers in a DNA sample are amplified by PCR, and the PCR products are separated by electrophoresis. The procedure reveals how many repeats are present for each STR locus in the sample. An individual has two alleles per STR locus, each with a certain number of repeats. This table shows the number of repeats for three STR markers in three samples: from semen found on the victim, from Washington, and from another man named Kenneth Tinsley, who was in prison because of an unrelated conviction. These and other STR data (not shown) exonerated Washington and led Tinsley to plead guilty to the murder.

▲ **Figure 20.24 STR analysis used to release an innocent man from prison.**

similar process can produce "biodiesel" from plant oils. Either product can be mixed with gasoline or used alone to power vehicles. Proponents say these fuels have less impact on the environment than fossil fuels, but others disagree, asserting that the environmental effects of growing these crops make their total impact greater than that of fossil fuels.

Agricultural Applications

Scientists are working to learn more about the genomes of agriculturally important plants and animals. For a number of years, they have been using DNA technology in an effort to improve agricultural productivity.

Animal Husbandry

The selective breeding of livestock, or animal husbandry, has exploited naturally occurring mutations and genetic recombination for centuries. As we described earlier, DNA technology enables scientists to produce transgenic animals, which speeds up the selective breeding process. The goals of creating a transgenic animal are often the same as the goals of traditional breeding—for instance, to make a sheep with better quality wool, a pig with leaner meat, or a cow that will mature in a shorter time. Scientists might, for example, identify and clone a gene that causes the development of larger muscles (muscles make up most of the meat we eat) in one breed of cattle and transfer it to other cattle or even to sheep.

However, problems such as low fertility or increased susceptibility to disease are not uncommon among farm animals carrying genes from humans and other foreign species. Animal health and welfare are important issues to consider when developing transgenic animals.

Genetic Engineering in Plants

Agricultural scientists have already endowed a number of crop plants with genes for desirable traits, such as delayed ripening and resistance to spoilage and disease. In one striking way, plants are easier to genetically engineer than most animals. For many plant species, a single tissue cell grown in culture can give rise to an adult plant (see Figure 20.16). Thus, genetic manipulations can be performed on an ordinary somatic cell and the cell then used to generate an organism with new traits.

The most commonly used vector for introducing new genes into plant cells is a plasmid, called the **Ti plasmid**, from the soil bacterium *Agrobacterium tumefaciens*. This plasmid integrates a segment of its DNA, known as T DNA, into the chromosomal DNA of its host plant cells. For vector purposes, researchers work with versions of the plasmid that do not cause disease (unlike the wild-type version) and that have been engineered to carry genes of interest within the borders of the T DNA. **Figure 20.25** outlines one method for using the Ti plasmid to produce transgenic plants. Scientists can intro-

▼ **Figure 20.25** **Research Method**

Using the Ti Plasmid to Produce Transgenic Plants

APPLICATION Genes conferring useful traits, such as pest resistance, herbicide resistance, delayed ripening, and increased nutritional value, can be transferred from one plant variety or species to another using the Ti plasmid as a vector.

TECHNIQUE

❶ The Ti plasmid is isolated from the bacterium *Agrobacterium tumefaciens*. The segment of the plasmid that integrates into the genome of host cells is called T DNA.

❷ The foreign gene of interest is inserted into the middle of the T DNA using methods shown in Figure 20.4.

❸ Recombinant plasmids can be introduced into cultured plant cells by electroporation. Or plasmids can be returned to *Agrobacterium*, which is then applied as a liquid suspension to the leaves of susceptible plants, infecting them. Once a plasmid is taken into a plant cell, its T DNA integrates into the cell's chromosomal DNA.

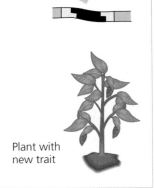

RESULTS Transformed cells carrying the transgene of interest can regenerate complete plants that exhibit the new trait conferred by the transgene.

duce recombinant Ti plasmids into plant cells by electroporation. Alternatively, the recombinant plasmid can be put back into *Agrobacterium*; susceptible plants or plant cells growing in culture are then infected with bacteria that contain the recombinant plasmid.

Genetic engineering is rapidly replacing traditional plant-breeding programs, especially for useful traits, such as herbicide or pest resistance, determined by one or a few genes. Crops engineered with a bacterial gene making the plants resistant to herbicides can grow while weeds are destroyed, and genetically engineered crops that can resist destructive insects reduce the need for chemical insecticides. In India, the insertion of a salinity resistance gene from a coastal mangrove plant into the genomes of several rice varieties has resulted in rice plants that can grow in water three times as salty as seawater. The research foundation that carried out this feat of genetic engineering estimates that one-third of all irrigated land has high salinity owing to overirrigation and intensive use of chemical fertilizers, representing a serious threat to the food supply. Thus, salinity-resistant crop plants would be enormously valuable worldwide.

Genetic engineering also has great potential for improving the nutritional value of crop plants. For instance, scientists have developed transgenic rice plants that produce yellow rice grains containing beta-carotene, which our body uses to make vitamin A (see Figure 38.18). This "golden" rice could help prevent vitamin A deficiency in the half of the world's population that depends on rice as a staple food. Currently, large numbers of young children in Southeast Asia suffer from vitamin A deficiency, which leads to vision impairment and increases susceptibility to disease.

Safety and Ethical Questions Raised by DNA Technology

Early concerns about potential dangers associated with recombinant DNA technology focused on the possibility that hazardous new pathogens might be created. What might happen, for instance, if cancer cell genes were transferred into bacteria or viruses? To guard against such rogue microbes, scientists developed a set of guidelines that were adopted as formal government regulations in the United States and some other countries. One safety measure is a set of strict laboratory procedures designed to protect researchers from infection by engineered microbes and to prevent the microbes from accidentally leaving the laboratory. In addition, strains of microorganisms to be used in recombinant DNA experiments are genetically crippled to ensure that they cannot survive outside the laboratory. Finally, certain obviously dangerous experiments have been banned.

Today, most public concern about possible hazards centers not on recombinant microbes but on **genetically modified (GM) organisms** used as food. In common language, a GM organism is one that has acquired by artificial means one or more genes from another species or even from another variety of the same species. Some salmon, for example, have been genetically modified by addition of a more active salmon growth hormone gene. However, the majority of the GM organisms that contribute to our food supply are not animals, but crop plants.

GM crops are widespread in the United States, Argentina, and Brazil; together these countries account for over 80% of the world's acreage devoted to such crops. In the United States, the majority of corn, soybeans, and canola are GM crops, and GM products are not required to be labeled. However, the same foods are an ongoing subject of controversy in Europe, where the GM revolution has met with strong opposition. Many Europeans are concerned about the safety of GM foods and the possible environmental consequences of growing GM plants. Early in 2000, negotiators from 130 countries (including the United States) agreed on a Biosafety Protocol that requires exporters to identify GM organisms present in bulk food shipments and allows importing countries to decide whether the products pose environmental or health risks. Since then, European countries have, on occasion, refused crops from the United States and other countries, leading to trade disputes. Although a small number of GM crops have been grown on European soil, these products have generally failed in local markets, and the future of GM crops in Europe is uncertain.

Advocates of a cautious approach toward GM crops fear that transgenic plants might pass their new genes to close relatives in nearby wild areas. We know that lawn and crop grasses, for example, commonly exchange genes with wild relatives via pollen transfer. If crop plants carrying genes for resistance to herbicides, diseases, or insect pests pollinated wild ones, the offspring might become "super weeds" that are very difficult to control. Another possible hazard, suggested by one laboratory-based study, is that a transgene encoding a pesticide-like protein might cause plants to produce pollen toxic to butterflies. However, scientists with the Agricultural Research Service concluded from a two-year field study that butterflies were unlikely to be exposed to toxic levels of pollen.

As for the risks to human health from GM foods, some people fear that the protein products of transgenes might lead to allergic reactions. Although there is some evidence that this could happen, advocates claim that these proteins could be tested in advance to avoid producing ones that cause allergic reactions.

Today, governments and regulatory agencies throughout the world are grappling with how to facilitate the use of biotechnology in agriculture, industry, and medicine while ensuring that new products and procedures are safe. In the United States, such applications of biotechnology are evaluated for potential risks by various regulatory agencies, including the FDA, the Environmental Protection Agency, the National Institutes of Health, and the Department of Agriculture. Meanwhile, these same agencies and the public must consider the ethical implications of biotechnology.

Advances in biotechnology have allowed us to obtain complete genome sequences for humans and many other species, providing a vast treasure trove of information about genes. We can ask how certain genes differ from species to species, as well as how genes and, ultimately, entire genomes have evolved.

(These are the subjects of Chapter 21.) At the same time, the increasing speed and falling cost of determining the genome sequences of individuals are raising significant ethical questions. Who should have the right to examine someone else's genetic information? How should that information be used? Should a person's genome be a factor in determining eligibility for a job or insurance? Ethical considerations, as well as concerns about potential environmental and health hazards, will likely slow some applications of biotechnology. There is always a danger that too much regulation will stifle basic research and its potential benefits. However, the power of DNA technology and genetic engineering—our ability to profoundly and rapidly alter species that have been evolving for millennia—demands that we proceed with humility and caution.

CONCEPT CHECK **20.4**

1. What is the advantage of using stem cells for gene therapy?
2. List at least three different properties that have been acquired by crop plants via genetic engineering.
3. **WHAT IF?** As a physician, you have a patient with symptoms that suggest a hepatitis A infection. The symptoms come and go, but you have not been able to detect viral proteins in the blood. Knowing that hepatitis A is an RNA virus, what lab tests could you perform to support your diagnosis? Explain what the results would mean.

For suggested answers, see Appendix A.

Chapter 20 Review

MEDIA Go to the Study Area at **www.masteringbio.com** for BioFlix 3-D Animations, MP3 Tutors, Videos, Practice Tests, an eBook, and more.

SUMMARY OF KEY CONCEPTS

CONCEPT **20.1**

DNA cloning yields multiple copies of a gene or other DNA segment (pp. 396–405)

▶ **DNA Cloning and Its Applications: *A Preview*** DNA cloning and other techniques, collectively termed DNA technology, can be used to manipulate and analyze DNA and to produce useful new products and organisms.

▶ **Using Restriction Enzymes to Make Recombinant DNA** Bacterial restriction enzymes cut DNA molecules within short, specific nucleotide sequences to yield a set of double-stranded DNA fragments with single-stranded sticky ends. The sticky ends on fragments from one DNA source can base-pair with complementary sticky ends on fragments from other DNA molecules; sealing of the base-paired fragments with DNA ligase produces recombinant DNA molecules.

▶ **Cloning a Eukaryotic Gene in a Bacterial Plasmid**

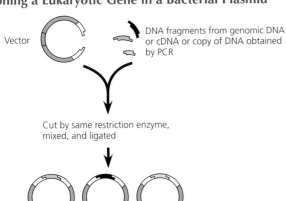

Recombinant DNA plasmids

Recombinant plasmids are returned to host cells, each of which divides to form a clone of cells. Collections of clones are stored as libraries.

▶ **Expressing Cloned Eukaryotic Genes** Several technical difficulties hinder the expression of cloned eukaryotic genes in bacterial host cells. The use of cultured eukaryotic cells as host cells and yeast artificial chromosomes (YACs) as vectors helps avoid these problems.

▶ **Amplifying DNA *in Vitro*: The Polymerase Chain Reaction (PCR)** PCR can produce many copies of a specific target segment of DNA, using primers that bracket the desired sequence and a heat-resistant DNA polymerase.

MEDIA
Activity Applications of DNA Technology
Activity Restriction Enzymes
Activity Cloning a Gene in Bacteria
Investigation How Can Antibiotic-Resistant Plasmids Transform *E. coli*?

CONCEPT **20.2**

DNA technology allows us to study the sequence, expression, and function of a gene (pp. 405–411)

▶ **Gel Electrophoresis and Southern Blotting** DNA restriction fragments of different lengths can be separated by gel electrophoresis. Specific fragments can be identified by Southern blotting, using labeled probes that hybridize to the DNA immobilized on a "blot" of the gel.

▶ **DNA Sequencing** Relatively short DNA fragments can be sequenced by the dideoxy chain termination method, which can be performed in automated sequencing machines.

▶ **Analyzing Gene Expression** Expression of a gene can be investigated using hybridization with labeled probes to look for specific mRNAs, either on a gel (Northern blotting) or in a whole organism (*in situ* hybridization). Also, RNA can be transcribed into cDNA by reverse transcriptase and the cDNA amplified with specific primers (RT-PCR). Microarrays allow researchers to compare the expression of many genes at once in different tissues, at different times, or under different conditions.

► **Determining Gene Function** For a gene of unknown function, experimental inactivation of the gene and observation of the resulting phenotypic effects can provide clues to its function.

MEDIA

Activity Gel Electrophoresis of DNA
Activity Analyzing DNA Fragments Using Gel Electrophoresis
Investigation How Can Gel Electrophoresis Be Used to Analyze DNA?

CONCEPT 20.3

Cloning organisms may lead to production of stem cells for research and other applications (pp. 412–416)

► Studies showing genomic equivalence (that an organism's cells have the same genome) were the first examples of organismal cloning.

► **Cloning Plants: Single-Cell Cultures** Differentiated cells from mature plants are often capable of generating a complete new plant.

► **Cloning Animals: Nuclear Transplantation** The nucleus from a differentiated animal cell can sometimes give rise to a new animal if transplanted to an enucleated egg.

► **Stem Cells of Animals** Certain stem cells from animal embryos or adult tissues can reproduce and differentiate *in vitro* as well as *in vivo*, offering the potential for medical use.

CONCEPT 20.4

The practical applications of DNA technology affect our lives in many ways (pp. 416–423)

► **Medical Applications** DNA technology is increasingly being used in the diagnosis of genetic and other diseases and offers potential for better treatment of genetic disorders or even permanent cures. Single nucleotide polymorphisms (SNPs) and restriction fragment length polymorphisms (RFLPs) are useful as genetic markers linked to disease-causing alleles. Large-scale production of protein hormones and other proteins with therapeutic uses, including safer vaccines, is possible with DNA technology. Some therapeutic proteins are being produced in transgenic "pharm" animals and plants.

► **Forensic Evidence and Genetic Profiles** Analysis of genetic markers such as short tandem repeats (STRs) in DNA isolated from tissue or body fluids found at crime scenes can provide definitive evidence that a suspect is guilty or innocent. Such analysis is also useful in parenthood disputes and in identifying the remains of crime victims.

► **Environmental Cleanup** Genetically engineered microorganisms can be used to extract minerals from the environment or degrade various types of potentially toxic waste materials.

► **Agricultural Applications** The aim of developing transgenic plants and animals is to improve agricultural productivity and food quality.

► **Safety and Ethical Questions Raised by DNA Technology** The potential benefits of genetic engineering must be carefully weighed against the potential hazards of creating products or developing procedures that are harmful to humans or the environment.

MEDIA

Activity DNA Fingerprinting
Activity Making Decisions About DNA Technology: Golden Rice
Activity The Human Genome Project: Genes on Human Chromosome 17

424 UNIT THREE Genetics

TESTING YOUR KNOWLEDGE

SELF-QUIZ

1. Which of the following tools of recombinant DNA technology is *incorrectly* paired with its use?
   a. restriction enzyme—production of RFLPs
   b. DNA ligase—enzyme that cuts DNA, creating the sticky ends of restriction fragments
   c. DNA polymerase—used in a polymerase chain reaction to amplify sections of DNA
   d. reverse transcriptase—production of cDNA from mRNA
   e. electrophoresis—separation of DNA fragments

2. Which of the following would *not* be true of cDNA produced using human brain tissue as the starting material?
   a. It could be amplified by the polymerase chain reaction.
   b. It could be used to create a complete genomic library.
   c. It is produced from mRNA using reverse transcriptase.
   d. It could be used as a probe to detect genes expressed in the brain.
   e. It lacks the introns of the human genes.

3. Plants are more readily manipulated by genetic engineering than are animals because
   a. plant genes do not contain introns.
   b. more vectors are available for transferring recombinant DNA into plant cells.
   c. a somatic plant cell can often give rise to a complete plant.
   d. genes can be inserted into plant cells by microinjection.
   e. plant cells have larger nuclei.

4. A paleontologist has recovered a bit of tissue from the 400-year-old preserved skin of an extinct dodo (a bird). The researcher would like to compare a specific region of the DNA from the sample with DNA from living birds. Which of the following would be most useful for increasing the amount of dodo DNA available for testing?
   a. RFLP analysis
   b. polymerase chain reaction (PCR)
   c. electroporation
   d. gel electrophoresis
   e. Southern blotting

5. Expression of a cloned eukaryotic gene in a bacterial cell involves many challenges. The use of mRNA and reverse transcriptase is part of a strategy to solve the problem of
   a. post-transcriptional processing.
   b. electroporation.
   c. post-translational processing.
   d. nucleic acid hybridization.
   e. restriction fragment ligation.

6. DNA technology has many medical applications. Which of the following is *not* done routinely at present?
   a. production of hormones for treating diabetes and dwarfism
   b. production of viral proteins for vaccines
   c. introduction of genetically engineered genes into human gametes
   d. prenatal identification of genetic disease genes
   e. genetic testing for carriers of harmful alleles

7. Which of the following sequences in double-stranded DNA is most likely to be recognized as a cutting site for a restriction enzyme?
a. AAGG   b. AGTC   c. GGCC   d. ACCA   e. AAAA
    TTCC   TCAG   CCGG   TGGT   TTTT

8. In recombinant DNA methods, the term *vector* can refer to
a. the enzyme that cuts DNA into restriction fragments.
b. the sticky end of a DNA fragment.
c. a RFLP marker.
d. a plasmid used to transfer DNA into a living cell.
e. a DNA probe used to identify a particular gene.

9. **DRAW IT** You are making a genomic library for the aard-vark, using a bacterial plasmid as a vector. The green diagram below shows the plasmid, which contains the restriction site for the enzyme used in Figure 20.3. Above the plasmid is a region of linear aardvark DNA. Diagram your cloning procedure, showing what would happen to these two molecules during each step. Use one color for the aardvark DNA and its bases and another color for those of the plasmid. Label each step.

5′   TCCATGAATTCTAAAGCGCTTATGAATTCACGGC   3′
3′   AGGTACTTAAGATTTCGCGAATACTTAAGTGCCG   5′
Aardvark DNA

Plasmid

10. **WHAT IF?** Imagine you want to study human crystallins, proteins present in the lens of the eye. To obtain a sufficient amount of the protein, you decide to clone the crystallin gene. Would you construct a genomic library or a cDNA library? What material would you use as a source of DNA or RNA?

For Self-Quiz answers, see Appendix A.

MEDIA Visit the Study Area at **www.masteringbio.com** for a Practice Test.

EVOLUTION CONNECTION

11. If DNA-based technologies become widely used, how might they change the way evolution proceeds, as compared with the natural evolutionary mechanisms of the past 4 billion years?

SCIENTIFIC INQUIRY

12. You hope to study a gene that codes for a neurotransmitter protein in human brain cells. You know the amino acid sequence of the protein. Explain how you might (a) identify the genes expressed in a specific type of brain cell, (b) identify the gene for the neurotransmitter, (c) produce multiple copies of the gene for study, and (d) produce a quantity of the neurotransmitter for evaluation as a potential medication.

SCIENCE, TECHNOLOGY, AND SOCIETY

13. Is there danger of discrimination based on testing for "harmful" genes? What policies can you suggest that would prevent such abuses?

14. Government funding of embryonic stem cell research has been a contentious political issue. Why has this debate been so heated? Summarize the arguments for and against embryonic stem cell research, and explain your own position on the issue.

21

Genomes and Their Evolution

▲ Figure 21.1 **What genomic information makes a human or a chimpanzee?**

KEY CONCEPTS

21.1 New approaches have accelerated the pace of genome sequencing

21.2 Scientists use bioinformatics to analyze genomes and their functions

21.3 Genomes vary in size, number of genes, and gene density

21.4 Multicellular eukaryotes have much noncoding DNA and many multigene families

21.5 Duplication, rearrangement, and mutation of DNA contribute to genome evolution

21.6 Comparing genome sequences provides clues to evolution and development

OVERVIEW

Reading the Leaves from the Tree of Life

The woman in **Figure 21.1** and her chimpanzee companions are sharing a laugh—or are they? Does each of them perceive a "joke" and react with this joyful facial expression and its accompanying vocalization? With the advent of recent techniques for rapidly sequencing complete genomes, we can now start to address the genetic basis of intriguing questions like this.

The chimpanzee (*Pan troglodytes*) is our closest living relative on the evolutionary tree of life. Its genome was sequenced in 2005, two years after sequencing of the human genome was largely completed. Now that we can compare our genome with that of the chimpanzee base by base, we can tackle the more general issue of what differences in the genetic information account for the distinct characteristics of these two species of primates.

In addition to determining the sequences of the human and chimpanzee genomes, researchers have obtained complete genome sequences for *E. coli* and numerous other prokaryotes,

as well as many eukaryotes, including *Saccharomyces cerevisiae* (brewer's yeast), *Caenorhabditis elegans* (a nematode), *Drosophila melanogaster* (fruit fly), *Mus musculus* (house mouse), and *Macaca mulatta* (rhesus macaque). Fragments of DNA have been sequenced even from extinct species, such as the cave bear and the woolly mammoth! These whole and partial genomes are of great interest in their own right and are also providing important insights into evolution and other biological processes. Broadening the human-chimpanzee comparison to the genomes of other primates and more distantly related animals should reveal the sets of genes that control group-defining characteristics. Beyond that, comparisons with the genomes of bacteria, archaea, fungi, protists, and plants should enlighten us about the long evolutionary history of shared ancient genes and their products.

With the genomes of many species fully sequenced, scientists can study whole sets of genes and their interactions, an approach called **genomics**. The sequencing efforts that feed this approach have generated, and continue to generate, enormous volumes of data. The need to deal with this ever-increasing flood of information has spawned the new field of **bioinformatics**, the application of computational methods to the storage and analysis of biological data.

We will begin this chapter by discussing two approaches to genome sequencing and some of the advances in and applications of bioinformatics. We will then summarize what has been learned from the genomes that have been sequenced thus far. Next, we will describe the composition of the human genome as a representative genome of a complex multicellular eukaryote. Finally, we will explore current ideas about how genomes evolve and about how the evolution of developmental mechanisms could have generated the great diversity of life found on Earth today.

CONCEPT 21.1

New approaches have accelerated the pace of genome sequencing

Sequencing of the human genome, an ambitious undertaking, officially began as the **Human Genome Project** in 1990. Organized by an international, publicly funded consortium of scientists at universities and research institutes, the project involved 20 large sequencing centers in six countries plus a host of other labs working on small projects.

After sequencing of the human genome was largely completed in 2003, the sequence of each chromosome was carefully analyzed and described in a series of papers, the last of which covered chromosome 1 and was published in 2006. With this refinement, researchers termed the sequencing "virtually complete." To reach these milestones, the project proceeded through three stages that provided progressively more detailed views of the human genome: linkage mapping, physical mapping, and DNA sequencing.

Three-Stage Approach to Genome Sequencing

Even before the Human Genome Project began, earlier research had sketched a rough picture of the organization of the genomes of many organisms. For instance, the karyotyping of many species had revealed their chromosome numbers and banding patterns (see Figure 13.3). And some genes had already been located on a particular region of a chromosome by fluorescence *in situ* hybridization (FISH), a method in which fluorescently labeled probes are allowed to hybridize to an immobilized array of whole chromosomes (see Figure 15.1). Cytogenetic maps based on this type of information provided the starting point for more detailed mapping.

With these cytogenetic maps of the chromosomes in hand, the initial stage in sequencing the human genome was to construct a **linkage map** (a type of genetic map; see Chapter 15) of several thousand genetic markers spaced throughout the chromosomes (**Figure 21.2** stage ❶). The order of the markers and the relative distances between them on such a map are based on recombination frequencies (see Figure 15.11). The markers can be genes or any other identifiable sequences in the DNA, such as RFLPs or the short tandem repeats (STRs) discussed in Chapter 20. By 1992, researchers had compiled a human linkage map with some 5,000 markers. Such a map enabled them to locate other markers, including genes, by testing for genetic linkage to the known markers. It was also valuable as a framework for organizing more detailed maps of particular regions.

The next stage was the physical mapping of the human genome. In a **physical map**, the distances between markers are expressed by some physical measure, usually the number

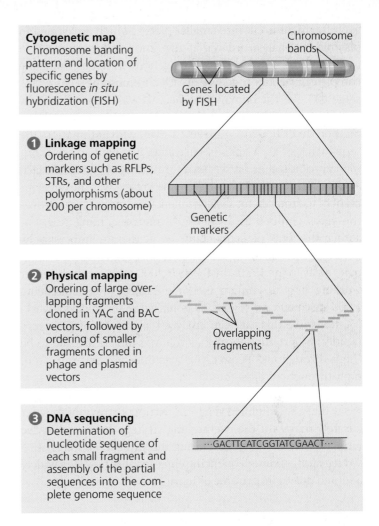

▲ Figure 21.2 Three-stage approach to sequencing an entire genome. Starting with a cytogenetic map of each chromosome, researchers with the Human Genome Project proceeded through three stages to reach the ultimate goal, the virtually complete nucleotide sequence of every chromosome.

of base pairs along the DNA. For whole-genome mapping, a physical map is made by cutting the DNA of each chromosome into a number of restriction fragments and then determining the original order of the fragments in the chromosomal DNA. The key is to make fragments that overlap and then use probes or automated nucleotide sequencing of the ends to find the overlaps (Figure 21.2, stage ❷). In this way, fragments can be assigned to a sequential order that corresponds to their order in a chromosome.

Supplies of the DNA fragments used for physical mapping are prepared by DNA cloning. In working with large genomes, researchers carry out several rounds of DNA cutting, cloning, and physical mapping. The first cloning vector is often a yeast artificial chromosome (YAC), which can carry inserted fragments a million base pairs long, or a bacterial artificial chromosome (BAC), which typically carries inserts of 100,000 to 300,000 base pairs. After such long fragments are put in order, each fragment is cut into smaller pieces, which are cloned in plasmids or phages, ordered in turn, and finally sequenced.

The ultimate goal in mapping a genome is to determine the complete nucleotide sequence of each chromosome (Figure 21.2, stage ❸). For the human genome, this was accomplished by sequencing machines, using the dideoxy chain-termination method described in Figure 20.12. Even with automation, the sequencing of all 3.2 billion base pairs in a haploid set of human chromosomes presented a formidable challenge. In fact, a major thrust of the Human Genome Project was the development of technology for faster sequencing. Improvements over the years chipped away at each time-consuming step, enabling the rate of sequencing to accelerate impressively: Whereas a productive lab could typically sequence 1,000 base pairs a day in the 1980s, by the year 2000 each research center working on the Human Genome Project was sequencing 1,000 base pairs *per second*, 24 hours a day, seven days a week. Methods like this that can analyze biological materials very rapidly and produce enormous volumes of data are said to be "high-throughput." Sequencing machines are an example of high-throughput devices.

In practice, the three stages shown in Figure 21.2 overlap in a way that our simplified version does not portray, but they accurately represent the overarching strategy employed in the Human Genome Project. During the project, an alternative strategy for genome sequencing emerged that has been widely adopted due to its extreme efficiency.

Whole-Genome Shotgun Approach to Genome Sequencing

In 1992, emboldened by advances in sequencing and computer technology, molecular biologist J. Craig Venter devised an alternative approach to the sequencing of whole genomes. Called the *whole-genome shotgun approach*, it essentially skips the linkage mapping and physical mapping stages and starts directly with the sequencing of random DNA fragments. Powerful computer programs then assemble the resulting very large number of overlapping short sequences into a single continuous sequence **(Figure 21.3)**.

Despite the skepticism of many scientists, the value of Venter's approach became clear in 1995 when he and colleagues reported the first complete genome sequence of an organism, the bacterium *Haemophilus influenzae*. In 1998, he set up a company, Celera Genomics, and declared his intention to sequence the entire human genome. Five years later, Celera Genomics and the public consortium jointly announced that sequencing of the human genome was largely complete, two years before the original target date of the Human Genome Project.

Representatives of the public consortium point out that Celera's accomplishment relied heavily on the consortium's maps and sequence data and that the infrastructure estab-

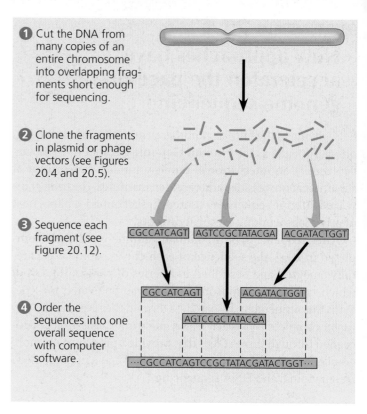

❶ Cut the DNA from many copies of an entire chromosome into overlapping fragments short enough for sequencing.

❷ Clone the fragments in plasmid or phage vectors (see Figures 20.4 and 20.5).

❸ Sequence each fragment (see Figure 20.12).

CGCCATCAGT AGTCCGCTATACGA ACGATACTGGT

❹ Order the sequences into one overall sequence with computer software.

CGCCATCAGT
AGTCCGCTATACGA
ACGATACTGGT

···CGCCATCAGTCCGCTATACGATACTGGT···

▲ **Figure 21.3 Whole-genome shotgun approach to sequencing.** In this approach, developed by Craig Venter and colleagues at the company he founded, Celera Genomics, random DNA fragments are sequenced and then ordered relative to each other. Compare this approach with the hierarchical, three-stage approach shown in Figure 21.2.

? *The fragments in stage 2 of this figure are depicted as scattered, whereas those in stage 2 of Figure 21.2 are drawn in a much more orderly fashion. How do these depictions reflect the two approaches?*

lished by their approach was a tremendous aid to Celera's efforts. Venter, on the other hand, argues for the efficiency and economy of Celera's methods, and indeed, the public consortium has made some use of them as well. Clearly, both approaches are valuable and have contributed to the rapid completion of genome sequencing for quite a few species.

Today, the whole-genome shotgun approach is widely used. Typically, the fragments are cloned into three different vectors, each of which takes a defined size of insert. The known distance between the ends of the inserted DNA is one more piece of information the computer can use to assemble the sequences properly. A recent study comparing the two approaches has shown that whole-genome shotgun sequencing can miss some duplicated sequences, thus underestimating the size of the genome and missing some genes in those regions. The hybrid approach that ended up being used for the human genome, with the more rapid shotgun sequencing being augmented by some mapping of clones, may in fact prove to be most useful in the long run.

As of 2007, there were still some small sections of the human genome that had not been sequenced. Because of the presence of repetitive DNA and for other poorly understood reasons, certain parts of the chromosomes of multicellular organisms resist detailed sequencing by the usual methods.

At first glance, genome sequences of humans and other organisms are simply dry lists of nucleotide bases—millions of A's, T's, C's, and G's in mind-numbing succession. Crucial to making sense of this massive amount of data have been new analytical approaches, which we discuss next.

CONCEPT CHECK 21.1

1. What is the major difference between a linkage map and a physical map of a chromosome?
2. In general, how does the approach to genome mapping used in the Human Genome Project differ from the whole-genome shotgun approach?
3. **WHAT IF?** Imagine you decide to sequence the genome of a field mouse, a species closely related to the lab mouse whose genome has already been sequenced. Why might having the lab mouse sequence available lead you to use the whole-genome shotgun approach instead of the three-stage approach?

For suggested answers, see Appendix A.

CONCEPT 21.2

Scientists use bioinformatics to analyze genomes and their functions

Each of the 20 or so sequencing centers around the world working on the Human Genome Project churned out voluminous amounts of DNA sequence day after day. As the data began to accumulate, the need to coordinate efforts to keep track of all the sequences became clear. Thanks to the foresight of scientists and government officials involved in the Human Genome Project, its goals included the establishment of banks of data, or databases, and the refining of analytical software. These databases and software programs would then be centralized and made readily accessible on the Internet. Accomplishing this aim has accelerated progress in DNA sequence analysis by making bioinformatics resources available to researchers worldwide and by speeding up the dissemination of information.

Centralized Resources for Analyzing Genome Sequences

Government-funded agencies carried out their mandate to establish databases and provide software with which scientists could analyze the sequence data. For example, in the United States, a joint endeavor between the National Library of Medicine and the National Institutes of Health (NIH) created the National Center for Biotechnology Information (NCBI), which

maintains a website (www.ncbi.nlm.nih.gov) with extensive bioinformatics resources. On this site are links to databases, software, and a wealth of information about genomics and related topics. Similar websites have also been established by the European Molecular Biology Laboratory and the DNA Data Bank of Japan, two genome centers with which the NCBI collaborates. These large, comprehensive websites are complemented by others maintained by individual or small groups of laboratories. Smaller websites often provide databases and software designed for a narrower purpose, such as studying genetic and genomic changes in one particular type of cancer.

The NCBI database of sequences is called Genbank. As of August 2007, it included the sequences of 76 million fragments of genomic DNA, totaling 80 billion base pairs! Genbank is constantly updated, and the amount of data it contains is estimated to double approximately every 18 months. Any sequence in the database can be retrieved and analyzed using software from the NCBI website or elsewhere.

One software program available on the NCBI website, called BLAST, allows the visitor to compare a DNA sequence with every sequence in Genbank, base by base, to look for similar regions. Another program allows comparison of predicted protein sequences. Yet a third can search any protein sequence for common stretches of amino acids (domains) for which a function is known or suspected, and it can show a three-dimensional model of the domain alongside other relevant information (**Figure 21.4**, on the next page). There is even a software program that can compare a collection of sequences, either nucleic acids or polypeptides, and diagram them in the form of an evolutionary tree based on the sequence relationships. (You'll learn more about such diagrams in Chapter 26.)

The NCBI website also maintains a database that includes all three-dimensional protein structures that have been determined. (To review how protein structures are analyzed, see Figure 5.25.) These structures can be rotated by the viewer to see all sides of the protein. Let's say a researcher has an amino acid sequence for all or part of an unknown protein, and it is similar to an amino acid sequence for which the structure has been worked out. In this event, the possible structure of the unknown protein can be predicted by one software program and compared with all other known protein structures using another program. This information can aid the researcher in determining the function of the unknown protein.

There is a vast array of resources available for researchers anywhere in the world to use. Let us now consider the types of questions scientists can address using these resources.

Identifying Protein-Coding Genes Within DNA Sequences

Using available DNA sequences, geneticists can study genes directly, without having to infer genotype from phenotype, as in classical genetics. But this approach poses a new challenge:

In this window, a partial amino acid sequence from an unknown muskmelon protein ("Query") is aligned with sequences from other proteins that the computer program found to be similar. Each sequence represents a domain called WD40. Four hallmarks of this domain are highlighted in yellow. (Sequence similarity is based on chemical aspects of the amino acids, so the amino acids in each hallmark region are not always identical.)

WD40 - Sequence Alignment Viewer

Query	~~~ktGGIRL~RHfksVSAVEWHRk~~gDYLSTlvLreSRAVLIHQlsk
Cow [transducin]	~nvrvSRELA~GHtgyLSCCRFLDd~~nQIVTs~~Sg~DTTCALWDie~
Mustard weed [transducin]	gtvpvSRMLT~GHrgyVSCCQYVPnedaHLITs~~Sg~DQTCILWDvtt
Corn [GNB protein]	gnmpvSRILT~GHkgyVSSCQYVPdgetRLITs~~Sg~DQTCVLWDvt~
Human [PAFA protein]	~~~ecIRTMH~GHdhnVSSVAIMPng~dHIVSA~~Sr~DKTIKMWEvg~
Nematode [unknown protein #1]	~~~rcVKTLK~GHtnyVFCCCFNPs~~gTLIAS~~GsfDETIRIWCar~
Nematode [unknown protein #2]	~~~rmTKTLK~GHnnyVFCCNFNPq~~sSLVVS~~GsfDESVRIWDvk~
Fission yeast [FWDR protein]	~~~seCISILhGHtdsVLCLTFDS~~~~TLLVS~~GsaDCTVKLWHfs~

The Cn3D program displays a three-dimensional ribbon model of cow transducin (the protein highlighted in purple in the Sequence Alignment Viewer). This protein is the only one of those shown for which a structure has been determined. The sequence similarity of the other proteins to cow transducin suggests that their structures are likely to be similar.

WD40 - Cn3D 4.1

This window displays information about the WD40 domain from the Conserved Domain Database.

CDD Descriptive Items

Name: WD40

WD40 domain, found in a number of eukaryotic proteins that cover a wide variety of functions including adaptor/regulatory modules in signal transduction, pre-mRNA processing and cytoskeleton assembly; typically contains a GH dipeptide 11-24 residues from its N-terminus and the WD dipeptide at its C-terminus and is 40 residues long, hence the name WD40;

Cow transducin contains seven WD40 domains, one of which is highlighted here in gray.

The yellow areas correspond to the WD40 hallmarks highlighted in yellow in the window above.

▲ **Figure 21.4 Bioinformatics tools available on the Internet.** A website maintained by the National Center for Biotechnology Information allows scientists and the public to access DNA and protein sequences and other stored data. The site includes a link to a protein structure database (Conserved Domain Database, CDD) that can find and describe similar domains in related proteins, as well as software (Cn3D, "see in 3D") that displays three-dimensional models of domains for which the structure has been determined. Some results are shown from a search for regions of proteins similar to an amino acid sequence in a muskmelon protein.

determining the phenotype from the genotype. Given a long DNA sequence from a database such as Genbank, how can we recognize as-yet unknown protein-coding genes and determine their function?

The usual approach is to use software to scan these stored sequences for transcriptional and translational start and stop signals, for RNA-splicing sites, and for other telltale signs of protein-coding genes. The software also looks for certain short sequences that correspond to sequences present in known mRNAs. Thousands of such sequences, called *expressed sequence tags*, or *ESTs*, have been collected from cDNA sequences and are cataloged in computer databases. This type of analysis identifies sequences that may be previously unknown protein-coding genes.

The identities of about half of the human genes were known before the Human Genome Project began. But what about the others, the previously unknown genes revealed by analysis of DNA sequences? Clues about their identities come from comparing the sequences of gene candidates with those of known

genes from other organisms, using the software described previously. Due to redundancy in the genetic code, the DNA sequence itself may vary more than the protein sequence does. Thus, scientists interested in proteins often compare the predicted amino acid sequence of the protein to that of other proteins.

Sometimes a newly identified sequence will match, at least partially, the sequence of a gene or protein whose function is well known. For example, part of a new gene may match a known gene that encodes an important signaling pathway protein such as a protein kinase (see Chapter 11), suggesting that the new gene does, too. Alternatively, the new gene sequence may be similar to a previously encountered sequence whose function is still unknown. Another possibility is that the sequence is entirely unlike anything ever seen before. This was true for about a third of the genes of *E. coli* when its genome was sequenced. In the last case, protein function is usually deduced through a combination of biochemical and functional studies. The biochemical approach aims to determine the three-dimensional structure of the protein as well as other attributes, such as potential binding sites for other molecules. Functional studies usually involve blocking or disabling the gene to see what effect that has on the phenotype. RNAi, described in Chapter 20, is an example of an experimental technique used to block gene function.

Understanding Genes and Their Products at the Systems Level

The impressive computational power provided by the tools of bioinformatics allows the study of whole sets of genes and their interactions, as well as the comparison of genomes from different species. Genomics is a rich source of new insights into fundamental questions about genome organization, regulation of gene expression, growth and development, and evolution.

The success in sequencing genomes and studying entire sets of genes has encouraged scientists to attempt similar systematic study of the full protein sets (*proteomes*) encoded by genomes, an approach called **proteomics**. Proteins, not the genes that encode them, actually carry out most of the activities of the cell. Therefore, we must study when and where proteins are produced in an organism, as well as how they interact in networks, if we are to understand the functioning of cells and organisms.

How Systems Are Studied: An Example

Genomics and proteomics are enabling biologists to approach the study of life from an increasingly global perspective. Using the tools we have described, biologists have begun to compile catalogs of genes and proteins—listings of all the "parts" that contribute to the operation of cells, tissues, and organisms. With such catalogs in hand, researchers have shifted their attention from the individual parts to their functional integration in biological systems. As you may recall, in Chapter 1 we discussed this systems biology approach, which aims to model the dynamic behavior of whole biological systems.

One basic application of the systems biology approach is to define gene circuits and protein interaction networks. To map the protein interaction network in *Drosophila* that was mentioned in Chapter 1, for instance, researchers started with over 10,000 predicted RNA transcripts. They then used molecular techniques to test interactions between the whole or partial protein products of these transcripts. Using statistical tests to select the interactions for which the data were strongest, they ended up with approximately 4,700 proteins that appeared to participate in more than 4,000 interactions. A subset of these interactions is displayed graphically in **Figure 21.5**; the details are more easily seen in the two successive blowups in the figure. To process the vast number of protein-protein interactions generated by this experiment and integrate them into the graphic model required powerful computers, mathematical tools, and newly developed software. Thus, the systems biology approach has really been made possible by advances in bioinformatics.

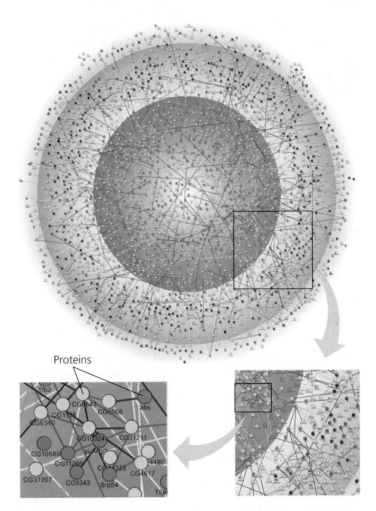

Proteins

▲ Figure 21.5 **The systems biology approach to protein interactions.** This global protein interaction map shows a subset of the most statistically likely interactions (lines) among about 2,300 proteins (small circles) in *Drosophila*. The three background colors in the map correspond to the general location of each protein: Green is the nucleus, blue the cytoplasm, and yellow the plasma membrane. The proteins are also color-coded according to their specific subcellular localization; for example, green circles represent nuclear proteins.

Application of Systems Biology to Medicine

The Cancer Genome Atlas is another example of systems biology in which a large group of interacting genes and gene products are analyzed together. This project, under the joint leadership of the National Cancer Institute and the NIH, aims to understand how changes in biological systems lead to cancer. In a three-year pilot project running from 2007 to 2010, three types of cancer—lung cancer, ovarian cancer, and glioblastoma of the brain—are being analyzed by comparing gene sequences and patterns of gene expression in cancer cells with those of normal cells. A set of approximately 2,000 genes from the cancer cells will be sequenced at several different times during the progression of the disease to monitor changes due to mutations and rearrangements. If this approach proves fruitful, it will be extended to other types of cancer.

◀ **Figure 21.6 A human gene microarray chip.** Tiny dots of DNA arranged in a grid on this silicon wafer represent almost all of the genes in the human genome. Using this chip, researchers can analyze expression patterns for all human genes at the same time, minimizing the amount of reagents used and ensuring uniform conditions for all the genes.

Systems biology has tremendous potential in human medicine that is just starting to be explored. Silicon and glass "chips" have already been developed that hold a microarray of most of the known human genes (Figure 21.6). Such chips are being used to analyze gene expression patterns in patients suffering from various cancers and other diseases, with the eventual aim of tailoring their treatment to their unique genetic makeup and the specifics of their cancers. This approach has already had modest success in characterizing subsets of several cancers.

Ultimately, every person may carry with their medical records a catalog of their DNA sequence, a sort of genetic bar code, with regions highlighted that predispose them to specific diseases. The potential application for disease prevention and treatment is substantial.

Systems biology is a highly efficient way to study emergent properties at the molecular level. Recall from Chapter 1 that according to the concept of emergent properties, novel properties arise at each successive level of biological complexity as a result of the arrangement of building blocks at the underlying level. The more we are able to learn about the arrangement and interactions of the components of genetic systems, the deeper will be our understanding of organisms. The remaining sections of this chapter will survey what we've learned from genomic studies thus far.

CONCEPT CHECK 21.2

1. What role does the Internet play in current genomics and proteomics research?
2. Explain the advantage of the systems biology approach to studying cancer versus the approach of studying a single gene at a time.
3. **WHAT IF?** Let's say you used the classic genetic approach to study a certain inherited trait in *Drosophila*— that is, you mutated flies and selected those with a phenotype of interest to you. Assuming you could use molecular biological tools to obtain the region of DNA that is mutated, how would you analyze it further to determine how it is involved in the trait of interest?

For suggested answers, see Appendix A.

Genomes vary in size, number of genes, and gene density

By early 2008, the sequencing of over 700 genomes had been completed and that of more than 2,700 genomes was in progress. In the completely sequenced group, about 600 are genomes of bacteria, and 50 are archaeal genomes. Among the 65 eukaryotic species in the group are vertebrates, invertebrates, protists, fungi, and plants. The accumulated genome sequences contain a wealth of information that we are just beginning to mine. What have we learned so far by comparing the genomes that have now been sequenced? In this section, we will examine the characteristics of genome size, number of genes, and gene density. Because these characteristics are so broad, we will focus on general trends, for which there are often exceptions.

Genome Size

Comparing the three domains (Bacteria, Archaea, and Eukarya), we find a general difference in genome size between prokaryotes and eukaryotes (Table 21.1). While there are some exceptions, most bacterial genomes have between 1 and 6 million base pairs (Mb); the genome of *E. coli*, for instance, has 4.6 Mb. Genomes of archaea are, for the most part, within the size range of bacterial genomes. (Keep in mind, however, that many fewer archaeal genomes have been completely sequenced, so this picture may change.) Eukaryotic genomes tend to be larger: The genome of the single-celled yeast *Saccharomyces cerevisiae* (a fungus) has about 13 Mb, while most animals and plants, which are multicellular, have genomes of at least 100 Mb. There are 180 Mb in the fruit fly genome, while humans have 3,200 Mb, about 500 to 3,000 times as many as a typical bacterium.

Aside from this general difference between prokaryotes and eukaryotes, a comparison of genome sizes among eukaryotes fails to reveal any systematic relationship between genome size and the organism's phenotype. For instance, the genome of *Fritillaria assyriaca*, a flowering plant in the lily family, contains 120 billion base pairs (120,000 Mb), about 40 times the size of the human genome. Even more striking, there is a single-celled amoeba, *Amoeba dubia*, whose genome has 670,000 Mb. (This genome has not yet been sequenced.) On a finer scale, comparing two insect species, the cricket (*Anabrus simplex*) genome turns out to have 11 times as many base pairs as the *Drosophila melanogaster* genome. There is a wide range of genome sizes within the groups of protists, insects, amphibians, and plants and less of a range within mammals and reptiles.

Number of Genes

A similar difference holds true for the number of genes: Bacteria and archaea, in general, have fewer genes than eukaryotes.

Free-living bacteria and archaea have from 1,500 to 7,500 genes, while the number of genes in eukaryotes ranges from about 5,000 for unicellular fungi to at least 40,000 for some multicellular eukaryotes (see Table 21.1).

Within the eukaryotes, the number of genes in a species is often lower than expected from simply considering the size of its genome. Looking at Table 21.1, you can see that the genome of the nematode *C. elegans* is 100 Mb in size and contains roughly 20,000 genes. The *Drosophila* genome, in comparison, is almost twice as big (180 Mb) but has about two-thirds the number of genes—only 13,700 genes.

Considering an example closer to home, we noted that the human genome contains 3,200 Mb, well over ten times the size of either the *Drosophila* or *C. elegans* genome. At the outset of the Human Genome Project, biologists expected somewhere between 50,000 and 100,000 genes to be identified in the completed sequence, based on the number of known human proteins. As the project progressed, the estimate was revised downward several times, and, as of 2007, the most reliable count places the number at 20,488. This relatively low number, similar to the number of genes in the nematode *C. elegans*, has surprised biologists, who had clearly expected many more human genes.

What genetic attributes allow humans (and other vertebrates) to get by with no more genes than nematodes? An important factor is that vertebrate genomes "get more bang for the buck" from their coding sequences because of extensive alternative splicing of RNA transcripts. Recall that this process generates more than one functional protein from a single gene (see Figure 18.11). For instance, nearly all human genes contain multiple exons, and an estimated 75% of these multi-exon genes are spliced in at least two different ways. If we assume that each alternatively spliced human gene on average specifies three different polypeptides, then the total number of different human polypeptides would be about 75,000. Additional polypeptide diversity could result from post-translational modifications such as cleavage or addition of carbohydrate groups in different cell types or at different developmental stages.

Gene Density and Noncoding DNA

In addition to genome size and number of genes, we can compare gene density in different species—in other words, how many genes there are in a given length of DNA. When we compare the genomes of bacteria, archaea, and eukaryotes, we see that eukaryotes generally have larger genomes but fewer genes in a given number of base pairs. Humans have hundreds or thousands of times as many base pairs in their genome as most bacteria, as we already noted, but they have only 5 to 15 times as many genes; thus, gene density is lower in humans (see Table 21.1). Even unicellular eukaryotes, such as yeasts, have fewer genes per million base pairs than bacteria and archaea. Among the genomes that have been sequenced completely thus far, humans and other mammals have the lowest gene density.

In all bacterial genomes studied so far, most of the DNA consists of genes for protein, tRNA, or rRNA; the small amount of other DNA consists mainly of nontranscribed regulatory sequences, such as promoters. The sequence of nucleotides along a bacterial protein-coding gene proceeds from start to finish without interruption by noncoding sequences (introns). In eukaryotic genomes, by contrast, most of the DNA neither encodes protein nor is transcribed into known functional RNA molecules (such as tRNAs), and the DNA includes more complex regulatory sequences. In fact, humans have 10,000 times as much noncoding DNA as bacteria. Some of this DNA in multicellular eukaryotes is present as introns within genes. Indeed, introns account for most of the difference in average length between human genes (27,000 base pairs) and bacterial genes (1,000 base pairs).

Table 21.1 Genome Sizes and Estimated Numbers of Genes*			
Organism	Haploid Genome Size (Mb)	Number of Genes	Genes per Mb
Bacteria			
Haemophilus influenzae	1.8	1,700	940
Escherichia coli	4.6	4,400	950
Archaea			
Archaeoglobus fulgidus	2.2	2,500	1,130
Methanosarcina barkeri	4.8	3,600	750
Eukaryotes			
Saccharomyces cerevisiae (yeast, a fungus)	13	6,200	480
Caenorhabditis elegans (nematode)	100	20,000	200
Arabidopsis thaliana (mustard family plant)	118	25,500	215
Drosophila melanogaster (fruit fly)	180	13,700	76
Oryza sativa (rice)	390	40,000	140
Danio rerio (zebrafish)	1,700	23,000	13
Mus musculus (house mouse)	2,600	22,000	11
Homo sapiens (human)	3,200	20,500	7
Fritillaria assyriaca (lily family plant)	120,000	ND	ND

*Some values given here are likely to be revised as genome analysis continues. Mb = million base pairs. ND = not determined.

In addition to introns, multicellular eukaryotes have a vast amount of noncoding DNA between genes. In the next section, we will describe the composition and arrangement of these great stretches of DNA in the human genome.

CONCEPT 21.4
Multicellular eukaryotes have much noncoding DNA and many multigene families

We have spent most of this chapter, and indeed this unit, focusing on genes that code for proteins. Yet the coding regions of these genes and the genes for RNA products such as rRNA, tRNA, and microRNA (miRNA) make up only a small portion of the genomes of most multicellular eukaryotes. The bulk of most eukaryotic genomes consists of DNA sequences that neither code for proteins nor are transcribed to produce known RNAs; this noncoding DNA was often described in the past as "junk DNA." However, much evidence is accumulating that this DNA plays important roles in the cell, an idea supported by its persistence in diverse genomes over many hundreds of generations. For example, comparison of the genomes of humans, rats, and mice has revealed the presence of almost 500 regions of noncoding DNA that are identical in sequence in all three species. This is a higher level of sequence conservation than is seen for protein-coding regions in these species, strongly suggesting that the noncoding regions have important functions. In this section, we examine how genes and noncoding DNA sequences are organized within genomes of multicellular eukaryotes, using the human genome as our main example. Genome organiza-

tion tells us much about how genomes have evolved and continue to evolve, the next subject we'll consider.

Once the sequencing of the human genome was completed, it became clear that only a tiny part—1.5%—codes for proteins or is transcribed into rRNAs or tRNAs. **Figure 21.7** shows what is known about the makeup of the remaining 98.5%. Gene-related regulatory sequences and introns account for 24% of the human genome; the rest, located between functional genes, includes some unique noncoding DNA, such as gene fragments and **pseudogenes**, former genes that have accumulated mutations over a long time and have become nonfunctional. Most intergenic DNA, however, is **repetitive DNA**, which consists of sequences that are present in multiple copies in the genome. Somewhat surprisingly, about three-fourths of this repetitive DNA (44% of the entire human genome) is made up of units called transposable elements and sequences related to them.

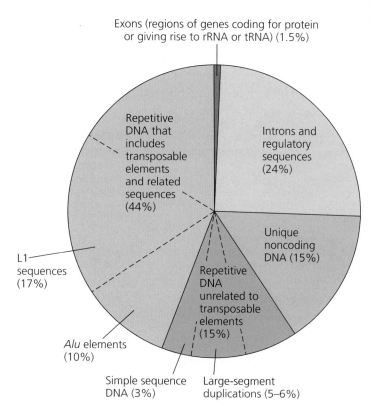

▲ **Figure 21.7 Types of DNA sequences in the human genome.** The gene sequences that code for proteins or are transcribed into rRNA or tRNA molecules make up only about 1.5% of the human genome (dark purple in the pie chart), while introns and regulatory sequences associated with genes (light purple) make up about a quarter. The vast majority of the human genome does not code for proteins or give rise to known RNAs, and much of it is repetitive DNA (dark and light green). Because repetitive DNA is the most difficult to sequence and analyze, classification of some portions is tentative, and the percentages given here may shift slightly as genome analysis proceeds. The genes that are transcribed into miRNAs, which were recently discovered, are found among unique noncoding DNA sequences and within introns; thus, they are included in two segments of this chart.

Transposable Elements and Related Sequences

Both prokaryotes and eukaryotes have stretches of DNA that can move from one location to another within the genome. These stretches are known as *transposable genetic elements*, or simply **transposable elements**. During the process called *transposition*, a transposable element moves from one site in a cell's DNA to a different target site by a type of recombination process. Transposable elements are sometimes called "jumping genes," but the phrase is misleading because they never completely detach from the cell's DNA. (The original and new DNA sites are brought together by DNA bending.)

The first evidence for wandering DNA segments came from American geneticist Barbara McClintock's breeding experiments with Indian corn (maize) in the 1940s and 1950s **(Figure 21.8)**. As she tracked corn plants through multiple generations, McClintock identified changes in the color of corn kernels that made sense only if she postulated the existence of genetic elements capable of moving from other locations in the genome into the genes for kernel color, disrupting the genes so that the kernel color was changed. McClintock's discovery was met with great skepticism and virtually discounted at the time. Her careful work and insightful ideas were finally validated many years later when transposable elements were found in bacteria and microbial geneticists learned more about the molecular basis of transposition.

Movement of Transposons and Retrotransposons

Eukaryotic transposable elements are of two types. The first type are **transposons**, which move within a genome by means of a DNA intermediate. Transposons can move by a "cut-and-paste" mechanism, which removes the element from the original site, or by a "copy-and-paste" mechanism, which leaves a copy behind **(Figure 21.9a)**.

Most transposable elements in eukaryotic genomes are of the second type, **retrotransposons**, which move by means of an RNA intermediate that is a transcript of the retrotransposon DNA. Retrotransposons always leave a copy at the original site during transposition, since they are initially transcribed into an RNA intermediate **(Figure 21.9b)**. To insert at another site, the RNA intermediate is first converted back to DNA by reverse transcriptase, an enzyme encoded in the retrotransposon itself. Thus, reverse transcriptase can be present in cells not infected with retroviruses. (In fact, retroviruses, which were discussed in Chapter 19, may have evolved from retrotransposons.) A cellular enzyme catalyzes insertion of the reverse-transcribed DNA at a new site.

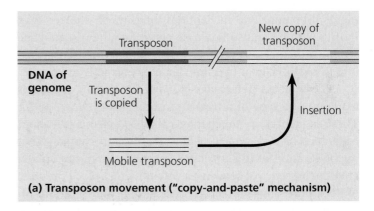

(a) Transposon movement ("copy-and-paste" mechanism)

(b) Retrotransposon movement

▲ **Figure 21.9 Movement of eukaryotic transposable elements. (a)** Movement of transposons by either the cut-and-paste mechanism or the copy-and-paste mechanism (shown here) involves a double-stranded DNA intermediate that is inserted into the genome. **(b)** Movement of retrotransposons begins with formation of a single-stranded RNA intermediate. The remaining steps are essentially identical to part of the retrovirus reproductive cycle (see Figure 19.8). In the movement of transposons by the copy-and-paste mechanism and in the movement of retrotransposons, the DNA sequence remains in the original site as well as appearing in a new site.

? *How would part (a) differ if it showed the cut-and-paste mechanism?*

▲ **Figure 21.8 The effect of transposable elements on corn kernel color.** Barbara McClintock first proposed the idea of mobile genetic elements after observing variegations in corn kernel color. Although her idea was met with skepticism when she proposed it in the 1940s, it was later fully validated. She received the Nobel Prize in 1983, at the age of 81, for her pioneering research.

Sequences Related to Transposable Elements

Multiple copies of transposable elements and sequences related to them are scattered throughout eukaryotic genomes. A single unit is usually hundreds to thousands of base pairs long, and the dispersed "copies" are similar but usually not identical to each other. Some of these are transposable elements that can move; the enzymes required for this movement may be encoded by any transposable element, including the one that is moving. Others are related sequences that have lost the ability to move altogether. Transposable elements and related sequences make up 25–50% of most mammalian genomes (see Figure 21.7) and even higher percentages in amphibians and many plants.

In humans and other primates, a large portion of transposable element–related DNA consists of a family of similar sequences called *Alu elements*. These sequences alone account for approximately 10% of the human genome. *Alu* elements are about 300 nucleotides long, much shorter than most functional transposable elements, and they do not code for any protein. However, many *Alu* elements are transcribed into RNA; its cellular function, if any, is currently unknown.

An even larger percentage (17%) of the human genome is made up of a type of retrotransposon called *LINE-1*, or *L1*. These sequences are much longer than *Alu* elements—about 6,500 base pairs—and have a low rate of transposition. What might account for this low rate? Recent research has uncovered the presence of sequences within L1 that block progress of RNA polymerase, which is necessary for transposition. An accompanying genomic analysis found L1 sequences within the introns of nearly 80% of the human genes that were analyzed, suggesting that L1 may help regulate gene expression. Other researchers have proposed that L1 retrotransposons may have differential effects on gene expression in developing neurons, contributing to the great diversity of neuronal cell types (see Chapter 48).

Although many transposable elements encode proteins, these proteins do not carry out normal cellular functions. Therefore, transposable elements are often included in the "noncoding" DNA category, along with other repetitive sequences.

Other Repetitive DNA, Including Simple Sequence DNA

Repetitive DNA that is not related to transposable elements probably arises due to mistakes during DNA replication or recombination. Such DNA accounts for about 15% of the human genome (see Figure 21.7). About a third of this (5–6% of the human genome) consists of duplications of long stretches of DNA, with each unit ranging from 10,000 to 300,000 base pairs. The large segments seem to have been copied from one chromosomal location to another site on the same or a different chromosome.

In contrast to scattered copies of long sequences, **simple sequence DNA** contains many copies of tandemly repeated short sequences, as in the following example (showing one DNA strand only):

. . . GTTACGTTACGTTACGTTACGTTACGTTAC . . .

In this case, the repeated unit (GTTAC) consists of five nucleotides. Repeated units may contain as many as 500 nucleotides, but often contain fewer than 15 nucleotides, as seen for this example. When the unit contains 2 to 5 nucleotides, the series of repeats is called a **short tandem repeat**, or **STR**; we discussed the use of STR analysis in preparing genetic profiles in Chapter 20. The number of copies of the repeated unit can vary from site to site within a given genome. There could be as many as several hundred thousand repetitions of the GTTAC unit at one site, but only half that number at another. The repeat number can also vary from person to person, producing the variation represented in the genetic profiles that result from STR analysis. Altogether, simple sequence DNA makes up 3% of the human genome.

The nucleotide composition of simple sequence DNA is often different enough from the rest of the cell's DNA to have an intrinsically different density. If genomic DNA is cut into pieces and centrifuged at high speed, segments of different density migrate to different positions in the centrifuge tube. Repetitive DNA isolated in this way was originally called *satellite DNA* because it appeared as a "satellite" band in the centrifuge tube, separate from the rest of the DNA. Now the term is often used interchangeably with simple sequence DNA.

Much of a genome's simple sequence DNA is located at chromosomal telomeres and centromeres, suggesting that this DNA plays a structural role for chromosomes. The DNA at centromeres is essential for the separation of chromatids in cell division (see Chapter 12). Centromeric DNA, along with simple sequence DNA located elsewhere, may also help organize the chromatin within the interphase nucleus. The simple sequence DNA located at telomeres, at the tips of chromosomes, prevents genes from being lost as the DNA shortens with each round of replication (see Chapter 16). Telomeric DNA also binds proteins that protect the ends of a chromosome from degradation and from joining to other chromosomes.

Genes and Multigene Families

We finish our discussion of the various types of DNA sequences in eukaryotic genomes with a closer look at genes. Recall that DNA sequences that code for proteins or give rise to tRNA or rRNA compose a mere 1.5% of the human genome (see Figure 21.7). If we include introns and regulatory sequences associated with genes, the total amount of gene-related DNA—coding and noncoding—constitutes about 25%

of the human genome. Put another way, only about 6% (1.5% out of 25%) of the length of the average gene is represented in the final gene product.

Like the genes of bacteria, many eukaryotic genes are present as unique sequences, with only one copy per haploid set of chromosomes. But in the human genome and the genomes of many other animals and plants, such solitary genes make up less than half of the total transcribed DNA. The rest occurs in **multigene families**, collections of two or more identical or very similar genes.

In multigene families that consist of *identical* DNA sequences, those sequences are usually clustered tandemly and, with the notable exception of the genes for histone proteins, have RNAs as their final products. An example is the family of identical DNA sequences that are the genes for the three largest rRNA molecules **(Figure 21.10a)**. These rRNA molecules are transcribed from a single transcription unit that is repeated tandemly hundreds to thousands of times in one or several clusters in the genome of a multicellular eukaryote.

The many copies of this rRNA transcription unit help cells to quickly make the millions of ribosomes needed for active protein synthesis. The primary transcript is cleaved to yield the three rRNA molecules. These are then combined with proteins and one other kind of rRNA (5S rRNA) to form ribosomal subunits.

The classic examples of multigene families of *nonidentical* genes are two related families of genes that encode globins, a group of proteins that include the α and β polypeptide subunits of hemoglobin. One family, located on chromosome 16 in humans, encodes various forms of α-globin; the other, on chromosome 11, encodes forms of β-globin **(Figure 21.10b)**. The different forms of each globin subunit are expressed at different times in development, allowing hemoglobin to function effectively in the changing environment of the developing animal. In humans, for example, the embryonic and fetal forms of hemoglobin have a higher affinity for oxygen than the adult forms, ensuring the efficient transfer of oxygen from mother to fetus. Also found in the globin gene family clusters are several pseudogenes.

(a) **Part of the ribosomal RNA gene family.** Three of the hundreds of copies of rRNA transcription units in a salamander genome are shown at the top (TEM). Each "feather" corresponds to a single transcription unit being transcribed by about 100 molecules of RNA polymerase (the dark dots along the DNA), moving left to right. The growing RNA transcripts extend out from the DNA. In the diagram below the TEM, one transcription unit is shown. It includes the genes for three types of rRNA (blue), adjacent to regions that are transcribed but later removed (yellow). A single transcript is made and then processed to yield one molecule of each of the three rRNAs, which are crucial components of the ribosome. A fourth rRNA (5S rRNA) is also found in the ribosome, but the gene encoding it is not part of this transcription unit.

(b) **The human α-globin and β-globin gene families.** Hemoglobin is composed of two α-globin and two β-globin polypeptide subunits. The genes (dark blue) encoding α- and β-globins are found in two families, organized as shown here. The noncoding DNA separating the functional genes within each family cluster includes pseudogenes (green), nonfunctional versions of the functional genes. Genes and pseudogenes are named with Greek letters.

▲ **Figure 21.10 Gene families.**

? *In (a), how could you determine the direction of transcription if it wasn't indicated by the red arrow?*

The arrangement of the genes in gene families has given biologists insight into the evolution of genomes. We will consider some of the processes that have shaped the genomes of different species over evolutionary time in the next section.

CONCEPT 21.5
Duplication, rearrangement, and mutation of DNA contribute to genome evolution

The basis of change at the genomic level is mutation, which underlies much of genome evolution. It seems likely that the earliest forms of life had a minimal number of genes—those necessary for survival and reproduction. If this were indeed the case, one aspect of evolution must have been an increase in the size of the genome, with the extra genetic material providing the raw material for gene diversification. In this section, we will first describe how extra copies of all or part of a genome can arise and then consider subsequent processes that can lead to the evolution of proteins (or RNA products) with slightly different or entirely new functions.

Duplication of Entire Chromosome Sets

An accident in meiosis can result in one or more extra sets of chromosomes, a condition known as polyploidy. Although such accidents would most often be lethal, in rare cases they could facilitate the evolution of genes. In a polyploid organism, one set of genes can provide essential functions for the organism. The genes in the one or more extra sets can diverge by accumulating mutations; these variations may persist if the organism carrying them survives and reproduces. In this way, genes with novel functions can evolve. As long as one copy of an essential gene is expressed, the divergence of another copy can lead to its encoded protein acting in a novel

way, thereby changing the organism's phenotype. The outcome of this accumulation of mutations may be the branching off of a new species, as happens often in plants (see Chapter 24). Polyploid animals also exist, but they are rare.

Alterations of Chromosome Structure

Scientists have long known that sometime in the last 6 million years, when the ancestors of humans and chimpanzees diverged as species, the fusion of two ancestral chromosomes in the human line led to different haploid numbers for humans ($n = 23$) and chimpanzees ($n = 24$). With the recent explosion in genomic sequence information, we can now compare the chromosomal organization of many different species on a much finer scale. This information allows us to make inferences about the evolutionary processes that shape chromosomes and may drive speciation.

In one study, for example, researchers compared the DNA sequence of each human chromosome with the whole genome sequence of the mouse. **Figure 21.11** shows the results of this comparison for human chromosome 16: Large blocks of genes on this chromosome are found on four mouse chromosomes, indicating that the genes in each block stayed together during the evolution of the mouse and human lineages. Performing the same comparative analysis between chromosomes of humans

Human chromosome 16

Blocks of DNA sequence

Blocks of similar sequences in four mouse chromosomes:

7   8   16   17

▲ **Figure 21.11 Similar blocks of sequences on human and mouse chromosomes.** DNA sequences very similar to large blocks of human chromosome 16 are found on mouse chromosomes 7, 8, 16, and 17. This suggests that the DNA sequence in each block has stayed together in the mouse and human lineages since the time they diverged from a common ancestor.

and six other mammalian species allowed the researchers to reconstruct the evolutionary history of chromosomal rearrangements in these eight species. They found many duplications and inversions of large portions of chromosomes, the result of mistakes during meiotic recombination in which the DNA broke and was rejoined incorrectly. The rate of these events seems to have accelerated about 100 million years ago, around the time large dinosaurs became extinct and the number of mammalian species increased rapidly. The apparent coincidence is interesting because chromosomal rearrangements are thought to contribute to the generation of new species. Although two individuals with different arrangements could still mate and produce offspring, the offspring would have two nonequivalent sets of chromosomes, making meiosis inefficient or even impossible. Thus, chromosomal rearrangements would lead to two populations that could not successfully mate with each other, a step on the way to their becoming two separate species. (You'll learn more about this in Chapter 24.)

Somewhat unexpectedly, the same study also unearthed a pattern with medical relevance. Analysis of the chromosomal breakage points associated with the rearrangements showed that they were not randomly distributed, but that specific sites were used over and over again. A number of these recombination "hot spots" correspond to locations of chromosomal rearrangements within the human genome that are associated with congenital diseases. Researchers are, of course, looking at the other sites as well for their possible association with as yet unidentified diseases.

Duplication and Divergence of Gene-Sized Regions of DNA

Errors during meiosis can also lead to the duplication of chromosomal regions that are smaller than the ones we've just discussed, including segments the length of individual genes. Unequal crossing over during prophase I of meiosis, for instance, can result in one chromosome with a deletion and another with a duplication of a particular gene. As illustrated in **Figure 21.12**, transposable elements in the genome can provide sites where nonsister chromatids can cross over, even when their homologous sequences are not correctly aligned.

Also, slippage can occur during DNA replication, such that the template shifts with respect to the new complementary strand, and a part of the template strand is either skipped by the replication machinery or used twice as a template. As a result, a segment of DNA is deleted or duplicated. It is easy to imagine how such errors could occur in regions of repeats like the simple sequence DNA described previously. The variable number of repeated units of simple sequence DNA at a given site, used for STR analysis, is probably due to errors like these. Evidence that unequal crossing over and template slippage during DNA replication lead to duplication of genes is found in the existence of multigene families.

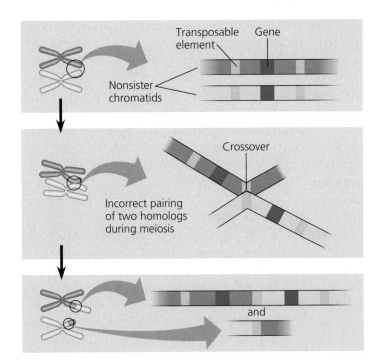

▲ **Figure 21.12 Gene duplication due to unequal crossing over.** One mechanism by which a gene (or other DNA segment) can be duplicated is recombination during meiosis between copies of a transposable element flanking the gene. Such recombination between misaligned nonsister chromatids of homologous chromosomes produces one chromatid with two copies of the gene and one chromatid with no copy.

Evolution of Genes with Related Functions: The Human Globin Genes

Duplication events can lead to the evolution of genes with related functions, such as those of the α-globin and β-globin gene families (see Figure 21.10b). A comparison of gene sequences within a multigene family can suggest the order in which the genes arose. This approach to re-creating the evolutionary history of the globin genes indicates that they all evolved from one common ancestral globin gene that underwent duplication and divergence into the α-globin and β-globin ancestral genes about 450–500 million years ago (**Figure 21.13**, on the next page). Each of these genes was later duplicated several times, and the copies then diverged from each other in sequence, yielding the current family members. In fact, the common ancestral globin gene also gave rise to the oxygen-binding muscle protein myoglobin and to the plant protein leghemoglobin. The latter two proteins function as monomers, and their genes are included in a "globin superfamily."

After the duplication events, the differences between the genes in the globin families undoubtedly arose from mutations that accumulated in the gene copies over many generations. The current model is that the necessary function provided by an α-globin protein, for example, was fulfilled by one gene, while other copies of the α-globin gene accumulated random mutations. Many mutations may have had an adverse effect on the organism and others may have had no effect, but a few mutations must have altered the function of the protein product in a way that was advantageous to the organism at a particular life stage without substantially changing the protein's oxygen-carrying function. Presumably, natural selection acted on these altered genes, maintaining them in the population.

The similarity in the amino acid sequences of the various α-globin and β-globin polypeptides supports this model of gene duplication and mutation **(Table 21.2)**. The amino acid sequences of the β-globins, for instance, are much more similar to each other than to the α-globin sequences. The existence of several pseudogenes among the functional globin genes provides additional evidence for this model (see Figure 21.10b): Random mutations in these "genes" over evolutionary time have destroyed their function.

Evolution of Genes with Novel Functions

In the evolution of the globin gene families, gene duplication and subsequent divergence produced family members whose protein products performed similar functions (oxygen transport). Alternatively, one copy of a duplicated gene can undergo alterations that lead to a completely new function for the protein product. The genes for lysozyme and α-lactalbumin are good examples.

Lysozyme is an enzyme that helps protect animals against bacterial infection by hydrolyzing bacterial cell walls; α-lactalbumin is a nonenzymatic protein that plays a role in milk production in mammals. The two proteins are quite similar in their amino acid sequences and three-dimensional structures. Both genes are found in mammals, whereas only the lysozyme gene is present in birds. These findings suggest that at some time after the lineages leading to mammals and birds had separated, the lysozyme gene underwent a duplication event in the mammalian lineage but not in the avian lineage. Subsequently, one copy of the duplicated lysozyme gene evolved into a gene encoding α-lactalbumin, a protein with a completely different function.

Rearrangements of Parts of Genes: Exon Duplication and Exon Shuffling

Rearrangement of existing DNA sequences within genes has also contributed to genome evolution. The presence of introns in most genes of multicellular eukaryotes may have promoted the evolution of new and potentially useful proteins by facilitating the duplication or repositioning of exons in the genome. Recall from Chapter 17 that an exon often codes for a domain, a distinct structural or functional region of a protein.

We've already seen that unequal crossing over during meiosis can lead to duplication of a gene on one chromosome and its loss from the homologous chromosome (see Figure 21.12). By a similar process, a particular exon within a gene could be duplicated on one chromosome and deleted from the other. The gene with the duplicated exon would code for a protein containing a second copy of the encoded domain. This change in the protein's structure could augment its function by increasing its stability, enhancing

▲ **Figure 21.13 A model for the evolution of the human α-globin and β-globin gene families from a single ancestral globin gene.**

? *The green elements are pseudogenes. Explain how they could have arisen after gene duplication.*

Table 21.2 Percentage of Similarity in Amino Acid Sequence Between Human Globin Proteins

		α-Globins		β-Globins		
		α	ζ	β	γ	ε
α-Globins	α	—	58	42	39	37
	ζ	58	—	34	38	37
β-Globins	β	42	34	—	73	75
	γ	39	38	73	—	80
	ε	37	37	75	80	—

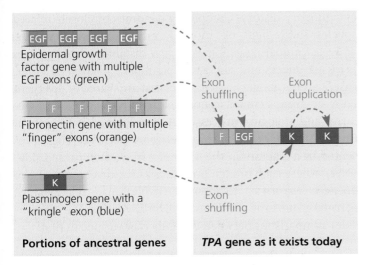

| Portions of ancestral genes | TPA gene as it exists today |

EGF **EGF** **EGF** **EGF**
Epidermal growth
factor gene with multiple
EGF exons (green)

F **F** **F** **F**
Fibronectin gene with multiple
"finger" exons (orange)

K
Plasminogen gene with a
"kringle" exon (blue)

Exon
shuffling

Exon
duplication

F **EGF** **K** **K**

Exon
shuffling

▲ **Figure 21.14 Evolution of a new gene by exon shuffling.** Exon shuffling could have moved exons from ancestral forms of the genes for epidermal growth factor, fibronectin, and plasminogen (left) into the evolving gene for tissue plasminogen activator, TPA (right). The order in which these events might have occurred is unknown. Duplication of the "kringle" exon from the plasminogen gene after its movement could account for the two copies of this exon in the *TPA* gene. Each type of exon encodes a particular domain in the TPA protein.

? *How could the presence of transposable elements in introns have facilitated the exon shuffling shown here?*

its ability to bind a particular ligand, or altering some other property. Quite a few protein-coding genes have multiple copies of related exons, which presumably arose by duplication and then diverged. The gene encoding the extracellular matrix protein collagen is a good example. Collagen is a structural protein with a highly repetitive amino acid sequence, which is reflected in the repetitive pattern of exons in the collagen gene.

Alternatively, we can imagine the occasional mixing and matching of different exons either within a gene or between two nonallelic genes owing to errors in meiotic recombination. This process, termed *exon shuffling*, could lead to new proteins with novel combinations of functions. As an example, let's consider the gene for tissue plasminogen activator (TPA). The TPA protein is an extracellular protein that helps control blood clotting. It has four domains of three types, each encoded by an exon; one exon is present in two copies. Because each type of exon is also found in other proteins, the gene for TPA is thought to have arisen by several instances of exon shuffling and duplication (**Figure 21.14**).

How Transposable Elements Contribute to Genome Evolution

The persistence of transposable elements as a large fraction of some eukaryotic genomes is consistent with the idea that they play an important role in shaping a genome over evolutionary time. These elements can contribute to the evolution of the genome in several ways. They can promote recombination,

disrupt cellular genes or control elements, and carry entire genes or individual exons to new locations.

Transposable elements of similar sequence scattered throughout the genome facilitate recombination between different chromosomes by providing homologous regions for crossing over. Most such alterations are probably detrimental, causing chromosomal translocations and other changes in the genome that may be lethal to the organism. But over the course of evolutionary time, an occasional recombination event of this sort may be advantageous to the organism.

The movement of a transposable element can also have direct consequences. For instance, if a transposable element "jumps" into the middle of a protein-coding sequence, it will prevent the production of a normal transcript of the gene. If a transposable element inserts within a regulatory sequence, the transposition may lead to increased or decreased production of one or more proteins. Transposition caused both types of effects on the genes coding for pigment-synthesizing enzymes in McClintock's corn kernels. Again, while such changes may usually be harmful, in the long run some may prove beneficial by providing a survival advantage.

During transposition, a transposable element may carry along a gene or group of genes to a new position in the genome. This mechanism probably accounts for the location of the α-globin and β-globin gene families on different human chromosomes, as well as the dispersion of the genes of certain other gene families. By a similar tag-along process, an exon from one gene may be inserted into another gene in a mechanism similar to that of exon shuffling during recombination. For example, an exon may be inserted by transposition into the intron of a protein-coding gene. If the inserted exon is retained in the RNA transcript during RNA splicing, the protein that is synthesized will have an additional domain, which may confer a new function on the protein.

A recent study reveals yet another way that transposable elements can bring about new coding sequences. This work shows that an *Alu* element may hop into an intron in a way that creates a weak alternative splice site in the RNA transcript. During processing of the transcript, the regular splice sites are used more often, so that the original protein is made. On occasion, however, splicing occurs at the new weak site, with the result that some of the *Alu* element ends up in the mRNA, coding for a new portion of the protein. In this way, alternative genetic combinations may be "tried out" while the function of the original gene product is retained.

Clearly, all the processes discussed in this section most often produce either harmful effects, which may be lethal, or no effect at all. In a few cases, however, small beneficial changes may occur. Over many generations, the resulting genetic diversity provides valuable raw material for natural selection. Diversification of genes and their products is an important factor in the evolution of new species. Thus, the accumulation of changes in the genome of each species provides a record of its evolutionary history. To read this record, we must be able to identify genomic changes. Comparing the genomes of different species allows us to do that and has increased our understanding of how genomes evolve. You will learn more about these topics in the final section.

CONCEPT CHECK 21.5

1. Describe three examples of errors in cellular processes that lead to DNA duplications.
2. Explain how multiple exons might have arisen in the ancestral EGF and fibronectin genes shown in Figure 21.14 (left).
3. What are three ways that transposable elements are thought to contribute to genome evolution?
4. **WHAT IF?** In 2005, Icelandic scientists reported finding a large chromosomal inversion present in 20% of northern Europeans, and they noted that Icelandic women with this inversion had significantly more children than women without it. What would you expect to happen to the frequency of this inversion in the Icelandic population in future generations?

For suggested answers, see Appendix A.

CONCEPT 21.6
Comparing genome sequences provides clues to evolution and development

One researcher has likened the current state of biology to the Age of Exploration in the 15th century after major improvements in navigation and the building of faster ships. In the last 20 years, we have seen rapid advances in genome sequencing and data collection, new techniques for assessing gene activity across the whole genome, and refined approaches for understanding how genes and their products work together in complex systems. We are truly poised on the brink of a new world.

Comparisons of genome sequences from different species reveal much about the evolutionary history of life, from very ancient to more recent. Similarly, comparative studies of the genetic programs that direct embryonic development in different species are beginning to clarify the mechanisms that generated the great diversity of life-forms present today. In this final section of the chapter, we will discuss what has been learned from these two approaches.

Comparing Genomes

The more similar in sequence the genes and genomes of two species are, the more closely related those species are in their evolutionary history. Comparing genomes of closely related species sheds light on more recent evolutionary events, whereas comparing genomes of very distantly related species helps us understand ancient evolutionary history. In either case, learning about characteristics that are shared or divergent between groups enhances our picture of the evolution of life-forms and biological processes. As you learned in Chapter 1, the evolutionary relationships between species can be represented by a diagram in the form of a tree (often turned sideways), where each branch point marks the divergence of two lineages. **Figure 21.15** shows the evolutionary relationships of some groups and species we will be discussing. We will consider comparisons between distantly related species first.

Comparing Distantly Related Species

Analyzing which genes have remained similar—that is, are *highly conserved*—in distantly related species can help clarify evolutionary relationships among species that diverged from each other long ago. Indeed, comparisons of the complete genome sequences of bacteria, archaea, and eukaryotes indicate that these three groups diverged between 2 and 4 billion years ago and strongly support the theory that they are the fundamental domains of life (see Figure 21.15).

In addition to their value in evolutionary biology, comparative genomic studies confirm the relevance of research on model organisms to our understanding of biology in general and human biology in particular. Genes that evolved a very long time ago can still be surprisingly similar in disparate species. As a case in point, several genes in yeast are so similar to certain human disease genes that researchers have deduced the functions of the disease genes by studying their yeast counterparts. This striking similarity underscores the common origin of these two distantly related species.

Comparing Closely Related Species

The genomes of two closely related species are likely to be organized similarly because of their relatively recent divergence. As we mentioned earlier, this allows the fully sequenced genome of one species to be used as a scaffold for assembling the genomic sequences of a closely related species, accelerating mapping of the second genome. For instance, using the human genome sequence as a guide, researchers were able to quickly sequence the mouse genome.

The recent divergence of two closely related species also underlies the small number of gene differences that are found when their genomes are compared. The particular genetic differences can therefore be more easily correlated with phenotypic differences between the two species. An exciting application of this type of analysis is seen as researchers compare the human genome with the genomes of the chimpanzee, mouse, rat, and other mammals. Identifying the genes shared by all of these species but not by nonmammals should give clues about what it

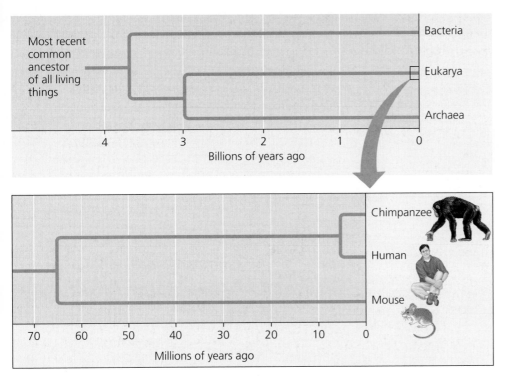

▲ **Figure 21.15 Evolutionary relationships of the three domains of life.** This tree diagram shows the ancient divergence of bacteria, archaea, and eukaryotes. A portion of the eukaryote lineage is expanded in the inset to show the more recent divergence of three mammalian species discussed in this chapter.

takes to make a mammal, while finding the genes shared by chimpanzees and humans but not by rodents should tell us something about primates. And, of course, comparing the human genome with that of the chimpanzee should help us answer the tantalizing question we asked at the beginning of the chapter: What genomic information makes a human or a chimpanzee?

An analysis of the overall composition of the human and chimpanzee genomes, which are thought to have diverged only about 6 million years ago (see Figure 21.15), reveals some general differences. Considering single base substitutions, the two genomes differ by only 1.2%. When researchers looked at longer stretches of DNA, however, they were surprised to find a further 2.7% difference due to insertions or deletions of larger regions in the genome of one or the other species; many of the insertions were duplications or other repetitive DNA. In fact, a third of the human duplications are not present in the chimpanzee genome, and some of these duplications contain regions associated with human diseases. There are more *Alu* elements in the human genome than in that of the chimpanzee, and the latter contains many copies of a retroviral provirus not present in humans. All of these observations provide clues to the forces that might have swept the two genomes along different paths, but we don't have a complete picture yet. We also don't know how these differences might account for the distinct characteristics of each species.

To discover the basis for the phenotypic differences between the two species, biologists are studying specific genes

and types of genes that differ between humans and chimpanzees and comparing them with their counterparts in other mammals. This approach has revealed a number of genes that are apparently changing (evolving) faster in the human than in either the chimpanzee or the mouse. Among them are genes involved in defense against malaria and tuberculosis and at least one gene that regulates brain size. When genes are classified by function, the genes that seem to be evolving the fastest are those that code for transcription factors. This is exciting news because transcription factors regulate gene expression and thus play a key role in orchestrating the overall genetic program.

One transcription factor whose gene shows evidence of rapid change in the human lineage is called FOXP2. Several lines of evidence suggest that the *FOXP2* gene functions in vocalization in vertebrates. For one thing, mutations in this gene can produce severe speech and language impairment in humans. Moreover, the *FOXP2* gene is expressed in the brains of zebra finches and canaries at the time when these songbirds are learning their songs. But perhaps the strongest evidence comes from a "knock-out" experiment in which Joseph Buxbaum and colleagues disrupted the *FOXP2* gene in mice and analyzed the resulting phenotype (**Figure 21.16**, on the next page). The homozygous mutant mice had malformed brains and failed to emit normal ultrasonic vocalizations, and mice with one faulty copy of the gene also showed significant problems with vocalization. These results support the idea that the *FOXP2* gene product turns on genes involved in vocalization.

Expanding on this notion, researchers are exploring the question of whether differences between the human and chimpanzee FOXP2 proteins could account for the ability of humans, but not chimpanzees, to communicate by speech. There are only two amino acid differences between the human and chimpanzee FOXP2 proteins, and the effect of these differences on the function of the human protein is an intriguing question, whose answer is not yet known.

The *FOXP2* story is an excellent example of how different approaches complement each other in uncovering biological phenomena of widespread importance. The experiment described in Figure 21.16 uses mice as a model for humans because it would be unethical (as well as impractical) to carry out such an experiment in humans. Mice and humans diverged about 65.5 million years ago (see Figure 21.15) and share about 85% of their genes. This genetic similarity can be exploited in

What is the function of a gene (*FOXP2*) that is rapidly evolving in the human lineage?

EXPERIMENT   Several lines of evidence support a role for the *FOXP2* gene in the development of speech and language in humans and of vocalization in other vertebrates. In 2005, Joseph Buxbaum and collaborators at the Mount Sinai School of Medicine and several other institutions set out to test the function of *FOXP2*. They used the mouse, a model organism in which genes can be easily knocked out, as a representative vertebrate that vocalizes. Mice produce ultrasonic squeaks, referred to as whistles, to communicate stress. The researchers applied genetic engineering techniques to produce mice in which one or both copies of *FOXP2* were disrupted.

| **Wild type: two normal copies of *FOXP2*** | **Heterozygote: one copy of *FOXP2* disrupted** | **Homozygote: both copies of *FOXP2* disrupted** |

They then compared the phenotypes of these mice. Two of the characters they examined are included here: brain anatomy and vocalization.

Experiment 1: Researchers cut thin sections of brain and stained them with reagents, allowing visualization of brain anatomy in a UV fluorescence microscope.

Experiment 2: Researchers separated each newborn pup from its mother and recorded the number of ultrasonic whistles produced by the pup.

RESULTS

Experiment 1: Disruption of both copies of *FOXP2* led to brain abnormalities in which the cells were disorganized. Phenotypic effects on the brain of heterozygotes, with one disrupted copy, were less severe.

Wild type

Heterozygote

Homozygote

Experiment 2: Disruption of both copies of *FOXP2* led to an absence of ultrasonic vocalization in response to stress. The effect on vocalization in the heterozygote was also extreme.

CONCLUSION   *FOXP2* plays a significant role in the development of functional communication systems in mice. The results augment evidence from studies of birds and humans, supporting the hypothesis that *FOXP2* may act similarly in diverse organisms.

SOURCE   W. Shu et al., Altered ultrasonic vocalization in mice with a disruption in the *Foxp2* gene, *Proceedings of the National Academy of Sciences* 102:9643–9648 (2005).

WHAT IF?   Since the results support a role for mouse *FOXP2* in vocalization, you might wonder whether the human FOXP2 protein is a key regulator of speech. If you were given the amino acid sequences of wild-type and mutant human FOXP2 proteins and the wild-type chimpanzee FOXP2 protein, how would you investigate this question? What further clues could you obtain by comparing these sequences to that of the mouse FOXP2 protein?

studying other human genetic disorders. If researchers know the organ or tissue that is affected by a particular genetic disorder, they can look for genes that are expressed in these locations in experiments using mice. This approach has revealed several human genes of interest, including one that may contribute to Down syndrome.

Further research efforts are under way to extend genomic studies to many more microbial species, additional primates, and neglected species from diverse branches of the tree of life. These studies will advance our understanding of all aspects of biology, including health and ecology as well as evolution.

Comparing Genomes Within a Species

Another exciting prospect that stems from our ability to analyze genomes is increasing our understanding of the spectrum of genetic variation in humans. Because the history of the human species is so short—probably about 200,000 years—the amount of DNA variation among humans is small compared to that of many other species. Much of our diversity seems to be in the form of single nucleotide polymorphisms (SNPs, described in Chapter 20), usually detected by DNA sequencing. In the human genome, SNPs occur on average about once in 100 to 300 base pairs.

Scientists have already identified the location of several million SNP sites in the human genome and continue to find more. In the course of this search, they have also found other variations—including inversions, deletions, and duplications—that occur without apparent ill effect on the individual carrying them. These variations, as well as SNPs, will be useful genetic markers for studying human evolution, the differences between human populations, and the migratory routes of human populations throughout history. Such polymorphisms in human DNA will also be valuable markers for identifying genes that cause diseases or affect our health in more subtle ways. As well as informing us about evolution, analysis of the differences in individual genomes is likely to change the practice of medicine later in the 21st century.

Comparing Developmental Processes

Biologists in the field of evolutionary developmental biology, or **evo-devo** as it is often called, compare developmental processes of different multicellular organisms. Their aim is to understand how these processes have evolved and how changes in them can modify existing organismal features or lead to new ones. With the advent of molecular techniques and the recent flood of genomic information, we are beginning to realize that the genomes of related species with strikingly different forms may have only minor differences in gene sequence or regulation. Discovering the molecular basis underlying these differences in turn helps us understand the origin of the myriad diverse forms that cohabit this planet, thus informing our study of evolution.

Widespread Conservation of Developmental Genes Among Animals

In Chapter 18, you learned about the homeotic genes in *Drosophila*, which specify the identity of body segments in the fruit fly (see Figure 18.18). Molecular analysis of the homeotic genes in *Drosophila* has shown that they all include a 180-nucleotide sequence called a **homeobox**, which specifies a 60-amino-acid *homeodomain* in the encoded proteins. An identical or very similar nucleotide sequence has been discovered in the homeotic genes of many invertebrates and ver-

tebrates. The sequences are so similar between humans and fruit flies, in fact, that one researcher has whimsically referred to flies as "little people with wings." The resemblance even extends to the organization of these genes: The vertebrate genes homologous to the homeotic genes of fruit flies have kept the same chromosomal arrangement **(Figure 21.17)**. Homeobox-containing sequences have also been found in regulatory genes of much more distantly related eukaryotes, including plants and yeasts. From these similarities, we can deduce that the homeobox DNA sequence evolved very early in the history of

▲ **Figure 21.17 Conservation of homeotic genes in a fruit fly and a mouse.** Homeotic genes that control the form of anterior and posterior structures of the body occur in the same linear sequence on chromosomes in *Drosophila* and mice. Each colored band on the chromosomes shown here represents a homeotic gene. In fruit flies, all homeotic genes are found on one chromosome. The mouse and other mammals have the same or similar sets of genes on four chromosomes. The color code indicates the parts of the embryos in which these genes are expressed and the adult body regions that result. All of these genes are essentially identical in flies and mice, except for those represented by black bands, which are less similar in the two animals.

life and was sufficiently valuable to organisms to have been conserved in animals and plants virtually unchanged for hundreds of millions of years.

Homeotic genes in animals were named *Hox* genes, short for *homeobox*-containing genes, because homeotic genes were the first genes found to have this sequence. Other homeobox-containing genes were later found that do not act as homeotic genes; that is, they do not directly control the identity of body parts. However, most of these genes, in animals at least, are associated with development, suggesting their ancient and fundamental importance in that process. In *Drosophila*, for example, homeoboxes are present not only in the homeotic genes but also in the egg-polarity gene *bicoid* (see Chapter 18), in several of the segmentation genes, and in a master regulatory gene for eye development.

Researchers have discovered that the homeobox-encoded homeodomain is the part of a protein that binds to DNA when the protein functions as a transcriptional regulator. However, the shape of the homeodomain allows it to bind to any DNA segment; by itself it cannot select a specific sequence. Rather, other domains in a homeodomain-containing protein, ones that are more variable, determine which genes the protein regulates. Interaction of these latter domains with still other transcription factors helps a homeodomain-containing protein recognize specific enhancers in the DNA. Proteins with homeodomains probably regulate development by coordinating the transcription of batteries of developmental genes, switching them on or off. In embryos of *Drosophila* and other animal species, different combinations of homeobox genes are active in different parts of the embryo. This selective expression of regulatory genes, varying over time and space, is central to pattern formation.

Developmental biologists have found that in addition to homeotic genes, many other genes involved in development are highly conserved from species to species. These include numerous genes encoding components of signaling pathways. The extraordinary similarity among particular developmental genes in different animal species raises a question: How can the same genes be involved in the development of animals whose forms are so very different from each other?

Current studies are suggesting answers to this question. In some cases, small changes in regulatory sequences of particular genes cause changes in gene expression patterns that can lead to major changes in body form. For example, the differing patterns of expression of the *Hox* genes along the body axis in insects and crustaceans can explain the variation in number of leg-bearing segments among these segmented animals **(Figure 21.18)**. Also, recent research suggests that the same *Hox* gene product may have subtly dissimilar effects in different species, turning on new genes or turning on the same genes at higher or lower levels. In other cases, similar genes direct distinct developmental processes in different organisms, resulting in diverse body shapes. Several *Hox* genes, for instance, are expressed in the embryonic and larval stages of the sea urchin, a nonsegmented animal that has a body plan quite different from those of insects and mice. Sea urchin adults make the pincushion-shaped shells you may have seen on the beach. They are among the organisms long used in classical embryological studies (see Chapter 47).

Comparison of Animal and Plant Development

The last common ancestor of animals and plants was probably a single-celled eukaryote that lived hundreds of millions of years ago, so the processes of development must have evolved independently in the two multicellular lineages of organisms. Plants evolved with rigid cell walls, which rule out the morphogenetic movements of cells and tissues that are so important in animals. Instead, morphogenesis in plants relies primarily on differing planes of cell division and on selective cell enlargement. (You will learn about these processes in

▲ **Figure 21.18 Effect of differences in *Hox* gene expression during development in crustaceans and insects.** Changes in the expression patterns of four *Hox* genes have occurred over evolutionary time. These changes account in part for the different body plans of the brine shrimp *Artemia*, a crustacean (top), and the grasshopper, an insect. Shown here are regions of the adult body color-coded for expression of the *Hox* genes that determine formation of particular body parts during embryonic development. Each color represents a specific *Hox* gene.

Chapter 35.) But despite the differences between animals and plants, there are similarities in the molecular mechanisms of development, which are legacies of their shared unicellular origin.

In both animals and plants, development relies on a cascade of transcriptional regulators turning on or turning off genes in a finely tuned series. For example, work on a small flowering plant in the mustard family, *Arabidopsis thaliana*, has shown that establishing the radial pattern of flower parts, like setting up the head-to-tail axis in *Drosophila*, involves a cascade of transcription factors. The genes that direct these processes, however, differ considerably in animals and plants. While quite a few of the master regulatory switches in *Drosophila* are homeobox-containing *Hox* genes, those in *Arabidopsis* belong to a completely different family of genes, called the *Mads-box* genes. And although homeobox-containing genes can be found in plants and *Mads-box* genes in animals, in neither case do they perform the same major roles in development that they do in the other group. Thus, molecular evidence supports the supposition that developmental programs evolved separately in animals and plants.

In this final chapter of the genetics unit, you have learned how studying genomic composition and comparing the genomes of different species can disclose much about how genomes evolve. Further, comparing developmental programs, we can see that the unity of life is reflected in the similarity of molecular and cellular mechanisms used to establish body pattern, although the genes directing development may differ among organisms. The similarities between genomes reflect the common ancestry of life on Earth. But the differences are also crucial, for they have created the huge diversity of organisms that have evolved. In the remainder of the book, we expand our perspective beyond the level of molecules, cells, and genes to explore this diversity on the organismal level.

CONCEPT CHECK 21.6

1. Would you expect the genome of the macaque (a monkey) to be more similar to the mouse genome or the human genome? Why?
2. The DNA sequences called homeoboxes, which help homeotic genes in animals direct development, are common to flies and mice. Given this similarity, explain why these animals are so different.
3. **WHAT IF?** There are three times as many *Alu* elements in the human genome as in the chimpanzee genome. How do you think these extra *Alu* elements arose in the human genome? Propose a role they might have played in the divergence of these two species.

For suggested answers, see Appendix A.

Chapter 21 Review

SUMMARY OF KEY CONCEPTS

CONCEPT 21.1
New approaches have accelerated the pace of genome sequencing (pp. 427–429)

▶ **Three-Stage Approach to Genome Sequencing** In linkage mapping, the order of genes and other inherited markers in the genome and the relative distances between them can be determined from recombination frequencies. Next, physical mapping uses overlaps between DNA fragments to order the fragments and determine the distance in base pairs between markers. Finally, the ordered fragments are sequenced, providing the finished genome sequence.

▶ **Whole-Genome Shotgun Approach to Genome Sequencing** The whole genome is cut into many small, overlapping fragments that are sequenced; computer software then assembles the complete sequence. Correct assembly is made easier when mapping information is also available.

Activity The Human Genome Project: Genes on Human Chromosome 17

CONCEPT 21.2
Scientists use bioinformatics to analyze genomes and their functions (pp. 429–432)

▶ **Centralized Resources for Analyzing Genome Sequences** Websites on the Internet provide centralized access to genome sequence databases, analytical tools, and genome-related information.

▶ **Identifying Protein-Coding Genes Within DNA Sequences** Computer analysis of genome sequences helps researchers identify sequences likely to encode proteins. Comparison of the sequences of "new" genes with those of known genes in other species may help identify functions of new genes. For a gene of unknown function, experimental inactivation of the gene and observation of the resulting phenotypic effects can provide clues to its function.

▶ **Understanding Genes and Their Products at the Systems Level** Using the computer-based tools of bioinformatics, scientists can compare genomes and study sets of genes and proteins as whole systems (genomics and proteomics). Studies include large-scale analyses of protein interactions.

CONCEPT ■ 21.3

Genomes vary in size, number of genes, and gene density (pp. 432–434)

	Bacteria	Archaea	Eukarya
Genome size	Most are 1–6 Mb		Most are 10–4,000 Mb, but a few are much larger
Number of genes	1,500–7,500		5,000–40,000
Gene density	Higher than in eukaryotes		Lower than in prokaryotes (Within eukaryotes, lower density is correlated with larger genomes.)
Introns	None in protein-coding genes	Present in some genes	Unicellular eukaryotes: present, but prevalent only in some species Multicellular eukaryotes: present in most genes
Other noncoding DNA	Very little		Can be large amounts; generally more repetitive noncoding DNA in multicellular eukaryotes

CONCEPT ■ 21.4

Multicellular eukaryotes have much noncoding DNA and many multigene families (pp. 434–438)

▶ Only 1.5% of the human genome codes for proteins or gives rise to rRNAs or tRNAs; the rest is noncoding DNA, including repetitive DNA.

▶ **Transposable Elements and Related Sequences** The most abundant type of repetitive DNA in multicellular eukaryotes consists of transposable elements and related sequences. Two types of transposable elements occur in eukaryotes: transposons, which move via a DNA intermediate, and retrotransposons, which are more prevalent and move via an RNA intermediate. Each element may be hundreds or thousands of base pairs long, and similar but usually not identical copies are dispersed throughout the genome.

▶ **Other Repetitive DNA, Including Simple Sequence DNA** Short noncoding sequences that are tandemly repeated thousands of times (simple sequence DNA, which includes STRs) are especially prominent in centromeres and telomeres, where they probably play structural roles in the chromosome.

▶ **Genes and Multigene Families** Though many eukaryotic genes are present in one copy per haploid chromosome set, others (most, in some species) are members of a family of related genes. The transcription unit corresponding to the three largest rRNAs is tandemly repeated hundreds to thousands of times at one or several chromosomal sites, enabling the cell to quickly make the rRNA for millions of ribosomes. The multiple, slightly different genes in the two globin gene families encode polypeptides used at different developmental stages of an animal.

CONCEPT ■ 21.5

Duplication, rearrangement, and mutation of DNA contribute to genome evolution (pp. 438–442)

▶ **Duplication of Entire Chromosome Sets** Accidents in cell division can lead to extra copies of all or part of a genome, which may then diverge if one set accumulates sequence changes.

▶ **Alterations of Chromosome Structure** The chromosomal organization of genomes can be compared among species, providing information about evolutionary relationships. Within a given species, rearrangements of chromosomes are thought to contribute to the emergence of new species.

▶ **Duplication and Divergence of Gene-Sized Regions of DNA** The genes encoding the various globin proteins evolved from one common ancestral globin gene, which duplicated and diverged into α-globin and β-globin ancestral genes. Subsequent duplication and random mutation gave rise to the present globin genes, all of which code for oxygen-binding proteins. The copies of some duplicated genes have diverged so much that the functions of their encoded proteins are now substantially different.

▶ **Rearrangements of Parts of Genes: Exon Duplication and Exon Shuffling** Rearrangement of exons within and between genes during evolution has led to genes containing multiple copies of similar exons and/or several different exons derived from other genes.

▶ **How Transposable Elements Contribute to Genome Evolution** Movement of transposable elements or recombination between copies of the same element occasionally generates new sequence combinations that are beneficial to the organism. Such mechanisms can alter the functions of genes or their patterns of expression and regulation.

MEDIA

Biology Labs On-Line HemoglobinLab

CONCEPT ■ 21.6

Comparing genome sequences provides clues to evolution and development (pp. 442–447)

▶ **Comparing Genomes** Comparative studies of genomes from widely divergent and closely related species provides valuable information about ancient and more recent evolutionary history, respectively. Human and chimpanzee sequences show about 4% difference, mostly due to insertions, deletions, and duplications in one lineage. Along with nucleotide variations in specific genes (such as *FOXP2*, a gene affecting speech), these differences may account for the distinct characteristics of the two species. Single nucleotide polymorphisms among individuals in a species can also yield information about the history of that species.

▶ **Comparing Developmental Processes** Homeotic genes and some other genes associated with animal development contain a homeobox region, whose sequence is identical or similar in diverse species. Related sequences are present in the genes of plants and yeasts. Other developmental genes also are highly conserved among animal species, but they may play different roles in the development of different species. During embryonic development in both plants and animals, a cascade of transcription regulators turns genes on or off in a carefully regulated sequence. However, the genes that direct analogous developmental processes differ considerably in sequence in plants and animals as a result of their remote ancestry.

TESTING YOUR KNOWLEDGE

SELF-QUIZ

1. Bioinformatics includes all of the following *except*
   a. using computer programs to align DNA sequences.
   b. analyzing protein interactions in a species.
   c. using molecular biology to combine DNA from two different sources in a test tube.
   d. development of computer-based tools for genome analysis.
   e. use of mathematical tools to make sense of biological systems.

2. Which of the following has the largest genome and the fewest genes per million base pairs?
   a. *Haemophilus influenzae* (bacterium)
   b. *Saccharomyces cerevisiae* (yeast)
   c. *Arabidopsis thaliana* (plant)
   d. *Drosophila melanogaster* (fruit fly)
   e. *Homo sapiens* (human)

3. One of the characteristics of retrotransposons is that
   a. they code for an enzyme that synthesizes DNA using an RNA template.
   b. they are found only in animal cells.
   c. they generally move by a cut-and-paste mechanism.
   d. they contribute a significant portion of the genetic variability seen within a population of gametes.
   e. their amplification is dependent on a retrovirus.

4. Multigene families are
   a. groups of enhancers that control transcription.
   b. usually clustered at the telomeres.
   c. equivalent to the operons of prokaryotes.
   d. sets of genes that are coordinately controlled.
   e. sets of identical or similar genes that have evolved by gene duplication.

5. Two eukaryotic proteins have one domain in common but are otherwise very different. Which of the following processes is most likely to have contributed to this similarity?
   a. gene duplication
   b. RNA splicing
   c. exon shuffling
   d. histone modification
   e. random point mutations

6. Homeotic genes
   a. encode transcription factors that control the expression of genes responsible for specific anatomical structures.
   b. are found only in *Drosophila* and other arthropods.
   c. are the only genes that contain the homeobox domain.
   d. encode proteins that form anatomical structures in the fly.
   e. are responsible for patterning during plant development.

7. **DRAW IT** At the top of the next column are the amino acid sequences (using the single-letter code; see Figure 5.17) of four short segments of the FOXP2 protein from six species: chimpanzee, orangutan, gorilla, rhesus macaque, mouse, and human. These segments contain all of the amino acid differences between the FOXP2 proteins of these species.

   1. ATETI...PKSSD...TSSTT...NARRD
   2. ATETI...PKSSE...TSSTT...NARRD
   3. ATETI...PKSSD...TSSTT...NARRD
   4. ATETI...PKSSD...TSSNT...SARRD
   5. ATETI...PKSSD...TSSTT...NARRD
   6. VTETI...PKSSD...TSSTT...NARRD

   Use a highlighter to color any amino acid that varies among the species. (Color that amino acid in all sequences.) Then answer the following questions.
   a. The chimpanzee, gorilla, and rhesus macaque (C, G, R) sequences are identical. Which lines correspond to those sequences?
   b. The human sequence differs from that of the C, G, R species at two amino acids. Which line corresponds to the human sequence? Underline the two differences.
   c. The orangutan sequence differs from the C, G, R sequence at one amino acid (having valine instead of alanine) and from the human sequence at three amino acids. Which line corresponds to the orangutan sequence?
   d. How many amino acid differences are there between the mouse and the C, G, R species? Circle the amino acid(s) that differ(s) in the mouse. How many amino acid differences are there between the mouse and the human? Draw a square around the amino acid(s) that differ(s) in the mouse.
   e. Primates and rodents diverged between 60 and 100 million years ago, and chimpanzees and humans diverged about 6 million years ago. Knowing that, what can you conclude by comparing the amino acid differences between the mouse and the C, G, R species with the differences between the human and the C, G, R species?

For Self-Quiz answers, see Appendix A.

MEDIA Visit the Study Area at **www.masteringbio.com** for a Practice Test.

EVOLUTION CONNECTION

8. Genes important in the embryonic development of animals, such as homeobox-containing genes, have been relatively well conserved during evolution; that is, they are more similar among different species than are many other genes. Why is this?

SCIENTIFIC INQUIRY

9. The scientists mapping the SNPs in the human genome noticed that groups of SNPs tended to be inherited together, in blocks known as haplotypes, ranging in length from 5,000 to 200,000 base pairs. There are as few as four or five commonly occurring combinations of SNPs per haplotype. Propose an explanation for this observation, integrating what you've learned throughout this chapter and this unit.

UNIT 4

Mechanisms of Evolution

AN INTERVIEW WITH
Scott V. Edwards

Birds—and the birds of Australia in particular—might seem a surprising focus for a scientist who grew up in New York City, but they are the main subjects of Scott Edwards's research on evolution. A graduate of Harvard College, with a Ph.D. from the University of California, Berkeley, and postdoctoral work at the University of Florida, Dr. Edwards was at the University of Washington until he returned to Harvard in 2003 as Professor of Organismic and Evolutionary Biology. Jane Reece and Michael Cain interviewed Dr. Edwards at Harvard's Museum of Comparative Zoology, where he is Curator of Ornithology and the head of an active research group.

How big is the bird collection here?
Since the Museum of Comparative Zoology was founded in 1859, its collection of bird specimens has grown to 350,000 specimens, the largest university collection in the world. Each specimen is tagged with data about the location where it was obtained, the date, often the bird's sex and weight, and other pertinent information. The collection provides a remarkable record of how bird species have changed over the years, as environments have changed. Using the oldest specimens here, we can now compare the sizes, shapes, and genes of birds from populations separated by more than a century. What's exciting now is that all the information is being digitized, so that we can easily look at large amounts of data from multiple museums.

Were you interested in birds as a child?
When I was about six years old, we moved from an urban neighborhood to Riverdale, in the northwest corner of the Bronx. There were actually trees there, and we were close to the Hudson River. A few years later, a neighbor took me bird watching—and the rest is history. I'll never forget how impressed I was with my first Northern flicker; it was just remarkable to

me that this bizarrely colored woodpecker lived right in my backyard.

Later, as an undergraduate biology major, I really needed a break after taking organic chemistry, and I was able to take a year off. I volunteered at the Smithsonian for several months and then at national parks in Hawaii and California. It was that first exposure to fieldwork that showed me what biologists do. And when I came back to college, I was much more focused and motivated. I think it should be mandatory for biology majors to work in the field or in a lab for a few months, because that's how you find out what science is all about.

How did you get interested in evolution?
I was impressed with the precision that molecular tools seemed to bring to the study of evolution. I realize now that things are not as precise as I thought, but the DNA code is still a remarkable yardstick for comparing different species on the same scale. I actually didn't like biochemistry or molecular biology until I could connect them with evolution. But coming back from my year off, I worked in a lab that helped me make the connection. The world is very diverse biologically—there are millions of species—and the fact that these species can be compared at the DNA level was a revelation to me.

What led you to study Australian birds?
After entering grad school, I volunteered for a research project on birds of paradise in New Guinea; these are flamboyant songbirds that live in the rain forest. I was hunting around for a project of my own. Several ornithologists directed me to a group of songbirds called babblers, which mostly live in Australia. These birds are fascinating: They live in family groups, using large, domed nests with a hole on the side. Eight or nine of them will clamber into one of these nests. It was very interesting to see the organization of their family groups in the wild and also to study the birds on the DNA level. Were they all related to each other, or not? How different were different families in a single locality? So I ended up doing my dissertation on babblers, comparing individuals within a family,

families within a region, and populations in different parts of the continent.

As a postdoc in Florida, you studied the evolution of genes involved in disease resistance in birds. What were these genes?
They're called MHC genes, for Major Histocompatibility Complex. These genes are important components of the immune systems of all vertebrates. In humans, they are the genes you try to match when looking for a compatible donor for an organ transplant. The MHC genes encode proteins that bind to fragments of pathogens and other foreign cells that have been phagocytized. The MHC proteins then move to the cell surface and present the fragments to the rest of the immune system, saying, "Hey, I found something foreign." The MHC is fascinating from an evolutionary standpoint, because pathogens and parasites seem to be major drivers of evolutionary change. They're constantly playing cat and mouse with the host. In the pathogens, more efficient ways of infecting the host keep evolving, while evolving defenses keep pace in their hosts. So MHC genes are under strong selection by pathogens, and we can see signs of that selection when we look at the DNA sequences. In mammals, these genes are wildly diverse compared to typical "housekeeping" genes. I was curious to see if they were as diverse in birds as they are in mammals.

How did so much variation evolve in MHC genes?
There are a couple of different hypotheses. One comes from the idea that the primary drivers of MHC diversity are pathogens. It says that if you are heterozygous—if you have two different alleles for each of these MHC genes—you have a better surveillance system for dealing with the pathogenic world. You're going to be able to recognize at least twice as many pathogens compared to a homozygous individual. When you have a situation where heterozygotes are more fit because they can combat disease, it results in a lot of diversity. The other hypothesis focuses on mating preferences, though it's not inconsistent with the

450

pathogen hypothesis. If it's true that being heterozygous is advantageous, then it would make sense for females to choose mates whose MHC alleles are different from theirs. Scientists in the lab where I was a postdoc documented this in lab mice. We're interested in documenting it in birds, as well. Birds are good organisms for this kind of study because many bird populations are being monitored in great detail. For these populations, researchers know who has mated with whom, and they have blood samples from offspring. So we can look at many different pairings and see if the members of each pair are significantly more different in MHC genes than, say, random pairs in the human population. We have an ongoing project on MHC genes and parasitism in red-winged blackbirds.

Does this research have relevance to avian flu and other bird diseases that threaten humans?

It certainly relates to the important question of whether all individuals of a species are equally susceptible to such a disease. For avian flu and West Nile virus, this is being studied now in chicken and songbird populations. We know that many different species of birds are carrying the highly pathogenic type of flu virus, so a logical next step is to compare different individual birds, both susceptible and resistant, to see if they differ in their MHC genes. One of my postdocs is addressing this kind of question for a bacterial pathogen of the house finch.

What is some other research you're doing?

We want to understand how the MHC evolved in the transition from early reptiles to birds, which are in the reptilian family tree. We've made genomic libraries of DNA from five different species: an emu (an Australian bird that resembles an ostrich), an alligator, a turtle, a tuatara (an ancient reptile that lives in New

Zealand), and a garter snake. They make a great system for doing comparative genomics. In addition to looking at MHC genes, which seem to be under strong selection, we also look at neutral markers, which aren't under selection, to track species through space and time.

I go to Australia pretty regularly. Australia is a good natural laboratory for my work because the geography and the geographic ranges of birds are very consistent across different species. We're interested in using genetic tools to understand the times of speciation in different groups of birds. When did an eastern species diverge from the western species? And are those times the same across different species? We're comparing the evolution and geography of different species.

What is a species?

You'd think that a concept like species would be very well hammered out and agreed upon by scientists, but it's actually one of the more contentious areas of biology! I tend to be a traditionalist in this matter; I regard species as reproductively isolated groups of related individuals, as Ernst Mayr defined them in 1942. That is, individuals of one species don't breed with those of other species. The isolation can come about by many different mechanisms. For example, it can result from divergence after a population has colonized a new area. New species arise when gene flow (transfer) between different populations mostly ceases.

Can evolutionary trees give insights into mechanisms of evolution?

One way to use evolutionary trees to look at mechanisms is to focus on the tempo of evolution and the shape of the tree. Do we see a rapid burst of speciation, of many rapid branchings toward the tips, for example? Or do we see very long branches that are un-

broken by speciation events? We try to link the branching patterns in these trees to environmental events in the past. In Australia, we're looking at related species in the east and west of the continent, and if we know how long ago these species separated, we may be able to link their separation to specific events, such as intrusions of the sea near a coast or desert formation in inland areas. There are records of such environmental changes going back several hundred thousand years in Australia.

Do you have evidence that speciation can be driven by sexual selection?

In sexual selection, individuals with certain inherited traits—bright plumage, for instance—are more likely than others to obtain mates. We have a lot of indirect evidence that sexual selection can play a role in the formation of new species. When DNA evidence shows that two species that look very different are actually extremely closely related, we can reasonably conclude that the species evolved recently and that some sort of selection was involved. We find this situation in Australian birds of paradise, where different species may have different plumage, different calls, and different behaviors, while being very similar in the neutral components of their genomes. So clearly some sort of selection, probably sexual selection, has driven the phenotypes apart. Birds of paradise, which are fantastically diverse in phenotype, have diverged into different species in the blink of an eye.

Is it true that all the world's songbirds got their start in Australia?

Many lines of evidence suggest that Australia and nearby New Guinea may have been the cradle of songbird evolution. And more broadly, Gondwana may have been the origin of many groups of birds. Gondwana was an ancient supercontinent that included most of the landmasses that are now in the Southern Hemisphere. Some of the oldest fossil songbirds have been found in Australia. The evidence suggests that many new groups of songbirds arose in Australia around 55–65 million years ago. They then spread around the globe. Also, our North American crows and jays trace their roots back to Australia. It's interesting that taxonomists in the early 20th century thought that Australian bird species were all just twigs of evolutionary trees rooted in the Northern Hemisphere. But really, it's the opposite.

. . . we can now compare the sizes, shapes, and genes of birds from populations separated by more than a century.

Inquiry in Action

Learn about an experiment by Scott Edwards in Inquiry Figure 24.3 on page 489.

Left to right: Scott Edwards, Jane Reece, Michael Cain

Descent with Modification
A Darwinian View of Life

22

22.1 The Darwinian revolution challenged traditional views of a young Earth inhabited by unchanging species

22.2 Descent with modification by natural selection explains the adaptations of organisms and the unity and diversity of life

22.3 Evolution is supported by an overwhelming amount of scientific evidence

OVERVIEW
Endless Forms Most Beautiful

The *Onymacris unguicularis* beetle lives in the coastal Namib desert of southwestern Africa, a land where fog is common, but virtually no rain falls. To obtain the water it needs to survive, the beetle relies on a peculiar "head-standing" behavior **(Figure 22.1)**. Tilting head-downward, the beetle faces into the winds that blow fog across the dunes. Droplets of moisture from the fog collect on the beetle's body and run down into its mouth.

This headstander beetle shares many features with the more than 350,000 other beetle species on Earth, including six pairs of legs, a hard outer surface, and two pairs of wings. But how did there come to be so many variations on the basic beetle theme? The headstander beetle and its many close relatives illustrate three key observations about life: the striking ways in which organisms are suited for life in their environments; the many shared characteristics (unity) of life; and the rich diversity of life. A century and a half ago, Charles Darwin was inspired to develop a scientific explanation for these three broad observations. When he published his hypothesis in *The Origin of Species,* Darwin ushered in a scientific revolution—the era of evolutionary biology.

For now, we will define **evolution** as *descent with modification,* a phrase Darwin used in proposing that Earth's many

▲ Figure 22.1 **How can this beetle survive in the desert, and what is it doing?**

species are descendants of ancestral species that were different from the present-day species. Evolution can also be defined more narrowly as a change in the genetic composition of a population from generation to generation, as we'll explore in Chapter 23. Whether it is defined broadly or narrowly, we can view evolution in two related but different ways: as a pattern and as a process. The *pattern* of evolutionary change is revealed by data from a range of scientific disciplines, including biology, geology, physics, and chemistry. These data are facts—they are observations about the natural world. The *process* of evolution consists of the mechanisms that produce the observed pattern of change. These mechanisms represent natural causes of the natural phenomena we observe. Indeed, the power of evolution as a unifying theory is its ability to explain and connect a vast array of observations about the living world.

As with all general theories in science, we continue to test our theory of evolution by examining whether it can account for new observations and experimental results. In this and the following chapters, we'll examine how ongoing discoveries shape our current understanding of the pattern and process of evolution. To set the stage, we'll first retrace Darwin's quest to explain the adaptations, unity, and diversity of life's "endless forms most beautiful."

CONCEPT 22.1
The Darwinian revolution challenged traditional views of a young Earth inhabited by unchanging species

What impelled Darwin to challenge the prevailing views of his time about Earth and its life? His revolutionary proposal actually had its roots in the work of many other individuals **(Figure 22.2)**.

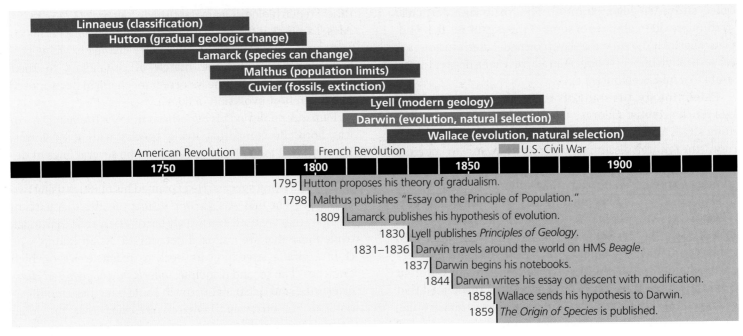

Linnaeus (classification)		
Hutton (gradual geologic change)		
Lamarck (species can change)		
Malthus (population limits)		
Cuvier (fossils, extinction)		
Lyell (modern geology)		
Darwin (evolution, natural selection)		
Wallace (evolution, natural selection)		

American Revolution   French Revolution   U.S. Civil War

1750   1800   1850   1900

1795 | Hutton proposes his theory of gradualism.
1798 | Malthus publishes "Essay on the Principle of Population."
1809 | Lamarck publishes his hypothesis of evolution.
1830 | Lyell publishes *Principles of Geology*.
1831–1836 | Darwin travels around the world on HMS *Beagle*.
1837 | Darwin begins his notebooks.
1844 | Darwin writes his essay on descent with modification.
1858 | Wallace sends his hypothesis to Darwin.
1859 | *The Origin of Species* is published.

▲ **Figure 22.2 The historical context of Darwin's life and ideas.** The dark blue bars represent the lives of some individuals whose ideas contributed to Darwin's thinking about evolution.

Scala Naturae and Classification of Species

Long before Darwin was born, several Greek philosophers suggested that life might have changed gradually over time. But one philosopher who greatly influenced early Western science, Aristotle (384–322 B.C.), viewed species as fixed (unchanging). Through his observations of nature, Aristotle recognized certain "affinities" among organisms. He concluded that life-forms could be arranged on a ladder, or scale, of increasing complexity, later called the *scala naturae* ("scale of nature"). Each form of life, perfect and permanent, had its allotted rung on this ladder.

These ideas coincided with the Old Testament account of creation, which holds that species were individually designed by God and therefore perfect. In the 1700s, many scientists interpreted the often remarkable match of organisms to their environment as evidence that the Creator had designed each species for a particular purpose.

One such scientist was Carolus Linnaeus (1707–1778), a Swedish physician and botanist who sought to classify life's diversity, in his words, "for the greater glory of God." Linnaeus developed the two-part, or binomial, system of naming species (such as *Homo sapiens* for humans) that is still used today. In contrast to the linear hierarchy of the *scala naturae*, Linnaeus adopted a nested classification system, grouping similar species into increasingly general categories. For example, similar species are grouped in the same genus, similar genera (plural of genus) are grouped in the same family, and so on (see Figure 1.14).

Linnaeus did not ascribe the resemblances among species to evolutionary kinship, but rather to the pattern of their creation. However, a century later his classification system would play a role in Darwin's argument for evolution.

Ideas About Change over Time

Darwin drew many of his ideas from the work of scientists studying **fossils**, the remains or traces of organisms from the past. Most fossils are found in sedimentary rocks formed from the sand and mud that settle to the bottom of seas, lakes, and swamps **(Figure 22.3)**. New layers of sediment cover older ones and compress them into superimposed layers of rock

1 Rivers carry sediment into seas and swamps. Over time, sedimentary rock layers (strata) form under water. Some strata contain fossils.

2 As water levels change and the seafloor is pushed upward, the strata and their fossils are exposed.

Younger stratum with more recent fossils

Older stratum with older fossils

▲ **Figure 22.3 Formation of sedimentary strata with fossils.**

called **strata** (singular, *stratum*). The fossils in a particular stratum provide a glimpse of some of the organisms that populated Earth at the time that layer formed. Later, erosion may carve through upper (younger) strata, revealing deeper (older) strata that had been buried.

Paleontology, the study of fossils, was largely developed by French scientist Georges Cuvier (1769–1832). In examining strata near Paris, Cuvier noted that the older the stratum, the more dissimilar its fossils were to current life-forms. He also observed that from one layer to the next, some new species appeared while others disappeared. He inferred that extinctions must have been a common occurrence in the history of life. Yet Cuvier staunchly opposed the idea of evolution. To explain his observations, he advocated **catastrophism**, the principle that events in the past occurred suddenly and were caused by mechanisms different from those operating in the present. Cuvier speculated that each boundary between strata represented a catastrophe, such as a flood, that had destroyed many of the species living at that time. He proposed that these periodic catastrophes were usually confined to local regions, which were later repopulated by species immigrating from other areas.

In contrast, other scientists suggested that profound change could take place through the cumulative effect of slow but continuous processes. In 1795, Scottish geologist James Hutton (1726–1797) proposed that Earth's geologic features could be explained by gradual mechanisms still operating. For example, he suggested that valleys were often formed by rivers wearing through rocks and that rocks containing marine fossils were formed when sediments that had eroded from the land were carried by rivers to the sea, where they buried dead marine organisms. The leading geologist of Darwin's time, Charles Lyell (1797–1875), incorporated Hutton's thinking into his principle of **uniformitarianism**, which stated that mechanisms of change are constant over time. Lyell proposed that the same geologic processes are operating today as in the past, and at the same rate.

Hutton and Lyell's ideas strongly influenced Darwin's thinking. Darwin agreed that if geologic change results from slow, continuous actions rather than from sudden events, then Earth must be much older than the widely accepted age of a few thousand years. It would, for example, take a very long time for a river to carve a canyon by erosion. He later reasoned that perhaps similarly slow and subtle processes could produce substantial biological change. Darwin was not the first to apply the idea of gradual change to biological evolution, however.

Lamarck's Hypothesis of Evolution

During the 18th century, several naturalists (including Darwin's grandfather, Erasmus Darwin) suggested that life evolves as environments change. But only one of Charles Darwin's predecessors proposed a mechanism for *how* life changes over time: French biologist Jean-Baptiste de Lamarck (1744–1829). Alas, Lamarck is primarily remembered today *not* for his visionary recognition that evolutionary change explains patterns in fossils and the match of organisms to their environments, but for the incorrect mechanism he proposed to explain how evolution occurs.

Lamarck published his hypothesis in 1809, the year Darwin was born. By comparing living species with fossil forms, Lamarck had found what appeared to be several lines of descent, each a chronological series of older to younger fossils leading to a living species. He explained his findings using two principles. The first was *use and disuse*, the idea that parts of the body that are used extensively become larger and stronger, while those that are not used deteriorate. As an example, he cited a giraffe stretching its neck to reach leaves on high branches. The second principle, *inheritance of acquired characteristics*, stated that an organism could pass these modifications to its offspring. Lamarck reasoned that the long, muscular neck of the living giraffe had evolved over many generations as giraffes stretched their necks ever higher.

Lamarck also thought that evolution happens because organisms have an innate drive to become more complex. Darwin rejected this idea, but he, too, thought that variation was introduced into the evolutionary process in part through inheritance of acquired characteristics. Today, however, our understanding of genetics refutes this mechanism: There is no evidence that acquired characteristics can be inherited in the way proposed by Lamarck **(Figure 22.4)**.

Lamarck was vilified in his own time, especially by Cuvier, who denied that species ever evolve. In retrospect, however, Lamarck deserves credit for recognizing that the match of organisms to their environments can be explained by gradual evolutionary change and for proposing a testable mechanism for this change.

▲ **Figure 22.4 Acquired traits cannot be inherited.** This bonsai tree was "trained" to grow as a dwarf by pruning and shaping. However, seeds from this tree would produce offspring of normal size.

1. How did Hutton's and Lyell's ideas influence Darwin's thinking about evolution?
2. **WHAT IF?** In Chapter 1, you read that scientific hypotheses must be testable and falsifiable. If you apply these criteria, are Cuvier's explanation of the fossil record and Lamarck's hypothesis of evolution scientific? Explain your answer in each case.

For suggested answers, see Appendix A.

CONCEPT 22.2

Descent with modification by natural selection explains the adaptations of organisms and the unity and diversity of life

As the 19th century dawned, it was generally believed that species had remained unchanged since their creation. A few clouds of doubt about the permanence of species were beginning to gather, but no one could have forecast the thundering storm just beyond the horizon. How did Charles Darwin become the lightning rod for a revolutionary view of life?

Darwin's Research

Charles Darwin (1809–1882) was born in Shrewsbury in western England. Even as a boy, he had a consuming interest in nature. When he was not reading nature books, he was fishing, hunting, and collecting insects. Darwin's father, a physician, could see no future for his son as a naturalist and sent him to medical school in Edinburgh. But Charles found medicine boring and surgery before the days of anesthesia horrifying. He quit medical school and enrolled at Cambridge University, intending to become a clergyman. (At that time in England, many scholars of science belonged to the clergy.)

At Cambridge, Darwin became the protégé of the Reverend John Henslow, a botany professor. Soon after Darwin graduated, Henslow recommended him to Captain Robert FitzRoy, who was preparing the survey ship HMS *Beagle* for a long voyage around the world. Darwin would pay his own way and serve as a conversation partner to the young captain. FitzRoy accepted Darwin because of his education and because they were of the same social class and about the same age.

The Voyage of the Beagle

Darwin embarked from England on the *Beagle* in December 1831. The primary mission of the voyage was to chart poorly known stretches of the South American coastline (Figure 22.5). While the ship's crew surveyed the coast, Darwin spent most of his time on shore, observing and collecting thousands of South American plants and animals. He noted the characteristics of plants and animals that made them well suited to such diverse environments as the humid jungles of Brazil, the expansive grasslands of Argentina, and the towering peaks of the Andes.

Darwin observed that the plants and animals in temperate regions of South America more closely resembled species living in the South American tropics than species living in

Darwin in 1840, after his return from the voyage

HMS *Beagle* in port

The Galápagos Islands

▲ Figure 22.5 **The voyage of HMS *Beagle*.**

temperate regions of Europe. Furthermore, the fossils he found, though clearly different from living species, were distinctly South American in their resemblance to the living organisms of that continent.

Darwin also spent much time thinking about geology during the voyage. Despite bouts of seasickness, he read Lyell's *Principles of Geology* while aboard the *Beagle*. He experienced geologic change firsthand when a violent earthquake rocked the coast of Chile, and he observed afterward that rocks along the coast had been thrust upward by several feet. Finding fossils of ocean organisms high in the Andes, Darwin inferred that the rocks containing the fossils must have been raised there by a series of many similar earthquakes. These observations reinforced what he had learned from Lyell: The physical evidence did not support the traditional view of a static Earth only a few thousand years old.

Darwin's interest in the geographic distribution of species was further stimulated by the *Beagle*'s stop at the Galápagos, a group of volcanic islands located near the equator about 900 km (540 miles) west of South America. Darwin was fascinated by the unusual organisms he found there. The birds he collected on the Galápagos included several kinds of mockingbirds that, although similar, seemed to be different species. Some were unique to individual islands, while others lived on two or more adjacent islands. Furthermore, although the animals on the Galápagos resembled species living on the South American mainland, most of the Galápagos species were not known from anywhere else in the world. Darwin hypothesized that the Galápagos had been colonized by organisms that had strayed from South America and then diversified, giving rise to new species on the various islands.

Darwin's Focus on Adaptation

During the voyage of the *Beagle*, Darwin observed many examples of **adaptations**, characteristics of organisms that enhance their survival and reproduction in specific environments. Later, as he reassessed his observations, he began to perceive adaptation to the environment and the origin of new species as closely related processes. Could a new species arise from an ancestral form by the gradual accumulation of adaptations to a different environment? From studies made years after Darwin's voyage, biologists have concluded that this is indeed what happened to the diverse group of Galápagos finches we discussed in Chapter 1 (see Figure 1.22). The finches' various beaks and behaviors are adapted to the specific foods available on their home islands **(Figure 22.6)**. Darwin realized that explaining such adaptations was

essential to understanding evolution. As we'll explore further, his explanation of how adaptations arise centered on **natural selection**, a process in which individuals with certain inherited traits leave more offspring than individuals with other traits.

By the early 1840s, Darwin had worked out the major features of his hypothesis. He set these ideas on paper in 1844, when he wrote a long essay on descent with modification and its underlying mechanism, natural selection. Yet he was still reluctant to publish his ideas, apparently because he anticipated the uproar they would cause. Even as he procrastinated, Darwin continued to compile evidence in support of his hypothesis. By the mid-1850s, he had described his ideas to Lyell and a few others. Lyell, who was not yet convinced of evolution, nevertheless urged Darwin to publish on the subject before someone else came to the same conclusions and published first.

In June 1858, Lyell's prediction came true. Darwin received a manuscript from Alfred Russel Wallace (1823–1913), a British naturalist working in the East Indies who had developed a hypothesis of natural selection similar to Darwin's. Wallace asked Darwin to evaluate his paper and forward it to Lyell if it merited publication. Darwin complied, writing to Lyell: "Your words have come true with a vengeance. . . . I never saw a more striking coincidence . . . so all my originality, whatever it may amount to, will be smashed." Lyell and a colleague then presented Wallace's paper, along with extracts from Darwin's unpublished 1844 essay, to the Linnean Society of London on July 1, 1858. Darwin quickly finished his book, titled *On the Origin of Species by Means of Natural Selection* (commonly referred to as *The Origin of Species*), and published it the next year. Although Wallace had

(a) Cactus-eater. The long, sharp beak of the cactus ground finch (*Geospiza scandens*) helps it tear and eat cactus flowers and pulp.

(b) Insect-eater. The green warbler finch (*Certhidea olivacea*) uses its narrow, pointed beak to grasp insects.

(c) Seed-eater. The large ground finch (*Geospiza magnirostris*) has a large beak adapted for cracking seeds that fall from plants to the ground.

▲ **Figure 22.6 Beak variation in Galápagos finches.** The Galápagos Islands are home to more than a dozen species of closely related finches, some found only on a single island. The most striking differences among them are their beaks, which are adapted for specific diets.

submitted his ideas for publication first, he admired Darwin and thought that Darwin had developed the idea of natural selection so extensively that he should be known as its main architect.

Within a decade, Darwin's book and its proponents had convinced most biologists that life's diversity is the product of evolution. Darwin succeeded where previous evolutionists had failed, mainly because he had presented a plausible scientific mechanism with immaculate logic and an avalanche of evidence.

The Origin of Species

In his book, Darwin developed two main ideas: that descent with modification explains life's unity and diversity and that natural selection brings about the match between organisms and their environment.

Descent with Modification

In the first edition of *The Origin of Species*, Darwin never used the word *evolution* (although the final word of the book is "evolved"). Rather, he discussed *descent with modification*, a phrase that summarized his view of life. Darwin perceived unity in life, which he attributed to the descent of all organisms from an ancestor that lived in the remote past. He also thought that as the descendants of that ancestral organism lived in various habitats over millions of years, they had accumulated diverse modifications, or adaptations, that fit them to specific ways of life. Darwin reasoned that over long periods of time, descent with modification eventually led to the rich diversity of life we see today.

Darwin viewed the history of life as a tree, with multiple branchings from a common trunk out to the tips of the youngest twigs (**Figure 22.7**). The tips of the twigs represent the diversity of organisms living in the present. Each fork of the tree represents an ancestor of all the lines of evolution that subsequently branch from that point. As shown in the tree diagram in **Figure 22.8**, closely related species, such as the Asian elephant and African elephants, are very similar because they shared the same line of descent until a relatively recent split from

▶ **Figure 22.7 "I think. . ."** In this 1837 sketch, Darwin envisioned the branching pattern of evolution.

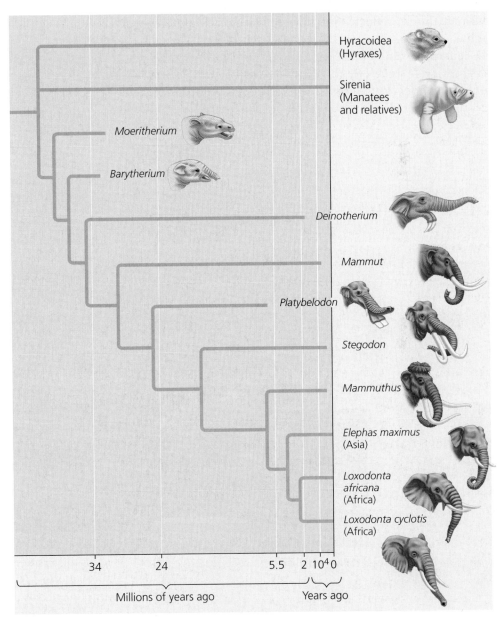

▲ **Figure 22.8 Descent with modification.** This evolutionary tree of elephants and their relatives is based mainly on fossils—their anatomy, order of appearance in strata, and geographic distribution. Note that most branches of descent ended in extinction. (Time line not to scale.)

? *Based on the tree shown here, approximately when did the most recent ancestor shared by Mammuthus (woolly mammoths), Asian elephants, and African elephants live?*

their common ancestor. Note that seven lineages related to elephants have become extinct over the past 30 million years. As a result, there are no living species that fill the gap between the elephants and their nearest relatives today, the manatees and hyraxes. In fact, many branches of evolution, even some major ones, are dead ends: Scientists estimate that over 99% of all species that have ever lived are now extinct.

In his efforts at classification, Linnaeus had realized that some organisms resemble each other more closely than others, but he had not linked these resemblances to evolution. Nonetheless, because he had recognized that the great diversity of organisms could be organized into "groups subordinate to groups" (Darwin's phrase), Linnaeus's system meshed well with Darwin's hypothesis. To Darwin, the Linnaean hierarchy reflected the branching history of the tree of life, with organisms at the various levels related through descent from common ancestors.

Artificial Selection, Natural Selection, and Adaptation

Darwin proposed a mechanism, natural selection, to explain the observable patterns of evolution. He crafted his argument carefully, to persuade even the most skeptical readers. First he discussed familiar examples of selective breeding of domesticated plants and animals. Humans have modified other species over many generations by selecting and breeding individuals that possess desired traits—a process called **artificial selection (Figure 22.9)**.

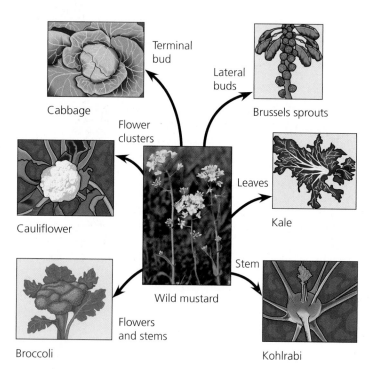

▲ **Figure 22.9 Artificial selection.** These different vegetables have all been selected from one species of wild mustard. By selecting variations in different parts of the plant, breeders have obtained these divergent results.

▲ **Figure 22.10 Variation in a population.** To the extent that the variation in color and banding patterns in this snail population is heritable, it can be acted on by natural selection.

As a result of artificial selection, crop plants and animals bred as livestock or pets often bear little resemblance to their wild ancestors.

Darwin then described four observations of nature from which he drew two inferences:

Observation #1: Members of a population often vary greatly in their traits (**Figure 22.10**).

Observation #2: Traits are inherited from parents to offspring.

Observation #3: All species are capable of producing more offspring than their environment can support (**Figure 22.11**).

Observation #4: Owing to lack of food or other resources, many of these offspring do not survive.

Inference #1: Individuals whose inherited traits give them a higher probability of surviving and reproducing in a given environment tend to leave more offspring than other individuals.

Inference #2: This unequal ability of individuals to survive and reproduce will lead to the accumulation of favorable traits in the population over generations.

Darwin perceived an important connection between natural selection and the capacity of organisms to "overreproduce." He began to make this connection after reading an essay by economist Thomas Malthus, who contended that much of human suffering—disease, famine, and war—was the inescapable consequence of the human population's potential to increase faster than food supplies and other resources. Darwin realized that the capacity to overreproduce was characteristic of all species. Of the many eggs laid, young born, and seeds spread, only a tiny fraction complete their development and leave offspring of their own. The rest are eaten, starved, diseased, un-

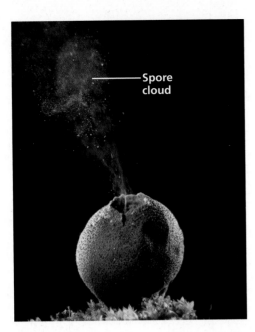

Spore cloud

▲ **Figure 22.11 Overproduction of offspring.** A single puffball fungus can produce billions of offspring. If all of these offspring and their descendants survived to maturity, they would carpet the surrounding land surface.

(a) A flower mantid in Malaysia

(b) A stick mantid in Africa

▲ **Figure 22.12 Camouflage as an example of evolutionary adaptation.** Related species of the insects called mantids have diverse shapes and colors that evolved in different environments.

mated, or unable to tolerate physical conditions of the environment such as salinity or temperature.

An organism's traits can influence not only its own performance, but also how well its offspring cope with environmental challenges. For example, an organism might have a heritable trait that gives its offspring an advantage in escaping predators, obtaining food, or tolerating physical conditions. When such advantages increase the number of offspring that survive and reproduce, the traits that are favored will likely appear at a greater frequency in the next generation. Thus, over time, natural selection imposed by factors such as predators, lack of food, or adverse physical conditions can increase the proportion of favorable traits in a population.

How rapidly do such changes occur? Darwin reasoned that if artificial selection can bring about dramatic change in a relatively short period of time, then natural selection should be capable of substantial modification of species over many hundreds of generations. Even if the advantages of some heritable traits over others are slight, the advantageous variations will gradually accumulate in the population, and less favorable variations will diminish. Over time, this process will increase the frequency of individuals with favorable adaptations and hence refine the match between organisms and their environment.

Natural Selection: A Summary

Let's now recap the main ideas of natural selection:

▶ Natural selection is a process in which individuals that have certain heritable characteristics survive and reproduce at a higher rate than other individuals.

▶ Over time, natural selection can increase the match between organisms and their environment (Figure 22.12).

▶ If an environment changes, or if individuals move to a new environment, natural selection may result in adaptation to these new conditions, sometimes giving rise to new species in the process.

One subtle but important point is that although natural selection occurs through interactions between individual organisms and their environment, *individuals do not evolve.* Rather, it is the population that evolves over time.

A second key point is that natural selection can amplify or diminish *only heritable traits*—traits that are passed from organisms to their offspring. Though an organism may become modified during its lifetime, and these acquired characteristics may even help the organism in its environment, there is little evidence that such acquired characteristics can be inherited by offspring.

Third, remember that environmental factors vary from place to place and over time. A trait that is favorable in one place or time may be useless—or even detrimental—in other places or times. Natural selection is always operating, but which traits are favored depends on the environmental context.

Next, we'll survey the wide range of observations that support a Darwinian view of evolution by natural selection.

1. How does the concept of descent with modification explain both the unity and diversity of life?
2. Describe how overreproduction and heritable variation relate to evolution by natural selection.
3. **WHAT IF?** If you discovered a fossil of an extinct mammal that lived high in the Andes, would you predict that it would more closely resemble present-day mammals from South American jungles or present-day mammals that live high in African mountains? Explain.

For suggested answers, see Appendix A.

CONCEPT **22.3**
Evolution is supported by an overwhelming amount of scientific evidence

In *The Origin of Species*, Darwin marshaled a broad range of evidence to support the concept of descent with modification. Still—as he readily acknowledged—there were instances in which key evidence was lacking. For example, Darwin referred to the origin of flowering plants as an "abominable mystery," and he lamented the lack of fossils showing how earlier groups of organisms gave rise to new groups.

In the 150 years since, new discoveries have filled many of the gaps that Darwin identified. The origin of flowering plants, for example, is better understood (see Chapter 29), and many fossils have been discovered that signify the origin of new groups of organisms (see Chapter 25). In this section, we'll consider four types of data that document the pattern of evolution and illuminate the processes by which it occurs: direct observations of evolution, the fossil record, homology, and biogeography.

Direct Observations of Evolutionary Change

Biologists have documented evolutionary change in thousands of scientific studies. We'll examine many such studies throughout this unit, but let's look here at two examples.

Predation and Coloration in Guppies: Scientific Inquiry

Predators (organisms that feed on other species, called prey) are a potent force in shaping the adaptations of their food source. The predator is most likely to feed on prey individuals that are least able to avoid detection, escape, or defend themselves. As a result, such prey individuals are less likely to reproduce and pass their traits to their offspring than are individuals whose traits help them evade predators.

For many years, John Endler, of the University of California, Santa Barbara, has studied the impact of predators on guppies (*Poecilia reticulata*), small freshwater fish that you may know as aquarium pets. He observed that among wild

▼ Figure 22.13 **Inquiry**

Can predation result in natural selection for color patterns in guppies?

EXPERIMENT John Endler, of the University of California, Santa Barbara, studied wild guppies in the Aripo River system on the Caribbean island of Trinidad. He transplanted 200 guppies from pools containing pike-cichlids, intense guppy predators, to pools containing killifish, less active predators of guppies. He tracked the number of bright-colored spots and the total area of those spots on male guppies in each generation.

Predator: Killifish; preys mainly on juvenile guppies (which do not express the color genes)

Guppies: Adult males have brighter colors than those in "pike-cichlid pools"

Pools with killifish, but no guppies prior to transplant

Experimental transplant of guppies

Predator: Pike-cichlid; preys mainly on adult guppies

Guppies: Adult males are more drab in color than those in "killifish pools"

RESULTS After 22 months (15 generations), the number and total area of colored spots on male guppies in the transplanted population had increased compared to those of males in the source population.

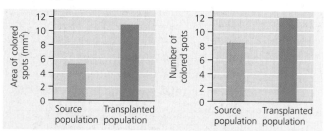

CONCLUSION Endler concluded that the change in predator resulted in different variations (brighter color patterns) being favored in the transplanted population. Over a relatively short time, an observable evolutionary change occurred in this population.

SOURCE J. A. Endler, Natural selection on color patterns in *Poecilia reticulata*, *Evolution* 34:76–91 (1980).

WHAT IF? What would happen if, after 22 months, guppies from the transplanted population were returned to the source pool?

guppy populations in Trinidad, the male guppies' color patterns are so variable that no two males look alike. These highly variable colors are controlled by a number of genes that, in the wild, are only expressed in adult males. Female guppies are attracted to males with bright colors, choosing them as mates more often than they choose males with drab coloring. But the bright colors that attract females might also make the males more conspicuous to predators. Thus, if a guppy population contained both brightly colored and drab males, we might predict that predators would tend to eat more of the brightly colored fish.

Endler wondered how the trade-off between attracting mates and attracting predators affects coloration in male guppies. In the field, he observed that the color patterns of male guppies appeared to correspond to the intensity of predation. In pools that had few predator species, male guppies tended to be brightly colored, whereas in pools that had many predators, males were less brightly colored. Based on these observations, Endler hypothesized that intense predation caused natural selection in male guppies, favoring the trait of drab coloration. He tested this hypothesis by transferring brightly colored guppies to a pool with many predators. As he predicted, over time the transplanted guppy population became less brightly colored.

One guppy predator, the killifish, preys on juvenile guppies that have not yet displayed their adult coloration. Endler predicted that if guppies with drab colors were transferred to a pool with only killifish, eventually the descendants of these guppies would be more brightly colored (because females prefer males with bright colors). **Figure 22.13**, on the facing page, describes this experiment. Indeed, in their new environment, the guppy population rapidly came to feature brighter colors, demonstrating that selection can cause rapid evolution in wild populations.

The Evolution of Drug-Resistant HIV

An example of ongoing natural selection that affects our own lives dramatically is the evolution of drug-resistant pathogens (disease-causing organisms and viruses). This is a particular problem with bacteria and viruses that reproduce rapidly, because individuals that are resistant to a particular drug can increase in number very quickly.

Consider the example of HIV (human immunodeficiency virus), the virus that causes AIDS (see Chapters 19 and 43). Researchers have developed numerous drugs to combat this pathogen, but using these medications selects for viruses resistant to the drugs. A few drug-resistant viruses may be present by chance at the beginning of treatment. Those that survive the early doses reproduce, passing on the alleles that enable them to resist the drug. In this way, the frequency of resistant viruses increases rapidly in the population.

Figure 22.14 illustrates the evolution of HIV resistance to the drug 3TC. Scientists designed 3TC to interfere with reverse transcriptase. HIV uses this enzyme to make a DNA version of

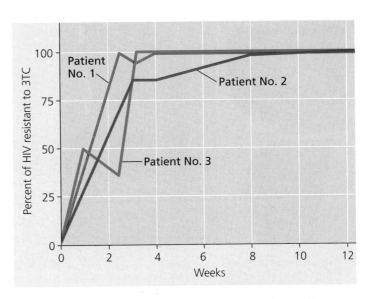

▲ **Figure 22.14 Evolution of drug resistance in HIV.** Rare resistant viruses multiplied quickly when each of these patients was treated with the anti-HIV drug 3TC. Within just a few weeks, 3TC-resistant organisms made up 100% of the virus population in each case.

its RNA genome, which is then inserted into the DNA of the human host cell (see Figure 19.8). Because the 3TC molecule is similar in shape to the cytosine-bearing (C-bearing) nucleotide of DNA, HIV's reverse transcriptase picks up a 3TC molecule instead of a C-bearing nucleotide and inserts the 3TC into a growing DNA chain. This error terminates further elongation of the DNA and thus blocks reproduction of HIV.

The 3TC-resistant varieties of HIV have versions of reverse transcriptase that are able to discriminate between the drug and the normal C-bearing nucleotide. These viruses have no advantage in the absence of 3TC; in fact, they replicate more slowly than viruses that carry the typical version of reverse transcriptase. But once 3TC is added to their environment, it becomes a powerful selecting force, favoring the survival of resistant viruses (see Figure 22.14).

Both the guppy example and the HIV example highlight two key points about natural selection. First, natural selection is a process of editing rather than a creative mechanism. A drug does not *create* resistant pathogens; it *selects for* resistant individuals that were already present in the population. Second, natural selection depends on time and place. It favors those characteristics in a genetically variable population that provide advantage in the current, local environment. What is beneficial in one situation may be useless or even harmful in another. In the guppy example, individuals that have drab colors are at an advantage in pools with fierce predators but at a disadvantage in pools without them.

The Fossil Record

A second type of evidence for evolution comes from fossils. The fossil record shows that past organisms differed from present-day organisms and that many species have become

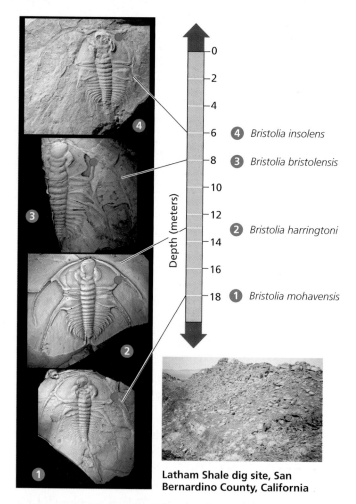

▲ Figure 22.15 Fossil evidence of evolution in a group of trilobites. These fossils are just a few in a series discovered in the Latham Shale bed, which was deposited between 513 and 512 million years ago. The sequence shows change over time in the location and angle of the spines of the head shield (the area marked by red dots).

Depth (meters)

0
2
4
6 — ④ *Bristolia insolens*
8 — ③ *Bristolia bristolensis*
10
12
14 — ② *Bristolia harringtoni*
16
18 — ① *Bristolia mohavensis*

Latham Shale dig site, San Bernardino County, California

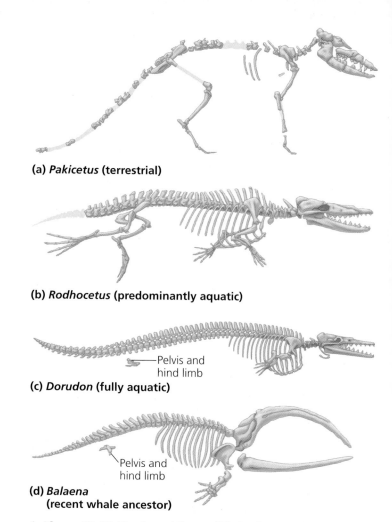

(a) *Pakicetus* (terrestrial)

(b) *Rodhocetus* (predominantly aquatic)

Pelvis and hind limb
(c) *Dorudon* (fully aquatic)

Pelvis and hind limb
(d) *Balaena* (recent whale ancestor)

▲ Figure 22.16 The transition to life in the sea. The hypothesis that whales and other cetaceans evolved from terrestrial organisms predicts that cetacean ancestors were four-legged. Indeed, paleontologists have unearthed fossils of extinct cetaceans that had hind limbs, including the four species whose skeletons are depicted here (not drawn to scale). Additional fossils show that *Pakicetus* and *Rodhocetus* had a type of ankle bone that is otherwise unique to a group of land mammals that includes pigs, hippos, cows, camels, and deer. This similarity strongly suggests that cetaceans are most closely related to this group of land mammals.

extinct. Fossils also show the evolutionary changes that have occurred over time in various groups of organisms **(Figure 22.15)**.

Over longer time scales, fossils document the origins of major new groups of organisms. An example is the fossil record of early cetaceans, the mammalian order that includes whales, dolphins, and porpoises. The earliest cetaceans lived 50–60 million years ago. The fossil record indicates that prior to that time, most mammals were terrestrial. Although scientists had long realized that whales and other cetaceans must have originated from land mammals, few fossils had been found that revealed how cetacean limb structure had changed over time, leading eventually to the loss of hind limbs and the development of flippers. In the past few decades, however, a series of remarkable fossils have been discovered in Pakistan, Egypt, and North America that document the transition from life on land to life in the sea. Each organism shown in **Figure 22.16** differs from present-day mammals, including present-day whales, and is now extinct. Collectively, these and other early fossils document the formation of new species and the origin of a major new group of mammals, the cetaceans.

In addition to providing evidence of how life on Earth has changed over time—the pattern of evolution—the fossil record also can be used to test evolutionary hypotheses arising from other kinds of evidence. For example, based on anatomical data, scientists think that early land vertebrates evolved from a group of fishes and that early amphibians evolved from descendants of early land vertebrates. If these relationships are correct, we would predict that the earliest fossils of fishes should be older than the earliest fossils of land vertebrates. Similarly, we would predict that the earliest fossil land vertebrates should be older than the earliest fossil amphibians. These predictions can be tested using radioactive dating techniques (see Chapter 25) to determine the age of fossils. To date, all of these predictions have been upheld, which suggests that our understanding of the evolutionary relationships on which the predictions were based is correct.

Homology

A third type of evidence for evolution comes from analyzing similarities among different organisms. As we've discussed, evolution is a process of descent with modification: Characteristics present in an ancestral organism are altered (by natural selection) in its descendants over time as they face different environmental conditions. As a result, related species can have characteristics with an underlying similarity even though they may have very different functions. Such similarity resulting from common ancestry is known as **homology**.

Anatomical and Molecular Homologies

The view of evolution as a remodeling process leads to the prediction that closely related species should share similar features—and they do. Of course, closely related species share the features used to determine their relationship, but they also share many other features. Some of these shared features make little sense except in the context of evolution. For example, the forelimbs of all mammals, including humans, cats, whales, and bats, show the same arrangement of bones from the shoulder to the tips of the digits, even though these appendages have very different functions: lifting, walking, swimming, and flying (**Figure 22.17**). Such striking anatomical resemblances would be highly unlikely if these structures had arisen anew in each species. Rather, the underlying skeletons of the arms, forelegs, flippers, and wings of different mammals are **homologous structures** that represent variations on a structural theme that was present in their common ancestor.

Comparing early stages of development in different animal species reveals additional anatomical homologies not visible in adult organisms. For example, at some point in their devel-

Chick embryo (LM)　　　　Human embryo

▲ **Figure 22.18 Anatomical similarities in vertebrate embryos.** At some stage in their embryonic development, all vertebrates have a tail located posterior to the anus (referred to as a post-anal tail), as well as pharyngeal (throat) pouches. Descent from a common ancestor can explain such similarities.

opment, all vertebrate embryos have a tail located posterior to (behind) the anus, as well as structures called pharyngeal (throat) pouches (**Figure 22.18**). These homologous throat pouches ultimately develop into structures with very different functions, such as gills in fishes and parts of the ears and throat in humans and other mammals.

Some of the most intriguing homologies concern "leftover" structures of marginal, if any, importance to the organism. These **vestigial structures** are remnants of features that served important functions in the organism's ancestors. For instance, the skeletons of some snakes retain vestiges of the pelvis and leg bones of walking ancestors. Another example is the decreased size and loss of function in cetaceans' hind limbs as these organisms faced the challenges of life in water (see Figure 22.16). We would not expect to see these vestigial structures if snakes and whales had origins separate from other vertebrate animals.

Biologists also observe similarities among organisms at the molecular level. All forms of life use the same genetic language of DNA and RNA, and the genetic code is essentially universal (see Chapter 17). Thus, it is likely that all species descended from common ancestors that used this code. But molecular homologies go beyond a shared code. For example, organisms as dissimilar as humans and bacteria share genes inherited from a very distant common ancestor. Like the forelimbs of humans and whales, these genes have often acquired different functions.

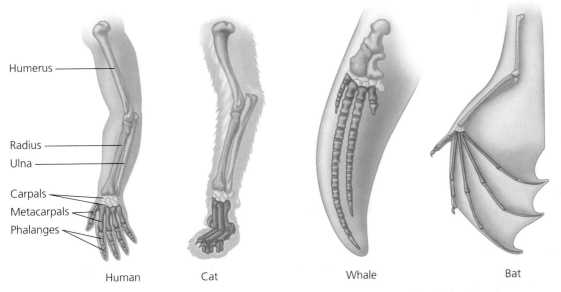

Humerus

Radius
Ulna

Carpals
Metacarpals
Phalanges

Human　　　　Cat　　　　Whale　　　　Bat

▲ **Figure 22.17 Mammalian forelimbs: homologous structures.** Even though they have become adapted for different functions, the forelimbs of all mammals are constructed from the same basic skeletal elements: one large bone (purple), attached to two smaller bones (orange and tan), attached to several small bones (gold), attached to several metacarpals (green), attached to approximately five digits, or phalanges (blue).

Homologies and "Tree Thinking"

Some homologous characteristics, such as the genetic code, are shared by all species because they date to the deep ancestral past. In contrast, homologous characteristics that evolved more recently are shared only within smaller groups of organisms. Consider an example in the tetrapods (from the Greek *tetra*, four, and *pod*, foot), the vertebrate group that consists of amphibians, mammals, and reptiles (including birds—see Figure 22.19). All tetrapods possess the same basic limb bone structure illustrated in Figure 22.17, but the ancestors of tetrapods do not. Thus, homologous characteristics form a nested pattern: All life shares the deepest layer, and each successive smaller group adds their own homologies to those they share with larger groups. This nested pattern is exactly what we would expect to result from descent with modification from a common ancestor.

Biologists often represent the pattern of descent from common ancestors and the resulting homologies with an **evolutionary tree**, a diagram that reflects evolutionary relationships among groups of organisms. We will explore in detail how evolutionary trees are constructed in Chapter 26, but for now, let's consider how we can interpret and use such trees.

Figure 22.19 is an evolutionary tree of tetrapods and their closest living relatives, the lungfishes. In this diagram, each branch point represents the common ancestor of all species that descended from it. For example, lungfishes and all tetrapods descended from ancestor ❶, whereas mammals, lizards and snakes, crocodiles, and birds all descended from ancestor ❸. As expected, the three homologies shown on the tree—tetrapod limbs, the amnion (a protective embryonic membrane), and feathers—form a nested pattern. Tetrapod limbs were present in common ancestor ❷ and hence are found in all of the descendants of that ancestor (the tetrapods). The amnion was present only in ancestor ❸ and hence is shared only by some tetrapods (mammals and reptiles). Feathers were present only in common ancestor ❻ and hence are found only in birds.

To explore "tree thinking" further, note that in Figure 22.19, mammals are positioned closer to amphibians than to birds. As a result, you might conclude that mammals are more closely related to amphibians than they are to birds. However, mammals are actually more closely related to birds than to amphibians because mammals and birds share a more recent common ancestor (ancestor ❸) than do mammals and amphibians (ancestor ❷).

Evolutionary trees are hypotheses that summarize our current understanding of patterns of descent. Our confidence in these relationships, as with any hypothesis, depends on the strength of the supporting data. In the case of Figure 22.19, the tree is supported by a variety of independent data sets, including both anatomical and DNA sequence data. As a result, biologists feel confident that it accurately reflects actual evolutionary history. As you will read in Chapter 26, scientists can use such well-supported evolutionary trees to make specific and sometimes surprising predictions about the biology of organisms.

Convergent Evolution

Although organisms that are closely related share characteristics because of common descent, distantly related organisms can resemble one another for a different reason: **convergent evolution**, the independent evolution of similar features in different lineages. Consider marsupial mammals, many of which live in Australia. Marsupials are distinct from another group of mammals—the eutherians—that live elsewhere on Earth. (Eutherians complete their embryonic development in the uterus, whereas marsupials are born as embryos and complete their development in an external pouch.) Some Australian

Each branch point represents the common ancestor of the lineages beginning there or to the right of it.

Tetrapod limbs

Amnion

A hatch mark represents a homologous characteristic shared by all the groups to the right of the mark.

Feathers

Lungfishes

Amphibians

Mammals

Lizards and snakes

Crocodiles

Ostriches

Hawks and other birds

Tetrapods

Amniotes

Birds

▲ **Figure 22.19 Tree thinking: information provided in an evolutionary tree.** This evolutionary tree for tetrapods and their closest living relatives, the lungfishes, is based on anatomical and DNA sequence data. The purple bars indicate the origin of three important homologies, each of which evolved only once. Birds are nested within and evolved from reptiles; hence, the group of organisms called "reptiles" technically includes birds.

? *Are crocodiles more closely related to lizards or birds? Explain your answer.*

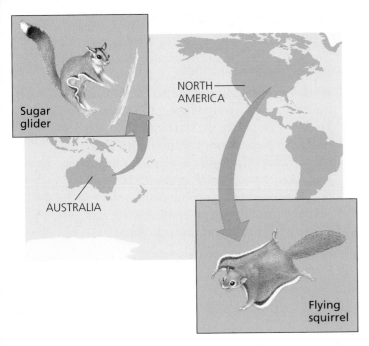

▲ **Figure 22.20 Convergent evolution.** The sugar glider is a marsupial mammal that evolved in isolation on the island continent of Australia. Although sugar gliders superficially resemble the eutherian flying squirrels of North America, the ability to glide through the air evolved independently in these two distantly related groups of mammals.

marsupials have eutherian look-alikes with similar adaptations. For instance, a forest-dwelling Australian marsupial called the sugar glider is superficially very similar to flying squirrels, gliding eutherians that live in North American forests **(Figure 22.20)**. But the sugar glider has many other characteristics that make it a marsupial, much more closely related to kangaroos and other Australian marsupials than to flying squirrels or other eutherians. Once again, our understanding of evolution can explain these observations. Although they evolved independently from different ancestors, these two mammals have adapted to similar environments in similar ways. In such examples in which species share features because of convergent evolution, the resemblance is said to be **analogous**, not homologous.

Biogeography

A fourth type of evidence for evolution comes from **biogeography**, the geographic distribution of species. The geographic distribution of organisms is influenced by many factors, including **continental drift**, the slow movement of Earth's continents over time. About 250 million years ago, these movements united all of Earth's landmasses into a single large continent, called **Pangaea** (see Figure 25.13). Roughly 200 million years ago, Pangaea began to break apart; by 20 million years ago, the continents we know today were within a few hundred kilometers of their present locations.

We can use our understanding of evolution and continental drift to predict where fossils of different groups of organisms might be found. For example, as you will read in Chapter 25, evolutionary biologists have constructed evolutionary trees for horses based on anatomical data. Based on these trees and on the ages of fossils of horse ancestors, researchers estimate that present-day horse species originated 5 million years ago in North America. At that time, North and South America were close to their present locations, but they were not yet connected to one another, making it difficult for horses to travel between them. Thus, we would predict that the oldest horse fossils should be found only on the continent on which horses originated—North America. This prediction and others like it for different groups of organisms have been upheld, providing more evidence for evolution.

We can also use our understanding of evolution to explain biogeographic data. For example, islands generally have many species of plants and animals that are **endemic**, which means they are found nowhere else in the world. Yet, as Darwin described in *The Origin of Species*, most island species are closely related to species from the nearest mainland or a neighboring island. He explained this observation by suggesting that islands are colonized by species from the nearest mainland. These colonists eventually give rise to new species as they adapt to their new environments. Such a process also explains why two islands with similar environments in different parts of the world are populated not by closely related species but rather by species that resemble those of the nearest mainland, where the environment is often quite different.

What Is Theoretical About Darwin's View of Life?

Some people dismiss Darwin's ideas as "just a theory." However, as we have seen, the pattern of evolution—the observation that life has evolved over time—has been documented directly and is supported by a great deal of evidence. In addition, Darwin's explanation of the process of evolution—that natural selection is the primary cause of the observed pattern of evolutionary change—makes sense of massive amounts of data. The effects of natural selection also can be observed and tested in nature.

What, then, is theoretical about evolution? Keep in mind that the scientific meaning of the term *theory* is very different from its meaning in everyday use. The colloquial use of the word *theory* comes close to what scientists mean by a hypothesis. In science, a theory is more comprehensive than a hypothesis. A theory, such as Darwin's theory of evolution by natural selection, accounts for many observations and explains and integrates a great variety of phenomena. Such a unifying theory does not become widely accepted unless its predictions stand up to thorough and continual testing by experiment and additional observation (see Chapter 1). As the next three chapters demonstrate, this has certainly been the case with the theory of evolution by natural selection.

The skepticism of scientists as they continue to test theories prevents these ideas from becoming dogma. For example, although Darwin thought that evolution was a very slow process, we now know that this isn't always true. New species can form in relatively short periods of time (a few thousand years or less; see Chapter 24). Furthermore, as we'll explore throughout this unit, evolutionary biologists now recognize that natural selection is not the only mechanism responsible for evolution. Indeed, the study of evolution today is livelier than ever as scientists find more ways to test the predictions of Darwin's theory.

Although Darwin's theory attributes the diversity of life to natural processes, the diverse products of evolution nevertheless remain elegant and inspiring. As Darwin wrote in the final sentence of *The Origin of Species*, "There is grandeur in this view of life . . . [in which] endless forms most beautiful and most wonderful have been, and are being, evolved."

CONCEPT CHECK 22.3

1. Explain how the following statement is inaccurate: "Anti-HIV drugs have created drug resistance in the virus."
2. How does evolution account for (a) the similar mammalian forelimbs with different functions shown in Figure 22.17 and (b) the similar lifestyle of the two distantly related mammals shown in Figure 22.20?
3. **WHAT IF?** The fossil record shows that dinosaurs originated 200–250 million years ago. Would you expect the geographic distribution of early dinosaur fossils to be broad (on many continents) or narrow (on one or a few continents only)? Explain.

For suggested answers, see Appendix A.

Chapter 22 Review

 MEDIA Go to the Study Area at **www.masteringbio.com** for BioFlix 3-D Animations, MP3 Tutors, Videos, Practice Tests, an eBook, and more.

SUMMARY OF KEY CONCEPTS

CONCEPT 22.1

The Darwinian revolution challenged traditional views of a young Earth inhabited by unchanging species (pp. 452–455)

▶ *Scala Naturae* and Classification of Species Darwin's proposal that life's diversity has arisen from ancestral species through natural selection was a radical departure from the prevailing views of Western culture.

▶ Ideas About Change over Time In contrast to the principle that events in the past occurred suddenly by mechanisms not operating today, geologists Hutton and Lyell perceived that changes in Earth's surface can result from slow, continuous actions still operating at the present time.

▶ Lamarck's Hypothesis of Evolution Lamarck hypothesized that species evolve, but the mechanisms he proposed are not supported by evidence.

CONCEPT 22.2

Descent with modification by natural selection explains the adaptations of organisms and the unity and diversity of life (pp. 455–460)

▶ Darwin's Research Darwin's experiences during the voyage of the *Beagle* gave rise to his idea that new species originate from ancestral forms through the accumulation of adaptations. He refined his theory for more than 20 years and finally published it in 1859 after learning that Wallace had come to the same idea.

▶ *The Origin of Species* Darwin's book proposed that evolution occurs by natural selection:

Observations

Individuals in a population vary in their heritable characteristics.	Organisms produce more offspring than the environment can support.

Inferences

Individuals that are well suited to their environment tend to leave more offspring than other individuals.

and

Over time, favorable traits accumulate in the population.

MEDIA

MP3 Tutor Natural Selection
Activity Darwin and the Galápagos Islands
Activity The Voyage of the *Beagle*: Darwin's Trip Around the World

CONCEPT 22.3

Evolution is supported by an overwhelming amount of scientific evidence (pp. 460–466)

▶ Direct Observations of Evolutionary Change Researchers have directly observed natural selection leading to adaptive evolution in many studies, including research on wild guppy populations and on pathogens such as HIV.

▶ The Fossil Record Fossils show that past organisms differed from living organisms, that many species have become extinct, and that species have evolved over long periods of time.

► **Homology** Organisms share characteristics because of common descent (homology) or because natural selection affects independently evolving species in similar environments in similar ways (convergent evolution).

► **Biogeography** The geographic distribution of organisms is consistent with evolutionary theory.

► **What Is Theoretical About Darwin's View of Life?** The theory of evolution by natural selection integrates diverse areas of study and stimulates many new questions.

MEDIA

Activity Reconstructing Forelimbs
Investigation How Do Environmental Changes Affect a Population?
Investigation What Are the Patterns of Antibiotic Resistance?

TESTING YOUR KNOWLEDGE

SELF-QUIZ

1. Which of the following is *not* an observation or inference on which natural selection is based?
   a. There is heritable variation among individuals.
   b. Poorly adapted individuals never produce offspring.
   c. Species produce more offspring than the environment can support.
   d. Individuals whose characteristics are best suited to the environment generally leave more offspring than those whose characteristics are less suited.
   e. Only a fraction of the offspring produced by an individual may survive.

2. The upper forelimbs of humans and bats have fairly similar skeletal structures, whereas the corresponding bones in whales have very different shapes and proportions. However, genetic data suggest that all three kinds of organisms diverged from a common ancestor at about the same time. Which of the following is the most likely explanation for these data?
   a. Humans and bats evolved by natural selection, and whales evolved by Lamarckian mechanisms.
   b. Forelimb evolution was adaptive in people and bats, but not in whales.
   c. Natural selection in an aquatic environment resulted in significant changes to whale forelimb anatomy.
   d. Genes mutate faster in whales than in humans or bats.
   e. Whales are not properly classified as mammals.

3. Which of the following observations helped Darwin shape his concept of descent with modification?
   a. Species diversity declines farther from the equator.
   b. Fewer species live on islands than on the nearest continents.
   c. Birds can be found on islands located farther from the mainland than the birds' maximum nonstop flight distance.
   d. South American temperate plants are more similar to the tropical plants of South America than to the temperate plants of Europe.
   e. Earthquakes reshape life by causing mass extinctions.

4. Within a few weeks of treatment with the drug 3TC, a patient's HIV population consists entirely of 3TC-resistant viruses. How can this result best be explained?
   a. HIV can change its surface proteins and resist vaccines.
   b. The patient must have become reinfected with 3TC-resistant viruses.
   c. HIV began making drug-resistant versions of reverse transcriptase in response to the drug.
   d. A few drug-resistant viruses were present at the start of treatment, and natural selection increased their frequency.
   e. The drug caused the HIV RNA to change.

5. DNA sequences in many human genes are very similar to the sequences of corresponding genes in chimpanzees. The most likely explanation for this result is that
   a. humans and chimpanzees share a relatively recent common ancestor.
   b. humans evolved from chimpanzees.
   c. chimpanzees evolved from humans.
   d. convergent evolution led to the DNA similarities.
   e. humans and chimpanzees are not closely related.

6. Which of the following pairs of structures is *least* likely to represent homology?
   a. the wings of a bat and the arms of a human
   b. the hemoglobin of a baboon and that of a gorilla
   c. the mitochondria of a plant and those of an animal
   d. the wings of a bird and those of an insect
   e. the brain of a cat and that of a dog

For Self-Quiz answers, see Appendix A.

MEDIA Visit the Study Area at **www.masteringbio.com** for a Practice Test.

EVOLUTION CONNECTION

7. Explain why anatomical and molecular homologies generally fit a similar nested pattern.

SCIENTIFIC INQUIRY

8. **DRAW IT** Mosquitoes resistant to the pesticide DDT first appeared in India in 1959, but now are found throughout the world. (a) Graph the data in the table below. (b) Examining the graph, hypothesize why the percentage of mosquitoes resistant to DDT rose rapidly. (c) Suggest an explanation for the global spread of DDT resistance.

Month	Percentage of Mosquitoes Resistant* to DDT
0	4%
8	45%
12	77%

*Mosquitoes were considered resistant if they were not killed within 1 hour of receiving a dose of 4% DDT.

Source: C. F. Curtis et al., Selection for and against insecticide resistance and possible methods of inhibiting the evolution of resistance in mosquitoes, *Ecological Entomology* 3:273–287 (1978).

23
The Evolution of Populations

OVERVIEW

The Smallest Unit of Evolution

One common misconception about evolution is that individual organisms evolve. It is true that natural selection *acts* on individuals: Each organism's combination of traits affects its survival and reproductive success compared to other individuals. But the evolutionary impact of natural selection is only apparent in the changes in a *population* of organisms over time.

Consider the medium ground finch (*Geospiza fortis*), a seed-eating bird that inhabits the Galápagos Islands **(Figure 23.1)**. In 1977, the *G. fortis* population on the island of Daphne Major was decimated by a long period of drought: Of some 1,200 birds, only 180 survived. Researchers Peter and Rosemary Grant observed that the surviving finches tended to have larger, deeper beaks than others in the population. The Grants also observed that during the drought, small, soft seeds were in short supply. The finches mostly fed on large, hard seeds that were more plentiful. The birds with larger, deeper beaks were able to crack these larger seeds, increasing their rate of survival compared to finches with smaller beaks. As a result, the average beak size in the next generation of *G. fortis* was greater than it had been in the pre-drought population. The finch population had evolved by natural selection. However, the *individual*

finches did not evolve. Each bird had a beak of a particular size, which did not grow larger during the drought. Rather, the proportion of large beaks in the population increased over generations: The population evolved, not its individual members.

Focusing on evolutionary change in populations, we can define evolution on its smallest scale, called **microevolution**, as change in allele frequencies in a population over generations. As we will see in this chapter, natural selection is not the only cause of microevolution. In fact, there are three main mechanisms that can cause allele frequency change: natural selection, genetic drift (chance events that alter allele frequencies), and gene flow (the transfer of alleles between populations). Each of these mechanisms has distinctive effects on the genetic composition of populations. However, only natural selection consistently improves the match between organisms and their environment, thus bringing about the type of change we refer to as adaptive evolution. Before we examine natural selection and adaptation more closely, let's revisit how the variations that are the raw material for evolutionary change arise.

CONCEPT 23.1
Mutation and sexual reproduction produce the genetic variation that makes evolution possible

In *The Origin of Species*, Darwin provided abundant evidence that life on Earth has evolved over time, and he proposed natural selection as the primary mechanism for that change. Darwin also emphasized the importance of heritable differences among individuals. He knew that natural selection could not cause evolutionary change unless individuals differed in their inherited characteristics. But Darwin could not explain precisely how organisms pass heritable traits to their offspring.

Just a few years after Darwin published *The Origin of Species*, Gregor Mendel wrote a groundbreaking paper on inheritance in pea plants (see Chapter 14). In that paper, Mendel proposed a particulate model of inheritance, which stated that organisms transmit discrete heritable units (now called genes) to their offspring. Although Darwin never learned about genes, Mendel's paper set the stage for understanding the genetic differences on which evolution is based. Here we'll examine such genetic differences along with two processes that produce them, mutation and sexual reproduction.

Genetic Variation

You probably have no trouble recognizing your friends in a crowd. Each person has a unique genotype, reflected in individual phenotypic variations such as facial features, height, and voice. Indeed, individual variation occurs in all species. In addition to the differences that we can see or hear, species have extensive genetic variation that can only be observed at the molecular level. For example, you cannot identify a person's blood group (A, B, AB, or O) from his or her appearance, but this and many other such inherited characters vary among individuals.

As you read in earlier chapters, however, some phenotypic variation is not heritable (**Figure 23.2** shows a striking example in a caterpillar of the southwestern United States). Phenotype is the product of an inherited genotype and many environmental influences. In a human example, bodybuilders alter their phenotypes dramatically but do not pass their huge muscles on to the next generation. Only the genetic part of variation can have evolutionary consequences.

Variation Within a Population

Characters that vary within a population may be discrete or quantitative. *Discrete characters*, such as the purple or white flower colors of Mendel's pea plants (see Figure 14.3), can be classified on an either-or basis (each plant has flowers that are either purple or white). Many discrete characters are determined by a single gene locus with different alleles that produce distinct phenotypes. However, most heritable variation involves *quantitative characters*, which vary along a continuum within a population. Heritable quantitative variation usually results from the influence of two or more genes on a single phenotypic character.

Whether considering discrete or quantitative characters, biologists can measure genetic variation in a population at both the whole-gene level (gene variability) and the molecular level of DNA (nucleotide variability). Gene variability can be quantified as the **average heterozygosity**, the average percent of loci that are heterozygous. (Recall that a heterozygous individual has two different alleles for a given locus, whereas a homozygous individual has two identical alleles for that locus.) As an example, consider the fruit fly *Drosophila melanogaster*, which has about 13,700 genes in its genome. On average, a fruit fly is heterozygous for about 1,920 of its loci (14%) and homozygous for all the rest. We can therefore say that a *D. melanogaster* population has an average heterozygosity of 14%.

Average heterozygosity is often estimated by surveying the protein products of genes using gel electrophoresis (see Figure 20.9). While useful, this approach cannot detect silent mutations that alter the DNA sequence of a gene but not the amino acid sequence of the protein (see Figure 17.23). To include silent mutations in their estimates of average heterozygosity, researchers must use other approaches, such as PCR-based methods and restriction fragment analyses (see Figures 20.8 and 20.10).

Nucleotide variability is measured by comparing the DNA sequences of two individuals in a population and then

▲ **Figure 23.2 Nonheritable variation.** These caterpillars of the moth *Nemoria arizonaria* owe their different appearances to chemicals in their diets, not to their genotypes. Caterpillars raised on a diet of oak flowers resembled the flowers **(a)**, whereas their siblings raised on oak leaves resembled oak twigs **(b)**.

averaging the data from many such comparisons. The genome of *D. melanogaster* has about 180 million nucleotides, and the sequences of any two fruit flies differ on average by approximately 1.8 million (1%) of their nucleotides. Thus, the nucleotide variability of *D. melanogaster* populations is about 1%.

As in this fruit fly example, gene variability (that is, average heterozygosity) tends to be greater than nucleotide variability. Why is this true? Remember that a gene can consist of thousands of nucleotides. A difference at only one of these nucleotides can be sufficient to make two alleles of that gene different and thereby increase gene variability.

Variation Between Populations

In addition to variation observed within a population, species also exhibit **geographic variation**, differences in the genetic composition of separate populations. **Figure 23.3** illustrates geographic variation in populations of house mice (*Mus musculus*) separated by mountains on the Atlantic island of Madeira. Inadvertently introduced by Portuguese settlers in the 15th century, several populations of mice have evolved in isolation from one another. Researchers have observed differences in the karyotypes (chromosome sets) of these isolated populations. In some of the populations, a

▲ **Figure 23.3 Geographic variation in isolated mouse populations on Madeira.** The number pairs represent fused chromosomes. For example, "2.4" indicates fusion of chromosome 2 and chromosome 4. Mice in the areas indicated by the yellow dots have the set of fused chromosomes in the yellow box; mice in the red-dot locales have the set of fusions in the red box.

▲ **Figure 23.4 A cline determined by temperature.** In mummichog fish, the frequency of the *Ldh-B^b* allele for the enzyme lactate dehydrogenase-B (which functions in metabolism) decreases in fish sampled from Maine to Georgia. The *Ldh-B^b* allele codes for a form of the enzyme that is a better catalyst in cold water than are other versions of the enzyme. Individuals with the *Ldh-B^b* allele can swim faster in cold water than can individuals with other alleles.

number of the original chromosomes have become fused. However, the patterns of fused chromosomes differ from one population to another. Because these chromosome-level changes leave genes intact, their phenotypic effects on the mice seem to be neutral. Thus, the variation between these populations appears to have resulted from chance events (drift) rather than natural selection.

Other examples of geographic variation occur as a **cline**, a graded change in a character along a geographic axis. Some clines are produced by a gradation in an environmental variable, as illustrated by the impact of temperature on the frequency of a cold-adaptive allele in mummichog fish (*Fundulus heteroclitus*). Clines such as the one depicted in **Figure 23.4** probably result from natural selection—otherwise there would be no reason to expect a close association between the environmental variable and the frequency of the allele. But selection can only operate if multiple alleles exist for a given locus. Such variation in alleles is the product of mutation, as we will discuss next.

Mutation

The ultimate source of new alleles is **mutation**, a change in the nucleotide sequence of an organism's DNA. A mutation is like a shot in the dark—we cannot predict accurately which segments of DNA will be altered or in what way. In multicellular organisms, only mutations in cell lines that produce gametes can be passed to offspring. In plants and fungi, this is not as limiting as it may sound, since many different cell lines can produce gametes (see Figures 29.13, 30.6, and 31.17). But in animals, most mutations occur in somatic cells and are lost when the individual dies.

Point Mutations

A change of as little as one base in a gene—a "point mutation"—can have a significant impact on phenotype, as in sickle-cell disease (see Figure 17.22). Organisms reflect thousands of generations of past selection, and hence their phenotypes generally provide a close match to their environment. As a result, it's unlikely that a new mutation that alters a phenotype will improve it. In fact, most such mutations are at least slightly harmful. But much of the DNA in eukaryotic genomes does not code for protein products, and point mutations in these noncoding regions are often harmless. Also, because of the redundancy in the genetic code, even a point mutation in a gene that encodes a protein will have no effect on the protein's function if the amino acid composition is not changed. Moreover, even if there is a change in an amino acid, this may not affect the protein's shape and function. However—as we will see—on rare occasions, a mutant allele may actually make its bearer better suited to the environment, enhancing reproductive success.

Mutations That Alter Gene Number or Sequence

Chromosomal changes that delete, disrupt, or rearrange many loci at once are almost certain to be harmful. However, when such large-scale mutations leave genes intact, their effects on organisms may be neutral (see Figure 23.3). In rare cases, chromosomal rearrangements may even be beneficial. For example, the translocation of part of one chromosome to a different chromosome could link DNA segments in a way that results in a positive effect.

An important source of variation begins when genes are duplicated due to errors in meiosis (such as unequal crossing over), slippage during DNA replication, or the activities of transposable elements (see Chapters 15 and 21). Duplications of large chromosome segments, like other chromosomal aberrations, are often harmful, but the duplication of smaller pieces of DNA may not be. Gene duplications that do not have severe effects can persist over generations, allowing mutations to accumulate. The result is an expanded genome with new loci that may take on new functions.

Such beneficial increases in gene number appear to have played a major role in evolution. For example, the remote ancestors of mammals carried a single gene for detecting odors that has been duplicated many times. As a result, humans today have about 1,000 olfactory receptor genes, and mice have 1,300. It is likely that such dramatic increases in the number of olfactory genes helped early mammals by enabling them to detect faint odors and to distinguish among many different smells. More recently, about 60% of human olfactory receptor genes have been inactivated by mutations, whereas mice have lost only 20% of theirs. This dramatic difference demonstrates that a versatile sense of smell is more important to mice than it is to us!

Mutation Rates

Mutation rates tend to be low in plants and animals, averaging about one mutation in every 100,000 genes per generation, and they are often even lower in prokaryotes. But prokaryotes typically have short generation spans, so mutations can quickly generate genetic variation in populations of these organisms. The same is true of viruses. For instance, HIV has a generation span of about two days. It also has an RNA genome, which has a much higher mutation rate than a typical DNA genome because of the lack of RNA repair mechanisms in host cells (see Chapter 19). For this reason, it is unlikely that a single-drug treatment would ever be effective against HIV; mutant forms of the virus that are resistant to a particular drug would no doubt proliferate in relatively short order. The most effective AIDS treatments to date have been drug "cocktails" that combine several medications. It is less likely that multiple mutations conferring resistance to *all* the drugs will occur in a short time period.

Sexual Reproduction

In organisms that reproduce sexually, most of the genetic variation in a population results from the unique combination of alleles that each individual receives. Of course, at the nucleotide level, all the differences among these alleles have originated from past mutations. But it is the mechanism of sexual reproduction that shuffles existing alleles and deals them at random to determine individual genotypes.

As described in Chapter 13, three mechanisms contribute to this shuffling: crossing over, independent assortment of chromosomes, and fertilization. During meiosis, homologous chromosomes, one inherited from each parent, trade some of their alleles by crossing over. These homologous chromosomes and the alleles they carry are then distributed at random into gametes. Then, because myriad possible mating combinations exist in a population, fertilization brings together gametes of individuals that are likely to have different genetic backgrounds. The combined effects of these three mechanisms ensure that sexual reproduction rearranges existing alleles into fresh combinations each generation, providing much of the genetic variation that makes evolution possible.

CONCEPT CHECK 23.1

1. (a) Explain why genetic variation within a population is a prerequisite for evolution. (b) What factors can produce genetic variation among populations?
2. Of all the mutations that occur in a population, why do only a small fraction become widespread among the population's members?
3. **WHAT IF?** If a population stopped reproducing sexually (but still reproduced asexually), how would its genetic variation be affected over time? Explain.

For suggested answers, see Appendix A.

The Hardy-Weinberg equation can be used to test whether a population is evolving

As we've seen, the individuals in a population must differ genetically for evolution to occur. But the presence of genetic variation does not guarantee that a population will evolve. For that to happen, one of the factors that cause evolution must be at work. In this section, we'll explore how to test whether evolution is occurring in a population. The first step in this process is to clarify what we mean by a population.

Gene Pools and Allele Frequencies

A **population** is a group of individuals of the same species that live in the same area and interbreed, producing fertile offspring. Different populations of a single species may be isolated geographically from one another, thus exchanging genetic material only rarely. Such isolation is common for species that live on widely separated islands or in different lakes. But not all populations are isolated, nor must populations have sharp boundaries (**Figure 23.5**). Still, members of a population typically breed with one another and thus on average are more closely related to each other than to members of other populations.

▲ **Figure 23.5 One species, two populations.** These two caribou populations in the Yukon are not totally isolated; they sometimes share the same area. Nonetheless, members of either population are more likely to breed with members of their own population than with members of the other population.

We can characterize a population's genetic makeup by describing its **gene pool**, which consists of all the alleles for all the loci in all individuals of the population. If only one allele exists for a particular locus in a population, that allele is said to be *fixed* in the gene pool, and all individuals are homozygous for that allele. But if there are two or more alleles for a particular locus in a population, individuals may be either homozygous or heterozygous.

Each allele has a frequency (proportion) in the population. For example, imagine a population of 500 wildflower plants with two alleles, C^R and C^W, for a certain locus that codes for flower pigment. These alleles show incomplete dominance (see Chapter 14); thus, each genotype has a distinct phenotype. Plants homozygous for the C^R allele ($C^R C^R$) produce red pigment and have red flowers; plants homozygous for the C^W allele ($C^W C^W$) produce no red pigment and have white flowers; and heterozygotes ($C^R C^W$) produce some red pigment and have pink flowers. In our population, suppose there are 320 plants with red flowers, 160 with pink flowers, and 20 with white flowers. Because these are diploid organisms, there are a total of 1,000 copies of genes for flower color in the population of 500 individuals. The C^R allele accounts for 800 of these genes ($320 \times 2 = 640$ for $C^R C^R$ plants, plus $160 \times 1 = 160$ for $C^R C^W$ plants).

When studying a locus with two alleles, the convention is to use p to represent the frequency of one allele and q to represent the frequency of the other allele. Thus, p, the frequency of the C^R allele in the gene pool of this population, is $800/1,000 = 0.8 = 80\%$. And because there are only two alleles for this gene, the frequency of the C^W allele, represented by q, must be $200/1,000 = 0.2 = 20\%$. For loci that have more than two alleles, the sum of all allele frequencies must still equal 1 (100%).

Next we'll see how allele and genotype frequencies can be used to test whether evolution is occurring in a population.

The Hardy-Weinberg Principle

One way to assess whether natural selection or other factors are causing evolution at a particular locus is to determine what the genetic makeup of a population would be if it were *not* evolving at that locus. We can then compare that scenario with data from a real population. If there are no differences, we can conclude that the real population is not evolving. If there are differences, we can conclude that the real population is evolving—and then we can try to figure out why.

Hardy-Weinberg Equilibrium

The gene pool of a population that is not evolving can be described by the **Hardy-Weinberg principle**, named for the British mathematician and German physician, respectively, who independently derived it in 1908. This principle states that the frequencies of alleles and genotypes in a population will remain constant from generation to generation, provided that only Mendelian segregation and recombination of alleles are at work. Such a gene pool is said to be in **Hardy-Weinberg equilibrium**.

To understand and use the Hardy-Weinberg principle, it is helpful to think about alleles and genetic crosses in a new way. Previously, we used Punnett squares to determine the genotypes of offspring in a genetic cross (see Figure 14.5). We can take a similar approach here, but instead of considering the possible allele combinations from one genetic cross, our focus now is on the combination of alleles in *all* of the genetic crosses in a population.

Imagine that alleles for a given locus from all of the individuals in a population could be mixed together in a large bin **(Figure 23.6)**. We can think of this bin as holding the population's gene pool for that locus. "Reproduction" occurs by selecting alleles at random from the bin; somewhat similar events occur in nature when fish release sperm and eggs into the water or when pollen (containing plant sperm) is blown about by the wind. By viewing reproduction as a random selection of alleles from the bin (the gene pool), we are in effect assuming that mating occurs at random—that is, that all male-female matings are equally likely.

Let's apply our bin analogy to the hypothetical wildflower population discussed earlier. In that population, the frequency of the allele for red flowers (C^R) is $p = 0.8$, and the frequency of the allele for white flowers (C^W) is $q = 0.2$. Thus, a bin holding all 1,000 flower-color alleles of the 500 wildflowers contains 800 C^R alleles and 200 C^W alleles. Assuming that gametes are formed by selecting alleles at random from the bin, the probability that an egg or sperm contains a C^R or C^W allele is equal to the frequency of these alleles in the bin. Thus, as shown in Figure 23.6, each egg has an 80% chance of containing a C^R allele and a 20% chance of containing a C^W allele; the same is true for each sperm.

Using the rule of multiplication (see Chapter 14), we can now calculate the frequencies of the three possible genotypes, assuming random unions of sperm and eggs. The probability that two C^R alleles will come together is $p \times p = p^2 = 0.8 \times 0.8 = 0.64$. Thus, about 64% of the plants in the next generation will have the genotype $C^R C^R$. The frequency of $C^W C^W$ individuals is expected to be about $q \times q = q^2 = 0.2 \times 0.2 = 0.04$, or 4%. $C^R C^W$ heterozygotes can arise in two different ways. If the sperm provides the C^R allele and the egg provides the C^W allele, the resulting heterozygotes will be $p \times q = 0.8 \times 0.2 = 16\%$ of the total. If the sperm provides the C^W allele and the egg the C^R allele, the heterozygous offspring will make up $q \times p = 0.2 \times 0.8 = 16\%$. The frequency of heterozygotes is thus the sum of these possibilities: $pq + qp = 0.16 + 0.16 = 0.32$, or 32%.

As shown in **Figure 23.7** on the next page, the genotype frequencies in the next generation must add up to 1 (100%). Thus, the equation for Hardy-Weinberg equilibrium states that at a locus with two alleles, the three genotypes will appear in the following proportions:

$$p^2 \quad + \quad 2pq \quad + \quad q^2 = 1$$

Expected frequency of genotype $C^R C^R$ — Expected frequency of genotype $C^R C^W$ — Expected frequency of genotype $C^W C^W$

Note that for a locus with two alleles, only three genotypes are possible (in this case, $C^R C^R$, $C^R C^W$, and $C^W C^W$). As a result, the sum of the frequencies of the three genotypes must equal 1 (100%) in *any* population—regardless of whether the population is in Hardy-Weinberg equilibrium. A population is in Hardy-Weinberg equilibrium only if the genotype frequencies are such that the actual frequency of one homozygote is p^2, the actual frequency of the other homozygote is q^2, and the actual frequency of heterozygotes is $2pq$. Finally, as suggested by Figure 23.7, if a population such as our wildflowers is in Hardy-Weinberg equilibrium and its members continue to mate randomly generation after generation, allele and genotype frequencies will remain constant. The system operates somewhat like a deck of cards: No matter how many times the deck is reshuffled to deal out new hands, the deck

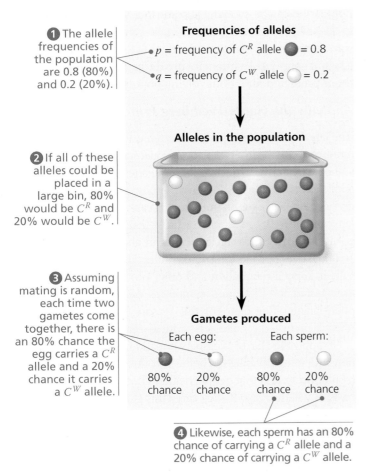

1 The allele frequencies of the population are 0.8 (80%) and 0.2 (20%).

Frequencies of alleles

p = frequency of C^R allele ● = 0.8
q = frequency of C^W allele ○ = 0.2

Alleles in the population

2 If all of these alleles could be placed in a large bin, 80% would be C^R and 20% would be C^W.

3 Assuming mating is random, each time two gametes come together, there is an 80% chance the egg carries a C^R allele and a 20% chance it carries a C^W allele.

Gametes produced

Each egg:
80% chance
20% chance

Each sperm:
80% chance
20% chance

4 Likewise, each sperm has an 80% chance of carrying a C^R allele and a 20% chance of carrying a C^W allele.

▲ **Figure 23.6 Selecting alleles at random from a gene pool.**

Gametes for each generation are drawn at random from the gene pool of the previous generation, as in Figure 23.6:

80% C^R ($p = 0.8$)   20% C^W ($q = 0.2$)

Sperm

	C^R (80%)	C^W (20%)
C^R (80%)	64% (p^2) $C^R C^R$	16% (pq) $C^R C^W$
C^W (20%)	16% (qp) $C^R C^W$	4% (q^2) $C^W C^W$

Eggs

If the gametes come together at random, the genotype frequencies of this generation are in Hardy-Weinberg equilibrium:

64% $C^R C^R$, 32% $C^R C^W$, and 4% $C^W C^W$

Gametes of this generation:

64% C^R (from $C^R C^R$ plants) + 16% C^R (from $C^R C^W$ plants) = 80% C^R = 0.8 = p

4% C^W (from $C^W C^W$ plants) + 16% C^W (from $C^R C^W$ plants) = 20% C^W = 0.2 = q

With random mating, these gametes will result in the same mix of genotypes in the next generation:

64% $C^R C^R$, 32% $C^R C^W$, and 4% $C^W C^W$ plants

▲ **Figure 23.7 The Hardy-Weinberg principle.** In our wildflower population, the gene pool remains constant from one generation to the next. Mendelian processes alone do not alter frequencies of alleles or genotypes.

? *If the frequency of the C^R allele is 60%, predict the frequencies of the $C^R C^R$, $C^R C^W$, and $C^W C^W$ genotypes.*

itself remains the same. Aces do not grow more numerous than jacks. And the repeated shuffling of a population's gene pool over the generations cannot, in itself, change the frequency of one allele relative to another.

Conditions for Hardy-Weinberg Equilibrium

The Hardy-Weinberg principle describes a hypothetical population that is not evolving. But in real populations, the allele and genotype frequencies often *do* change over time. Such

changes can occur when at least one of the following five conditions of Hardy-Weinberg equilibrium is not met:

1. **No mutations.** By altering alleles or (in large-scale changes) deleting or duplicating entire genes, mutations modify the gene pool.
2. **Random mating.** If individuals mate preferentially within a subset of the population, such as their close relatives (inbreeding), random mixing of gametes does not occur, and genotype frequencies change.
3. **No natural selection.** Differences in the survival and reproductive success of individuals carrying different genotypes can alter allele frequencies.
4. **Extremely large population size.** The smaller the population, the more likely it is that allele frequencies will fluctuate by chance from one generation to the next (genetic drift).
5. **No gene flow.** By moving alleles into or out of populations, gene flow can alter allele frequencies.

Departure from any of these conditions usually results in evolutionary change, which, as we've already described, is common in natural populations. But it is also common for natural populations to be in Hardy-Weinberg equilibrium for specific genes. This apparent contradiction occurs because a population can be evolving at some loci, yet simultaneously be in Hardy-Weinberg equilibrium at other loci. In addition, some populations evolve so slowly that the changes in their allele and genotype frequencies are difficult to distinguish from those predicted for a nonevolving population.

Applying the Hardy-Weinberg Principle

The Hardy-Weinberg equation is often used to test whether evolution is occurring in a population (you'll encounter an example in Concept Check 23.2, question 3). The equation also has medical applications, such as estimating the percentage of a population carrying the allele for an inherited disease. For example, phenylketonuria (PKU), a metabolic disorder that results from homozygosity for a recessive allele, occurs in about one out of every 10,000 babies born in the United States. Left untreated, PKU results in mental retardation and other problems. (Newborns are now tested for PKU, and symptoms can be lessened with a phenylalanine-free diet. For this reason, products that contain phenylalanine—diet colas, for example—carry warning labels.)

To apply the Hardy-Weinberg equation, we must assume that new PKU mutations are not being introduced into the population (condition 1), and that people neither choose their mates on the basis of whether or not they carry this gene nor generally mate with close relatives (condition 2). We must also neglect any effects of differential survival and reproductive success among PKU genotypes (condition 3) and assume that there are no effects of genetic drift (condition 4) or of gene flow from other populations into the United States (condition 5). These assumptions are reasonable: The mutation rate for the PKU gene is low, inbreeding is not common in the United States, selection occurs only against the rare homozygotes (and then only if dietary restrictions are not followed), the United States' population is very large, and populations outside the country have PKU allele frequencies similar to those seen in the United States. If all these assumptions hold, then the frequency of individuals in the population born with PKU will correspond to q^2 in the Hardy-Weinberg equation (q^2 = frequency of homozygotes). Because the allele is recessive, we must estimate the number of heterozygotes rather than counting them directly as we did with the pink flowers. Since we know there is one PKU occurrence per 10,000 births (q^2 = 0.0001), the frequency of the recessive allele for PKU is

$$q = \sqrt{0.0001} = 0.01$$

and the frequency of the dominant allele is

$$p = 1 - q = 1 - 0.01 = 0.99$$

The frequency of carriers, heterozygous people who do not have PKU but may pass the PKU allele to offspring, is

$$2pq = 2 \times 0.99 \times 0.01 = 0.0198$$
(approximately 2% of the U.S. population)

Remember, the assumption of Hardy-Weinberg equilibrium yields an approximation; the real number of carriers may differ. Still, our calculations suggest that harmful recessive alleles at this and other loci can be concealed in a population because they are carried by healthy heterozygotes.

CONCEPT CHECK 23.2

1. Suppose a population of organisms with 500 loci is fixed at half of these loci and has two alleles at each of the other loci. How many different alleles are found in its entire gene pool? Explain.

2. If p is the frequency of allele A, which parts of the Hardy-Weinberg equation correspond to the frequency of individuals that have at least one A allele?

3. **WHAT IF?** For a locus with two alleles (A and a) in a population at risk from an infectious neurodegenerative disease, 16 people had genotype AA, 92 had genotype Aa, and 12 had genotype aa. Use the Hardy-Weinberg equation to determine whether this population appears to be evolving.

For suggested answers, see Appendix A.

CONCEPT 23.3
Natural selection, genetic drift, and gene flow can alter allele frequencies in a population

Note again the five conditions required for a population to be in Hardy-Weinberg equilibrium. A deviation from any of these conditions is a potential cause of evolution. New mutations (violation of condition 1) can alter allele frequencies, but because mutations are rare, the change from one generation to the next is likely to be very small. Nevertheless, as we'll see, mutation ultimately can have a large effect on allele frequencies when it produces new alleles that strongly influence fitness in a positive or negative way. Nonrandom mating (violation of condition 2) can affect the frequencies of homozygous and heterozygous genotypes but by itself usually has no effect on allele frequencies in the gene pool. The three mechanisms that alter allele frequencies directly and cause most evolutionary change are natural selection, genetic drift, and gene flow (violations of conditions 3–5).

Natural Selection

As you read in Chapter 22, Darwin's concept of natural selection is based on differential success in survival and reproduction: Individuals in a population exhibit variations in their heritable traits, and those with traits that are better suited to their environment tend to produce more offspring than those with traits that are less well suited.

We now know that selection results in alleles being passed to the next generation in proportions different from their proportions in the present generation. For example, the fruit fly *Drosophila melanogaster* has an allele that confers resistance to several insecticides, including DDT. This allele has a frequency of 0% in laboratory strains of *D. melanogaster* established from flies collected in the wild in the early 1930s, prior to DDT usage. However, in strains established from flies collected after 1960 (following 20 or more years of DDT usage), the allele frequency is 37%. We can infer that this allele either arose by mutation between 1930 and 1960 or that this allele was present in the population in 1930, but was very rare. In any case, the observed increase in the frequency of this allele most likely occurred because DDT is a powerful poison that is a strong selective force in exposed fly populations.

As the *D. melanogaster* example shows, an allele that confers insecticide resistance will increase in frequency in a population exposed to that insecticide. Such changes are not coincidental. Instead, by consistently favoring some alleles over others, natural selection can cause *adaptive evolution* (evolution that results in a better match between organisms and their environment). We'll explore this process in more detail a little later in this chapter.

Genetic Drift

If you flip a coin 1,000 times, a result of 700 heads and 300 tails might make you suspicious about that coin. But if you flip a coin 10 times, an outcome of 7 heads and 3 tails would not be surprising. The smaller the number of coin flips, the more likely it is that chance alone will cause a deviation from the predicted result—in this case, the prediction is an equal number of heads and tails. Chance events can also cause allele frequencies

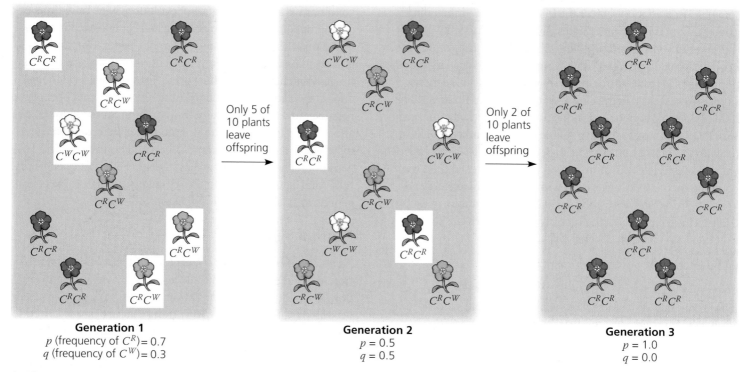

Generation 1
p (frequency of C^R) = 0.7
q (frequency of C^W) = 0.3

Generation 2
p = 0.5
q = 0.5

Generation 3
p = 1.0
q = 0.0

▲ **Figure 23.8 Genetic drift.** This small wildflower population has a stable size of ten plants. Suppose that by chance only five plants (those in white boxes) of generation 1 produce fertile offspring. This could occur, for example, if only those plants happened to grow in a location that provided enough nutrients to support the production of offspring. Again by chance, only two plants of generation 2 leave fertile offspring. As a result, by chance alone, the frequency of the C^W allele first increases in generation 2, then falls to zero in generation 3.

to fluctuate unpredictably from one generation to the next, especially in small populations—a process called **genetic drift**.

Figure 23.8 models how genetic drift might affect a small population of our wildflowers. In this example, an allele is lost from the gene pool, but it is purely a matter of chance that the C^W allele is lost, not the C^R allele. Such unpredictable changes in allele frequencies can be caused by chance events associated with survival and reproduction. Perhaps a large animal such as a moose stepped on the three $C^W C^W$ individuals in generation 2, killing them and increasing the chance that only the C^R allele would be passed to the next generation. Allele frequencies can also be affected by chance events that occur during fertilization. For example, suppose two individuals of genotype $C^R C^W$ had a small number of offspring. By chance alone, every egg and sperm pair that generated offspring could happen to have carried the C^R allele, not the C^W allele.

Certain circumstances can result in genetic drift having a significant impact on a population. Two examples are the founder effect and the bottleneck effect.

The Founder Effect

When a few individuals become isolated from a larger population, this smaller group may establish a new population whose gene pool differs from the source population; this is called the **founder effect**. The founder effect might occur, for example, when a few members of a population are blown by a

storm to a new island. Genetic drift—in which chance events alter allele frequencies—occurs in such a case because the storm indiscriminately transports some individuals (and their alleles), but not others, from the source population.

The founder effect probably accounts for the relatively high frequency of certain inherited disorders among isolated human populations. For example, in 1814, 15 British colonists founded a settlement on Tristan da Cunha, a group of small islands in the Atlantic Ocean midway between Africa and South America. Apparently, one of the colonists carried a recessive allele for retinitis pigmentosa, a progressive form of blindness that afflicts homozygous individuals. Of the founding colonists' 240 descendants on the island in the late 1960s, 4 had retinitis pigmentosa. The frequency of the allele that causes this disease is ten times higher on Tristan da Cunha than in the populations from which the founders came.

The Bottleneck Effect

A sudden change in the environment, such as a fire or flood, may drastically reduce the size of a population. A severe drop in population size can cause the **bottleneck effect**, so named because the population has passed through a restrictive "bottleneck" in size **(Figure 23.9)**. By chance alone, certain alleles may be overrepresented among the survivors, others may be underrepresented, and some may be absent altogether. Ongoing genetic drift is likely to have substantial effects on the gene pool

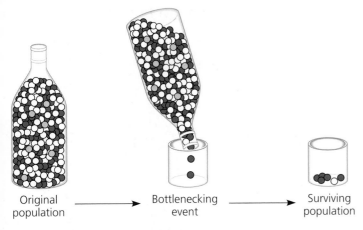

▲ **Figure 23.9 The bottleneck effect.** Shaking just a few marbles through the narrow neck of a bottle is analogous to a drastic reduction in the size of a population. By chance, blue marbles are overrepresented in the surviving population and gold marbles are absent.

Original population → Bottlenecking event → Surviving population

until the population becomes large enough that chance events have less effect. But even if a population that has passed through a bottleneck ultimately recovers in size, it may have low levels of genetic variation for a long period of time—a legacy of the genetic drift that occurred when the population was small.

One reason it is important to understand the bottleneck effect is that human actions sometimes create severe bottlenecks for other species. The following example illustrates the impact of genetic drift on an endangered population.

Case Study: *Impact of Genetic Drift on the Greater Prairie Chicken*

Millions of greater prairie chickens (*Tympanuchus cupido*) once lived on the prairies of Illinois. As these prairies were converted to farmland and other uses during the 19th and 20th centuries, the number of greater prairie chickens plummeted **(Figure 23.10a)**. By 1993, only two Illinois populations remained, which together harbored fewer than 50 birds. The few surviving birds had low levels of genetic variation, and less than 50% of their eggs hatched, compared to much higher hatching rates of the larger populations in Kansas, Nebraska, and Minnesota **(Figure 23.10b)**.

These data suggest that genetic drift during the bottleneck may have led to a loss of genetic variation and an increase in the frequency of harmful alleles. To investigate this hypothesis, Juan Bouzat, of Bowling Green State University, Ohio, and his colleagues extracted DNA from 15 museum specimens of Illinois greater prairie chickens. Of the 15 birds, 10 had been collected in the 1930s, when there were 25,000 greater prairie chickens in Illinois, and 5 had been collected in the 1960s, when there were 1,000 greater prairie chickens in Illinois. By studying the DNA of these specimens, the researchers were able to obtain a minimum, baseline estimate of how much genetic variation was present in the Illinois population *before* the population shrank to extremely low numbers.

Greater prairie chicken

Pre-bottleneck (Illinois, 1820)   Post-bottleneck (Illinois, 1993)

☐ Range of greater prairie chicken

Grasslands in which the prairie chickens live once covered most of the state.

In 1993, with less than 1% of the grasslands remaining, the prairie chickens were found in just two locations.

(a) The Illinois population of greater prairie chickens dropped from millions of birds in the 1800s to fewer than 50 birds in 1993.

Location	Population size	Number of alleles per locus	Percentage of eggs hatched
Illinois			
1930–1960s	1,000–25,000	5.2	93
1993	<50	3.7	<50
Kansas, 1998 (no bottleneck)	750,000	5.8	99
Nebraska, 1998 (no bottleneck)	75,000–200,000	5.8	96
Minnesota, 1998 (no bottleneck)	4,000	5.3	85

(b) As a consequence of the drastic reduction in the size of the Illinois population, genetic drift resulted in a drop in the number of alleles per locus (averaged across six loci studied) and a decrease in the percentage of eggs that hatched.

▲ **Figure 23.10 Bottleneck effect and reduction of genetic variation.**

The researchers surveyed six loci and found that the 1993 Illinois greater prairie chicken population had lost nine alleles present in the museum specimens. The 1993 population also had fewer alleles per locus than the pre-bottleneck Illinois or the current Kansas, Nebraska, and Minnesota populations (see Figure 23.10b). Thus, as predicted, drift had reduced the genetic variation of the small 1993 population. Drift may also have increased the frequency of harmful alleles, leading to the low egg-hatching rate. To counteract possible negative effects of genetic drift, the researchers added a total of 271 birds from neighboring states to the Illinois population over four years.

This strategy succeeded. New alleles entered the population, and the egg-hatching rate improved to over 90%. Overall, studies on the Illinois greater prairie chicken illustrate the powerful effects of genetic drift in small populations and provide hope that in at least some populations, these effects can be reversed.

Effects of Genetic Drift: A Summary

The examples we've described highlight four key points:

1. **Genetic drift is significant in small populations.** Chance events can cause an allele to be disproportionately over- or underrepresented in the next generation. Although chance events occur in populations of all sizes, they alter allele frequencies substantially only in small populations.

2. **Genetic drift can cause allele frequencies to change at random.** Because of genetic drift, an allele may increase in frequency one year, then decrease the next; the change from one year to the next is not predictable. Thus, unlike natural selection, which in a given environment consistently favors some alleles over others, genetic drift causes allele frequencies to change at random over time.

3. **Genetic drift can lead to a loss of genetic variation within populations.** By causing allele frequencies to fluctuate randomly over time, genetic drift can eliminate alleles from a population (see Figures 23.8 and 23.10). Because evolution depends on genetic variation, such losses can influence how effectively a population can adapt to a change in the environment.

4. **Genetic drift can cause harmful alleles to become fixed.** Alleles that are neither harmful nor beneficial can be lost or become fixed entirely by chance through genetic drift. In very small populations, genetic drift can also cause alleles that are slightly harmful to become fixed. When this occurs, the population's survival can be threatened (as for the Illinois greater prairie chicken).

Gene Flow

Natural selection and genetic drift are not the only phenomena affecting allele frequencies. Allele frequencies can also change by **gene flow**, the transfer of alleles into or out of a population due to the movement of fertile individuals or their gametes. For example, suppose that near our original hypothetical wildflower population there is another population consisting primarily of white-flowered individuals ($C^W C^W$). Insects carrying pollen from these plants may fly to and pollinate plants in our original population. The introduced C^W alleles would modify our original population's allele frequencies in the next generation.

Because alleles are exchanged among populations, gene flow tends to reduce the genetic differences between populations. If it is extensive enough, gene flow can result in neighboring populations combining into a single population with a common gene pool. For example, humans today move much

▲ **Figure 23.11 Gene flow and human evolution.** The migration of people throughout the world has increased gene flow between populations that once were isolated from one another. The computer-generated image on this magazine cover illustrates how gene flow can homogenize the gene pools of such populations, thereby reducing geographic variation in appearance.

more freely about the world than in the past. As a result, mating is more common between members of populations that previously were quite isolated **(Figure 23.11)**. The result is that gene flow has become an increasingly important agent of evolutionary change in human populations.

When neighboring populations live in different environments, alleles transferred by gene flow may prevent a population from fully adapting to its environment. Consider the example of bent grass (*Agrostis tenuis*) populations growing next to copper mines. These mine soils have high concentrations of copper, causing toxic effects in nontolerant plants. If alleles for copper tolerance are present in the bent grass population, these favorable alleles rapidly spread in the population. However, on nearby soils not contaminated with copper, copper-tolerant plants reproduce poorly compared to nontolerant ones. Thus we might expect that the percentage of plants that are copper tolerant would be close to 100% on mine soils and close to 0% on nearby (uncontaminated) soils. But bent grass is wind pollinated, and the wind can blow pollen from one population to another, moving alleles in the process. Thus, copper-tolerance alleles are transferred to non-mine soils; likewise, alleles associated with copper nontolerance are transferred to mine soils **(Figure 23.12)**.

Sometimes beneficial alleles are transferred very widely. For example, gene flow has resulted in the worldwide spread of several insecticide-resistance alleles in the mosquito *Culex pipiens*, a vector of West Nile virus and malaria. Each of these alleles has a unique genetic signature that allowed researchers

▼ **Figure 23.12 Gene flow and selection.** The bent grass in the foreground of the photo is growing on the tailings of an abandoned mine and is more copper tolerant than the bent grass in the pasture beyond the fence. The graph shows the degree of copper tolerance at various locations. These data suggest that ongoing gene flow prevents each population from adapting fully to its local conditions.

WHAT IF? *If prevailing winds blew the opposite way, how would copper tolerance change at the location marked by the red arrow?*

to document that it arose by mutation in one or a few geographic locations. In their population of origin, these alleles increased because they provided insecticide resistance. These alleles were then transferred to new populations, where again, their frequencies increased as a result of natural selection.

To sum up, gene flow, like mutation, can introduce new alleles into a population. But because it can occur at a higher rate than mutation, gene flow is more likely than mutation to alter allele frequencies directly. And once gene flow or mutation introduces a new allele to a population, natural selection may then cause the new allele to increase in frequency (as in the insecticide-resistance alleles in mosquitoes) or decrease in frequency (as in the copper-tolerance alleles in bent grass in non-mine soil).

CONCEPT CHECK 23.3

1. In what sense is natural selection more "predictable" than genetic drift?
2. Distinguish genetic drift from gene flow in terms of (a) how they occur and (b) their implications for future genetic variation in a population.
3. **WHAT IF?** Suppose two plant populations exchange pollen and seeds. In one population, individuals of genotype *AA* are most common (9,000 *AA*, 900 *Aa*, 100 *aa*), while the opposite is true in the other population (100 *AA*, 900 *Aa*, 9,000 *aa*). If neither allele has a selective advantage, what will happen over time to the allele and genotype frequencies of these populations?

For suggested answers, see Appendix A.

CONCEPT 23.4

Natural selection is the only mechanism that consistently causes adaptive evolution

Evolution by natural selection is a blend of chance and "sorting"—chance in the creation of new genetic variations (originally by mutation) and sorting as natural selection favors some alleles over others. Because of this sorting effect, only natural selection consistently increases the frequencies of alleles that provide reproductive advantage and thus leads to adaptive evolution.

A Closer Look at Natural Selection

In examining how natural selection brings about adaptive evolution, we'll begin with the concept of relative fitness and the different ways that an organism's phenotype is subject to natural selection.

Relative Fitness

The phrases "struggle for existence" and "survival of the fittest" are commonly used to describe natural selection, yet these expressions are misleading if taken to mean direct competitive contests among individuals. There *are* animal species in which individuals, usually the males, lock horns or otherwise do combat to determine mating privilege. But reproductive success is generally more subtle and depends on many factors besides outright battle. For example, a barnacle that is more efficient at collecting food than its neighbors may have greater stores of energy and hence be able to produce a larger number of eggs. A moth may have more offspring than other moths in the same population because its body colors more effectively conceal it from predators, improving its chance of surviving long enough to produce more offspring. These examples illustrate how adaptive advantage can lead to greater **relative fitness**: the contribution an individual makes to the gene pool of the next generation, *relative to* the contributions of other individuals.

Although we often refer to the relative fitness of a genotype, remember that the entity that is subjected to natural selection is the whole organism, not the underlying genotype. Thus, selection acts more directly on the phenotype than on the genotype; it acts on the genotype indirectly, via how the genotype affects the phenotype. Furthermore, the relative fitness conferred by a particular allele depends on the entire genetic and environmental context in which it is expressed. For example, an allele that is slightly disadvantageous might increase in frequency by "hitchhiking," that is, as a result of being located close to an allele at another locus that is strongly favored by natural selection (see Chapter 15 to review how distance between genes affects their inheritance).

Directional, Disruptive, and Stabilizing Selection

Natural selection can alter the frequency distribution of heritable traits in three ways, depending on which phenotypes in a population are favored. These three modes of selection are called directional selection, disruptive selection, and stabilizing selection.

Directional selection occurs when conditions favor individuals exhibiting one extreme of a phenotypic range, thereby shifting the frequency curve for the phenotypic character in one direction or the other **(Figure 23.13a)**. Directional selection is common when a population's environment changes or when members of a population migrate to a new (and different) habitat. For instance, fossil evidence indicates that the average size of black bears in Europe increased during each frigid glacial period, only to decrease again during warmer interglacial periods. Larger bears, with a smaller surface-to-

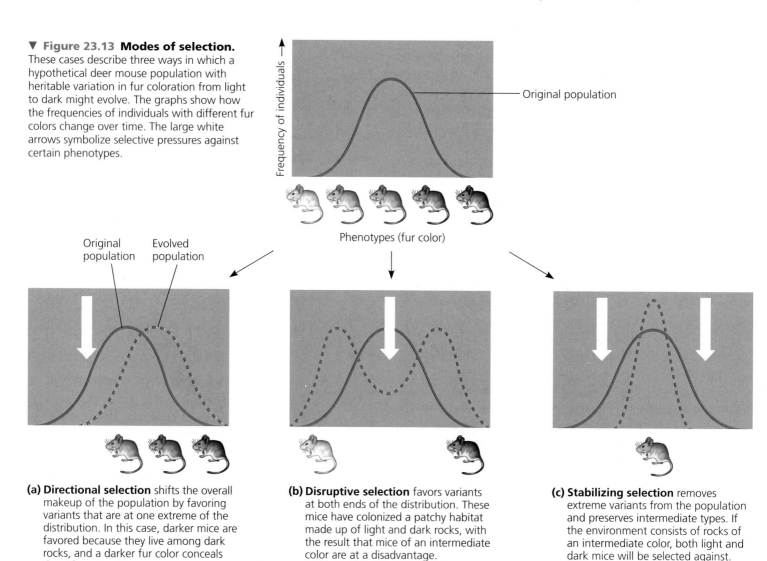

▼ **Figure 23.13 Modes of selection.** These cases describe three ways in which a hypothetical deer mouse population with heritable variation in fur coloration from light to dark might evolve. The graphs show how the frequencies of individuals with different fur colors change over time. The large white arrows symbolize selective pressures against certain phenotypes.

Frequency of individuals →

Original population

Phenotypes (fur color)

Original population   Evolved population

(a) Directional selection shifts the overall makeup of the population by favoring variants that are at one extreme of the distribution. In this case, darker mice are favored because they live among dark rocks, and a darker fur color conceals them from predators.

(b) Disruptive selection favors variants at both ends of the distribution. These mice have colonized a patchy habitat made up of light and dark rocks, with the result that mice of an intermediate color are at a disadvantage.

(c) Stabilizing selection removes extreme variants from the population and preserves intermediate types. If the environment consists of rocks of an intermediate color, both light and dark mice will be selected against.

volume ratio, are better at conserving body heat and surviving periods of extreme cold.

Disruptive selection (**Figure 23.13b**) occurs when conditions favor individuals at both extremes of a phenotypic range over individuals with intermediate phenotypes. One example is a population of black-bellied seedcracker finches in Cameroon whose members display two distinctly different beak sizes. Small-billed birds feed mainly on soft seeds, whereas large-billed birds specialize in cracking hard seeds. It appears that birds with intermediate-sized bills are relatively inefficient at cracking both types of seeds and thus have lower relative fitness.

Stabilizing selection (**Figure 23.13c**) acts against both extreme phenotypes and favors intermediate variants. This mode of selection reduces variation and tends to maintain the status quo for a particular phenotypic character. For example, the birth weights of most human babies lie in the range of 3–4 kg (6.6–8.8 pounds); babies who are either much smaller or much larger suffer higher rates of mortality.

Regardless of the mode of selection, however, the basic mechanism remains the same. Selection favors individuals whose heritable phenotypic traits provide higher reproductive success than do the traits of other individuals.

The Key Role of Natural Selection in Adaptive Evolution

The adaptations of organisms include many striking examples. Consider the ability of cuttlefish to rapidly change color, enabling them to blend into different backgrounds (**Figure 23.14a**). Another example is the remarkable jaws of snakes (**Figure 23.14b**), which enable them to swallow prey much larger than their own head (a feat analogous to a person swallowing a whole watermelon). Other adaptations, such as a version of an enzyme that shows improved function in cold environments (see Figure 23.4), may be less visually dramatic but just as important for survival and reproduction.

Such adaptations can arise gradually over time as natural selection increases the frequencies of alleles that enhance survival and reproduction. As the proportion of individuals that have favorable traits increases, the match between a species and its environment improves; that is, adaptive evolution occurs. However, as we saw in Chapter 22, the physical and biological components of an organism's environment may change over time. As a result, what constitutes a "good match" between an organism and its environment can be a moving target, making adaptive evolution a continuous, dynamic process.

And what about the two other important mechanisms of evolutionary change in populations, genetic drift and gene flow? Both can, in fact, increase the frequencies of alleles that improve the match between organisms and their environment—but neither does so consistently. Genetic drift can cause the frequency of a slightly beneficial allele to increase, but it also can cause the frequency of such an allele to decrease. Similarly, gene flow may

(a) Color-changing ability in cuttlefish. In a split second, this cuttlefish can blend against its background, enabling it to hide from predators and surprise its prey.

The bones of the upper jaw that are shown in purple are movable.

(b) Movable jaw bones in snakes. The skull bones of most terrestrial vertebrates are relatively rigidly attached to one another, limiting jaw movement. In contrast, most snakes have movable bones in their upper jaw, allowing them to swallow food much larger than their head.

▲ Figure 23.14 **Examples of adaptations.**

introduce alleles that are advantageous or ones that are disadvantageous. Natural selection is the only evolutionary mechanism that consistently leads to adaptive evolution.

Sexual Selection

Charles Darwin was the first to explore the implications of **sexual selection**, a form of natural selection in which individuals with certain inherited characteristics are more likely than other individuals to obtain mates. Sexual selection can result in **sexual dimorphism**, marked differences between the two sexes in secondary sexual characteristics,

▲ **Figure 23.15 Sexual dimorphism and sexual selection.**
Peacocks and peahens show extreme sexual dimorphism. There is
intrasexual selection between competing males, followed by intersexual
selection when the females choose among the showiest males.

which are not directly associated with reproduction or survival (**Figure 23.15**). These distinctions include differences in size, color, ornamentation, and behavior.

How does sexual selection operate? There are several ways. In **intrasexual selection**, meaning selection within the same sex, individuals of one sex compete directly for mates of the opposite sex. In many species, intrasexual selection occurs among males. For example, a single male may patrol a group of females and prevent other males from mating with them. The patrolling male may defend his status by defeating smaller, weaker, or less fierce males in combat. More often, this male is the psychological victor in ritualized displays that discourage would-be competitors but do not risk injury that would reduce his own fitness (see Figure 51.22). But intrasexual selection has also been observed among females in some species, including ring-tailed lemurs.

In **intersexual selection**, also called *mate choice*, individuals of one sex (usually the females) are choosy in selecting their mates from the other sex. In many cases, the female's choice depends on the showiness of the male's appearance or behavior (see Figure 23.15). What intrigued Darwin about mate choice is that male showiness may not seem adaptive in any other way and may in fact pose some risk. For example, bright plumage may make male birds more visible to predators. But if such characteristics help a male gain a mate, and if this benefit outweighs the risk from predation, then both the bright plumage and the female preference for it will be reinforced because they enhance overall reproductive success.

How do female preferences for certain male characteristics evolve in the first place? One hypothesis is that females prefer male traits that are correlated with "good genes." If the trait preferred by females is indicative of a male's overall genetic quality, both the male trait and female preference for it should increase in frequency. **Figure 23.16** describes one experiment testing this hypothesis in gray tree frogs (*Hyla versicolor*).

▼ **Figure 23.16** **Inquiry**

Do females select mates based on traits indicative of "good genes"?

EXPERIMENT   Female gray tree frogs prefer to mate with males that give long mating calls. Allison Welch and colleagues, at the University of Missouri, tested whether the genetic makeup of long-calling (LC) males is superior to that of short-calling (SC) males. The researchers fertilized half the eggs of each female with sperm from an LC male and fertilized the remaining eggs with sperm from an SC male. The resulting half-sibling offspring were raised in a common environment and tracked for two years.

RESULTS

Fitness Measure	1995	1996
Larval growth	NSD	LC better
Larval survival	LC better	NSD
Time to metamorphosis	LC better (shorter)	LC better (shorter)

NSD = no significant difference; LC better = offspring of LC males superior to offspring of SC males.

CONCLUSION   Because offspring fathered by an LC male had higher fitness than their half-siblings fathered by an SC male, the team concluded that the duration of a male's mating call is indicative of the male's overall genetic quality. This result supports the hypothesis that female mate choice can be based on a trait that indicates whether the male has "good genes."

SOURCE   A.M. Welch et al., Call duration as an indicator of genetic quality in male gray tree frogs, *Science* 280:1928–1930 (1998).

Inquiry in Action   Read and analyze the original paper in *Inquiry in Action: Interpreting Scientific Papers.*

WHAT IF?   Why did the researchers split each female frog's eggs into two batches for fertilization by different males? Why didn't they mate each female with a single male frog?

Other researchers have shown that in several bird species, the traits preferred by females are related to overall male health. Here, too, female preference appears to be based on traits that reflect "good genes," in this case alleles indicative of a robust immune system.

The Preservation of Genetic Variation

What prevents natural selection from reducing genetic variation by culling all unfavorable genotypes? The tendency for directional and stabilizing selection to reduce variation is countered by mechanisms that preserve or restore it.

Diploidy

Because most eukaryotes are diploid, a considerable amount of genetic variation is hidden from selection in the form of recessive alleles. Recessive alleles that are less favorable than their dominant counterparts, or even harmful in the current environment, can persist by propagation in heterozygous individuals. This latent variation is exposed to natural selection only when both parents carry the same recessive allele and two copies end up in the same zygote. This happens only rarely if the frequency of the recessive allele is very low. Heterozygote protection maintains a huge pool of alleles that might not be favored under present conditions, but which could bring new benefits if the environment changes.

Balancing Selection

Selection itself may preserve variation at some loci. **Balancing selection** occurs when natural selection maintains two or more forms in a population. This type of selection includes heterozygote advantage and frequency-dependent selection.

Heterozygote Advantage   If individuals who are heterozygous at a particular locus have greater fitness than do both kinds of homozygotes, they exhibit **heterozygote advantage**. In such a case, natural selection tends to maintain two or more alleles at that locus. Note that heterozygote advantage is defined in terms of *genotype*, not phenotype. Thus, whether heterozygote advantage represents stabilizing or directional selection depends on the relationship between the genotype and the phenotype. For example, if the phenotype of a heterozygote is intermediate to the phenotypes of both homozygotes, heterozygote advantage is a form of stabilizing selection.

There are relatively few well-documented examples of heterozygote advantage. One such example occurs at the locus in humans that codes for the β polypeptide subunit of hemoglobin, the oxygen-carrying protein of red blood cells. In homozygous individuals, a certain recessive allele at that locus causes sickle-cell disease. The red blood cells of people with sickle-cell disease become distorted in shape (see Figure 5.22), which can lead to serious complications, including damage to the kidney, heart, and brain. However, heterozygotes are pro-

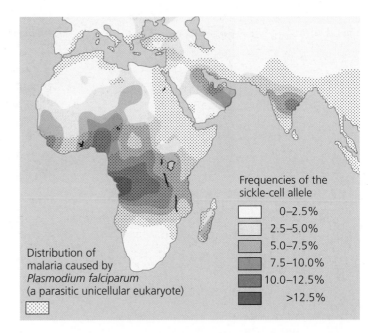

▲ **Figure 23.17 Mapping malaria and the sickle-cell allele.** The sickle-cell allele is most common in Africa, but it is not the only case of heterozygote advantage providing protection against malaria. Alleles at other loci are favored by heterozygote advantage in populations near the Mediterranean Sea and in southeast Asia, where malaria is also widespread.

tected against the most severe effects of malaria (although they are not resistant to malarial infection). This protection is important in tropical regions where malaria is a major killer. In such regions, selection favors heterozygotes over homozygous dominant individuals, who are more susceptible to malaria, and also over homozygous recessive individuals, who develop sickle-cell disease. The frequency of the sickle-cell allele in Africa is generally highest in areas where the malaria parasite is most common (**Figure 23.17**). In some populations, it accounts for 20% of the hemoglobin alleles in the gene pool, a very high frequency for such a harmful allele.

Frequency-Dependent Selection   In **frequency-dependent selection**, the fitness of a phenotype declines if it becomes too common in the population. Consider the scale-eating fish (*Perissodus microlepis*) of Lake Tanganyika in Africa. These fish attack other fish from behind, darting in to remove a few scales from the flank of their prey. Of interest here is a peculiar feature of the scale-eating fish: Some are "left-mouthed" and some are "right-mouthed." Simple Mendelian inheritance determines these phenotypes, with the right-mouthed allele being dominant to the left-mouthed allele. Because their mouth twists to the left, left-mouthed fish always attack their prey's right flank. (To see why, twist your lower jaw and lips to the left and imagine trying to take a bite from the left side of a fish, approaching it from behind.) Similarly, right-mouthed fish always attack from the left. Prey species guard against attack from whatever phenotype of scale-eating fish is most common in the lake. Thus, from year to

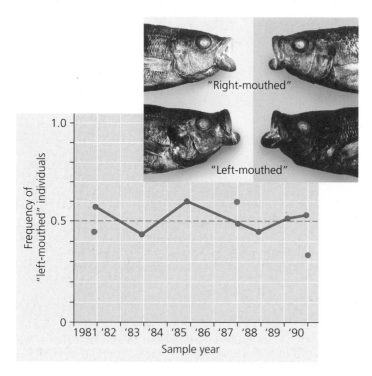

"Right-mouthed"

"Left-mouthed"

▲ **Figure 23.18 Frequency-dependent selection in scale-eating fish (*Perissodus microlepis*).** Michio Hori, of Kyoto University, Japan, noted that the frequency of left-mouthed individuals rises and falls in a regular manner. At each of three time periods when the phenotypes of breeding adults were assessed, adults that reproduced (represented by green dots) had the opposite phenotype of that which was most common in the population. Thus, it appeared that right-mouthed individuals were favored by selection when left-mouthed individuals were more common, and vice versa.

? *What did the researchers measure to determine which phenotype was favored by selection? Are any assumptions implied by this choice? Explain.*

year, selection favors whichever mouth phenotype is least common. As a result, the frequency of left- and right-mouthed fish oscillates over time, and balancing selection (due to frequency dependence) keeps the frequency of each phenotype close to 50% **(Figure 23.18)**.

Neutral Variation

Much of the DNA variation in populations probably has little or no impact on reproductive success, and thus natural selection does not affect this DNA. In humans, many of the nucleotide differences in noncoding sequences appear to confer no selective advantage or disadvantage and therefore are considered **neutral variation**. Mutations that cause changes in proteins also can be neutral. Data from *Drosophila* suggest that roughly half of the amino-acid-changing mutations that arise and subsequently become fixed have little or no selective effect because they have little effect on protein function and reproductive fitness (see Figure 17.23). Over time, the frequencies of alleles that are not affected by natural selection may increase or decrease as a result of genetic drift.

Why Natural Selection Cannot Fashion Perfect Organisms

Though natural selection leads to adaptation, there are several reasons why nature abounds with examples of organisms that are less than ideally "engineered" for their lifestyles.

1. **Selection can act only on existing variations.** Natural selection favors only the fittest phenotypes among those currently in the population, which may not be the ideal traits. New advantageous alleles do not arise on demand.
2. **Evolution is limited by historical constraints.** Each species has a legacy of descent with modification from ancestral forms. Evolution does not scrap the ancestral anatomy and build each new complex structure from scratch; rather, evolution co-opts existing structures and adapts them to new situations. We could imagine that if a terrestrial animal were to adapt to an environment in which flight would be advantageous, it might be best just to grow an extra pair of limbs that would serve as wings. However, evolution does not work in this way—it operates on the traits an organism already has. Thus, in birds and bats, an existing pair of limbs took on new functions for flight as these organisms evolved from walking ancestors.
3. **Adaptations are often compromises.** Each organism must do many different things. A seal spends part of its time on rocks; it could probably walk better if it had legs instead of flippers, but then it would not swim nearly as well. We humans owe much of our versatility and athleticism to our prehensile hands and flexible limbs, but these also make us prone to sprains, torn ligaments, and dislocations: Structural reinforcement has been compromised for agility. **Figure 23.19** depicts another example of evolutionary compromise.
4. **Chance, natural selection, and the environment interact.** Chance events can affect the subsequent evolutionary history of populations. For instance, when a storm blows insects or birds hundreds of kilometers over an ocean to an island, the wind does not necessarily transport those individuals that are best suited to the new environment. Thus, not all alleles present in the founding population's gene pool are better suited to the new environment than the alleles that are "left behind." In addition, the environment at a particular location may change unpredictably from year to year, again limiting the extent to which adaptive evolution results in a close match between the organism and current environmental conditions.

With these four constraints, evolution cannot craft perfect organisms. Natural selection operates on a "better than" basis. We can, in fact, see evidence for evolution in the many imperfections of the organisms it produces.

▲ Figure 23.19 **Evolutionary compromise.** The loud call that enables a Túngara frog to attract mates also attracts more unsavory characters in the neighborhood—in this case, a bat about to seize a meal.

Chapter 23 Review

SUMMARY OF KEY CONCEPTS

CONCEPT **23.1**

Mutation and sexual reproduction produce the genetic variation that makes evolution possible (pp. 468–471)

▶ **Genetic Variation** Genetic variation includes variation among individuals within a population in discrete and quantitative characters, as well as geographic variation between populations.

▶ **Mutation** New alleles ultimately originate by mutation. Most mutations are harmful or have no effect, but a few may be beneficial.

▶ **Sexual Reproduction** In sexually reproducing organisms, most of the genetic differences among individuals result from crossing over, the independent assortment of chromosomes, and fertilization.

MEDIA

Activity Genetic Variation from Sexual Reproduction

CONCEPT **23.2**

The Hardy-Weinberg equation can be used to test whether a population is evolving (pp. 472–475)

▶ **Gene Pools and Allele Frequencies** A population, a localized group of organisms belonging to one species, is united by its gene pool, the aggregate of all the alleles in the population.

▶ **The Hardy-Weinberg Principle** The Hardy-Weinberg principle states that the allele and genotype frequencies of a population will remain constant if the population is large, mating is random, mutation is negligible, there is no gene flow, and there is no natural selection. For such a population, if p and q represent the frequencies of the only two possible alleles at a particular locus, then p^2 is the frequency of one kind of homozygote, q^2 is the frequency of the other kind of homozygote, and $2pq$ is the frequency of the heterozygous genotype.

MEDIA

Investigation How Can the Frequencies of Alleles Be Calculated?

CONCEPT **23.3**

Natural selection, genetic drift, and gene flow can alter allele frequencies in a population (pp. 475–479)

▶ **Natural Selection** Differential success in reproduction results in certain alleles being passed to the next generation in greater proportions than others.

▶ **Genetic Drift** Chance fluctuations in allele frequencies from generation to generation tend to reduce genetic variation.

▶ **Gene Flow** Genetic exchange between populations tends to reduce differences between populations over time.

MEDIA

Activity Causes of Evolutionary Change
Biology Labs On-Line PopulationGeneticsLab

CONCEPT **23.4**

Natural selection is the only mechanism that consistently causes adaptive evolution (pp. 479–485)

▶ **A Closer Look at Natural Selection** One organism has greater fitness than another if it leaves more fertile descendants. The modes of natural selection differ in how selection acts on phenotype (arrows indicate selective pressure).

Original population   Evolved population

Directional selection   Disruptive selection   Stabilizing selection

▶ **The Key Role of Natural Selection in Adaptive Evolution**
Natural selection increases the frequencies of alleles that enhance survival and reproduction, thus improving the match between organisms and their environment.

▶ **Sexual Selection** Sexual selection leads to the evolution of secondary sex characteristics, which can give individuals advantages in mating.

▶ **The Preservation of Genetic Variation** Diploidy maintains a reservoir of concealed recessive variation in heterozygotes. Genetic variation also can be maintained by balancing selection.

▶ **Why Natural Selection Cannot Fashion Perfect Organisms** Natural selection can act only on available variation; structures result from modified ancestral anatomy; adaptations are often compromises; and chance, natural selection, and the environment interact.

MEDIA

Biology Labs On-Line EvolutionLab

TESTING YOUR KNOWLEDGE

SELF-QUIZ

1. A fruit fly population has a gene with two alleles, *A1* and *A2*. Tests show that 70% of the gametes produced in the population contain the *A1* allele. If the population is in Hardy-Weinberg equilibrium, what proportion of the flies carry both *A1* and *A2*?
   a. 0.7 b. 0.49 c. 0.21 d. 0.42 e. 0.09

2. There are 40 individuals in population 1, all of which have genotype *A1A1*, and there are 25 individuals in population 2, all of genotype *A2A2*. Assume that these populations are located far from one another and that their environmental conditions are very similar. Based on the information given here, the observed genetic variation is mostly likely an example of
   a. genetic drift.   d. discrete variation.
   b. gene flow.   e. directional selection.
   c. disruptive selection.

3. Natural selection changes allele frequencies because some _____ survive and reproduce more successfully than others.
   a. alleles   c. gene pools   e. individuals
   b. loci   d. species

4. No two people are genetically identical, except for identical twins. The chief cause of genetic variation among human individuals is
   a. new mutations that occurred in the preceding generation.
   b. the reshuffling of alleles in sexual reproduction.
   c. genetic drift due to the small size of the population.
   d. geographic variation within the population.
   e. environmental effects.

5. Sparrows with average-sized wings survive severe storms better than those with longer or shorter wings, illustrating
   a. the bottleneck effect.   d. neutral variation.
   b. stabilizing selection.   e. disruptive selection.
   c. frequency-dependent selection.

For Self-Quiz answers, see Appendix A.

MEDIA Visit the Study Area at **www.masteringbio.com** for a Practice Test.

EVOLUTION CONNECTION

6. How is the process of evolution revealed by the imperfections of living organisms?

SCIENTIFIC INQUIRY

7. **DRAW IT** Richard Koehn, of the State University of New York, Stony Brook, and Thomas Hilbish, of the University of South Carolina, studied genetic variation in the marine mussel *Mytilus edulis* around Long Island, New York. They measured the frequency of a particular allele (lap^{94}) for an enzyme involved in regulating the mussel's internal salt-water balance. The researchers presented their data as a series of pie charts linked to sampling sites within Long Island Sound, where the salinity is highly variable, and along the coast of the open ocean, where salinity is constant:

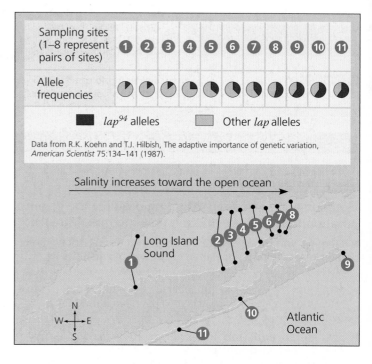

Data from R.K. Koehn and T.J. Hilbish, The adaptive importance of genetic variation, *American Scientist* 75:134–141 (1987).

Create a data table for the 11 sampling sites by estimating the frequency of lap^{94} from the pie charts. (*Hint*: Think of each pie chart as a clock face to help you estimate the proportion of the shaded area.) Then graph the frequencies for sites 1–8 to show how the frequency of this allele changes with increasing salinity in Long Island Sound (from southwest to northeast). How do the data from sites 9–11 compare with the data from the sites within the Sound?

   Construct a hypothesis that explains the patterns you observe in the data and that accounts for the following observations: (1) the lap^{94} allele helps mussels maintain osmotic balance in water with a high salt concentration but is costly to use in less salty water; and (2) mussels produce larvae that can disperse long distances before they settle on rocks and grow into adults.

SCIENCE, TECHNOLOGY, AND SOCIETY

8. To what extent are humans who live in a technological society exempt from natural selection? Justify your answer.

The Origin of Species

24

▲ **Figure 24.1 How did this flightless bird come to live on the isolated Galápagos Islands?**

OVERVIEW
That "Mystery of Mysteries"

Darwin came to the Galápagos Islands eager to explore landforms newly emerged from the sea. He noted that these volcanic islands, despite their geologic youth, were teeming with plants and animals found nowhere else in the world (**Figure 24.1**). Later he realized that these species, like the islands, were relatively new. He wrote in his diary: "Both in space and time, we seem to be brought somewhat near to that great fact—that mystery of mysteries—the first appearance of new beings on this Earth."

The "mystery of mysteries" that captivated Darwin is **speciation**, the process by which one species splits into two or more species. Speciation fascinated Darwin (and many biologists since) because it is responsible for the tremendous diversity of life, repeatedly yielding new species that differ from existing ones. Speciation explains not only differences between species, but also similarities between them (the unity of life). When one species splits, the species that result share many characteristics because they are descended from this common ancestral species. For example, DNA similarities indicate that the flightless cormorant (*Phalacrocorax harrisi*) in Figure 24.1 is closely related to flying cormorant species found on the west coast of the Americas. This suggests that the flightless cor-

morant may have originated from an ancestral cormorant species that migrated from the mainland to the Galápagos.

Speciation also forms a conceptual bridge between **microevolution**, changes over time in allele frequencies in a population, and **macroevolution**, the broad pattern of evolution over long time spans. An example of macroevolutionary change is the origin of new groups of organisms, such as mammals or flowering plants, through a series of speciation events. We examined microevolutionary mechanisms (mutation, natural selection, genetic drift, and gene flow) in Chapter 23, and we'll turn to macroevolution in Chapter 25. In this chapter, we will explore the "bridge"—the mechanisms by which new species originate from existing ones. First, however, we need to establish what we actually mean when we talk about "species."

CONCEPT 24.1
The biological species concept emphasizes reproductive isolation

The word *species* is Latin for "kind" or "appearance." In daily life, we commonly distinguish between various "kinds" of organisms—dogs and cats, for instance—from differences in their appearance. But are organisms truly divided into the discrete units we call species, or is this classification an arbitrary attempt to impose order on the natural world? To answer this question, biologists compare not only the morphology (body form) of different groups of organisms but also less obvious differences in physiology, biochemistry, and DNA sequences. The results generally confirm that morphologically distinct species are indeed discrete groups, with many differences in addition to morphological ones.

The Biological Species Concept

The primary definition of species used in this textbook is referred to as the **biological species concept**. According to this concept, as described in 1942 by biologist Ernst Mayr, a **species** is a group of populations whose members have the potential to interbreed in nature and produce viable, fertile offspring—but do not produce viable, fertile offspring with members of other such groups **(Figure 24.2)**. Thus, the members of a biological species are united by being reproductively compatible, at least potentially. All human beings, for example, belong to the same

(a) Similarity between different species. The eastern meadowlark (*Sturnella magna*, left) and the western meadowlark (*Sturnella neglecta*, right) have similar body shapes and colorations. Nevertheless, they are distinct biological species because their songs and other behaviors are different enough to prevent interbreeding should they meet in the wild.

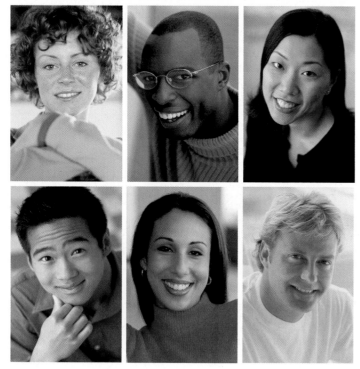

(b) Diversity within a species. As diverse as we may be in appearance, all humans belong to a single biological species (*Homo sapiens*), defined by our capacity to interbreed.

▲ **Figure 24.2 The biological species concept is based on the potential to interbreed rather than on physical similarity.**

species. A businesswoman in Manhattan may be unlikely to meet a dairy farmer in Mongolia, but if the two should happen to meet and mate, they could have viable babies that develop into fertile adults. In contrast, humans and chimpanzees remain distinct biological species even where they share territory, because many factors keep them from interbreeding and producing fertile offspring.

What holds the gene pool of a species together, causing its members to resemble each other more than they resemble other species? To answer this question, we need to reconsider an evolutionary mechanism discussed in Chapter 23: *gene flow*, the transfer of alleles between populations. Members of a species often resemble each other because their populations are connected by gene flow. As you might expect, populations located near one another exchange alleles relatively often. But what about populations separated by long distances? Evolutionary biologist Scott Edwards, interviewed on pages 450–451, examined this question for the grey-crowned babbler, *Pomatostomus temporalis* **(Figure 24.3)**. His results showed that a low level of gene flow occurred between even widely separated populations. Similar results have been found for other animal species, as well as for various fungi and plants. Such results illustrate that gene flow has the potential to hold the gene pool of a species together, so long as it is not outweighed by effects of selection or drift (either of which can result in populations diverging). As we'll explore in the next section, gene flow also plays a key role in the formation of new species.

Reproductive Isolation

Because biological species are defined in terms of reproductive compatibility, the formation of a new species hinges on **reproductive isolation**—the existence of biological factors (barriers) that impede members of two species from producing viable, fertile offspring. Such barriers block gene flow between the species and limit the formation of **hybrids**, offspring that result from an interspecific mating. Although a single barrier may not prevent all gene flow, a combination of several barriers can effectively isolate a species' gene pool.

Clearly, a fly cannot mate with a frog or a fern, but the reproductive barriers between more closely related species are not so obvious. These barriers can be classified according to whether they contribute to reproductive isolation before or after fertilization. **Prezygotic barriers** ("before the zygote") block fertilization from occurring. Such barriers typically act in one of three ways: by impeding members of different species from attempting to mate, by preventing an attempted mating from being completed successfully, or by hindering fertilization if mating is completed successfully. If a sperm cell from one species overcomes prezygotic barriers and fertilizes an ovum from another species, a variety of **postzygotic barriers** ("after the zygote") may contribute to reproductive isolation

▼ Figure 24.3 Inquiry

Does gene flow occur between widely separated populations?

EXPERIMENT   In many species, individuals disperse only short distances from their parent population. Can gene flow unify the gene pool of a species with widespread populations? Scott Edwards, then at the University of California, Berkeley, studied gene flow in a bird thought to disperse only short distances, the grey-crowned babbler (*Pomatostomus temporalis*). Edwards sequenced a segment of DNA from birds in 12 widely

separated populations (named populations A–L) located throughout Australia and Papua New Guinea. He used these data to construct *gene trees*, evolutionary trees showing patterns of relatedness among the alleles at the locus he studied. If a gene tree showed that some birds in one population had an allele that shared a recent common ancestor with alleles found in a different population, Edwards reasoned that gene flow must have occurred between those populations (see the example tree at right). In this way, Edwards analyzed allele relatedness for various combinations of the 12 study populations.

▼ **Example of a gene tree for population pair A-B**

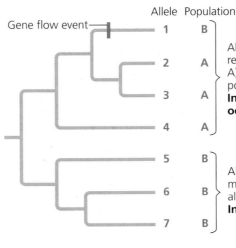

Allele 1 (found in population B) is more closely related to alleles 2, 3, and 4 (found in population A) than it is to alleles 5, 6, and 7 (found in population B).
Inference: Gene flow (at least one event) occurred.

Alleles 5, 6, and 7 (found in population B) are more closely related to one another than to alleles found in population A.
Inference: No gene flow occurred.

RESULTS   Among the 12 study populations, Edwards inferred that gene flow occurred in 7 population pairs.

Pair of populations with detected gene flow	Estimated minimum number of gene flow events to account for genetic patterns	Distance between populations (km)
A-B	5	340
K-L	3	720
A-C	2–3	1,390
B-C	2	1,190
F-G	2	760
G-I	2	1,110
C-E	1–2	1,310

CONCLUSION   Because gene flow was detected between populations separated by over 1,000 km, Edwards concluded that gene flow can potentially hold the grey-crowned babbler gene pool together even though individuals were thought to disperse only short distances. The long-distance movement of alleles could result from a series of shorter movements by individual birds, or from chance events such as a storm that transports birds to a distant location.

SOURCE   S. V. Edwards, Long-distance gene flow in a cooperative breeder detected in genealogies of mitochondrial DNA sequences, *Proceedings of the Royal Society of London, Series B, Biological Sciences* 252:177–185 (1993).

WHAT IF?   Do the data indicate that the gene flow event shown on the tree occurred as the transfer of an allele from population A to population B, or the reverse? Explain.

---

after the hybrid zygote is formed. For example, developmental errors may reduce survival among hybrid embryos. Or problems after birth may cause hybrids to be infertile or may de-crease their chance of surviving long enough to reproduce. **Figure 24.4**, on the next two pages, describes prezygotic and postzygotic barriers in more detail.

Exploring Reproductive Barriers

Prezygotic barriers impede mating or hinder fertilization if mating does occur

| Habitat Isolation | Temporal Isolation | Behavioral Isolation | Mechanical Isolation |

Individuals of different species

Mating attempt

Two species that occupy different habitats within the same area may encounter each other rarely, if at all, even though they are not isolated by obvious physical barriers, such as mountain ranges.

Example: Two species of garter snakes in the genus *Thamnophis* occur in the same geographic areas, but one lives mainly in water (a) while the other is primarily terrestrial (b).

Species that breed during different times of the day, different seasons, or different years cannot mix their gametes.

Example: In North America, the geographic ranges of the eastern spotted skunk (*Spilogale putorius*) (c) and the western spotted skunk (*Spilogale gracilis*) (d) overlap, but *S. putorius* mates in late winter and *S. gracilis* mates in late summer.

Courtship rituals that attract mates and other behaviors unique to a species are effective reproductive barriers, even between closely related species. Such behavioral rituals enable *mate recognition*—a way to identify potential mates of the same species.

Example: Blue-footed boobies, inhabitants of the Galápagos, mate only after a courtship display unique to their species. Part of the "script" calls for the male to high-step (e), a behavior that calls the female's attention to his bright blue feet.

Mating is attempted, but morphological differences prevent its successful completion.

Example: The shells of two species of snails in the genus *Bradybaena* spiral in different directions: Moving inward to the center, one spirals in a counter-clockwise direction (f, left), the other in a clockwise direction (f, right). As a result, the snails' genital openings (indicated by arrows) are not aligned, and mating cannot be completed.

(a)

(b)

(c)

(d)

(e)

(f)

| Gametic Isolation | Reduced Hybrid Viability | Reduced Hybrid Fertility | Hybrid Breakdown |

Fertilization

Viable, fertile offspring

Sperm of one species may not be able to fertilize the eggs of another species. For instance, sperm may not be able to survive in the reproductive tract of females of the other species, or biochemical mechanisms may prevent the sperm from penetrating the membrane surrounding the other species' eggs.

Example: Gametic isolation separates certain closely related species of aquatic animals, such as sea urchins (g). Sea urchins release their sperm and eggs into the surrounding water, where they fuse and form zygotes. Gametes of different species, such as the red and purple urchins shown here, are unable to fuse because proteins on the surfaces of the eggs and sperm cannot bind to each other.

The genes of different parent species may interact in ways that impair the hybrid's development or survival in its environment.

Example: Some salamander subspecies of the genus *Ensatina* live in the same regions and habitats, where they may occasionally hybridize. But most of the hybrids do not complete development, and those that do are frail (h).

Even if hybrids are vigorous, they may be sterile. If the chromosomes of the two parent species differ in number or structure, meiosis in the hybrids may fail to produce normal gametes. Since the infertile hybrids cannot produce offspring when they mate with either parent species, genes cannot flow freely between the species.

Example: The hybrid offspring of a donkey (i) and a horse (j) is a mule (k), which is robust but sterile.

Some first-generation hybrids are viable and fertile, but when they mate with one another or with either parent species, offspring of the next generation are feeble or sterile.

Example: Strains of cultivated rice have accumulated different mutant recessive alleles at two loci in the course of their divergence from a common ancestor. Hybrids between them are vigorous and fertile (l, left and right), but plants in the next generation that carry too many of these recessive alleles are small and sterile (l, center). Although these rice strains are not yet considered different species, they have begun to be separated by postzygotic barriers.

(h)

(i)

(l)

(g)

(j)

(k)

Limitations of the Biological Species Concept

One strength of the biological species concept is that it directs our attention to how speciation occurs: by the evolution of reproductive isolation. However, the number of species to which this concept can be usefully applied is limited. There is, for example, no way to evaluate the reproductive isolation of fossils. The biological species concept also does not apply to organisms that reproduce asexually all or most of the time, such as prokaryotes. (Many prokaryotes do transfer genes among themselves, as we will discuss in Chapter 27, but this is not part of their reproductive process.) Furthermore, in the biological species concept, species are designated by the *absence* of gene flow. There are, however, many pairs of species that are morphologically and ecologically distinct, and yet gene flow occurs between them. As we'll see, natural selection can cause such species to remain distinct despite gene flow. This observation has led some researchers to argue that the biological species concept overemphasizes gene flow and downplays the role of natural selection. Because of the limitations to the biological species concept, alternative species concepts are useful in certain situations.

Other Definitions of Species

While the biological species concept emphasizes the *separateness* of species from one another due to reproductive barriers, several other definitions emphasize the *unity within* a species. For example, the **morphological species concept** characterizes a species by body shape and other structural features. The morphological species concept has several advantages. It can be applied to asexual and sexual organisms, and it can be useful even without information on the extent of gene flow. In practice, this is how scientists distinguish most species. One disadvantage, however, is that this definition relies on subjective criteria; researchers may disagree on which structural features distinguish a species.

The **ecological species concept** views a species in terms of its ecological niche, the sum of how members of the species interact with the nonliving and living parts of their environment (see Chapter 54). For example, two species of amphibians might be similar in appearance but differ in the foods they eat or in their ability to tolerate dry conditions. Unlike the biological species concept, the ecological species concept can accommodate asexual as well as sexual species; it also emphasizes the role of disruptive natural selection as organisms adapt to different environmental conditions.

The **phylogenetic species concept** defines a species as the smallest group of individuals that share a common ancestor, forming one branch on the tree of life. Biologists trace the phylogenetic history of a species by comparing its characteristics, such as morphology or molecular sequences, with those of other organisms. Such analyses can distinguish groups of individuals that are sufficiently different to be considered separate species. Of course, the difficulty with this species concept is determining the degree of difference required to indicate separate species.

In addition to those discussed here, more than 20 other species definitions have been proposed. The usefulness of each definition depends on the situation and the research questions being asked. For our purposes of studying how species originate, the biological species concept, with its focus on reproductive barriers, is particularly helpful.

CONCEPT CHECK 24.1

1. (a) Which species concept(s) could you apply to both asexual and sexual species? (b) Which would be most useful for identifying species in the field? Explain.
2. **WHAT IF?** Suppose you are studying two bird species that live in a forest and are not known to interbreed. One species feeds and mates in the treetops and the other on the ground. But in captivity, the birds can interbreed and produce viable, fertile offspring. What type of reproductive barrier most likely keeps these species separate in nature? Explain.

For suggested answers, see Appendix A.

CONCEPT 24.2

Speciation can take place with or without geographic separation

Now that we have a clearer sense of what constitutes a unique species, let's return to our discussion of the process by which such species arise from existing species. Speciation can occur in two main ways, depending on how gene flow is interrupted between populations of the existing species (**Figure 24.5**).

Allopatric ("Other Country") Speciation

In **allopatric speciation** (from the Greek *allos*, other, and *patra*, homeland), gene flow is interrupted when a population is divided into geographically isolated subpopulations. For example, the water level in a lake may subside, resulting in two or more smaller lakes that are now home to separated populations (see Figure 24.5a). Or a river may change course and divide a population of animals that cannot cross it. Allopatric speciation can also occur without geologic remodeling, such as when individuals colonize a remote area and their descendants become geographically isolated from the parent population. The flightless cormorant shown in Figure 24.1 likely originated in this way from an ancestral flying species that migrated to the Galápagos Islands.

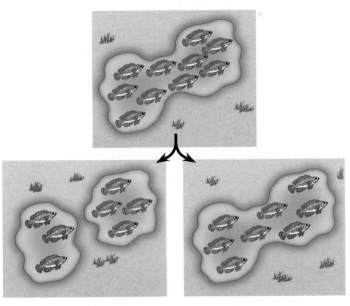

(a) Allopatric speciation. A population forms a new species while geographically isolated from its parent population.

(b) Sympatric speciation. A small population becomes a new species without geographic separation.

▲ **Figure 24.5 Two main modes of speciation.**

The Process of Allopatric Speciation

How formidable must a geographic barrier be to promote allopatric speciation? The answer depends on the ability of the organisms to move about. Birds, mountain lions, and coyotes can cross rivers and canyons. Nor do such barriers hinder the windblown pollen of pine trees or the seeds of many flowering plants. In contrast, small rodents may find a wide river or a deep canyon a formidable barrier **(Figure 24.6)**.

Once geographic separation has occurred, the separated gene pools may diverge through the mechanisms described in Chapter 23. Different mutations arise, natural selection acts on the separated organisms, and genetic drift alters allele frequencies. Reproductive isolation may then arise as a by-product of selection or drift having caused the populations to diverge genetically. For example, in the monkey flower *Mimulus guttatus*, selection has favored the evolution of copper tolerance in populations living near copper mines. Soil copper concentrations in these areas can reach levels that are lethal to nontolerant individuals. When members of copper-tolerant *M. guttatus* populations interbreed with individuals from other populations, the offspring survive poorly. Genetic analyses have shown that the gene for copper tolerance or an allele genetically linked to the copper-tolerance gene is responsible for the poor survival of the hybrid offspring. Thus, selection for copper tolerance appears to have had an important but coincidental side effect: partial reproductive isolation between *M. guttatus* populations.

The gene pools of highly isolated populations (such as those on remote islands) experience very little gene flow and hence are particularly likely to undergo allopatric speciation. For example, in less than 2 million years, the few animals and plants from the South and North American mainlands that colonized the Galápagos Islands gave rise to all the new species now found there.

Evidence of Allopatric Speciation

Many studies provide evidence that speciation can occur in allopatric populations. For example, biogeographic and genetic data together suggest that two present-day groups of frog species, the subfamilies Mantellinae and Rhacophorinae, began to diverge about 88 million years ago, when what is now the island of Madagascar started to separate from the Indian landmass. It appears that these two frog groups shared a common ancestor that lived on the Madagascar-India landmass

A. harrisi

A. leucurus

▲ **Figure 24.6 Allopatric speciation of antelope squirrels on opposite rims of the Grand Canyon.** Harris's antelope squirrel (*Ammospermophilus harrisi*) inhabits the canyon's south rim (left). Just a few kilometers away on the north rim (right) lives the closely related white-tailed antelope squirrel (*Ammospermophilus leucurus*). In contrast, birds and other organisms that can disperse easily across the canyon have not diverged into different species on the two rims.

► **Figure 24.7 Allopatric speciation in frogs.** The frog subfamilies Mantellinae and Rhacophorinae diverged when present-day Madagascar separated from India. The maps show the movement of Madagascar (red) and India (blue) over time.

Mantellinae (Madagascar only): 100 species

Rhacophorinae (India/southeast Asia): 310 species

Other Indian/ southeast Asian frogs

Millions of years ago (mya)

India

Madagascar

88 mya   65 mya   56 mya

before it began to break apart **(Figure 24.7)**. Following the breakup, allopatric speciation occurred within the separated populations of this common ancestor. The result was the formation of many new species in each location.

The importance of allopatric speciation is also suggested by the fact that regions that are highly subdivided by geographic barriers typically have more species than do regions with fewer barriers. For example, an unusually large number of bird species are found in the mountainous regions of New Guinea, and many unique plants and animals are found on the geographically isolated Hawaiian Islands (we'll return to the origin of Hawaiian species in Chapter 25).

Laboratory and field tests also provide evidence that reproductive isolation between two populations generally increases as the distance between them increases. In one such study of dusky salamanders (*Desmognathus ochrophaeus*), biologists brought individuals from different populations into the laboratory and tested their ability to produce viable, fertile offspring **(Figure 24.8)**. The researchers observed little reproductive isolation in salamanders from neighboring populations. In contrast, salamanders from widely separated populations often failed to reproduce. One possible explanation for these results is that long-distance gene flow is not occurring between the dusky salamander populations (unlike the grey-crowned babblers studied by Scott Edwards). Alternatively, long-distance gene flow between the salamander populations may be outweighed by the effects of natural selection or genetic drift, either of which can cause the populations to diverge. In other studies, researchers have tested whether intrinsic reproductive

barriers develop when populations are isolated experimentally and subjected to different environmental conditions. In such cases, too, the results provide strong support for allopatric speciation **(Figure 24.9**, on the facing page).

We need to emphasize here that although geographic isolation prevents interbreeding between allopatric populations, separation itself is not a biological barrier to reproduction. Biological reproductive barriers such as those described in Figure 24.4 are intrinsic to the organisms themselves. Hence, these barriers can prevent interbreeding when members of different populations come into contact with one another.

▲ **Figure 24.8 Variation in reproductive isolation with distance between populations of dusky salamanders.** The degree of reproductive isolation is represented here by an index ranging from 0 (no isolation) to 2 (complete isolation).

Can divergence of allopatric populations lead to reproductive isolation?

EXPERIMENT Diane Dodd, then at Yale University, divided a fruit fly population, raising some flies on a starch medium and others on a maltose medium. After one year (about 40 generations), natural selection resulted in divergent evolution: Populations raised on starch digested starch more efficiently, while those raised on maltose digested maltose more efficiently. Dodd then put flies from the same or different populations in mating cages and measured mating frequencies.

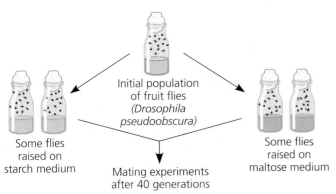

Some flies raised on starch medium

Initial population of fruit flies (*Drosophila pseudoobscura*)

Mating experiments after 40 generations

Some flies raised on maltose medium

RESULTS When flies from "starch populations" were mixed with flies from "maltose populations," the flies tended to mate with like partners. But in the control group shown here, flies from different populations adapted to starch were about as likely to mate with each other as with flies from their own population; similar results were obtained for control groups adapted to maltose.

	Female	
	Starch	Maltose
Male Starch	22	9
Male Maltose	8	20

Mating frequencies in experimental group

	Female	
	Starch population 1	Starch population 2
Male Starch population 1	18	15
Male Starch population 2	12	15

Mating frequencies in control group

CONCLUSION In the experimental group, the strong preference of "starch flies" and "maltose flies" to mate with like-adapted flies indicates that a reproductive barrier was forming between the divergent populations of flies. Although the barrier was not absolute (some mating between starch flies and maltose flies did occur), after 40 generations it appeared to be under way, the result of differing selective pressures as these allopatric populations adapted to different environments.

SOURCE D. M. B. Dodd, Reproductive isolation as a consequence of adaptive divergence in *Drosophila pseudoobscura*, *Evolution* 43:1308–1311 (1989).

WHAT IF? How would the results have changed if in each generation a few flies from the starch population had been placed in the maltose population and vice versa? Explain your prediction.

Sympatric ("Same Country") Speciation

In **sympatric speciation** (from the Greek *syn*, together), speciation occurs in populations that live in the same geographic area. How can reproductive barriers form between sympatric populations while their members remain in contact with each other? Although such contact (and the ongoing gene flow that results) makes sympatric speciation less common than allopatric speciation, sympatric speciation can occur if gene flow is reduced by such factors as polyploidy, habitat differentiation, and sexual selection. (Note that these factors can also promote allopatric speciation.)

Polyploidy

A species may originate from an accident during cell division that results in extra sets of chromosomes, a condition called **polyploidy**. There are two distinct forms of polyploidy. An **autopolyploid** (from the Greek *autos*, self) is an individual that has more than two chromosome sets that are all derived from a single species. For example, a failure of cell division could double a cell's chromosome number from the diploid number ($2n$) to a tetraploid number ($4n$) **(Figure 24.10)**. This mutation

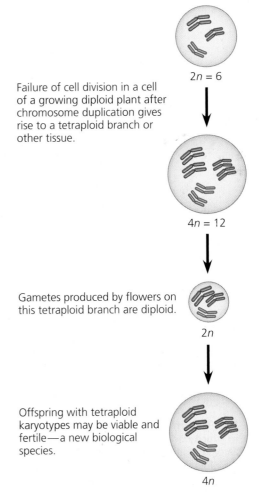

$2n = 6$

Failure of cell division in a cell of a growing diploid plant after chromosome duplication gives rise to a tetraploid branch or other tissue.

$4n = 12$

Gametes produced by flowers on this tetraploid branch are diploid.

$2n$

Offspring with tetraploid karyotypes may be viable and fertile—a new biological species.

$4n$

▲ **Figure 24.10 Sympatric speciation by autopolyploidy in plants.**

causes the tetraploid to be reproductively isolated from diploid plants of the original population, because the triploid (3*n*) offspring of such unions have reduced fertility. However, the tetraploid plants can produce fertile tetraploid offspring by self-pollinating or by mating with other tetraploids. Thus, in just one generation, autopolyploidy can generate reproductive isolation without any geographic separation.

A second form of polyploidy can occur when two different species interbreed and produce hybrid offspring. Most hybrids are sterile because the set of chromosomes from one species cannot pair during meiosis with the set of chromosomes from the other species. However, an infertile hybrid may be able to propagate itself asexually (as many plants can do). In subsequent generations, various mechanisms can change a sterile hybrid into a fertile polyploid called an **allopolyploid** (Figure 24.11). The allopolyploids are fertile when mating with each other but cannot interbreed with either parent species; thus, they represent a new biological species.

Polyploid speciation occasionally occurs in animals; for example, the gray tree frog *Hyla versicolor* (see Figure 23.16) is thought to have originated in this way. However, polyploidy is far more common in plants. Botanists estimate that more than 80% of the plant species alive today are descended from ancestors that formed by polyploid speciation. One documented example involves two new species of goatsbeard plants (genus *Tragopogon*) that originated in the Pacific Northwest in the mid-1900s. *Tragopogon* first arrived in the region when humans introduced three European species in the early 1900s. These species, *T. dubius, T. pratensis*, and *T. porrifolius*, are now common weeds in abandoned parking lots and other urban sites. In the 1950s, botanists identified two new *Tragopogon* species in regions of Idaho and Washington, where all three European species are also found. One new species, *T. miscellus*, is a tetraploid hybrid of *T. dubius* and *T. pratensis*; the other new species, *T. mirus*, is also an allopolyploid, but its ancestors are *T. dubius* and *T. porrifolius*. Although the *T. mirus* population grows mainly by reproduction of its own members, additional episodes of hybridization between the parent species continue to add new members to the *T. mirus* population—just one example of an ongoing speciation process that can be observed.

Many important agricultural crops—such as oats, cotton, potatoes, tobacco, and wheat—are polyploids. The wheat used for bread, *Triticum aestivum*, is an allohexaploid (six sets of chromosomes, two sets from each of three different species). The first of the polyploidy events that eventually led to modern wheat probably occurred about 8,000 years ago in the Middle East as a spontaneous hybrid of an early cultivated wheat species and a wild grass. Today, plant geneticists generate new polyploids in the laboratory by using chemicals that induce meiotic and mitotic errors. By harnessing the evolutionary process, researchers can produce new hybrid species with desired qualities, such as a hybrid that combines the high yield of wheat with the hardiness of rye.

▲ **Figure 24.11 One mechanism for allopolyploid speciation in plants.** Most hybrids are sterile because their chromosomes are not homologous and cannot pair during meiosis. However, such a hybrid may be able to reproduce asexually. This diagram traces one mechanism that can produce fertile hybrids (allopolyploids) as new species. The new species has a diploid chromosome number equal to the sum of the diploid chromosome numbers of the two parent species.

Habitat Differentiation

Sympatric speciation can also occur when genetic factors enable a subpopulation to exploit a habitat or resource not used by the parent population. Such is the case with the North American apple maggot fly (*Rhagoletis pomonella*). The fly's original habitat was the native hawthorn tree, but about 200 years ago, some populations colonized apple trees that had been introduced by European settlers. As apples mature more quickly than hawthorn fruit, natural selection has favored apple-feeding flies with rapid development. These apple-feeding populations now show temporal isolation from the hawthorn-feeding *R. pomonella*, providing a prezygotic restriction to gene flow between the two populations. Researchers also have identified alleles that benefit the flies that use one host plant but harm the flies that use the other host plant. As a result, natural selection operating on these alleles provides a postzygotic barrier to reproduction, further limiting gene flow. Altogether, although the two populations are still classified as subspecies rather than separate species, sympatric speciation appears to be well under way.

Sexual Selection

There is evidence that sympatric speciation can also be driven by sexual selection. Clues to how this can occur have been found in cichlid fish from one of Earth's hot spots of animal speciation, East Africa's Lake Victoria. This lake was once home to as many as 600 species of cichlids. Genetic data indicate that these species originated within the last 100,000 years from a small number of colonist species that arrived from rivers and lakes located elsewhere. How did so many species—more than double the number of freshwater fish species known in all of Europe—originate within a single lake?

One hypothesis is that subgroups of the original cichlid populations adapted to different food sources and that the resulting genetic divergence contributed to speciation in Lake Victoria. But sexual selection, in which (typically) females select males based on their appearance (see Chapter 23), may also have been a factor. Researchers have studied two closely related sympatric species of cichlids that differ mainly in the coloration of breeding males: Breeding *Pundamilia pundamilia* males have a blue-tinged back, whereas breeding *Pundamilia nyererei* males have a red-tinged back (**Figure 24.12**). Their results suggest that mate choice based on male breeding coloration is the main reproductive barrier that normally keeps the gene pools of these two species separate.

Allopatric and Sympatric Speciation: A Review

Now let's recap the two main modes by which new species form. In allopatric speciation, a new species forms in geographic isolation from its parent population. Geographic isolation severely restricts gene flow. As a result, other reproductive barriers from the ancestral species may arise as a by-product of genetic changes that occur within the isolated population. Many different processes can produce such genetic changes, including natural selection under different environ-

▼ **Figure 24.12** **Inquiry**

Does sexual selection in cichlids result in reproductive isolation?

EXPERIMENT Ole Seehausen and Jacques van Alphen, then at the University of Leiden, placed males and females of *Pundamilia pundamilia* and *P. nyererei* together in two aquarium tanks, one with natural light and one with a monochromatic orange lamp. Under normal light, the two species are noticeably different in male breeding coloration; under monochromatic orange light, the two species are very similar in color. The researchers then observed the mate choices of the females in each tank.

RESULTS Under normal light, females of each species strongly preferred males of their own species. But under orange light, females of each species responded indiscriminately to males of both species. The resulting hybrids were viable and fertile.

CONCLUSION Seehausen and van Alphen concluded that mate choice by females based on male breeding coloration is the main reproductive barrier that normally keeps the gene pools of these two species separate. Since the species can still interbreed when this prezygotic behavioral barrier is breached in the laboratory, the genetic divergence between the species is likely to be small. This suggests that speciation in nature has occurred relatively recently.

SOURCE O. Seehausen and J. J. M. van Alphen, The effect of male coloration on female mate choice in closely related Lake Victoria cichlids (*Haplochromis nyererei* complex), *Behavioral Ecology and Sociobiology* **42**:1–8 (1998).

WHAT IF? If changing the light to orange had not affected the mating behavior of the cichlids, how would the researchers' conclusion in this study have changed?

mental conditions, genetic drift, and sexual selection. Once formed, intrinsic reproductive barriers that arise in allopatric populations can prevent interbreeding with the parent population even if the populations come back into contact.

Sympatric speciation, in contrast, requires the emergence of a reproductive barrier that isolates a subset of a population from the remainder of the population in the same area. Though rarer than allopatric speciation, sympatric speciation can occur when gene flow to and from the isolated subpopulation is blocked. This can occur as a result of polyploidy, a condition in which an organism has extra sets of chromosomes. Sympatric speciation also can occur when a subset of a population becomes reproductively isolated because of natural selection that results from a switch to a habitat or food source not used by the parent population. Finally, sympatric speciation can result from sexual selection. Having reviewed the geographic context in which new species form, we'll next explore in more detail what can happen when allopatric populations come back into contact.

CONCEPT CHECK 24.2

1. Summarize key differences between allopatric and sympatric speciation. Which type of speciation is more common, and why?
2. Describe two mechanisms that can decrease gene flow in sympatric populations, thereby making sympatric speciation more likely to occur.
3. **WHAT IF?** Is allopatric speciation more likely to occur on an island close to a mainland or on a more isolated island of the same size? Explain your prediction.

For suggested answers, see Appendix A.

CONCEPT 24.3
Hybrid zones provide opportunities to study factors that cause reproductive isolation

What happens if allopatric populations come back into contact with one another? One possible outcome is the formation of a **hybrid zone**, a region in which members of different species meet and mate, producing at least some offspring of mixed ancestry. In this section, we'll explore hybrid zones and what they reveal about factors that cause the evolution of reproductive isolation.

Patterns Within Hybrid Zones

Hybrid zones exhibit a variety of structures. Some hybrid zones form as narrow bands, such as the one depicted in **Figure 24.13** for two species of toads in the genus *Bombina*, the yellow-bellied toad (*B. variegata*) and the fire-bellied toad (*B. bombina*). This

Yellow-bellied toad, *Bombina variegata*

Fire-bellied toad range
Hybrid zone
Yellow-bellied toad range

Fire-bellied toad, *Bombina bombina*

▲ **Figure 24.13 A narrow hybrid zone for *B. variegata* and *B. bombina* in Europe.** The graph shows the pattern of allele frequency changes across the width of the zone near Krakow, Poland.

hybrid zone, represented by the thick red line on the map, extends for 4,000 km but is less than 10 km wide in most places. Across a given "slice" of the hybrid zone, the frequency of alleles specific to yellow-bellied toads typically decreases from close to 100% at the edge where only yellow-bellied toads are found, to 50% in the central portion of the zone, to 0% at the edge where only fire-bellied toads are found.

What causes such a pattern of allele frequencies across a hybrid zone? We can infer that there is an obstacle to gene flow—otherwise alleles from one parent species would also be found in the gene pool of the other parent species. Are geographic barriers reducing gene flow? Not in this case, since the toads move freely throughout the zone. A more important factor is that hybrid toads have increased rates of embryonic mortality and a variety of morphological abnormalities, including ribs that are fused to the spine and malformed tadpole mouthparts. Because the hybrids have poor survival and reproduction, they produce few viable offspring with members of the parent species. As a result, hybrids rarely serve as a stepping-stone from which alleles are passed from one species to the other.

Other hybrid zones have more complicated spatial patterns. Consider the hybrid zone between the ground crickets *Allonemobius fasciatus* and *Allonemobius socius*, both found in the Appalachian Mountains in the eastern United States. The environment has a powerful impact on the fitness of the parent species. *A. fasciatus* is more successful than *A. socius* in colder portions of the zone, and the reverse is true in warm lo-

cations. Thus *A. fasciatus* predominates in cooler sites (high elevation or north-facing locations), and *A. socius* predominates in warmer sites (low elevation or south-facing locations). The topography of this region is complex, with many hills and valleys, so there are many areas where patches of the two species are closely interspersed. As a result, populations of the two parent species come into contact, and hybrids are formed. Unlike the situation in the *Bombina* hybrid zone, where hybrid individuals are consistently less fit than individuals of either parent species, the fitness of *Allonemobius* hybrids varies from year to year and sometimes exceeds that of both parent species. As we'll see, the differences in the fitness of the *Bombina* and *Allonemobius* hybrids lead to different predictions regarding how reproductive barriers for these species change over time.

Hybrid Zones over Time

Studying a hybrid zone is like observing a natural experiment on speciation. Will the result be the rapid formation of a new species, as occurred by polyploidy in the goatsbeard plants of the Pacific Northwest? If not, there are three possible outcomes for the hybrid zone over time (**Figure 24.14**). Reproductive barriers between species may be strengthened over time (limiting the formation of hybrids) or weakened over time (causing the two species to fuse into a single species). Or hybrids may continue to be produced, creating a long-term, stable hybrid zone. Let's examine what the field evidence suggests about these three possibilities.

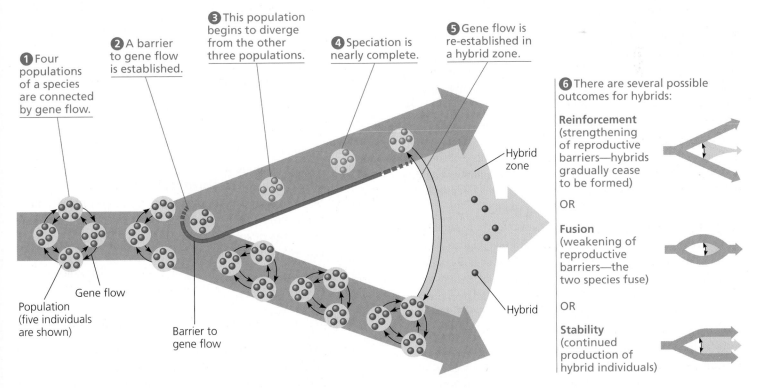

▲ **Figure 24.14 Formation of a hybrid zone and possible outcomes for hybrids over time.** The thick colored arrows represent the passage of time.

WHAT IF? *What might happen if gene flow were re-established at step 3 in this process?*

Reinforcement: Strengthening Reproductive Barriers

When hybrids are less fit than members of their parent species, as in the *Bombina* example, we might expect natural selection to strengthen prezygotic barriers to reproduction, thus reducing the formation of unfit hybrids. Because this process involves *reinforcing* reproductive barriers, it is called **reinforcement**. If reinforcement is occurring, we would predict that barriers to reproduction between species should be stronger for sympatric species than for allopatric species.

As an example, let's consider the evidence for reinforcement in two closely related species of European flycatcher, the pied flycatcher and the collared flycatcher. In allopatric populations of these birds, males of the two species closely resemble one another. But in sympatric populations, the males of the two species look very different: Male pied flycatchers are a dull brown, whereas male collared flycatchers have enlarged patches of white. Female pied and collared flycatchers do not select males of the other species when given a choice between males from sympatric populations, but they frequently do make mistakes when selecting between males from allopatric populations **(Figure 24.15)**. Thus, barriers to reproduction appear to be stronger in birds from sympatric populations than in birds from allopatric populations, as predicted by the reinforcement hypothesis. Similar results have been observed in a number of organisms, including fishes, insects, plants, and other birds. But interestingly, reinforcement does *not* appear to be at work in the case of the *Bombina* toads, as we'll discuss shortly.

Fusion: Weakening Reproductive Barriers

Next let's consider the case in which two species contact one another in a hybrid zone, but the barriers to reproduction are not strong. So much gene flow may occur that reproductive barriers weaken further and the gene pools of the two species become increasingly alike. In effect, the speciation process reverses, eventually causing the two hybridizing species to fuse into a single species.

Such a situation may be occurring among some of the Lake Victoria cichlids we discussed earlier. Many pairs of ecologically similar cichlid species are reproductively isolated by female mate choice—the females of one species prefer to mate with males of one color, while females of the other species prefer to mate with males of a different color (see Figure 24.12).

In the past 30 years, about 200 of the former 600 species of Lake Victoria cichlids have vanished. Some of these species were driven to extinction by an introduced predator, the Nile perch. But many species not eaten by Nile perch also have disappeared. Researchers think that murky waters caused by pollution may have reduced the ability of females to use color to distinguish males of their own species from males of closely related species. If further evidence supports this hypothesis, it would seem that pollution in Lake Victoria has produced a cascade of related effects. First, by decreasing the ability of fe-

Sympatric male pied flycatcher   **Allopatric male pied flycatcher**

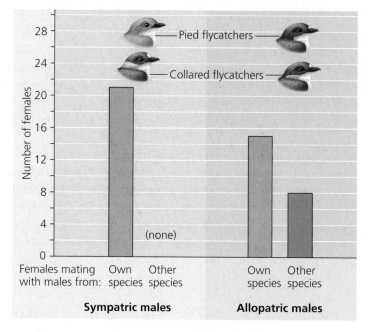

▲ **Figure 24.15 Reinforcement of barriers to reproduction in closely related species of European flycatchers.**

males to distinguish males of their own species, pollution has increased the frequency of mating between members of species that had been isolated reproductively from one another. Second, as a result of these matings, many hybrids have been produced, leading to fusion of the parent species' gene pools and a loss of species **(Figure 24.16)**. Third, future speciation events in Lake Victoria cichlids are now less likely because female mate choice based on male breeding color, which can promote speciation in these fish, is hindered.

Stability: Continued Formation of Hybrid Individuals

Many hybrid zones are stable in the sense that hybrids continue to be produced—a result you might not expect. For example, recall that hybrids are at a strong disadvantage in the *Bombina* hybrid zone. As a result, the offspring of individuals that prefer to mate with members of their own species should survive or

Pundamilia nyererei   *Pundamilia pundamilia*

Pundamilia "turbid water,"
hybrid offspring from a location
with turbid water

▲ **Figure 24.16 The breakdown of reproductive barriers.**
Increasingly cloudy water in Lake Victoria over the past 30 years may
have weakened reproductive barriers between *P. nyererei* and
P. pundamilia. In areas of cloudy water, the two species have
hybridized extensively, causing their gene pools to fuse.

reproduce better than the unfit hybrid offspring of individuals
that mate indiscriminately with members of the other species.
This suggests that reinforcement should occur, strengthening
reproductive barriers and thereby limiting the production of
hybrid toads. But in more than 20 years of study, no evidence
for reinforcement has been found, and hybrids continue to be
produced. What could explain this surprising finding? One
possibility relates to the narrowness of the *Bombina* hybrid
zone. Perhaps extensive gene flow from outside the zone leads
to the continued production of hybrids and overwhelms selection for increased reproductive isolation inside the hybrid
zone. If the hybrid zone were wider, this would be less likely to
occur, since the center of the zone would receive little gene flow
from distant populations outside the hybrid zone.

In the *Allonemobius* hybrid zone, hybrids sometimes have
higher fitness than the parent species. Thus, we might predict
that many hybrids would be formed, at least in some years. As
these hybrids mated with each other and with members of
both parent species, the gene pools of the parent species could
fuse, reversing the speciation process. However, although hybrids do continue to be formed, more than 20 years of data indicate that they are uncommon and that gene flow between
the parent species is not extensive. Why aren't hybrids more

common? Throughout much of the hybrid zone, the two parent species meet at locations where one or both of them are
near the limit of the environmental conditions that they can
tolerate. As a result, even a slight change in the local environment can cause one or the other of the parent species to disappear from that location. In a 14-year study, researchers
observed several such local extinctions. Thus, because locations where hybrids are formed may appear and disappear rapidly, hybrids remain uncommon, and fusion of the *A. fasciatus*
and *A. socius* gene pools may be prevented by insufficient time
for the reproductive barriers to break down.

In short, sometimes the outcomes in hybrid zones match
our predictions (European flycatchers and cichlid fishes),
and sometimes they don't (*Bombina* and *Allonemobius*). But
whether our predictions are upheld or not, events in hybrid
zones can shed light on how barriers to reproduction between
closely related species change over time. In the next section,
we'll examine how interactions between hybridizing species
can also provide a glimpse into the speed and genetic control
of speciation.

CONCEPT CHECK   24.3

1. What are hybrid zones, and why can they be viewed
   as "natural laboratories" in which to study speciation?
2. **WHAT IF?**   Consider two species that diverged
   while geographically separated but resumed contact
   before reproductive isolation was complete. Predict
   what would happen over time if the two species
   mated indiscriminately and (a) hybrid offspring survived and reproduced more poorly than offspring
   from intraspecific matings or (b) hybrid offspring
   survived and reproduced as well as offspring from
   intraspecific matings.

For suggested answers, see Appendix A.

CONCEPT 24.4
Speciation can occur rapidly or slowly and can result from changes in few or many genes

Darwin faced many unanswered questions when he began to
ponder that "mystery of mysteries," speciation. As you read in
Chapter 22, he found answers to some of those questions
when he realized that evolution by natural selection helped to
explain both the diversity of life and the adaptations of organisms. But biologists since Darwin have continued to ask fundamental questions about speciation, such as, How long does
it take new species to form? and, How many genes change
when one species splits into two? Answers to these questions
are also beginning to emerge.

The Time Course of Speciation

We can gather information about how long it takes new species to form from broad patterns in the fossil record and from studies that use morphological data (including fossils) or molecular data to assess the time interval between speciation events in particular groups of organisms.

Patterns in the Fossil Record

The fossil record includes many episodes in which new species appear suddenly in a geologic stratum, persist essentially unchanged through several strata, and then disappear. Paleontologists Niles Eldredge, of the American Museum of Natural History, and Stephen Jay Gould (1941–2002), of Harvard University, coined the term **punctuated equilibria** to describe these periods of apparent stasis punctuated by sudden change **(Figure 24.17a)**. Other species do not show a punctuated pattern; instead, they change more gradually over long periods of time **(Figure 24.17b)**.

What do punctuated and gradual patterns tell us about how long it takes new species to form? Suppose that a species survived for 5 million years, but most of the morphological changes that caused it to be designated a new species occurred during the first 50,000 years of its existence—just 1% of its total lifetime. Time periods this short (in geologic terms) often cannot be distinguished in fossil strata, in part because the rate of sediment accumulation is too slow to separate layers this close in time. Thus, based on its fossils, the species would seem to have appeared suddenly and then lingered with little or no change before becoming extinct. Even though such a species may have originated more slowly than its fossils suggest (in this case taking 50,000 years), a punctuated pattern indicates that speciation occurred relatively rapidly. For species whose fossils change much more gradually, we also cannot tell exactly when a new biological species forms, since information about reproductive isolation does not fossilize. However, it is likely that speciation in such groups occurred relatively slowly, perhaps taking millions of years.

Speciation Rates

The punctuated pattern suggests that once the process begins, speciation can be completed relatively rapidly—a suggestion confirmed by a growing number of studies.

For example, research conducted by Loren Rieseberg, then at Indiana University, and colleagues suggests that rapid speciation produced the wild sunflower *Helianthus anomalus*. This species is thought to have originated by the hybridization of two other sunflower species, *H. annuus* and *H. petiolaris*. The hybrid species *H. anomalus* is ecologically distinct and reproductively isolated from both parent species **(Figure 24.18)**. Unlike allopolyploid speciation, in which there is a change in chromosome number after hybridization, in these sunflowers the two parent species and the hybrid all have the same number of chromosomes ($2n = 34$). How then did speciation occur? In laboratory experiments designed to answer this question, only 5% of the F_1 hybrids were fertile. However, after just four more generations in which hybrids mated among themselves and also mated with the parent species, the fertility rose to more than 90%. To explain this finding, Rieseberg and colleagues hypothesized that experimental hybrids whose chromosomes contained blocks of DNA from the parent species that were not compatible with one another failed to reproduce and thus were eliminated by selection. As a result, the chromosomes of the experimental hybrids rapidly became similar in composition to the chromosomes of *H. anomalus* individuals from natural populations (see Figure 24.18).

(a) In a punctuated pattern, new species change most as they branch from a parent species and then change little for the rest of their existence.

Time ⟶

(b) Other species diverge from one another much more gradually over time.

▲ Figure 24.17 **Two models for the tempo of speciation.**

The sunflower example, along with the apple maggot fly, Lake Victoria cichlid, and fruit fly examples discussed earlier, suggests that new species can form rapidly once divergence begins. But what is the total length of time between speciation events? This interval consists of the time that elapses before populations of a newly formed species start to diverge from one another plus the time it takes for speciation to be complete once divergence begins. It turns out that the total time between speciation events varies considerably. For example, in a survey of data from 84 groups of plants and animals, the interval be-

tween speciation events ranged from 4,000 years (in cichlids of Lake Nabugabo, Uganda) to 40 million years (in some beetles). Overall, the time between speciation events averaged 6.5 million years and rarely took less than 500,000 years.

What can we learn from such data? First, the data suggest that on average, millions of years may pass before a newly formed species will itself give rise to another new species. As we'll see in Chapter 25, this result has implications for how long it takes Earth's life to recover from mass extinction events. Second, the extreme variability in the time it takes new species to form indicates that organisms do not have a "speciation clock" ticking inside them, causing them to produce new species at regular time intervals. Instead, speciation begins only after gene flow between populations is interrupted, perhaps by an unpredictable event such as a storm that transports a few individuals to an isolated area. Furthermore, once gene flow has been interrupted, the populations must diverge genetically to such an extent that they become reproductively isolated—all before another event causes gene flow to resume, reversing the speciation process (see Figure 24.16).

Studying the Genetics of Speciation

Studies of ongoing speciation (as in hybrid zones) can reveal traits that cause reproductive isolation. By identifying the genes that control those traits, scientists can explore a fundamental question of evolutionary biology: How many genes change when a new species forms?

In a few cases, the evolution of reproductive isolation is due to a change in a single gene. For example, in Japanese snails of the genus *Euhadra*, alleles of a single gene can induce a mechanical barrier to reproduction. This gene controls the direction in which the shells spiral (Figure 24.19). When their shells spiral in different directions, the snails' genitals are oriented in a manner that prevents mating (Figure 24.4f shows a similar example).

A major barrier to reproduction between two closely related species of monkey flower, *Mimulus lewisii* and *M. cardinalis*,

(a) The wild sunflower *Helianthus anomalus* lives in dry sand dune environments. *H. anomalus* originated via the hybridization of two other sunflowers, *H. annuus* and *H. petiolaris*, which live in nearby but moister environments.

Chromosome 1 { H. anomalus / Experimental hybrid
Chromosome 2 { H. anomalus / Experimental hybrid
Chromosome 3 { H. anomalus / Experimental hybrid

Key

■ Region diagnostic for parent species *H. petiolaris*
■ Region diagnostic for parent species *H. annuus*
■ Region lacking information on parental origin

(b) The genetic composition of three chromosomes in *H. anomalus* and in experimental hybrids. After a five-generation experiment, the chromosomes in the experimental hybrids were similar to the chromosomes of naturally occurring *H. anomalus*.

▲ **Figure 24.18 Rapid speciation in a sunflower hybrid zone.**

▲ **Figure 24.19 Single-gene speciation.** A mutation in one gene causes the shell of the Japanese land snail (*Euhadra*) to spiral in the opposite direction from others. Snails with opposite spirals cannot mate, resulting in reproductive isolation.

also appears to be influenced by a relatively small number of genes. These two species are isolated both by prezygotic barriers (pollinator choice and partial gametic isolation) and by postzygotic barriers (interspecific crosses produce fewer offspring than intraspecific crosses, and F_1 hybrids have reduced fertility and survival). Of these barriers, pollinator choice accounts for most of the isolation: In a hybrid zone between *M. lewisii* and *M. cardinalis*, nearly 98% of pollinator visits were restricted to one species or the other.

The two monkey flower species are visited by different pollinators: Bumblebees prefer the pink-flowered *M. lewisii* and hummingbirds prefer the red-flowered *M. cardinalis*. Douglas Schemske, of Michigan State University, and colleagues have shown that pollinator choice is affected by at least two loci in the monkey flowers, one of which, the "yellow upper," or *yup*, locus, influences flower color (**Figure 24.20**). By producing F_1

(a) Typical *Mimulus lewisii*

(b) *M. lewisii* with an *M. cardinalis* flower-color allele

(c) Typical *Mimulus cardinalis*

(d) *M. cardinalis* with an *M. lewisii* flower-color allele

▲ **Figure 24.20 A locus that influences pollinator choice.** Pollinator preferences provide a strong barrier to reproduction between *Mimulus lewisii* and *M. cardinalis*. After transferring the *M. lewisii* allele for a flower-color locus into *M. cardinalis* and vice versa, researchers observed a shift in some pollinators' preferences.

WHAT IF? *If* M. cardinalis *individuals that had the* M. lewisii yup *allele were planted in an area that housed both monkey flower species, how might the production of hybrid offspring be affected?*

hybrids and then performing repeated backcrosses to each parent species, Schemske and colleagues succeeded in transferring the *M. lewisii* allele at this locus into *M. cardinalis*, and vice versa. In a field experiment, *M. lewisii* plants with the *M. cardinalis yup* allele received 68-fold more visits from hummingbirds than did wild-type *M. lewisii*. Similarly, *M. cardinalis* plants with the *M. lewisii yup* allele received 74-fold more visits from bumblebees than did wild-type *M. cardinalis*. Thus, a mutation at a single locus can influence pollinator preference and hence contribute to reproductive isolation in monkey flowers.

In other organisms, the speciation process is influenced by larger numbers of genes and gene interactions. For example, hybrid sterility between two subspecies of *Drosophila pseudoobscura* results from gene interactions among at least four loci, and postzygotic isolation in the sunflower hybrid zone discussed earlier is influenced by at least 26 chromosomal segments (and an unknown number of genes). Overall, studies conducted to date suggest that few or many genes can influence the evolution of reproductive isolation and hence the emergence of a new species—a new addition to the great diversity of life.

From Speciation to Macroevolution

As you've seen in this chapter's examples, speciation may begin with differences as seemingly small as the color on a cichlid's back. However, as speciation occurs again and again, such differences can accumulate and become more pronounced, eventually leading to the formation of new groups of organisms that differ greatly from their ancestors (as in the origin of whales from land-dwelling mammals; see Figure 22.16). Furthermore, as one group of organisms increases in size by producing many new species, another group of organisms may shrink, losing species to extinction. The cumulative effects of many such speciation and extinction events have helped to shape the sweeping evolutionary changes that are documented in the fossil record. In the next chapter, we turn to such large-scale evolutionary changes as we begin our study of macroevolution.

CONCEPT CHECK 24.4

1. Speciation can occur rapidly between diverging populations, yet the length of time between speciation events is often more than a million years. Explain this apparent contradiction.
2. **WHAT IF?** Summarize experimental evidence that the *yup* locus acts as a prezygotic barrier to reproduction in two species of monkey flowers. Do these results demonstrate that the *yup* locus alone controls barriers to reproduction between these closely related monkey flower species? Explain your answer.

For suggested answers, see Appendix A.

Chapter 24 Review

SUMMARY OF KEY CONCEPTS

CONCEPT 24.1

The biological species concept emphasizes reproductive isolation (pp. 487–492)

▶ **The Biological Species Concept** A biological species is a group of populations whose individuals have the potential to interbreed and produce viable, fertile offspring with each other but not with members of other species. The biological species concept emphasizes reproductive isolation through prezygotic and postzygotic barriers that separate gene pools.

▶ **Other Definitions of Species** Although helpful in thinking about how speciation occurs, the biological species concept has limitations. For instance, it cannot be applied to organisms known only as fossils or to organisms that reproduce only asexually. Thus, scientists use other species concepts, such as the morphological species concept, in certain circumstances.

MEDIA

Activity Overview of Macroevolution

CONCEPT 24.2

Speciation can take place with or without geographic separation (pp. 492–498)

▶ **Allopatric ("Other Country") Speciation** Evidence indicates that allopatric speciation can occur when two populations of one species become geographically separated from each other. One or both populations may undergo evolutionary change during the period of separation, resulting in the establishment of prezygotic or postzygotic barriers to reproduction.

▶ **Sympatric ("Same Country") Speciation** A new species can originate while remaining in a geographically overlapping area with the parent species. Plant species (and, more rarely, animals) have evolved sympatrically through polyploidy. Sympatric speciation can also result from habitat shifts and sexual selection.

▶ **Allopatric and Sympatric Speciation:** *A Review*

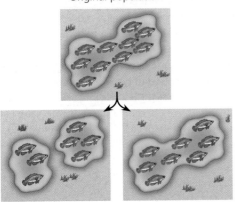

Original population

Allopatric speciation   Sympatric speciation

MEDIA

MP3 Tutor Speciation

CONCEPT 24.3

Hybrid zones provide opportunities to study factors that cause reproductive isolation (pp. 498–501)

▶ **Patterns Within Hybrid Zones** Many groups of organisms form hybrid zones in which members of different species meet and mate, producing at least some offspring of mixed ancestry.

▶ **Hybrid Zones over Time** In many hybrid zones, a limited number of hybrid offspring continue to be produced over time. In others, reinforcement strengthens prezygotic barriers to reproduction, thus decreasing the formation of unfit hybrids. In still other hybrid zones, barriers to reproduction may weaken over time, resulting in the fusion of the species' gene pools (reversing the speciation process).

CONCEPT 24.4

Speciation can occur rapidly or slowly and can result from changes in few or many genes (pp. 501–504)

▶ **The Time Course of Speciation** New species can form rapidly once divergence begins—but it can take millions of years for that to happen. The time interval between speciation events varies considerably, from a few thousand years to tens of millions of years.

▶ **Studying the Genetics of Speciation** New developments in genetics have enabled researchers to identify specific genes involved in some cases of speciation. Results show that speciation can be driven by few or many genes.

▶ **From Speciation to Macroevolution** Due to repeated events, small differences between organisms can accumulate, leading to the formation of new groups of organisms.

MEDIA

Investigation How Do New Species Arise by Genetic Isolation?
Biology Labs On-Line EvolutionLab

TESTING YOUR KNOWLEDGE

SELF-QUIZ

1. The *largest* unit within which gene flow can readily occur is a
   a. population.
   b. species.
   c. genus.
   d. hybrid.
   e. phylum.

2. Bird guides once listed the myrtle warbler and Audubon's warbler as distinct species. Recently, these birds have been classified as eastern and western forms of a single species, the yellow-rumped warbler. Which of the following pieces of evidence, if true, would be cause for this reclassification?
   a. The two forms interbreed often in nature, and their offspring have good survival and reproduction.
   b. The two forms live in similar habitats.
   c. The two forms have many genes in common.
   d. The two forms have similar food requirements.
   e. The two forms are very similar in coloration.

3. Males of different species of the fruit fly *Drosophila* that live in the same parts of the Hawaiian Islands have different elaborate courtship rituals that involve fighting other males and stylized movements that attract females. What type of reproductive isolation does this represent?
   a. habitat isolation
   b. temporal isolation
   c. behavioral isolation
   d. gametic isolation
   e. postzygotic barriers

4. Which of the following factors would *not* contribute to allopatric speciation?
   a. A population becomes geographically isolated from the parent population.
   b. The separated population is small, and genetic drift occurs.
   c. The isolated population is exposed to different selection pressures than the ancestral population.
   d. Different mutations begin to distinguish the gene pools of the separated populations.
   e. Gene flow between the two populations is extensive.

5. Plant species A has a diploid number of 12. Plant species B has a diploid number of 16. A new species, C, arises as an allopolyploid from A and B. The diploid number for species C would probably be
   a. 12.   b. 14.   c. 16.
   d. 28.   e. 56.

6. According to the punctuated equilibria model,
   a. natural selection is unimportant as a mechanism of evolution.
   b. given enough time, most existing species will branch gradually into new species.
   c. most new species accumulate their unique features relatively rapidly as they come into existence, then change little for the rest of their duration as a species.
   d. most evolution occurs in sympatric populations.
   e. speciation is usually due to a single mutation.

For Self-Quiz answers, see Appendix A.

MEDIA   Visit the Study Area at **www.masteringbio.com** for a Practice Test.

EVOLUTION CONNECTION

7. What is the biological basis for assigning all human populations to a single species? Can you think of a scenario by which a second human species could originate in the future?

SCIENTIFIC INQUIRY

8. **DRAW IT**   In this chapter, you read that bread wheat (*Triticum aestivum*) is an allohexaploid, containing two sets of chromosomes from each of three different parent species. Genetic analysis suggests that the three species pictured below each contributed chromosome sets to *T. aestivum*. (The capital letters here represent sets of chromosomes rather than individual genes.) Evidence also indicates that the first polyploidy event was a spontaneous hybridization of the early cultivated wheat species *T. monococcum* and a wild grass species. Based on this information, draw a diagram of one possible chain of events that could have produced the allohexaploid *T. aestivum*.

Ancestral species:

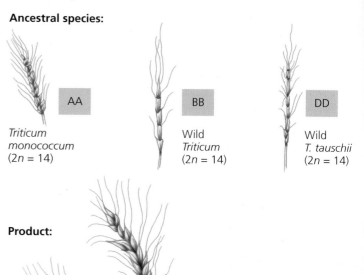

Triticum monococcum (2n = 14)   AA

Wild *Triticum* (2n = 14)   BB

Wild *T. tauschii* (2n = 14)   DD

Product:

AA BB DD

T. aestivum (bread wheat) (2n = 42)

SCIENCE, TECHNOLOGY, AND SOCIETY

9. In the United States, the rare red wolf (*Canis lupus*) has been known to hybridize with coyotes (*Canis latrans*), which are much more numerous. Although red wolves and coyotes differ in terms of morphology, DNA, and behavior, genetic evidence suggests that living red wolf individuals are actually hybrids. Red wolves are designated as an endangered species and hence receive legal protection under the Endangered Species Act. Some people think that their endangered status should be withdrawn because the remaining red wolves are hybrids, not members of a "pure" species. Do you agree? Why or why not?

25

The History of Life on Earth

OVERVIEW

Lost Worlds

Visitors to Antarctica today encounter one of Earth's harshest, most barren environments. In this land of extreme cold where there is almost no liquid water, life is sparse and small—the largest fully terrestrial animal is a fly 5 mm long. But even as early antarctic explorers struggled to survive, some of them made an astonishing discovery: fossil evidence that life once thrived where it now barely exists. Fossils reveal that 500 million years ago, the ocean waters surrounding Antarctica were warm and teeming with tropical invertebrates. Later, the continent was covered in forests for hundreds of millions of years. At various times, a wide range of animals stalked through these forests, including 3-meter-tall predatory "terror birds" and giant dinosaurs such as the voracious *Cryolophosaurus* **(Figure 25.1)**, a 7-meter-long relative of *Tyrannosaurus rex*.

Fossils discovered in other parts of the world tell a similar, if not quite as surprising, story: Past organisms were very different from

▲ **Figure 25.1 What does fossil evidence say about where these dinosaurs lived?**

▲ *Cryolophosaurus* **skull**

those now alive. The sweeping changes in life on Earth revealed by fossils illustrate **macroevolution**, the pattern of evolution over large time scales. Specific examples of macroevolutionary change include the origin of key biochemical processes such as photosynthesis, the emergence of the first terrestrial vertebrates, and the long-term impact of a mass extinction on the diversity of life.

Taken together, such changes provide a grand view of the evolutionary history of life on Earth. We'll examine that history in this chapter, beginning with hypotheses regarding the origin of life. The origin of life is the most speculative topic of the entire unit, for no fossil evidence of that seminal episode exists. We will then turn to the fossil record and what it tells us about major events in the history of life, paying particular attention to factors that have helped to shape the rise and fall of different groups of organisms over time.

CONCEPT 25.1

Conditions on early Earth made the origin of life possible

The earliest evidence of life on Earth comes from fossils of microorganisms that are about 3.5 billion years old. But when and how did the first living cells appear? Observations and experiments in chemistry, geology, and physics have led scientists to propose one scenario that we'll examine here. They hypothesize that chemical and physical processes on early Earth, aided by the emerging force of natural selection, could have produced very simple cells through a sequence of four main stages:

1. The abiotic (nonliving) synthesis of small organic molecules, such as amino acids and nucleotides
2. The joining of these small molecules into macromolecules, including proteins and nucleic acids
3. The packaging of these molecules into "protobionts," droplets with membranes that maintained an internal chemistry different from that of their surroundings
4. The origin of self-replicating molecules that eventually made inheritance possible

Though speculative, this scenario leads to predictions that can be tested in the laboratory. In this section, we will examine some of the evidence for each stage.

Synthesis of Organic Compounds on Early Earth

There is scientific evidence that Earth and the other planets of the solar system formed about 4.6 billion years ago, condensing from a vast cloud of dust and rocks that surrounded the young sun. For the first few hundred million years, life probably could not have originated or survived on Earth because the planet was still being bombarded by huge chunks of rock and ice left over from the formation of the solar system. The collisions generated enough heat to vaporize the available water and prevent seas from forming. This phase likely ended about 3.9 billion years ago.

As the bombardment of early Earth slowed, conditions on the planet were extremely different from those of today. The first atmosphere was probably thick with water vapor, along with various compounds released by volcanic eruptions, including nitrogen and its oxides, carbon dioxide, methane, ammonia, hydrogen, and hydrogen sulfide. As Earth cooled, the water vapor condensed into oceans, and much of the hydrogen quickly escaped into space.

In the 1920s, Russian chemist A. I. Oparin and British scientist J. B. S. Haldane independently hypothesized that Earth's early atmosphere was a reducing (electron-adding) environment, in which organic compounds could have formed from simple molecules. The energy for this organic synthesis could have come from lightning and intense UV radiation. Haldane suggested that the early oceans were a solution of organic molecules, a "primitive soup" from which life arose.

In 1953, Stanley Miller and Harold Urey, of the University of Chicago, tested the Oparin-Haldane hypothesis by creating laboratory conditions comparable to those that scientists at the time thought existed on early Earth (see Figure 4.2). Their apparatus yielded a variety of amino acids found in organisms today, along with other organic compounds. Many laboratories have since repeated the experiment using different recipes for the atmosphere. Some of these variations also produced organic compounds.

However, it is unclear whether the atmosphere of young Earth contained enough methane and ammonia to be reducing. Growing evidence suggests that the early atmosphere was made up primarily of nitrogen and carbon dioxide and was neither reducing nor oxidizing (electron removing). Some recent Miller-Urey-type experiments using such atmospheres have produced organic molecules. In any case, it is likely that small "pockets" of the early atmosphere—perhaps near volcanic openings—were reducing. Perhaps instead of forming in the atmosphere, the first organic compounds formed near submerged volcanoes and deep-sea vents, where hot water and minerals gush into the ocean from Earth's interior (Figure 25.2). These regions are also rich in inorganic sulfur and iron compounds, which are important in ATP synthesis by present-day organisms.

Miller-Urey-type experiments demonstrate that the abiotic synthesis of organic molecules is possible. Support for this idea also comes from analyses of the chemical composition of meteorites. Among the meteorites that land on Earth are carbonaceous chondrites, rocks that are 1–2% carbon compounds by mass. Fragments of a fallen 4.5-billion-year-old chondrite found in Australia in 1969 contain more than 80 amino acids, some in large amounts. Remarkably, the proportions of these amino acids are similar to those produced in the Miller-Urey experiment. The chondrite amino acids cannot

▲ **Figure 25.2 A window to early life?** An instrument on the research submarine *Alvin* samples the water around a hydrothermal vent in the Sea of Cortés. More than 1.5 km below the surface, the vent releases hydrogen sulfide and iron sulfide, which react and produce pyrite (fool's gold) and hydrogen gas. Prokaryotes that live near the vent use the hydrogen as an energy source. Such environments are among the most extreme in which life exists today, and some researchers favor the hypothesis that life may have begun in similar regions of early Earth.

be contaminants from Earth because they consist of an equal mix of D and L isomers (see Chapter 4). Organisms make and use only L isomers, with a few rare exceptions.

Abiotic Synthesis of Macromolecules

The presence of small organic molecules, such as amino acids, is not sufficient for the emergence of life as we know it. Every cell has a vast assortment of macromolecules, including enzymes and other proteins and the nucleic acids that are essential for self-replication. Could such macromolecules have formed on early Earth? By dripping solutions of amino acids onto hot sand, clay, or rock, researchers have been able to produce amino acid polymers. The polymers formed spontaneously, without the help of enzymes or ribosomes. But unlike proteins, these polymers are a complex mix of linked and cross-linked amino acids. Nevertheless, it is possible that such polymers may have acted as weak catalysts for a variety of reactions on early Earth.

Protobionts

Two key properties of life are accurate replication and metabolism. Neither property can exist without the other. DNA molecules carry genetic information, including the instructions needed to replicate themselves accurately. But the replication of DNA requires elaborate enzymatic machinery, along with a copious supply of nucleotide building blocks that must be provided by the cell's metabolism (see Chapter 16). While Miller-Urey-type experiments have yielded some of the nitrogenous bases of DNA and RNA, they have not produced anything like nucleotides. If building blocks of nucleic acids were not part of the early organic soup, self-replicating molecules and a metabolism-like source of the building blocks must have appeared together. How did that happen?

The necessary conditions may have been met by **protobionts**, collections of abiotically produced molecules surrounded by a membrane-like structure. Protobionts may exhibit some properties of life, including simple reproduction and metabolism, as well as the maintenance of an internal chemical environment different from that of their surroundings.

Laboratory experiments demonstrate that protobionts could have formed spontaneously from abiotically produced organic compounds. For example, certain small membrane-bounded droplets called liposomes can form when lipids or other organic molecules are added to water. The hydrophobic molecules in the mixture organize into a bilayer at the surface of the droplet, much like the lipid bilayer of a plasma membrane. Liposomes can "reproduce" (**Figure 25.3a**), and because their bilayer is selectively permeable, liposomes undergo osmotic swelling or shrinking when placed in solutions of different solute concentrations. Some of these liposomes can perform simple metabolic reactions, another important step toward the origin of life (**Figure 25.3b**).

Self-Replicating RNA and the Dawn of Natural Selection

The first genetic material was most likely RNA, not DNA. Thomas Cech, of the University of Colorado, and Sidney Altman, of Yale University, found that RNA, which plays a central role in protein synthesis, can also carry out a number of enzyme-like catalytic functions. Cech called these RNA catalysts **ribozymes**. Some ribozymes can make complementary copies of short pieces of RNA, provided that they are supplied with nucleotide building blocks.

Natural selection on the molecular level has produced ribozymes capable of self-replication in the laboratory. How does this occur? Unlike double-stranded DNA, which takes the form of a uniform helix, single-stranded RNA molecules assume a variety of specific three-dimensional shapes mandated by their nucleotide sequences. In a particular environment, RNA molecules with certain base sequences are more stable and replicate faster and with fewer errors than other sequences. The RNA molecule whose sequence is best suited to the surrounding environment and has the greatest ability to replicate itself will leave the most descendant molecules. Its descendants will not be a single RNA "species" but instead will be a family of sequences that differ slightly because of copying

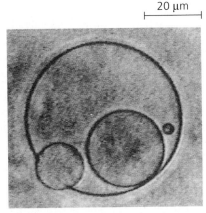

(a) **Simple reproduction.** This liposome is "giving birth" to smaller liposomes (LM).

▲ **Figure 25.3 Laboratory versions of liposome protobionts.**

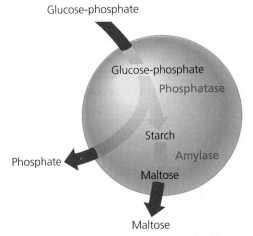

(b) **Simple metabolism.** If enzymes—in this case, phosphatase and amylase—are included in the solution from which the droplets self-assemble, some liposomes can carry out simple metabolic reactions and export the products.

errors. Occasionally, a copying error will result in a molecule that folds into a shape that is even more stable or more adept at self-replication than the ancestral sequence. Similar selection events may have occurred on early Earth. Thus, the molecular biology of today may have been preceded by an "RNA world," in which small RNA molecules that carried genetic information were able to replicate and to store information about the protobionts that carried them.

A protobiont with self-replicating, catalytic RNA would differ from its many neighbors that did not carry RNA or that carried RNA without such capabilities. If that protobiont could grow, split, and pass its RNA molecules to its daughters, the daughters would have some of the properties of their parent. Although the first such protobionts must have carried only limited amounts of genetic information, specifying only a few properties, their inherited characteristics could have been acted on by natural selection. The most successful of the early protobionts would have increased in number because they could exploit their resources effectively and pass their abilities on to subsequent generations. The emergence of such protobionts may seem unlikely, but remember that there could have been trillions of protobionts in bodies of water on early Earth. Even those with only a limited capacity for inheritance would have had a huge advantage over the rest.

Once RNA sequences that carried genetic information appeared in protobionts, many further changes would have been possible. For example, RNA could have provided the template on which DNA nucleotides were assembled. Double-stranded DNA is a much more stable repository for genetic information than the more fragile single-stranded RNA. DNA also can be replicated more accurately. Accurate replication was a necessity as genomes grew larger through gene duplication and other processes and as more properties of the protobionts became coded in genetic information. After DNA appeared, perhaps RNA molecules began to take on their present-day roles as intermediates in the translation of genetic programs, and the RNA world gave way to a "DNA world." The stage was now set for a blossoming of diverse life-forms—a change we see documented in the fossil record.

CONCEPT CHECK 25.1

1. What hypothesis did Miller and Urey test in their famous experiment?
2. How would the appearance of protobionts have represented a key step in the origin of life?
3. **WHAT IF?** If scientists built a protobiont with self-replicating RNA and metabolism under conditions similar to those on early Earth, would this prove that life began as in the experiment? Explain.

For suggested answers, see Appendix A.

CONCEPT 25.2
The fossil record documents the history of life

Starting with the earliest traces of life, the fossil record opens a window into the world of long ago and provides glimpses of the evolution of life over billions of years. In this section, we'll explore what the fossil record reveals about the major changes in the history of life—what those changes have been and how they may have occurred.

The Fossil Record

Recall from Chapter 22 that sedimentary rocks are the richest source of fossils. As a result, the fossil record is based primarily on the sequence in which fossils have accumulated in sedimentary rock layers called *strata* (see Figure 22.3). Useful information is also provided by other types of fossils, such as insects preserved in amber (fossilized tree sap) and mammals frozen in ice.

The fossil record shows that there have been great changes in the kinds of organisms that dominated life on Earth at different points in time (Figure 25.4). Many past organisms were unlike today's organisms, and many organisms that once were common are now extinct. As we'll see later, fossils also document how new groups of organisms arose from previously existing ones.

As substantial and significant as the fossil record is, keep in mind that it is an incomplete chronicle of evolutionary change. Many of Earth's organisms probably did not die in the right place at the right time to be preserved as fossils. Of those fossils that were formed, many were destroyed by later geologic processes, and only a fraction of the others have been discovered. As a result, the known fossil record is biased in favor of species that existed for a long time, were abundant and widespread in certain kinds of environments, and had hard shells, skeletons, or other parts that facilitated their fossilization. Even with its limitations, however, the fossil record is a remarkably detailed account of biological change over the vast scale of geologic time. Furthermore, as shown by the recently unearthed fossils of whale ancestors with hind limbs (see Figure 22.16), gaps in the fossil record continue to be filled by new discoveries.

How Rocks and Fossils Are Dated

Fossils are valuable data for reconstructing the history of life, but only if we can determine where they fit in that unfolding story. While the order of fossils in rock strata tells us the sequence in which the fossils were laid down—their relative ages—it does not tell us their actual (absolute) ages. Examining the relative positions of fossils in strata is like peeling off layers of wallpaper in an old house. You can determine the

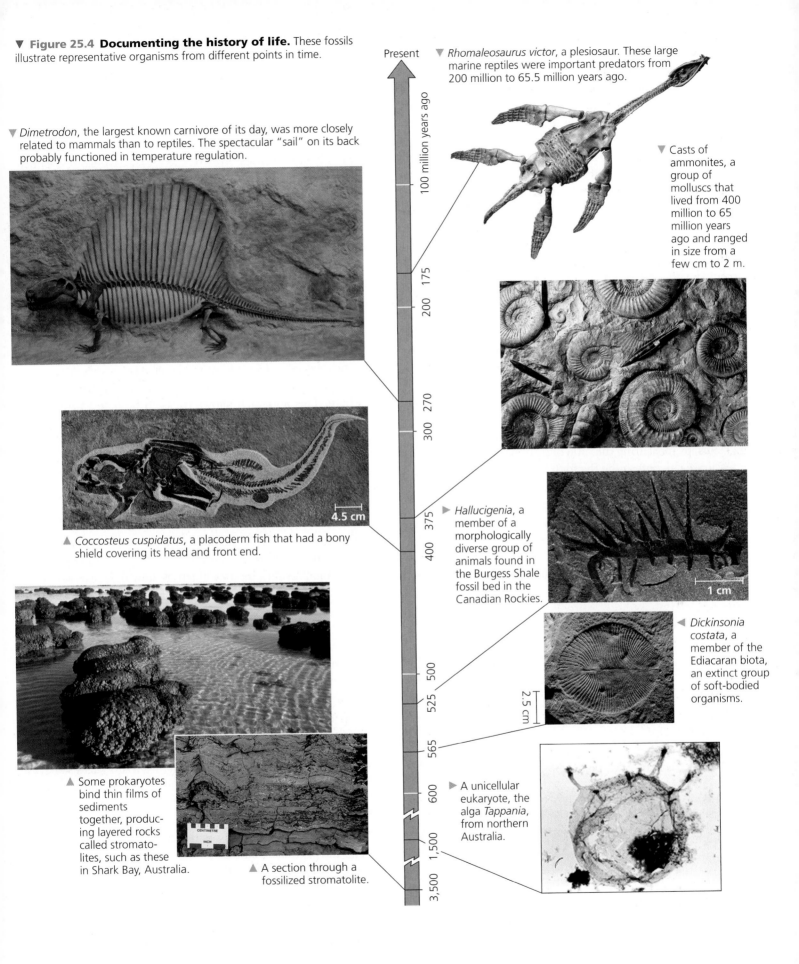

▼ **Figure 25.4 Documenting the history of life.** These fossils illustrate representative organisms from different points in time.

Present

100 million years ago

▼ *Rhomaleosaurus victor*, a plesiosaur. These large marine reptiles were important predators from 200 million to 65.5 million years ago.

▼ *Dimetrodon*, the largest known carnivore of its day, was more closely related to mammals than to reptiles. The spectacular "sail" on its back probably functioned in temperature regulation.

▼ Casts of ammonites, a group of molluscs that lived from 400 million to 65 million years ago and ranged in size from a few cm to 2 m.

175

200

270

300

4.5 cm

▲ *Coccosteus cuspidatus*, a placoderm fish that had a bony shield covering its head and front end.

375

400

▶ *Hallucigenia*, a member of a morphologically diverse group of animals found in the Burgess Shale fossil bed in the Canadian Rockies.

1 cm

◀ *Dickinsonia costata*, a member of the Ediacaran biota, an extinct group of soft-bodied organisms.

500

525

2.5 cm

▲ Some prokaryotes bind thin films of sediments together, producing layered rocks called stromatolites, such as these in Shark Bay, Australia.

565

600

▶ A unicellular eukaryote, the alga *Tappania*, from northern Australia.

▲ A section through a fossilized stromatolite.

1,500

3,500

sequence in which the layers were applied, but not the year each layer was added.

How can we determine the absolute age of a fossil? (Note that "absolute" dating does not mean errorless dating, but only that an age is given in years rather than relative terms such as *before* and *after*.) One of the most common techniques is **radiometric dating**, which is based on the decay of radioactive isotopes (see Chapter 2). A radioactive "parent" isotope decays to a "daughter" isotope at a constant rate. The rate of decay is expressed by the **half-life**, the time required for 50% of the parent isotope to decay **(Figure 25.5)**. Each variety of radioactive isotope has a characteristic half-life, which is not affected by temperature, pressure, or other such environmental variables. For example, carbon-14 decays relatively quickly; it has a half-life of 5,730 years. Uranium-238 decays slowly; its half-life is 4.5 billion years.

Fossils contain isotopes of elements that accumulated in the organisms when they were alive. For example, the carbon in a living organism includes the most common carbon isotope, carbon-12, as well as a radioactive isotope, carbon-14. When the organism dies, it stops accumulating carbon, and the amount of carbon-12 in its tissues does not change over time. However, the carbon-14 that it contains at the time of death slowly decays and becomes another element, nitrogen-14. Thus, by measuring the ratio of carbon-14 to carbon-12 in a fossil, we can determine the fossil's age. This method works for fossils up to about 75,000 years old; fossils older than that contain too little carbon-14 to be detected with current techniques. Radioactive isotopes with longer half-lives are used to date older fossils.

Determining the age of old fossils in sedimentary rocks can be challenging. One reason is that organisms do not use ra-dioisotopes that have long half-lives, such as uranium-238, to build their bones or shells. Moreover, the sedimentary rocks themselves tend to be composed of sediments of differing ages. Hence, we usually cannot date old fossils directly. However, geologists can apply an indirect method to infer the absolute age of fossils that are sandwiched between two layers of volcanic rocks. For example, researchers might measure the amount in each rock layer of the radioactive isotope potassium-40, which has a half-life of 1.3 billion years. If the two surrounding rock layers were determined to be 525 million and 535 million years old, the fossils likely represent organisms that lived about 530 million years ago.

The magnetism of rocks can also provide dating information. During the formation of volcanic and sedimentary rocks, iron particles in the rock align themselves with Earth's magnetic field. When the rock hardens, the particles' orientation is frozen in time. Measurements of the magnetism of various rock layers indicate that Earth's north and south magnetic poles have reversed repeatedly in the past. Because these magnetic reversals affect the entire planet at once, reversals in one location can be matched with corresponding patterns elsewhere. This approach allows rocks to be dated when other methods are not available. It also can be used to corroborate ages estimated in other ways.

Now that we've seen how fossils can be dated, let's turn to an example of what we can learn from them.

The Origin of New Groups of Organisms

Some fossils provide a detailed look at the origin of new groups of organisms. Such fossils are central to our understanding of evolution; they illustrate how new features of organisms arise and how long it takes for such changes to occur. We'll examine one such case here, the origin of mammals.

Along with amphibians and reptiles, mammals belong to the group of animals called *tetrapods* (from the Greek *tetra*, four, and *pod*, foot), named for having four limbs. Mammals have a number of unique anatomical features that fossilize readily, allowing scientists to trace their origin. For example, the lower jaw is composed of one bone (the dentary) in mammals but several bones in other tetrapods. In addition, the lower and upper jaws hinge between a different set of bones in mammals than in other tetrapods. As we'll explore in Chapter 34, mammals also have a unique set of three bones that transmit sound in the middle ear (the hammer, anvil, and stirrup), whereas other tetrapods have only one such bone (the stirrup). Finally, the teeth of mammals are differentiated into incisors (for tearing), canines (for piercing), and the multi-pointed premolars and molars (for grinding). In contrast, the teeth of other tetrapods usually consist of a row of undifferentiated, single-pointed teeth.

As detailed in **Figure 25.6**, the fossil record shows that the unique features of mammalian jaws and teeth evolved as a series of gradual modifications. As you study Figure 25.6, bear in

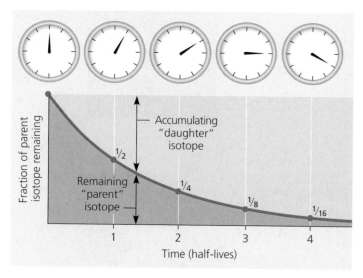

▲ **Figure 25.5 Radiometric dating.** In this diagram, each division of the clock face represents a half-life.

DRAW IT *Relabel the x-axis (time) of this graph to illustrate the radioactive decay of uranium-238 (half-life = 4.5 billion years).*

Exploring The Origin of Mammals

Over the course of 120 million years, mammals originated gradually from a group of tetrapods called synapsids. Shown here are a few of the many fossil organisms whose morphological features represent intermediate steps between living mammals and their synapsid ancestors. The evolutionary context of the origin of mammals is shown in the tree diagram at right.

Key

- Articular
- Quadrate
- Dentary
- Squamosal

Synapsid (300 mya)

Temporal fenestra

Synapsids had multiple bones in the lower jaw and single-pointed teeth. The jaw hinge was formed by the articular and quadrate bones. Synapsids also had an opening called the temporal fenestra behind the eye socket. Powerful cheek muscles for closing the jaws probably passed through the temporal fenestra. Over time, this opening enlarged and moved in front of the hinge between the lower and upper jaws, thereby increasing the power and precision with which the jaws could be closed (much as moving a doorknob away from the hinge makes a door easier to close).

Therapsid (280 mya)

Temporal fenestra

Later, a group of synapsids called therapsids appeared. Therapsids had large dentary bones, long faces, and the first signs of specialized teeth, large canines.

Early cynodont (260 mya)

Temporal fenestra

In early cynodont therapsids, the dentary was the largest bone in the lower jaw, the temporal fenestra was large and positioned forward of the jaw hinge, and teeth with several cusps first appeared (not visible in the diagram). As in earlier synapsids, the jaw had an articular-quadrate hinge.

Later cynodont (220 mya)

Later cynodonts had teeth with complex cusp patterns and their lower and upper jaws hinged in two locations: They retained the original articular-quadrate hinge and formed a new, second hinge between the dentary and squamosal bones.

Very late cynodont (195 mya)

In the common ancestor of this very late cynodont and mammals, the original articular-quadrate hinge was lost, leaving the dentary-squamosal hinge as the only hinge between the lower and upper jaws (as in living mammals). The articular and quadrate bones migrated into the ear region (not shown), where they functioned in transmitting sound. In the mammal lineage, these two bones later evolved into the familiar hammer and anvil (see Figure 34.31).

mind that it includes just a few examples of the fossil skulls that document the origin of mammals. If all the known fossils in the sequence were arranged by shape and placed side by side, their features would blend smoothly from one group to the next, reflecting how the features of a new group, the mammals, gradually arose in a previously existing group, the cynodonts.

CONCEPT 25.3
Key events in life's history include the origins of single-celled and multicelled organisms and the colonization of land

The study of fossils has helped geologists to establish a **geologic record** of Earth's history, which is divided into three eons (**Table 25.1**, on the facing page). The first two eons—the Archaean and the Proterozoic—together lasted approximately 4 billion years. The Phanerozoic eon, roughly the last half billion years, encompasses most of the time that animals have existed on Earth. It is divided into three eras: the Paleozoic, Mesozoic, and Cenozoic. Each era represents a distinct age in the history of Earth and its life. For example, the Mesozoic era is sometimes called the "age of reptiles" because of its abundance of reptilian fossils, including those of dinosaurs. The boundaries between the eras correspond to major extinction events seen in the fossil record, when many forms of life disappeared and were replaced by forms that evolved from the survivors.

As we've seen, the fossil record provides a sweeping overview of the history of life over geologic time. Here we will focus on a few major events in that history, returning to study the details in Unit Five. **Figure 25.7** uses the analogy of a clock to place these events in the context of the geologic record. This clock will reap-

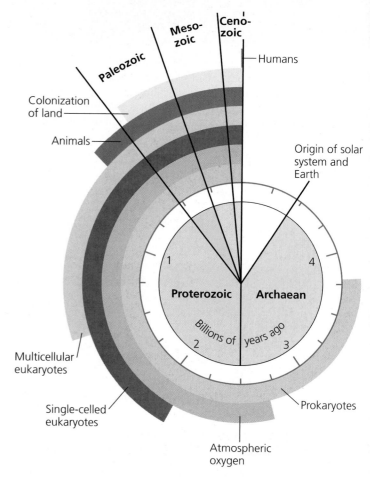

▲ **Figure 25.7 Clock analogy for some key events in Earth's history.** The clock ticks down from the origin of Earth 4.6 billion years ago to the present.

pear at various points in this section as a quick visual reminder of when the events we are discussing took place.

The First Single-Celled Organisms

The earliest evidence of life, dating from 3.5 billion years ago, comes from fossilized stromatolites (see Figure 25.4). **Stromatolites** are layered rocks that form when certain prokaryotes bind thin films of sediment together. Present-day stromatolites are found in a few warm, shallow, salty bays. If microbial communities complex enough to form stromatolites existed 3.5 billion years ago, it is a reasonable hypothesis that single-celled organisms originated much earlier, perhaps as early as 3.9 billion years ago.

Early prokaryotes were Earth's sole inhabitants from at least 3.5 billion years ago to about 2.1 billion years ago. As we will see, these prokaryotes transformed life on our planet.

Table 25.1 **The Geologic Record**

Relative Duration of Eons	Era	Period	Epoch	Age (Millions of Years Ago)	Some Important Events in the History of Life
Phan-erozoic	Cenozoic	Neogene	Holocene		Historical time
				0.01	
			Pleistocene		Ice ages; humans appear
				1.8	
			Pliocene		Origin of genus *Homo*
				5.3	
			Miocene		Continued radiation of mammals and angiosperms; apelike ancestors of humans appear
				23	
		Paleogene	Oligocene		Origins of many primate groups, including apes
				33.9	
			Eocene		Angiosperm dominance increases; continued radiation of most present-day mammalian orders
				55.8	
			Paleocene		Major radiation of mammals, birds, and pollinating insects
				65.5	
Proter-ozoic	Mesozoic	Cretaceous			Flowering plants (angiosperms) appear and diversify; many groups of organisms, including most dinosaurs, become extinct at end of period
				145.5	
		Jurassic			Gymnosperms continue as dominant plants; dinosaurs abundant and diverse
				199.6	
		Triassic			Cone-bearing plants (gymnosperms) dominate landscape; dinosaurs evolve and radiate; origin of mammals
				251	
	Paleozoic	Permian			Radiation of reptiles; origin of most present-day groups of insects; extinction of many marine and terrestrial organisms at end of period
				299	
		Carboniferous			Extensive forests of vascular plants form; first seed plants appear; origin of reptiles; amphibians dominant
				359.2	
		Devonian			Diversification of bony fishes; first tetrapods and insects appear
				416	
		Silurian			Diversification of early vascular plants
				443.7	
		Ordovician			Marine algae abundant; colonization of land by diverse fungi, plants, and animals
				488.3	
		Cambrian			Sudden increase in diversity of many animal phyla (Cambrian explosion)
				542	
Archaean		Ediacaran			Diverse algae and soft-bodied invertebrate animals appear
				635	
				2,100	Oldest fossils of eukaryotic cells appear
				2,500	
				2,700	Concentration of atmospheric oxygen begins to increase
				3,500	Oldest fossils of cells (prokaryotes) appear
				3,800	Oldest known rocks on Earth's surface
				Approx. 4,600	Origin of Earth

Photosynthesis and the Oxygen Revolution

Most atmospheric oxygen gas (O_2) is of biological origin, produced during the water-splitting step of photosynthesis. When oxygenic photosynthesis first evolved, the free O_2 it produced probably dissolved in the surrounding water until it reached a high enough concentration to react with dissolved iron. This would have caused the iron to precipitate as iron oxide, which accumulated as sediments. These sediments were compressed into banded iron formations, red layers of rock containing iron oxide that are a source of iron ore today (**Figure 25.8**). Once all of the dissolved iron had precipitated, additional O_2 dissolved in the water until the seas and lakes became saturated with O_2. After this occurred, the O_2 finally began to "gas out" of the water and enter the atmosphere. This change left its mark in the rusting of iron-rich terrestrial rocks, a process that began about 2.7 billion years ago. This chronology implies that bacteria similar to today's cyanobacteria (oxygen-releasing, photosynthetic bacteria) originated well before 2.7 billion years ago.

The amount of atmospheric O_2 increased gradually from about 2.7 to 2.2 billion years ago, but then shot up relatively rapidly to more than 10% of its present level. This "oxygen revolution" had an enormous impact on life. In certain of its chemical forms, oxygen attacks chemical bonds and can inhibit enzymes and damage cells. As a result the rising concentration of atmospheric O_2 probably doomed many prokaryotic groups. Some species survived in habitats that remained anaerobic, where we find their descendants living today (see Chapter 27). Among other survivors, diverse adaptations to the changing atmosphere evolved, including cellular respiration, which uses O_2 in the process of harvesting the energy stored in organic molecules.

▲ **Figure 25.8 Banded iron formations: evidence of oxygenic photosynthesis.** The reddish streaks in this sedimentary rock are bands of iron oxide.

As mentioned previously, the early, gradual rise in atmospheric O_2 levels was probably brought about by ancient cyanobacteria. A few hundred million years later, the rise in O_2 accelerated. What caused this acceleration? One hypothesis is that this rise followed the evolution of eukaryotic cells containing chloroplasts, as we will discuss in the next section.

The First Eukaryotes

The oldest widely accepted fossils of eukaryotic organisms are about 2.1 billion years old. Recall that eukaryotic cells have more complex organization than prokaryotic cells: Eukaryotic cells have a nuclear envelope, mitochondria, endoplasmic reticulum, and other internal structures that prokaryotes lack. Also, unlike prokaryotic cells, eukaryotic cells have a cytoskeleton, a feature that enables eukaryotic cells to change their shape and thereby surround and engulf other cells.

How did these eukaryotic features evolve from prokaryotic cells? A range of evidence supports a model called **endosymbiosis**, which posits that mitochondria and plastids (a general term for chloroplasts and related organelles) were formerly small prokaryotes that began living within larger cells. The term *endosymbiont* refers to a cell that lives within another cell, called the *host cell*. The prokaryotic ancestors of mitochondria and plastids probably gained entry to the host cell as undigested prey or internal parasites. Though such a process may seem unlikely, scientists have directly observed cases in which endosymbionts that began as prey or parasites came to have a mutually beneficial relationship with the host in as little as five years.

By whatever means the relationships began, we can hypothesize how the symbiosis could have become mutually beneficial. A heterotrophic host could use nutrients released from photosynthetic endosymbionts. And in a world that was becoming increasingly aerobic, a host that was itself an anaerobe would have benefited from endosymbionts that turned the oxygen to advantage. Over time, the host and endosymbionts would have become a single organism, its parts inseparable. Although all eukaryotes have mitochondria or remnants of these organelles, they do not all have plastids. Thus, the model of **serial endosymbiosis** supposes that mitochondria evolved before plastids through a sequence of endosymbiotic events (**Figure 25.9**).

A great deal of evidence supports the endosymbiotic origin of mitochondria and plastids. The inner membranes of both organelles have enzymes and transport systems that are homologous to those found in the plasma membranes of living prokaryotes. Mitochondria and plastids replicate by a splitting process that is similar to that of certain prokaryotes. In addition, each of these organelles contains a single, circular DNA molecule that, like the chromosomes of bacteria, is not associated with histones or large amounts of other proteins. As might be expected of organelles descended from free-living organisms, mitochondria and plastids also have the cellular machinery (including ribosomes) needed to transcribe and translate their DNA into proteins. Finally, in terms of size, nucleotide sequence, and sensitivity to certain antibiotics, the ribosomes of mitochondria and plastids are more similar to prokaryotic ribosomes than they are to the cytoplasmic ribosomes of eukaryotic cells.

The Origin of Multicellularity

An orchestra can play a greater variety of musical compositions than a violin soloist can; the increased complexity of the orchestra makes more variations possible. Likewise, the appearance of structurally complex eukaryotic cells sparked the evolution of greater morphological diversity than was possible for the simpler prokaryotic cells. After the first eukaryotes appeared, a great range of unicellular forms evolved, giving rise to the diversity of single-celled eukaryotes that continue to flourish today. Another wave of diversification also occurred: Some single-celled eukaryotes gave rise to multicellular forms, whose descendants include a variety of algae, plants, fungi, and animals.

The Earliest Multicellular Eukaryotes

Based on comparisons of DNA sequences, researchers have suggested that the common ancestor of multicellular eukaryotes lived 1.5 billion years ago. This result is in rough agreement with the fossil record; the oldest known fossils of multicellular eukaryotes are of relatively small algae that lived about 1.2 billion years ago. Larger and more diverse multicellular eukaryotes do not appear in the fossil record until about 565 million years ago (see Figure 25.4). These fossils, referred to as the Ediacaran biota, were of soft-bodied organisms—some over 1 m long—that lived from 565 to 535 million years ago.

Why were multicellular eukaryotes limited in size and diversity until the late Proterozoic? Geologic evidence indicates that a series of severe ice ages occurred from 750 to 580 million years ago. At various times during this period, glaciers covered all of the planet's landmasses, and the seas were largely iced over. The "snowball Earth" hypothesis suggests that most life would have been confined to areas near deep-sea vents and hot springs or to equatorial regions of the ocean that lacked ice cover. The fossil record of the first major diversification of multicellular eukaryotes (beginning about 565 million years ago) corresponds roughly to the time when snowball Earth thawed. As that diversification came to a close about 30 million years

▲ **Figure 25.9 A model of the origin of eukaryotes through serial endosymbiosis.** The proposed ancestors of mitochondria were aerobic, heterotrophic prokaryotes (meaning they used oxygen to metabolize organic molecules obtained from other organisms). The proposed ancestors of plastids were photosynthetic prokaryotes. Note that the arrows represent change over evolutionary time.

later, the stage was set for another, even more spectacular burst of evolutionary change.

The Cambrian Explosion

Many phyla of living animals appear suddenly in fossils formed early in the Cambrian period (535–525 million years ago), a phenomenon referred to as the **Cambrian explosion**. Fossils of at least three living animal phyla—Cnidaria (sea anemones and their relatives), Porifera (sponges), and Mollusca (molluscs)—appear in even older rocks dating from the late Proterozoic **(Figure 25.10)**.

Prior to the Cambrian explosion, all large animals were soft-bodied. The fossils of large pre-Cambrian animals reveal little evidence of predation. Instead, these animals appear to have been herbivores (feeding on algae), filter feeders, or scavengers, not hunters. The Cambrian explosion changed all of that. In a relatively short period of time (10 million years), predators over 1 m in length emerged that had claws and other features for capturing prey; simultaneously, new defensive adaptations, such as sharp spines and heavy body armor, appeared in their prey (see Figure 25.4). The safe, slow-moving

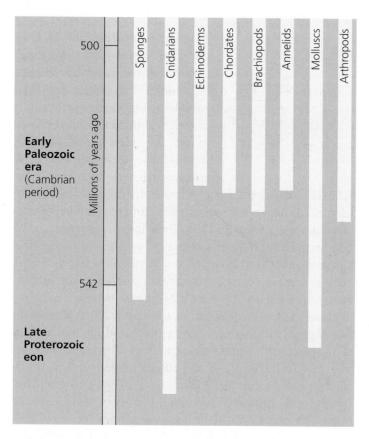

▲ **Figure 25.10 Appearance of selected animal phyla.** The yellow bars indicate earliest appearances of these phyla in the fossil record, although they could have originated earlier.

(a) Two-cell stage 150 μm **(b) Later stage** 200 μm

▲ **Figure 25.11 Proterozoic fossils that may be animal embryos (SEM).**

world that characterized larger forms of life before the Cambrian explosion was gone forever.

Although the Cambrian explosion had an enormous impact on life on Earth, it is possible that many animal phyla originated long before that time. Some DNA analyses suggest that most animal phyla originated and began to diverge from one another as early as 700 million to 1 billion years ago. Even if these estimates are not correct, recent fossil discoveries in China suggest that animals similar to members of living animal phyla were present tens of millions of years before the Cambrian explosion. The discoveries include 575-million-year-old fossils of beautifully preserved specimens interpreted by some scientists as animal embryos and by others as members of extinct groups closely related to animals **(Figure 25.11)**. Overall, as noted by Cambridge University paleontologist Simon Conway Morris, "the Cambrian explosion had a long fuse"—at least 40 million years long, based on the Chinese fossils. The fuse may have been hundreds of millions of years long if some animal phyla originated as far back as some DNA-based estimates suggest.

The Colonization of Land

Colonization of land

The colonization of land was another milestone in the history of life. There is fossil evidence that cyanobacteria and other photosynthetic prokaryotes coated damp terrestrial surfaces well over a billion years ago. However, larger forms of life, such as fungi, plants, and animals, did not begin to colonize land until about 500 million years ago. This gradual evolutionary venture out of aquatic environments was associated with adaptations that made it possible to reproduce on land and that helped prevent dehydration. For example, many land plants today have a vascular system for transporting materials internally and a waterproof coating of wax on their leaves that slows the loss of water to the air. Early signs of these adaptations were present 420 million years ago, at which time there were small plants (about 10 cm high) that had a vascular system but lacked true roots or leaves. About 50 million years later, plants had diversified greatly and included reeds and treelike plants with true roots and leaves.

Plants colonized land in the company of fungi. Even today, the roots of most plants are associated with fungi that aid in the absorption of water and minerals from the soil (see Chapter 31). These root fungi, in turn, obtain their organic nutrients from the plants. Such mutually beneficial associations of plants and fungi are evident in some of the oldest fossilized roots, dating this relationship back to the early spread of life onto land.

Although many animal groups are now represented in terrestrial environments, the most widespread and diverse land animals are arthropods (particularly insects and spiders) and tetrapods. The earliest tetrapods found in the fossil record lived about 365 million years ago and appear to have evolved from a group of lobe-finned fishes (see Chapter 34). Tetrapods include humans, although we are late arrivals on the scene. The human lineage diverged from other primates around 6–7 million years ago, and our species originated only about 195,000 years ago. If the clock of Earth's history were rescaled to represent an hour, humans appeared less than 0.2 second ago.

CONCEPT CHECK 25.3

1. The first appearance of free oxygen in the atmosphere likely triggered a massive wave of extinctions among the prokaryotes of the time. Why?
2. What evidence supports the hypothesis that mitochondria preceded plastids in the evolution of eukaryotic cells?
3. **WHAT IF?** What would a fossil record of life today look like?

For suggested answers, see Appendix A.

CONCEPT 25.4

The rise and fall of dominant groups reflect continental drift, mass extinctions, and adaptive radiations

From its beginnings, life on Earth has seen the rise and fall of groups of organisms. Anaerobic prokaryotes originated, flourished, and then declined as the oxygen content of the atmosphere rose. Billions of years later, the first tetrapods emerged from the sea, giving rise to amphibians that went on to dominate life on land for 100 million years—until other tetrapods (including dinosaurs and later, mammals) replaced them as the dominant terrestrial vertebrates. These and other major changes in life on Earth have been influenced by large-scale processes such as continental drift, mass extinctions, and adaptive radiations.

Continental Drift

If photographs of Earth were taken from space every 10,000 years and spliced together to make a movie, it would show something many of us find hard to imagine: The seemingly "rock solid" continents we live on move over time. Since the origin of multicellular eukaryotes roughly 1.5 billion years ago, there have been three occasions (1.1 billion, 600 million, and 250 million years ago) in which all of the landmasses of Earth came together to form a supercontinent, then later broke apart. Each time they yielded a different configuration of continents. Looking into the future, geologists estimate that the continents will come together again and form a new supercontinent roughly 250 million years from now.

The continents are part of great plates of Earth's crust that essentially float on the hot, underlying portion of the mantle **(Figure 25.12a)**. These plates move over time in a process

▼ **Figure 25.12 Earth and its continental plates.**

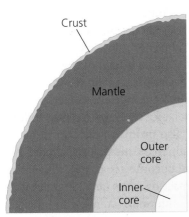

(a) Cutaway view of Earth. The thickness of the crust is exaggerated here.

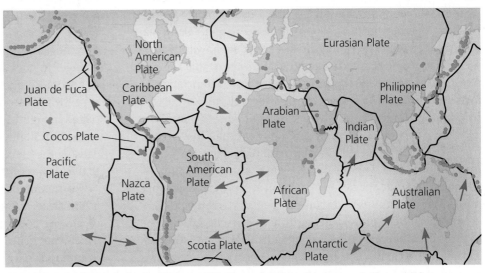

(b) Major continental plates. The arrows indicate direction of movement. The reddish-orange dots represent zones of violent tectonic activity.

called **continental drift**. Geologists can measure the rate at which the continental plates are moving today—usually only a few centimeters per year. They can also infer the past locations of the continents using the magnetic signal recorded in rocks at the time of their formation. This method works because as a continent shifts its position over time, the direction of magnetic north recorded in its newly formed rocks also changes.

Earth's major continental plates are shown in **Figure 25.12b**. Many important geologic processes, including the formation of mountains and islands, occur at plate boundaries. In some cases, two plates are moving away from one another, as are the North American and Eurasian plates, which are currently drifting apart at a rate of about 2 cm per year. In other cases, two plates are sliding past one another, forming regions where earthquakes are common. California's infamous San Andreas Fault is part of a border where two plates slide past each other. In still other cases, two plates are colliding. Typically, oceanic plates (those found on the bottom of the ocean) are more dense than terrestrial plates. As a result, when an oceanic plate collides with a terrestrial plate, the oceanic plate usually sinks below the terrestrial plate. When two oceanic plates or two terrestrial plates collide with one another, violent upheavals occur and mountains form along the plate boundaries. One spectacular example of this occurred 55 million years ago, when the Indian plate crashed into the Eurasian plate, starting the formation of the Himalayan mountains.

Consequences of Continental Drift

Plate movements rearrange geography slowly, but their cumulative effects are dramatic. In addition to reshaping the physical features of our planet, continental drift also has a major impact on life on Earth.

One reason for its great impact on life is that continental drift alters the habitats in which organisms live. Consider the changes shown in **Figure 25.13**. About 250 million years ago, plate movements brought all the previously separated landmasses together into a supercontinent named **Pangaea**, meaning "all land." Ocean basins became deeper, which lowered sea level and drained shallow coastal seas. At that time, as now, most marine species inhabited shallow waters, and the formation of Pangaea destroyed a considerable amount of that habitat. The interior of the vast continent was cold and dry, probably an even more severe environment than that of central Asia today. Overall, the formation of Pangaea had a tremendous impact on the physical environment and climate, which drove some species to extinction and provided new opportunities for groups of organisms that survived the crisis.

Another effect of continental drift is the climate change that results when a continent shifts northward or southward. The southern tip of Labrador, Canada, for example, once was located near the equator but has moved 40° to the north over the last 200 million years. To appreciate the impact of such a

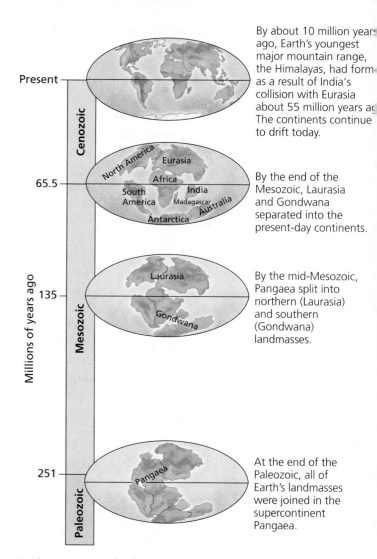

By about 10 million years ago, Earth's youngest major mountain range, the Himalayas, had formed as a result of India's collision with Eurasia about 55 million years ago. The continents continue to drift today.

By the end of the Mesozoic, Laurasia and Gondwana separated into the present-day continents.

By the mid-Mesozoic, Pangaea split into northern (Laurasia) and southern (Gondwana) landmasses.

At the end of the Paleozoic, all of Earth's landmasses were joined in the supercontinent Pangaea.

▲ **Figure 25.13 The history of continental drift during the Phanerozoic eon.**

shift, compare the climate of Wilmington, Delaware (about 40° north latitude), to that of Belem, Brazil (located near the equator). In the winter, temperatures in Wilmington have fallen as low as −26°C (−15°F), while temperatures in Belem have never dropped below 18°C (64°F). When faced with such changes in climate, organisms adapt, move to a new location, or become extinct (this last outcome occurred for most organisms stranded on Antarctica, such as *Cryolophosaurus*, depicted in Figure 25.1). The shifting positions of the continents are also thought to have rerouted the world's ocean currents, causing the global climate to become colder and contributing to the formation of polar ice caps over the past 15 million years.

Continental drift also promotes allopatric speciation on a grand scale. When supercontinents break apart, regions that once were connected become geographically isolated. As the continents drifted apart over the last 200 million years, each became a separate evolutionary arena, with lineages of plants and animals that diverged from those on other continents (see Figure 24.6 for one example).

Finally, continental drift can help explain puzzles about the geographic distribution of extinct organisms, such as why fossils of the same species of Permian freshwater reptiles have been discovered in both Brazil and the West African nation of Ghana. These two parts of the world, now separated by 3,000 km of ocean, were joined together when these reptiles were living. Continental drift also explains much about the current distributions of organisms, such as why Australian fauna and flora contrast so sharply with those of the rest of the world. Marsupial mammals fill ecological roles in Australia analogous to those filled by eutherians (placental mammals) on other continents (see Figure 22.20). Marsupials probably originated in what is now Asia and North America and reached Australia via South America and Antarctica while the continents were still joined. The subsequent breakup of the southern continents set Australia "afloat" like a great ark of marsupials. In Australia, marsupials diversified, and the few early eutherians that lived there became extinct; on other continents, most marsupials became extinct, and the eutherians diversified.

Mass Extinctions

The fossil record shows that the overwhelming majority of species that ever lived are now extinct. A species may become extinct for many reasons. Its habitat may have been destroyed, or its environment may have changed in a manner unfavorable to the species. For example, if ocean temperatures fall by even a few degrees, species that are otherwise well adapted may perish. Even if physical factors in the environment remain stable, biological factors may change—the origin of one species can spell doom for another.

Although extinction occurs on a regular basis, at certain times disruptive global environmental changes have caused the rate of extinction to increase dramatically. When this occurs, a **mass extinction** results, in which large numbers of species become extinct throughout Earth.

The "Big Five" Mass Extinction Events

Five mass extinctions are documented in the fossil record over the past 500 million years **(Figure 25.14)**. These events are particularly well documented for the decimation of hard-bodied animals that lived in shallow seas, the organisms for which the fossil record is most complete. In each mass extinction, 50% or more of Earth's marine species became extinct.

Two mass extinctions—the Permian and the Cretaceous—have received the most attention. The Permian mass extinction, which defines the boundary between the Paleozoic and Mesozoic eras (251 million years ago), claimed about 96% of marine animal species and drastically altered life in the ocean. Terrestrial life was also affected. For example, 8 out of 27 known orders of insects were wiped out. This mass extinction occurred in less than 5 million years, possibly in a few thousands of years—an instant in the context of geologic time.

The Permian mass extinction occurred at the time of enormous volcanic eruptions in what is now Siberia. This period was the most extreme episode of volcanism to have occurred during the past half billion years. Geologic data indicate that an area of 1.6 million km^2 (roughly half the size of western Europe) was covered with a layer of lava hundreds to thousands of meters thick. Besides spewing enormous amounts of lava and ash, the eruptions may have produced enough carbon

◀ **Figure 25.14 Mass extinction and the diversity of life.** The five generally recognized mass extinction events, indicated by red arrows, represent peaks in the extinction rate of marine animal families (red line and left vertical axis). These mass extinctions interrupted the overall increase in the number of marine animal families over time (blue line and right vertical axis).

dioxide to warm the global climate by an estimated 6°C. Reduced temperature differences between the equator and the poles would have slowed the mixing of ocean water, which in turn would have reduced the amount of oxygen available to marine organisms. This oxygen deficit may have been a major cause of the Permian extinction of marine life.

The Cretaceous mass extinction occurred about 65.5 million years ago and marks the boundary between the Mesozoic and Cenozoic eras. This event extinguished more than half of all marine species and eliminated many families of terrestrial plants and animals, including most of the dinosaurs. One clue to a possible cause of the Cretaceous mass extinction is a thin layer of clay enriched in iridium that separates sediments from the Mesozoic and Cenozoic eras. Iridium is an element that is very rare on Earth but common in many of the meteorites and other extraterrestrial objects that occasionally fall to Earth. Walter Alvarez and the late Luis Alvarez, of the University of California, Berkeley, and their colleagues proposed that this clay is fallout from a huge cloud of debris that billowed into the atmosphere when an asteroid or large comet collided with Earth. This cloud would have blocked sunlight and severely disturbed the global climate for several months.

Is there evidence of such an asteroid or comet? Research has focused on the Chicxulub crater, a 65-million-year-old scar beneath sediments off the Yucatán coast of Mexico (Figure 25.15). About 180 km in diameter, the crater is the right size to have been caused by an object with a diameter of 10 km. Critical evaluation of this and other hypotheses for mass extinctions continues.

Is a Sixth Mass Extinction Under Way?

As we will explore in Chapter 56, human actions, such as habitat destruction, are modifying the global environment to such an extent that many species are threatened with extinction. More than a thousand species have become extinct in the last 400 years. Scientists estimate that this rate is 100 to 1,000 times the typical background rate seen in the fossil record. Is a sixth mass extinction now in progress?

This question is difficult to answer, in part because it is hard to document the total number of extinctions occurring today. Tropical rain forests, for example, harbor many undiscovered species. As a result, destroying tropical forest may drive species to extinction before we even learn of their existence. Such uncertainties make it hard to assess the full extent of the current extinction crisis. Even so, it is clear that losses to date have not reached those of the "big five" mass extinctions, in which large percentages of Earth's species became extinct. This does not in any way discount the seriousness of today's situation. Monitoring programs show that many species are declining at an alarming rate. Such data suggest that unless dramatic actions are taken, a sixth (human-caused) mass extinction is likely to occur within the next few centuries or millennia.

Consequences of Mass Extinctions

By removing large numbers of species, a mass extinction can reduce a thriving and complex ecological community to a pale shadow of its former self. In addition, when an evolutionary lineage disappears, it cannot reappear. This changes the course of evolution forever. Consider what would have happened if the early primates living 66 million years ago had died out in the

▲ **Figure 25.15 Trauma for Earth and its Cretaceous life.** The 65-million-year-old Chicxulub impact crater is located in the Caribbean Sea near the Yucatán Peninsula of Mexico. The horseshoe shape of the crater and the pattern of debris in sedimentary rocks indicate that an asteroid or comet struck at a low angle from the southeast. This artist's interpretation represents the impact and its immediate effect—a cloud of hot vapor and debris that could have killed many of the plants and animals in North America within hours.

After the Permian mass extinction, the percentage of predators rose sharply and then stabilized near 22% for 150 million years—until it was disrupted again by the Cretaceous mass extinction.

The percentage of marine genera that were predators remained close to 15% for 200 million years.

▲ **Figure 25.16 Mass extinctions and ecology.** The Permian and Cretaceous mass extinctions (indicated by red arrows) altered the ecology of the oceans by increasing the percentage of marine genera that were predators.

Cretaceous mass extinction. Humans would not exist, and life on Earth would differ greatly from how we know it.

The fossil record shows that it typically takes 5–10 million years for the diversity of life to recover to previous levels after a mass extinction. In some cases, it has taken much longer than that: It took about 100 million years for the number of marine families to recover after the Permian mass extinction (see Figure 25.14). These data have sobering implications. If current trends continue and a sixth mass extinction occurs, it will take millions of years for life on Earth to recover.

Mass extinctions can also alter ecological communities by changing the types of organisms found in them. For example, after the Permian and Cretaceous mass extinctions, the percentage of marine organisms that were predators increased substantially **(Figure 25.16)**. A rise in the number of predator species can increase both the pressures faced by prey and the competition among predators for food. In addition, mass extinctions can remove lineages with highly advantageous features. For example, in the late Triassic a group of gastropods (snails and their relatives) arose that could drill through the shells of bivalves (such as clams) and feed on the animals inside. Although shell drilling provided access to a new and abundant source of food, this newly formed group was wiped out during the mass extinction at the end of the Triassic (about 200 million years ago). Another 120 million years passed before another group of gastropods (the oyster drills) exhibited the ability to drill through shells. As their predecessors might have done if they had not origi-

nated shortly before the Triassic mass extinction, oyster drills have since diversified into many new species. Finally, by eliminating so many of Earth's species, mass extinctions can pave the way for adaptive radiations, in which new groups of organisms rise to prominence.

Adaptive Radiations

The fossil record indicates that the diversity of life has increased over the past 250 million years (see Figure 25.14). This increase has been fueled by **adaptive radiations**, periods of evolutionary change in which groups of organisms form many new species whose adaptations allow them to fill different ecological roles, or niches, in their communities. Large-scale adaptive radiations occurred after each of the big five mass extinctions, when survivors became adapted to the many vacant ecological niches. Adaptive radiations have also occurred in groups of organisms that possessed major evolutionary innovations, such as seeds or armored body coverings, or that colonized regions in which they faced little competition from other species.

Worldwide Adaptive Radiations

Fossil evidence indicates that mammals underwent a dramatic adaptive radiation after the extinction of terrestrial dinosaurs 65.5 million years ago **(Figure 25.17)**. Although mammals originated about 180 million years ago, the mammal fossils older than 65.5 million years are mostly small and not morphologically diverse. Many species appear to have been nocturnal based on their large eye sockets, similar to those in living nocturnal mammals. A few early mammals were intermediate in

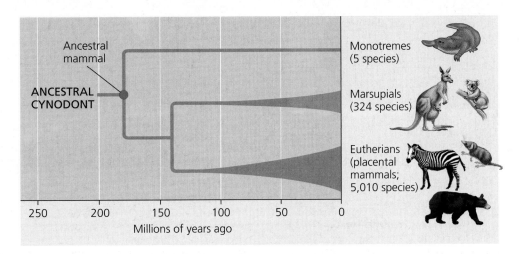

▲ **Figure 25.17 Adaptive radiation of mammals.**

size, such as *Repenomamus giganticus*, a 1-meter-long predator that lived 130 million years ago—but none approached the size of many dinosaurs. Early mammals may have been restricted in size and diversity because they were eaten or outcompeted by the larger and more diverse dinosaurs. With the disappearance of the dinosaurs (except for birds, which are considered members of the same group; see Chapter 34), mammals expanded greatly in both diversity and size, filling the ecological roles once occupied by terrestrial dinosaurs.

The history of life has also been greatly altered by radiations in which groups of organisms increased in diversity as they came to play entirely new ecological roles in their communities. Examples include the rise of photosynthetic prokaryotes, the evolution of large predators in the Cambrian explosion, and the radiations following the colonization of land by plants, insects, and tetrapods. Each of these last three radiations was associated with major evolutionary innovations that facilitated life on land. The radiation of land plants, for example, was associated

with key adaptations, such as stems that support plants against gravity and a waxy coat that protects leaves from water loss. Finally, organisms that arise in an adaptive radiation can serve as a new source of food for still other organisms. In fact, the diversification of land plants stimulated a series of adaptive radiations in insects that ate or pollinated plants, helping to make insects the most diverse group of animals on Earth today.

Regional Adaptive Radiations

Striking adaptive radiations have also occurred over more limited geographic areas. Such radiations can be initiated when a few organisms make their way to a new, often distant location in which they face relatively little competition from other organisms. The Hawaiian archipelago is one of the world's great showcases of this type of adaptive radiation **(Figure 25.18)**. Located about 3,500 km from the nearest continent, the volcanic islands are progressively older as one follows the chain toward

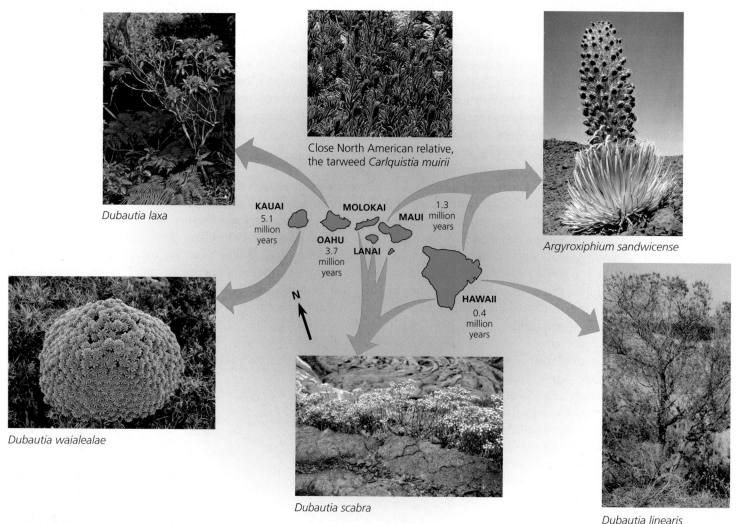

Close North American relative, the tarweed *Carlquistia muirii*

Dubautia laxa

Argyroxiphium sandwicense

KAUAI
5.1 million years

MOLOKAI

MAUI
1.3 million years

OAHU
3.7 million years

LANAI

HAWAII
0.4 million years

N

Dubautia waialealae

Dubautia scabra

Dubautia linearis

▲ **Figure 25.18 Adaptive radiation on the Hawaiian Islands.** Molecular analysis indicates that these remarkably varied Hawaiian plants, known collectively as the "silversword alliance," are all descended from an ancestral tarweed that arrived on the islands about 5 million years ago from North America. Members of the silversword alliance have since spread into different habitats and formed new species with strikingly different adaptations.

the northwest; the youngest island, Hawaii, is less than a million years old and still has active volcanoes. Each island was born "naked" and was gradually populated by stray organisms that rode the ocean currents and winds either from far-distant land areas or from older islands of the archipelago itself. The physical diversity of each island, including immense variation in elevation and rainfall, provides many opportunities for evolutionary divergence by natural selection. Multiple invasions followed by speciation events have ignited an explosion of adaptive radiation in Hawaii. Most of the thousands of species that inhabit the islands are found nowhere else on Earth.

CONCEPT CHECK 25.4

1. Explain consequences of continental drift for life on Earth.
2. What factors promote adaptive radiations?
3. **WHAT IF?** If a mass extinction were caused by a single, catastrophic event (such as an asteroid impact), what pattern would you expect regarding the dates when formerly common species lost in the extinction are last observed in the fossil record?

For suggested answers, see Appendix A.

CONCEPT **25.5**
Major changes in body form can result from changes in the sequences and regulation of developmental genes

The fossil record tells us what the great changes in the history of life have been and when they occurred. Moreover, an understanding of continental drift, mass extinction, and adaptive radiation provides a picture of how those changes came about. But we can also seek to understand the intrinsic biological mechanisms that underlie changes seen in the fossil record. For this, we turn to genetic mechanisms of change, paying particular attention to genes that influence development.

Evolutionary Effects of Developmental Genes

As you read in Chapter 21, "evo-devo"—research at the interface between evolutionary biology and developmental biology—is illuminating how slight genetic divergences can produce major morphological differences between species. Genes that control development influence the rate, timing, and spatial pattern of change in an organism's form as it develops from a zygote into an adult.

Changes in Rate and Timing

Many striking evolutionary transformations are the result of **heterochrony** (from the Greek *hetero*, different, and *chronos*,

time), an evolutionary change in the rate or timing of developmental events. For example, an organism's shape depends in part on the relative growth rates of different body parts during development. **Figure 25.19a** tracks how changes in such growth rates alter human body proportions during development. Even slight changes in relative rates of growth can change the adult form substantially, as seen in the contrasting shapes of human and chimpanzee skulls **(Figure 25.19b)**.

Heterochrony can also alter the timing of reproductive development relative to the development of nonreproductive organs. If reproductive-organ development accelerates compared to other organs, the sexually mature stage of a species may retain

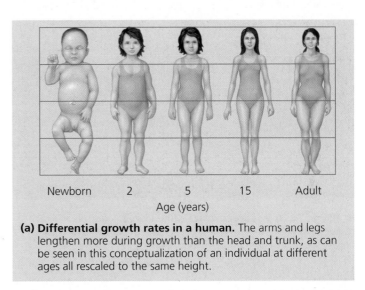

Newborn 2 5 15 Adult
Age (years)

(a) Differential growth rates in a human. The arms and legs lengthen more during growth than the head and trunk, as can be seen in this conceptualization of an individual at different ages all rescaled to the same height.

Chimpanzee fetus   Chimpanzee adult

Human fetus   Human adult

(b) Comparison of chimpanzee and human skull growth. The fetal skulls of chimpanzees and humans are similar in shape. However, growth in the jaw is accelerated in chimpanzees relative to humans, producing the characteristic elongated skull and sloping forehead of an adult chimpanzee.

▲ **Figure 25.19 Relative growth rates of body parts.**

body features that were juvenile structures in an ancestral species—a condition called **paedomorphosis** (from the Greek *paedos*, of a child, and *morphosis*, formation). For example, most salamander species have aquatic larvae that undergo metamorphosis in becoming adults. But some species grow to adult size and become sexually mature while retaining gills and other larval features **(Figure 25.20)**. Such an evolutionary alteration of developmental timing can produce animals that appear very different from their ancestors, even though the overall genetic change may be small. Indeed, recent evidence indicates that a change at a single locus was probably sufficient to bring about paedomorphosis in the axolotl salamander, although other genes may have contributed as well.

Changes in Spatial Pattern

Substantial evolutionary changes can also result from alterations in genes that control the placement and spatial organization of body parts. For example, master regulatory genes called **homeotic genes** (described in Chapters 18 and 21) determine such basic features as where a pair of wings and a pair of legs will develop on a bird or how a plant's flower parts are arranged.

The products of one class of homeotic genes, the *Hox* genes, provide positional information in an animal embryo. This information prompts cells to develop into structures appropriate for a particular location. Changes in *Hox* genes or in how they are expressed can have a profound impact on morphology. For example, among crustaceans, a change in the location where two *Hox* genes (*Ubx* and *Scr*) are expressed correlates with the conversion of a swimming appendage to a feeding appendage.

The evolution of vertebrates from invertebrate animals was an even larger evolutionary change, and it, too, may have been influenced by alterations in *Hox* genes and the genes that regulate them. Two duplications of *Hox* genes have occurred in the vertebrate lineage, and all vertebrate genomes tested to date have both of these duplications. As outlined in **Figure 25.21**,

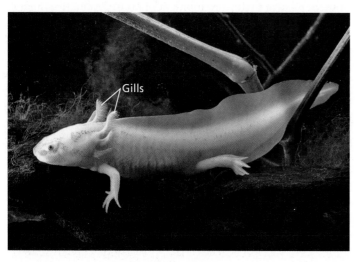

▲ Figure 25.20 **Paedomorphosis.** The adults of some species retain features that were juvenile in ancestors. This salamander is an axolotl, an aquatic species that grows to full size, becomes sexually mature, and reproduces while retaining certain larval (tadpole) characteristics, including gills.

Hypothetical vertebrate ancestor (invertebrate) with a single *Hox* cluster

First *Hox* duplication

Hypothetical early vertebrates (jawless) with two *Hox* clusters

Second *Hox* duplication

Vertebrates (with jaws) with four *Hox* clusters

1 Most invertebrates have one cluster of homeotic genes (the *Hox* complex), shown here as bands on a chromosome. *Hox* genes direct development of major body parts.

2 A mutation (duplication) of the single *Hox* complex occurred about 520 million years ago and may have provided genetic material associated with the origin of the first vertebrates.

3 In an early vertebrate, the duplicate set of genes took on entirely new roles, such as directing the development of a backbone.

4 A second duplication of the *Hox* complex, yielding the four clusters found in most present-day vertebrates, occurred later, about 425 million years ago. This duplication, probably the result of a polyploidy event, may have allowed the development of even greater structural complexity, such as jaws and limbs.

5 The vertebrate *Hox* complex contains duplicates of many of the same genes as the single invertebrate cluster, in virtually the same linear order on chromosomes, and they direct the sequential development of the same body regions. Scientists infer that the four clusters of the vertebrate *Hox* complex are homologous to the single cluster in invertebrates.

▲ Figure 25.21 *Hox* **mutations and the origin of vertebrates.**

these duplications may have been instrumental in the origin of novel characteristics in the vertebrates. This hypothesis remains controversial, however, in part because in addition to the *Hox* genes, many other genes (perhaps the entire genome) were duplicated in the vertebrate ancestor. Thus, the origin of novel characteristics cannot be ascribed solely to new *Hox* genes.

The Evolution of Development

The 565-million-year-old fossils of Ediacaran animals suggest that a set of genes sufficient to produce complex animals existed at least 30 million years *before* the Cambrian explosion. If developmental genes have existed for so long, how can we explain the astonishing increases in diversity seen during and since the Cambrian explosion?

Adaptive evolution by natural selection provides one answer to this question. As we've seen throughout this unit, by sorting among differences in the sequence of protein-encoding genes, selection can improve adaptations rapidly. In addition, new genes (created by gene duplication events) may have taken on a wide range of new metabolic and structural functions. Thus, adaptive evolution of new and existing genes may have played a key role in shaping the great diversity of life.

Examples in the previous section suggest that developmental genes may play a critical role. For the remainder of this section, we'll focus on how new morphological forms arise by changing the nucleotide sequences or regulation of developmental genes.

Changes in Genes

New developmental genes arising after gene duplication events very likely facilitated the origin of new morphological forms. But as we discussed regarding the possible role of new *Hox* genes in the origin of vertebrates, it can be difficult to establish causal links between genetic and morphological changes that occurred in the past.

This difficulty was sidestepped in a recent study of developmental changes associated with the divergence of six-legged insects from crustacean-like ancestors that had more than six legs. In insects, such as *Drosophila*, the *Ubx* gene is expressed in the abdomen, while in crustaceans, such as *Artemia*, it is expressed in the main trunk of the body **(Figure 25.22)**. When expressed, the *Ubx* gene suppresses leg formation in insects but not in crustaceans. To examine the workings of this gene, researchers cloned the *Ubx* gene from *Drosophila* and *Artemia*. Next, they genetically engineered fruit fly embryos to express either the *Drosophila Ubx* gene or the *Artemia Ubx* gene throughout their bodies. The *Drosophila* gene suppressed 100% of the limbs in the embryos, as expected, whereas the *Artemia* gene suppressed only 15%.

The researchers then sought to uncover key steps involved in the evolutionary transition from a crustacean *Ubx* gene to an insect *Ubx* gene. Their approach was to identify mutations that would cause the *Artemia Ubx* gene to suppress leg for-

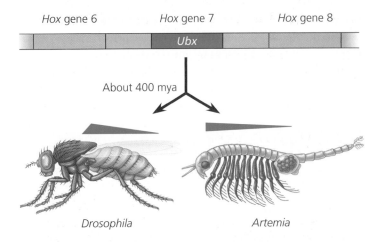

▲ **Figure 25.22 Origin of the insect body plan.** Expression of the *Hox* gene *Ubx* suppresses the formation of legs in fruit flies (*Drosophila*) but not in brine shrimp (*Artemia*), thus helping to build the insect body plan. Fruit fly and brine shrimp *Hox* genes have evolved independently for 400 million years.

mation, thus making the crustacean gene act more like an insect *Ubx* gene. To do this, they constructed a series of "hybrid" *Ubx* genes, each of which contained known segments of the *Drosophila Ubx* gene and known segments of the *Artemia Ubx* gene. By inserting these hybrid genes into fruit fly embryos (one hybrid gene per embryo) and observing their effects on leg development, the researchers were able to pinpoint the exact amino acid changes responsible for the suppression of additional limbs in insects. In so doing, this study provided experimental evidence linking a particular change in the sequence of a developmental gene to a major evolutionary change—the origin of the six-legged insect body plan.

Changes in Gene Regulation

A change in the nucleotide sequence of a gene may affect its function wherever the gene is expressed. In contrast, changes in the regulation of gene expression can be limited to a single cell type (see Chapter 18). Thus, a change in the regulation of a developmental gene may have fewer harmful side effects than a change to the sequence of the gene. This line of reasoning has prompted researchers to suggest that changes in the form of organisms often may be caused by mutations that affect the regulation of developmental genes—not their sequence.

This idea is supported by studies in a variety of species, including three-spine stickleback fish. These fish live in the open ocean and in shallow, coastal waters. In western Canada, they also live in lakes formed when the coastline receded in the past 12,000 years. David Kingsley, of Stanford University, and colleagues have identified a key developmental gene, *Pitx1*, that influences whether the fish have a set of large spines on their ventral (lower) surface, in addition to the three dorsal spines that give them their name. Marine populations have the ventral spines, which help to deter some predators. However, the spines are reduced or absent in lake populations. The loss of ventral spines may have been driven by natural selection because the lakes harbor large invertebrate predators, such as dragonfly larvae, which may at times capture juvenile sticklebacks by grasping onto the spines.

Was the reduction of spines due to changes in the *Pitx1* gene or due to changes in how the gene is expressed **(Figure 25.23)**? The researchers' results indicate that the regulation of gene expression has changed, not the DNA sequence of the gene. Furthermore, lake sticklebacks do express the *Pitx1* gene in tissues not related to the production of spines (for example, the mouth), illustrating how morphological change can be caused by altering the expression of a developmental gene in some parts of the body but not others.

▼ **Figure 25.23** **Inquiry**

What causes the loss of spines in lake stickleback fish?

EXPERIMENT   Marine populations of the three-spine stickleback fish (*Gasterosteus aculeatus*) have a set of protective spines on their lower (ventral) surface; these spines are lost or reduced in lake populations of this fish. Working at Stanford University, Michael Shapiro, David Kingsley, and colleagues tested two hypotheses about the cause of this morphological change.

Hypothesis A: A change in the DNA sequence of a key developmental gene, *Pitx1*, caused the loss of spines in lake populations. To test this idea, the team used DNA sequencing to compare the coding sequence of the *Pitx1* gene between marine and lake stickleback populations.

Hypothesis B: A change in the regulation of the expression of *Pitx1* caused the loss of spines. To test this idea, the researchers monitored where in the developing embryo the *Pitx1* gene is expressed. They conducted whole-body *in situ* hybridization experiments (see Chapter 20) using *Pitx1* DNA as a probe to detect *Pitx1* mRNA in the fish.

RESULTS

Test of Hypothesis A: Are there differences in the coding sequence of the *Pitx1* gene in marine and lake sticklebacks?   **Result: No** →   The 283 amino acids of the *Pitx1* protein are identical in marine and lake stickleback populations.

Test of Hypothesis B: Are there any differences in the regulation of expression of *Pitx1*?   **Result: Yes** →   Red arrows indicate regions of *Pitx1* gene expression in the photographs below. *Pitx1* is expressed in the ventral spine and mouth regions of developing marine sticklebacks but only in the mouth region of developing lake sticklebacks.

Marine stickleback embryo

Close-up of mouth

Close-up of ventral surface

Lake stickleback embryo

CONCLUSION   The loss or reduction of ventral spines in lake populations of three-spine stickleback fish results from a change in the regulation of *Pitx1* gene expression, not from a change in the gene's sequence.

SOURCE   M. D. Shapiro et al., Genetic and developmental basis of evolutionary pelvic reduction in three-spine sticklebacks, *Nature* 428:717–723 (2004).

WHAT IF?   Describe the set of results that would have led researchers to the conclusion that a change in the coding sequence of the *Pitx1* gene was more important than a change in regulation of gene expression.

1. How can heterochrony cause the evolution of different body forms?
2. Why is it likely that *Hox* genes have played a major role in the evolution of novel morphological forms?
3. **WHAT IF?** Given that changes in morphology are often caused by changes in gene regulation, predict whether noncoding DNA is likely to be affected by natural selection. (Noncoding DNA includes the sequences called control elements that regulate gene expression by binding to transcription factors.)

For suggested answers, see Appendix A.

CONCEPT **25.6**
Evolution is not goal oriented

What does our study of macroevolution tell us about how evolution works? To paraphrase the Nobel Prize-winning geneticist François Jacob, evolution is like tinkering—a process in which new forms arise by the slight modification of existing forms. Even large changes, like the ones that produced the first mammals or the six-legged body plan of insects, can result from the gradual modification of existing structures or the slight modification of existing developmental genes.

Evolutionary Novelties

François Jacob's view of evolution harkens back to Darwin's concept of descent with modification. As new species form, novel and complex structures can arise as gradual modifications of ancestral structures. In many cases, complex structures have evolved in increments from simpler versions that performed the same basic function. For example, consider the human eye, an intricate organ constructed from numerous parts that work together in forming an image and transmitting it to the brain. How could the human eye have evolved in gradual increments? Some argue that if the eye needs all of its components to function, a partial eye could not have been of use to our ancestors.

The flaw in this argument, as Darwin himself noted, lies in the assumption that only complicated eyes are useful. In fact, many animals depend on eyes that are far less complex than our own **(Figure 25.24)**. The simplest eyes that we know of are patches of light-sensitive photoreceptor cells. These simple eyes appear to have had a single evolutionary origin and are now found in a variety of animals, including small molluscs called limpets. Such eyes have no equipment for focusing images, but they do enable the animal to distinguish light from dark. Limpets cling more tightly to their rock when a shadow falls on them—a behavioral adaptation that reduces the risk of being eaten. Because limpets have had a long evolutionary history, we can conclude that their "simple" eyes are quite adequate to support their survival and reproduction.

(a) Patch of pigmented cells. The limpet *Patella* has a simple patch of photoreceptors.

(b) Eyecup. The slit shell mollusc *Pleurotomaria* has an eyecup.

(c) Pinhole camera-type eye. The *Nautilus* eye functions like a pinhole camera (an early type of camera lacking a lens).

(d) Eye with primitive lens. The marine snail *Murex* has a primitive lens consisting of a mass of crystal-like cells. The cornea is a transparent region of tissue that protects the eye and helps focus light.

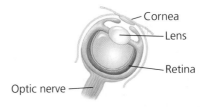

(e) Complex camera-type eye. The squid *Loligo* has a complex eye whose features (cornea, lens, and retina), though similar to those of vertebrate eyes, evolved independently.

▲ **Figure 25.24 A range of eye complexity among molluscs.**

In the animal kingdom, complex eyes have evolved independently from such basic structures many times. Some molluscs, such as squids and octopuses, have eyes as complex as those of humans and other vertebrates (see Figure 25.24). Although complex mollusc eyes evolved independently of vertebrate eyes, both evolved from a simple cluster of photoreceptor cells present in a common ancestor. In each case, the evolution of the complex eye took place through a series of incremental modifications that benefited the eyes' owners at every stage. Evidence for these evolutionary paths comes from phylogenetic analysis of the genes that act as "master regulators" of eye development and are shared by all animals with eyes.

Throughout their evolutionary history, eyes retained their basic function of vision. But evolutionary novelties can also arise when structures that originally played one role gradually acquire a different one. For example, as cynodonts gave rise to early mammals, bones that formerly comprised the jaw hinge (the articular and quadrate; see Figure 25.6) were incorporated into the ear region of mammals, where they eventually took on a new function: the transmission of sound (see Chapter 34).

Structures that evolve in one context but become co-opted for another function are sometimes called *exaptations* to distinguish them from the adaptive origin of the original structure. Note that the concept of exaptation does not imply that a structure somehow evolves in anticipation of future use. Natural selection cannot predict the future; it can only improve a structure in the context of its *current* utility. Novel features, such as the new jaw hinge and ear bones of early mammals, can arise gradually via a series of intermediate stages, each of which has some function in the organism's current context.

Evolutionary Trends

What else can we learn from patterns of macroevolution? Consider evolutionary "trends" observed in the fossil record. For instance, some evolutionary lineages exhibit a trend toward larger or smaller body size. An example is the evolution of the present-day horse (genus *Equus*), a descendant of the 55-million-year-old *Hyracotherium* **(Figure 25.25)**. About the size of a large dog, *Hyracotherium* had four toes on its front feet, three toes on its hind feet, and teeth adapted for browsing on bushes and trees. In

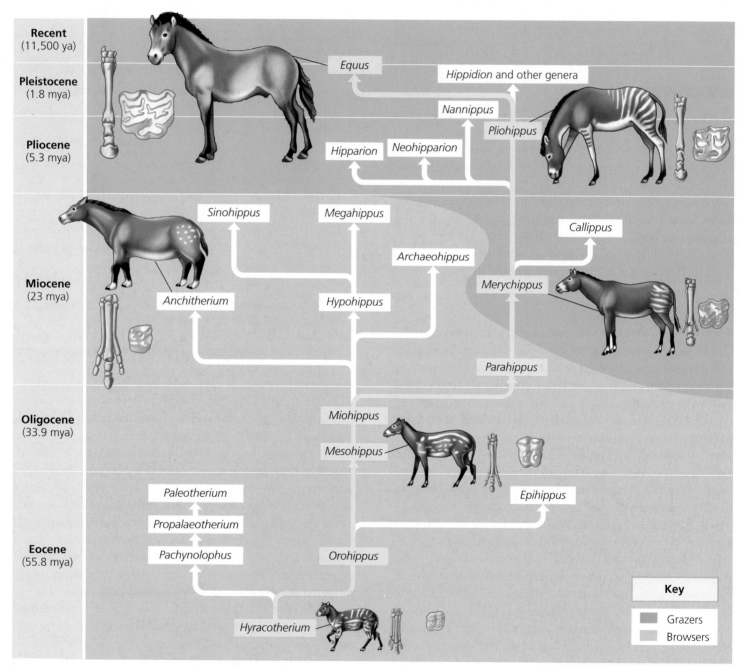

▲ **Figure 25.25 The branched evolution of horses.** Using yellow to trace the sequence of fossil horses that are intermediate in form between the present-day horse (*Equus*) and its Eocene ancestor *Hyracotherium* creates the illusion of a progressive trend toward larger size, reduced number of toes, and teeth modified for grazing. In fact, *Equus* is the only surviving twig of an evolutionary bush with many divergent trends.

comparison, present-day horses are larger, have only one toe on each foot, and possess teeth modified for grazing on grasses.

Extracting a single evolutionary progression from the fossil record can be misleading, however; it is like describing a bush as growing toward a single point by tracing only the branches that lead to that twig. For example, by selecting certain species from the available fossils, it is possible to arrange a succession of animals intermediate between *Hyracotherium* and living horses that shows a trend toward large, single-toed species (follow the lineage highlighted in yellow in Figure 25.25). However, if we consider *all* fossil horses known today, this apparent trend vanishes. The genus *Equus* did not evolve in a straight line; it is the only surviving twig of an evolutionary tree that is so branched that it is more like a bush. *Equus* actually descended through a series of speciation episodes that included several adaptive radiations, not all of which led to large, one-toed, grazing horses. For instance, notice in Figure 25.25 that only those lineages derived from *Parahippus* include grazers; other lineages derived from *Miohippus,* all of which are now extinct, remained multi-toed browsers for 35 million years.

Branching evolution *can* result in a real evolutionary trend even if some species counter the trend. One model of long-term trends proposed by Steven Stanley, of Johns Hopkins University, views species as analogous to individuals: Speciation is their birth, extinction is their death, and new species that diverge from them are their offspring. In this model, Stanley suggests that just as individual organisms undergo natural selection, species undergo *species selection.* The species that endure the longest and generate the most new offspring species determine the direction of major evolutionary trends. The species selection model suggests that "differential speciation success" plays a

role in macroevolution similar to the role of differential reproductive success in microevolution. Evolutionary trends can also result directly from natural selection. For example, when horse ancestors invaded the grasslands that spread during the mid-Cenozoic, there was strong selection for grazers that could escape predators by running faster. This trend would not have occurred without open grasslands.

Whatever its cause, an evolutionary trend does not imply that there is some intrinsic drive toward a particular phenotype. Evolution is the result of the interactions between organisms and their current environments; if environmental conditions change, an evolutionary trend may cease or even reverse itself. The cumulative effect of these ongoing interactions between organisms and their environments is enormous: It is through them that the staggering diversity of life—Darwin's "endless forms most beautiful"—has arisen.

CONCEPT CHECK **25.6**

1. How can the Darwinian concept of descent with modification explain the evolution of such complex structures as the vertebrate eye?
2. **WHAT IF?**   The myxoma virus is highly lethal to European rabbits (*Oryctolagus cuniculus*). In a naive rabbit population (one with no previous exposure to the virus), the virus kills up to 99.8% of infected rabbits. The virus is transmitted between living rabbits by mosquitoes. Describe an evolutionary trend (in either the rabbits or the virus) that might occur after a naive rabbit population first encounters the virus.

For suggested answers, see Appendix A.

Chapter 25 Review

SUMMARY OF KEY CONCEPTS

CONCEPT **25.1**

Conditions on early Earth made the origin of life possible (pp. 507–510)

▶ **Synthesis of Organic Compounds on Early Earth** Earth formed about 4.6 billion years ago. Laboratory experiments simulating a reducing atmosphere have produced organic molecules from inorganic precursors. Amino acids have also been found in meteorites.

▶ **Abiotic Synthesis of Macromolecules** Amino acids polymerize when added to hot sand, clay, or rock.

▶ **Protobionts** Organic compounds can spontaneously assemble in the laboratory into protobionts, membrane-bounded droplets that have some of the properties of cells.

▶ **Self-Replicating RNA and the Dawn of Natural Selection** The first genetic material may have been short pieces of RNA capable of guiding polypeptide synthesis and self-replication. Early protobionts containing such RNA would have been more effective at using resources and would have increased in number through natural selection.

MEDIA

Investigation How Did Life Begin on Early Earth?

CONCEPT **25.2**

The fossil record documents the history of life (pp. 510–514)

▶ **The Fossil Record** The fossil record, based largely on fossils found in sedimentary rocks, documents the rise and fall of different groups of organisms over time.

▶ **How Rocks and Fossils Are Dated** Sedimentary strata reveal the relative ages of fossils. The absolute ages of fossils can be estimated by radiometric dating and other methods.

► **The Origin of New Groups of Organisms** The fossil record shows how new groups of organisms can arise via the gradual modification of preexisting organisms.

CONCEPT 25.3

Key events in life's history include the origins of single-celled and multicelled organisms and the colonization of land (pp. 514–519)

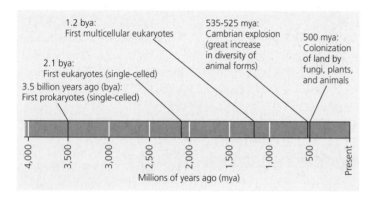

MEDIA

Activity A Scrolling Geologic Record
Activity The History of Life

CONCEPT 25.4

The rise and fall of dominant groups reflect continental drift, mass extinctions, and adaptive radiations (pp. 519–525)

► **Continental Drift** Continental plates move gradually over time, altering the physical geography and climate of Earth; these changes lead to extinctions in some groups of organisms and bursts of speciation in others.

► **Mass Extinctions** Evolutionary history has been punctuated by five mass extinctions that radically altered the history of life. Some of these extinctions may have been caused by changes in continent positions, volcanic activity, or impacts from meteorites or comets.

► **Adaptive Radiations** Large increases in the diversity of life have resulted from adaptive radiations that followed mass extinctions. Adaptive radiations have also occurred in groups of organisms that possessed major evolutionary innovations or that colonized new regions in which there was little competition from other organisms.

CONCEPT 25.5

Major changes in body form can result from changes in the sequences and regulation of developmental genes (pp. 525–529)

► **Evolutionary Effects of Developmental Genes** Developmental genes affect morphological differences between species by influencing the rate, timing, and spatial patterns of change in an organism's form as it develops into an adult.

► **The Evolution of Development** The evolution of new morphological forms can be caused by changes in the nucleotide sequences or regulation of developmental genes.

CONCEPT 25.6

Evolution is not goal oriented (pp. 529–531)

► **Evolutionary Novelties** Novel and complex biological structures can evolve through a series of incremental modifications, each of which benefits the organism that possesses it.

► **Evolutionary Trends** Evolutionary trends can be caused by factors such as natural selection in a changing environment or species selection. Like all aspects of evolution, evolutionary trends result from interactions between organisms and their current environments.

TESTING YOUR KNOWLEDGE

SELF-QUIZ

1. Fossilized stromatolites
   a. all date from 2.7 billion years ago.
   b. formed around deep-sea vents.
   c. resemble structures formed by bacterial communities that are found today in some warm, shallow, salty bays.
   d. provide evidence that plants moved onto land in the company of fungi around 500 million years ago.
   e. contain the first undisputed fossils of eukaryotes and date from 2.1 billion years ago.

2. The oxygen revolution changed Earth's environment dramatically. Which of the following adaptations took advantage of the presence of free oxygen in the oceans and atmosphere?
   a. the evolution of cellular respiration, which used oxygen to help harvest energy from organic molecules
   b. the persistence of some animal groups in anaerobic habitats
   c. the evolution of photosynthetic pigments that protected early algae from the corrosive effects of oxygen
   d. the evolution of chloroplasts after early protists incorporated photosynthetic cyanobacteria
   e. the evolution of multicellular eukaryotic colonies from communities of prokaryotes

3. Select the factor most likely to have caused the animals and plants of India to differ greatly from species in nearby southeast Asia.
   a. The species have become separated by convergent evolution.
   b. The climates of the two regions are similar.
   c. India is in the process of separating from the rest of Asia.
   d. Life in India was wiped out by ancient volcanic eruptions.
   e. India was a separate continent until 55 million years ago.

4. Adaptive radiations can be a direct consequence of four of the following five factors. Select the exception.
   a. vacant ecological niches
   b. genetic drift
   c. colonization of an isolated region that contains suitable habitat and few competitor species
   d. evolutionary innovation
   e. an adaptive radiation in a group of organisms (such as plants) that another group uses as food

532 UNIT FOUR Mechanisms of Evolution

5. A genetic change that caused a certain *Hox* gene to be expressed along the tip of a vertebrate limb bud instead of farther back helped make possible the evolution of the tetrapod limb. This type of change is illustrative of
   a. the influence of environment on development.
   b. paedomorphosis.
   c. a change in a developmental gene or in its regulation that altered the spatial organization of body parts.
   d. heterochrony.
   e. gene duplication.

6. Which of the following steps has *not* yet been accomplished by scientists studying the origin of life?
   a. synthesis of small RNA polymers by ribozymes
   b. abiotic synthesis of polypeptides
   c. formation of molecular aggregates with selectively permeable membranes
   d. formation of protobionts that use DNA to direct the polymerization of amino acids
   e. abiotic synthesis of organic molecules

7. A swim bladder is a gas-filled sac that helps fish maintain buoyancy. The evolution of the swim bladder from lungs of an ancestral fish is an example of
   a. an evolutionary trend.   d. paedomorphosis.
   b. exaptation.   e. adaptive radiation.
   c. changes in *Hox* gene expression.

8. **DRAW IT** Use the unlabeled clock diagram below to test your memory of the sequence of key events in the history of life described in this chapter by labeling the colored bars. As a visual aid to help you study, add labels that represent other significant events, including the Cambrian explosion, origin of mammals, and Permian and Cretaceous mass extinctions.

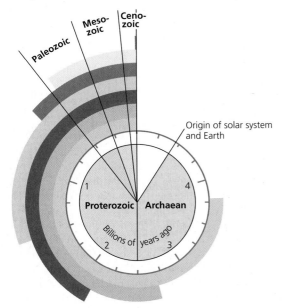

EVOLUTION CONNECTION

9. Describe how gene flow, genetic drift, and natural selection all can influence macroevolution.

SCIENTIFIC INQUIRY

10. Herbivory (plant-eating) has evolved repeatedly in insects, typically from meat-eating or detritus-feeding ancestors (detritus is dead organic matter). Moths and butterflies, for example, eat plants, whereas their "sister group" (the insect group to which they are most closely related), the caddisflies, feed on animals, fungi, or detritus. As illustrated in the phylogenetic tree below, the combined moth/butterfly and caddisfly group shares a common ancestor with flies and fleas. Like caddisflies, flies and fleas are thought to have evolved from ancestors that did not eat plants.
   There are 140,000 species of moths and butterflies and 7,000 species of caddisflies. State a hypothesis about the impact of herbivory on adaptive radiations in insects. How could this hypothesis be tested?

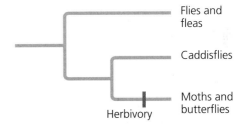

SCIENCE, TECHNOLOGY, AND SOCIETY

11. Experts estimate that human activities cause the extinction of hundreds of species every year. In contrast, the natural rate of extinction is thought to average only a few species per year. If we continue to alter the global environment, especially by destroying tropical rain forests and altering Earth's climate, the likely result will be a wave of extinctions that could rival those at the end of the Cretaceous period. Considering that life has endured five mass extinctions, should we be concerned that we may cause a sixth mass extinction? How would such an extinction differ from previous extinctions? What might be some of the consequences for the surviving species, including ourselves?

   Biology Inquiry: A Workbook of Investigative Cases Life on Earth has gone through repeated cycles of mass extinction and diversification. Explore the latter with the case "Unveiling the Carboniferous."

For Self-Quiz answers, see Appendix A.

MEDIA Visit the Study Area at **www.masteringbio.com** for a Practice Test.

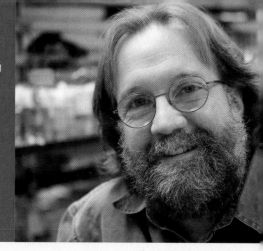

UNIT 5

The Evolutionary History of Biological Diversity

Sean B. Carroll

Passionately committed to sharing the revelations of evo-devo with students and the public, Sean Carroll is a popular speaker and the author of several acclaimed trade books—as well as a leading researcher on the genetics and evolution of animal development. He completed his formal education in record time, earning a B.A. in Biology at Washington University and a Ph.D. in Immunology at Tufts University School of Medicine in less than six years. Dr. Carroll is now an investigator at the Howard Hughes Medical Institute and a professor of molecular biology and genetics at the University of Wisconsin, Madison. He is a member of the National Academy of Sciences.

How did you get interested in evolutionary biology?

As a kid, I really enjoyed flipping over logs and seeing what was underneath. I was fascinated by reptiles, snakes in particular, and also liked to catch frogs and salamanders. That attraction to wildlife has always nurtured my interest in biology. At Washington University, students like myself could get exposed to almost anything in biology. I would go to seminars on subjects ranging from wolf ecology to the molecular biology of viruses. There I started to learn something about the big questions that were being asked in various disciplines at the time. I was smitten with immunology because of the big questions still open in that field and because of its practical side—vaccines and the treatment of infectious diseases.

But while working on my Ph.D. in immunology, I started reading a lot on my own—Stephen Jay Gould, for example—and going to science talks all over the Boston area. I would just hop on the subway and go to talks at any of three or four different universities. The unanswered questions in evolutionary biology drew me in that direction. At the time, the debate over punctuated equilibrium was fresh,

and this new idea was changing interpretations of the fossil record and raising questions about the rate of morphological change. All this prompted a simple question in my mind: How can we have this debate when we don't know anything about how form is made? And how can we start to get a grip on that?

At around that time, I came across some of the early papers on the developmental genetics of fruit flies, which described fascinating body-pattern mutants—homeotic mutants [see Figure 18.18]. I got it in my head that homeotic genes were the ones that people would have to study to understand the evolution of form. Despite advice to the contrary, I committed myself to studying these kinds of genes in fruit flies.

Let's talk about your book *Endless Forms Most Beautiful: The New Science of Evo Devo and the Making of the Animal Kingdom.* What does the title mean?

The first part of the title is borrowed from the last sentence of Charles Darwin's *Origin of Species*: "from so simple a beginning endless forms most beautiful . . . have been and are being evolved." The "most beautiful" part is important to me because I think that part of our attraction to nature is aesthetic. The book tries to explain what the new science of the last 20 years—advances in developmental genetics and the evolutionary study of development—has revealed about the generation of the physical diversity of the animal kingdom.

There is an intimate connection between development and evolution. Development is the process that gives rise to form, and so the evolution of form comes about through the evolution of development. Understanding how development happens in the first place is the starting point. Then we want to understand how changes in development can evolve. Only a small percentage of our genes are devoted to building body form, maybe a couple of thousand in us and six or seven hundred in a fruit fly. But when those genes are disrupted by mutation, the effects can be pretty catastrophic.

The book looks at the central ideas in evolutionary developmental biology—*evo-devo*, for short. A few of the key discoveries in this area were stunning, completely unanticipated. So the book traces those discoveries and discusses how they force us to look at the evolution of diversity very differently from how previous generations of evolutionary biologists did. The biggest discovery of evo-devo has been that the genes that build the bodies and body parts of fruit flies are shared with us and with virtually every other creature in the animal kingdom. That shows us a deep connection shared by all animals, no matter how different the bodies are. Gene for gene, we are essentially the same as a mouse, a rat, or a dog, and especially a chimpanzee. And the genes involved in building our eyes and our hearts and our bones have been around for 500 million years. So much like astronomy did four centuries ago, evo-devo is contributing to the realization that humans are not the center of everything. The human species is a member of the animal kingdom and not really above or very distinct from the other members.

What are you doing research on now?

We're working on the question of *how* the differences between animal species arise. There has been an idea around biology for a long time that to get new things you need new genes—for new structures, for new capabilities, or for whole new types of animals. But it doesn't look like that at all. Instead, it looks like new things arise because very old genes learn new tricks. We are focusing on understanding the mechanisms of these changes. This involves the question of how a gene involved in setting up the basic body plan and building body parts can change its roles without the whole machine falling apart. How do you change the car while the engine is running? It turns out that body-building genes have very sophisticated and extensive sets of regulatory instructions—control elements in the DNA nearby or embedded within the genes. An individual gene might act in a dozen places in the body in the course of development, but its action in a particular body part at a particular moment in development is controlled independently from its action in other places. We are trying to understand how these regulatory instructions are used, because we think that these are the hot spots of evolution. It is becoming more clear how and why these regulatory elements are the keys to understanding how so much diversity can be generated with a limited set of body-building genes.

The rules for the evolution of body form and physiology are different: In the evolution of physiological processes—for example, respiration, olfaction, or immunity—the evolution of new protein-coding genes has been more important. For example, the multiple types of globins that act at different stages of our life arose as genes were duplicated and the copies then diverged.

Are you using fruit flies currently?

Yes. To get at some of the *general* rules about the evolution of form, we often studied animals that are distant relatives; we might compare a snake with a bird. But if you really want to trace the specific genetic steps involved in the evolution of form, you need to have greater resolving power. The strategy we have taken is to study closely related species, which share a very recent common ancestor. If you take two such "sister" species, you can actually identify the genetic changes that cause the differences in the appearance and behavior of these animals. Fruit flies provide a great opportunity to do that, because *Drosophila melanogaster*, the familiar lab fruit fly, has hundreds of relatives out there in the wild, different species with all sorts of differences in body appearance. For instance, there are *Drosophila* species where the male has large black spots on the tips of the wings that are used in a courtship display. Now, genes that influence mating are among the most important targets of natural selection, because whether the male passes his genes on depends on whether the female is induced to mate. We can compare these flies with flies of sister species that do not have these spots and do not use the same mating ritual. Because the relationship is close, we can pinpoint very specifically the bits of regulatory DNA that have changed. So we are looking at the smoking guns of evolution.

What can one learn about animal phylogeny from DNA sequences versus fossils and morphology?

It's useful to have both—independent but intersecting lines of evidence. There are things you cannot see in fossils that you can learn about by studying DNA, and there is a lot that the molecules cannot tell you about the history of life. You can't look at DNA and know that the dinosaurs existed. Fossils tell you what animals roamed the earth, what structures existed, and even how the structures evolved, if the fossil record is rich enough. When you have extant species, the molecular record is good for figuring out other things. For example, if you want to know whether annelids are more closely related to molluscs or to arthropods—an issue that for a hundred-plus years was argued on the basis of appearance—the molecules now weigh in on the problem. Sometimes the results from molecules are consistent with long-held notions, and sometimes they throw the old notions for a loop.

What does evo-devo tell us about the Cambrian explosion?

Evo-devo tells us that the body-building genes we've been talking about must have been in place in the very early ancestors of most animals, in the ancestors of the animals seen in fossils from the geologic period we call the Cambrian. We can infer that the earliest bilateral animals—"bilaterians," which have left and right sides—had a pretty sophisticated genetic toolkit, and that those animals must have lived prior to the Cambrian. The Cambrian coming-out party may not have been so much a matter of new genes as an ecologically driven explosion of diversity. My personal view is that all the key genes and circuits were probably in place cryptically in small creatures before the Cambrian. So evo-devo is a great window to understanding the mechanism of diversification, but there's a huge ecological story, too.

Going back before the Cambrian, when did the first animals arise, and what did they look like?

The first animals probably appeared about 600 million years ago, give or take a week. I tend to believe that a lot of the early evolution of animals is cryptic because the earliest animals were tiny, soft-bodied organisms and didn't leave a good fossil record. These first animals would have been, by today's standards, dull-looking spongelike things. The first bilaterians probably looked like worms. Also, because there are significant differences between sponges and cnidarians and cnidarians and bilaterians, I think there were all sorts of intermediate phyla that we don't know anything about. Maybe some tremendous breakthrough in finding and analyzing microfossils will lead to discovery of some of the missing phyla.

Why should people who are not going to be evolutionary biologists learn about the evolution of biological diversity?

I think the study of evolution and diversity is as fundamental as studying the history of human civilizations. That's just the last 10,000 years! But our history as animals goes back some 600 million years and as organisms several billion years. In addition, there are important practical reasons. We humans are managing the natural resources on the planet. If we don't understand the basic principles of evolutionary biology, we cannot conduct those activities intelligently for the long term. To take one example, what's the effect of trawling for ocean fish with a 7-cm mesh net? Organisms that are smaller than 7 cm escape and flourish, and ones that are larger than 7 cm are removed. How does that influence the harvest ten years later? We have to understand the fundamental role that selection plays in the real world and that we are a major agent of selection. We can foresee some of the consequences of our activities from the first principles of evolutionary biology.

Evo-devo tells us that the body-building genes . . . must have been in place in the very early ancestors of most animals . . .

Inquiry in Action

Learn about an experiment by Sean Carroll and colleagues in Inquiry Figure 33.28 on page 684.

Jane Reece and Sean Carroll

Phylogeny and the Tree of Life

KEY CONCEPTS

26.1 Phylogenies show evolutionary relationships

26.2 Phylogenies are inferred from morphological and molecular data

26.3 Shared characters are used to construct phylogenetic trees

26.4 An organism's evolutionary history is documented in its genome

26.5 Molecular clocks help track evolutionary time

26.6 New information continues to revise our understanding of the tree of life

OVERVIEW

Investigating the Tree of Life

Look closely at the organism in **Figure 26.1**. Although it resembles a snake, this animal is actually an Australian legless lizard known as the common scaly-foot (*Pygopus lepidopodus*). Why isn't the scaly-foot considered a snake? More generally, how do biologists distinguish and categorize the millions of species on Earth?

An understanding of evolutionary relationships suggests one way to address these questions: We can decide in which "container" to place a species by comparing its traits to those of potential close relatives. For example, the scaly-foot does not have a fused eyelid, a highly mobile jaw, or a short tail posterior to the anus, three traits of snakes. These and other characteristics suggest that despite a superficial resemblance, the scaly-foot is not a snake. Furthermore, a survey of the lizards reveals that the scaly-foot is not alone; the legless condition has evolved repeatedly in lizards. Most legless lizards are burrowers or live in grasslands, and like snakes, these species lost their legs over generations as they adapted to their environments.

Snakes and lizards are part of the continuum of life extending from the earliest organisms to the great variety of species alive today. In this unit, we will survey this diversity and de-

scribe hypotheses regarding how it evolved. As we do so, our emphasis will shift from the *process* of evolution (the evolutionary mechanisms described in Unit Four) to its *pattern* (observations of evolution's products over time).

To set the stage for our survey of life's diversity, in this chapter we consider how biologists trace **phylogeny**, the evolutionary history of a species or group of species. A phylogeny of lizards and snakes, for example, indicates that both the scaly-foot and snakes evolved from lizards with legs—but they evolved from different lineages of legged lizards. Thus, it appears that their legless conditions evolved independently.

To construct a phylogeny such as that of lizards and snakes, biologists utilize **systematics**, a discipline focused on classifying organisms and determining their evolutionary relationships. Systematists use data ranging from fossils to molecules and genes to infer evolutionary relationships **(Figure 26.2)**. This information is enabling biologists to construct a comprehensive tree of life, which will continue to be refined as additional data are collected.

▲ **Figure 26.2 An unexpected family tree.** What are the evolutionary relationships between a human, a mushroom, and a tulip? A phylogeny based on DNA data reveals that—despite appearances—animals (including humans) and fungi (including mushrooms) are more closely related to each other than either is to plants.

CONCEPT 26.1
Phylogenies show evolutionary relationships

As we discussed in Chapter 22, organisms share homologous characteristics because of common ancestry. As a result, we can learn a great deal about a species if we know its evolutionary history. For example, an organism is likely to share many of its genes, metabolic pathways, and structural proteins with its close relatives. We'll consider practical applications of such information at the close of this section, but first we'll examine how organisms are named and classified, the scientific discipline of **taxonomy**. We'll also look at how we can interpret and use diagrams that represent evolutionary history.

Binomial Nomenclature

Common names for organisms—such as monkey, finch, and lilac—convey meaning in casual usage, but they can also cause confusion. Each of these names, for example, refers to more than one species. Moreover, some common names do not accurately reflect the kind of organism they signify. Consider these three "fishes": jellyfish (a cnidarian), crayfish (a small lobsterlike crustacean), and silverfish (an insect). And of course, different languages have different words for various organisms.

To avoid ambiguity when communicating about their research, biologists refer to organisms by Latin scientific names. The two-part format of the scientific name, commonly called a **binomial**, was instituted in the 18th century by Carolus Linnaeus (see Chapter 22). The first part of a binomial is the name of the **genus** (plural, *genera*) to which the species belongs. The second part, called the specific epithet, is unique for each species within the genus. An example of a binomial is *Panthera pardus*, the scientific name for the large cat commonly called the leopard. Notice that the first letter of the genus is capitalized and the entire binomial is italicized. (Newly created scientific names are also "latinized": You can name an insect you discover after a friend, but you must add a Latin ending.) Many of the more than 11,000 binomials assigned by Linnaeus are still used today, including the optimistic name he gave our own species—*Homo sapiens*, meaning "wise man."

Hierarchical Classification

In addition to naming species, Linnaeus also grouped them into a hierarchy of increasingly inclusive categories. The first grouping is built into the binomial: Species that appear to be closely related are grouped into the same genus. For example, the leopard (*Panthera pardus*) belongs to a genus that also includes the African lion (*Panthera leo*), the tiger (*Panthera tigris*), and the jaguar (*Panthera onca*). Beyond genera, taxonomists employ progressively more comprehensive categories of classification. The taxonomic system named after Linnaeus, the Linnaean system, places related genera in the same **family**, families into **orders**, orders into **classes**, classes into **phyla** (singular, *phylum*), phyla into **kingdoms**, and, more recently, kingdoms into **domains** (Figure 26.3). The resulting biological classification of a particular organism is somewhat like a postal address identifying a person in a particular apartment, in a building with many apartments, on a street with many apartment buildings, in a city with many streets, and so on.

The named taxonomic unit at any level of the hierarchy is called a **taxon** (plural, *taxa*). In the leopard example, *Panthera* is a taxon at the genus level, and Mammalia is a taxon at the class level that includes all the many orders of mammals. Note that in the Linnaean system, taxa broader than the genus are not italicized, though they are capitalized.

Classifying species seems to come naturally to humans—it is a way to structure our view of the world. We lump together various species of trees to which we give the common name of pines and distinguish them from other trees that we call firs. Taxonomists have decided that pines and firs are different enough to be placed in separate genera, yet similar enough to be grouped into the same family, the Pineaceae. As with pines and firs,

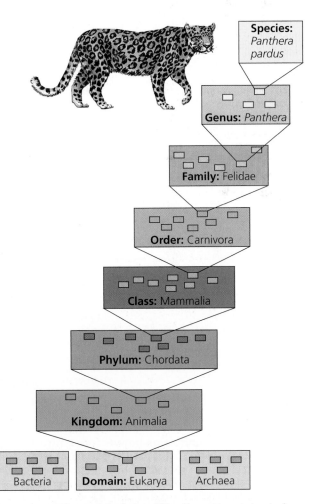

▲ **Figure 26.3 Hierarchical classification.** At each level of the Linnaean classification system, species are placed into groups belonging to more comprehensive groups.

higher levels of classification are usually defined by particular morphological characters chosen by taxonomists, rather than by measurements applicable to all organisms. For this reason, the larger categories often are not comparable between lineages; that is, an order of snails does not exhibit the same degree of morphological or genetic diversity as an order of mammals. Furthermore, as we'll see, the placement of species into orders, classes, and so on, does not necessarily reflect evolutionary history.

Linking Classification and Phylogeny

The evolutionary history of a group of organisms can be represented in a branching diagram called a **phylogenetic tree**. The branching pattern in some cases matches the hierarchical classification of groups nested within more inclusive groups **(Figure 26.4)**. In other situations, however, certain similarities among organisms may lead taxonomists to place a species within a group of organisms (for example, a genus or family) other than the group to which it is most closely related. If systematists conclude that such a mistake has occurred, the organism may be reclassified (that is, placed in a different genus or family) to accurately reflect its evolutionary history. In addition, the categories in the Linnaean classification system may provide little information about phylogeny: We may distinguish 17 families of lizards, but that tells us nothing about their evolutionary relationships to one another.

In fact, such difficulties in aligning Linnaean classification with phylogeny have led some systematists to propose that classification be based entirely on evolutionary relationships. A recent example of this approach is the **PhyloCode**, which only names groups that include a common ancestor and all of its descendants. While PhyloCode would change the way taxa are defined and recognized, the taxonomic names of most species would remain the same. But species would no longer necessarily have "ranks" attached to them, such as family, order, or class. Also, some commonly recognized groups would become part of other groups previously of the same rank. For example, because birds evolved from a group of reptiles, Aves (the Linnaean class to which birds are assigned) would be considered a subgroup of Reptilia (also a class in the Linnaean system). Although PhyloCode is controversial and still being developed, many systematists are adopting the phylogenetic approach on which it is based.

Whether groups are named according to PhyloCode or to Linnaean classification, a phylogenetic tree represents a hypothesis about evolutionary relationships. These relationships often are depicted as a series of dichotomies, or two-way **branch points (Figure 26.5)**. Each branch point represents the divergence of two evolutionary lineages from a common ancestor. For example, in Figure 26.5, branch point ❶ represents the common ancestor of taxa A, B, and C. The position of branch point ❹ to the right of branch point ❶ indicates that taxa B and C diverged after their shared lineage split from that of taxon A. Note that tree branches can be rotated around a branch point without changing their evolutionary relationships.

In Figure 26.5, taxa B and C are **sister taxa**, groups of organisms that share an immediate common ancestor (branch point ❹) and hence are each other's closest relatives. Note also that this tree, like most of the phylogenetic trees in this book, is **rooted**, which means that a branch point within the

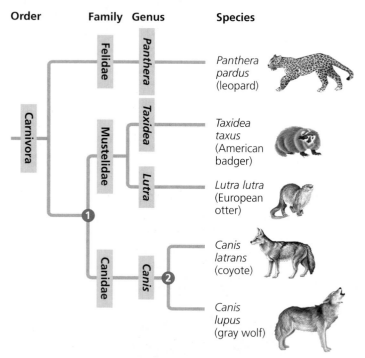

▲ **Figure 26.4 The connection between classification and phylogeny.** Hierarchical classification is reflected in the progressively finer branching of phylogenetic trees. This tree traces possible evolutionary relationships between some of the taxa within order Carnivora, itself a branch of class Mammalia. The branch point ❶ represents the most recent common ancestor of all members of the weasel (Mustelidae) and dog (Canidae) families. The branch point ❷ represents the most recent common ancestor of coyotes and gray wolves.

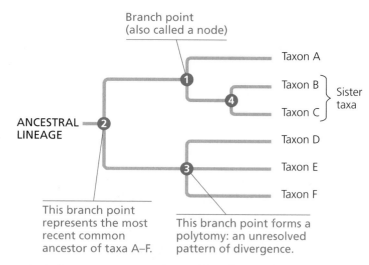

▲ **Figure 26.5 How to read a phylogenetic tree.**
DRAW IT *Redraw this tree, rotating the branches around branch points ❷ and ❹. Does your new version tell a different story about the evolutionary relationships between the taxa? Explain.*

tree (typically, the one farthest to the left) represents the last common ancestor of all taxa in the tree. Finally, the lineage leading to taxa D–F includes a **polytomy**, a branch point from which more than two descendant groups emerge. A polytomy indicates that evolutionary relationships among the descendant taxa are not yet clear.

What We Can and Cannot Learn from Phylogenetic Trees

Let's pause to summarize two key points about phylogenetic trees and what they signify. First, the sequence of branching in a tree does not necessarily indicate the actual (absolute) ages of the particular species. For example, the tree in Figure 26.4 does *not* indicate that the wolf evolved more recently than the European otter; rather, the tree shows only that the most recent common ancestor of the wolf and European otter (branch point ❶) lived before the most recent common ancestor of the wolf and coyote (branch point ❷). To indicate when wolves and European otters evolved, the tree would need to include additional divergences in each evolutionary lineage, as well as the dates when those splits occurred. More generally, unless given specific information about what the branch lengths in a phylogenetic tree mean—for example, that they are proportional to time or genetic change—we should interpret the diagram solely in terms of patterns of descent. No assumptions should be made about when particular species evolved or how much genetic change occurred in each evolutionary lineage.

Second, we cannot assume that a taxon on a phylogenetic tree evolved from the taxon next to it. Figure 26.4 does not indicate that wolves evolved from coyotes or vice versa. We can infer only that the lineage leading to wolves and the lineage leading to coyotes both evolved from the common ancestor ❷.

Applying Phylogenies

Why do biologists care about studying phylogenies? One reason is that a species' phylogeny provides an enormous amount of information. Consider maize (corn), the second most important source of food worldwide (after wheat). From a phylogeny of maize based on DNA data, researchers identified two species of wild grasses that may be the closest living relatives to maize. These two close relatives may prove useful as "reservoirs" of beneficial genes that can be transferred to cultivated maize by plant breeding or genetic engineering. The phylogenetic analysis of maize also led to the identification of the gene responsible for maize's unique fruiting body, the cob.

Phylogenetic trees have played a key role in a wide range of other applications. One example is an investigation into whether food sold as "whale meat" in Japan was illegally harvested from whale species protected under international law **(Figure 26.6)**. Although it is legal to harvest some whales for food, such as Minke whales that are caught in the Southern Hemisphere, this phylogeny indicated that meat from

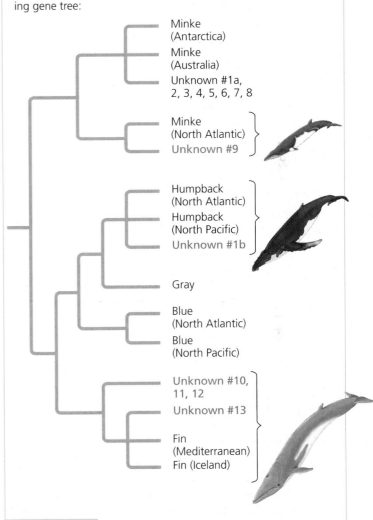

▼ **Figure 26.6** **Inquiry**

What is the species identity of food being sold as whale meat?

EXPERIMENT   C. S. Baker, at the University of Auckland, New Zealand, and S. R. Palumbi, then at the University of Hawaii, purchased 13 samples of "whale meat" from several Japanese fish markets. They sequenced a region with the mitochondrial DNA from each sample and compared their results with the comparable DNA sequence from known whale species. To infer the species identity of their samples, Baker and Palumbi constructed a *gene tree*, a phylogenetic tree that shows patterns of relatedness among DNA sequences rather than among taxa.

RESULTS   Baker and Palumbi's analysis yielded the following gene tree:

- Minke (Antarctica)
- Minke (Australia)
- Unknown #1a, 2, 3, 4, 5, 6, 7, 8
- Minke (North Atlantic)
- Unknown #9
- Humpback (North Atlantic)
- Humpback (North Pacific)
- Unknown #1b
- Gray
- Blue (North Atlantic)
- Blue (North Pacific)
- Unknown #10, 11, 12
- Unknown #13
- Fin (Mediterranean)
- Fin (Iceland)

CONCLUSION   This analysis indicated that DNA sequences of six of the unknown samples (in red) were most closely related to DNA sequences of whales that are not legal to harvest.

SOURCE   C. S. Baker and S. R. Palumbi, Which whales are hunted? A molecular genetic approach to monitoring whaling, *Science* 265:1538–1539 (1994).

WHAT IF?   What are some potential sources of error in this study? How might the chances of reaching an erroneous conclusion be reduced?

humpback, fin, and Minke whales caught in the Northern Hemisphere was being sold illegally in fish markets.

Another newsworthy application of phylogeny relates to bioterrorism. In fall 2001, several politicians and journalists were sent envelopes containing anthrax bacteria. Researchers used phylogenetic trees based on DNA data to identify the strain of the bacterium used in the 2001 attacks—information that may eventually help trace the source of the attacks.

How do researchers construct trees like those we've considered here? In the next section, we'll begin to answer that question by examining the data used to estimate phylogenies.

CONCEPT 26.2
Phylogenies are inferred from morphological and molecular data

To infer phylogeny, systematists must gather as much information as possible about the morphology, genes, and biochemistry of the relevant organisms. It is important to focus on features that result from common ancestry, because only these features reflect evolutionary relationships.

Morphological and Molecular Homologies

Recall that similarities due to shared ancestry are called homologies. For example, the similarity in the number and arrangement of bones in the forelimbs of mammals is due to their descent from a common ancestor with the same bone

structure; this is an example of a morphological homology (see Figure 22.17). In the same way, genes or other DNA sequences are homologous if they are descended from sequences carried by a common ancestor.

In general, organisms that share very similar morphologies or similar DNA sequences are likely to be more closely related than organisms with vastly different structures or sequences. In some cases, however, the morphological divergence between related species can be great and their genetic divergence small (or vice versa). Consider the Hawaiian silversword plants discussed in Chapter 25. These species vary dramatically in appearance throughout the islands. Some are tall, twiggy trees, and others are dense, ground-hugging shrubs (see Figure 25.18). But despite these striking phenotypic differences, the silverswords' genes are very similar. Based on these small molecular divergences, scientists estimate that the silversword group began to diverge 5 million years ago, which is also about the time when the oldest of the current islands formed. We'll discuss how scientists use molecular data to make such estimates later in this chapter.

Sorting Homology from Analogy

A potential red herring in constructing a phylogeny is similarity due to convergent evolution—called **analogy**—rather than to shared ancestry (homology). As you read in Chapter 22, convergent evolution occurs when similar environmental pressures and natural selection produce similar (analogous) adaptations in organisms from different evolutionary lineages. For example, the two mole-like animals illustrated in **Figure 26.7** are very similar in their external appearance. However, their internal anatomy, physiology, and reproductive systems are very dissimilar. Australian "moles" are marsupials; their young complete

▲ **Figure 26.7 Convergent evolution of analogous burrowing characteristics.** An elongated body, enlarged front paws, small eyes, and a pad of thickened skin that protects a tapered nose all evolved independently in the marsupial Australian "mole" (top) and a eutherian North American mole (bottom).

their embryonic development in a pouch on the outside of the mother's body. North American moles, in contrast, are eutherians; their young complete their embryonic development in the uterus within the mother's body. Indeed, genetic comparisons and the fossil record provide evidence that the common ancestor of these moles lived 140 million years ago, about the time the marsupial and eutherian mammals diverged. This ancestor and most of its descendants were not mole-like, but analogous characteristics evolved independently in these two mole lineages as they became adapted to similar lifestyles.

Distinguishing between homology and analogy is critical in reconstructing phylogenies. To see why, consider bats and birds, both of which have adaptations that enable flight. This superficial resemblance might imply that bats are more closely related to birds than they are to cats, which cannot fly. But a closer examination reveals that a bat's wing is far more similar to the forelimbs of cats and other mammals than to a bird's wing. Bats and birds descended from a common tetrapod ancestor that lived about 320 million years ago. This common ancestor could not fly. Thus, although the underlying skeletal systems of bats and birds are homologous, their *wings* are not. Flight is enabled in different ways—stretched membranes in the bat wing versus feathers in the bird wing. Fossil evidence also documents that bat wings and bird wings arose independently from the forelimbs of different tetrapod ancestors. Thus, with respect to flight, a bat's wing is *analogous*, not homologous, to a bird's wing. Analogous structures that arose independently are also called **homoplasies** (from the Greek for "to mold in the same way").

Besides corroborative similarities and fossil evidence, another clue to distinguishing between homology and analogy is the complexity of the characters being compared. The more points of resemblance that two complex structures have, the more likely it is that they evolved from a common ancestor. For instance, the skulls of an adult human and an adult chimpanzee both consist of many bones fused together. The compositions of the skulls match almost perfectly, bone for bone. It is highly improbable that such complex structures, matching in so many details, have separate origins. More likely, the genes involved in the development of both skulls were inherited from a common ancestor. The same argument applies to comparisons at the gene level. Genes are sequences of thousands of nucleotides, each of which represents an inherited character in the form of one of the four DNA bases: A (adenine), G (guanine), C (cytosine), or T (thymine). If genes in two organisms share many portions of their nucleotide sequences, it is highly likely that the genes are homologous.

Evaluating Molecular Homologies

Molecular comparisons of nucleic acids often pose technical challenges for researchers. The first step after sequencing the molecules is to align comparable sequences from the species being studied. If the species are very closely related, the sequences probably differ at only one or a few sites. In contrast, comparable nucleic acid sequences in distantly related species usually have different bases at many sites and may have different lengths. This is because insertions and deletions accumulate over long periods of time (see Chapter 23).

Suppose, for example, that particular noncoding DNA sequences in a particular gene in two species are very similar, except that the first base of the sequence has been deleted in one of the species. The effect is that the remaining sequence shifts back one notch. A comparison of the two sequences that does not take this deletion into account would overlook what in fact is a very good match. To address such problems, systematists have developed computer programs that estimate the best way to align comparable DNA segments of differing lengths (Figure 26.8).

Such molecular comparisons reveal that a large number of base substitutions and other differences have accumulated between the comparable genes of the Australian mole and a North American mole. The many differences indicate that their lineages have diverged greatly since their common ancestor; thus, we say that the living species are not closely related. In contrast, the high degree of gene sequence similarity among the silverswords supports the hypothesis that they are all very closely related, in spite of their considerable morphological differences.

Just as with morphological characters, it is necessary to distinguish homology from analogy in evaluating molecular

① Ancestral homologous DNA segments are identical as species 1 and species 2 begin to diverge from their common ancestor.

1 C C A T C A G A G T C C
2 C C A T C A G A G T C C

② Deletion and insertion mutations shift what had been matching sequences in the two species.

Deletion

1 C C A T C A⟨G⟩A G T C C
2 C C A T C A G A G T C C

⟨G T A⟩ Insertion

③ Of the three homologous regions, two (shaded orange) do not align because of these mutations.

1 C C A T C A A G T C C
2 C C A T G T A C A G A G T C C

④ Homologous regions realign after a computer program adds gaps in sequence 1.

1 C C A T _ _ _ C A _ A G T C C
2 C C A T G T A C A G A G T C C

▲ **Figure 26.8 Aligning segments of DNA.** Systematists use computer software to find and align similar sequences along DNA segments from two species. (In this example, no bases have changed in these sequences since divergence, and so the comparable sequences are still identical once the length is adjusted.)

ACGGATAGTCCACTAGGCACTA

TCACCGACAGGTCTTTGACTAG

▲ **Figure 26.9 A molecular homoplasy.** These two DNA sequences from organisms that are not closely related coincidentally share 25% of their bases. Statistical tools have been developed to determine whether DNA sequences that share more than 25% of their bases do so because they are homologous.

? *Why might you expect organisms that are not closely related to nevertheless share roughly 25% of their bases?*

similarities for evolutionary studies. Two sequences that resemble each other at many points along their length most likely are homologous (see Figure 26.8). But in organisms that do not appear to be closely related, the bases that their otherwise very different sequences happen to share may simply be coincidental matches, called molecular homoplasies **(Figure 26.9)**. Scientists have developed statistical tools that can help distinguish "distant" homologies from such coincidental matches in extremely divergent sequences.

Scientists have so far sequenced more than 100 billion bases' worth of nucleic acid data from thousands of species. This enormous collection of data has fed a boom in the study of phylogeny. The new data have supported earlier hypotheses regarding many evolutionary relationships, such as that between the Australian and North American moles, and have clarified other relationships, such as those between the various silverswords. In the rest of this chapter and unit, you will see many examples of the tremendous impact of **molecular systematics**, the discipline that uses DNA and other molecular data to determine evolutionary relationships.

CONCEPT **26.3**

Shared characters are used to construct phylogenetic trees

In reconstructing phylogenies, the first step is to distinguish homologous features from analogous features (since only the former reflect evolutionary history). Once that task is accomplished, biologists must choose a method of inferring phylogeny from these homologous characters. In this section, we'll examine a widely used set of methods known as cladistics.

Cladistics

In the approach to systematics called **cladistics**, common ancestry is the primary criterion used to classify organisms. Using this methodology, biologists place species into groups called **clades**, each of which includes an ancestral species and all of its descendants **(Figure 26.10a)**. Clades, like taxonomic

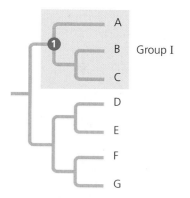

(a) Monophyletic group (clade). Group I, consisting of three species (A, B, C) and their common ancestor ❶, is a clade, also called a monophyletic group. A monophyletic group consists of an ancestral species and *all* of its descendants.

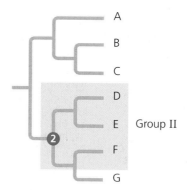

(b) Paraphyletic group. Group II is paraphyletic, meaning that it consists of an ancestral species ❷ and some of its descendants (species D, E, F) but not all of them (missing species G).

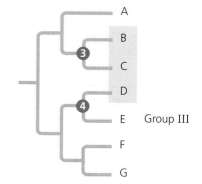

(c) Polyphyletic group. Group III is polyphyletic, meaning that its members have different ancestors. In this case, species B and C share common ancestor ❸, but species C has a different ancestor: ❹.

▲ **Figure 26.10 Monophyletic, paraphyletic, and polyphyletic groups.**

ranks, are nested within larger clades. For example, the cat group represents a clade within a larger clade that also includes the dog group. However, a taxon is equivalent to a clade only if it is **monophyletic** (from the Greek meaning "single tribe"), signifying that it consists of an ancestral species and all its descendants (see Figure 26.10a). Contrast this with a **paraphyletic** ("beside the tribe") group, which consists of an ancestral species and some, but not all, of its descendants **(Figure 26.10b)**, or a **polyphyletic** ("many tribes") group, which includes taxa with different ancestors **(Figure 26.10c)**. Next we'll discuss how clades are identified: using shared derived characters.

Shared Ancestral and Shared Derived Characters

As a result of descent with modification, organisms both share characteristics with their ancestors and differ from them (see Chapter 22). For example, all mammals have backbones, but the presence of a backbone does not distinguish mammals from other vertebrates because *all* vertebrates have backbones. The backbone predates the branching of the mammalian clade from other vertebrates. Thus, we say that for mammals, the backbone is a **shared ancestral character**, a character that originated in an ancestor of the taxon. In contrast, hair is a character shared by all mammals but *not* found in their ancestors. Thus, in mammals, hair is considered a **shared derived character**, an evolutionary novelty unique to a particular clade.

Note that a backbone can also qualify as a shared derived character, but only at a deeper branch point that distinguishes all vertebrates from other animals. Among vertebrates, a backbone is considered a shared ancestral character because it was present in the ancestor common to all vertebrates.

Inferring Phylogenies Using Derived Characters

Shared derived characters are unique to particular clades. Because all features of organisms arose at some point in the history of life, it should be possible to determine the clade in which each shared derived character first appeared and to use that information to infer evolutionary relationships.

To see how this analysis is done, consider the set of characters shown in **Figure 26.11a** for each of five vertebrates—a leopard, turtle, salamander, tuna, and lamprey (a jawless aquatic vertebrate). As a basis of comparison, we need to select an outgroup. An **outgroup** is a species or group of species from an evolutionary lineage that is known to have diverged before the lineage that includes the species we are studying (the **ingroup**). A suitable outgroup can be determined based on evidence from morphology, paleontology, embryonic development, and gene sequences. An appropriate outgroup for our example is the lancelet, a small animal that lives in mudflats and (like vertebrates) is a member of the Chordata. Unlike the vertebrates, however, the lancelet does not have a backbone.

By comparing members of the ingroup to each other and to the outgroup, we can determine which characters were derived at the various branch points of vertebrate evolution. For example, *all* of the vertebrates in the ingroup have backbones: This character was present in the ancestral vertebrate, but not in the outgroup. Now note that hinged jaws are a character absent in lampreys but present in other members of the ingroup; this character helps us to identify an early branch point in the vertebrate clade. Proceeding in this way, we can translate the data in our table of characters into a phylogenetic tree **(Figure 26.11b)**.

	TAXA					
CHARACTERS	Lancelet (outgroup)	Lamprey	Tuna	Salamander	Turtle	Leopard
Vertebral column (backbone)	0	1	1	1	1	1
Hinged jaws	0	0	1	1	1	1
Four walking legs	0	0	0	1	1	1
Amniotic (shelled) egg	0	0	0	0	1	1
Hair	0	0	0	0	0	1

(a) Character table. A 0 indicates that a character is absent; a 1 indicates that a character is present.

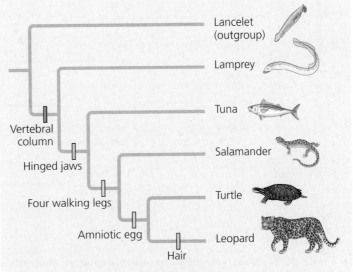

(b) Phylogenetic tree. Analyzing the distribution of these derived characters can provide insight into vertebrate phylogeny.

▲ Figure 26.11 **Constructing a phylogenetic tree.**

Phylogenetic Trees with Proportional Branch Lengths

In the phylogenetic trees we have presented so far, the lengths of the tree's branches do not indicate the degree of evolutionary change in each lineage. Furthermore, the chronology represented by the branching pattern of the tree is relative (earlier versus later) rather than absolute (how many millions of years ago). But in some tree diagrams, branch lengths are proportional to amount of evolutionary change or to the times at which particular events occurred.

For example, the branch length of a phylogenetic tree can reflect the number of changes that have taken place in a particular DNA sequence in that lineage (Figure 26.12). Note that in Figure 26.12, the *total length* of the horizontal lines from the base of the tree to the mouse is less than that of the line leading to the outgroup species, the fruit fly *Drosophila*. This implies that in the time since the mouse and fly diverged from a common ancestor, more genetic changes have occurred in the *Drosophila* lineage than in the mouse lineage.

Even though the branches of a phylogenetic tree may have different lengths, among organisms alive today, all the different lineages that descend from a common ancestor have survived for the same number of years. To take an extreme example, humans and bacteria had a common ancestor that lived over 3 billion years ago. Fossils and genetic evidence indicate that this ancestor was a single-celled prokaryote. Even though bacteria have apparently changed little in their structure since that common ancestor, there have nonetheless been 3 billion years of evolution in the bacterial lineage, just as there have been 3 billion years of evolution in the eukaryotic lineage that includes humans.

These equal spans of chronological time can be represented in a phylogenetic tree whose branch lengths are proportional to time (Figure 26.13). Such a tree draws on fossil data to place branch points in the context of geologic time. Additionally, it is possible to combine these two types of trees by labeling branch points with information about rates of genetic change or dates of divergence.

Maximum Parsimony and Maximum Likelihood

As the growing database of DNA sequences enables us to study more species, the difficulty of building the phylogenetic tree that best describes their evolutionary history also grows. What if you are analyzing data for 50 species? There are 3×10^{76} different ways to arrange 50 species into a tree! And which tree in this huge forest reflects the true phylogeny? Systematists can never be sure of finding the most accurate tree in such a large data set, but they can narrow the possibilities by applying the principles of maximum parsimony and maximum likelihood.

According to the principle of **maximum parsimony**, we should first investigate the simplest explanation that is consistent with the facts. (The parsimony principle is also called "Occam's razor" after William of Occam, a 14th-century English philosopher who advocated this minimalist problem-solving approach of "shaving away" unnecessary complications.) In the case of trees based on morphology, the most parsimonious tree requires the fewest evolutionary events, as measured by the origin of shared derived morphological characters. For phylogenies based on DNA, the most parsimonious tree requires the fewest base changes.

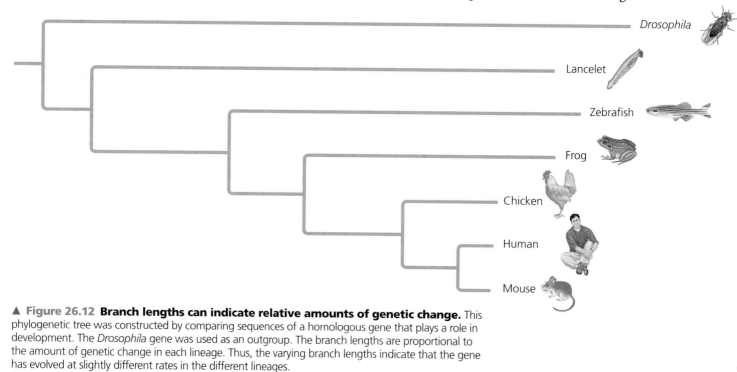

▲ **Figure 26.12 Branch lengths can indicate relative amounts of genetic change.** This phylogenetic tree was constructed by comparing sequences of a homologous gene that plays a role in development. The *Drosophila* gene was used as an outgroup. The branch lengths are proportional to the amount of genetic change in each lineage. Thus, the varying branch lengths indicate that the gene has evolved at slightly different rates in the different lineages.

[?] *In which vertebrate lineage has the studied gene evolved most rapidly? Explain.*

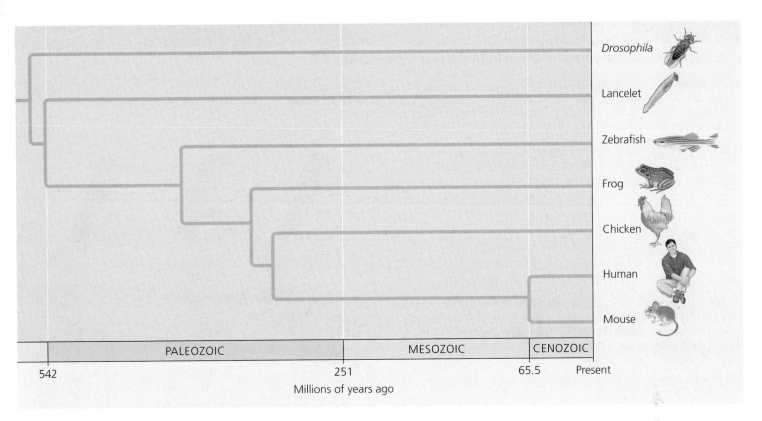

▲ Figure 26.13 Branch lengths can indicate time. The relationships shown in this tree are based on the same molecular data as the tree in Figure 26.12. Branch lengths were then drawn to fit the dates of the different branch points based on fossil evidence. As a result, branch lengths are proportional to time. Each evolutionary lineage has the same total length from the base of the tree to the branch tip, indicating that all the lineages have diverged from the common ancestor for equal amounts of time.

The principle of **maximum likelihood** states that given certain rules about how DNA changes over time, a tree can be found that reflects the most likely sequence of evolutionary events. Maximum-likelihood methods are complex, but as a simple example, let us return to the phylogenetic relationships between a human, a mushroom, and a tulip. **Figure 26.14** shows two possible, equally parsimonious trees for this trio. Tree 1 is more likely if we assume that DNA changes have occurred at equal rates along all the branches of the tree from the common ancestor. Tree 2 requires assuming that the rates of evolution slowed greatly in the mushroom lineage and sped up greatly in the tulip lineage. Thus, assuming that equal rates are more common than unequal rates, tree 1 is more likely. We will soon see that many genes do evolve at approximately equal rates in different lineages. But note that if we find new evidence

	Human	Mushroom	Tulip
Human	0	30%	40%
Mushroom		0	40%
Tulip			0

(a) Percentage differences between sequences

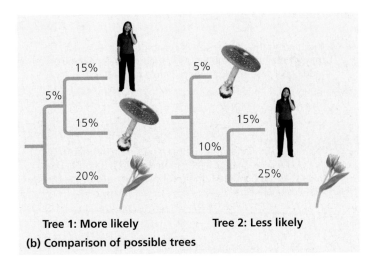

Tree 1: More likely   Tree 2: Less likely

(b) Comparison of possible trees

► Figure 26.14 Trees with different likelihoods. Based on percentage differences between genes carried by a human, a mushroom, and a tulip (a), we can construct two possible phylogenetic trees with the same total branch length (b). The sum of the percentages from a point of divergence in a tree equals the percentage differences as listed in (a). For example, in tree 1, the human–tulip divergence is 15% + 5% + 20% = 40%. In tree 2, this divergence also equals 40% (15% + 25%). Assuming that the genes have evolved at the same rate in the different branches, tree 1 is more likely than tree 2.

Research Method

Applying Parsimony to a Problem in Molecular Systematics

APPLICATION   In considering possible phylogenies for a group of species, systematists compare molecular data for the species. An efficient way to begin is by identifying the most parsimonious hypothesis—the one that requires the fewest evolutionary events (molecular changes) to have occurred.

TECHNIQUE   Follow the numbered steps as we apply the principle of parsimony to a hypothetical phylogenetic problem involving three closely related bird species.

Species I   Species II   Species III

1 First, draw the three possible phylogenies for the species. (Although only 3 trees are possible when ordering 3 species, the number of possible trees increases rapidly with the number of species: There are 15 trees for 4 species and 34,459,425 trees for 10 species.)

Three phylogenetic hypotheses:

2 Tabulate the molecular data for the species. In this simplified example, the data represent a DNA sequence consisting of just four nucleotide bases. Data from several outgroup species (not shown) were used to infer the ancestral DNA sequence.

	Site			
	1	2	3	4
Species I	C	T	A	T
Species II	C	T	T	C
Species III	A	G	A	C
Ancestral sequence	A	G	T	T

3 Now focus on site 1 in the DNA sequence. In the tree on the left, a single base-change event, represented by the purple hatchmark on the branch leading to species I and II (and labeled 1/C, indicating a change at site 1 to nucleotide C), is sufficient to account for the site 1 data. In the other two trees, two base-change events are necessary.

4 Continuing the comparison of bases at sites 2, 3, and 4 reveals that each of the three trees requires a total of five additional base-change events (purple hatchmarks).

RESULTS   To identify the most parsimonious tree, we total all of the base-change events noted in steps 3 and 4. We conclude that the first tree is the most parsimonious of the three possible phylogenies.

6 events   7 events   7 events

of unequal rates, tree 2 might be more likely! The likelihood of a tree depends on the assumptions on which it is based.

Many computer programs have been developed to search for trees that are parsimonious and likely. When a large amount of accurate data is available, the methods used in these programs usually yield similar trees. As an example of one method, **Figure 26.15**, on the facing page, walks you through the process of identifying the most parsimonious molecular tree for a three-species problem. Computer programs based on parsimony estimate phylogenies in a similar way: They exhaustively examine all possible trees and select the tree or trees that require fewest evolutionary changes.

Phylogenetic Trees as Hypotheses

This is a good place to reiterate that any phylogenetic tree represents a hypothesis about how the various organisms in the tree are related to one another. The best hypothesis is the one that best fits all the available data. A phylogenetic hypothesis may be modified when new evidence compels systematists to revise their trees. Indeed, while many older phylogenetic hypotheses have been supported, others have been changed or rejected based on new morphological and molecular data.

Thinking of phylogenies as hypotheses also allows us to use them in a powerful way: We can make and test predictions based on the assumption that a phylogeny—our hypothesis—is correct. For example, in an approach known as **phylogenetic bracketing**, we can predict (by parsimony) that features shared by two groups of closely related organisms are present in their common ancestor and all of its descendants, unless independent data indicate otherwise. (Note that here the term *prediction* includes past events, not only future evolutionary change.)

This approach has been used to make novel predictions about dinosaurs. For example, there is evidence that birds descended from the theropods, a group of bipedal dinosaurs within the Saurischian clade. As seen in **Figure 26.16**, the closest living relatives of birds are crocodiles. Birds and crocodiles share numerous features: They have four-chambered hearts, they "sing" to defend territories and attract mates (although a crocodile "song" is more like a bellow), and they build nests. Both birds and crocodiles also care for their eggs by *brooding*, a behavior in which a parent warms the eggs with its body. Birds brood by sitting on their eggs, whereas crocodiles cover their eggs with their neck. Reasoning that any feature shared by birds and crocodiles is likely to have been present in their common ancestor (denoted by the blue dot in Figure 26.16) and *all* of its descendants, biologists predicted that dinosaurs had four-chambered hearts, sang, built nests, and exhibited brooding.

Internal organs, such as the heart, rarely fossilize, and it is, of course, difficult to test whether dinosaurs sang to defend territories and attract mates. However, fossilized dinosaur eggs and nests have provided evidence supporting the prediction of brooding in dinosaurs. First, a fossil embryo of an *Oviraptor* dinosaur was found, still inside its egg. This egg was identical to those found in another fossil, one that showed an *Oviraptor* adult crouching over a group of eggs in a posture similar to that in brooding birds today **(Figure 26.17)**. Researchers suggested

Front limb
Hind limb
Eggs

(a) Fossil remains of *Oviraptor* and eggs. The orientation of the bones, which surround and cover the eggs, suggests that the dinosaur died while incubating or protecting its eggs.

(b) Artist's reconstruction of the dinosaur's posture based on the fossil findings.

▲ **Figure 26.17 Fossils support a phylogenetic prediction: Dinosaurs built nests and brooded their eggs.**

Lizards and snakes

Crocodilians

Ornithischian dinosaurs

Common ancestor of crocodilians, dinosaurs, and birds

Saurischian dinosaurs

Birds

▲ **Figure 26.16 A phylogenetic tree of birds and their close relatives.**

that the *Oviraptor* dinosaur preserved in this second fossil died while incubating or protecting its eggs. The broader conclusion that emerged from this work—that dinosaurs built nests and exhibited brooding—has since been supported by additional fossil discoveries that show that other species of dinosaurs built nests and sat on their eggs. Finally, by supporting predictions based on the phylogenetic hypothesis shown in Figure 26.16, fossil discoveries of nests and brooding in dinosaurs provide independent data that suggest the hypothesis is correct.

CONCEPT CHECK 26.3

1. To distinguish a particular clade of mammals within the larger clade that corresponds to class Mammalia, would hair be a useful character? Why or why not?
2. Why might the most parsimonious tree not necessarily be the most accurate in representing evolutionary relationships for a particular group of species?
3. **WHAT IF?** Draw a phylogenetic tree that includes the relationships from both Figure 25.6 and Figure 26.16. Traditionally, all the taxa shown besides birds and mammals were classified as reptiles. Using a cladistic approach, critique that classification.

For suggested answers, see Appendix A.

CONCEPT 26.4
An organism's evolutionary history is documented in its genome

You have seen throughout this chapter that molecular systematics—using comparisons of nucleic acids or other molecules to deduce relatedness—is a valuable tool for tracing evolutionary history. The molecular approach helps us to understand phylogenetic relationships that cannot be determined by nonmolecular methods such as comparative anatomy. For example, molecular systematics helps us uncover evolutionary relationships between groups that have little common ground for morphological comparison, such as animals and fungi. And molecular methods allow us to reconstruct phylogenies among groups of present-day prokaryotes and other microorganisms for which we have no fossil record at all. Molecular biology has helped to extend systematics to evolutionary relationships far above and below the species level, ranging from the major branches of the tree of life to its finest twigs. Still, the findings are often inconclusive, as in cases where several taxa diverged at nearly the same time in the distant past. The differences may be apparent, but not the order of their appearance.

Different genes evolve at different rates, even in the same evolutionary lineage. As a result, molecular trees can repre-

sent short or long periods of time, depending on what genes are used. For example, the DNA that codes for ribosomal RNA (rRNA) changes relatively slowly, and so comparisons of DNA sequences in these genes are useful for investigating relationships between taxa that diverged hundreds of millions of years ago. Studies of rRNA sequences indicate, for example, that fungi are more closely related to animals than to green plants (see Figure 26.2). In contrast, mitochondrial DNA (mtDNA) evolves relatively rapidly and can be used to explore recent evolutionary events. One research team has traced the relationships among Native American groups through their mtDNA sequences. The molecular findings corroborate other evidence that the Pima of Arizona, the Maya of Mexico, and the Yanomami of Venezuela are closely related, probably descending from the first of three waves of immigrants that crossed the Bering land bridge from Asia to the Americas about 13,000 years ago.

Gene Duplications and Gene Families

What does molecular systematics reveal about the evolutionary history of genome change? Consider gene duplication, which plays a particularly important role in evolution because it increases the number of genes in the genome, providing more opportunities for further evolutionary changes. Molecular techniques now allow us to trace the phylogenies of gene duplications and the influence of these duplications on genome evolution. These molecular phylogenies must account for repeated duplications that have resulted in *gene families*, groups of related genes within an organism's genome (see Figure 21.10). Like homologous genes in different species, these duplicated genes have a common ancestor. We distinguish these types of homologous genes by different names: orthologous genes and paralogous genes.

The term **orthologous genes** (from the Greek *orthos*, straight) refers to homologous genes that are found in different species because of speciation (Figure 26.18a). The cytochrome *c* genes (which code for an electron transport chain protein) in humans and dogs are orthologous. **Paralogous genes** (from the Greek *para*, beside) result from gene duplication, so they are found in more than one copy in the same genome (Figure 26.18b). In Chapter 23, you encountered the example of olfactory receptor genes, which have undergone many gene duplications in vertebrates. Humans and mice both have huge families of more than 1,000 of these paralogous genes.

It is possible to describe most of the genes that make up genomes as representing one of these two types of homology. Note that orthologous genes can only diverge after speciation has taken place, with the result that the genes are found in separate gene pools. For example, although the cytochrome *c* genes in humans and dogs serve a similar function, the

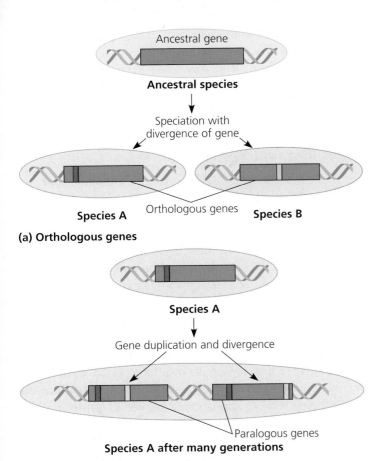

▲ **Figure 26.18 How two types of homologous genes originate.** The colored bands mark regions of the genes where differences in base sequences have accumulated.

gene's sequence in humans has diverged from that in dogs in the time since these species last shared a common ancestor. Paralogous genes, on the other hand, can diverge within a species because they are present in more than one copy in the genome. The paralogous genes that make up the olfactory receptor gene family in humans have diverged from each other during our long evolutionary history. They now specify proteins that confer sensitivity to a wide variety of odors, ranging from various foods to sex pheromones.

Genome Evolution

Now that we can compare the entire genomes of different organisms, including our own, two remarkable facts have emerged. First, orthologous genes are widespread and can extend over huge evolutionary distances. Ninety-nine percent of the genes of humans and mice are detectably orthologous, and 50% of our genes are orthologous with those of yeast. This remarkable commonality demonstrates that all living organisms share many biochemical and developmental pathways.

Second, the number of genes seems not to have increased through duplication at the same rate as perceived phenotypic complexity. Humans have only about four times as many genes as yeast, a single-celled eukaryote, even though—unlike

yeast cells—we have a large, complex brain and a body that contains more than 200 different types of tissues. Evidence is emerging that many human genes are more versatile than those of yeast in that the proteins they encode carry out a wider variety of tasks in various body tissues. Before us lies a huge and exciting scientific challenge: unraveling the mechanisms that enable this genomic versatility.

CONCEPT CHECK 26.4

1. Explain how comparisons between the proteins of two species can yield data about their evolutionary relationship.
2. **WHAT IF?** Suppose gene A is orthologous in species 1 and species 2, and gene B is paralogous to gene A in species 1. Suggest a sequence of two evolutionary events that could result in the following: Gene A differs considerably between species, yet gene A and gene B show little sequence divergence from each other.

For suggested answers, see Appendix A.

CONCEPT 26.5
Molecular clocks help track evolutionary time

One of the long-term goals of evolutionary biology is to understand the relationships among all organisms, including those for which there is no fossil record. When we extend molecular phylogenies beyond the fossil record, however, we must rely on an important assumption about how change occurs at the molecular level.

Molecular Clocks

We stated earlier that researchers have estimated that the common ancestor of Hawaiian silverswords lived about 5 million years ago. How did they make this estimate? They relied on the concept of a **molecular clock**, a yardstick for measuring the absolute time of evolutionary change based on the observation that some genes and other regions of genomes appear to evolve at constant rates. The assumption underlying the molecular clock is that the number of nucleotide substitutions in orthologous genes is proportional to the time that has elapsed since the species branched from their common ancestor (divergence time). In the case of paralogous genes, the number of substitutions is proportional to the time since the genes became duplicated.

We can calibrate the molecular clock of a gene that has a reliable average rate of evolution by graphing the number of genetic differences—for example, nucleotide, codon, or amino acid differences—against the dates of evolutionary branch

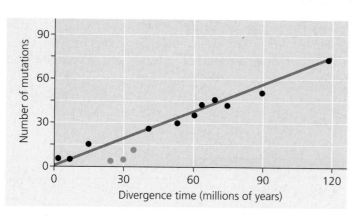

▲ **Figure 26.19 A molecular clock for mammals.** The number of accumulated mutations in seven proteins increased over time in a consistent manner for most mammal species. The three green data points represent primate species, whose proteins appear to have evolved more slowly than those of other mammals. The divergence time for each data point was based on fossil evidence.

? *Use the clock to estimate the divergence time for a mammal with a total of 30 mutations in the seven proteins.*

points that are known from the fossil record **(Figure 26.19)**. Such graphs can then be used to estimate the dates of evolutionary episodes that cannot be discerned from the fossil record, such as the origin of the silverswords discussed earlier.

Of course, no gene marks time with complete precision. In fact, some portions of the genome appear to have evolved in irregular fits and starts that are not at all clocklike. And even those genes that seem to have reliable molecular clocks are accurate only in the statistical sense of showing a fairly smooth *average* rate of change. Over time, there may still be chance deviations above and below that average rate. Furthermore, the same gene may evolve at different rates in different groups of organisms, making it necessary to calibrate and use molecular clocks with care. Finally, even among genes that are clocklike, the rate of the clock may vary greatly from one gene to another; some genes evolve a million times faster than others.

Neutral Theory

The regularity of change that enables us to use some genes as molecular clocks raises the possibility that many of the changes in these sequences result from genetic drift (see Chapter 23) and that the changes are mostly neutral—neither adaptive nor detrimental. In the 1960s, Jack King and Thomas Jukes, at the University of California, Berkeley, and Motoo Kimura, at the Japanese National Institute of Genetics, published papers supporting this **neutral theory**—that much evolutionary change in genes and proteins has no effect on fitness and therefore is not influenced by Darwinian selection. Kimura pointed out that many new mutations are harmful and are removed quickly. But if most of the rest are neutral and have little or no effect on fitness, then the rate of molecular change should indeed be regular like a clock. Differences in the clock rate for different genes are a function of how important a gene is. If the

exact sequence of amino acids that a gene specifies is essential to survival, most of the mutational changes will be harmful and only a few will be neutral. As a result, such genes change only slowly. But if the exact sequence of amino acids is less critical, fewer of the new mutations will be harmful and more will be neutral. Such genes change more quickly.

Difficulties with Molecular Clocks

In fact, molecular clocks do not run as smoothly as neutral theory predicts. Many irregularities are likely to be the result of natural selection in which certain DNA changes are favored over others. Consequently, some scientists question the utility of molecular clocks for timing evolution. Their skepticism is part of a broader debate about the extent to which neutral genetic variation can account for some kinds of DNA diversity. Indeed, evidence suggests that almost half the amino acid differences in proteins of two *Drosophila* species, *D. simulans* and *D. yakuba*, are not neutral but have resulted from directional natural selection. But because the direction of natural selection may change repeatedly over long periods of time (and hence may average out), some genes experiencing selection can nevertheless serve as approximate markers of elapsed time.

Another question arises when researchers attempt to extend molecular clocks beyond the time span documented by the fossil record. Although some fossils are more than 3 billion years old, these are very rare. An abundant fossil record extends back only about 550 million years, but molecular clocks have been used to date evolutionary divergences that occurred a billion or more years ago. These estimates assume that the clocks have been constant for all that time. Such estimates are highly uncertain.

In some cases, problems may be avoided by calibrating molecular clocks with many genes rather than just one or a few genes (as is often done). By using many genes, fluctuations in evolutionary rate due to natural selection or other factors that vary over time may average out. For example, one group of researchers constructed molecular clocks of vertebrate evolution from published sequence data for 658 nuclear genes. Despite the broad period of time covered (nearly 600 million years) and the fact that natural selection probably affected some of these genes, their estimates of divergence times agreed closely with fossil-based estimates.

Applying a Molecular Clock: The Origin of HIV

Researchers at Los Alamos National Laboratory in New Mexico used a molecular clock to date the origin of HIV infection in humans. Phylogenetic analysis shows that HIV, the virus that causes AIDS, is descended from viruses that infect chimpanzees and other primates. (The viruses do not cause any AIDS-like diseases in nonhuman hosts.) When did HIV jump to humans? There is no simple answer, because the virus has

Figure 26.20 Dating the origin of HIV-1 M with a molecular clock. The numerous data points in the upper right-hand corner of this graph are based on DNA sequences for a specific HIV gene in blood samples collected from patients at different known times. If we project the relatively constant rate at which changes occurred in this gene in the 1980s and 1990s back in time, we intersect the *x*-axis of the graph in the 1930s.

spread to humans more than once. The multiple origins of HIV are reflected in the variety of strains (genetic types) of the virus. HIV's genetic material is made of RNA, and like other RNA viruses, it evolves quickly.

The most widespread strain in humans is HIV-1 M. To pinpoint the earliest HIV-1 M infection, the researchers compared samples of the virus from various times during the epidemic, including one sample from 1959. A comparison of gene sequences showed that the virus has evolved in a clock-like fashion since 1959 **(Figure 26.20)**. By extrapolating from their molecular clock, the researchers concluded that the HIV-1 M strain first spread to humans during the 1930s.

CONCEPT CHECK 26.5

1. What is a molecular clock? What assumption underlies the use of a molecular clock?
2. Explain how numerous base changes could occur in DNA, yet have no effect on an organism's fitness.
3. **WHAT IF?** Suppose a molecular clock dates the divergence of two taxa at 80 million years ago, but new fossil evidence shows that the taxa diverged at least 120 million years ago. Explain how this could happen.

For suggested answers, see Appendix A.

CONCEPT 26.6
New information continues to revise our understanding of the tree of life

The discovery that the scaly-foot in Figure 26.1 evolved from a different lineage of legless lizards than did snakes is one example of how systematics is used to reconstruct the evolutionary relationships of life's diverse forms. In recent decades, we have gained insight into even the very deepest branches of the tree of life through molecular systematics.

From Two Kingdoms to Three Domains

Early taxonomists classified all known species into two kingdoms: plants and animals. Even with the discovery of the diverse microbial world, the two-kingdom system persisted: Noting that bacteria had a rigid cell wall, taxonomists placed them in the plant kingdom. Eukaryotic unicellular organisms with chloroplasts were also considered plants. Fungi, too, were classified as plants, partly because most fungi, like most plants, are unable to move about, and despite the fact that fungi are not photosynthetic and have little in common structurally with plants. In the two-kingdom system, unicellular organisms that move and ingest food—protozoans—were classified as animals. Microorganisms such as *Euglena* that move and are photosynthetic were claimed by both botanists and zoologists and showed up in both kingdoms.

Taxonomic schemes with more than two kingdoms did not gain broad acceptance until the late 1960s, when many biologists recognized five kingdoms: Monera (prokaryotes), Protista (a diverse kingdom consisting mostly of unicellular organisms), Plantae, Fungi, and Animalia. This system highlighted the two fundamentally different types of cells, prokaryotic and eukaryotic, and set the prokaryotes apart from all eukaryotes by placing them in their own kingdom, Monera.

However, shortly after the widespread adoption of the five-kingdom approach, phylogenies based on genetic data began to reveal a fundamental problem with this system: Some prokaryotes differed as much from each other as they did from eukaryotes. Such difficulties have led biologists to adopt a three-domain system. The three domains—Bacteria, Archaea, and Eukarya—are a taxonomic level higher than the kingdom level. The validity of these domains has now been confirmed by many studies, including an analysis of nearly 100 of the many hundreds of completely sequenced genomes.

The domain Bacteria contains most of the currently known prokaryotes, including the bacteria closely related to chloroplasts and mitochondria. The second domain, Archaea, consists of a diverse group of prokaryotic organisms that inhabit a wide variety of environments. Some archaea can use hydrogen as an energy source, and others were the chief source of the

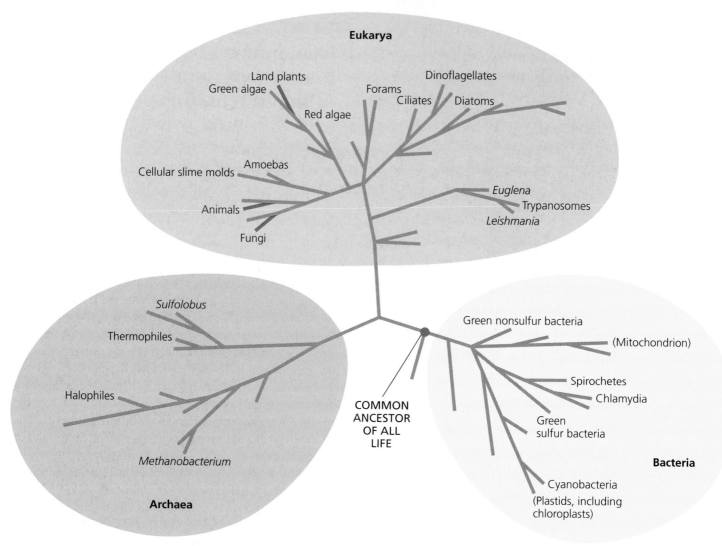

▲ **Figure 26.21 The three domains of life.** Based on rRNA gene sequences, all of life can be grouped into three domains. Branch lengths are proportional to the amount of genetic change in each lineage. (To simplify the figure, only some branches are labeled.) In this diagram, the lineages within Eukarya that are dominated by multicellular organisms (plants, fungi, and animals) are shown in red. All other lineages consist solely or primarily of single-celled organisms.

? *Based on this diagram, which domain was the first to diverge? Which is the sister domain to Eukarya?*

natural gas deposits that are found throughout Earth's crust. As you will read in Chapter 27, bacteria differ from archaea in many structural, biochemical, and physiological characteristics. The third domain, Eukarya, consists of all the organisms that have cells containing true nuclei. This domain includes many groups of single-celled organisms (see Chapter 28) as well as multicellular plants (Chapters 29 and 30), fungi (Chapter 31), and animals (Chapters 32–34). **Figure 26.21** represents one possible phylogenetic tree for the three domains and the many lineages they encompass.

The three-domain system highlights the fact that much of the history of life has been about single-celled organisms. The two prokaryotic domains consist entirely of single-celled organisms, and even in Eukarya, only the branches shown in red (plants, fungi, and animals) are dominated by multicellular organisms. Of the five kingdoms previously recognized by

taxonomists, most biologists continue to recognize Plantae, Fungi, and Animalia, but not Monera and Protista. The kingdom Monera is obsolete because it would have members in two different domains. As you'll read in Chapter 28, the kingdom Protista has also crumbled because it is polyphyletic—it includes members that are more closely related to plants, fungi, or animals than to other protists.

A Simple Tree of All Life

The evolutionary relationships shown in Figure 26.21 can be summarized in a simpler tree **(Figure 26.22)**. In this tree, the first major split in the history of life occurred when the bacteria diverged from other organisms. If this tree is correct, eukaryotes and archaea are more closely related to each other than either is to bacteria.

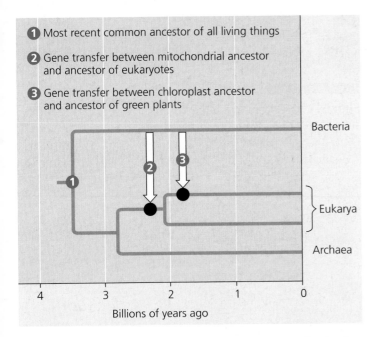

① Most recent common ancestor of all living things

② Gene transfer between mitochondrial ancestor and ancestor of eukaryotes

③ Gene transfer between chloroplast ancestor and ancestor of green plants

Billions of years ago

▲ **Figure 26.22 The role of horizontal gene transfer in the history of life.** This tree shows two major episodes of horizontal gene transfer, the dates of which are uncertain. It is known that many more such events occurred.

This reconstruction of the tree of life is based largely on sequence comparisons of rRNA genes, which code for the RNA parts of ribosomes. Because ribosomes are fundamental to the workings of the cell, rRNA genes have evolved so slowly that homologies between distantly related organisms can still be detected—making these genes very useful for determining evolutionary relationships among deep branches in the history of life. However, other genes reveal a different set of relationships. For example, researchers have found that many of the genes that influence metabolism in yeast (a single-celled eukaryote) are more similar to genes in the domain Bacteria than they are to genes in the domain Archaea—a finding that suggests that the eukaryotes may share a more recent common ancestor with bacteria than with archaea.

Comparisons of complete genomes from the three domains show that there have been substantial movements of genes between organisms in the different domains (see Figure 26.22). These took place through **horizontal gene transfer**, a process in which genes are transferred from one genome to another through mechanisms such as exchange of transposable elements and plasmids, viral infection (see Chapter 19), and perhaps fusions of organisms. Some biologists hypothesize that the first eukaryote may have arisen through a fusion between an ancestral bacterium and an ancestral archaean. Because phylogenetic trees are based on the assumption that genes are passed vertically from one generation to the next, the occurrence of such horizontal transfer events helps to explain why universal trees built using different genes can give inconsistent results.

▲ **Figure 26.23 A ring of life.** In this hypothesis, the earliest organisms form a "ring of life" through horizontal gene transfer. Three great domains (Bacteria, Eukarya, and Archaea) eventually emerged from the ring and gave rise to the tremendous diversity of life we observe today.

Is the Tree of Life Really a Ring?

Some scientists have argued that horizontal gene transfers were so common that the early history of life should be represented as a tangled network of connected branches—not a simple, dichotomously branching tree like that in Figure 26.22. Others have suggested that relationships among early organisms are best represented by a ring, not a tree (**Figure 26.23**). In an analysis based on hundreds of genes, these researchers hypothesized that eukaryotes arose as an endosymbiosis between an early bacterium and an early archaean. If correct, eukaryotes are simultaneously most closely related to bacteria *and* archaea—an evolutionary relationship that cannot be depicted in a tree of life, but can be depicted in a *ring* of life.

Although scientists continue to debate whether early steps in the history of life are best represented as a tree, a ring, or a tangled web, in recent decades there have been many exciting discoveries about evolutionary events that occurred later in time. We'll explore such discoveries in the rest of this unit's chapters, beginning with Earth's earliest inhabitants, the prokaryotes.

CONCEPT CHECK **26.6**

1. Why is the kingdom Monera no longer considered a valid taxon?

2. Explain why phylogenies based on different genes can yield different branching patterns for the universal tree of life.

3. **WHAT IF?** Draw the three possible dichotomously branching trees showing evolutionary relationships for the domains Bacteria, Archaea, and Eukarya. Two of these trees have been supported by genetic data. Is it likely that the third tree might also receive such support? Explain your answer.

For suggested answers, see Appendix A.

MEDIA Go to the Study Area at **www.masteringbio.com** for BioFlix 3-D Animations, MP3 Tutors, Videos, Practice Tests, an eBook, and more.

SUMMARY OF KEY CONCEPTS

CONCEPT 26.1

Phylogenies show evolutionary relationships (pp. 537–540)

▶ **Binomial Nomenclature** Linnaeus's system gives organisms two-part names: a genus plus a specific epithet.

▶ **Hierarchical Classification** Linnaeus introduced a formal system for grouping species in increasingly broad categories: related genera are placed in the same family, families into orders, orders into classes, classes into phyla, phyla into kingdoms, and (more recently) kingdoms into domains.

▶ **Linking Classification and Phylogeny** Systematists depict evolutionary relationships as branching phylogenetic trees. Some systematists propose that classification be based entirely on evolutionary relationships.

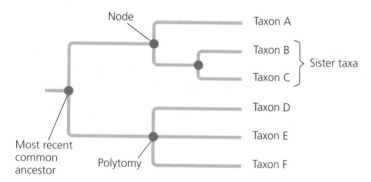

▶ **What We Can and Cannot Learn from Phylogenetic Trees** Unless branch lengths are proportional to time or genetic change, a phylogenetic tree indicates only patterns of descent.

▶ **Applying Phylogenies** Much information can be learned about a species from its evolutionary history; hence, phylogenies are useful in a wide range of applications.

MEDIA Activity Classification Schemes

CONCEPT 26.2

Phylogenies are inferred from morphological and molecular data (pp. 540–542)

▶ **Morphological and Molecular Homologies** Organisms that share very similar morphologies or DNA sequences are likely to be more closely related than organisms with very different structures and genetic sequences.

▶ **Sorting Homology from Analogy** Homology (similarity due to shared ancestry) must be sorted from analogy (similarity due to convergent evolution).

▶ **Evaluating Molecular Homologies** Computer programs are used to align comparable nucleic acid sequences and to distinguish molecular homologies from coincidental matches between taxa that diverged long ago.

CONCEPT 26.3

Shared characters are used to construct phylogenetic trees (pp. 542–548)

▶ **Cladistics** A clade is a monophyletic grouping that includes an ancestral species and all of its descendants. Clades can be distinguished by their shared derived characters.

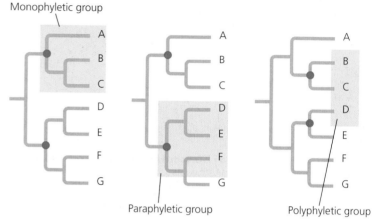

▶ **Phylogenetic Trees with Proportional Branch Lengths** Branch lengths can be drawn proportional to the amount of evolutionary change or time.

▶ **Maximum Parsimony and Maximum Likelihood** Among phylogenies, the most parsimonious tree is the one that requires the fewest evolutionary changes. The most likely tree is the one based on the most likely pattern of changes.

▶ **Phylogenetic Trees as Hypotheses** Well-supported phylogenetic hypotheses are consistent with a wide range of data.

MEDIA Investigation How Is Phylogeny Determined by Comparing Proteins?

CONCEPT 26.4

An organism's evolutionary history is documented in its genome (pp. 548–549)

▶ **Gene Duplications and Gene Families** Orthologous genes are homologous genes found in different species because of speciation. Paralogous genes arise through duplication within a genome and can diverge within a clade, often adding new functions.

▶ **Genome Evolution** Distantly related species often have orthologous genes. The small variation in gene number in organisms of varying complexity suggests that genes are versatile and may have multiple functions.

CONCEPT 26.5

Molecular clocks help track evolutionary time (pp. 549–551)

▶ **Molecular Clocks** The base sequences of some regions of DNA change at a rate consistent enough to allow dating of episodes in past evolution. Other genes change in a less predictable way.

▶ **Applying a Molecular Clock: The Origin of HIV** A molecular clock analysis suggests that the most common strain of HIV jumped from primates to humans in the 1930s.

CONCEPT 26.6

New information continues to revise our understanding of the tree of life (pp. 551–553)

▶ **From Two Kingdoms to Three Domains** Past classification systems have given way to the current view of the tree of life, which consists of three great domains: Bacteria, Archaea, and Eukarya.

▶ **A Simple Tree of All Life** Phylogenies based on rRNA genes suggest that eukaryotes are most closely related to archaea, while data from other genes suggest a closer relationship to bacteria.

▶ **Is the Tree of Life Really a Ring?** Genetic analyses suggest that the earliest organisms may have formed a "ring of life" in which eukaryotes are equally closely related to bacteria and to archaea.

TESTING YOUR KNOWLEDGE

SELF-QUIZ

1. In Figure 26.4, which similarly inclusive taxon descended from the same common ancestor as Canidae?
   a. Felidae
   b. Mustelidae
   c. Carnivora
   d. *Canis*
   e. *Lutra*

2. Three living species X, Y, and Z share a common ancestor T, as do extinct species U and V. A grouping that includes species T, X, Y, and Z makes up
   a. a valid taxon.
   b. a monophyletic clade.
   c. an ingroup, with species U as the outgroup.
   d. a paraphyletic group.
   e. a polyphyletic group.

3. In a comparison of birds and mammals, having four appendages is
   a. a shared ancestral character.
   b. a shared derived character.
   c. a character useful for distinguishing birds from mammals.
   d. an example of analogy rather than homology.
   e. a character useful for sorting bird species.

4. Based on this tree, which statement is *not* correct?

   a. The lineage leading to salamanders was the first to diverge from the other lineages.
   b. Salamanders are a sister group to the group containing lizards, goats, and humans.
   c. Salamanders are as closely related to goats as to humans.
   d. Lizards are more closely related to salamanders than to humans.
   e. The group highlighted by shading is paraphyletic.

5. If you were using cladistics to build a phylogenetic tree of cats, which of the following would be the best outgroup?
   a. lion
   b. domestic cat
   c. wolf
   d. leopard
   e. tiger

6. The relative lengths of the amphibian and mouse branches in the phylogeny in Figure 26.12 indicate that
   a. amphibians evolved before mice.
   b. mice evolved before amphibians.
   c. the genes of amphibians and mice have only coincidental homoplasies.
   d. the homologous gene has evolved more slowly in mice.
   e. the homologous gene has evolved more rapidly in mice.

7. To apply parsimony to constructing a phylogenetic tree,
   a. choose the tree that assumes all evolutionary changes are equally probable.
   b. choose the tree in which the branch points are based on as many shared derived characters as possible.
   c. base phylogenetic trees only on the fossil record, as this provides the simplest explanation for evolution.
   d. choose the tree that represents the fewest evolutionary changes, either in DNA sequences or morphology.
   e. choose the tree with the fewest branch points.

For Self-Quiz answers, see Appendix A.

MEDIA Visit the Study Area at **www.masteringbio.com** for a Practice Test.

EVOLUTION CONNECTION

8. Darwin suggested looking at a species' close relatives to learn what its ancestors may have been like. How does his suggestion anticipate recent methods, such as phylogenetic bracketing and the use of outgroups in cladistic analysis?

Biological Inquiry: A Workbook of Investigative Cases Explore the use of outgroups and other aspects of cladistic analysis in "Tree Thinking."

SCIENTIFIC INQUIRY

9. **DRAW IT** (a) Draw a phylogenetic tree based on the first five characters in the table below. Place hatch marks on the tree to indicate the origin(s) of each of the six characters. (b) Assume that tuna and dolphins are sister species and redraw the phylogenetic tree accordingly, keeping other evolutionary relationships the same as in the first tree. Place hatch marks on the tree to indicate the origin(s) of each of the six characters. (c) How many evolutionary changes are required in each tree? Which tree is most parsimonious?

| Character | SPECIES | | | | | | |
	Lancelet (outgroup)	Lamprey	Tuna	Salamander	Turtle	Leopard	Dolphin
Backbone	0	1	1	1	1	1	1
Hinged jaw	0	0	1	1	1	1	1
Four limbs	0	0	0	1	1	1	1*
Amniotic egg	0	0	0	0	1	1	1
Milk	0	0	0	0	0	1	1
Dorsal fin	0	0	1	0	0	0	1

*Although adult dolphins have only two obvious limbs (their flippers), as embryos they have two hind-limb buds, for a total of four limbs.

Bacteria and Archaea

OVERVIEW

Masters of Adaptation

After a heavy summer rain, California's Owens Lake can contain waters so hot and salty that they would burn and dehydrate your skin on contact. The salt concentration can reach 32%, more than nine times that of seawater. Yet despite these harsh conditions, the briny lakebed's reddish color, shown in **Figure 27.1**, is caused by organisms, not by minerals or other nonliving sources. What organisms can live in such an inhospitable environment, and how do they do it?

The pink color of Owens Lake comes from trillions of cells of *Halobacterium*, a single-celled prokaryote in domain Archaea that is one of the few kinds of organisms living in the lake. This archaean has a red membrane pigment, bacteriorhodopsin, that uses light energy to drive ATP synthesis. *Halobacterium* is among the most salt-tolerant organisms on Earth—it thrives in salinities that dehydrate and kill other cells. This archaean compensates for osmotic water loss by pumping potassium ions (K^+) or other ions into the cell until the ionic concentration inside the cell matches the concentration outside.

▲ Figure 27.1 **Why is this lakebed red?**

Like *Halobacterium*, many other prokaryotes are master adapters. Examples include *Deinococcus radiodurans*, which can survive 3 million rads of radiation (3,000 times the dose fatal to humans), and *Picrophilus oshimae*, which can grow at a pH of 0.03 (acidic enough to dissolve metal). Other prokaryotes live in environments that are too cold or too hot for most other organisms, and some have even been found living in rocks 3.2 km (2 miles) below Earth's surface.

Prokaryotic species are also very well adapted to more "normal" habitats—the lands and waters in which most other species are found. Their ability to adapt to a broad range of habitats helps to explain why prokaryotes are the most abundant organisms on Earth: Their collective biological mass (biomass) is at least ten times that of all eukaryotes, and the number of prokaryotes in a handful of fertile soil is greater than the number of people who have ever lived. In this chapter, we'll examine the adaptations, diversity, ecological impact, and importance to humans of these small but amazing organisms that comprise two of the three domains of life.

CONCEPT 27.1

Structural and functional adaptations contribute to prokaryotic success

As we discussed in Chapter 25, the first organisms to inhabit Earth are thought to have been prokaryotes. Throughout their long evolutionary history, prokaryotic populations have been (and continue to be) subjected to natural selection under many different environmental conditions. This process ultimately has resulted in the great diversity of adaptations found among prokaryotes today.

In this and the following sections, we'll survey the biology of prokaryotes. Most prokaryotes are unicellular, although some species aggregate temporarily or permanently in colonies.

Prokaryotic cells typically have diameters in the range of 0.5–5 μm, much smaller than the 10–100 μm diameter of many eukaryotic cells. (One notable exception is the giant prokaryote *Thiomargarita namibiensis*, which is about 750 μm in diameter—just visible to the unaided eye.) Prokaryotic cells have a variety of

1 μm

2 μm

5 μm

(a) Spherical (cocci)   **(b) Rod-shaped (bacilli)**   **(c) Spiral**

▲ **Figure 27.2 The most common shapes of prokaryotes.**
(a) Cocci (singular, *coccus*) are spherical prokaryotes. They occur singly, in pairs (diplococci), in chains of many cells (streptococci, shown here), and in clusters resembling bunches of grapes (staphylococci). **(b)** Bacilli (singular, *bacillus*) are rod-shaped prokaryotes. They are usually solitary, but in some forms the rods are arranged in chains (streptobacilli). **(c)** Spiral prokaryotes include spirilla, which range from comma-like shapes to long coils, and spirochetes (shown here), which are corkscrew-shaped (colorized SEMs).

shapes, the three most common of which are spheres (cocci), rods (bacilli), and spirals **(Figure 27.2)**. Finally, although they are unicellular and small, prokaryotes are well organized, achieving all of an organism's life functions within a single cell.

Cell-Surface Structures

A key feature of nearly all prokaryotic cells is the cell wall, which maintains cell shape, provides physical protection, and prevents the cell from bursting in a hypotonic environment (see Chapter 7). In a hypertonic environment, most prokaryotes lose water and shrink away from their wall (plasmolyze), like other walled cells. Severe water loss inhibits cell reproduction. Salt thus can be used to preserve foods because it causes prokaryotes to lose water.

The cell walls of prokaryotes differ in molecular composition and construction from those of eukaryotes. As you read in Chapter 5, eukaryotic cell walls are usually made of cellulose or chitin. In contrast, most bacterial cell walls contain **peptidoglycan**, a network of modified-sugar polymers cross-linked by short polypeptides. This molecular fabric encloses the entire bacterium and anchors other molecules that extend from its surface. Archaeal cell walls contain a variety of polysaccharides and proteins but lack peptidoglycan.

Using a technique called the **Gram stain**, developed by the nineteenth-century Danish physician Hans Christian Gram, scientists can classify many bacterial species into two groups based on differences in cell wall composition. **Gram-positive** bacteria have simpler walls with a relatively large amount of peptidoglycan **(Figure 27.3a)**. **Gram-negative** bacteria have less peptidoglycan and are structurally more complex, with an outer membrane that contains lipopolysaccharides (carbohydrates bonded to lipids) **(Figure 27.3b)**.

(a) Gram-positive. Gram-positive bacteria have a thick cell wall made of peptidoglycan that traps the crystal violet in the cytoplasm. The alcohol rinse does not remove the crystal violet, which masks the added red safranin dye.

(b) Gram-negative. Gram-negative bacteria have a thinner layer of peptidoglycan, and it is located in a layer between the plasma membrane and an outer membrane. The crystal violet is easily rinsed from the cytoplasm, and the cell appears pink or red.

▲ **Figure 27.3 Gram staining.** Samples are first stained with crystal violet dye and iodine, then rinsed in alcohol, and finally stained with a red dye such as safranin. The structure of a bacterium's cell wall determines the staining response (LM).

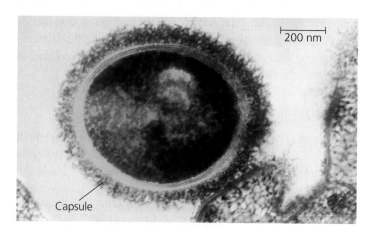

▲ **Figure 27.4 Capsule.** The polysaccharide capsule around this *Streptococcus* bacterium enables the prokaryote to attach to cells in the respiratory tract—in this colorized TEM, a tonsil cell.

▲ **Figure 27.5 Fimbriae.** These numerous appendages enable some prokaryotes to attach to surfaces or to other prokaryotes (colorized TEM).

Gram staining is a valuable tool in medicine for quickly determining if a patient's infection is due to gram-negative or to gram-positive bacteria. This information has treatment implications. The lipid portions of the lipopolysaccharides in the walls of many gram-negative bacteria are toxic, causing fever or shock. Furthermore, the outer membrane of a gram-negative bacterium helps protect it from the body's defenses. Gram-negative bacteria also tend to be more resistant than gram-positive species to antibiotics because the outer membrane impedes entry of the drugs. However, certain gram-positive species (for example, *Mycobacterium tuberculosis*, which causes tuberculosis) have virulent strains that are resistant to one or more antibiotics.

The effectiveness of certain antibiotics, such as penicillin, derives from their inhibition of the peptidoglycan cross-linking. The resulting cell wall may not be functional, particularly in gram-positive bacteria. Such drugs destroy many species of pathogenic bacteria without adversely affecting human cells, which do not contain peptidoglycan.

The cell wall of many prokaryotes is covered by a **capsule**, a sticky layer of polysaccharide or protein **(Figure 27.4)**. The capsule enables prokaryotes to adhere to their substrate or to other individuals in a colony. Some capsules protect against dehydration, and some shield pathogenic prokaryotes from attacks by their host's immune system.

Some prokaryotes stick to their substrate or to one another by means of hairlike protein appendages called **fimbriae** (singular, *fimbria*) **(Figure 27.5)**; thus, fimbriae are also known as *attachment pili*. The bacterium that causes gonorrhea, *Neisseria gonorrhoeae*, uses fimbriae to fasten itself to the mucous membranes of its host. Fimbriae are usually shorter and more numerous than **sex pili** (singular, *sex pilus*), appendages that pull two cells together prior to DNA transfer from one cell to the other.

Motility

About half of all prokaryotes are capable of directional movement. Some species can move at velocities exceeding 50 μm/sec—up to 50 times their body length per second. For perspective, consider that a person 1.7 m tall moving that fast would be running 306 km (190 miles) per hour!

Of the various structures that enable prokaryotes to move, the most common are flagella **(Figure 27.6)**. Flagella (singular, *flagellum*) may be scattered over the entire surface of the cell or concentrated at one or both ends. Prokaryotic flagella are one-tenth the width of eukaryotic flagella and are not covered by an

▲ **Figure 27.6 Prokaryotic flagellum.** The motor of the prokaryotic flagellum is the basal apparatus, a system of rings embedded in the cell wall and plasma membrane (TEM). ATP-driven pumps transport protons out of the cell, and the diffusion of protons back into the cell directly powers the basal apparatus, which turns a curved hook. The hook is attached to a filament composed of chains of flagellin, a globular protein. (This diagram shows flagellar structures characteristic of gram-negative bacteria.)

extension of the plasma membrane (see Figures 6.24 and 6.25 to review eukaryotic flagella). The flagella of prokaryotes are also very different from those of eukaryotes in their molecular composition and their mechanism of propulsion.

In a relatively uniform environment, flagellated prokaryotes may move randomly. In a heterogeneous environment, however, many prokaryotes exhibit **taxis**, movement toward or away from a stimulus (from the Greek *taxis*, to arrange). For example, prokaryotes that exhibit *chemotaxis* change their movement pattern in response to chemicals. They may move *toward* nutrients or oxygen (positive chemotaxis) or *away from* a toxic substance (negative chemotaxis). Consider movement patterns in *Escherichia coli*, the well-studied bacterial species that has been called the "lab rat of molecular biology." In 2003, scientists at Princeton University and the Institut Curie in Paris demonstrated that solitary *E. coli* cells exhibit positive chemotaxis toward other members of their species, enabling the formation of colonies.

Internal and Genomic Organization

The cells of prokaryotes are simpler than those of eukaryotes, in both their internal structure and their genomic organization (see Figure 6.6). Prokaryotic cells lack the complex compartmentalization found in eukaryotic cells. However, some prokaryotic cells do have specialized membranes that perform metabolic functions **(Figure 27.7)**. These membranes are usually infoldings of the plasma membrane.

The genome of a prokaryote is structurally different from a eukaryotic genome and in most cases has considerably less DNA. In the majority of prokaryotes, the genome consists of a circular chromosome whose structure includes fewer proteins than found in the linear chromosomes of eukaryotes **(Figure 27.8)**. Also unlike eukaryotes, prokaryotes lack a membrane-bounded nucleus; their chromosome is located in the **nucleoid**, a region of cytoplasm that appears lighter than the surrounding cytoplasm

(a) Aerobic prokaryote   **(b) Photosynthetic prokaryote**

▲ **Figure 27.7 Specialized membranes of prokaryotes.**
(a) Infoldings of the plasma membrane, reminiscent of the cristae of mitochondria, function in cellular respiration in some aerobic prokaryotes (TEM). **(b)** Photosynthetic prokaryotes called cyanobacteria have thylakoid membranes, much like those in chloroplasts (TEM).

Chromosome   Plasmids

▲ **Figure 27.8 A prokaryotic chromosome and plasmids.** The thin, tangled loops surrounding this ruptured *E. coli* cell are parts of the cell's large, circular chromosome (colorized TEM). Three of the cell's plasmids, the much smaller rings of DNA, are also shown.

in electron micrographs. In addition to its single chromosome, a typical prokaryotic cell may also have much smaller rings of separately replicating DNA called **plasmids** (see Figure 27.8), most carrying only a few genes.

As explained in Chapters 16 and 17, DNA replication, transcription, and translation are fundamentally similar processes in prokaryotes and eukaryotes, although there are some differences. For example, prokaryotic ribosomes are slightly smaller than eukaryotic ribosomes and differ in their protein and RNA content. These differences allow certain antibiotics, such as erythromycin and tetracycline, to bind to ribosomes and block protein synthesis in prokaryotes but not in eukaryotes. As a result, we can use these antibiotics to kill bacteria without harming ourselves.

Reproduction and Adaptation

Prokaryotes are highly successful in part because of their potential to reproduce quickly in a favorable environment. By binary fission (see Figure 12.11), a single prokaryotic cell divides into 2 cells, which then divide into 4, 8, 16, and so on. Under optimal conditions, many prokaryotes can divide every 1–3 hours; some species can produce a new generation in only 20 minutes. If reproduction continued unchecked at this rate, a single prokaryotic cell could give rise to a colony outweighing Earth in only three days!

In reality, of course, prokaryotic reproduction is limited. The cells eventually exhaust their nutrient supply, poison themselves with metabolic wastes, face competition from other microorganisms, or are consumed by other organisms. Thus, *E. coli*, which can divide as often as every 20 minutes under ideal conditions, more typically divides once every 12 to 24 hours in a

Endospore

0.3 μm

▲ **Figure 27.9 An endospore.** *Bacillus anthracis*, the bacterium that causes the disease anthrax, produces endospores (TEM). An endospore's thick, protective coat helps it survive in the soil for years.

human intestine. But whether cell division occurs every 20 minutes or every few days, reproduction in prokaryotes draws attention to three key features of their biology: *They are small, they reproduce by binary fission, and they have short generation times*. As a result, prokaryotic populations can consist of many trillions of individuals—far more than populations of multicellular eukaryotes, such as plants and animals.

The ability of some prokaryotes to withstand harsh conditions also contributes to their success. Some, like *Halobacterium*, have biochemical adaptations; others have structural adaptations. Certain bacteria, for example, develop resistant cells called **endospores** when an essential nutrient is lacking **(Figure 27.9)**. The original cell produces a copy of its chromosome and surrounds it with a tough wall, forming the endospore. Water is removed from the endospore, and its metabolism halts. The rest of the original cell then disintegrates, leaving the endospore behind. Most endospores are so durable that they can survive in boiling water; killing them requires heating lab equipment to 121°C under high pressure. In less hostile environments, endospores can remain dormant but viable for centuries, able to rehydrate and resume metabolism when their environment improves.

Finally, in part because of their short generation times, prokaryotic populations can evolve substantially in short periods of time. For example, in a remarkable study that spanned 20,000 generations (roughly eight years) of evolution, Vaughn Cooper and Richard Lenski, of Michigan State University, documented adaptive evolution in bacterial populations **(Figure 27.10)**. The ability of prokaryotes to adapt rapidly to new conditions highlights the fact that although the structure of their cells is simpler than that of eukaryotic cells, prokaryotes are not "primitive" or "inferior" in an evolutionary sense. They are, in fact, highly evolved: For over 3.5 billion years, prokaryotic populations have responded successfully to many different types of environmental challenges. As we will see, one reason for this is that their populations harbor high levels of genetic diversity on which selection can act.

▼ **Figure 27.10** **Inquiry**

Can prokaryotes evolve rapidly in response to environmental change?

EXPERIMENT   Vaughn Cooper and Richard Lenski, of Michigan State University, tested the ability of *E. coli* populations to adapt to a new environment. They established 12 populations, each founded by a single cell from an asexual strain of *E. coli*, and followed these populations for 20,000 generations (3,000 days). To maintain a continual supply of resources, each day the researchers performed a *serial transfer*: They transferred 0.1 mL of each population to a new tube containing 9.9 mL of fresh growth medium. The growth medium used throughout the experiment represented a challenging environment that contained only low levels of glucose and other resources needed for growth.

Daily serial transfer

0.1 mL
(population sample)

Old tube
(discarded after transfer)

New tube
(9.9 mL growth medium)

Samples were periodically removed from the 12 populations and grown in competition with the common ancestor in the experimental (low-glucose) environment.

RESULTS   The fitness of the experimental populations, as measured by the rate at which each population grew, increased rapidly for the first 5,000 generations (two years) and more slowly for the next 15,000 generations. The graph below shows the averages for the 12 populations.

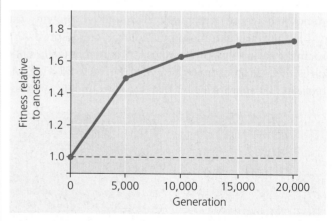

CONCLUSION   Asexual populations of *E. coli* continued to accumulate beneficial mutations for 20,000 generations, allowing rapid evolution of improved performance in their new environment.

SOURCE   V. S. Cooper and R. E. Lenski, The population genetics of ecological specialization in evolving *Escherichia coli* populations, *Nature* 407:736–739 (2000).

WHAT IF?   Suggest possible functions of the genes whose sequence or expression was altered as the experimental populations evolved in the low-glucose environment.

1. Identify and explain at least two adaptations that enable prokaryotes to survive in environments too harsh for other organisms.
2. Contrast the cellular and genomic organization of prokaryotes and eukaryotes.
3. **WHAT IF?** Researchers discover bacterial endospores in silt at the bottom of a lake that has been contaminated with an industrial pollutant for 50 years. This silt was deposited in annual layers; thus, the age of an endospore can be estimated from the layer in which it is found. Predict how 40- and 150-year-old endospores each would grow if placed in flasks containing growth medium along with the pollutant.

For suggested answers, see Appendix A.

CONCEPT 27.2

Rapid reproduction, mutation, and genetic recombination promote genetic diversity in prokaryotes

As we discussed in Unit Four, genetic variation is a prerequisite for natural selection to occur in a population. The fact that prokaryotes exhibit such a range of adaptations suggests that their populations must have considerable genetic variation—and they do. For example, a ribosomal RNA gene differs more between two strains of *E. coli* than it does between a human and a platypus. In this section, we'll examine three factors that give rise to high levels of genetic diversity in prokaryotes: rapid reproduction, mutation, and genetic recombination.

Rapid Reproduction and Mutation

In sexually reproducing species, the generation of a novel allele by a new mutation is rare at any particular gene. Instead, most of the genetic variation in sexual populations results from the way existing alleles are arranged in new combinations during meiosis and fertilization (see Chapter 13). Prokaryotes do not reproduce sexually, so at first glance their extensive genetic variation may seem puzzling. A closer look, however, reveals that prokaryotic populations may have large amounts of genetic variation as a result of rapid reproduction and mutation.

Consider a prokaryote reproducing by binary fission. After repeated rounds of division, most of the offspring cells are genetically identical to the original parent cell. However, owing to insertions, deletions, and base-pair substitutions in their DNA, some of the offspring cells may differ genetically. The probability of a spontaneous mutation occurring in a

given *E. coli* gene averages only about one in 10 million (1×10^{-7}) per cell division. But among the 2×10^{10} new *E. coli* cells that arise each day in a person's intestine, there will be approximately $(2 \times 10^{10}) \times (1 \times 10^{-7}) = 2,000$ bacteria that have a mutation in that gene. The total number of mutations when all 4,300 *E. coli* genes are considered is about $4,300 \times 2,000 = 9$ million per day per human host.

The important point is that new mutations, though individually rare, can greatly increase genetic diversity in species like *E. coli* that have short generation times and large population sizes. This diversity, in turn, can lead to rapid evolution: Individuals that are genetically better equipped for their local environment tend to survive and reproduce more prolifically than less fit individuals.

Genetic Recombination

Although new mutations are a major source of variation in prokaryotic populations, additional diversity arises from genetic recombination, the combining of DNA from two sources. In eukaryotes, the sexual processes of meiosis and fertilization combine DNA from two individuals in a single zygote. But meiosis and fertilization do not occur in prokaryotes. Instead, three other processes—transformation, transduction, and conjugation—can bring together prokaryotic DNA from different individuals.

Transformation and Transduction

In **transformation**, the genotype and possibly phenotype of a prokaryotic cell are altered by the uptake of foreign DNA from its surroundings. For example, bacteria from a harmless strain of *Streptococcus pneumoniae* can be transformed to pneumonia-causing cells if they are placed into a medium containing dead, broken-open cells of the pathogenic strain (see Figure 16.2). This transformation occurs when a live nonpathogenic cell takes up a piece of DNA carrying the allele for pathogenicity. The foreign allele is then incorporated into the cell's chromosome, replacing the existing nonpathogenic allele—an exchange of homologous DNA segments. The cell is now a recombinant: Its chromosome contains DNA derived from two different cells.

For many years after transformation was discovered in laboratory cultures, most biologists thought the process to be too rare and haphazard to play an important role in natural bacterial populations. But researchers have since learned that many bacteria have cell-surface proteins that recognize DNA from closely related species and transport it into the cell. Once inside the cell, the foreign DNA can be incorporated into the genome by homologous DNA exchange.

In **transduction**, bacteriophages (also called phages, the viruses that infect bacteria) carry bacterial genes from one host cell to another; transduction is a type of horizontal gene transfer (see Chapter 26). For most phages, transduction results from accidents that occur during the phage reproductive

① Phage infects a bacterial cell that has alleles A^+ and B^+.

② Host DNA (brown) is fragmented, and phage DNA and proteins are made. This is the donor cell.

Donor cell

③ A bacterial DNA fragment (in this case a fragment with the A^+ allele) may be packaged in a phage capsid.

A^+

④ Phage with the A^+ allele from the donor cell infects a recipient A^-B^- cell, and recombination between donor DNA (brown) and recipient DNA (green) occurs at two places (dotted lines).

Recombination

A^+

A^- B^-

Recipient cell

⑤ The genotype of the resulting recombinant cell (A^+B^-) differs from the genotypes of both the donor (A^+B^+) and the recipient (A^-B^-).

A^+ B^-

Recombinant cell

▲ **Figure 27.11 Transduction.** Phages occasionally carry random pieces of the host chromosome containing bacterial genes from one cell (the donor) to another (the recipient). Recombination may cause the transferred DNA to be incorporated into the genome of the recipient.

cycle **(Figure 27.11)**. A virus that carries bacterial DNA may not be able to reproduce because it lacks its own genetic material. However, the virus may be able to attach to another bacterium (a recipient) and inject the piece of bacterial DNA acquired from the first cell (the donor). Some of this DNA may subsequently replace the homologous region of the recipient cell's chromosome by DNA recombination. In such a case, the recipient cell's chromosome becomes a combination of DNA derived from two cells; genetic recombination has occurred.

Conjugation and Plasmids

In a process called **conjugation**, genetic material is transferred between two bacterial cells (of the same or different

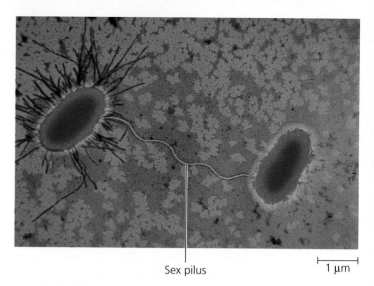

Sex pilus
⊢ 1 μm ⊣

▲ **Figure 27.12 Bacterial conjugation.** The *E. coli* donor cell (left) extends a sex pilus that attaches to a recipient cell. The two cells will be drawn close together, allowing a mating bridge to form between them (not shown). Through this bridge, the donor will transfer DNA to the recipient (colorized TEM).

WHAT IF? *In a rapidly changing environment, which population would likely be more successful, one that included individuals capable of conjugation or one that did not? Explain.*

species) that are temporarily joined. The DNA transfer is one-way: One cell donates the DNA, and the other receives it. The donor uses sex pili to attach to the recipient **(Figure 27.12)**. After contacting a recipient cell, each sex pilus retracts, pulling the two cells together, much like a grappling hook. A temporary "mating bridge" then forms between the two cells, providing an avenue for DNA transfer.

In most cases, the ability to form sex pili and donate DNA during conjugation results from the presence of a particular piece of DNA called the **F factor** (F for *fertility*). The F factor consists of about 25 genes, most required for the production of sex pili. The F factor can exist either as a plasmid or as a segment of DNA within the bacterial chromosome.

The F Factor as a Plasmid   The F factor in its plasmid form is called the **F plasmid**. Cells containing the F plasmid, designated F^+ cells, function as DNA donors during conjugation. Cells lacking the F factor, designated F^-, function as DNA recipients during conjugation. The F^+ condition is transferable in the sense that an F^+ cell converts an F^- cell to F^+ if a copy of the entire F^+ plasmid is transferred **(Figure 27.13a)**.

The F Factor in the Chromosome   Chromosomal genes can be transferred during conjugation when the donor cell's F factor is integrated into the chromosome. A cell with the F factor built into its chromosome is called an *Hfr cell* (for *high frequency of recombination*). Like an F^+ cell, an Hfr cell functions as a donor during conjugation with an F^- cell **(Figure 27.13b)**. When chromosomal DNA from an Hfr cell enters an F^- cell, homologous regions of the Hfr and F^- chromosomes may align, allowing

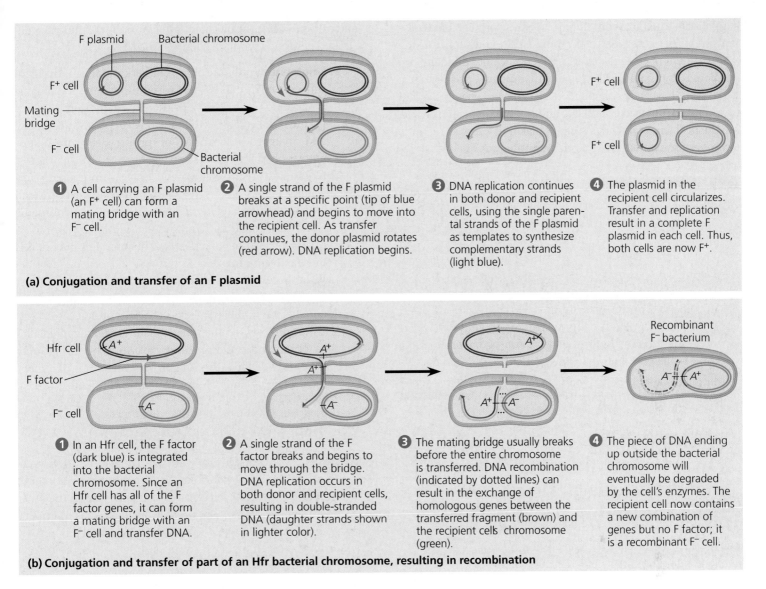

(a) Conjugation and transfer of an F plasmid

❶ A cell carrying an F plasmid (an F⁺ cell) can form a mating bridge with an F⁻ cell.

❷ A single strand of the F plasmid breaks at a specific point (tip of blue arrowhead) and begins to move into the recipient cell. As transfer continues, the donor plasmid rotates (red arrow). DNA replication begins.

❸ DNA replication continues in both donor and recipient cells, using the single parental strands of the F plasmid as templates to synthesize complementary strands (light blue).

❹ The plasmid in the recipient cell circularizes. Transfer and replication result in a complete F plasmid in each cell. Thus, both cells are now F⁺.

(b) Conjugation and transfer of part of an Hfr bacterial chromosome, resulting in recombination

❶ In an Hfr cell, the F factor (dark blue) is integrated into the bacterial chromosome. Since an Hfr cell has all of the F factor genes, it can form a mating bridge with an F⁻ cell and transfer DNA.

❷ A single strand of the F factor breaks and begins to move through the bridge. DNA replication occurs in both donor and recipient cells, resulting in double-stranded DNA (daughter strands shown in lighter color).

❸ The mating bridge usually breaks before the entire chromosome is transferred. DNA recombination (indicated by dotted lines) can result in the exchange of homologous genes between the transferred fragment (brown) and the recipient cell's chromosome (green).

❹ The piece of DNA ending up outside the bacterial chromosome will eventually be degraded by the cell's enzymes. The recipient cell now contains a new combination of genes but no F factor; it is a recombinant F⁻ cell.

▲ **Figure 27.13 Conjugation and recombination in *E. coli*.** The DNA replication that accompanies transfer of an F plasmid or part of an Hfr bacterial chromosome is called *rolling circle replication*. This is sometimes referred to as the "toilet paper model" because of the way the single strand rolls off the donor cell DNA and moves into the recipient cell.

segments of their DNA to be exchanged. This results in the production of a recombinant bacterium that has genes derived from two different cells—a new genetic variant on which evolution can act. Though these processes of horizontal gene transfer have so far been studied almost exclusively in bacteria, it is assumed that they are similarly important in archaea.

R Plasmids and Antibiotic Resistance   During the 1950s in Japan, physicians started noticing that some hospital patients with bacterial dysentery, which produces severe diarrhea, did not respond to antibiotics that had generally been effective in the past. Apparently, resistance to these antibiotics had evolved in certain strains of *Shigella*, the bacterium that causes the disease.

Eventually, researchers began to identify the specific genes that confer antibiotic resistance in *Shigella* and other pathogenic bacteria. Sometimes, mutation in a chromosomal gene of the

pathogen can confer resistance. For example, a mutation in one gene may make it less likely that the pathogen will transport a particular antibiotic into the cell. Mutation in a different gene may alter the intracellular target protein for an antibiotic molecule, reducing its inhibitory effect. In other cases, bacteria have "resistance genes," which code for enzymes that specifically destroy or otherwise hinder the effectiveness of certain antibiotics, such as tetracycline or ampicillin. Such resistance genes are carried by plasmids known as **R plasmids** (R for *r*esistance).

Exposing a bacterial population to a specific antibiotic, whether in a laboratory culture or within a host organism, will kill antibiotic-sensitive bacteria but not those that happen to have R plasmids with genes that counter the antibiotic. The theory of natural selection predicts that under these circumstances, the fraction of the bacterial population carrying genes for antibiotic resistance will increase, and that is exactly what happens. The medical consequences are also predictable: Resistant strains of pathogens are becoming more common, making the treatment of certain bacterial infections more difficult. The problem is compounded by the fact that many R plasmids, like F plasmids, have genes that encode sex pili and enable plasmid transfer from one bacterial cell to another by conjugation. Making the problem still worse, some R plasmids carry as many as ten genes for resistance to that many antibiotics.

CONCEPT CHECK 27.2

1. What features of prokaryotes make it likely that considerable genetic variation will be added to their populations in each generation?
2. Distinguish between the three mechanisms of transferring DNA from one bacterial cell to another.
3. **WHAT IF?** If a nonpathogenic bacterium were to acquire resistance to antibiotics, could this strain pose a health risk to people? Explain. In general, how does genetic recombination among bacteria affect the spread of resistance genes?

For suggested answers, see Appendix A.

CONCEPT 27.3
Diverse nutritional and metabolic adaptations have evolved in prokaryotes

The mechanisms discussed in the previous section—rapid reproduction, mutation, and genetic recombination—underlie the extensive genetic variation found in prokaryotic populations. This variation is reflected in the nutritional adaptations found in prokaryotes. Like all organisms, prokaryotes can be categorized by their nutrition—how they obtain energy and the carbon used in building the organic molecules that make up cells. Nutritional diversity is greater among prokaryotes than among eukaryotes: Every type of nutrition observed in eukaryotes is represented among prokaryotes, along with some nutritional modes unique to prokaryotes.

Organisms that obtain energy from light are called *phototrophs*, and those that obtain energy from chemicals are called *chemotrophs*. Organisms that need only an inorganic compound such as CO_2 as a carbon source are called *autotrophs*. In contrast, *heterotrophs* require at least one organic nutrient—such as glucose—to make other organic compounds. Combining these possibilities for energy sources and carbon sources results in four major modes of nutrition, described here and summarized in **Table 27.1**.

1. **Photoautotrophs** are photosynthetic organisms that capture light energy and use it to drive the synthesis of organic compounds from CO_2 or other inorganic carbon compounds, such as bicarbonate (HCO_3^-). Cyanobacteria and many other groups of prokaryotes are photoautotrophs, as are plants and algae.
2. **Chemoautotrophs** also need only an inorganic compound such as CO_2 as a carbon source. However, instead of using light as an energy source, they oxidize inorganic substances, such as hydrogen sulfide (H_2S), ammonia (NH_3), or ferrous ions (Fe^{2+}). This mode of nutrition is unique to certain prokaryotes.
3. **Photoheterotrophs** harness energy from light but must obtain carbon in organic form. This mode is unique to certain marine and halophilic (salt-loving) prokaryotes.
4. **Chemoheterotrophs** must consume organic molecules to obtain both energy and carbon. This nutritional mode is widespread among prokaryotes. Fungi, animals, most protists, and even some parasitic plants are also chemoheterotrophs.

The Role of Oxygen in Metabolism

Prokaryotic metabolism also varies with respect to oxygen. **Obligate aerobes** use O_2 for cellular respiration (see Chapter 9) and cannot grow without it. **Obligate anaerobes**, on the other hand, are poisoned by O_2. Some obligate anaerobes live exclusively by fermentation; others extract chemical energy by **anaerobic respiration**, in which substances other than O_2, such as nitrate ions (NO_3^-) or sulfate ions (SO_4^{2-}), accept electrons at the "downhill" end of electron transport chains. **Facultative anaerobes** use O_2 if it is present but can also carry out anaerobic respiration or fermentation in an anaerobic environment.

Table 27.1 Major Nutritional Modes

Mode of Nutrition	Energy Source	Carbon Source	Types of Organisms
Autotroph			
Photoautotroph	Light	CO_2	Photosynthetic prokaryotes (for example, cyanobacteria); plants; certain protists (for example, algae)
Chemoautotroph	Inorganic chemicals	CO_2	Certain prokaryotes (for example, *Sulfolobus*)
Heterotroph			
Photoheterotroph	Light	Organic compounds	Certain prokaryotes (for example, *Rhodobacter*, *Chloroflexus*)
Chemoheterotroph	Organic compounds	Organic compounds	Many prokaryotes (for example, *Clostridium*) and protists; fungi; animals; some plants

Nitrogen Metabolism

Nitrogen is essential for the production of amino acids and nucleic acids in all organisms. Whereas eukaryotes can obtain nitrogen from only a limited group of nitrogen compounds, prokaryotes can metabolize nitrogen in a wide variety of forms. For example, some cyanobacteria and some methanogens (a group of archaea) convert atmospheric nitrogen (N_2) to ammonia (NH_3), a process called **nitrogen fixation**. The cells can then incorporate this "fixed" nitrogen into amino acids and other organic molecules. In terms of their nutrition, nitrogen-fixing cyanobacteria are some of the most self-sufficient organisms, since they need only light, CO_2, N_2, water, and some minerals to grow.

Nitrogen fixation by prokaryotes has a large impact on other organisms. For example, nitrogen-fixing prokaryotes can increase the nitrogen available to plants, which cannot use atmospheric nitrogen but can use the nitrogen compounds that the prokaryotes produce from ammonia. Chapter 55 discusses this and other essential roles that prokaryotes play in the nitrogen cycles of ecosystems.

Metabolic Cooperation

Cooperation between prokaryotes allows them to use environmental resources they could not use as individual cells. In some cases, this cooperation takes place between specialized cells of a colony. For instance, the cyanobacterium *Anabaena* has genes that encode proteins for photosynthesis and for nitrogen fixation, but a single cell cannot carry out both processes at the same time. The reason is that photosynthesis produces O_2, which inactivates the enzymes involved in nitrogen fixation. Instead of living as isolated cells, *Anabaena* forms filamentous colonies (Figure 27.14). Most cells in a filament carry out only photosynthesis, while a few specialized cells called **heterocytes** (formerly called *heterocysts*) carry out only nitrogen fixation. Each heterocyte is surrounded by a thickened cell wall that restricts entry of O_2 produced by neighboring photosynthetic cells. Intercellular connections allow heterocytes to transport fixed nitrogen to neighboring cells and to receive carbohydrates.

Metabolic cooperation between different prokaryotic species often occurs in surface-coating colonies known as **biofilms** (Figure 27.15). Cells in a biofilm secrete signaling molecules that recruit nearby cells, causing the colonies to grow. The cells also produce proteins that stick the cells to the substrate and to one another. Channels in the biofilm allow nutrients to reach cells in the interior and wastes to be expelled. Biofilms damage industrial and medical equipment, contaminate products, and contribute to tooth decay and more serious health problems, altogether costing billions of dollars annually.

In another example of cooperation between prokaryotes, sulfate-consuming bacteria coexist with methane-consuming archaea in ball-shaped aggregates on the ocean floor. The bacteria appear to use the archaea's waste products, such as organic

▲ **Figure 27.14 Metabolic cooperation in a colonial prokaryote.** In the filamentous cyanobacterium *Anabaena*, cells called heterocytes fix nitrogen, while the other cells carry out photosynthesis (LM). *Anabaena* is found in many freshwater lakes.

▲ **Figure 27.15 A biofilm.** The yellow mass in this colorized SEM is dental plaque, a biofilm consisting of numerous bacterial species that forms on tooth surfaces.

compounds and hydrogen. In turn, the bacteria produce compounds that facilitate methane consumption by the archaea. This partnership has global ramifications: Each year, these archaea consume an estimated 300 billion kilograms of methane, a major contributor to the greenhouse effect (see Chapter 55).

CONCEPT CHECK 27.3

1. Distinguish between the four major modes of nutrition, noting which are unique to prokaryotes.
2. A bacterium requires only the amino acid methionine as an organic nutrient and lives in lightless caves. What mode of nutrition does it employ? Explain.
3. **WHAT IF?** Describe what you might eat for a typical meal if humans, like cyanobacteria, could fix nitrogen.

For suggested answers, see Appendix A.

CONCEPT 27.4

Molecular systematics is illuminating prokaryotic phylogeny

Until the late 20th century, systematists based prokaryotic taxonomy on phenotypic criteria such as shape, motility, nutritional mode, and response to Gram staining. These criteria are still valuable in certain contexts, such as the rapid identification of pathogenic bacteria cultured from a patient's blood. But when it comes to prokaryotic phylogeny, comparing these characteristics does not reveal a clear evolutionary history. Applying molecular systematics to the investigation of prokaryotic phylogeny, however, has led to some dramatic conclusions.

Lessons from Molecular Systematics

As discussed in Chapter 26, microbiologists began comparing the sequences of prokaryotic genes in the 1970s. Using small-subunit ribosomal RNA as a marker for evolutionary relationships, Carl Woese and his colleagues concluded that many prokaryotes once classified as bacteria are actually more closely related to eukaryotes and belong in a domain of their own: Archaea. Microbiologists have since analyzed larger amounts of genetic data—in some cases, entire genomes—and have concluded that a few traditional taxonomic groups, such as cyanobacteria, do appear to be monophyletic. However, other groups, such as gram-negative bacteria, are scattered throughout several lineages. **Figure 27.16** shows one phylogenetic hypothesis for some of the major taxa of prokaryotes based on molecular systematics.

One lesson from studying prokaryotic phylogeny is that the genetic diversity of prokaryotes is immense. When researchers began to sequence the genes of prokaryotes, they could investigate only those species that could be cultured in the laboratory—a small fraction of all prokaryotic species. In the 1980s, Norman Pace, of the University of Colorado, pioneered the use of the polymerase chain reaction (PCR; see Chapter 20) to analyze the genes of prokaryotes collected directly from their environment (such as from soil or water samples). Such "genetic prospecting" is now widely used, and each year it adds new branches to the tree of life. (Some researchers suggest that certain branches represent entire new kingdoms.) While only about 6,300 prokaryotic species have been assigned scientific names, a single handful of soil could contain 10,000 prokaryotic species, according to some estimates. You can see why taking full stock of this diversity will require many years of research.

Another important lesson from molecular systematics is the apparent significance of horizontal gene transfer in the evolution of prokaryotes. Over hundreds of millions of years, prokaryotes have acquired genes from even distantly related species, and they continue to do so today. As a result, significant portions of the genomes of many prokaryotes are actually mosaics of genes imported from other species. As we saw in Chapter 26, horizontal gene transfer obscures the location of the root of the tree of life. Still, it is clear that very early in the history of life, the prokaryotes diverged into two main lineages, the archaea and the bacteria (see Figure 27.16).

Archaea

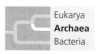

Archaea share certain traits with bacteria and others with eukaryotes **(Table 27.2)**. However, archaea also have many unique characteristics, as we would expect in a taxon that has followed a separate evolutionary path for so long.

The first prokaryotes assigned to domain Archaea live in environments so extreme that few other organisms can survive there. Such organisms are called **extremophiles**, meaning "lovers" of extreme conditions (from the Greek *philos*, lover), and include extreme halophiles and extreme thermophiles.

Extreme halophiles (from the Greek *halo*, salt) live in highly saline environments, such as the Great Salt Lake, the Dead Sea, and Owens Lake (see Figure 27.1). Some species merely tolerate salinity, while others require an environment that is several times saltier than seawater (which has a salinity of 3.5%). For example, the proteins and cell wall of *Halobacterium* have unusual features that improve function in extremely salty environments but render these organisms incapable of survival if the salinity drops below 9%.

Extreme thermophiles (from the Greek *thermos*, hot) thrive in very hot environments **(Figure 27.17)**. For example, archaea in the genus *Sulfolobus* live in sulfur-rich volcanic springs as hot as 90°C. At temperatures this high, the cells of most organisms die because their DNA does not stay together in a double helix, and many of their proteins denature. *Sulfolobus* and other extreme thermophiles avoid this fate because their DNA and proteins have adaptations that make them stable at high temperatures. One extreme thermophile that lives near deep-sea hydrothermal vents in the Pacific Ocean, *Geogemma barossii*, is informally

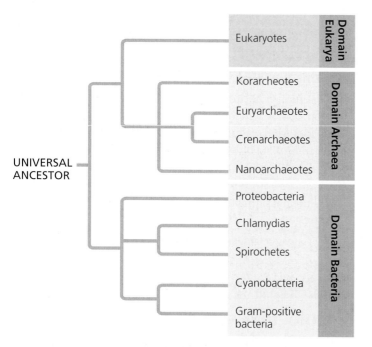

▲ **Figure 27.16 A simplified phylogeny of prokaryotes.** This phylogenetic tree based on molecular data highlights the relationships between the major prokaryotic groups discussed in this chapter. Within Archaea, the placement of the korarcheotes and nanoarchaeotes remains unclear.

Domain Eukarya
- Eukaryotes

Domain Archaea
- Korarcheotes
- Euryarchaeotes
- Crenarchaeotes
- Nanoarchaeotes

Domain Bacteria
- Proteobacteria
- Chlamydias
- Spirochetes
- Cyanobacteria
- Gram-positive bacteria

UNIVERSAL ANCESTOR

Table 27.2 A Comparison of the Three Domains of Life

CHARACTER	DOMAIN		
	Bacteria	Archaea	Eukarya
Nuclear envelope	Absent	Absent	Present
Membrane-enclosed organelles	Absent	Absent	Present
Peptidoglycan in cell wall	Present	Absent	Absent
Membrane lipids	Unbranched hydrocarbons	Some branched hydrocarbons	Unbranched hydrocarbons
RNA polymerase	One kind	Several kinds	Several kinds
Initiator amino acid for protein synthesis	Formyl-methionine	Methionine	Methionine
Introns in genes	Very rare	Present in some genes	Present
Response to the antibiotics streptomycin and chloramphenicol	Growth inhibited	Growth not inhibited	Growth not inhibited
Histones associated with DNA	Absent	Present in some species	Present
Circular chromosome	Present	Present	Absent
Growth at temperatures > 100°C	No	Some species	No

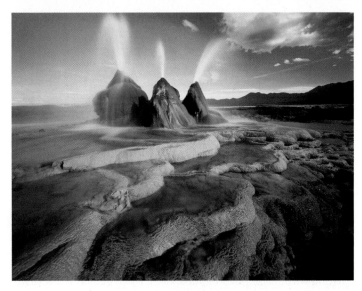

▲ **Figure 27.17 Extreme thermophiles.** Orange and yellow colonies of thermophilic prokaryotes grow in the hot water of a Nevada geyser.

? *How might the enzymes of thermophiles differ from those in other organisms?*

known as "strain 121," since it can double its cell numbers even at 121°C. Another extreme thermophile, *Pyrococcus furiosus*, is used in biotechnology as a source of DNA polymerase for the PCR technique (see Chapter 20).

Other archaea live in more moderate environments. Some of these are included among the **methanogens**, a group of archaea named for the unique way they obtain energy: They use CO_2 to oxidize H_2, releasing methane as a waste product. Among the strictest of anaerobes, methanogens are poisoned by O_2. Although some methanogens live in extreme environments, such as under kilometers of ice in Greenland, others live in swamps and marshes where other microorganisms have consumed all the O_2. The "marsh gas" found in such environments is the methane produced by these archaea. Other species of methanogens inhabit the anaerobic environment within the guts of cattle, termites, and other herbivores, playing an essential role in the nutrition of these animals. Methanogens also have an important application as decomposers in sewage treatment facilities.

Many extreme halophiles and all known methanogens are archaea in the clade Euryarchaeota (from the Greek *eurys*, broad, a reference to the habitat range of these prokaryotes).

The euryarchaeotes also include some extreme thermophiles, though most thermophilic species belong to a second clade, Crenarchaeota (*cren* means "spring," such as a hydrothermal spring). Recently, genetic prospecting has revealed many species of euryarchaeotes and crenarchaeotes that are not extremophiles. These archaea exist in habitats ranging from farm soils to lake sediments to the surface waters of the open ocean.

New findings continue to update the picture of archaeal phylogeny. In 1996, researchers sampling a hot spring in Yellowstone National Park discovered archaea that do not appear to belong to either Euryarchaeota or Crenarchaeota. They placed these archaea in a new clade, Korarchaeota (from the Greek *koron*, young man). In 2002, researchers exploring hydrothermal vents off the coast of Iceland discovered archaeal cells only 0.4 μm in diameter attached to a much larger crenarchaeote. The genome of the smaller archaean is one of the smallest known of any organism, containing only 500,000 base pairs. Genetic analysis indicates that this prokaryote belongs to a fourth archaeal clade, called Nanoarchaeota (from the Greek *nanos*, dwarf). Within a year after this clade was named, three other DNA sequences from nanoarchaeote species were isolated: one from Yellowstone's hot springs, one from hot springs in Siberia, and one from a hydrothermal vent in the Pacific. As prospecting continues, it seems likely that the tree in Figure 27.16 will undergo further changes.

Bacteria

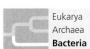

Eukarya
Archaea
Bacteria

Examine **Figure 27.18**, on the following two pages, for a closer look at several major groups of bacteria. Bacteria include the vast majority of prokaryotes that most people are aware of, from the pathogenic species that cause strep throat and tuberculosis to

Exploring Major Groups of Bacteria

PROTEOBACTERIA

This large and diverse clade of gram-negative bacteria includes photoautotrophs, chemoautotrophs, and heterotrophs. Some proteobacteria are anaerobic, while others are aerobic. Molecular systematists currently recognize five subgroups of proteobacteria; the phylogenetic tree at right shows their relationships based on molecular data.

Subgroup: Alpha Proteobacteria

Many of the species in this subgroup are closely associated with eukaryotic hosts. For example, *Rhizobium* species live in nodules within the roots of legumes (plants of the pea/bean family), where the bacteria convert atmospheric N_2 to compounds the host plant can use to make proteins. Species in the genus *Agrobacterium* produce tumors in plants; genetic engineers use these bacteria to carry foreign DNA into the genomes of crop plants (see Figure 20.25). As explained in Chapter 25, scientists hypothesize that mitochondria evolved from aerobic alpha proteobacteria through endosymbiosis.

Rhizobium (arrows) inside a root cell of a legume (TEM)

Subgroup: Beta Proteobacteria

This nutritionally diverse subgroup includes *Nitrosomonas*, a genus of soil bacteria that play an important role in nitrogen recycling by oxidizing ammonium (NH_4^+), producing nitrite (NO_2^-) as a waste product.

Nitrosomonas (colorized TEM)

Subgroup: Gamma Proteobacteria

This subgroup's autotrophic members include sulfur bacteria such as *Thiomargarita namibiensis*, which obtain energy by oxidizing H_2S, producing sulfur as a waste product (the small globules in the photograph at right). Some heterotrophic gamma proteobacteria are pathogens; for example, *Legionella* causes Legionnaires' disease, *Salmonella* is responsible for some cases of food poisoning, and *Vibrio cholerae* causes cholera. *Escherichia coli*, a common resident of the intestines of humans and other mammals, normally is not pathogenic.

Thiomargarita namibiensis containing sulfur wastes (LM)

Subgroup: Delta Proteobacteria

This subgroup includes the slime-secreting myxobacteria (left). When the soil dries out or food is scarce, the cells congregate into a fruiting body that releases resistant "myxospores." These cells found new colonies in favorable environments. Bdellovibrios (right) are delta proteobacteria that attack other bacteria, charging at up to 100 µm/sec (comparable to a human running 600 km/hr) and boring into their prey by spinning at 100 revolutions/sec.

Fruiting bodies of *Chondromyces crocatus,* a myxobacterium (SEM)

Bdellovibrio bacteriophorus attacking a larger bacterium (colorized TEM)

Subgroup: Epsilon Proteobacteria

Most species in this subgroup are pathogenic to humans or other animals. Epsilon proteobacteria include *Campylobacter*, which causes blood poisoning and intestinal inflammation, and *Helicobacter pylori*, which causes stomach ulcers.

Helicobacter pylori (colorized TEM)

CHLAMYDIAS

These parasites can survive only within animal cells, depending on their hosts for resources as basic as ATP. The gram-negative walls of chlamydias are unusual in that they lack peptidoglycan. One species, *Chlamydia trachomatis*, is the most common cause of blindness in the world and also causes nongonococcal urethritis, the most common sexually transmitted disease in the United States.

Chlamydia (arrows) inside an animal cell (colorized TEM)

SPIROCHETES

These helical heterotrophs spiral through their environment by means of rotating, internal, flagellum-like filaments. Many spirochetes are free-living, but others are notorious pathogenic parasites: *Treponema pallidum* causes syphilis, and *Borrelia burgdorferi* causes Lyme disease (see Figure 27.21).

Leptospira, a spirochete (colorized TEM)

CYANOBACTERIA

These photoautotrophs are the only prokaryotes with plantlike, oxygen-generating photosynthesis. (In fact, chloroplasts likely evolved from an endosymbiotic cyanobacterium; see Chapter 25.) Both solitary and colonial cyanobacteria are abundant wherever there is water, providing an enormous amount of food for freshwater and marine ecosystems. Some filamentous colonies have cells specialized for nitrogen fixation, the process that incorporates atmospheric N_2 into inorganic compounds that can be used in the synthesis of amino acids and other organic molecules (see Figure 27.14).

Two species of *Oscillatoria,* filamentous cyanobacteria (LM)

GRAM-POSITIVE BACTERIA

Gram-positive bacteria rival the proteobacteria in diversity. Species in one subgroup, the actinomycetes (from the Greek *mykes,* fungus, for which these bacteria were once mistaken), form colonies containing branched chains of cells. Two species of actinomycetes cause tuberculosis and leprosy. However, most actinomycetes are free-living species that help decompose the organic matter in soil; their secretions are partly responsible for the "earthy" odor of rich soil. Soil-dwelling species in the genus *Streptomyces* (top) are cultured by pharmaceutical companies as a source of many antibiotics, including streptomycin.

In addition to the colonial actinomycetes, gram-positive bacteria include many solitary species, such as *Bacillus anthracis* (see Figure 27.9), which causes anthrax, and *Clostridium botulinum,* which causes botulism. The various species of *Staphylococcus* and *Streptococcus* are also gram-positive bacteria.

Mycoplasmas (bottom) are the only bacteria known to lack cell walls. They are also the tiniest of all known cells, with diameters as small as 0.1 µm, only about five times as large as a ribosome. Mycoplasmas have remarkably small genomes—*Mycoplasma genitalium* has only 517 genes, for example. Many mycoplasmas are free-living soil bacteria, but others are pathogens.

Streptomyces, the source of many antibiotics (colorized SEM)

Hundreds of mycoplasmas covering a human fibroblast cell (colorized SEM)

the beneficial species used to make Swiss cheese and yogurt. Every major mode of nutrition and metabolism is represented among bacteria, and even a small taxonomic group of bacteria may contain species exhibiting many different nutritional modes. As we'll see, the diverse nutritional and metabolic capabilities of bacteria—and archaea—are behind the great impact of these tiny organisms on Earth and its life.

CONCEPT CHECK 27.4

1. Explain how molecular systematics has contributed to our understanding of prokaryotic phylogeny.
2. How has genetic prospecting contributed to our understanding of prokaryotic diversity and phylogeny?
3. **WHAT IF?** What would the discovery of a bacterial species that is a methanogen imply about the evolution of that metabolic pathway?

For suggested answers, see Appendix A.

CONCEPT 27.5
Prokaryotes play crucial roles in the biosphere

If humans were to disappear from the planet tomorrow, life on Earth would change for many species, but few would be driven to extinction. In contrast, prokaryotes are so important to the biosphere that if they were to disappear, the prospects of survival for many other species would be dim.

Chemical Recycling

The atoms that make up the organic molecules in all living things were at one time part of inorganic substances in the soil, air, and water. Sooner or later, those atoms will return there. Ecosystems depend on the continual recycling of chemical elements between the living and nonliving components of the environment, and prokaryotes play a major role in this process. For example, chemoheterotrophic prokaryotes function as **decomposers**, breaking down corpses, dead vegetation, and waste products, and thereby unlocking supplies of carbon, nitrogen, and other elements. Without the actions of prokaryotes and other decomposers such as fungi, all life would cease. (See Chapter 55 for a detailed discussion of chemical cycles.)

Prokaryotes also convert inorganic compounds to forms that can be taken up by other organisms. Autotrophic prokaryotes, for example, use CO_2 to make organic compounds, which are then passed up through food chains. Cyanobacteria produce atmospheric O_2, and a variety of prokaryotes fix atmospheric nitrogen (N_2) into forms that other organisms can use to make the building blocks of proteins and nucleic acids. Under some conditions, prokaryotes can increase the availability of nutrients that plants require for growth, such as nitrogen, phosphorus, and potassium **(Figure 27.19)**. Prokaryotes can also *decrease* the availability of

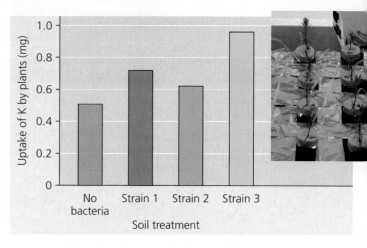

▲ **Figure 27.19 Impact of bacteria on soil nutrient availability.** Pine seedlings grown in soils to which one of three strains of the bacterium *Burkholderia glathei* had been added absorbed more potassium (K) than did seedlings grown in soil without any bacteria. Other results (not shown) demonstrated that strain 3 increased the amount of K released from mineral crystals to the soil.

WHAT IF? *Estimate the average uptake of K for seedlings in soils with bacteria. What would you expect this average to be if bacteria had no effect on nutrient availability?*

key plant nutrients; this occurs when prokaryotes "immobilize" nutrients by using them to synthesize molecules that remain within their cells. Thus, prokaryotes can have complex effects on soil nutrient concentrations. In marine environments, a 2005 study found that an archaean from the clade Crenarchaeota can perform nitrification, a key step in the nitrogen cycle (see Figure 55.14). Crenarchaeotes dominate the oceans by numbers, comprising an estimated 10^{28} cells. The sheer abundance of these organisms suggests that they may have a large impact on the global nitrogen cycle; scientists are investigating this question.

Ecological Interactions

Prokaryotes play a central role in many ecological interactions. Consider **symbiosis** (from a Greek word meaning "living together"), an ecological relationship in which two species live in close contact with one another. Prokaryotes are small, and they often form symbiotic associations with much larger organisms. In general, the larger organism in a symbiotic relationship is known as the **host**, and the smaller is known as the **symbiont**. There are many cases in which a prokaryote and its host participate in **mutualism**, an ecological interaction between two species in which both benefit **(Figure 27.20)**. In other cases, the interaction takes the form of **commensalism**, an ecological relationship in which one species benefits while the other is not harmed or helped in any significant way. For example, more than 150 bacterial species live on the surface of your body, covering portions of your skin with up to 10 million cells per square centimeter. Some of these species are commensalists: You provide them with food, such as the oils that exude from your pores, and a place to live, while they do not harm or benefit you. Finally, some prokaryotes engage in **parasitism**, an ecological relationship in which a **parasite** eats the cell contents, tissues, or body

▲ **Figure 27.20 Mutualism: bacterial "headlights."** The glowing oval below the eye of the flashlight fish (*Photoblepharon palpebratus*) is an organ harboring bioluminescent bacteria. The fish uses the light to attract prey and to signal potential mates. The bacteria receive nutrients from the fish.

fluids of its host; as a group, parasites harm but usually do not kill their host, at least not immediately (unlike a predator). Parasites that cause disease are known as **pathogens**, many of which are prokaryotic. (We'll discuss mutualism, commensalism, and parasitism in greater detail in Chapter 54.)

The well-being of many eukaryotes—yourself included—depends on mutualistic prokaryotes. Human intestines are home to an estimated 500 to 1,000 species of bacteria; their cells outnumber all human cells in the body by as much as ten times. Different species live in different portions of the intestines, and they vary in their ability to process different foods. Many of these species are mutualists, digesting food that our own intestines cannot break down. In 2003, scientists at Washington University in St. Louis published the first complete genome of one of these gut mutualists, *Bacteroides thetaiotaomicron*. The genome includes a large array of genes involved in synthesizing carbohydrates, vitamins, and other nutrients needed by humans. Signals from the bacterium activate human genes that build the network of intestinal blood vessels necessary to absorb nutrient molecules. Other signals induce human cells to produce antimicrobial compounds to which *B. thetaiotaomicron* is not susceptible. This action may reduce the population sizes of other, competing species, thus potentially benefiting both *B. thetaiotaomicron* and its human host.

CONCEPT CHECK 27.5

1. Explain how individual prokaryotes, though small, can be considered giants in their collective impact on Earth and its life.
2. Explain how the relationship between humans and *B. thetaiotaomicron* is an example of mutualism.
3. **WHAT IF?** If you suddenly and dramatically changed your diet, how might this affect the diversity of prokaryotic species that live in your intestine?

For suggested answers, see Appendix A.

CONCEPT 27.6

Prokaryotes have both harmful and beneficial impacts on humans

Though the best-known prokaryotes tend to be the bacteria that cause illness in humans, these pathogens represent only a small fraction of prokaryotic species. Many other prokaryotes have positive interactions with humans, and some play essential roles in agriculture and industry.

Pathogenic Bacteria

All the pathogenic prokaryotes known to date are bacteria, and they deserve their negative reputation. Bacteria cause about half of all human diseases. Roughly 2 million people a year die of the lung disease tuberculosis, caused by *Mycobacterium tuberculosis*. And another 2 million people die each year from diarrheal diseases caused by various bacteria.

Some bacterial diseases are transmitted by other species, such as fleas or ticks. In the United States, the most widespread pest-carried disease is Lyme disease, which infects 15,000 to 20,000 people each year **(Figure 27.21)**. Caused by a bacterium carried by ticks that live on deer and field mice, Lyme disease can produce debilitating arthritis, heart disease, and nervous disorders if untreated.

Pathogenic prokaryotes usually cause illness by producing poisons, which are classified as exotoxins or endotoxins. **Exotoxins** are proteins secreted by certain bacteria and other organisms. Cholera, a dangerous diarrheal disease, is caused by an exotoxin secreted by the proteobacterium *Vibrio cholerae*. The exotoxin stimulates intestinal cells to release chloride ions into the gut, and water follows by osmosis. In another example, the potentially fatal disease botulism is caused by botulinum toxin, an exotoxin secreted by the gram-positive bacterium *Clostridium botulinum* as it ferments various foods, including improperly canned meat, seafood, and vegetables. Like other exotoxins, the botulinum toxin can produce disease

5 μm

▲ **Figure 27.21 Lyme disease.** Ticks in the genus *Ixodes* spread the disease by transmitting the spirochete *Borrelia burgdorferi* (colorized SEM). A rash may develop at the site of the tick's bite; the rash may be large and ring-shaped (as shown) or much less distinctive.

even if the bacteria that manufacture it are not present. In one such case, eight people contracted botulism after eating salted fish that did not contain any *C. botulinum* bacteria, but did contain the botulinum toxin. Even though the bacterium was no longer present, at some point in the fish preparation process, the bacterium had been able to grow and secrete the toxin.

Endotoxins are lipopolysaccharide components of the outer membrane of gram-negative bacteria. In contrast to exotoxins, endotoxins are released only when the bacteria die and their cell walls break down. Examples of endotoxin-producing bacteria include species in the genus *Salmonella*, which are not normally present in healthy animals. *Salmonella typhi* causes typhoid fever, and several other *Salmonella* species, some of which are frequently found in poultry, cause food poisoning.

Since the 19th century, improved sanitation systems in the industrialized world have greatly reduced the threat of pathogenic bacteria. Antibiotics have saved a great many lives and reduced the incidence of disease. However, resistance to antibiotics is currently evolving in many bacterial strains. As you read earlier, the rapid reproduction of bacteria enables genes conferring resistance to multiply quickly throughout bacterial populations as a result of natural selection, and these genes can spread to other species by horizontal gene transfer.

Horizontal gene transfer can also spread genes associated with virulence, turning normally harmless bacteria into lethal pathogens. *E. coli*, for instance, is ordinarily a harmless symbiont in the human intestines, but pathogenic strains that cause bloody diarrhea have emerged. One of the most dangerous strains, called O157:H7, is a global threat; in the United States alone, there are 75,000 cases of O157:H7 infection per year, often from contaminated beef or produce. In 2001, scientists sequenced the genome of O157:H7 and compared it with the genome of a harmless strain of *E. coli* called K-12. They discovered that 1,387 out of the 5,416 genes in O157:H7 have no counterpart in K-12. Many of these 1,387 genes are found in chromosomal regions that include DNA sequences related to bacteriophage DNA. This result suggests that at least some of the 1,387 genes were incorporated into the genome of O157:H7 through bacteriophage-mediated horizontal gene transfer (see Figure 27.11). Some of the genes found only in O157:H7 are associated with virulence, including genes that code for adhesive fimbriae that enable O157:H7 to attach itself to the intestinal wall and extract nutrients.

Pathogenic bacteria pose a potential threat as weapons of bioterrorism. For example, endospores of *Bacillus anthracis* sent through the mail caused 18 people—5 of whom died—to develop inhalation anthrax (see also Chapter 26). Such scenarios have stimulated intense research on pathogenic prokaryotic species in the hope of developing new vaccines and antibiotics.

Prokaryotes in Research and Technology

On a positive note, we reap many benefits from the metabolic capabilities of both bacteria and archaea. For example, humans have long used bacteria to convert milk into cheese and yogurt. In recent years, our greater understanding of prokaryotes has led to an explosion of new applications in biotechnology; two examples are the use of *E. coli* in gene cloning and of *Agrobacterium tumefaciens* in producing transgenic plants such as Golden Rice (see Chapter 20).

Prokaryotes are the principal agents in **bioremediation**, the use of organisms to remove pollutants from soil, air, or water. For example, anaerobic bacteria and archaea decompose the organic matter in sewage, converting it to material that can be used as landfill or fertilizer after chemical sterilization. Other bioremediation applications include cleaning up oil spills **(Figure 27.22a)** and precipitating radioactive material (such as uranium) out of groundwater.

Bacteria may soon figure prominently in a major industry: plastics. Globally, each year about 350 billion pounds of plastic are produced from petroleum and used to make toys, storage containers, soft drink bottles, and many other items. These products degrade slowly, creating environmental problems. Bacteria can now be used to make natural plastics **(Figure 27.22b)**. For example, some bacteria synthesize a type of polyester known as PHA (polyhydroxyalkanoate), which they use to store chemical energy. When these bacteria are fed sugars derived from corn, the PHA they produce can be extracted, formed into pellets, and used to make durable, biodegradable plastics.

Through genetic engineering, humans can now modify bacteria to produce vitamins, antibiotics, hormones, and other products (see Chapter 20). Researchers are seeking to reduce fossil fuel use by engineering bacteria that can produce ethanol from various forms of biomass, including agricultural waste, switchgrass, fast-growing woody plants such as willows, and corn **(Figure 27.22c)**. One radical idea for modifying bacteria

▲ **Figure 27.22 Some applications of prokaryotes. (a)** Spraying fertilizers on an oil-soaked area stimulates growth of native bacteria that metabolize the oil, speeding the natural breakdown process up to fivefold. **(b)** These bacteria synthesize and store the polyester PHA. The PHA can be extracted and used to make biodegradable plastic products. **(c)** Current research seeks to develop bacteria that produce ethanol (E-85) fuel efficiently from renewable plant products.

comes from Craig Venter, head of The Institute for Genomic Research (TIGR). Venter and his colleagues are attempting to build "synthetic chromosomes" for bacteria—in effect, producing new species from scratch. They hope to "design" bacteria that can perform specific tasks, such as producing large amounts of hydrogen to reduce dependence on fossil fuels. Some scientists, however, question whether this approach may have unanticipated harmful effects.

The usefulness of prokaryotes largely derives from their diverse forms of nutrition and metabolism. All this metabolic versatility evolved prior to the appearance of the structural novelties that heralded the evolution of eukaryotic organisms, to which we devote the remainder of this unit.

CONCEPT CHECK 27.6

1. Identify at least two ways that prokaryotes have affected you positively today.
2. A pathogenic bacterium's toxin causes symptoms that increase the bacterium's chance of spreading from host to host. Does this information indicate whether the poison is an exotoxin or endotoxin? Explain.
3. WHAT IF? In addition to horizontal gene transfer, propose another hypothesis that could account for *E. coli* strain O157:H7 having genes not found in strain K-12. How could your hypothesis be tested?

For suggested answers, see Appendix A.

Chapter 27 Review

MEDIA Go to the Study Area at **www.masteringbio.com** for BioFlix 3-D Animations, MP3 Tutors, Videos, Practice Tests, an eBook, and more.

SUMMARY OF KEY CONCEPTS

CONCEPT 27.1

Structural and functional adaptations contribute to prokaryotic success (pp. 556–561)

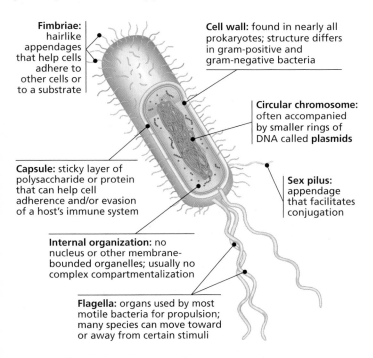

Fimbriae: hairlike appendages that help cells adhere to other cells or to a substrate

Cell wall: found in nearly all prokaryotes; structure differs in gram-positive and gram-negative bacteria

Circular chromosome: often accompanied by smaller rings of DNA called **plasmids**

Capsule: sticky layer of polysaccharide or protein that can help cell adherence and/or evasion of a host's immune system

Sex pilus: appendage that facilitates conjugation

Internal organization: no nucleus or other membrane-bounded organelles; usually no complex compartmentalization

Flagella: organs used by most motile bacteria for propulsion; many species can move toward or away from certain stimuli

▶ **Reproduction and Adaptation** Prokaryotes can reproduce quickly by binary fission. Some form endospores, which can remain viable in harsh conditions for centuries. Prokaryotic populations can evolve in short periods of time in response to changing environmental conditions.

MEDIA

Activity Prokaryotic Cell Structure and Function

CONCEPT 27.2

Rapid reproduction, mutation, and genetic recombination promote genetic diversity in prokaryotes (pp. 561–564)

▶ **Rapid Reproduction and Mutation** Because prokaryotes can often proliferate rapidly, mutations can quickly increase a population's genetic variation, enabling adaptive evolution.

▶ **Genetic Recombination** Genetic diversity in prokaryotes also can arise by recombination of the DNA from two different cells (in bacteria, via transformation, transduction, or conjugation). By transferring advantageous alleles, such as those for antibiotic resistance, genetic recombination can promote adaptive evolution in prokaryotic populations.

MEDIA

Investigation What Are the Patterns of Antibiotic Resistance?

CONCEPT 27.3

Diverse nutritional and metabolic adaptations have evolved in prokaryotes (pp. 564–565)

▶ Examples of all four modes of nutrition—photoautotrophy, chemoautotrophy, photoheterotrophy, and chemoheterotrophy—are found among prokaryotes.

▶ **The Role of Oxygen in Metabolism** Obligate aerobes require O_2, obligate anaerobes are poisoned by O_2, and facultative anaerobes can survive with or without O_2.

▶ **Nitrogen Metabolism** Prokaryotes can metabolize a wide variety of nitrogenous compounds. Some can convert atmospheric nitrogen to ammonia in a process called nitrogen fixation.

▶ **Metabolic Cooperation** Many prokaryotes depend on the metabolic activities of other prokaryotes. In *Anabaena*, photosynthetic cells and nitrogen-fixing cells exchange metabolic products. Some prokaryotes form surface-coating biofilms, typically including different species.

MEDIA

Investigation What Are the Modes of Nutrition in Prokaryotes?

CONCEPT 27.4
Molecular systematics is illuminating prokaryotic phylogeny (pp. 565–570)

▶ **Lessons from Molecular Systematics** Molecular systematics is leading to a phylogenetic classification of prokaryotes, allowing systematists to identify major new clades.

▶ **Archaea** Archaea share certain traits with bacteria and other traits with eukaryotes. Some archaea, such as extreme thermophiles and extreme halophiles, live in extreme environments. Other archaea, including most methanogens and species in soils, lakes, and oceans, live in moderate environments.

▶ **Bacteria** Diverse nutritional types are scattered among the major groups of bacteria. The two largest groups are the proteobacteria and the gram-positive bacteria.

> **MEDIA**
> Activity Classification of Prokaryotes

CONCEPT 27.5
Prokaryotes play crucial roles in the biosphere (pp. 570–571)

▶ **Chemical Recycling** Decomposition by heterotrophic prokaryotes and the synthetic activities of autotrophic and nitrogen-fixing prokaryotes contribute to the recycling of elements in ecosystems.

▶ **Ecological Interactions** Many prokaryotes have a symbiotic relationship with a host; the relationships between prokaryotes and their hosts range from mutualism to commensalism to parasitism.

CONCEPT 27.6
Prokaryotes have both harmful and beneficial impacts on humans (pp. 571–573)

▶ **Pathogenic Bacteria** Pathogenic bacteria typically cause disease by releasing exotoxins or endotoxins and are potential weapons of bioterrorism. Horizontal gene transfer can spread genes associated with virulence to harmless strains.

▶ **Prokaryotes in Research and Technology** Experiments involving bacteria such as *E. coli* and *A. tumefaciens* have led to important advances in DNA technology. Prokaryotes can be used in bioremediation, production of biodegradable plastics, and the synthesis of vitamins, antibiotics, and other products.

TESTING YOUR KNOWLEDGE

SELF-QUIZ

1. Genetic variation in bacterial populations cannot result from
   a. transduction.
   b. transformation.
   c. conjugation.
   d. mutation.
   e. meiosis.

2. Photoautotrophs use
   a. light as an energy source and CO_2 as a carbon source.
   b. light as an energy source and methane as a carbon source.
   c. N_2 as an energy source and CO_2 as a carbon source.
   d. CO_2 as both an energy source and a carbon source.
   e. H_2S as an energy source and CO_2 as a carbon source.

3. Which of the following statements is *not* true?
   a. Archaea and bacteria have different membrane lipids.
   b. Both archaea and bacteria generally lack membrane-enclosed organelles.
   c. The cell walls of archaea lack peptidoglycan.
   d. Only bacteria have histones associated with DNA.
   e. Only some archaea use CO_2 to oxidize H_2, releasing methane.

4. Which of the following features of prokaryotic biology involves metabolic cooperation among cells?
   a. binary fission
   b. endospore formation
   c. endotoxin release
   d. biofilms
   e. photoautotrophy

5. Which prokaryotic group is mismatched with its members?
   a. Proteobacteria—diverse gram-negative bacteria
   b. Gram-positive bacteria—symbionts in legume root nodules
   c. Spirochetes—helical heterotrophs
   d. Chlamydias—intracellular parasites
   e. Cyanobacteria—solitary and colonial photoautotrophs

6. Plantlike photosynthesis that releases O_2 occurs in
   a. cyanobacteria.
   b. chlamydias.
   c. archaea.
   d. actinomycetes.
   e. chemoautotrophic bacteria.

For Self-Quiz answers, see Appendix A.

> **MEDIA** Visit the Study Area at **www.masteringbio.com** for a Practice Test.

EVOLUTION CONNECTION

7. Health officials worldwide are concerned about antibiotic resistance in bacteria that cause disease. In patients infected with nonresistant strains of the bacterium that causes tuberculosis, antibiotics can relieve symptoms in a few weeks. However, it takes much longer to halt the infection, and patients may discontinue treatment while bacteria are still present. How can bacteria quickly cause symptoms again if they are not wiped out? How might this result in the evolution of drug-resistant pathogens?

SCIENTIFIC INQUIRY

8. **DRAW IT** The nitrogen-fixing bacterium *Rhizobium* infects the roots of some plant species, forming a mutualism in which the bacterium provides the plant with nitrogen, and the plant provides the bacterium with carbohydrates. Scientists measured how well one such plant species (*Acacia irrorata*) grew when its roots were infected by six different *Rhizobium* strains.

(a) Graph the data. (b) Interpret your graph.

Rhizobium strain	Plant mass (g) after 12 weeks of growth
1	0.91
2	0.06
3	1.56
4	1.72
5	0.14
6	1.03

Source: J. J. Burdon, et al., Variation in the effectiveness of symbiotic associations between native rhizobia and temperate Australian *Acacia*: within species interactions, *Journal of Applied Ecology*, 36:398-408 (1999).

Note: In the absence of *Rhizobium*, after 12 weeks of growth, *Acacia* plants have a mass of about 0.1 g.

47 Animal Development

▲ Figure 47.1 **How did this complex embryo form from a single cell?**

KEY CONCEPTS

47.1 After fertilization, embryonic development proceeds through cleavage, gastrulation, and organogenesis

47.2 Morphogenesis in animals involves specific changes in cell shape, position, and adhesion

47.3 The developmental fate of cells depends on their history and on inductive signals

OVERVIEW

A Body-Building Plan

The 7-week-old human embryo in **Figure 47.1** has already achieved an astounding number of milestones in its development. Many of its organs are in place: Its digestive tract traverses the length of its body, and its heart (the red spot in the center) is pulsating. Its brain is forming at the upper left, and the blocks of tissue that will construct the vertebrae are lined up along its back. How did this intricately detailed embryo develop from a single-celled zygote no bigger than the period at the end of the previous sentence?

The question of how a zygote becomes an animal has intrigued scientists for centuries. In the 1700s, the prevailing notion was *preformation*: the idea that the egg or sperm contains an embryo—a preformed, miniature infant, or "homunculus"— that simply becomes larger during development **(Figure 47.2)**. The competing explanation of embryonic development was *epigenesis*: the idea that the form of an animal emerges gradually from a relatively formless egg. Epigenesis was originally proposed 2,000 years earlier by Aristotle, who had snipped open a window in the shell of a chicken egg and observed the developing embryo daily during its three-week incubation. As microscopy improved during the 1800s, biologists following in Aristotle's

▲ Figure 47.2 **A "homunculus" inside the head of a human sperm.** This engraving was made in 1694.

footsteps could see that embryos took shape in a series of progressive stages, and epigenesis displaced preformation as the favored explanation among embryologists.

An organism's development is orchestrated by a genetic program involving not only the genome of the zygote but also molecules placed into the egg by the mother. These molecules, which include proteins and RNAs, are called **cytoplasmic determinants**. As the zygote divides, differences arise between early embryonic cells due to the uneven distribution of cytoplasmic determinants and to signals from neighboring cells. These differences set the stage for distinct programs of gene expression to be carried out in each cell and its descendants. As cell division continues during embryonic development, the specific pattern of gene expression in particular cells sends them down unique paths toward their ultimate fates in the fully formed organism. This process of cell specialization in structure and function is called **cell differentiation**. Along with cell division and differentiation, development involves **morphogenesis**, the process by which an organism takes shape and the differentiated cells occupy their appropriate locations.

By combining molecular genetics with classical approaches to embryology, developmental biologists have learned a great deal about the transformation of a fertilized egg into an animal with multiple tissues and organs. Because animals display a wide variety of body plans, it is not surprising that embryonic development occurs by different schemes. Studies of numerous species, however, have revealed that animals share many basic mechanisms of development and use a common genetic toolkit.

In Chapter 18, we described the development of the fruit fly (*Drosophila melanogaster*). *Drosophila* is well suited to genetic analysis because mutants are easy to obtain in this species, so its genetic program is probably the best understood of any animal. *Drosophila* is a good example of a **model organism**, a species that lends itself to the study of a particular question, is representative of a larger group, and is easy to grow in the lab. In this chapter, we will concentrate mainly on model organisms that have been the subject of classical embryological studies as well as more recent molecular analyses: the sea urchin, the frog, the chick, and the nematode *Caenorhabditis elegans*. We will also explore some aspects of human embryonic development; even though humans are not model organisms, we are, of course, intensely interested in our own species.

We will begin with a description of the basic stages of embryonic development common to most animals. Then we will look at the cellular and molecular mechanisms that result in generation of the body form. Finally, we will consider the process by which embryonic cells travel down differentiation pathways that enable them to play their roles in a fully functional animal.

CONCEPT 47.1

After fertilization, embryonic development proceeds through cleavage, gastrulation, and organogenesis

Important processes regulating development occur during fertilization and the three stages that begin to build the body of most animals. During the first stage, called *cleavage*, cell division creates a hollow ball of cells, the blastula, from the zygote. The second stage, *gastrulation*, rearranges the blastula into a three-layered embryo, the gastrula. During the third stage, *organogenesis*, interactions and movements of the three layers generate rudimentary organs from which adult structures grow.

In our discussion, we will focus on a few species that have been used to investigate each of these processes. For each stage of development, we first consider the species about which the most is known and then compare the same process in other species. We begin by looking at the fertilization of an egg by a sperm.

Fertilization

A complex series of developmental events in the gonads of the parents produces sperm and eggs (gametes), the highly specialized cell types that unite during fertilization (see Figure 46.12). The main function of fertilization is the combining of haploid sets of chromosomes from two individuals into a single diploid cell, the zygote. Contact of the sperm with the egg's surface also initiates metabolic reactions within the egg that trigger the onset of embryonic development, thus "activating" the egg.

Fertilization has been studied most extensively in sea urchins. Their gametes can simply be combined in seawater in the lab-oratory, and subsequent events are easily observed. Although sea urchins (members of phylum Echinodermata) are not vertebrates or even chordates, they share with those two groups the characteristic of deuterostome development (see Figure 32.9). Despite differences in the details, fertilization and early development in sea urchins provide good general models for similar events in vertebrates.

The Acrosomal Reaction

The eggs of sea urchins are fertilized externally after the animals release their gametes into the surrounding seawater. The jelly coat that surrounds the egg exudes soluble molecules that attract the sperm, which swim toward the egg.

When the head of a sea urchin sperm contacts the jelly coat of a sea urchin egg, molecules in the egg's coat trigger the **acrosomal reaction** in the sperm **(Figure 47.3)**. This reaction begins when a specialized vesicle at the tip of the sperm, called the **acrosome**, discharges hydrolytic enzymes. These enzymes digest the jelly coat, enabling a sperm structure called the *acrosomal process* to elongate, penetrating the coat. Molecules of a protein on the tip of the acrosomal process then adhere to specific sperm receptor proteins that extend from the egg plasma membrane through the surrounding meshwork of extracellular matrix, called the *vitelline layer*. In sea urchins and many other animals, this "lock-and-key" recognition of molecules ensures that eggs will be fertilized only by sperm of the same species. Such specificity is especially important when fertilization occurs externally in water, which may be teeming with gametes of other species.

Contact of the tip of the acrosomal process with the egg membrane leads to the fusion of sperm and egg plasma membranes. The sperm nucleus then enters the egg cytoplasm. Contact and fusion of the membranes causes ion channels to open in the egg's plasma membrane, allowing sodium ions to flow into the egg and change the membrane potential (see Chapter 7). This change in membrane potential, called depolarization, is a common feature of fertilization in animals. Occurring within about 1–3 seconds after a sperm binds to an egg, depolarization prevents additional sperm from fusing with the egg's plasma membrane. Without this **fast block to polyspermy**, multiple sperm could fertilize the egg, resulting in an aberrant number of chromosomes in the zygote.

The Cortical Reaction

The membrane depolarization lasts for only a minute or so, thus blocking polyspermy only in the short term. However, fusion of the egg and sperm plasma membranes also triggers a series of changes in the egg that cause a longer-lasting block.

Key players in the longer-lasting block are numerous vesicles lying just beneath the egg plasma membrane, in the rim of cytoplasm known as the *cortex*. Within seconds after a sperm binds to the egg, these vesicles, called **cortical granules**, fuse

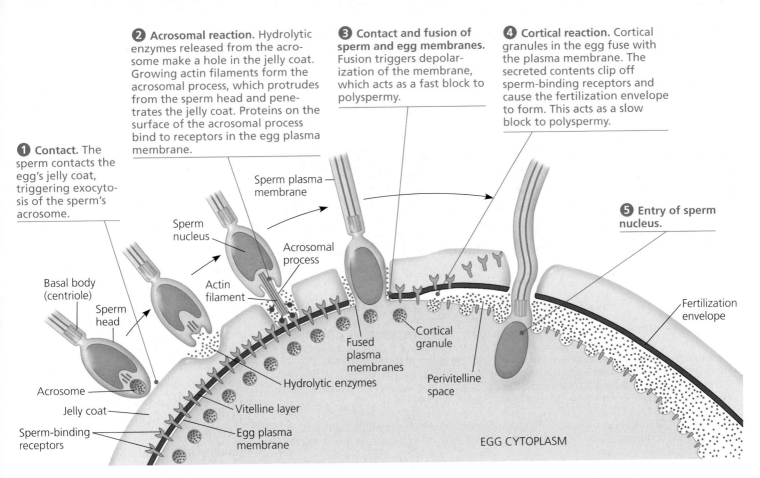

2 **Acrosomal reaction.** Hydrolytic enzymes released from the acrosome make a hole in the jelly coat. Growing actin filaments form the acrosomal process, which protrudes from the sperm head and penetrates the jelly coat. Proteins on the surface of the acrosomal process bind to receptors in the egg plasma membrane.

3 **Contact and fusion of sperm and egg membranes.** Fusion triggers depolarization of the membrane, which acts as a fast block to polyspermy.

4 **Cortical reaction.** Cortical granules in the egg fuse with the plasma membrane. The secreted contents clip off sperm-binding receptors and cause the fertilization envelope to form. This acts as a slow block to polyspermy.

1 **Contact.** The sperm contacts the egg's jelly coat, triggering exocytosis of the sperm's acrosome.

5 **Entry of sperm nucleus.**

Sperm plasma membrane

Sperm nucleus

Acrosomal process

Basal body (centriole)

Actin filament

Fertilization envelope

Sperm head

Acrosome

Fused plasma membranes

Cortical granule

Jelly coat

Hydrolytic enzymes

Perivitelline space

Sperm-binding receptors

Vitelline layer

Egg plasma membrane

EGG CYTOPLASM

▲ **Figure 47.3 The acrosomal and cortical reactions during sea urchin fertilization.** The events following contact of a single sperm and egg ensure that the nucleus of only one sperm enters the egg cytoplasm. The icon at left is a simplified drawing of an adult sea urchin. Throughout the chapter, this and other icons of an adult frog, chicken, and human indicate the animals whose embryos are featured in certain figures.

with the egg plasma membrane, initiating the **cortical reaction** (see Figure 47.3, step 4). Cortical granules contain a treasure trove of molecules that are now secreted into the *perivitelline space*, which lies between the plasma membrane and the vitelline layer. The secreted enzymes and other macromolecules together push the vitelline layer away from the egg and harden the layer, forming a protective **fertilization envelope** that resists the entry of additional sperm nuclei. Another enzyme clips off and releases the external portions of the remaining receptor proteins, along with any attached sperm. The fertilization envelope and other changes in the egg's surface function together as a longer-term **slow block to polyspermy**.

Experimental evidence, including the results described in **Figure 47.4** on the next page, indicates that a high concentration of calcium ions (Ca^{2+}) in the egg is essential for the cortical reaction to occur. Sperm binding activates a signal transduction pathway that causes Ca^{2+} to be released from the egg's endoplasmic reticulum into the cytosol (see Figure 11.12). The elevated Ca^{2+} levels then cause cortical granules to fuse with the plasma membrane. Although understood in greatest detail in sea urchins, the cortical reaction triggered by Ca^{2+} also occurs in vertebrates such as fishes and mammals.

Activation of the Egg

Another outcome of the sharp rise in Ca^{2+} concentration in the egg's cytosol is a substantial increase in the rates of cellular respiration and protein synthesis by the egg, known as *egg activation*. Although egg activation is normally triggered by the binding and fusion of sperm, the unfertilized eggs of many species can be artificially activated by the injection of Ca^{2+} or by various mildly injurious treatments, such as temperature shock. Artificial activation switches on the metabolic responses of the egg and causes it to begin developing by parthenogenesis (without fertilization by a sperm; see Chapter 46). It is even possible to artificially activate an egg that has had its own nucleus removed. This finding shows that proteins and mRNAs present in the cytoplasm of the unfertilized egg are sufficient for egg activation.

About 20 minutes after it enters the egg, the sperm nucleus merges with the egg nucleus, creating the diploid nucleus of the zygote. DNA synthesis begins, and the first cell division occurs after about 90 minutes in the case of sea urchins and some frogs, marking the end of the fertilization stage.

Fertilization in other species shares many features with the process in sea urchins. However, the timing of events differs

Is the distribution of Ca²⁺ in an egg correlated with formation of the fertilization envelope?

EXPERIMENT During fertilization, fusion of cortical granules with the egg plasma membrane causes the fertilization envelope to rise and spread around the egg from the point of sperm binding.

10 sec after fertilization	25 sec	35 sec	1 min

500 μm

Knowing that calcium ion (Ca²⁺) signaling is involved in exocytosis, Rick Steinhardt, Gerald Schatten, and colleagues, then at the University of California at Berkeley, hypothesized that an increase in Ca²⁺ levels triggers cortical granule fusion. To test this hypothesis, they tracked the release of free Ca²⁺ in sea urchin eggs after sperm binding to see if it correlated with formation of the fertilization envelope. A fluorescent dye that glows when it binds free Ca²⁺ was injected into unfertilized eggs. The researchers then added sea urchin sperm and observed the eggs with a fluorescence microscope. Schatten and colleagues later repeated the experiment using a more sensitive dye, producing the results shown here.

RESULTS A rise in cytosolic Ca²⁺ concentration began at the point of sperm entry and spread in a wave to the other side of the egg. Soon after the wave passed, the fertilization envelope rose.

1 sec before fertilization	10 sec after fertilization	20 sec	30 sec

500 μm

CONCLUSION The researchers concluded that Ca²⁺ release is correlated with cortical granule exocytosis and formation of the fertilization envelope, supporting their hypothesis that an increase in Ca²⁺ levels triggers cortical granule fusion.

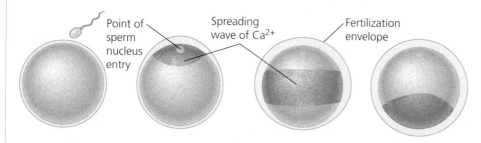

Point of sperm nucleus entry

Spreading wave of Ca²⁺

Fertilization envelope

SOURCES R. Steinhardt et al., Intracellular calcium release at fertilization in the sea urchin egg, *Developmental Biology* 58:185–197 (1977). M. Hafner et al., Wave of free calcium at fertilization in the sea urchin egg visualized with Fura-2, *Cell Motility and the Cytoskeleton* 9:271–277 (1988).

WHAT IF? Suppose you were given a chemical compound that could enter the egg and bind to Ca²⁺, blocking its function. How would you use this compound to further test the hypothesis that a rise in Ca²⁺ levels triggers exocytosis?

---

among species, as does the stage of meiosis the egg has reached by the time it is fertilized. When they are released from the female, sea urchin eggs have completed meiosis. In other species, the eggs are arrested at a specific stage of meiosis; upon fertilization, meiosis is quickly completed along with many of the events already described. Human eggs, for example, are arrested at metaphase of meiosis II (see Figure 46.12) until they are fertilized in the female reproductive tract.

Fertilization in Mammals

In contrast to the external fertilization of sea urchins and most other marine invertebrates, fertilization in terrestrial animals, including mammals, is generally internal. This ensures a moist environment through which the sperm can move toward the egg. Secretions in the mammalian female reproductive tract are responsible for an increase in sperm motility. In humans, this enhancement of sperm function requires about 6 hours of exposure to the female reproductive tract.

The mammalian egg is cloaked by follicle cells released along with the egg during ovulation. A sperm must travel through this layer of follicle cells before it reaches the **zona pellucida**, the extracellular matrix of the egg. One component of the zona pellucida functions as a sperm receptor. Binding of a sperm to this receptor induces an acrosomal reaction similar to that of sea urchin sperm, facilitating sperm passage through the zona pellucida to the egg and exposing a protein on the sperm that binds with the egg plasma membrane. At this point, the two cells fuse **(Figure 47.5)**.

As in sea urchin fertilization, the binding of a sperm to the egg triggers changes within the egg that lead to a cortical reaction, the release of enzymes from cortical granules to the outside of the cell via exocytosis. The released enzymes catalyze changes in the zona pellucida, which then functions as the slow block to polyspermy. (No fast block to polyspermy is known to exist in mammals.)

After the egg and sperm membranes fuse, the whole sperm, tail and all, is taken into the egg. The centriole that acted as the basal body of the sperm's flagellum ultimately generates the mitotic spindle for the first cell division. The haploid nuclei of the mammalian sperm and egg do not fuse immediately as they do in sea urchin fertilization. Instead, the envelopes of both nuclei disperse, and the two sets of chromosomes (one set from each gamete) share a common spindle apparatus during the first mitotic division of the zygote. Thus, only after this first division do the chromosomes from the two parents coex-

ist in a true diploid nucleus with a nuclear membrane. Fertilization is much slower in mammals than in sea urchins: The first cell division occurs 12–36 hours after sperm binding in mammals, compared with about 90 minutes in sea urchins. This cell division marks the beginning of the next stage, cleavage.

Cleavage

Once fertilization is completed, a succession of rapid cell divisions ensues in many species. During this period, called **cleavage**, the cells carry out the S (DNA synthesis) and M (mitosis) phases of the cell cycle; however, they often virtually skip the G_1 and G_2 (gap) phases, and little or no protein synthesis occurs (see Figure 12.5 for a review of the cell cycle). As a result, the embryo does not enlarge significantly during this period of development. Cleavage simply partitions the cytoplasm of one large cell, the zygote, into many smaller cells called **blastomeres**, each with its own nucleus, as depicted for an echinoderm embryo in **Figure 47.6**.

The first five to seven divisions produce a cluster of cells, within which a fluid-filled cavity called the **blastocoel** begins to form. The blastocoel is fully formed in the **blastula** (plural, *blastulae*), which is thus a hollow ball of cells. During cleavage, different regions of cytoplasm present in the original undivided egg end up in separate blastomeres. Because the regions may contain different cytoplasmic determinants, such as specific mRNAs and proteins, in many species this partitioning sets the stage for subsequent developmental events.

The eggs and zygotes of sea urchins and other animals, with the possible exception of mammals, have a definite polarity, established as the egg developed within the mother during oogenesis. During cleavage in such organisms, the planes of division

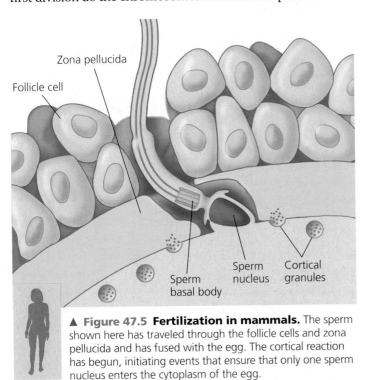

Zona pellucida

Follicle cell

Sperm basal body

Sperm nucleus

Cortical granules

▲ **Figure 47.5 Fertilization in mammals.** The sperm shown here has traveled through the follicle cells and zona pellucida and has fused with the egg. The cortical reaction has begun, initiating events that ensure that only one sperm nucleus enters the cytoplasm of the egg.

(a) Fertilized egg. Shown here is the zygote shortly before the first cleavage division, surrounded by the fertilization envelope.

(b) Four-cell stage. Remnants of the mitotic spindle can be seen between the two pairs of cells that have just completed the second cleavage division.

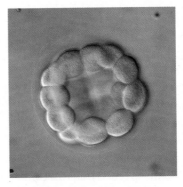

(c) Early blastula. After further cleavage divisions, the embryo is a multicellular ball that is still surrounded by the fertilization envelope. The blastocoel has begun to form in the center.

(d) Later blastula. A single layer of cells surrounds a large blastocoel. Although not visible here, the fertilization envelope is still present; the embryo will soon hatch from it and begin swimming.

▲ **Figure 47.6 Cleavage in an echinoderm embryo.** Cleavage is a series of mitotic cell divisions that transform the zygote into a blastula, a hollow ball composed of cells called blastomeres. These light micrographs show the embryonic stages of a sand dollar, which are virtually identical to those of a sea urchin.

follow a specific pattern relative to the poles of the zygote. The polarity is defined by the uneven distribution of substances in the cytoplasm, including not only cytoplasmic determinants but also **yolk** (stored nutrients). In frogs and many other animals, the distribution of yolk is a key factor influencing the pattern of cleavage. Yolk is often concentrated toward one pole of the egg, called the **vegetal pole**; the yolk concentration decreases significantly toward the opposite pole, the **animal pole**. The animal pole is also the site where the polar bodies of oogenesis bud from the cell (see Figure 46.12).

Establishment of the three body axes occurs early in development **(Figure 47.7a)**. This process has been well studied in particular frog species where the animal and vegetal hemispheres of the zygote, named for their respective poles, can be distinguished by color. The animal hemisphere is a deep gray because dark-colored melanin granules are embedded in the cortex in this region. The lack of melanin granules in the vegetal hemisphere allows the yellow color of the yolk to be visible.

The animal-vegetal axis of the egg determines the anterior-posterior (head-tail) axis of the embryo, so we can consider the anterior-posterior axis to be already in place in the egg. (Note, however, that these two axes are not equivalent: The head does not form where the animal pole is.) Following fusion of the egg and the sperm, rearrangement of the amphibian egg cytoplasm establishes the dorsal-ventral (back-belly) axis **(Figure 47.7b)**. The plasma membrane and associated cortex rotate with respect to the inner cytoplasm, a movement called *cortical rotation*. The animal hemisphere cortex moves toward the vegetal inner cytoplasm on the side where the sperm nucleus entered, which is always in the animal hemisphere. The vegetal hemisphere cortex across from the side of sperm nucleus entry moves toward the inner cytoplasm of the animal hemisphere.

Cortical rotation allows molecules in the unpigmented vegetal cortex on the side opposite sperm nucleus entry, placed there during oogenesis, to interact with molecules in the inner cytoplasm of the animal hemisphere. These interactions activate previously inactive proteins of the vegetal cortex. This in turn leads to the formation of cytoplasmic determinants that will later affect gene expression in the cells that inherit them, initiating development of dorsal structures. In this way, cortical rotation establishes the dorsal-ventral axis of the zygote. In some species, this rotation also exposes a light gray region of cytoplasm, the **gray crescent**, that had previously been covered by the pigmented animal cortex near the equator of the egg (see Figure 47.7b). Located on the side opposite sperm nucleus entry, the gray crescent serves as a marker for the future dorsal side of the embryo. The lighter pigment of the gray crescent can persist through many rounds of cell division.

Figure 47.8 shows the cleavage planes during the initial cell divisions in frogs. The first two divisions in frogs are merid-

(a) **The three axes of the fully developed embryo.**

❶ The polarity of the egg determines the anterior-posterior axis before fertilization.

❷ At fertilization, the pigmented cortex slides over the underlying cytoplasm toward the point of sperm nucleus entry. This rotation (black arrows) exposes a region of lighter-colored cytoplasm, the gray crescent, which is a marker of the future dorsal side.

❸ The first cleavage division bisects the gray crescent. Once the anterior-posterior and dorsal-ventral axes are defined, so is the left-right axis.

(b) **Establishing the axes.** The polarity of the egg and cortical rotation are critical in setting up the body axes.

▲ **Figure 47.7 The body axes and their establishment in an amphibian.** All three axes are established before the zygote begins to undergo cleavage.

? *To study axis establishment, researchers can block cortical rotation or force it to occur in a specific direction. One such study resulted in a two-headed embryo because the "back" developed on both sides. What do you think the researchers did to obtain such an embryo?*

ional (vertical), resulting in four blastomeres of equal size, each extending from the animal pole to the vegetal pole. The third division is equatorial (horizontal), producing an eight-celled embryo. However, the highly uneven distribution of yolk in the frog zygote displaces the mitotic apparatus and eventual cytokinesis toward the animal end of the dividing cells in equatorial divisions. As a result, the four blastomeres in the animal hemisphere are smaller than those in the vegetal

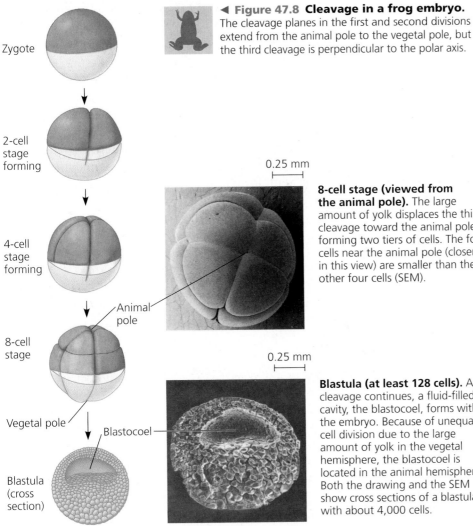

Zygote

2-cell stage forming

4-cell stage forming

8-cell stage

Animal pole

Vegetal pole

Blastocoel

Blastula (cross section)

◀ **Figure 47.8 Cleavage in a frog embryo.** The cleavage planes in the first and second divisions extend from the animal pole to the vegetal pole, but the third cleavage is perpendicular to the polar axis.

0.25 mm

8-cell stage (viewed from the animal pole). The large amount of yolk displaces the third cleavage toward the animal pole, forming two tiers of cells. The four cells near the animal pole (closer, in this view) are smaller than the other four cells (SEM).

0.25 mm

Blastula (at least 128 cells). As cleavage continues, a fluid-filled cavity, the blastocoel, forms within the embryo. Because of unequal cell division due to the large amount of yolk in the vegetal hemisphere, the blastocoel is located in the animal hemisphere. Both the drawing and the SEM show cross sections of a blastula with about 4,000 cells.

hemisphere at the eight-cell stage. The displacing effect of the yolk persists in subsequent divisions, which produce a blastula. In frogs, this unequal cell division causes the blastocoel to be located in the animal hemisphere.

Although the eggs of sea urchins and some other animals have less yolk than frog eggs, they still have an animal-vegetal axis, owing to uneven distribution of other substances. Without the restraint imposed by yolk, however, the blastomeres formed during cleavage are more likely to be of similar size, particularly during the first few divisions (see Figure 47.6). Nonetheless, the general cleavage pattern in frogs is seen in sea urchins and other echinoderms, in most chordates, and indeed in most deuterostomes. In animals whose eggs contain relatively little yolk, the blastocoel is centrally located, and the cleavage furrow passes all the way through the cells, a pattern called **holoblastic cleavage**.

Yolk is most plentiful and has its most pronounced effect on cleavage in the eggs of birds, other reptiles, many fishes, and insects. In these species, the volume of yolk is so great that cleavage furrows cannot pass through it, and only the re-

gion of the egg lacking yolk undergoes cleavage. This incomplete division of a yolk-rich egg is known as **meroblastic cleavage**.

In birds, for example, the part of the egg we commonly call the yolk is actually the entire egg cell, swollen with yolk nutrients. If you crack open a chicken egg and observe the yolk, you may see a small whitish area, which is a pool of cytoplasm located at the animal pole. Cleavage of the fertilized egg is restricted to this yolk-free cytoplasm; the dense yolk remains uncleaved. Early cleavage divisions in a bird embryo produce a cap of cells that rest on the undivided yolk and sort into upper and lower layers. The cavity between these two layers is the avian version of the blastocoel, and this embryonic stage is the avian equivalent of the blastula, although its form is different from the hollow ball of an early sea urchin or frog embryo.

In insects such as *Drosophila*, the zygote's nucleus is situated *within* a mass of yolk. Cleavage begins with the nucleus undergoing mitotic divisions that are not accompanied by cytokinesis. In other words, no cell membranes form around the early nuclei. The first several hundred nuclei are spread throughout the yolk and later migrate to the outer edge of the embryo. After several more rounds of mitosis, a plasma membrane forms around each nucleus, and the embryo, now the equivalent of a blastula, consists of a single layer of about 6,000 cells surrounding a mass of yolk.

Gastrulation

After cleavage, the rate of cell division slows dramatically. Groups of cells then undergo the morphogenetic process called **gastrulation**, taking up new locations that will allow the later formation of tissues and organs. During this process, the embryo is called a **gastrula** (plural, *gastrulae*). For organisms with a two-layered body plan, such as the cnidarian *Hydra*, this rearrangement can be fairly simple. For most animals, however, gastrulation is a dramatic rearrangement of the cells of the blastula that produces a three-layered embryo with a primitive digestive tube. Although gastrulation differs in detail from one animal group to another, the process is driven by the same general mechanisms in all species: changes in cell motility, changes in cell shape, and changes in cellular adhesion to other cells and to molecules of the extracellular matrix. The result of gastrulation is that some cells at or near the surface of the blastula move to an interior location, and three cell layers are established. The positioning of the three cell layers in the fully developed gastrula allows cells to interact with each other in new ways, leading to the generation of the body's organs.

The three layers produced by gastrulation are embryonic tissues collectively called the embryonic **germ layers**. In the late gastrula, the **ectoderm** forms the outer layer, the **endoderm** lines the embryonic digestive tract, and the **mesoderm** partly fills the space between the ectoderm and the endoderm. Eventually, these three cell layers develop into all the tissues and organs of the adult animal. Here we examine the events that occur during gastrulation in the sea urchin, frog, and chick.

Figure 47.9 outlines gastrulation in a sea urchin embryo. The sea urchin blastula consists of a single layer of cells enclosing the central blastocoel. Gastrulation begins at the vegetal pole, where individual cells detach from the blastocoel wall and enter the blastocoel as migratory cells called *mesenchyme cells*. The remaining cells near the vegetal pole flatten slightly and form a *vegetal plate* that buckles inward as a result of cell shape changes we will discuss later. This process is called **invagination**. The buckled vegetal plate then undergoes extensive rearrangement of its cells, transforming the shallow invagination into a deeper, narrower, blind-ended tube called the **archenteron**. The open end of the archenteron, which will become the anus, is called the **blastopore**. A second opening, which will become the mouth, forms when the opposite end of the archenteron touches the inside of the ectoderm and the two layers fuse, producing a rudimentary digestive tube. As you learned in Chapter 32, the developmental mode of animals can be categorized in part by whether the mouth is the first opening formed (protostome development) or the second (deuterostome development). Sea urchins and other echinoderms have deuterostome development, as do chordates like ourselves and other vertebrates.

Gastrulation in sea urchins produces an embryo with a primitive digestive tube and three germ layers, which developmental biologists commonly color-code in diagrams: blue for ectoderm, red for mesoderm, and yellow for endoderm (see Figure 47.9). This three-layered body plan is characteristic of most animal phyla and is established very early in development. In the sea urchin, the gastrula develops into a ciliated larva that drifts in ocean surface waters as zooplankton, feeding on bacteria and unicellular algae. Eventually, the larva metamorphoses into the adult form of the sea urchin, which takes up residence on the ocean floor.

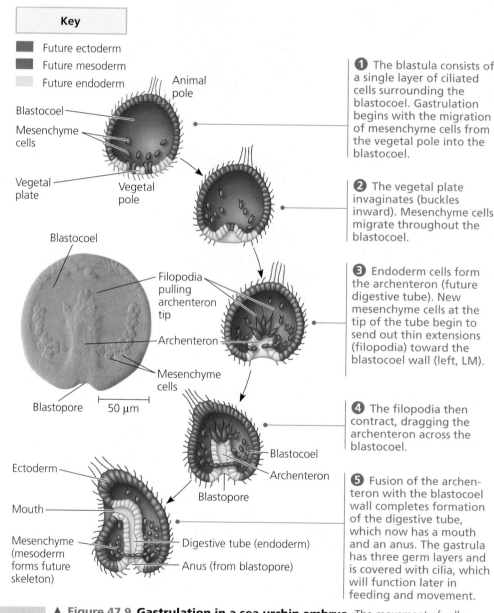

Key

- Future ectoderm
- Future mesoderm
- Future endoderm

Animal pole
Blastocoel
Mesenchyme cells
Vegetal plate
Vegetal pole

Blastocoel
Filopodia pulling archenteron tip
Archenteron
Mesenchyme cells
Blastopore
50 μm

Ectoderm
Mouth
Mesenchyme (mesoderm forms future skeleton)

Blastocoel
Archenteron
Blastopore
Digestive tube (endoderm)
Anus (from blastopore)

❶ The blastula consists of a single layer of ciliated cells surrounding the blastocoel. Gastrulation begins with the migration of mesenchyme cells from the vegetal pole into the blastocoel.

❷ The vegetal plate invaginates (buckles inward). Mesenchyme cells migrate throughout the blastocoel.

❸ Endoderm cells form the archenteron (future digestive tube). New mesenchyme cells at the tip of the tube begin to send out thin extensions (filopodia) toward the blastocoel wall (left, LM).

❹ The filopodia then contract, dragging the archenteron across the blastocoel.

❺ Fusion of the archenteron with the blastocoel wall completes formation of the digestive tube, which now has a mouth and an anus. The gastrula has three germ layers and is covered with cilia, which will function later in feeding and movement.

▲ **Figure 47.9 Gastrulation in a sea urchin embryo.** The movement of cells during gastrulation forms an embryo with a primitive digestive tube and three germ layers. Some of the mesodermal mesenchyme cells that migrate inward (step ❶) will eventually secrete calcium carbonate and form a simple internal skeleton. Embryos in steps ❶–❸ are viewed from the front, those in ❹ and ❺ from the side.

In the frog, gastrulation also produces a three-layered embryo with an archenteron. The mechanics of gastrulation are more complicated in a frog, however, because of the large, yolk-laden cells of the vegetal hemisphere and because the wall of the blastula is more than one cell thick in most species. Gastrulation begins on the dorsal side of the blastula when a group of cells begins to invaginate—change shape and push inward—forming a crease along the region where the gray crescent formed in the zygote (see Figure 47.7). It may help to

think of this crease as the site where two thin lips are pressed together. The part above this crease becomes the dorsal side of the blastopore, called the **dorsal lip** (Figure 47.10). Like a slowly widening frown, the blastopore extends at each end of the crease as new cells push inward. Finally, the two ends of the blastopore meet on the ventral side. The blastopore is now a complete circle.

As the blastopore is forming, future endoderm and mesoderm cell layers on the surface of the embryo roll over the edge

❶ Gastrulation begins when a small indented crease, the blastopore, appears on the dorsal side of the late blastula. The crease is formed by cells changing shape and pushing inward from the surface (invagination). Sheets of outer cells then roll inward over the dorsal lip (involution) and move into the interior (shown by the dashed arrow), where they will form endoderm and mesoderm. Meanwhile, cells at the animal pole, the future ectoderm, change shape and begin spreading over the outer surface.

SURFACE VIEW · CROSS SECTION

Animal pole · Blastocoel · Dorsal lip of blastopore · Blastopore · Dorsal lip of blastopore

Early gastrula · Vegetal pole

❷ The blastopore extends around both sides of the embryo (red arrows), as more cells invaginate. When the ends finally meet on the other side, the blastopore forms a circle that becomes smaller as ectoderm spreads downward over the surface. Internally, continued involution expands the endoderm and mesoderm, and the archenteron begins to form; as a result, the blastocoel becomes smaller.

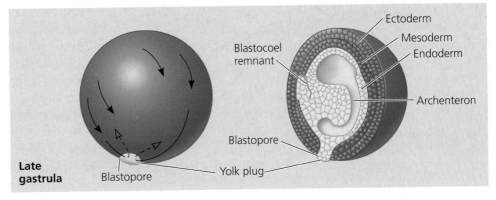

Blastocoel shrinking · Archenteron

❸ Late in gastrulation, the endoderm-lined archenteron has completely replaced the blastocoel and the three germ layers are in place. The circular blastopore surrounds a plug of yolk-filled cells.

Ectoderm · Mesoderm · Endoderm · Blastocoel remnant · Archenteron · Blastopore · Yolk plug

Late gastrula · Blastopore

Key

- Future ectoderm
- Future mesoderm
- Future endoderm

 ▲ **Figure 47.10 Gastrulation in a frog embryo.**
In the frog blastula, the blastocoel is displaced toward the animal pole and is surrounded by a wall several cells thick. The cell movements that begin gastrulation occur on the dorsal side of the blastula, where the gray crescent was located in the zygote (see Figure 47.7b). Although still visible as gastrulation begins, the gray crescent is not shown here.

of the lip into the interior of the embryo, a process called **involution**. Once inside the embryo, these cells move away from the blastopore toward the animal pole and become organized into layers of endoderm and mesoderm, with the endoderm on the inside. The blastocoel collapses during this process, displaced by the archenteron that is formed by the tube of endoderm. As gastrulation is completed, the circular lip of the blastopore encircles a **yolk plug** consisting of the outer nutrient-laden cells; these protruding cells will move inward as expansion of the ectoderm causes the blastopore to shrink further. At this point, the cells remaining on the surface make up the ectoderm, the tube of endoderm is the innermost layer, and the mesoderm lies between them. As in the sea urchin, the frog's anus develops from the blastopore, and the mouth eventually breaks through at the opposite end of the archenteron after it extends to the ventral side near the animal pole.

Gastrulation in the chick is similar to frog gastrulation in that it involves cells moving from the surface of the embryo to an interior location. In birds, however, the inward movement of cells during gastrulation is affected by the large mass of yolk pressing against the bottom of the embryo. Recall that cleav-

age in the chick results in a stage equivalent to the blastula. This stage, called the *blastoderm*, consists of upper and lower layers—the *epiblast* and *hypoblast*—lying atop the yolk mass. All the cells that will form the embryo come from the epiblast. During gastrulation, some epiblast cells move toward the midline of the blastoderm and then detach and move inward toward the yolk **(Figure 47.11)**. The pileup of cells moving inward at the blastoderm's midline produces a thickening called the **primitive streak**, which runs along the embryo's anterior-posterior axis. The primitive streak is functionally equivalent to the blastopore in the frog, but the two structures are oriented differently in the two embryos. Some of the inward-moving epiblast cells displace hypoblast cells and form the endoderm; other epiblast cells move laterally once they are midway into the blastocoel, forming the mesoderm. The epiblast cells that remain on the surface give rise to the ectoderm. Although the hypoblast contributes no cells to the embryo, it seems to help direct the formation of the primitive streak before the onset of gastrulation and is required for normal development. The hypoblast cells later segregate from the endoderm and eventually form portions of a sac that surrounds the yolk and a stalk that connects the yolk mass to the embryo.

Despite variations in how the three germ layers form in different species, once they are in place, gastrulation is complete. Now is the time when the embryo's organs begin to form.

Organogenesis

Various regions of the three embryonic germ layers develop into the rudiments of organs during the process of **organogenesis**. Whereas gastrulation involves mass movements of cells, organogenesis involves more localized shape changes in both tissues and individual cells. The first evidence of organ building is the appearance of tissue folds and splits and dense clustering (condensation) of cells.

Figure 47.12 shows some events during early organogenesis in a frog. The organs that begin to take shape first in the embryos of frogs and other chordates are the neural tube and the **notochord**, the skeletal rod characteristic of all chordate embryos. The notochord is formed from dorsal mesoderm that condenses when cells associate tightly as a group just above the archenteron (Figure 47.12a). The ectoderm above the notochord becomes the *neural plate* in response to a number of signaling molecules secreted by mesodermal and other tissues. Changes in cell shape then cause the neural plate to curve inward, rolling itself into the **neural tube**, which runs along the anterior-posterior axis of the embryo (Figure 47.12b). The neural tube will become the animal's central nervous system—the brain in the head and the spinal cord down the rest of the body. The signaling received by the ectoderm is a good example of a process seen often during organogenesis: One germ layer sends molecular signals to

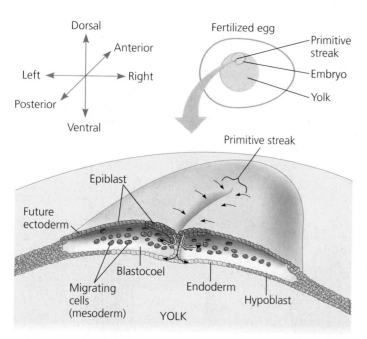

▲ **Figure 47.11 Gastrulation in a chick embryo.**
The chick blastula consists of an upper layer of cells, the epiblast, and a lower layer, the hypoblast, with a space (the blastocoel) lying between them. This is a cross section at a right angle to the primitive streak, looking toward the anterior end of a gastrulating embryo. During gastrulation, some cells of the epiblast migrate (arrows) into the interior of the embryo through the primitive streak. Some of these cells move downward and form endoderm, pushing aside the hypoblast cells, while others migrate laterally and form mesoderm. The cells left behind on the surface of the embryo at the end of gastrulation will become ectoderm.

Neural folds

Neural fold   Neural plate

1 mm

Neural fold   Neural plate

Notochord
Ectoderm
Mesoderm
Endoderm
Archenteron

(a) Neural plate formation. By this stage, the notochord has developed from dorsal mesoderm, and the dorsal ectoderm has thickened, forming the neural plate, in response to signals from other embryonic tissues. The neural folds are the two ridges that form the lateral edges of the neural plate. These folds are visible in the LM of a whole embryo.

Neural crest cells

Outer layer of ectoderm

Neural crest cells

Neural tube

(b) Neural tube formation. Infolding and pinching off of the neural plate generates the neural tube. Note the neural crest cells, which will migrate and give rise to numerous structures. (See also Figure 34.7.)

Eye   Somites   Tail bud

SEM   1 mm

Neural tube   Neural crest cells
Notochord
Coelom   Somite

Archenteron (digestive cavity)

(c) Somites. The SEM is a side view of the whole embryo at the tail-bud stage. Part of the ectoderm has been removed to reveal the somites, blocks of tissue that will give rise to segmental structures such as vertebrae. The drawing shows a similar-stage embryo after formation of the neural tube, as if the embryo in the SEM were cut and viewed in cross section. By this time, the lateral mesoderm has begun to separate into two tissue layers that line the coelom, or body cavity. The somites, formed from mesoderm, flank the notochord.

▲ **Figure 47.12 Early organogenesis in a frog embryo.**

another, thereby affecting gene expression and determining the fate of the second.

In vertebrate embryos, a band of cells called the *neural crest* develops along the borders where the neural tube pinches off from the ectoderm. **Neural crest cells** subsequently migrate to various parts of the embryo, forming peripheral nerves, parts of teeth, skull bones, and so many other different cell types that some developmental biologists have suggested that the neural crest could be considered a fourth germ layer.

Other condensations of cells occur in strips of mesoderm lateral to the notochord, which separate into blocks called **somites** (Figure 47.12c). The somites are arranged serially on both sides along the length of the notochord. Parts of the somites dissociate into mesenchyme cells, which migrate individually to new locations. Note that these cells are both

mesodermal and mesenchymal (migratory). (Be careful not to confuse the two terms.) Some mesenchyme cells gather around the notochord and form the vertebrae. Parts of the notochord between the vertebrae persist as the inner portions of the vertebral disks in adults. (These are the disks that can "slip," causing back pain.) Somite cells that become mesenchymal later also form the muscles associated with the vertebral column and the ribs. Note that serially repeating structures of the embryo (somites) form repeated structures in the adult. The serial origin of the vertebral column, ribs, and their muscles reinforces the idea that chordates are basically segmented animals, although the segmentation becomes less obvious later in development. Lateral to the somites, the mesoderm splits into two layers that form the lining of the body cavity, or coelom (see Figure 32.8).

► **Figure 47.13**
Organogenesis in a chick embryo.

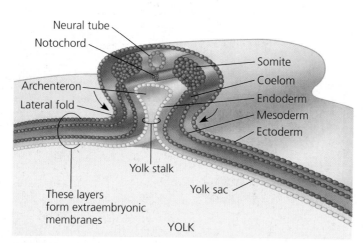

Neural tube
Notochord
Archenteron
Lateral fold
Somite
Coelom
Endoderm
Mesoderm
Ectoderm
Yolk stalk
Yolk sac
These layers form extraembryonic membranes
YOLK

(a) Early organogenesis. The archenteron forms when lateral folds pinch the embryo away from the yolk. The embryo remains open to the yolk, attached by the yolk stalk, about midway along its length, as shown in this cross section. The notochord, neural tube, and somites subsequently develop much as they do in the frog. The germ layers lateral to the embryo itself form extraembryonic membranes (to be discussed later).

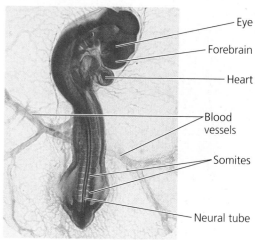

Eye
Forebrain
Heart
Blood vessels
Somites
Neural tube

(b) Late organogenesis. Rudiments of most major organs have already formed in this chick embryo, which is about 56 hours old and about 2–3 mm long. The extraembryonic membranes eventually are supplied by blood vessels extending from the embryo; several major blood vessels are seen here (LM).

As organogenesis progresses, morphogenesis and cell differentiation continue to refine the organs that arise from the three embryonic germ layers; many of the internal organs are derived from two of the three layers. Embryonic development of the frog leads to a larval stage, the tadpole, which hatches from the jelly coat that originally protected the egg and developing embryo. Later, metamorphosis transforms the frog from the aquatic, herbivorous tadpole to the terrestrial, carnivorous adult.

Organogenesis in the chick is quite similar to that in the frog. After the three germ layers are formed, the borders of the blastoderm fold downward and come together, pinching the embryo into a three-layered tube joined under the middle of the body to the yolk **(Figure 47.13a)**. Neural tube formation, development of the notochord and somites, and other events in organogenesis occur much as in the frog embryo. The rudiments of the major organs are evident in a 2- to 3-day-old chick embryo **(Figure 47.13b)**.

In invertebrates, organogenesis is somewhat different, which makes sense, given that their body plans diverge significantly from those of vertebrates. The underlying mechanisms, however, involve many of the same cellular activities: cell migration, cell condensations, cell signaling between different tissues, and cell shape changes generating new organs. For example, in flies and other insects, tissues of the nervous system form when ectoderm along the anterior-posterior axis rolls into a tube inside the embryo, like the vertebrate neural tube. Interestingly, however, the tube is on the ventral side of the fly embryo rather than the dorsal side, where it is in vertebrates. In spite of the different locations, the molecular signaling pathways that bring about the events in the two groups are very similar, underscoring their ancient shared evolutionary history.

Specifying the location of the three germ layers in a gastrula is quite straightforward, but during organogenesis, as you can see, the layers move and change shape, defying generalization. **Figure 47.14** summarizes organogenesis by listing the germ

► **Figure 47.14 Adult derivatives of the three embryonic germ layers in vertebrates.**

? *Given what you know about the three germ layers and morphogenesis, propose an explanation for how the epithelial linings of the mouth and anus are formed.*

ECTODERM	MESODERM	ENDODERM
• Epidermis of skin and its derivatives (including sweat glands, hair follicles) • Epithelial lining of mouth and anus • Cornea and lens of eye • Nervous system • Sensory receptors in epidermis • Adrenal medulla • Tooth enamel • Epithelium of pineal and pituitary glands	• Notochord • Skeletal system • Muscular system • Muscular layer of stomach and intestine • Excretory system • Circulatory and lymphatic systems • Reproductive system (except germ cells) • Dermis of skin • Lining of body cavity • Adrenal cortex	• Epithelial lining of digestive tract • Epithelial lining of respiratory system • Lining of urethra, urinary bladder, and reproductive system • Liver • Pancreas • Thymus • Thyroid and parathyroid glands

layers that produce the major organs and tissues in frogs, chicks, and other vertebrates.

Developmental Adaptations of Amniotes

All vertebrate embryos require an aqueous environment for development. In the case of fishes and amphibians, the egg is usually laid in the surrounding sea or pond and needs no special water-filled enclosure. The movement of vertebrates onto land could occur only after the evolution of structures that would allow reproduction in dry environments. Two such structures exist today: (1) the shelled egg of birds and other reptiles, as well as a few mammals (monotremes), and (2) the uterus of marsupial and eutherian mammals. Inside the shell or uterus, the embryos of these animals are surrounded by fluid within a sac formed by a membrane called the amnion. Reptiles (including birds) and mammals are therefore called **amniotes** (see Chapter 34).

Amnion. The amnion protects the embryo in a fluid-filled cavity that prevents dehydration and cushions mechanical shock.

Allantois. The allantois functions as a disposal sac for certain metabolic wastes produced by the embryo. The membrane of the allantois also functions with the chorion as a respiratory organ.

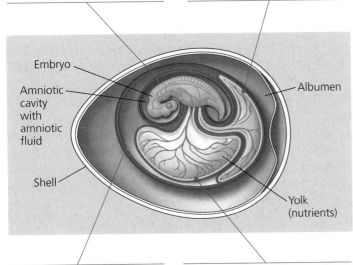

Embryo

Amniotic cavity with amniotic fluid

Shell

Albumen

Yolk (nutrients)

Chorion. The chorion and the membrane of the allantois exchange gases between the embryo and the surrounding air. Oxygen and carbon dioxide diffuse freely across the egg's shell.

Yolk sac. The yolk sac surrounds the yolk, a stockpile of nutrients stored in the egg. Blood vessels in the yolk sac membrane transport nutrients from the yolk into the embryo. Other nutrients are stored in the albumen (the "egg white").

▲ **Figure 47.15 Extraembryonic membranes in birds and other reptiles.** There are four extra-embryonic membranes: the amnion, the allantois, the chorion, and the yolk sac. Each membrane is a sheet of cells that develops from portions of two germ layers that are outside the embryo (see Figure 47.13a).

You have already seen that embryonic development of the chick, an amniote, is very similar to that of the frog, a vertebrate that lacks an amnion. However, in the chick, development also includes the formation of **extraembryonic membranes**, membranes located outside the embryo. Notice in Figure 47.13a that only part of each germ layer contributes to the embryo itself. The parts of the germ layers located outside the embryo proper develop into four extraembryonic membranes, each a sheet of cells derived from two germ layers **(Figure 47.15)**. The **chorion**, which completely surrounds the embryo and the other extraembryonic membranes, functions in gas exchange. The **amnion** eventually encloses the embryo in a protective, fluid-filled amniotic cavity. Below the developing embryo proper, the **yolk sac** encloses the yolk, which provides nutrients until the time of hatching. The **allantois** disposes of waste products and contributes to gas exchange. These four extraembryonic membranes provide a "life-support system" for further embryonic development within the shelled egg or the uterus of an amniote.

We will discuss mammalian extraembryonic membranes next as we describe early development in mammalian embryos. Formation of the placenta, a structure found only in marsupial and eutherian mammals, is an important part of this process.

Mammalian Development

In contrast with the large, yolky eggs of birds, other reptiles, and monotremes, mammalian eggs are typically quite small, storing little in the way of food reserves. In most mammalian species, fertilization takes place in the oviduct, and the earliest stages of development occur while the embryo completes its journey down the oviduct to the uterus (see Figure 46.15). As already mentioned, the mammalian egg and zygote have not yet been shown to exhibit polarity with respect to cytoplasmic contents, and cleavage of the zygote, which lacks yolk, is holoblastic. Despite the lack of yolk, however, mammalian gastrulation and early organogenesis follow a pattern similar to that of birds and other reptiles.

Because ethical concerns preclude experimentation on human embryos, knowledge about human development has been based partly on what we can extrapolate from other mammals, such as the mouse, and partly on observation of very early human development following *in vitro* fertilization. In humans, the first division is complete about 36 hours after fertilization, the second division at about 60 hours, and the third division at about 72 hours. The blastomeres are equal in size. At the eight-cell stage, the blastomeres become tightly adhered to one another, causing the outer surface of the embryo to take on a smooth appearance. **Figure 47.16**, on the next page, depicts development of the human embryo starting about 6 days after fertilization. Our description in the text follows the numbers in the figure.

Endometrial epithelium (uterine lining)

Inner cell mass

Trophoblast

Blastocoel

Uterus

❶ Blastocyst reaches uterus.

Maternal blood vessel

Expanding region of trophoblast

Epiblast

Hypoblast

Trophoblast

❷ Blastocyst implants (7 days after fertilization).

Expanding region of trophoblast

Amniotic cavity

Epiblast

Hypoblast

Yolk sac (from hypoblast)

Extraembryonic mesoderm cells (from epiblast)

Chorion (from trophoblast)

❸ Extraembryonic membranes start to form (10–11 days), and gastrulation begins (13 days).

Amnion

Chorion

Ectoderm

Mesoderm

Endoderm

Yolk sac

Extraembryonic mesoderm

Allantois

❹ Gastrulation has produced a three-layered embryo with four extraembryonic membranes.

▲ Figure 47.16 **Four stages in early embryonic development of a human.** The epiblast gives rise to the three germ layers, which form the embryo proper. See the text for a description of each stage.

❶ At the completion of cleavage, the embryo has more than 100 cells arranged around a central cavity and has traveled down the oviduct to the uterus. This embryonic stage, the **blastocyst**, is the mammalian version of a blastula. Clustered at one end of the blastocyst cavity is a group of cells called the **inner cell mass**, which will subsequently develop into the embryo proper and form or contribute to all the extraembryonic membranes. It is the cells of the very early blastocyst stage that are the source of embryonic stem cell lines.

❷ The **trophoblast**, the outer epithelium of the blastocyst, does not contribute to the embryo itself but instead provides support services. First, it initiates implantation by secreting enzymes that break down molecules of the endometrium, the lining of the uterus. This allows the blastocyst to invade the endometrium. Then, as the trophoblast thickens through cell division, it extends fingerlike projections into the surrounding maternal tissue, which is rich in blood vessels. Invasion by the trophoblast leads to erosion of capillaries in the endometrium, causing blood to spill out and bathe trophoblast tissues. Around the time of implantation, the inner cell mass of the blastocyst forms a flat disk with an upper layer of cells, the *epiblast*, and a lower layer, the *hypoblast*, which are homologous to the epiblast and hypoblast of birds. As in birds, the human embryo develops almost entirely from epiblast cells.

❸ As implantation is completed, gastrulation begins. Cells move inward from the epiblast through a primitive streak and form mesoderm and endoderm, just as in the chick (see Figure 47.11). At the same time, extraembryonic membranes begin to form. The trophoblast continues to expand into the endometrium. The invading trophoblast, mesodermal cells derived from the epiblast, and adjacent endometrial tissue all contribute to formation of the placenta (see Figure 46.16). The placenta is a vital organ that mediates exchange of nutrients, gases, and nitrogenous wastes between the embryo and the mother. The placenta also produces hormones and protects the embryo from a maternal immune response.

❹ By the end of gastrulation, the embryonic germ layers have formed. The three-layered embryo is now surrounded by proliferating extraembryonic mesoderm and the four extraembryonic membranes.

The extraembryonic membranes in mammals are homologous to those of birds and other reptiles (see Figure 47.15) and develop in a similar way. Gas exchange occurs across the chorion, and the amnion cushions the developing embryo. The fluid from the amniotic cavity is the "water" expelled from the mother's vagina when the amnion breaks just prior to childbirth. Below the developing mammalian embryo, the yolk sac encloses more fluid. Although this cavity contains no yolk, the membrane that surrounds it is given the same name as the homologous membrane in birds and other reptiles. The yolk sac membrane of mammals is a site of early formation of blood cells, which later migrate into the embryo proper. The allantois in mammals is incorporated into the umbilical cord. Here it forms blood vessels that transport oxygen and nutrients from the placenta to the embryo and rid the embryo of carbon dioxide and nitrogenous wastes. Thus, the extraembryonic membranes of shelled eggs, where embryos are nourished with yolk, were conserved in mammals as they diverged from reptiles in the course of evolution, but with modifications adapted to development within the reproductive tract of the mother.

As you learned in Chapter 46, identical (monozygotic) twins can arise when embryonic cells become separated. The timing of the separation determines the nature of the twins' arrangement in the uterus with regard to their extraembryonic membranes. If the separation occurs quite early, before the trophoblast and inner cell mass become differentiated, then two embryos will grow, each with its own chorion and amnion. This is the case in about a third of twin births. In most of the remainder, the separation occurs a little later, after the chorion forms but before the amnion forms. The two embryos that develop therefore share a chorion but have separate amnions. In very rare cases, two groups of cells become separated even later, and the two embryos share a common chorion and amnion.

In this section, you have learned about the main events of embryonic development in animals. Next, we will address the cellular and molecular mechanisms by which these events occur.

1. How does the fertilization envelope form in sea urchins? What is its function?
2. A frog zygote and frog blastula are nearly the same size. Explain this observation.
3. Contrast the effects of cleavage and gastrulation on development of the embryo.
4. Explain how the neural tube forms and how neural crest cells arise.
5. **WHAT IF?** Predict what would happen if you injected Ca^{2+} into an unfertilized sea urchin egg.
6. **WHAT IF?** How many chorions and amnions are present in the case of conjoined ("Siamese") twins? (These twins are always monozygotic.)

For suggested answers, see Appendix A.

CONCEPT 47.2
Morphogenesis in animals involves specific changes in cell shape, position, and adhesion

Although biologists are far from fully understanding cellular and molecular developmental mechanisms, several key principles have emerged as being fundamental to the development of all animals. Morphogenesis is a major aspect of development in both animals and plants, but only in animals does it involve the *movement* of cells. The rigid cell wall that surrounds plant cells prevents complex movements like those occurring during gastrulation. In animals, movement of parts of a cell can bring about changes in cell shape or enable a cell to migrate from one place to another within the embryo. Changes in both cell shape and cell position are involved in cleavage, gastrulation, and organogenesis. Here we consider some of the cellular components and behaviors that contribute to these events.

The Cytoskeleton, Cell Motility, and Convergent Extension

Changes in the shape of a cell usually involve reorganization of the cytoskeleton (see Table 6.1). Consider, for example, how the cells of the neural plate form the neural tube (Figure 47.17). First, microtubules oriented parallel to the dorsal-ventral axis of the embryo apparently help lengthen the cells in that direction. At the dorsal end of each cell is a parallel array of microfilaments (actin filaments) oriented crosswise. These microfilaments contract, giving the cells a wedge shape that forces the ectoderm layer to

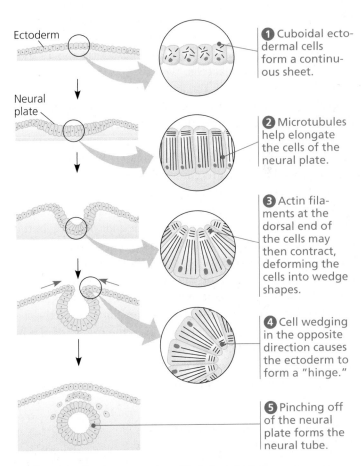

Ectoderm

Neural plate

❶ Cuboidal ectodermal cells form a continuous sheet.

❷ Microtubules help elongate the cells of the neural plate.

❸ Actin filaments at the dorsal end of the cells may then contract, deforming the cells into wedge shapes.

❹ Cell wedging in the opposite direction causes the ectoderm to form a "hinge."

❺ Pinching off of the neural plate forms the neural tube.

▲ **Figure 47.17 Change in cell shape during morphogenesis.** Reorganization of the cytoskeleton is associated with morphogenetic changes in embryonic tissues, as shown here for the formation of the neural tube in vertebrates.

bend inward. Similar changes in cell shape occur throughout development in other places, such as the hinge regions where the neural tube is pinching off from the ectoderm and sites where evaginations (outpocketings) of tissue layers form.

The cytoskeleton also drives cell migration, the active movement of cells from one place to another in developing animals. Cells "crawl" within the embryo by using cytoskeletal fibers to extend and retract cellular protrusions. This type of motility is akin to the amoeboid movement described in Figure 6.27b; but in contrast with the thick pseudopodia of some amoeboid cells, the cellular protrusions of migrating embryonic cells are usually flat sheets (lamellipodia) or spikes (filopodia).

During gastrulation in some organisms, invagination begins when cuboidal cells on the surface of the blastula become wedge-shaped. However, the movement of cells deeper into the embryo involves the extension of filopodia by cells at the leading edge of the migrating tissue. The cells that first move through the blastopore and up along the inside of the blastocoel wall drag others behind them, thus helping direct movement of the entire sheet of cells from the embryo's surface into appropriate locations in the blastocoel. The involuted sheet then forms the endoderm and mesoderm of the embryo (see Figure 47.10). There are also many situations in which cells migrate individually, as when the cells of a somite or the neural crest disperse to various parts of the embryo. In fact, during gastrulation in many species, the mesoderm moves into the embryo as individual cells. We have seen two such examples thus far, in the sea urchin and the chick.

Cell crawling is also involved in **convergent extension**, a type of morphogenetic movement in which the cells of a tissue layer rearrange themselves so that the sheet becomes narrower (converges) while it becomes longer (extends). It's as if a crowd of people waiting to enter a theater for a concert were told that the doors would not open until they formed a single-file line; the line would become much longer as it narrowed. In the embryo, the cells elongate, with their ends pointing in the direction they will move, and they wedge between each other into fewer columns of cells **(Figure 47.18)**. When many cells converge this way, the tissue can extend dramatically. Convergent extension is important in early embryonic development. It occurs, for example, as the archenteron elongates in the sea urchin embryo and during involution in the frog gastrula. In the latter case, convergent extension is responsible for changing the spherical shape of the gastrula to the rounded rectangular shape of the frog embryo seen in Figure 47.12c.

Role of Cell Adhesion Molecules and the Extracellular Matrix

Scientists are refining their understanding of the signaling pathways that trigger and guide cell movement and cell interactions during morphogenesis. A key group of proteins that contribute to cell migration and stable tissue structure are glycoproteins called **cell adhesion molecules (CAMs)**, transmembrane cell-surface proteins that bind to CAMs on other cells. CAMs vary in amount, chemical identity, or both from one type of cell to another. These differences help regulate morphogenetic movements and tissue building.

One important class of CAMs is the **cadherins**, which require calcium ions outside the cell for proper function. There are many different cadherins, and the gene for each cadherin is expressed in specific locations at specific times during embryonic development. Janet Heasman, Chris Wylie, and colleagues have vividly demonstrated the importance of one particular cadherin in the formation of the frog blastula **(Figure 47.19)**. Cadherins are also involved in the tight adhesion of cells in the mammalian embryo that first occurs at the eight-cell stage, when cadherin production begins.

The processes of cell migration and tissue organization also involve the extracellular matrix (ECM), the meshwork of secreted glycoproteins and other macromolecules lying outside the plasma membranes of cells (see Figure 6.30). The ECM helps to guide cells in many types of morphogenetic movements, such as migration of individual cells or shape changes of cell sheets. On the cells that undergo movement, membrane proteins act as receptors that bind specific ECM molecules. An organized array of ECM fibers may function as tracks, directing migrating cells along particular routes. Other substances in the ECM keep cells on the correct paths by *inhibiting* migration off the path. Thus, nonmigratory cells along migration pathways may promote or inhibit movement of other cells, depending on the specific molecules they secrete into the ECM.

Several kinds of extracellular glycoproteins, such as fibronectin, promote cell migration by providing specific molecular anchorage for moving cells. For example, fibronectin plays such a role at the leading edge of the involuting tissue during frog gastrulation. Fibronectin fibers line the roof of the blastocoel, and as the future mesoderm moves into the interior of the embryo, the cells at the free edge of the involuting sheet migrate along the fibers (see Figure 47.10). Researchers can prevent the attachment of cells to fibronectin by injecting embryos with antibodies against either fibronectin or the

▶ **Figure 47.18 Convergent extension of a sheet of cells.** In this simplified diagram, the cells elongate in a particular direction and crawl between each other (convergence), as the sheet becomes longer and narrower (extension).

Convergence

Extension

▼ Figure 47.19 Inquiry

Is cadherin required for development of the blastula?

EXPERIMENT In 1994, Janet Heasman, Chris Wylie, and colleagues, then at the Wellcome/CRC Institute in Cambridge, England, injected frog eggs with nucleic acid complementary to the mRNA encoding a cadherin known as EP cadherin. This "antisense" nucleic acid leads to destruction of EP cadherin mRNA, so no EP cadherin protein is produced. Frog sperm were then added to experimental (injected) eggs and to control (noninjected) eggs. The embryos that developed were observed with a scanning electron microscope.

RESULTS As shown in these SEMs of cut-open embryos, fertilized control eggs developed into normal blastulae, but fertilized experimental eggs did not. In the absence of EP cadherin, the blastocoel did not form properly, and the cells were arranged in a disorganized fashion.

0.25 mm   0.25 mm
|———| |———|

Control embryo   Embryo without EP cadherin

CONCLUSION During embryonic development in the frog, the cell adhesion molecule EP cadherin is required for proper cell organization in the blastula.

SOURCE J. Heasman et al., A functional test for maternally inherited cadherin in *Xenopus* shows its importance in cell adhesion at the blastula stage, *Development* 120:49–57 (1994).

WHAT IF? What do you predict would be the effect on embryos if you placed frog blastulae in water from which all the calcium had been removed?

---

receptors that bind fibronectin at the cell surface. Either treatment prevents the crawling of mesoderm.

A wealth of evidence supports the conclusion that moving cells engage in an ongoing dialogue with the ECM and other cells in the vicinity. As migrating cells move along specific paths, a variety of receptor proteins on their surfaces pick up directional cues from the immediate environment. Such signaling molecules, which may be ECM molecules or small soluble factors (see Chapter 11), can initiate intracellular signaling pathways that direct the orientation of cytoskeletal elements so that the cell moves in the proper direction. Such signaling may also affect the expression or function of other proteins involved in the migration.

Based on previous studies, Mungo Marsden and Doug DeSimone were intrigued by the possibility that cell-ECM and cell-cell binding systems might affect each other during convergent extension. **Figure 47.20** describes their initial experi-

---

▼ Figure 47.20 Inquiry

Is an organized fibronectin matrix required for convergent extension?

EXPERIMENT Mungo Marsden and Doug DeSimone, at the University of Virginia, wondered whether an organized fibronectin matrix was essential for convergent extension. Into the blastocoels of frog blastulae, they injected molecules that would block the interaction of fibronectin with its receptor protein on cell surfaces, knowing from previous work that this would block organization of the fibronectin matrix. As a control, they injected a very similar molecule that did not block matrix assembly. They compared convergent extension in matrix-blocked and control embryos in a series of experiments, two of which are shown here.

Experiment 1: In whole embryos, a probe was used to detect the presence of an mRNA that marks tissues normally undergoing convergent extension.

Experiment 2: Certain tissues that normally undergo convergent extension were removed from embryos, placed between glass cover slips, allowed to develop, and observed through a microscope.

RESULTS

Experiment 1: The marked tissue in the matrix-blocked whole embryo was shorter and wider than that in the control embryo.

Control   Matrix blocked

Experiment 2: Cells (nuclei marked by yellow arrowheads) were tightly packed in a column in the control tissues but not in the matrix-blocked tissues. (Red arrows indicate column widths.)

Control   Matrix blocked

CONCLUSION Fibronectin matrix assembly is crucial for the cell behaviors underlying convergent extension.

SOURCE M. Marsden and D. W. DeSimone, Integrin-ECM interactions regulate cadherin-dependent cell adhesion and are required for convergent extension in *Xenopus*, *Current Biology* 13:1182–1191 (2003).

WHAT IF? Suppose you wanted to determine if convergent extension can occur on a *preexisting* fibronectin matrix or if it requires a matrix formed *during* convergent extension. If you could make an artificial fibronectin matrix on glass cover slips, how would you design an experiment to ask this question?

---

ments to investigate this possibility. The results of their full study support a model in which fibronectin binding to its receptor provides a molecular signal to the cell that ultimately affects the function of cadherins. ECM molecules and cadherins thus appear to be linked in a single pathway driving convergent extension.

As you have seen, cell behavior and the molecular mechanisms underlying it are crucial to the morphogenesis of the embryo. In the next section, you'll learn that the same basic cellular and genetic processes ensure that the various types of cells end up in the right places in each embryo.

CONCEPT CHECK 47.2

1. During formation of the neural tube, cube-shaped cells change to wedge-shaped cells. Describe the roles of microtubules and microfilaments in this process.
2. In the frog embryo, convergent extension is thought to elongate the notochord along the anterior-posterior axis. Explain how the words *convergent* and *extension* apply to this process.
3. WHAT IF? Predict what would happen if, just before neural tube formation, you treated embryos with a drug that blocks the function of microfilaments.

For suggested answers, see Appendix A.

CONCEPT 47.3
The developmental fate of cells depends on their history and on inductive signals

Coupled with the morphogenetic changes that give an animal and its parts their characteristic shapes, development also requires the timely differentiation of many kinds of cells in specific locations. In Chapter 20, you learned about the principle of genomic equivalence: Virtually every cell in an organism has the same genome. However, different cell types make different sets of proteins because they end up expressing different sets of genes. Therefore, during differentiation, some mechanism must send cells down different pathways of gene expression. Two general principles integrate our current knowledge of the genetic and cellular mechanisms that underlie differentiation during embryonic development.

First, *during early cleavage divisions, embryonic cells must somehow become different from one another.* In many animal species, initial differences between cells result from the uneven distribution of cytoplasmic determinants in the unfertilized egg. By partitioning the heterogeneous cytoplasm of a polarized egg, cleavage parcels out different mRNAs, proteins, and other molecules to blastomeres in a type of asymmetrical cell division (see Figure 18.15a). These cytoplasmic determinants are in many cases transcription factors, DNA-binding proteins that activate one set of genes rather than another.

Thus, the resulting differences in the cells' cytoplasmic composition help specify the body axes and influence the expression of genes that affect the cells' developmental fate. In amniotes, local environmental differences play the principal role in establishing early differences between embryonic cells. For example, cells of the inner cell mass are located internally in the early human embryo, whereas trophoblast cells are located on the outside surface of the blastocyst. The different environments of these two groups of cells appear to determine their very different fates.

Second, *once initial cell asymmetries are set up, subsequent interactions among the embryonic cells influence their fate, usually by causing changes in gene expression.* This mechanism, called **induction**, eventually brings about the differentiation of the many specialized cell types making up an animal. Induction may be mediated by diffusible signaling molecules or, if the cells are in contact, by cell-surface interactions.

It will help to keep these two principles in mind as we delve into the molecular and cellular mechanisms of differentiation and morphogenesis during embryonic development of the species we're focusing on in this chapter. But to ask questions about *how* the fate of an early embryonic cell is determined, we need to know what that fate is. So let's first look at some historic experiments that provided early researchers with information about cell fates.

Fate Mapping

Biologists have studied the early development of many species, carefully scrutinizing each cell division, in an attempt to follow the fate and trace the ancestry of each embryonic cell. These labor-intensive studies have produced extremely useful territorial diagrams of embryonic development, called **fate maps**.

In classic studies performed in the 1920s, German embryologist Walther Vogt charted fate maps for the different regions of early amphibian embryos. Vogt's results were among the earliest indications that the lineages of cells making up the three germ layers created by gastrulation are traceable to cells in the blastula, before gastrulation has begun **(Figure 47.21a)**. Later researchers developed techniques that allowed them to mark an individual blastomere during cleavage and then follow the marker as it was distributed to all the mitotic descendants of that cell **(Figure 47.21b)**.

Perhaps the ultimate approach to fate mapping has been carried out on the soil-dwelling nematode *Caenorhabditis elegans*. This worm is easily raised in the laboratory in petri dishes. It is about 1 mm long, has a simple transparent body with only a few types of cells, and grows from zygote to mature adult in only 3½ days. Most individuals are hermaphrodites, producing both eggs and sperm, which has advantages for genetic studies.

The attributes of *C. elegans* allowed Sydney Brenner, Robert Horvitz, and Jonathan Sulston to determine the complete

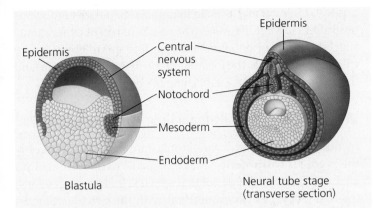

(a) Fate map of a frog embryo. The fates of groups of cells in a frog blastula (left) were determined in part by marking different regions of the blastula surface with nontoxic dyes of various colors. The embryos were sectioned at later stages of development, such as the neural tube stage shown on the right, and the locations of the dyed cells determined. The two embryonic stages shown here represent the result of numerous such experiments.

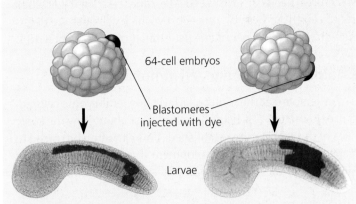

(b) Cell lineage analysis in a tunicate. In lineage analysis, an individual blastomere is injected with a dye during cleavage, as indicated in the drawings of 64-cell embryos of a tunicate, an invertebrate chordate (top). The dark regions in the light micrographs of larvae (bottom) correspond to the cells that developed from the two different blastomeres indicated in the drawings.

▲ **Figure 47.21 Fate mapping for two chordates.**

cell lineage of this organism, using a multi-pronged approach. Every adult hermaphrodite of the species has exactly 959 somatic cells, which arise from the zygote in virtually the same way for every individual. Careful microscopic observations during the entire period of development, coupled with experiments in which particular cells or groups of cells were destroyed by a laser beam or through mutations, resulted in the cell lineage diagram shown in **Figure 47.22**. In 2002, these researchers shared a Nobel Prize for their accomplishment, which led to *C. elegans* becoming the model organism of choice for many developmental biologists.

Developmental biologists have combined fate-mapping studies with experimental manipulation of parts of embryos to ascertain whether a cell's fate can be changed. Starting with the normal embryo's fate map, researchers can examine how the differentiation of cells is altered in experimental situations or in mutant embryos. Two important conclusions have emerged. First, in most animals, specific tissues of the older embryo are the products of certain early "founder cells" that contain unique factors as the result of asymmetrical cell divisions. Second, as development proceeds, a cell's *developmental potential*—the range of

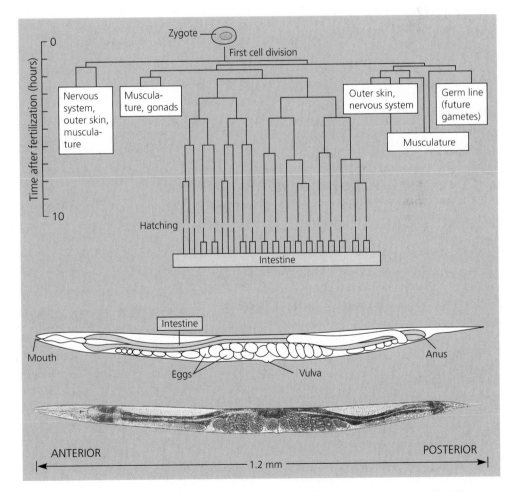

▲ **Figure 47.22 Cell lineage in *Caenorhabditis elegans*.** The *C. elegans* embryo is transparent, making it possible for researchers to trace the lineage of every cell, from the zygote to the adult worm (LM). The diagram shows a detailed lineage only for the intestine, which is derived exclusively from one of the first four cells formed from the zygote. The eggs will be fertilized internally and released through the vulva.

structures that it can give rise to—becomes restricted. Let's look more closely at these two aspects by which cell fates are determined. (For review of cell fate determination, see Chapter 18.)

Establishing Cellular Asymmetries

To understand at the molecular level how embryonic cells acquire their fates, it is helpful to think first about how the basic axes of the embryo are established. This can often be traced to a specific event in early development that sets up a particular cellular asymmetry, thus beginning to lay out the body plan.

The Axes of the Basic Body Plan

As you have learned, a bilaterally symmetrical animal has an anterior-posterior axis, a dorsal-ventral axis, and left and right sides (see Figure 47.7a). Establishing this basic body plan is the first step in morphogenesis and a prerequisite for the development of tissues and organs.

In nonamniote vertebrates, basic instructions for forming the body axes are established early, during oogenesis or fertilization. For example, in many frogs, including the species we've discussed, the locations of melanin and yolk in the unfertilized egg define the animal and vegetal hemispheres, respectively. The animal-vegetal axis indirectly determines the anterior-posterior body axis. Fertilization then triggers cortical rotation, which establishes the dorsal-ventral axis and at the same time leads to the appearance of the gray crescent, whose position marks the dorsal side (see Figure 47.7b). Once any two axes are established, the third (in this case, the left-right) axis is specified by default. (Of course, specific molecular mechanisms must then establish which side is left and which is right.)

In amniotes, the body axes are not fully established until later. In chicks, gravity is apparently involved in establishing the anterior-posterior axis as the egg travels down the hen's oviduct before being laid. Later, pH differences between the two sides of the blastoderm cells establish the dorsal-ventral axis. If the pH is artificially reversed above and below the blastoderm, the part facing the egg white will turn into the belly (ventral side) and the side facing the yolk will turn into the back (dorsal side), op-

posite to their normal fates. In mammals, no polarity is obvious until after cleavage. However, the results of recent experiments suggest that the orientation of the egg and sperm nuclei before they fuse influences the location of the first cleavage plane and thus may play a role in establishing the embryonic axes.

Restriction of the Developmental Potential of Cells

In many species that have cytoplasmic determinants, only the zygote is **totipotent**—that is, capable of developing into all the different cell types of that species. In these organisms, the first cleavage is asymmetrical, with the two blastomeres

▼ Figure 47.23 **Inquiry**

How does distribution of the gray crescent affect the developmental potential of the first two daughter cells?

EXPERIMENT Hans Spemann, at the University of Freiburg-im-Breisgau in Germany, carried out the following experiment in 1938 to test whether substances were located asymmetrically in the gray crescent.

Control egg (dorsal view)

Gray crescent

1a Control group: Fertilized salamander eggs were allowed to divide normally, resulting in the gray crescent being evenly divided between the two blastomeres.

1b Experimental group: Fertilized eggs were constricted by a thread, causing the first cleavage to occur at the thread. The thread was placed so that the gray crescent was on one side of the thread, and only one blastomere received the gray crescent.

Expermental egg (side view)

Gray crescent

Thread

2 In each group, the two blastomeres were then separated and allowed to develop.

RESULTS

Normal

Belly piece   Normal

Blastomeres that received half or all of the material in the gray crescent developed into normal embryos, but a blastomere that received none of the gray crescent gave rise to an abnormal embryo without dorsal structures. Spemann called it a "belly piece."

CONCLUSION The developmental potential of the two blastomeres normally formed during the first cleavage division depends on their acquisition of cytoplasmic determinants localized in the gray crescent.

SOURCE H. Spemann, *Embryonic Development and Induction*, Yale University Press, New Haven (1938).

WHAT IF? In a similar experiment 40 years earlier, embryologist Hans Roux allowed the first cleavage to occur and then used a needle to kill just one blastomere. The embryo that developed from the remaining blastomere (plus remnants of the dead cell) was abnormal, resembling a half-embryo. Propose a hypothesis to explain why Roux's result differed from the control result in Spemann's experiment.

receiving different cytoplasmic determinants. However, even in species that have cytoplasmic determinants, the first cleavage may occur along an axis that produces two identical blastomeres, which then have equal developmental potential. This occurs in amphibians, for instance, as demonstrated in 1938 in an experiment by German zoologist Hans Spemann (Figure 47.23). Thus, the fates of embryonic cells can be affected not only by the distribution of cytoplasmic determinants but also by how this distribution relates to the zygote's characteristic pattern of cleavage.

In contrast with the embryonic cells of many other animals, the cells of mammalian embryos remain totipotent until the 16-cell stage, when their location determines whether they will give rise to cells of the trophoblast or of the inner cell mass of the blastocyst, thus establishing their ultimate fates. Through the 8-cell stage, the blastomeres of a mammalian embryo all look alike, and each can form a complete embryo if isolated. Researchers have taken this as evidence that the early blastomeres of mammals probably receive equivalent amounts of cytoplasmic components from the egg. Recent work, however, suggests that the very early cells (even the first two) are not actually equivalent in a normal embryo, and their ability to form a complete embryo if isolated shows that they may be able to regulate their fate, depending on their environment. The jury is still out on this matter, which is an area of great interest to researchers.

Regardless of how similar or different early embryonic cells are in a particular species, the progressive restriction of developmental potential is a general feature of development in all animals. In some species, the cells of the early gastrula retain the capacity to give rise to more than one kind of cell, though they have lost their totipotency. If left alone, the dorsal ectoderm of an early amphibian gastrula will develop into a neural plate above the notochord. And if the dorsal ectoderm is experimentally replaced with ectoderm from some other location in the same gastrula, the transplanted tissue will form a neural plate. But if the same experiment is performed on a late-stage gastrula, the transplanted ectoderm will not respond to its new environment and will not form a neural plate. In general, the tissue-specific fates of cells in a late gastrula are fixed. Even when they are manipulated experimentally, these cells usually give rise to the same types of cells as in the normal embryo, indicating that their fate is already determined.

Cell Fate Determination and Pattern Formation by Inductive Signals

Once embryonic cell division creates cells that differ from each other, the cells begin to influence each other's fates by induction. At the molecular level, the response to an inductive signal is usually to switch on a set of genes that make the receiving cells differentiate into a specific tissue. Here we examine two examples of induction, an essential process in the development of many tissues in most animals.

The "Organizer" of Spemann and Mangold

The importance of induction during development of amphibians was dramatically demonstrated in transplantation experiments performed by Hans Spemann and his student Hilde Mangold in the 1920s. Based on the results of their most famous experiment, summarized in **Figure 47.24**, they concluded that

▼ **Figure 47.24** **Inquiry**

Can the dorsal lip of the blastopore induce cells in another part of the amphibian embryo to change their developmental fate?

EXPERIMENT In 1924, Hans Spemann and Hilde Mangold, at the University of Freiburg-im-Breisgau in Germany, transplanted a piece of the dorsal lip from a pigmented newt gastrula to the ventral side of a nonpigmented newt gastrula to investigate the inductive ability of the dorsal lip. Cross sections of the gastrulae are shown here.

Dorsal lip of blastopore

Pigmented gastrula (donor embryo)

Nonpigmented gastrula (recipient embryo)

RESULTS The recipient embryo formed a second notochord and neural tube in the region of the transplant, and eventually most of a second embryo developed. Examination of the interior of the double embryo revealed that the secondary structures were formed partly, but not wholly, from recipient tissue.

Primary embryo

Secondary (induced) embryo

Primary structures:
Neural tube
Notochord

Secondary structures:
Notochord (pigmented cells)
Neural tube (mostly nonpigmented cells)

CONCLUSION The transplanted dorsal lip was able to induce cells in a different region of the recipient to form structures different from their normal fate. In effect, the transplanted dorsal lip "organized" the later development of an entire extra embryo.

SOURCE H. Spemann and H. Mangold, Induction of embryonic primordia by implantation of organizers from a different species, Trans. V. Hamburger (1924). Reprinted in *International Journal of Developmental Biology* 45:13–38 (2001).

WHAT IF? Because the transplanted dorsal lip caused the recipient tissue to become something it would not otherwise have become, a signal of some sort must have passed from the dorsal lip. If you identified a protein candidate for the signaling molecule, how could you test whether it actually functions in signaling?

the dorsal lip of the blastopore in the early gastrula functions as an "organizer" of the embryo's body plan by initiating a chain of inductions that results in the formation of the notochord, the neural tube, and other organs.

Developmental biologists are still working intensively to identify the molecular basis of induction by *Spemann's organizer* (also called the *gastrula organizer* or simply the *organizer*). An important clue has come from studies of a growth factor called bone morphogenetic protein 4 (BMP-4). (Bone morphogenetic proteins, a family of related proteins with a variety of developmental roles, derive their name from members of the family that are important in bone formation.) In amphibians, a high concentration of BMP-4 signals cells on the ventral side of the gastrula to travel down the pathway toward formation of ventral structures. One major function of the cells of the organizer seems to be to *inactivate* BMP-4 on the dorsal side of the embryo by producing proteins that bind to BMP-4, rendering it unable to signal. This inactivation, along with signaling by other molecules not yet identified, promotes formation of dorsal structures such as the notochord and neural tube. In tissues between the dorsal and ventral sides, a lower concentration of BMP-4 results in lateral structures appropriate for the specific location along the dorsal-ventral axis. The varying concentration of BMP-4 along this axis is an example of a morphogen gradient (see Chapter 18). Proteins related to BMP-4 and its inhibitors are also found in other animals, including invertebrates such as the fruit fly, where they also regulate the dorsal-ventral axis. The ubiquity of these molecules suggests that they evolved long ago and may participate in the development of many different organisms.

The induction by BMP-4 of ventral and lateral structures is only one example of many cell-cell interactions that transform the three germ layers into organ systems. Many inductions seem to involve a sequence of inductive steps from different surrounding tissues that progressively determine the fate of cells. In the eye, for example, lens formation by ectodermal cells involves precisely timed inductive signals from ectodermal, mesodermal, and endodermal cells.

Formation of the Vertebrate Limb

The action of the gastrula organizer is a classic example of induction, and we can see that the organizer induces cells to take on their fates in appropriate locations relative to each other. Thus, inductive signals play a major role in **pattern formation**—the development of an animal's spatial organization, the arrangement of organs and tissues in their characteristic places in three-dimensional space. The molecular cues that control pattern formation, called **positional information**, tell a cell where it is with respect to the animal's body axes and help to determine how the cell and its descendants will respond to molecular signaling.

(a) Organizer regions. Vertebrate limbs develop from protrusions called limb buds, each consisting of mesoderm cells covered by a layer of ectoderm. Two regions in each limb bud, the apical ectodermal ridge (AER, shown in this SEM) and the zone of polarizing activity (ZPA), play key roles as organizers in limb pattern formation.

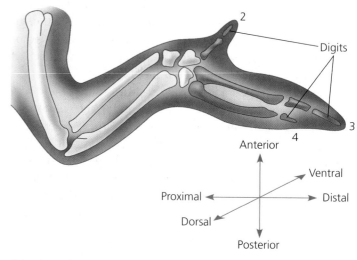

(b) Wing of chick embryo. As the bud develops into a limb, a specific pattern of tissues emerges. In the chick wing, for example, the digits are always present in the arrangement shown here. Pattern formation requires each embryonic cell to receive some kind of positional information indicating location along the three axes of the limb. The AER and ZPA secrete molecules that help provide this information. (Numbers are assigned to the digits based on a convention established for vertebrate limbs. The chicken wing has only four digits; the first digit points backward and is not shown in the diagram.)

▲ **Figure 47.25 Vertebrate limb development.**

In Chapter 18, we discussed pattern formation in the development of *Drosophila*. For the study of pattern formation in vertebrates, a classic model system has been limb development in the chick. The wings and legs of chicks, like all vertebrate limbs, begin as limb buds, bumps of mesodermal tissue covered by a layer of ectoderm (**Figure 47.25a**). Each component of a chick limb, such as a specific bone or muscle, develops with a precise location and orientation relative to three axes: the proximal-distal axis (the "shoulder-to-fingertip" axis), the anterior-posterior axis (the "thumb-to-little finger" axis), and the dorsal-ventral axis (the "knuckle-to-palm" axis). The embryonic cells within a limb bud respond to positional information indicating location along these three axes (**Figure 47.25b**).

Two critical organizer regions in a limb bud have profound effects on the limb's development. These regions are present in all vertebrate limb buds, including those that will develop into forelimbs (such as wings or arms) and those destined to become hind limbs. The cells of these regions secrete proteins that provide key positional information to the other cells of the bud.

One limb-bud organizer region is the **apical ectodermal ridge (AER)**, a thickened area of ectoderm at the tip of the bud (see Figure 47.25a). Removing the AER blocks outgrowth of the limb along the proximal-distal axis. The cells of the AER secrete several protein signals in the fibroblast growth factor (FGF) family that promote limb-bud outgrowth. If the AER is surgically removed and beads soaked with FGF are put in its place, a nearly normal limb will develop. In 2006, researchers identified an FGF-secreting AER that appears to be responsible for building a shark's unpaired (median) fins. This finding suggests that the AER may have predated the appearance of paired limbs in the vertebrate lineage, giving the AER a longer evolutionary history than previously thought.

The second major limb-bud organizer region is the **zone of polarizing activity (ZPA)**, a block of mesodermal tissue located underneath the ectoderm where the posterior side of the bud is attached to the body (see Figure 47.25a). The ZPA is necessary for proper pattern formation along the anterior-posterior axis of the limb. Cells nearest the ZPA give rise to the posterior structures, such as the most posterior of the chick's three digits (positioned like our little finger); cells farthest from the ZPA form anterior structures, including the most anterior digit (like our thumb).

The tissue transplantation experiment outlined in **Figure 47.26** supports the hypothesis that the ZPA produces an inductive signal that conveys positional information indicating "posterior." Indeed, researchers have discovered that the cells of the ZPA secrete an important protein growth factor called Sonic hedgehog.* These cells set up a gradient of Sonic hedgehog and other growth factors that Sonic hedgehog causes to be expressed. If cells genetically engineered to produce large amounts of Sonic hedgehog are implanted in the anterior region of a normal limb bud, a mirror-image limb results—just as if a

---

ZPA had been grafted there. Studies of the mouse version of Sonic hedgehog suggest that extra toes in mice—and perhaps also in humans—can result when the wrong amounts of this protein are produced in part of the limb bud.

---

* Sonic hedgehog gets its name from two sources: its similarity to a *Drosophila* protein called Hedgehog, which is involved in segmentation of the fly embryo, and a video game character.

The *Hox* genes that you learned about in Chapter 21 also seem to play various roles at several distinct points during limb pattern formation. The importance of these genes in humans is illustrated by a condition called polysyndactyly ("many digits joined together"), which is caused by a specific mutation in a *Hox* gene named *HoxD13* (**Figure 47.27**).

Such observations, along with experiments like those previously described, support the notion that pattern formation requires cells to receive and interpret environmental cues that vary from one location to another. These cues, acting together along three axes, often in gradients, tell cells where they are in the three-dimensional realm of a developing organ. For instance, we now know that in vertebrate limb development, specific proteins serve as some of these cues and that organizer regions such as the AER and the ZPA function as signaling centers. Researchers have recently established that these two regions also interact with each other by way of signaling molecules and signaling pathways that influence each other's developmental fates. Such mutual signaling interactions between mesoderm and ectoderm also occur during formation of the neural tube and many other tissues and organs.

What determines whether a limb bud develops into a forelimb or a hind limb? The cells receiving the signals from the AER and ZPA respond according to their developmental histories. Before the AER or ZPA issues its signals, earlier developmental signaling has set up patterns of *Hox* gene expression that distinguish the future forelimbs from the future hind limbs and the different regions within a limb from each other. These differences cause cells of the forelimb and hind limb buds—and cells in different parts of each limb bud—to react differently to the same positional cues.

Thus, constructing the fully formed animal involves a sequence of events that include many steps of signaling and differentiation. Initial cell asymmetries allow different types of cells to influence each other, resulting in the expression of specific sets of genes. The products of these genes then direct cells to differentiate into specific types. Coordinated with morphogenesis, various pathways of pattern formation occur in all the different parts of the developing embryo. These processes ultimately produce a complex arrangement of multiple tissues and organs, each functioning in its appropriate location and each coordinated with the other tissues and organs of the whole organism.

▲ **Figure 47.27 Human polysyndactyly in a baby's foot due to a homozygous mutation in a *Hox* gene.**

CONCEPT CHECK 47.3

1. Although there are three body axes, only two must be determined during development. Why?
2. **WHAT IF?** If the ventral cells of an early frog gastrula are experimentally induced to express large amounts of a protein that inhibits BMP-4, could a second embryo develop? Explain.
3. **WHAT IF?** If you removed the ZPA from a limb bud and then placed a bead soaked in Sonic hedgehog in the middle of the limb bud, what would be the most likely result?

For suggested answers, see Appendix A.

Chapter 47 Review

SUMMARY OF KEY CONCEPTS

CONCEPT 47.1

After fertilization, embryonic development proceeds through cleavage, gastrulation, and organogenesis (pp. 1022–1035)

▶ **Fertilization** Fertilization brings together the nuclei of sperm and egg, forming a diploid zygote, and activates the egg, initiating embryonic development. The acrosomal reaction, which is triggered when the sperm meets the egg,

releases hydrolytic enzymes that digest material surrounding the egg. Gamete contact and/or fusion depolarizes the egg cell membrane and sets up a fast block to polyspermy in many animals. Sperm-egg fusion also initiates the cortical reaction:

Sperm-egg fusion and depolarization of egg membrane (fast block to polyspermy)

Cortical granule release (cortical reaction)

Formation of fertilization envelope (slow block to polyspermy)

In mammalian fertilization, the cortical reaction modifies the zona pellucida as a slow block to polyspermy.

▶ **Cleavage** Fertilization is followed by cleavage, a period of rapid cell division without growth, which results in the production of a large number of cells called blastomeres. Cleavage planes usually follow a specific pattern relative to the animal and vegetal poles of the zygote. In many species, cleavage creates a multicellular ball called the blastula, which contains a fluid-filled cavity, the blastocoel.

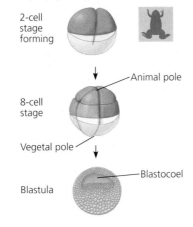

Holoblastic cleavage (division of the entire egg) occurs in species whose eggs have little or moderate amounts of yolk (as in sea urchins, frogs, and mammals). Meroblastic cleavage (incomplete division of the egg) occurs in species with yolk-rich eggs (as in birds and other reptiles).

▶ **Gastrulation** Gastrulation transforms the blastula into a gastrula, which has a primitive digestive cavity (the archenteron) and three embryonic germ layers: the ectoderm (blue), mesoderm (red), and endoderm (yellow).

▶ **Organogenesis** The organs of the animal body develop from specific portions of the three embryonic germ layers. Early events in organogenesis in vertebrates include formation of the notochord by condensation of dorsal mesoderm, formation of the coelom from splitting of lateral mesoderm, and development of the neural tube from infolding of the ectodermal neural plate:

▶ **Developmental Adaptations of Amniotes** The embryos of birds, other reptiles, and mammals develop within a fluid-filled sac that is contained within a shell or the uterus. In these organisms, the three germ layers give rise not only to embryonic tissue but also to the four extraembryonic membranes: the amnion, chorion, yolk sac, and allantois.

▶ **Mammalian Development** The eggs of marsupial and eutherian mammals are small and store few nutrients. They exhibit holoblastic cleavage and show no obvious polarity. Gastrulation and organogenesis, however, resemble the processes in birds and other reptiles. After fertilization and early cleavage in the oviduct, the blastocyst implants in the uterus. The trophoblast initiates formation of the fetal portion of the placenta, and the embryo proper develops from a single layer of cells, the epiblast, within the blastocyst. Extraembryonic membranes homologous to those of birds and other reptiles function in intrauterine development.

▶ **MEDIA**

Activity Sea Urchin Development
Investigation What Determines Cell Differentiation in the Sea Urchin?
Activity Frog Development

CONCEPT 47.2

Morphogenesis in animals involves specific changes in cell shape, position, and adhesion (pp. 1035–1038)

▶ **The Cytoskeleton, Cell Motility, and Convergent Extension** Cytoskeletal rearrangements are responsible for changes in both the shape and position of cells. Both kinds of changes are involved in tissue invaginations, as occurs in gastrulation, for example. In convergent extension, cell movements cause a sheet of cells to become narrower and longer.

▶ **Role of Cell Adhesion Molecules and the Extracellular Matrix** Cell adhesion molecules such as cadherins help hold cells together in tissues. Fibers of the extracellular matrix provide anchorage for cells and also help guide migrating cells toward their destinations. Fibronectin and other glycoproteins located on cell surfaces are important for cell migration and appear to affect cadherin function.

CONCEPT 47.3

The developmental fate of cells depends on their history and on inductive signals (pp. 1038–1044)

▶ **Fate Mapping** Experimentally derived fate maps of embryos have shown that specific regions of the zygote or blastula develop into specific parts of older embryos. The complete cell lineage has been worked out for *C. elegans*.

▶ **Establishing Cellular Asymmetries** In nonamniotes, unevenly distributed cytoplasmic determinants in the egg are important in establishing the body axes and in setting up differences between the blastomeres resulting from cleavage of the zygote. Cells that receive different cytoplasmic determinants undergo different fates. In amniotes, local environmental differences play the major role in establishing initial differences between cells and later the body axes. As embryonic development proceeds, the developmental potential of cells becomes progressively more limited in all species.

▶ **Cell Fate Determination and Pattern Formation by Inductive Signals** Cells in a developing embryo receive and respond to positional information that varies with location. This information is often in the form of signaling molecules secreted by cells in special "organizer" regions of the embryo, such as the dorsal lip of the blastopore in the amphibian gastrula and the AER and ZPA of the vertebrate limb bud. The signaling molecules influence gene expression in the cells that receive them, leading to differentiation and the development of particular structures.

SELF-QUIZ

1. The cortical reaction of sea urchin eggs functions directly in
   a. the formation of a fertilization envelope.
   b. the production of a fast block to polyspermy.
   c. the release of hydrolytic enzymes from the sperm.
   d. the generation of an electrical impulse by the egg.
   e. the fusion of egg and sperm nuclei.

2. Which of the following is common to the development of both birds and mammals?
   a. holoblastic cleavage   d. yolk plug
   b. epiblast and hypoblast   e. gray crescent
   c. trophoblast

3. The archenteron develops into
   a. the mesoderm.   d. the placenta.
   b. the blastocoel.   e. the lumen of the digestive tract.
   c. the endoderm.

4. In a frog embryo, the blastocoel is
   a. completely obliterated by yolk.
   b. lined with endoderm during gastrulation.
   c. located in the animal hemisphere.
   d. the cavity that becomes the coelom.
   e. the cavity that later forms the archenteron.

5. What structural adaptation in chickens allows them to lay their eggs in arid environments, rather than in water?
   a. extraembryonic membranes
   b. yolk
   c. cleavage
   d. gastrulation
   e. development of the brain from ectoderm

6. In an amphibian embryo, a group of cells called neural crest cells
   a. rolls up and forms the neural tube.
   b. develops into the main sections of the brain.
   c. produces cells that migrate to form teeth, skull bones, and other structures in the embryo.
   d. has been shown by experiments to be the organizer region of the developing embryo.
   e. induces the formation of the notochord.

7. In the early development of an amphibian embryo, Spemann's "organizer" is located in the
   a. neural tube.
   b. notochord.
   c. archenteron roof.
   d. dorsal ectoderm.
   e. dorsal lip of the blastopore.

8. **DRAW IT** Fill in the blanks in the figure below, and draw arrows showing the movement of ectoderm, mesoderm, and endoderm.

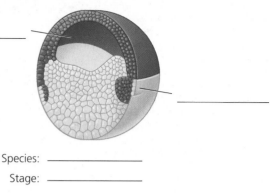

Species: _____

Stage: _____

For Self-Quiz answers, see Appendix A.

MEDIA Visit the Study Area at **www.masteringbio.com** for a Practice Test.

EVOLUTION CONNECTION

9. Evolution in insects and vertebrates has involved the repeated duplication of body segments, followed by fusion of some segments and specialization of their structure and function. What parts of vertebrate anatomy reflect the vertebrate segmentation pattern?

SCIENTIFIC INQUIRY

10. The "snout" of a frog tadpole bears a sucker. A salamander tadpole has a mustache-shaped structure called a balancer in the same area. Suppose that you perform an experiment in which you transplant ectoderm from the side of a young salamander embryo to the snout of a frog embryo. The tadpole that develops has a balancer. When you transplant ectoderm from the side of a slightly older salamander embryo to the snout of a frog embryo, the frog tadpole ends up with a patch of salamander skin on its snout. Suggest a hypothesis to explain these results in terms of developmental mechanisms. How might you test your hypothesis?

SCIENCE, TECHNOLOGY, AND SOCIETY

11. Many scientists think that fetal tissue transplants offer great potential for treating Parkinson's disease, epilepsy, diabetes, Alzheimer's disease, and spinal cord injuries. Why might tissues from a fetus be particularly useful for replacing diseased or damaged cells in patients with such conditions? Some people would allow only tissues from miscarriages to be used in fetal transplant research. However, most researchers prefer to use tissues from surgically aborted fetuses. Why? Explain your position on this controversial issue.

EVOLUTION CONNECTION

9. We often explain our behavior in terms of subjective feelings, motives, or reasons, but evolutionary explanations are based on reproductive fitness. What is the relationship between the two kinds of explanation? For instance, is a human explanation for behavior, such as "falling in love," incompatible with an evolutionary explanation? Does falling in love become more meaningful or less meaningful (or neither) if it has an evolutionary basis?

SCIENTIFIC INQUIRY

10. Scientists studying scrub jays found that "helpers" often assist mated pairs of birds in raising their young. The helpers lack territories and mates of their own. Instead, they help the territory owner gather food for their offspring. Propose a hypothesis to explain what advantage there might be for the helpers to engage in this behavior instead of seeking their own territories and mates. How would you test your hypothesis? If it is correct, what results would you expect your tests to yield?

Biological Inquiry: A Workbook of Investigative Cases Explore the behavior of a large gull population in a marina, and human attempts to control the population, in the case "Back to the Bay."

SCIENCE, TECHNOLOGY, AND SOCIETY

11. Researchers are very interested in studying identical twins separated at birth and raised apart. So far, the data suggest that such twins are much more alike than researchers predicted; they frequently have similar personalities, mannerisms, habits, and interests. What general question do you think researchers hope to answer by studying such twins? Why do identical twins make good subjects for this research? What are the potential pitfalls of this research? What abuses might occur if the studies are not evaluated critically and if the results are carelessly cited to support a social agenda?

UNIT 8

Ecology

AN INTERVIEW WITH
Diana H. Wall

As a past president of the Ecological Society of America and the American Institute of Biological Sciences, and in many other national and international roles, Diana Wall has made major contributions to science and the public interest. She has also distinguished herself as a researcher on carbon cycling and other ecosystem processes, focusing on the tiny roundworms called nematodes. Dr. Wall has B.A. and Ph.D. degrees from the University of Kentucky. She was a professor at the University of California, Riverside before coming to Colorado State University, where she is a professor of biology and senior research scientist at the Natural Resource Ecology Laboratory. She does much of her fieldwork in Antarctica.

How did you get started in ecology?
In graduate school, where I studied plant pathology, I focused on the interactions between two species of nematodes and the plant roots they parasitize. Later, as a post-doc at UC Riverside, I participated in the International Biological Program (IBP). My job was to go to deserts in the western U.S. and try to find out how soil nematodes contributed to the energy balance in those ecosystems.

What was the International Biological Program?
The IBP was the first truly global research project in ecology. The overall goal was to understand Earth's productivity by taking comparable measurements across different ecosystems. (Productivity is the amount of new material—biomass—that's produced in an ecosystem.) Grassland researchers from all around the world were measuring the same things, desert researchers were measuring the same things, and so forth, enabling us to combine all the data and make global comparisons. It was a jump for me from studying the interactions between two species to be asking how such interactions fit into the global scheme of things.

Why are nematodes of interest to ecologists?
Although many people know nematodes as harmful parasites of animals or plants, most nematodes are good guys, especially the free-living ones in soil. As part of my work in the desert, I got interested in free-living soil nematodes, which feed on fungi or bacteria, or sometimes on smaller animals. The "good" nematodes accelerate the turnover of organic matter by feeding on soil microbes and then releasing compounds of carbon and nitrogen to the soil. Experiments have shown that soils without nematodes have slower rates of decomposition.

Nematodes are everywhere: in soils, in streams, in ocean sediments, and in many animals and plants. It's been estimated that four out of five animals on Earth are nematodes! The geographic distribution of different species of nematodes is something we're studying. We're doing a global-scale "latitudinal gradient" experiment, where we take soil samples at different latitudes—for example, from Sweden to South Africa. We're going into places that are hotspots of biodiversity above ground—and "coldspots" as well—and looking at what's below ground. We're classifying the nematodes to see how many species there are in the soil and how species distribution differs with latitude.

What impact have modern molecular methods had on this kind of study?
They've been great for research on the diversity of all kinds of microscopic organisms. We can now go beyond asking general questions about what such organisms do in the soil and ask exactly what they are. With soil invertebrates such as nematodes and mites, it can be very difficult to tell species apart morphologically. Now we can look at DNA sequences and say, whoa, this one is really different from that one, or, hey, this one is endemic to Antarctica but it's got a really close relative hanging out in Argentina.

Why is soil biodiversity important?
From a practical perspective, soil biodiversity—the number and abundance of different species living in soils—is probably critically important for soil fertility, and soil fertility is crucial for

feeding and clothing the world's people. There's still much to be learned about the role of soil biodiversity in soil fertility. Simply how soils differ over the range from a forest to a desert is still a big question. Based on climate, geologic history, and biology, there are about 13,000 kinds of soil (called "series") in the United States alone. Each is a distinct habitat where microscopic soil creatures have evolved, and so not every species is widespread. Where the species are different, can you scale up from a difference between two farms, say, or between a farm and a nearby forest, and generalize about the connections between soil biodiversity and soil fertility? How do species that are just about everywhere contribute to soil fertility? Those questions are wide open for more research.

Another important question is whether there's a correlation between biodiversity above ground and below ground. Can we predict that an area of great biodiversity above ground will have a great diversity of mites, nematodes, and so forth below ground? And will their functions in the ecosystem be predictable, too? Because I don't want to go around digging up all the soils in the world! Once we understand something about that issue, we can start to think about the relationship between diversity and soil fertility. My big push now is to persuade people that you can't think of soil biodiversity as being unrelated to what's above ground. We used to think of the ocean as a dark garbage can, and we still tend to think of the soil that way. But we found out there are a lot of organisms in the ocean that carry out processes that benefit us, even if we don't have names for all of them. I think the same is true for soils.

How did you begin doing research in Antarctica? And what do you study there?
After the IBP, I continued working in hot deserts. They're a simpler system than a forest, for example, and therefore are more suitable for working out the factors that determine different food webs in the soil. To tease out the contribution of organisms other than plants, we would compare areas with and without plants. But that's hard to do, because plant roots seem to go

everywhere, even in the desert. I wanted to find an even simpler system, with fewer variables—soils where there are no plant roots. I wrote to a colleague who was in Antarctica, and he sent me some soil for analysis. It certainly didn't have plant roots, and it did have nematodes.

But when I searched the scientific literature, I read that the soils of the Antarctic Dry Valleys, where my sample had come from, were sterile, with no organisms at all, not even prokaryotes! Only in melt streams had some life been found. Researchers had looked for bacteria in the soil, but only by trying to culture them, and nothing had shown up. This was before molecular methods had been developed for identifying microorganisms from DNA alone.

We went down to Antarctica for the first time in 1989. Only 2% of Antarctica is actually soil; the rest is rock and ice. And the Dry Valleys area has no visible vegetation; when you fly in, it looks like Mars. We had enough financial support for only one field season—so only two months to find out what lived in the soil there. We adapted our hot-desert methods for this cold desert, which has precipitation the equivalent of less than 3 cm of rain per year. And as we'd hoped, we soon saw that there was an abundance of life in the soil, as much as in the Chihuahuan Desert in New Mexico. We could not believe that other people had missed it.

Our method was simple: We would take a handful of soil, about 100 g, stir it up with a sugar solution, and centrifuge it. The nematodes float in the solution, and the rock particles sink. After rinsing off the nematodes, we count them and determine their species. It was amazing to me to see these animals, knowing that they spend nine months of the year in a hard, frozen, and dark environment. It turned out that they live in water films around soil pores, and use survival mechanisms similar to those of hot-desert nematodes. When they receive certain environmental cues, such as dryness, they shrink their long bodies and curl up in a spiral, losing 99% of their water. When they're that small, they can disperse in wind. So this is a mechanism for spreading, as well as for surviving in a particular location.

These nematodes participate in very, very simple food chains, with only one to three tiers. For example, we have one chain with only two species of nematode: The one at the bottom eats bacteria, and the one above it may eat the bacteria-eater. It's remarkably simple compared with what is found in the soils up here.

In the last two years, we've been looking more closely at the different habitats. We've found that one species is almost everywhere in the valleys, *Scottnema lindsayae*; it's really tough, our "Rambo." But if there's too much salt in the soil or too much water, it's not present. We now have a model enabling us to predict where this species will be found around the valleys. In Antarctica, unlike elsewhere, I can look at individual nematode species and see that they have different niches; there's little overlap.

How is climate change affecting Antarctica?
Antarctica is the only continent that hasn't *on average* shown warming yet. The Antarctic Peninsula is warming rapidly, but the Dry Valleys are cooling, at least partly an indirect effect of ocean currents. Some people have made a big fuss about this cooling in attempts to disprove global warming. What we emphasize is that, while the continent as a whole is not warming, various regions are undergoing major changes, and there is warming and cooling occurring in different regions. In the Dry Valleys, we're seeing changes in every component of the ecosystem. For instance, we're seeing a decline in the abundance of the widespread *S. lindsayae*.

To look at this decline over a period of time, we've set up experiments in each valley basin.

We've made the soil wetter in places—because if an unusual amount of melting occurs when climate warms in this region, that's going to be the biggest driver of change. We want to see what that does to the *S. lindsayae* population and to the turnover of carbon in the soil. Because it's the only nematode species in many Dry Valley areas, we can easily use a carbon-isotope tracer to see how much carbon that one species is assimilating. The nematode population has very low biomass compared to what you see in the grassland here in Colorado, but it assimilates a greater percentage of organic carbon from the soil than do all the species here together. So it's a very important player in the ecosystem.

In places where we've manipulated the environment in the past, we're looking at how long it takes the soils to return to their original states. We're also looking at the effects of human trampling because the numbers of scientists and tourists are increasing tremendously. What we see is that human movement along a path disturbs the soil enough to cause a significant decline in nematodes. Furthermore, new, potentially invasive organisms are coming in on people's shoes and and clothing.

Antarctica is not isolated from the rest of the planet. The continents are all connected by ocean and atmosphere, and there is much more movement than we once thought. So future changes are something to worry about.

What is it like doing ecological research?
It's fun. You have an idea, you come up with a hypothesis, and then you get to test it in the lab or field. But as you test the hypothesis, you learn new things, and there are unexpected challenges. You have to try to fit everything you learn into a bigger picture. The process is like gathering all the blocks in a playpen and building a structure—without having the whole thing fall over.

Fieldwork has other kinds of pleasures. When you're in the field, you get to focus on one question that really interests you—during the Antarctic summer, there's a temptation to work 24 hours a day! At the same time, you usually have colleagues with different specialties there, and it's a great opportunity for freewheeling discussion and new insights. There's a great feeling of camaraderie.

Of course, there are frustrations, too. Collecting your data may be uncomfortable or boring. And you can spend a lot of time in the field that's not very productive or even a total failure. But the result of analyzing the data from a successful field trip can be a satisfying contribution to what we know about the world.

. . . the Dry Valleys area has no visible vegetation; when you fly in, it looks like Mars.

Inquiry in Action
Learn about an experiment by Diana Wall and a colleague in Inquiry Figure 54.19 on page 1210.

Left to right: Diana Wall, Jane Reece, Rob Jackson

An Introduction to Ecology and the Biosphere

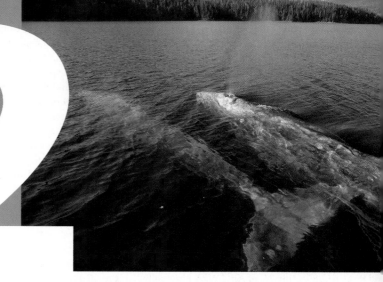

52

KEY CONCEPTS

52.1 Ecology integrates all areas of biological research and informs environmental decision making

52.2 Interactions between organisms and the environment limit the distribution of species

52.3 Aquatic biomes are diverse and dynamic systems that cover most of Earth

52.4 The structure and distribution of terrestrial biomes are controlled by climate and disturbance

OVERVIEW

The Scope of Ecology

High in the sky, a series of satellites circle Earth. These satellites aren't relaying the chatter of cell phones. Instead, they are transmitting data on the annual migration of gray whales **(Figure 52.1)**. Leaving their calving grounds near Baja California, adult and newborn gray whales (*Eschrichtius robustus*) swim side by side on a remarkable 8,000-km journey. They are headed to the Arctic Ocean to feed on the crustaceans, tube worms, and other creatures that thrive there in summer. The satellites also help biologists track a second journey, the recovery of the gray whales from the brink of extinction. A century ago, whaling had reduced the population to only a few hundred individuals. Today, after 70 years of protection from whaling, more than 20,000 travel to the Arctic each year.

What environmental factors determine the geographic distribution of gray whales? How do variations in their food supply affect the size of the gray whale population? Questions such as these are the subject of **ecology** (from the Greek *oikos*, home, and *logos*, to study), the scientific study of the interactions between organisms and the en-

▲ **Figure 52.1 Why do gray whales migrate?**

vironment. These interactions occur at a hierarchy of scales that ecologists study, from organismal to global **(Figure 52.2)**.

In addition to providing a conceptual framework for understanding the field of ecology, Figure 52.2 provides the organizational framework for our final unit. This chapter begins the unit by describing the breadth of ecology and some of the factors, both living and nonliving, that influence the distribution and abundance of organisms. The next three chapters examine population, community, and ecosystem ecology in detail. In the final chapter, we'll explore both landscape ecology and global ecology as we consider how ecologists apply biological knowledge to predict the global consequences of human activities, to conserve Earth's biodiversity, and to restore our planet's ecosystems.

CONCEPT 52.1

Ecology integrates all areas of biological research and informs environmental decision making

Ecology's roots are in discovery science (see Chapter 1). Naturalists, including Aristotle and Darwin, have long observed organisms in nature and systematically recorded their observations. Because extraordinary insight can be gained through this descriptive approach, called *natural history*, it remains a fundamental part of the science of ecology. Present-day ecologists still observe the natural world, albeit with genes-to-globe tools that would astound Aristotle and Darwin.

Modern ecology has become a rigorous experimental science as well. Ecologists generate hypotheses, manipulate the environment, and observe the outcome. Scientists interested in the effects of climate change on tree survival, for instance, might create drought and wet conditions in experimental plots instead

Exploring The Scope of Ecological Research

Ecologists work at different levels of the biological hierarchy, from individual organisms to the planet. Here we present a sample research question for each level in the biological hierarchy.

1 Organismal Ecology

Organismal ecology, which includes the subdisciplines of physiological, evolutionary, and behavioral ecology, is concerned with how an organism's structure, physiology, and (for animals) behavior meet the challenges posed by its environment.

◄ *How do hammerhead sharks select a mate?*

2 Population Ecology

A **population** is a group of individuals of the same species living in an area. **Population ecology** analyzes factors that affect population size and how and why it changes through time.

◄ *What environmental factors affect the reproductive rate of deer mice?*

3 Community Ecology

A **community** is a group of populations of different species in an area. **Community ecology** examines how interactions between species, such as predation and competition, affect community structure and organization.

◄ *What factors influence the diversity of species that make up a forest?*

4 Ecosystem Ecology

An **ecosystem** is the community of organisms in an area and the physical factors with which those organisms interact. **Ecosystem ecology** emphasizes energy flow and chemical cycling between organisms and the environment.

◄ *What factors control photosynthetic productivity in a temperate grassland ecosystem?*

5 Landscape Ecology

A **landscape** (or seascape) is a mosaic of connected ecosystems. Research in **landscape ecology** focuses on the factors controlling exchanges of energy, materials, and organisms across multiple ecosystems.

◄ *To what extent do the trees lining a river serve as corridors of dispersal for animals?*

6 Global Ecology

The **biosphere** is the global ecosystem—the sum of all the planet's ecosystems and landscapes. **Global ecology** examines how the regional exchange of energy and materials influences the functioning and distribution of organisms across the biosphere.

◄ *How does ocean circulation affect the global distribution of crustaceans?*

Trough

Pipe

"Dry"

"Wet"

"Ambient"

Troughs collect one-third of precipitation that falls on "dry" plot.

Pipes carry water from "dry" plot to "wet" plot.

"Ambient" plot receives natural amounts of rainfall.

▲ **Figure 52.3 Studying how a forest responds to altered precipitation.** At the Walker Branch Watershed in Tennessee, researchers used a system of troughs and pipes to create artificial "dry" and "wet" conditions within parts of a forest.

of waiting decades for the dry or wet years that could be representative of future rainfall. Paul Hanson and colleagues, at Oak Ridge National Laboratory in Tennessee, used just such an experimental approach in a Herculean study that lasted more than ten years. In one large plot of native forest, they collected one-third of the incoming precipitation and moved it to a second plot, while leaving a third plot unchanged as a control **(Figure 52.3)**. By comparing the growth and survival of trees in each plot, the researchers found that flowering dogwoods (*Cornus florida*) were more likely to die in drought conditions than were members of any other woody species examined.

Throughout this unit, you will encounter many more examples of ecological field experiments, whose complex challenges have made ecologists innovators in the areas of experimental design and statistical inference. As these examples also demonstrate, the interpretation of ecological experiments often depends on a broad knowledge of biology.

Linking Ecology and Evolutionary Biology

As we discussed in Chapter 23, organisms adapt to their environment over many generations through the process of natural selection; this adaptation occurs over many generations—the time frame of *evolutionary time*. The differential survival and reproduction of individuals that leads to evolution occurs in *ecological time*, the minute-to-minute time frame of interactions between organisms and the environment. One example of how events in ecological time have led to evolution was the selection for beak size in Galápagos finches (see Figure 23.1). Finches with bigger beaks were better able to eat the large, hard seeds available during the drought. Smaller-beaked birds, which required smaller, softer seeds that were in short supply, were less likely to survive.

We can see the link between ecology and evolution all around us. Suppose a farmer applies a new fungicide to protect a wheat crop from a fungus. The fungicide works well at first,

reducing the population size of the fungus—an ecological effect—and allowing the farmer to obtain higher yields from the crop. After a few years, however, the farmer has to apply higher and higher doses of the fungicide to obtain the same protection. The fungicide has altered the gene pool of the fungus—an evolutionary effect—by selecting for individuals that are resistant to the chemical. Eventually, the fungicide works so poorly that the farmer must find a different, more potent chemical to control the fungus.

Ecology and Environmental Issues

Ecology and evolutionary biology help us understand the emergence of pesticide-resistant organisms and many other environmental problems. Ecology also provides the scientific understanding needed to help us conserve and sustain life on Earth. Because of ecology's usefulness in conservation and environmental efforts, many people associate ecology with *environmentalism* (advocating the protection of nature).

Ecologists make an important distinction between science and advocacy. Many ecologists feel a responsibility to educate legislators and the public about environmental issues. How society uses ecological knowledge, however, depends on much more than science alone. If we know that phosphate promotes the growth of algae in lakes, for instance, policy-makers may weigh the environmental benefits of limiting the use of phosphate-rich fertilizers against the costs of doing so. This distinction between knowledge and advocacy is clear in the guiding principles of the Ecological Society of America, a scientific organization that strives to "ensure the appropriate use of ecological science in environmental decision making."

An important milestone in applying ecological data to environmental problems was the publication of Rachel Carson's *Silent Spring* in 1962 **(Figure 52.4)**. In her book, which

◄ **Figure 52.4 Rachel Carson.**

was seminal to the modern environmental movement, Carson (1907–1964) had a broad message: "The 'control of nature' is a phrase conceived in arrogance, born of the Neanderthal age of biology and philosophy, when it was supposed that nature exists for the convenience of man." Recognizing the network of connections among species, Carson warned that the widespread use of pesticides such as DDT was causing population declines in many more organisms than the insects targeted for control. She applied ecological principles to recommend a less wasteful, safer use of pesticides. Through her writing and her testimony before the U.S. Congress, Carson helped promote a new environmental ethic to lawmakers and the public. Her efforts led to a ban on DDT use in the United States and more stringent controls on the use of other chemicals.

CONCEPT 52.2

Interactions between organisms and the environment limit the distribution of species

Earlier we introduced the range of scales at which ecologists work and explained how ecology can be used to understand, and make decisions about, our environment. In this section, we will examine how ecologists determine what controls the distribution of species, such as the gray whale in Figure 52.1.

In Chapter 22, we explored *biogeography*, the study of the past and present distribution of species, in the context of evolutionary theory. Ecologists have long recognized global and regional patterns in the distribution of organisms. Kangaroos, for instance, are found in Australia but nowhere else on Earth. Ecologists ask not only *where* species occur, but also *why* species occur where they do: What factors determine their distribution? In seeking to answer this question, ecologists focus on two kinds of factors: **biotic**, or living, factors—all the organisms that are part of the individual's environment—and **abiotic**, or nonliving, factors—all the chemical and physical factors, such as temperature, light, water, and nutrients, that influence the distribution and abundance of organisms.

Figure 52.5 presents an example of how both kinds of factors might affect the distribution of a species, in this case the red kangaroo (*Macropus rufus*). As the figure shows, red kangaroos are most abundant in a few areas in the interior of Australia, where precipitation is relatively sparse and variable. They are not found around most of the periphery of the continent, where

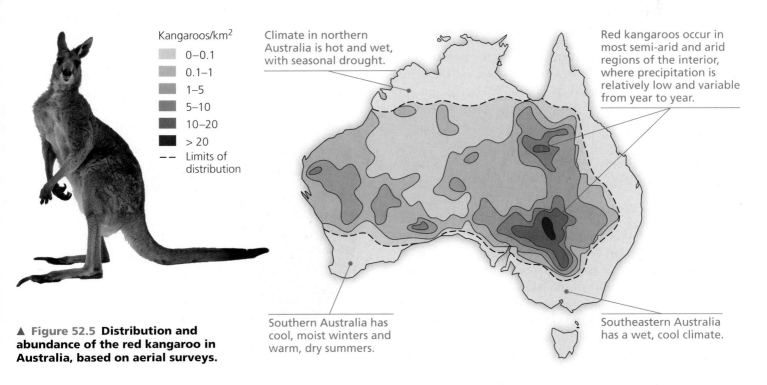

Kangaroos/km²
- 0–0.1
- 0.1–1
- 1–5
- 5–10
- 10–20
- > 20
- – – Limits of distribution

Climate in northern Australia is hot and wet, with seasonal drought.

Red kangaroos occur in most semi-arid and arid regions of the interior, where precipitation is relatively low and variable from year to year.

Southern Australia has cool, moist winters and warm, dry summers.

Southeastern Australia has a wet, cool climate.

▲ **Figure 52.5 Distribution and abundance of the red kangaroo in Australia, based on aerial surveys.**

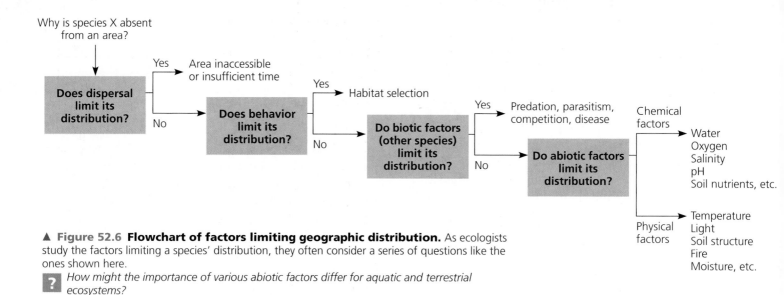

▲ Figure 52.6 Flowchart of factors limiting geographic distribution. As ecologists study the factors limiting a species' distribution, they often consider a series of questions like the ones shown here.

? *How might the importance of various abiotic factors differ for aquatic and terrestrial ecosystems?*

the climate ranges from moist to wet. At first glance, this distribution might suggest that an abiotic factor—the amount and variability of precipitation—directly determines where red kangaroos live. However, it is also possible that climate influences red kangaroo populations indirectly through biotic factors, such as pathogens, parasites, predators, competitors, and food availability. Ecologists generally need to consider multiple factors and alternative hypotheses when attempting to explain the distribution of species.

To see how ecologists might arrive at such an explanation, let's work our way through the series of questions in the flowchart in **Figure 52.6**.

Dispersal and Distribution

The movement of individuals away from their area of origin or from centers of high population density, called **dispersal**, contributes to the global distribution of organisms. A biogeographer might consider dispersal in hypothesizing why there are no kangaroos in North America: Kangaroos could not get there because a barrier to their dispersal existed. While land-bound kangaroos have not reached North America under their own power, other organisms that disperse more readily, such as some birds, have. The dispersal of organisms is critical to understanding both geographic isolation in evolution (see Chapter 24) and the broad patterns of current geographic distributions of species.

Natural Range Expansions

The importance of dispersal is most evident when organisms reach an area where they did not exist previously. For instance, 200 years ago, the cattle egret was found only in Africa and southwestern Europe. But in the late 1800s, some of these strong-flying birds managed to cross the Atlantic Ocean and colonize northeastern South America. From there, cattle egrets gradually spread southward and also northward through Central America and into North America, reaching

Florida by 1960 **(Figure 52.7)**. Today they have breeding populations as far west as the Pacific coast of the United States and as far north as southern Canada.

Natural range expansions clearly show the influence of dispersal on distribution, but opportunities to observe such dispersal directly are rare. As a consequence, ecologists often turn to experimental methods to better understand the role of dispersal in limiting the distribution of species.

▲ Figure 52.7 Dispersal of the cattle egret in the Americas. Native to Africa, cattle egrets were first reported in South America in 1877.

Species Transplants

To determine if dispersal is a key factor limiting the distribution of a species, ecologists may observe the results of intentional or accidental transplants of the species to areas where it was previously absent. For a transplant to be considered successful, some of the organisms must not only survive in the new area but also reproduce there. If a transplant is successful, then we can conclude that the *potential* range of the species is larger than its *actual* range; in other words, the species *could* live in certain areas where it currently does not.

Species introduced to new geographic locations often disrupt the communities and ecosystems to which they have been introduced and spread far beyond the area of intended introduction (see Chapter 56). Consequently, ecologists rarely conduct transplant experiments across geographic regions. Instead, they document the outcome when a species has been transplanted for other purposes, such as to introduce game animals or predators of pest species, or when a species has been accidentally transplanted.

Behavior and Habitat Selection

As transplant experiments show, some organisms do not occupy all of their potential range, even though they may be physically able to disperse into the unoccupied areas. To follow our line of questioning from Figure 52.6, does behavior play a role in limiting distribution in such cases? When individuals seem to avoid certain habitats, even when the habitats are suitable, the organism's distribution may be limited by habitat selection behavior.

Although habitat selection is one of the least understood of all ecological processes, some instances in insects have been closely studied. Female insects often deposit eggs only in response to a very narrow set of stimuli, which may restrict distribution of the insects to certain host plants. Larvae of the European corn borer, for example, can feed on a wide variety of plants but are found almost exclusively on corn (maize) because egg-laying females are attracted by odors produced by the plant. Habitat selection behavior clearly restricts the plant species on which the corn borer is found.

Biotic Factors

If behavior does not limit the distribution of a species, our next question is whether biotic factors—that is, other species—are responsible (see Figure 52.6). In many cases, a species cannot complete its full life cycle if transplanted to a new area. This inability to survive and reproduce may be due to negative interactions with other organisms in the form of predation, parasitism, or competition. Alternatively, survival and reproduction may be limited by the absence of other species on which the transplanted species depends, such as pollinators for many flowering plants. Predators (organisms that kill their prey) and herbivores (organisms that eat plants or algae) are common examples of biotic factors that limit the distribution of species. Simply put, organisms that eat can limit the distribution of organisms that get eaten.

Let's examine one specific case of an herbivore limiting the distribution of a food species (**Figure 52.8**). In certain marine ecosystems, there is often an inverse relationship between the abundance of sea urchins and seaweeds (large marine algae, such as kelp). Where sea urchins that graze on

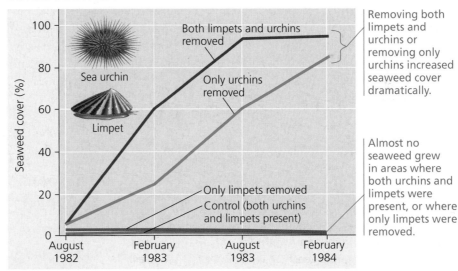

▼ Figure 52.8 **Inquiry**

Does feeding by sea urchins limit seaweed distribution?

EXPERIMENT   W. J. Fletcher, of the University of Sydney, Australia, reasoned that if sea urchins are a limiting biotic factor, then more seaweeds should invade an area from which sea urchins have been removed. To isolate the effect of sea urchins from that of another seaweed-eating animal, the limpet, he removed only urchins, only limpets, or both from study areas adjacent to a control site.

RESULTS   Fletcher observed a large difference in seaweed growth between areas with and without sea urchins.

CONCLUSION   Removing both limpets and urchins resulted in the greatest increase in seaweed cover, indicating that both species have some influence on seaweed distribution. But since removing only urchins greatly increased seaweed growth while removing only limpets had little effect, Fletcher concluded that sea urchins have a much greater effect than limpets in limiting seaweed distribution.

SOURCE   W. J. Fletcher, Interactions among subtidal Australian sea urchins, gastropods, and algae: effects of experimental removals, *Ecological Monographs* 57:89–109 (1989).

WHAT IF?   Seaweed cover increased the most when both urchins *and* limpets were removed. How might you explain this result?

seaweeds and other algae are common, large stands of seaweeds do not become established. Thus, sea urchins appear to limit the local distribution of seaweeds. This kind of interaction can be tested by "removal and addition" experiments. In studies near Sydney, Australia, W. J. Fletcher tested the hypothesis that sea urchins are a biotic factor limiting seaweed distribution. Because there are often other herbivores in the habitats where seaweeds may grow, Fletcher performed a series of manipulative field experiments to isolate the influence of sea urchins on seaweeds in his study area (see Figure 52.8). By removing sea urchins from certain plots and observing the dramatic increase in seaweed cover, he showed that urchins limited the distribution of seaweeds.

In addition to predation and herbivory, the presence or absence of food resources, parasites, pathogens, and competing organisms can act as biotic limitations on species distribution. Some of the most striking cases of limitation occur when humans accidentally or intentionally introduce exotic predators or pathogens into new areas and wipe out native species. You will encounter examples of these impacts in Chapter 56, which discusses conservation ecology.

Abiotic Factors

The last question in the flowchart in Figure 52.6 considers whether abiotic factors, such as temperature, water, salinity, sunlight, or soil, might be limiting a species' distribution. If the physical conditions at a site do not allow a species to survive and reproduce, then the species will not be found there. Throughout this discussion, keep in mind that the environment is characterized by both *spatial heterogeneity* and *temporal heterogeneity*; that is, most abiotic factors vary in space and time. Although two regions of Earth may experience different conditions at any given time, daily and annual fluctuations of abiotic factors may either blur or accentuate regional distinctions. Furthermore, organisms can avoid some stressful conditions temporarily through behaviors such as dormancy or hibernation.

Temperature

Environmental temperature is an important factor in the distribution of organisms because of its effect on biological processes. Cells may rupture if the water they contain freezes (at temperatures below 0°C), and the proteins of most organisms denature at temperatures above 45°C. In addition, few organisms can maintain an active metabolism at very low or very high temperatures, though extraordinary adaptations enable some organisms, such as thermophilic prokaryotes (see Chapter 27), to live outside the temperature range habitable by other life. Most organisms function best within a specific range of environmental temperature. Temperatures outside that range may force some animals to expend energy regulating their internal temperature, as mammals and birds do (see Chapter 40).

Water

The dramatic variation in water availability among habitats is another important factor in species distribution. Species living at the seashore or in tidal wetlands can desiccate (dry out) as the tide recedes. Terrestrial organisms face a nearly constant threat of desiccation, and the distribution of terrestrial species reflects their ability to obtain and conserve water. Desert organisms, for example, exhibit a variety of adaptations for acquiring and conserving water in dry environments, as described in Chapter 44.

Salinity

As you learned in Chapter 7, the salt concentration of water in the environment affects the water balance of organisms through osmosis. Most aquatic organisms are restricted to either freshwater or saltwater habitats by their limited ability to osmoregulate (see Chapter 44). Although many terrestrial organisms can excrete excess salts from specialized glands or in feces, salt flats and other high-salinity habitats typically have few species of plants or animals.

Sunlight

Sunlight absorbed by photosynthetic organisms provides the energy that drives most ecosystems, and too little sunlight can limit the distribution of photosynthetic species. In forests, shading by leaves in the treetops makes competition for light especially intense, particularly for seedlings growing on the forest floor. In aquatic environments, every meter of water depth selectively absorbs about 45% of the red light and about 2% of the blue light passing through it. As a result, most photosynthesis in aquatic environments occurs relatively near the surface.

Too much light can also limit the survival of organisms. The atmosphere is thinner at higher elevations, absorbing less ultraviolet radiation, so the sun's rays are more likely to damage DNA and proteins in alpine environments (Figure 52.9). In other ecosystems, such as deserts, high light levels can increase temperature stress if animals are unable to avoid the light or to cool themselves through evaporation (see Chapter 40).

Rocks and Soil

The pH, mineral composition, and physical structure of rocks and soil limit the distribution of plants and thus of the animals that feed on them, contributing to the patchiness of terrestrial ecosystems. The pH of soil and water can limit the distribution of organisms directly, through extreme acidic or basic conditions, or indirectly, through the solubility of nutrients and toxins. In streams and rivers, the composition of the substrate (bottom surface) can affect water chemistry, which in turn influences the resident organisms. In freshwater and marine environments, the

▲ **Figure 52.9 Alpine tree.** Organisms living at high elevations are exposed to high levels of ultraviolet radiation. They face other challenges as well, including freezing temperatures and strong winds, which increase water loss and inhibit the growth of limbs on the windward side of trees.

structure of the substrate determines the organisms that can attach to it or burrow into it.

Now that we have surveyed some of the abiotic factors that affect the distribution of organisms, let's focus on how those factors vary with climate, as we consider the major role that climate plays in determining species distribution.

Climate

Four abiotic factors—temperature, precipitation, sunlight, and wind—are the major components of **climate**, the long-term, prevailing weather conditions in a particular area. Climatic factors, particularly temperature and water availability, have a major influence on the distribution of terrestrial organisms. We can describe climate patterns on two scales: **macroclimate**, patterns on the global, regional, and local level; and **microclimate**, very fine patterns, such as those encountered by the community of organisms that live beneath a fallen log. First let's consider Earth's macroclimate.

Global Climate Patterns

Earth's global climate patterns are determined largely by the input of solar energy and the planet's movement in space.

The sun's warming effect on the atmosphere, land, and water establishes the temperature variations, cycles of air movement, and evaporation of water that are responsible for dramatic latitudinal variations in climate. **Figure 52.10**, on the next two pages, summarizes Earth's climate patterns and how they are formed.

Regional, Local, and Seasonal Effects on Climate

Proximity to bodies of water and topographic features such as mountain ranges create regional climatic variations, and smaller features of the landscape contribute to local climatic variation. Seasonal variation is another influence on climate.

Bodies of Water Ocean currents influence climate along the coasts of continents by heating or cooling overlying air masses, which may then pass across the land. Coastal regions are also generally moister than inland areas at the same latitude. The cool, misty climate produced by the cold California current that flows southward along the western United States supports a coniferous rain forest ecosystem in the Pacific Northwest and large redwood groves farther south. Similarly, the west coast of northern Europe has a mild climate because the Gulf Stream carries warm water from the equator to the North Atlantic, driven in part by the "great ocean conveyor belt" (Figure 52.11). As a result, northwest Europe is warmer during winter than New England, which is farther south but is cooled by the Labrador Current flowing south from the coast of Greenland.

Because of the high specific heat of water (see Chapter 3), oceans and large lakes tend to moderate the climate of nearby land. During a hot day, when the land is warmer than the nearby body of water, air over the land heats up and

▲ **Figure 52.11 The great ocean conveyor belt.** Water is warmed at the equator and flows along the ocean surface to the North Atlantic, where it cools, becomes denser, and sinks thousands of meters. The deep, cold water may not return to the ocean surface for as long as 1,000 years.

Exploring Global Climate Patterns

Latitudinal Variation in Sunlight Intensity

Earth's curved shape causes latitudinal variation in the intensity of sunlight. Because sunlight strikes the **tropics** (those regions that lie between 23.5° north latitude and 23.5° south latitude) most directly, more heat and light per unit of surface area are delivered there. At higher latitudes, sunlight strikes Earth at an oblique angle, and thus the light energy is more diffuse on Earth's surface.

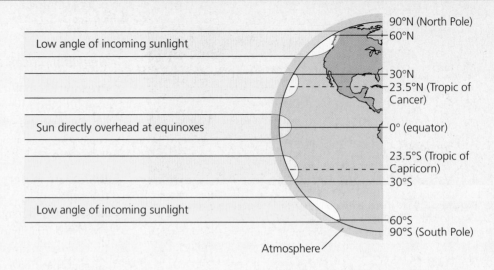

Seasonal Variation in Sunlight Intensity

March equinox: Equator faces sun directly; neither pole tilts toward sun; all regions on Earth experience 12 hours of daylight and 12 hours of darkness.

June solstice: Northern Hemisphere tilts toward sun and has longest day and shortest night; Southern Hemisphere tilts away from sun and has shortest day and longest night.

December solstice: Northern Hemisphere tilts away from sun and has shortest day and longest night; Southern Hemisphere tilts toward sun and has longest day and shortest night.

September equinox: Equator faces sun directly; neither pole tilts toward sun; all regions on Earth experience 12 hours of daylight and 12 hours of darkness.

Earth's tilt causes seasonal variation in the intensity of solar radiation. Because the planet is tilted on its axis by 23.5° relative to its plane of orbit around the sun, the tropics experience the greatest annual input of solar radiation and the least seasonal variation. The seasonal variations of light and temperature increase toward the poles.

Global Air Circulation and Precipitation Patterns

Intense solar radiation near the equator initiates a global pattern of air circulation and precipitation. High temperatures in the tropics evaporate water from Earth's surface and cause warm, wet air masses to rise (blue arrows) and flow toward the poles. The rising air masses release much of their water content, creating abundant precipitation in tropical regions. The high-altitude air masses, now dry, descend (brown arrows) toward Earth, absorbing moisture from the land and creating an arid climate conducive to the development of the deserts that are common at latitudes around 30° north and south. Some of the descending air then flows toward the poles. At latitudes around 60° north and south, the air masses again rise and release abundant precipitation (though less than in the tropics). Some of the cold, dry rising air then flows to the poles, where it descends and flows back toward the equator, absorbing moisture and creating the comparatively rainless and bitterly cold climates of the polar regions.

Global Wind Patterns

Air flowing close to Earth's surface creates predictable global wind patterns. As Earth rotates on its axis, land near the equator moves faster than that at the poles, deflecting the winds from the vertical paths shown above and creating more easterly and westerly flows. Cooling trade winds blow from east to west in the tropics; prevailing westerlies blow from west to east in the temperate zones, defined as the regions between the Tropic of Cancer and the Arctic Circle and between the Tropic of Capricorn and the Antarctic Circle.

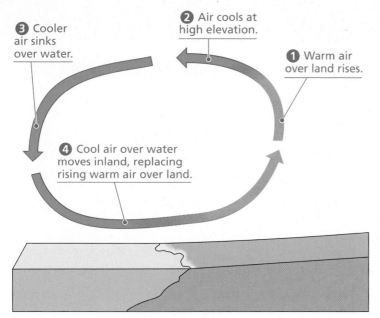

3 Cooler air sinks over water.

2 Air cools at high elevation.

1 Warm air over land rises.

4 Cool air over water moves inland, replacing rising warm air over land.

▲ Figure 52.12 **Moderating effects of a large body of water on climate.** This figure illustrates what happens on a hot summer day.

rises, drawing a cool breeze from the water across the land **(Figure 52.12)**. At night, air over the now warmer water rises, drawing cooler air from the land back out over the water, replacing it with warmer air from offshore. The moderation of climate may be limited to the coast itself, however. In certain regions, such as southern California, cool, dry ocean breezes in summer are warmed when they contact the land, absorbing moisture and creating a hot, arid climate just a few kilometers inland (see Figure 3.5). This climate pattern also occurs around the Mediterranean Sea, which gives it the name *Mediterranean climate.*

Mountains Mountains affect the amount of sunlight reaching an area and consequently the local temperature and rainfall. South-facing slopes in the Northern Hemisphere receive more sunlight than nearby north-facing slopes and are therefore warmer and drier. These abiotic differences influence species distribution; for example, in many mountains of western North America, spruce and other conifers occupy the cooler north-facing slopes, whereas shrubby, drought-resistant plants inhabit the south-facing slopes. In addition, every 1,000-m increase in elevation produces a temperature drop of approximately 6°C, equivalent to that produced by an 880-km increase in latitude. This is one reason the biological communities of mountains are similar to those at lower elevations but farther from the equator.

When warm, moist air approaches a mountain, the air rises and cools, releasing moisture on the windward side of the peak **(Figure 52.13)**. On the leeward side, cooler, dry air descends, absorbing moisture and producing a "rain shadow." Deserts commonly occur on the leeward side of mountain ranges, a phenomenon evident in the Great Basin and the Mojave Desert of western North America, the Gobi Desert of Asia, and the small deserts found in the southwest corners of some Caribbean islands.

Seasonality As described earlier, Earth's tilted axis of rotation and its annual passage around the sun cause strong seasonal cycles in middle to high latitudes (see Figure 52.10). In addition to these global changes in day length, solar radiation, and temperature, the changing angle of the sun over the course of the year affects local environments. For example, the belts of wet and dry air on either side of the equator move slightly northward and southward with the changing angle of the sun, producing marked wet and dry seasons around 20° north and 20° south latitude, where many tropical deciduous forests grow. In addition, seasonal changes in wind patterns produce variations in ocean currents, sometimes causing the upwelling of cold water from deep ocean layers. This nutrient-rich water stimulates the growth of surface-dwelling phytoplankton and the organisms that feed on them.

Microclimate

Many features in the environment influence microclimates by casting shade, affecting evaporation from soil, or changing wind patterns. For example, forest trees frequently moderate the microclimate below them. Consequently, cleared areas generally experience greater temperature extremes than the

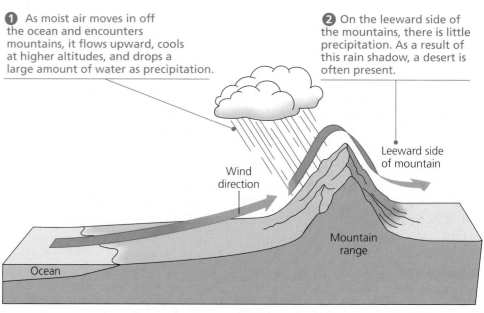

1 As moist air moves in off the ocean and encounters mountains, it flows upward, cools at higher altitudes, and drops a large amount of water as precipitation.

2 On the leeward side of the mountains, there is little precipitation. As a result of this rain shadow, a desert is often present.

Leeward side of mountain

Wind direction

Ocean

Mountain range

▲ Figure 52.13 **How mountains affect rainfall.**

forest interior because of greater solar radiation and wind currents that are established by the rapid heating and cooling of open land. Within a forest, low-lying ground is usually wetter than high ground and tends to be occupied by different species of trees. A log or large stone can shelter organisms such as salamanders, worms, and insects, buffering them from the extremes of temperature and moisture. Every environment on Earth is similarly characterized by a mosaic of small-scale differences in the abiotic factors that influence the local distributions of organisms.

Long-Term Climate Change

If temperature and moisture are the most important factors limiting the geographic ranges of plants and animals, then the global climate change currently under way will profoundly affect the biosphere (see Chapter 55). One way to predict the possible effects of climate change is to look back at the changes that have occurred in temperate regions since the last ice age ended.

Until about 16,000 years ago, continental glaciers covered much of North America and Eurasia. As the climate warmed and the glaciers retreated, tree distributions expanded northward. A detailed record of these migrations is captured in fossil pollen deposited in lakes and ponds. (It may seem odd to think of trees "migrating," but recall from Chapter 38 that wind and animals can disperse seeds, sometimes over great distances.) If researchers can determine the climatic limits of current geographic distributions for organisms, they can make predictions about how distributions will change with climatic warming. A major question when applying this approach to plants is whether seed dispersal is rapid enough to sustain the migration of each species as climate changes. For example, fossils suggest that the eastern hemlock was delayed nearly 2,500 years in its movement north at the end of the last ice age. This delay in seed dispersal was partly attributable to the lack of "wings" on the seeds, causing the seeds to fall close to their parent tree.

Let's look at a specific case of how the fossil record of past tree migrations can inform predictions about the biological impact of the current global warming trend. **Figure 52.14** shows the current and predicted geographic ranges of the American beech (*Fagus grandifolia*) under two different climate-change models. These models predict that the northern limit of the beech's range will move 700–900 km northward in the next century, and its southern range limit will move northward an even greater distance. If these predictions are even approximately correct, the beech must move 7–9 km per year northward to keep pace with the warming climate. However, since the end of the last ice age, the beech has migrated into its present range at a rate of only 0.2 km per year. Without human as-

(a) 4.5°C warming over next century **(b) 6.5°C warming over next century**

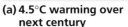
Current range
Predicted range
Overlap

▲ **Figure 52.14 Current range and predicted range for the American beech (*Fagus grandifolia*) under two scenarios of climate change.**

? *The predicted range in each scenario is based on climate factors alone. What other factors might alter the distribution of this species?*

sistance in moving into new ranges where they can survive as the climate warms, species such as the American beech may have much smaller ranges and may even become extinct.

CONCEPT CHECK 52.2

1. Give examples of human actions that could expand a species' distribution by changing its (a) dispersal or (b) biotic interactions.
2. Explain how the sun's unequal heating of Earth's surface influences global climate patterns.
3. **WHAT IF?** You suspect that deer are restricting the distribution of a tree species by preferentially eating the seedlings of the tree. How might you test that hypothesis?

For suggested answers, see Appendix A.

CONCEPT 52.3

Aquatic biomes are diverse and dynamic systems that cover most of Earth

We have seen how both biotic and abiotic factors influence the distribution of organisms on Earth. Combinations of these factors determine the nature of Earth's many **biomes**, major terrestrial or aquatic life zones, characterized by vegetation type in terrestrial biomes or the physical environment in aquatic biomes. We'll begin by examining Earth's aquatic biomes.

Aquatic biomes account for the largest part of the biosphere in terms of area, and all types are found around the globe **(Figure 52.15)**. Ecologists distinguish between freshwater biomes and marine biomes on the basis of physical and chemical differences. For example, marine biomes generally have salt concentrations that average 3%, whereas freshwater biomes are usually characterized by a salt concentration of less than 0.1%.

The oceans make up the largest marine biome, covering about 75% of Earth's surface. Because of their vast size, they have an enormous impact on the biosphere. The evaporation of water from the oceans provides most of the planet's rainfall, and ocean temperatures have a major effect on world climate and wind patterns. In addition, marine algae and

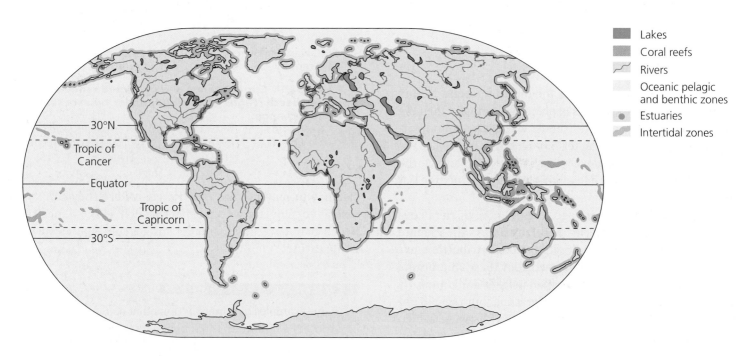

▲ **Figure 52.15 The distribution of major aquatic biomes.**

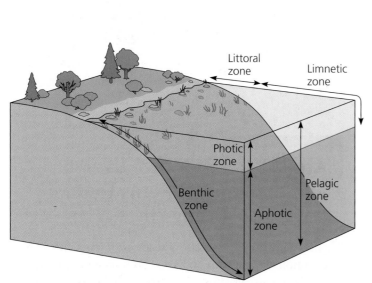

(a) Zonation in a lake. The lake environment is generally classified on the basis of three physical criteria: light penetration (photic and aphotic zones), distance from shore and water depth (littoral and limnetic zones), and whether it is open water (pelagic zone) or bottom (benthic zone).

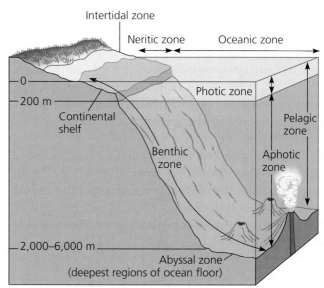

(b) Marine zonation. Like lakes, the marine environment is generally classified on the basis of light penetration (photic and aphotic zones), distance from shore and water depth (intertidal, neritic, and oceanic zones), and whether it is open water (pelagic zone) or bottom (benthic and abyssal zones).

▲ **Figure 52.16 Zonation in aquatic environments.**

photosynthetic bacteria supply a substantial portion of the world's oxygen and consume large amounts of atmospheric carbon dioxide.

Freshwater biomes are closely linked to the soils and biotic components of the terrestrial biomes through which they pass or in which they are situated. The particular characteristics of a freshwater biome are also influenced by the patterns and speed of water flow and the climate to which the biome is exposed.

Stratification of Aquatic Biomes

Many aquatic biomes are physically and chemically stratified (layered), as illustrated for both a lake and a marine environment in **Figure 52.16**, on the facing page. Light is absorbed by both the water itself and the photosynthetic organisms in it, so its intensity decreases rapidly with depth, as mentioned earlier. Ecologists distinguish between the upper **photic zone**, where there is sufficient light for photosynthesis, and the lower **aphotic zone**, where little light penetrates. At the bottom of all aquatic biomes, the substrate is called the **benthic zone**. Made up of sand and organic and inorganic sediments, the benthic zone is occupied by communities of organisms collectively called the **benthos**. A major source of food for many benthic species is dead organic matter called **detritus**, which "rains" down from the productive surface waters of the photic zone. In the ocean, the part of the benthic zone that lies between 2,000 and 6,000 m below the surface is known as the **abyssal zone**.

Thermal energy from sunlight warms surface waters to whatever depth the sunlight penetrates, but the deeper waters remain quite cold. In the ocean and in most lakes, a narrow layer of abrupt temperature change called a **thermocline** separates the more uniformly warm upper layer from more uniformly cold deeper waters. Lakes tend to be particularly layered with respect to temperature, especially during summer and winter, but many temperate lakes undergo a semiannual mixing of their waters as a result of changing temperature profiles **(Figure 52.17)**. This **turnover**, as it is called, brings oxygenated water from a lake's surface to the bottom and nutrient-rich water from the bottom to the surface in both spring and autumn. These cyclic changes in the abiotic properties of lakes are essential for the survival and growth of organisms at all levels within this ecosystem.

In both freshwater and marine environments, communities are distributed according to water depth, degree of light penetration, distance from shore, and whether they are found in open water or near the bottom. Marine communities, in particular, illustrate the limitations on species distribution that result from these abiotic factors. Plankton and many fish species occur in the relatively shallow photic zone (see Figure 52.16b). Because water absorbs light so well and the

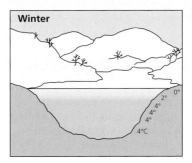

1 In winter, the coldest water in the lake (0°C) lies just below the surface ice; water is progressively warmer at deeper levels of the lake, typically 4°C at the bottom.

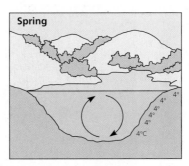

2 In spring, as the sun melts the ice, the surface water warms to 4°C and sinks below the cooler layers immediately below, eliminating the thermal stratification. Spring winds mix the water to great depth, bringing oxygen to the bottom waters and nutrients to the surface.

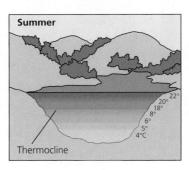

3 In summer, the lake regains a distinctive thermal profile, with warm surface water separated from cold bottom water by a narrow vertical zone of abrupt temperature change, called a thermocline.

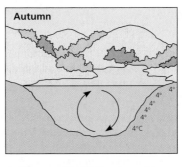

4 In autumn, as surface water cools rapidly, it sinks below the underlying layers, remixing the water until the surface begins to freeze and the winter temperature profile is reestablished.

▲ **Figure 52.17 Seasonal turnover in lakes with winter ice cover.** Because of the seasonal turnover shown here, lake waters are well oxygenated at all depths in spring and autumn; in winter and summer, when the lake is stratified by temperature, oxygen concentrations are lower in deeper waters and higher near the surface of the lake.

ocean is so deep, most of the ocean volume is virtually devoid of light (the aphotic zone) and harbors relatively little life, except for microorganisms and relatively sparse populations of fishes and invertebrates. Similar factors limit species distribution in deep lakes as well.

Figure 52.18, on the next four pages, surveys the major aquatic biomes.

Exploring Aquatic Biomes

Lakes

Physical Environment   Standing bodies of water range from ponds a few square meters in area to lakes covering thousands of square kilometers. Light decreases with depth, creating stratification (see Figure 52.16a). Temperate lakes may have a seasonal thermocline (see Figure 52.17); tropical lowland lakes have a thermocline year-round.

An oligotrophic lake in Grand Teton National Park, Wyoming

A eutrophic lake in the Okavango Delta, Botswana

Chemical Environment   The salinity, oxygen concentration, and nutrient content differ greatly among lakes and can vary with season. **Oligotrophic lakes** are nutrient-poor and generally oxygen-rich; **eutrophic lakes** are nutrient-rich and often depleted of oxygen in the deepest zone in summer and if ice covered in winter. The amount of decomposable organic matter in bottom sediments is low in oligotrophic lakes and high in eutrophic lakes; high rates of decomposition in deeper layers of eutrophic lakes cause periodic oxygen depletion.

Geologic Features   Oligotrophic lakes may become more eutrophic over time as runoff adds sediments and nutrients. They tend to have less surface area relative to their depth than eutrophic lakes have.

Photosynthetic Organisms   Rooted and floating aquatic plants live in the **littoral zone**, the shallow, well-lighted waters close to shore. Farther from shore, where water is too deep to support rooted aquatic plants, the **limnetic zone** is inhabited by a variety of phytoplankton and cyanobacteria.

Heterotrophs   In the limnetic zone, small drifting heterotrophs, or zooplankton, graze on the phytoplankton. The benthic zone is inhabited by assorted invertebrates whose species composition depends partly on oxygen levels. Fishes live in all zones with sufficient oxygen.

Human Impact   Runoff from fertilized land and dumping of wastes lead to nutrient enrichment, which can produce algal blooms, oxygen depletion, and fish kills.

Wetlands

Physical Environment   A **wetland** is a habitat that is inundated by water at least some of the time and that supports plants adapted to water-saturated soil. Some wetlands are inundated at all times, whereas others flood infrequently.

Chemical Environment   Because of high organic production by plants and decomposition by microbes and other organisms, both the water and the soils are periodically low in dissolved oxygen. Wetlands have a high capacity to filter dissolved nutrients and chemical pollutants.

Geologic Features   *Basin wetlands* develop in shallow basins, ranging from upland depressions to filled-in lakes and ponds. *Riverine wetlands* develop along shallow and periodically flooded banks of rivers and streams. *Fringe wetlands* occur along the coasts of large lakes and seas, where water flows back and forth because of rising lake levels or tidal action. Thus, fringe wetlands include both freshwater and marine biomes.

Photosynthetic Organisms   Wetlands are among the most productive biomes on Earth. Their water-saturated soils favor the growth of plants such as floating pond lilies and emergent cattails, many sedges, tamarack, and black spruce, which have adaptations enabling them to grow in water or in soil that is periodically anaerobic owing to the presence of unaerated water. Woody plants dominate the vegetation of swamps, while bogs are dominated by sphagnum mosses.

Heterotrophs   Wetlands are home to a diverse community of invertebrates, which in turn support a wide variety of birds. Herbivores,

Okefenokee National Wetland Reserve in Georgia

from crustaceans and aquatic insect larvae to muskrats, consume algae, detritus, and plants. Carnivores are also varied and may include dragonflies, otters, alligators, and owls.

Human Impact   Draining and filling have destroyed up to 90% of wetlands, which help purify water and reduce peak flooding.

Streams and Rivers

Physical Environment The most prominent physical characteristic of streams and rivers is their current. Headwater streams are generally cold, clear, turbulent, and swift. Farther downstream, where numerous tributaries may have joined, forming a river, the water is generally warmer and more turbid because of suspended sediment. Streams and rivers are stratified into vertical zones.

Chemical Environment The salt and nutrient content of streams and rivers increases from the headwaters to the mouth. Headwaters are generally rich in oxygen. Downstream water may also contain substantial oxygen, except where there has been organic enrichment. A large fraction of the organic matter in rivers consists of dissolved or highly fragmented material that is carried by the current from forested streams.

Geologic Features Headwater stream channels are often narrow, have a rocky bottom, and alternate between shallow sections and deeper pools. The downstream stretches of rivers are generally wide and meandering. River bottoms are often silty from sediments deposited over long periods of time.

Photosynthetic Organisms Headwater streams that flow through grasslands or deserts may be rich in phytoplankton or rooted aquatic plants.

Heterotrophs A great diversity of fishes and invertebrates inhabit unpolluted rivers and streams, distributed according to, and throughout, the vertical zones. In streams flowing through temperate or tropical forests, organic matter from terrestrial vegetation is the primary source of food for aquatic consumers.

Human Impact Municipal, agricultural, and industrial pollution degrade water quality and kill aquatic organisms. Damming and flood control impair the natural functioning of stream and river ecosystems and threaten migratory species such as salmon.

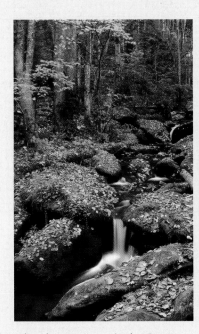
A headwater stream in the Great Smoky Mountains

The Mississippi River far from its headwaters

Estuaries

An estuary in a low coastal plain of Georgia

Physical Environment An **estuary** is a transition area between river and sea. Seawater flows up the estuary channel during a rising tide and flows back down during the falling tide. Often, higher-density seawater occupies the bottom of the channel and mixes little with the lower-density river water at the surface.

Chemical Environment Salinity varies spatially within estuaries, from nearly that of fresh water to that of seawater. Salinity also varies with the rise and fall of the tides. Nutrients from the river make estuaries, like wetlands, among the most productive biomes.

Geologic Features Estuarine flow patterns combined with the sediments carried by river and tidal waters create a complex network of tidal channels, islands, natural levees, and mudflats.

Photosynthetic Organisms Saltmarsh grasses and algae, including phytoplankton, are the major producers in estuaries.

Heterotrophs Estuaries support an abundance of worms, oysters, crabs, and many fish species that humans consume. Many marine invertebrates and fishes use estuaries as a breeding ground or migrate through them to freshwater habitats upstream. Estuaries are also crucial feeding areas for waterfowl and some marine mammals.

Human Impact Pollution from upstream, and also filling and dredging, have disrupted estuaries worldwide.

Continued on next page

Exploring Aquatic Biomes

Intertidal Zones

Rocky intertidal zone on the Oregon coast

Physical Environment   An **intertidal zone** is periodically submerged and exposed by the tides, twice daily on most marine shores. Upper zones experience longer exposures to air and greater variations in temperature and salinity. Changes in physical conditions from the upper to the lower intertidal zones limit the distributions of many organisms to particular strata, as shown in the photograph.

Chemical Environment   Oxygen and nutrient levels are generally high and are renewed with each turn of the tides.

Geologic Features   The substrates of intertidal zones, which are generally either rocky or sandy, select for particular behavior and anatomy among intertidal organisms. The configuration of bays or coastlines influences the magnitude of tides and the relative exposure of intertidal organisms to wave action.

Photosynthetic Organisms   A high diversity and biomass of attached marine algae inhabit rocky intertidal zones, especially in the lower zone. Sandy intertidal zones exposed to vigorous wave action generally lack attached plants or algae, while sandy intertidal zones in protected bays or lagoons often support rich beds of sea grass and algae.

Heterotrophs   Many of the animals in rocky intertidal environments have structural adaptations that enable them to attach to the hard substrate. The composition, density, and diversity of animals change markedly from the upper to the lower intertidal zones. Many of the animals in sandy or muddy intertidal zones, such as worms, clams, and predatory crustaceans, bury themselves and feed as the tides bring sources of food. Other common animals are sponges, sea anemones, echinoderms, and small fishes.

Human Impact   Oil pollution has disrupted many intertidal areas.

Oceanic Pelagic Zone

Physical Environment   The **oceanic pelagic zone** is a vast realm of open blue water, constantly mixed by wind-driven oceanic currents. Because of higher water clarity, the photic zone extends to greater depths than in coastal marine waters.

Chemical Environment   Oxygen levels are generally high. Nutrient concentrations are generally lower than in coastal waters. Because they are thermally stratified year-round, some tropical areas of the oceanic pelagic zone have lower nutrient concentrations than temperate oceans. Turnover between fall and spring renews nutrients in the photic zones of temperate and high-latitude ocean areas.

Geologic Features   This biome covers approximately 70% of Earth's surface and has an average depth of nearly 4,000 m. The deepest point in the ocean is more than 10,000 m beneath the surface.

Photosynthetic Organisms   The dominant photosynthetic organisms are phytoplankton, including photosynthetic bacteria, that drift with the oceanic currents. Spring turnover and renewal of nutrients in temperate oceans produces a surge of phytoplankton growth. Because of the large extent of this biome, photosynthetic plankton account for about half of the photosynthetic activity on Earth.

Heterotrophs   The most abundant heterotrophs in this biome are zooplankton. These protists, worms, copepods, shrimp-like krill, jellies, and the small larvae of invertebrates and fishes graze on photosynthetic plankton. The oceanic pelagic zone also includes free-swimming animals, such as large squids, fishes, sea turtles, and marine mammals.

Human Impact   Overfishing has depleted fish stocks in all Earth's oceans, which have also been polluted by waste dumping.

Open ocean off the island of Hawaii

Coral Reefs

Physical Environment   **Coral reefs** are formed largely from the calcium carbonate skeletons of corals. Shallow reef-building corals live in the photic zone of relatively stable tropical marine environments with high water clarity, primarily on islands and along the edge of some continents. They are sensitive to temperatures below about 18–20°C and above 30°C. Deep-sea coral reefs, found between 200 and 1,500 m deep, are less known than their shallow counterparts but harbor as much diversity as many shallow reefs do.

Chemical Environment   Corals require high oxygen levels and are excluded by high inputs of fresh water and nutrients.

Geologic Features   Corals require a solid substrate for attachment. A typical coral reef begins as a *fringing reef* on a young, high island, forming an offshore *barrier reef* later in the history of the island and becoming a *coral atoll* as the older island submerges.

Photosynthetic Organisms   Unicellular algae live within the tissues of the corals, forming a mutualistic relationship that provides the corals with organic molecules. Diverse multicellular red and green algae growing on the reef also contribute substantial amounts of photosynthesis.

Heterotrophs   Corals, a diverse group of cnidarians (see Chapter 33), are themselves the predominant animals on coral reefs. However, fish and invertebrate diversity is exceptionally high. Overall animal diversity on coral reefs rivals that of tropical forests.

A coral reef in the Red Sea

Human Impact   Collecting of coral skeletons and overfishing have reduced populations of corals and reef fishes. Global warming and pollution may be contributing to large-scale coral death. Development of coastal mangroves for aquaculture has also reduced spawning grounds for many species of reef fishes.

Marine Benthic Zone

Physical Environment   The **marine benthic zone** consists of the seafloor below the surface waters of the coastal, or **neritic**, zone and the offshore, pelagic zone (see Figure 52.16b). Except for shallow, near-coastal areas, the marine benthic zone receives no sunlight. Water temperature declines with depth, while pressure increases. As a result, organisms in the very deep benthic, or **abyssal**, zone are adapted to continuous cold (about 3°C) and very high water pressure.

Chemical Environment   Except in some areas of organic enrichment, oxygen is present at sufficient concentrations to support a diversity of animals.

Geologic Features   Soft sediments cover most of the benthic zone. However, there are areas of rocky substrate on reefs, submarine mountains, and new oceanic crust.

Autotrophs   Photosynthetic organisms, mainly seaweeds and filamentous algae, are limited to shallow benthic areas with sufficient light to support them. Unique assemblages of organisms, such as those shown in the photo, are found near **deep-sea hydrothermal vents** on mid-ocean ridges. In these dark, hot environments, the food producers are chemoautotrophic prokaryotes (see Chapter 27) that obtain energy by oxidizing H_2S formed by a reaction of the hot water with dissolved sulfate (SO_4^{2-}).

Heterotrophs   Neritic benthic communities include numerous invertebrates and fishes. Beyond the photic zone, most consumers depend entirely on organic matter raining down from above. Among the animals of the deep-sea hydrothermal vent communities are giant tube worms (pictured at left), some more than 1 m long. They are nourished by chemoautotrophic prokaryotes that live as symbionts within their bodies. Many other invertebrates, including arthropods and echinoderms, are also abundant around the hydrothermal vents.

Human Impact   Overfishing has decimated important benthic fish populations, such as the cod of the Grand Banks off Newfoundland. Dumping of organic wastes has created oxygen-deprived benthic areas.

A deep-sea hydrothermal vent community

The first two questions refer to Figure 52.18.

1. Many organisms living in estuaries experience fresh- and saltwater conditions each day with the rising and falling of tides. What challenge does this pose for the physiology of the organisms?
2. Why are phytoplankton, and not benthic algae or rooted aquatic plants, the dominant photosynthetic organisms of the oceanic pelagic zone?
3. **WHAT IF?** Water leaving a reservoir behind a dam is often taken from deep layers of the reservoir. Would you expect fish found in a river below a dam in summer to be species that prefer colder or warmer water than fish found in an undammed river? Explain.

For suggested answers, see Appendix A.

CONCEPT **52.4**

The structure and distribution of terrestrial biomes are controlled by climate and disturbance

All the abiotic factors discussed in this chapter, but especially climate, are important in determining why a particular terrestrial biome is found in a certain area. Because there are latitudinal patterns of climate over Earth's surface (see Figure 52.10), there are also latitudinal patterns of biome distribution (Figure 52.19). These biome patterns in turn are modified by **disturbance**, an event (such as a storm, fire, or human activ-

ity) that changes a community, removing organisms from it and altering resource availability. Frequent fires, for instance, can kill woody plants and keep a savanna from becoming the woodland that climate alone would otherwise support.

Climate and Terrestrial Biomes

We can see the great impact of climate on the distribution of organisms by constructing a **climograph**, a plot of the temperature and precipitation in a particular region. **Figure 52.20** is a climograph of annual mean temperature and precipitation for some of the biomes found in North America. Notice that the range of precipitation in northern coniferous forests is similar to that in temperate forests, but the temperature ranges are different. Grasslands are generally drier than either kind of forest, and deserts are drier still.

Factors other than mean temperature and precipitation also play a role in determining where biomes exist. For example, certain areas in North America with a particular combination of temperature and precipitation support a temperate broadleaf forest, but other areas with similar values for these variables support a coniferous forest. How do we explain this variation? First, remember that the climograph is based on annual *averages*. Often, however, the *pattern* of climatic variation is as important as the average climate. Some areas may receive regular precipitation throughout the year, whereas other areas with the same annual precipitation have distinct wet and dry seasons. A similar phenomenon may occur with respect to temperature. Other environmental characteristics, such as the type of bedrock in an area, may greatly affect mineral nutrient availability and soil structure, which in turn affect the kind of vegetation that can grow.

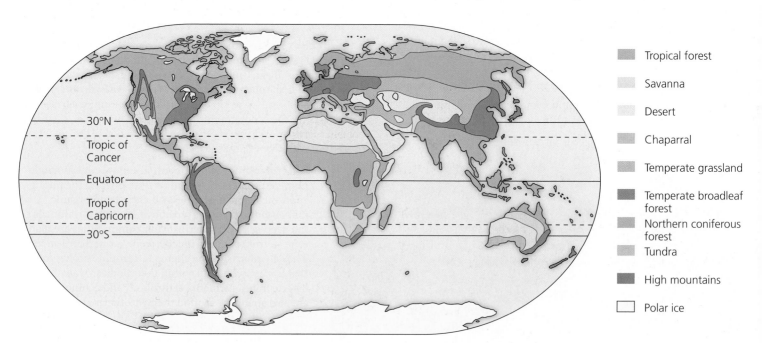

▲ **Figure 52.19 The distribution of major terrestrial biomes.** Although biomes are mapped here with sharp boundaries, biomes actually grade into one another, sometimes over large areas.

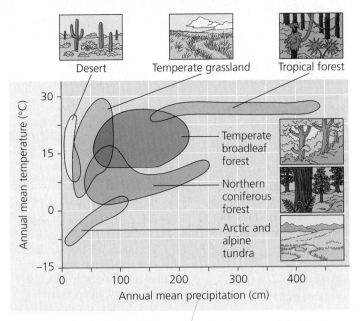

Desert   Temperate grassland   Tropical forest

▲ **Figure 52.20 A climograph for some major types of biomes in North America.** The areas plotted here encompass the range of annual mean temperature and precipitation in the biomes.

General Features of Terrestrial Biomes and the Role of Disturbance

Most terrestrial biomes are named for major physical or climatic features and for their predominant vegetation. Temperate grasslands, for instance, are generally found in middle latitudes, where the climate is more moderate than in the tropics or polar regions, and are dominated by various grass species (see Figure 52.19). Each biome is also characterized by microorganisms, fungi, and animals adapted to that particular environment. For example, temperate grasslands are more likely than forests to be populated by large grazing mammals.

Although Figure 52.19 shows distinct boundaries between the biomes, in actuality, terrestrial biomes usually grade into each other without sharp boundaries. The area of intergradation, called an **ecotone**, may be wide or narrow.

Vertical layering is an important feature of terrestrial biomes, and the shapes and sizes of plants largely define that layering. In many forests, for example, the layers from top to bottom consist of the upper **canopy**, the low-tree layer, the shrub understory, the ground layer of herbaceous plants, the forest floor (litter layer), and the root layer. Nonforest biomes have similar, though usually less pronounced, layers. Grasslands have an herbaceous layer of grasses and forbs (small broadleaf plants), a litter layer, and a root layer. Layering of vegetation provides many different habitats for animals, which often occupy well-defined feeding groups, from the insectivorous birds and bats that feed above canopies to the small mammals, numerous worms, and arthropods that search for food in the litter and root layers.

The species composition of each kind of biome varies from one location to another. For instance, in the northern conifer-

ous forest (taiga) of North America, red spruce is common in the east but does not occur in most other areas, where black spruce and white spruce are abundant. In an example of convergent evolution (see Figure 26.7), cacti living in North American deserts appear very similar to plants called euphorbs found in African deserts, although cacti and euphorbs belong to different evolutionary lineages.

Biomes are dynamic, and disturbance rather than stability tends to be the rule. For example, hurricanes create openings for new species in tropical and temperate forests. In northern coniferous forests, gaps are produced when old trees die and fall over or when snowfall breaks branches. These gaps allow deciduous species, such as aspen and birch, to grow. As a result, biomes usually exhibit extensive patchiness, with several different communities represented in any particular area.

In many biomes, the dominant plants depend on periodic disturbance. For example, natural wildfires are an integral component of grasslands, savannas, chaparral, and many coniferous forests. However, fires are no longer common across much of the Great Plains because tallgrass prairie ecosystems have been converted to agricultural fields that rarely burn. Before agricultural and urban development, much of the southeastern United States was dominated by a single conifer species, the longleaf pine. Without periodic burning, broadleaf trees tended to replace the pines. Forest managers now use fire as a tool to help maintain many coniferous forests.

Figure 52.21, on the next four pages, summarizes the major features of terrestrial biomes. As you read about the characteristics of each biome, remember that humans have altered much of Earth's surface, replacing original biomes with urban and agricultural ones. Most of the eastern United States, for example, is classified as temperate broadleaf forest, but little of that original forest remains.

Throughout this chapter, you have seen how the distributions of organisms and biomes depend on both abiotic and biotic factors. In the next chapter, we will begin to work our way down the hierarchy outlined in Figure 52.2, focusing on how abiotic and biotic factors influence the ecology of populations.

CONCEPT CHECK 52.4

1. Based on the climograph in Figure 52.20, what mainly differentiates dry tundra and deserts?
2. Identify the natural biome in which you live and summarize its abiotic and biotic characteristics. Do these reflect your actual surroundings? Explain.
3. **WHAT IF?** If global warming increases average temperatures on Earth by 4°C in this century, predict which biome is most likely to replace tundra in some locations as a result. Explain your answer.

For suggested answers, see Appendix A.

Exploring Terrestrial Biomes

Tropical Forest

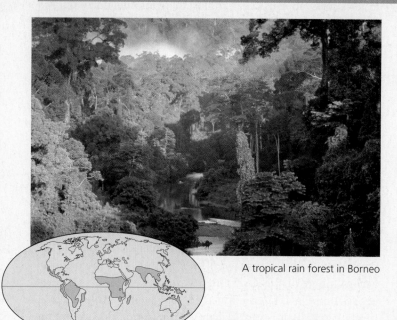

A tropical rain forest in Borneo

Distribution Equatorial and subequatorial regions.

Precipitation In **tropical rain forests**, rainfall is relatively constant, about 200–400 cm annually. In **tropical dry forests**, precipitation is highly seasonal, about 150–200 cm annually, with a six- to seven-month dry season.

Temperature Air temperatures are high year-round, averaging 25–29°C with little seasonal variation.

Plants Tropical forests are vertically layered, and competition for light is intense. Layers in rain forests include emergent trees that grow above a closed canopy, the canopy trees, one or two layers of subcanopy trees, and shrub and herb layers. There are generally fewer layers in tropical dry forests. Broadleaf evergreen trees are dominant in tropical rain forests, whereas tropical dry forest trees drop their leaves during the dry season. Epiphytes such as bromeliads and orchids generally cover tropical forest trees but are less abundant in dry forests. Thorny shrubs and succulent plants are common in some tropical dry forests.

Animals Earth's tropical forests are home to millions of species, including an estimated 5–30 million still undescribed species of insects, spiders, and other arthropods. In fact, animal diversity is higher in tropical forests than in any other terrestrial biome. The animals, including amphibians, birds and other reptiles, mammals, and arthropods, are adapted to the vertically layered environment and are often inconspicuous.

Human Impact Humans long ago established thriving communities in tropical forests. Rapid population growth leading to agriculture and development is now destroying some tropical forests.

Desert

A desert in the southwestern United States

Distribution **Deserts** occur in bands near 30° north and south latitude or at other latitudes in the interior of continents (for instance, the Gobi Desert of north central Asia).

Precipitation Precipitation is low and highly variable, generally less than 30 cm per year.

Temperature Temperature is variable seasonally and daily. Maximum air temperature in hot deserts may exceed 50°C; in cold deserts air temperature may fall below −30°C.

Plants Desert landscapes are dominated by low, widely scattered vegetation; the proportion of bare ground is high compared with other terrestrial biomes. The plants include succulents such as cacti, deeply rooted shrubs, and herbs that grow during the infrequent moist periods. Desert plant adaptations include heat and desiccation tolerance, water storage, and reduced leaf surface area. Physical defenses, such as spines, and chemical defenses, such as toxins in the leaves of shrubs, are common. Many of the plants exhibit C_4 or CAM photosynthesis (see Chapter 10).

Animals Common desert animals include many kinds of snakes and lizards, scorpions, ants, beetles, migratory and resident birds, and seed-eating rodents. Many species are nocturnal. Water conservation is a common adaptation, with some species surviving on water from metabolic breakdown of carbohydrates in seeds.

Human Impact Long-distance transport of water and deep groundwater wells have allowed humans to maintain substantial populations in deserts. Conversion to irrigated agriculture and urbanization have reduced the natural biodiversity of some deserts.

Savanna

Distribution   Equatorial and subequatorial regions.

Precipitation   Rainfall, which is seasonal, averages 30–50 cm per year. The dry season can last up to eight or nine months.

Temperature   The **savanna** is warm year-round, averaging 24–29°C, but with somewhat more seasonal variation than in tropical forests.

Plants   The scattered trees found at different densities in the savanna often are thorny and have small leaves, an apparent adaptation to the relatively dry conditions. Fires are common in the dry season, and the dominant plant species are fire-adapted and tolerant of seasonal drought. Grasses and forbs, which make up most of the ground cover, grow rapidly in response to seasonal rains and are tolerant of grazing by large mammals and other herbivores.

Animals   Large plant-eating mammals, such as wildebeests and bison, and predators, including lions and hyenas, are common inhabitants. However, the dominant herbivores are actually insects, especially termites. During seasonal droughts, grazing mammals often migrate to parts of the savanna with more forage and scattered watering holes.

Human Impact   There is evidence that the earliest humans lived in savannas. Fires set by humans may help maintain this biome. Cattle ranching and over-hunting have led to declines in large-mammal populations.

A savanna in Kenya

Chaparral

Distribution   This biome occurs in midlatitude coastal regions on several continents, and its many names reflect its far-flung distribution: **chaparral** in North America, *matorral* in Spain and Chile, *garigue* and *maquis* in southern France, and *fynbos* in South Africa.

Precipitation   Precipitation is highly seasonal, with rainy winters and long, dry summers. Annual precipitation generally falls within the range of 30–50 cm.

Temperature   Fall, winter, and spring are cool, with average temperatures in the range of 10–12°C. Average summer temperature can reach 30°C, and daytime maximum temperature can exceed 40°C.

Plants   Chaparral is dominated by shrubs and small trees, along with a many kinds of grasses and herbs. Plant diversity is high, with many species confined to a specific, relatively small geographic area. Adaptations to drought include the tough evergreen leaves of woody plants, which reduce water loss. Adaptations to fire are also prominent. Some of the shrubs produce seeds that will germinate only after a hot fire; food reserves stored in their fire-resistant roots enable them to resprout quickly and use nutrients released by the fire.

Animals   Native mammals include browsers, such as deer and goats, that feed on twigs and buds of woody vegetation, and a high diversity of small mammals. Chaparral areas also support many species of amphibians, birds and other reptiles, and insects.

Human Impact   Chaparral areas have been heavily settled and reduced through conversion to agriculture and urbanization. Humans contribute to the fires that sweep across the chaparral.

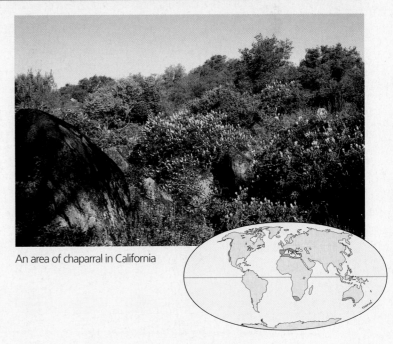

An area of chaparral in California

Continued on next page

Exploring Terrestrial Biomes

Temperate Grassland

Sheyenne National Grassland in North Dakota

Distribution The veldts of South Africa, the *puszta* of Hungary, the pampas of Argentina and Uruguay, the steppes of Russia, and the plains and prairies of central North America are all **temperate grasslands**.

Precipitation Precipitation is often highly seasonal, with relatively dry winters and wet summers. Annual precipitation generally averages between 30 and 100 cm. Periodic drought is common.

Temperature Winters are generally cold, with average temperatures frequently falling well below −10°C. Summers, with average temperatures often approaching 30°C, are hot.

Plants The dominant plants are grasses and forbs, which vary in height from a few centimeters to 2 m in tallgrass prairie. Many have adaptations that help them survive periodic, protracted droughts and fire: For example, grasses can sprout quickly following fire. Grazing by large mammals helps prevent establishment of woody shrubs and trees.

Animals Native mammals include large grazers such as bison and wild horses. Temperate grasslands are also inhabited by a wide variety of burrowing mammals, such as prairie dogs in North America.

Human Impact Deep, fertile soils make temperate grasslands ideal places for agriculture, especially for growing grains. As a consequence, most grassland in North America and much of Eurasia has been converted to farmland. In some drier grasslands, cattle and other grazers have helped change parts of the biome into desert.

Northern Coniferous Forest

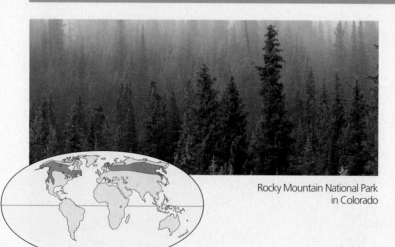

Rocky Mountain National Park in Colorado

Distribution Extending in a broad band across northern North America and Eurasia to the edge of the arctic tundra, the **northern coniferous forest**, or *taiga*, is the largest terrestrial biome on Earth.

Precipitation Annual precipitation generally ranges from 30 to 70 cm, and periodic droughts are common. However, some coastal coniferous forests of the U.S. Pacific Northwest are temperate rain forests that may receive over 300 cm of annual precipitation.

Temperature Winters are usually cold and long; summers may be hot. Some areas of coniferous forest in Siberia typically range in temperature from −50°C in winter to over 20°C in summer.

Plants Cone-bearing trees, such as pine, spruce, fir, and hemlock, dominate northern coniferous forests. The conical shape of many conifers prevents too much snow from accumulating and breaking their branches. The diversity of plants in the shrub and herb layers of these forests is lower than in temperate broadleaf forests.

Animals While many migratory birds nest in northern coniferous forests, other species reside there year-round. The mammals of this biome, which include moose, brown bears, and Siberian tigers, are diverse. Periodic outbreaks of insects that feed on the dominant trees can kill vast tracts of trees.

Human Impact Although they have not been heavily settled by human populations, northern coniferous forests are being logged at an alarming rate, and the old-growth stands of these trees may soon disappear.

Temperate Broadleaf Forest

Distribution   Found mainly at midlatitudes in the Northern Hemisphere, with smaller areas in New Zealand and Australia.

Precipitation   Precipitation can average from about 70 to over 200 cm annually. Significant amounts fall during all seasons, including summer rain and, in some forests, winter snow.

Temperature   Winter temperatures average around 0°C. Summers, with maximum temperatures near 35°C, are hot and humid.

Plants   A mature **temperate broadleaf forest** has distinct vertical layers, including a closed canopy, one or two strata of understory trees, a shrub layer, and an herbaceous stratum. There are few epiphytes. The dominant plants in the Northern Hemisphere are deciduous trees, which drop their leaves before winter, when low temperatures would reduce photosynthesis and make water uptake from frozen soil difficult. In Australia, evergreen eucalyptus dominate these forests.

Animals   In the Northern Hemisphere, many mammals hibernate in winter, while many bird species migrate to warmer climates. The mammals, birds, and insects make use of all vertical layers of the forest.

Human Impact   Temperate broadleaf forest has been heavily settled on all continents. Logging and land clearing for agriculture and urban development destroyed virtually all the original deciduous forests in North America. However, owing to their capacity for recovery, these forests are returning over much of their former range.

Great Smoky Mountains National Park in North Carolina

Tundra

Distribution   **Tundra** covers expansive areas of the Arctic, amounting to 20% of Earth's land surface. High winds and low temperatures create similar plant communities, called *alpine tundra*, on very high mountaintops at all latitudes, including the tropics.

Precipitation   Precipitation averages from 20 to 60 cm annually in arctic tundra but may exceed 100 cm in alpine tundra.

Temperature   Winters are long and cold, with averages in some areas below −30°C. Summers are short with low temperatures, generally averaging less than 10°C.

Plants   The vegetation of tundra is mostly herbaceous, consisting of a mixture of mosses, grasses, and forbs, along with some dwarf shrubs and trees and lichens. A permanently frozen layer of soil called **permafrost** restricts the growth of plant roots.

Animals   Large grazing musk oxen are resident, while caribou and reindeer are migratory. Predators include bears, wolves, and foxes. Many bird species migrate to the tundra for summer nesting.

Human Impact   Tundra is sparsely settled but has become the focus of significant mineral and oil extraction in recent years.

Denali National Park, Alaska, in autumn

MEDIA Go to the Study Area at **www.masteringbio.com** for BioFlix 3-D Animations, MP3 Tutors, Videos, Practice Tests, an eBook, and more.

SUMMARY OF KEY CONCEPTS

CONCEPT **52.1**

Ecology integrates all areas of biological research and informs environmental decision making (pp. 1148–1151)

▶ **Linking Ecology and Evolutionary Biology** Events that occur in ecological time affect life in evolutionary time.

▶ **Ecology and Environmental Issues** Ecologists distinguish between the science of ecology and environmental advocacy. Ecology provides a scientific basis for solving environmental problems, but policymakers must also balance social, economic, and political factors in reaching their decisions.

MEDIA

Activity Science, Technology, and Society: DDT

CONCEPT **52.2**

Interactions between organisms and the environment limit the distribution of species (pp. 1151–1159)

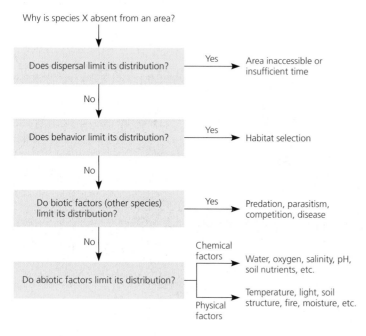

Why is species X absent from an area?

Does dispersal limit its distribution? → Yes → Area inaccessible or insufficient time

No

Does behavior limit its distribution? → Yes → Habitat selection

No

Do biotic factors (other species) limit its distribution? → Yes → Predation, parasitism, competition, disease

No

Do abiotic factors limit its distribution?
Chemical factors → Water, oxygen, salinity, pH, soil nutrients, etc.
Physical factors → Temperature, light, soil structure, fire, moisture, etc.

▶ **Climate** Global climate patterns are largely determined by the input of solar energy and Earth's revolution around the sun. Bodies of water, mountains, and the changing angle of the sun over the year exert regional, local, and seasonal effects on climate. Fine-scale differences in abiotic factors determine microclimates.

MEDIA

Activity Adaptations to Biotic and Abiotic Factors
Investigation How Do Abiotic Factors Affect Distribution of Organisms?

CONCEPT **52.3**

Aquatic biomes are diverse and dynamic systems that cover most of Earth (pp. 1159–1166)

▶ **Stratification of Aquatic Biomes** Aquatic biomes account for the largest part of the biosphere in terms of area and are generally stratified (layered) with regard to light penetration, temperature, and community structure. Marine biomes have a higher salt concentration than freshwater biomes.

MEDIA

Activity Aquatic Biomes

CONCEPT **52.4**

The structure and distribution of terrestrial biomes are controlled by climate and disturbance (pp. 1166–1171)

▶ **Climate and Terrestrial Biomes** Climographs show that temperature and precipitation are correlated with biomes, but because biomes overlap, other abiotic factors play a role in biome location.

▶ **General Features of Terrestrial Biomes and the Role of Disturbance** Terrestrial biomes are often named for major physical or climatic factors and for their predominant vegetation. Vertical layering is an important feature of terrestrial biomes. Disturbance, both natural and human induced, influences the type of vegetation found in biomes.

MEDIA

Activity Terrestrial Biomes

TESTING YOUR KNOWLEDGE

SELF-QUIZ

1. Which of the following areas of study focuses on the exchange of energy, organisms, and materials between ecosystems?
   a. population ecology
   b. organismal ecology
   c. landscape ecology
   d. ecosystem ecology
   e. community ecology

2. **WHAT IF?** If Earth's axis of rotation suddenly became perpendicular to the plane of its orbit, the most predictable effect would be
   a. no more night and day.
   b. a big change in the length of the year.
   c. a cooling of the equator.
   d. a loss of seasonal variation at high latitudes.
   e. the elimination of ocean currents.

3. When climbing a mountain, we can observe transitions in biological communities that are analogous to the changes
   a. in biomes at different latitudes.
   b. at different depths in the ocean.
   c. in a community through different seasons.
   d. in an ecosystem as it evolves over time.
   e. across the United States from east to west.

4. The oceans affect the biosphere in all of the following ways *except*
   a. producing a substantial amount of the biosphere's oxygen.
   b. removing carbon dioxide from the atmosphere.
   c. moderating the climate of terrestrial biomes.
   d. regulating the pH of freshwater biomes and terrestrial groundwater.
   e. being the source of most of Earth's rainfall.

5. Which lake zone would be absent in a very shallow lake?
   a. benthic zone
   b. aphotic zone
   c. pelagic zone
   d. littoral zone
   e. limnetic zone

6. Which of the following is true with respect to oligotrophic lakes and eutrophic lakes?
   a. Oligotrophic lakes are more subject to oxygen depletion.
   b. Rates of photosynthesis are lower in eutrophic lakes.
   c. Eutrophic lake water contains lower concentrations of nutrients.
   d. Eutrophic lakes are richer in nutrients.
   e. Sediments in oligotrophic lakes contain larger amounts of decomposable organic matter.

7. Which of the following is characteristic of most terrestrial biomes?
   a. annual average rainfall in excess of 250 cm
   b. a distribution predicted almost entirely by rock and soil patterns
   c. clear boundaries between adjacent biomes
   d. vegetation demonstrating stratification
   e. cold winter months

8. Which of the following biomes is correctly paired with the description of its climate?
   a. savanna—low temperature, precipitation uniform during the year
   b. tundra—long summers, mild winters
   c. temperate broadleaf forest—relatively short growing season, mild winters
   d. temperate grasslands—relatively warm winters, most rainfall in summer
   e. tropical forests—nearly constant day length and temperature

9. Suppose that the number of bird species is determined mainly by the number of vertical strata found in the environment. If so, in which of the following biomes would you find the greatest number of bird species?
   a. tropical rain forest
   b. savanna
   c. desert
   d. temperate broadleaf forest
   e. temperate grassland

10. **DRAW IT** After reading the experiment of W. J. Fletcher described in Figure 52.8, you decide to study feeding relationships among sea otters, sea urchins, and kelp on your own. You know that sea otters prey on sea urchins and that urchins eat kelp. At four coastal sites, you measure kelp abundance. Then you spend one day at each site and mark whether otters are present or absent every 5 minutes during daylight hours. Make a graph that shows how otter density depends on kelp abundance, using the data shown below. Then formulate a hypothesis to explain the pattern you observed.

Site	Kelp Abundance (% cover)	Otter Density (# sightings per day)
1	75	98
2	15	18
3	60	85
4	25	36

For Self-Quiz answers, see Appendix A.

MEDIA Visit the Study Area at **www.masteringbio.com** for a Practice Test.

EVOLUTION CONNECTION

11. Discuss how the concept of time applies to ecological situations and evolutionary changes. Do ecological time and evolutionary time ever overlap? If so, what are some examples?

SCIENTIFIC INQUIRY

12. Jens Clausen and colleagues, at the Carnegie Institution of Washington, studied how the size of yarrow plants (*Achillea lanulosa*) growing on the slopes of the Sierra Nevada varied with elevation. They found that plants from low elevations were generally taller than plants from high elevations, as shown below:

Source: J. Clausen et al., Experimental studies on the nature of species. III. Environmental responses of climatic races of *Achillea,* Carnegie Institution of Washington Publication No. 581 (1948).

Clausen and colleagues proposed two hypotheses to explain this variation within a species: (1) There are genetic differences between populations of plants found at different elevations. (2) The species has developmental flexibility and can assume tall or short growth forms, depending on local abiotic factors. If you had seeds from yarrow plants found at low and high elevations, what experiments would you perform to test these hypotheses?

Population Ecology 53

▲ Figure 53.1 **What causes a sheep population to fluctuate in size?**

KEY CONCEPTS

53.1 Dynamic biological processes influence population density, dispersion, and demographics

53.2 Life history traits are products of natural selection

53.3 The exponential model describes population growth in an idealized, unlimited environment

53.4 The logistic model describes how a population grows more slowly as it nears its carrying capacity

53.5 Many factors that regulate population growth are density dependent

53.6 The human population is no longer growing exponentially but is still increasing rapidly

OVERVIEW

Counting Sheep

On the rugged Scottish island of Hirta, ecologists have been studying a population of sheep for more than 50 years **(Figure 53.1)**. What makes these animals worth studying for such a long time? Soay sheep are a rare and ancient breed, the closest living relative of the domesticated sheep that lived in Europe thousands of years ago. To help preserve the breed, in 1932 conservationists captured sheep on Soay Island, at the time the animals' only home, and released them on nearby Hirta. There, the sheep became valuable for a second reason: They provided an ideal opportunity to study how an isolated population of animals changes in size when food is plentiful and predators are absent. Surprisingly, ecologists found that the number of sheep on Hirta swung dramatically under these conditions, sometimes changing by more than 50% from one year to the next.

Why do populations of some species fluctuate greatly while populations of other species do not? To answer this question, we turn to the field of **population ecology**, the study of populations in relation to their environment. Population ecology explores how biotic and abiotic factors influence the density, distribution, size, and age structure of populations.

Our earlier study of populations in Chapter 23 emphasized the relationship between population genetics—the structure and dynamics of gene pools—and evolution. Evolution remains a central theme as we now view populations in the context of ecology. In this chapter, we will first examine some of the structural and dynamic aspects of populations. We will then explore the tools and models ecologists use to analyze populations and the factors that regulate the abundance of organisms. Finally, we will apply these basic concepts as we examine recent trends in the size and makeup of the human population.

CONCEPT 53.1

Dynamic biological processes influence population density, dispersion, and demographics

A **population** is a group of individuals of a single species living in the same general area. Members of a population rely on the same resources, are influenced by similar environmental factors, and are likely to interact and breed with one another. Populations can evolve as natural selection acts on heritable variations among individuals and changes the frequencies of various traits over time (see Chapter 23).

Three fundamental characteristics of a population are its density, dispersion, and demographics.

Density and Dispersion

At any given moment, a population has specific boundaries and a specific size (the number of individuals living within those boundaries). Ecologists usually begin investigating a population by defining boundaries appropriate to the organism under study and to the questions being asked. A population's boundaries may be natural ones, as in the case of the sheep on Hirta Island, or they may be arbitrarily defined by an investigator—for example, the oak trees within a specific county in Minnesota. Once defined, the population can be described in terms of its density and dispersion. **Density** is the number of individuals per unit area or volume: the number of oak trees per square kilometer in the Minnesota county or the number of *Escherichia coli* bacteria per milliliter in a test tube. **Dispersion** is the pattern of spacing among individuals within the boundaries of the population.

Density: A Dynamic Perspective

In rare cases, population size and density can be determined by counting all individuals within the boundaries of the population. We could count all the Soay sheep on Hirta Island or all the sea stars in a tide pool, for example. Large mammals that live in herds, such as buffalo or elephants, can sometimes be counted accurately from airplanes. In most cases, however, it is impractical or impossible to count all individuals in a population. Instead, ecologists use a variety of sampling techniques to estimate densities and total population sizes. For example, they might count the number of oak trees in several randomly located 100 × 100 m plots (samples), calculate the average density in the samples, and then extrapolate to estimate the population size in the entire area. Such estimates are most accurate when there are many sample plots and when the habitat is fairly homogeneous. In other cases, instead of counting individual organisms, population ecologists estimate density from an index (indicator) of population size, such as the number of nests, burrows, tracks, or fecal droppings. Ecologists also use the **mark-recapture method** to estimate the size of wildlife populations **(Figure 53.2)**.

Density is not a static property but changes as individuals are added to or removed from a population **(Figure 53.3)**.

▼ Figure 53.2 **Research Method**

Determining Population Size Using the Mark-Recapture Method

APPLICATION   Ecologists cannot count all the individuals in a population if the organisms move too quickly or are hidden from view. In such cases, researchers often use the mark-recapture method to estimate population size. Andrew Gormley and colleagues at the University of Otago applied this method to a population of endangered Hector's dolphins (*Cephalorhynchus hectori*) near Banks Peninsula, in New Zealand.

Hector's dolphins

TECHNIQUE   Scientists typically begin by capturing a random sample of individuals in a population. They tag, or "mark," each individual and then release it. With some species, researchers can identify individuals without physically capturing them. For example, Gormley and colleagues identified 180 Hector's dolphins by photographing their distinctive dorsal fins from boats.

After waiting for the marked or otherwise identified individuals to mix back into the population, usually a few days or weeks, scientists capture or sample a second set of individuals. At Banks Peninsula, Gormley's team encountered 44 dolphins in their second sampling, 7 of which they had photographed before. The number of marked animals recaptured in the second sampling (x) divided by the total number of individuals recaptured (n) should equal the number of individuals marked and released in the first sampling (m) divided by the estimated population size (N):

$$\frac{x}{n} = \frac{m}{N} \qquad \text{or, solving for population size,} \qquad N = \frac{mn}{x}$$

The method assumes that marked and unmarked individuals have the same probability of being captured or sampled, that the marked organisms have mixed completely back into the population, and that no individuals are born, die, immigrate, or emigrate during the resampling interval.

RESULTS   Based on these initial data, the estimated population size of Hector's dolphins at Banks Peninsula would be 180 × 44/7 = 1,131 individuals. Repeated sampling by Gormley and colleagues suggested a true population size closer to 1,100.

SOURCE   A. M. Gormley et al., Capture-recapture estimates of Hector's dolphin abundance at Banks Peninsula, New Zealand, *Marine Mammal Science* 21:204–216 (2005).

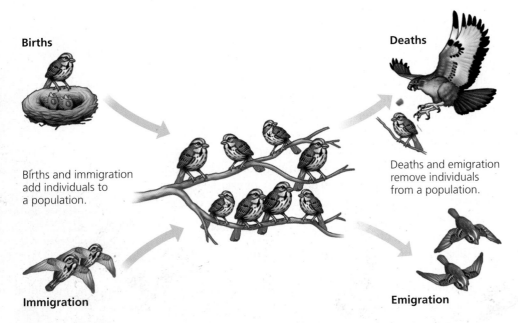

Births

Births and immigration add individuals to a population.

Immigration

Deaths

Deaths and emigration remove individuals from a population.

Emigration

▲ Figure 53.3 **Population dynamics.**

Additions occur through birth (which we will define in this context to include all forms of reproduction) and **immigration**, the influx of new individuals from other areas. The factors that remove individuals from a population are death (mortality) and **emigration**, the movement of individuals out of a population.

While birth and death rates influence the density of all populations, immigration and emigration also alter the density of many populations. For example, long-term studies of Belding's ground squirrels (*Spermophilus beldingi*) in the vicinity of Tioga Pass, in the Sierra Nevada of California, show that some of the squirrels move nearly 2 km from where they are born, making them immigrants to other populations. Paul Sherman and Martin Morton, then at Cornell University and Occidental College, respectively, estimated that immigrants made up 1–8% of the males and 0.7–6% of the females in the study population. Although these immigrant percentages may seem small, they represent biologically significant exchanges between populations over time.

Patterns of Dispersion

Within a population's geographic range, local densities may vary substantially. Variations in local density are among the most important characteristics for a population ecologist to study, since they provide insight into the environmental associations and social interactions of individuals in the population. Environmental differences—even at a local level—contribute to variation in population density; some habitat patches are simply more suitable for a species than are others. Social interactions between members of the population, which may maintain patterns of spacing between individuals, can also contribute to variation in population density.

The most common pattern of dispersion is *clumped*, with the individuals aggregated in patches. Plants and fungi are often clumped where soil conditions and other environmental factors favor germination and growth. Mushrooms, for instance, may be clumped within and on top of a rotting log. Insects and salamanders may be clumped under the same log because of the higher humidity there. Clumping of animals may also be associated with mating behavior. Mayflies, which survive only a day or two as mating adults, often swarm in great numbers, a behavior that increases their chance of mating. Sea stars group together in tide pools, where food is readily available and where they can breed successfully **(Figure 53.4a)**. Forming groups may also increase the effectiveness of certain predators; for example, a wolf pack is more likely than a single wolf to subdue a moose or other large prey animal.

A *uniform*, or evenly spaced, pattern of dispersion may result from direct interactions between individuals in the population. For example, some plants secrete chemicals that inhibit the germination and growth of nearby individuals that could compete for resources. Animals often exhibit uniform dispersion as a result of antagonistic social interactions, such as **territoriality**—the defense of a bounded physical space against encroachment

(a) Clumped. Many animals, such as these sea stars, group together where food is abundant.

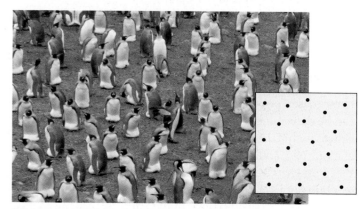

(b) Uniform. Birds nesting on small islands, such as these king penguins on South Georgia Island in the South Atlantic Ocean, often exhibit uniform spacing, maintained by aggressive interactions between neighbors.

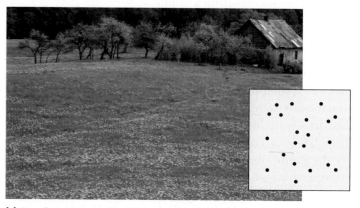

(c) Random. Many plants, such as these dandelions, grow from windblown seeds that land at random and later germinate.

▲ **Figure 53.4 Patterns of dispersion within a population's geographic range.**
WHAT IF? *Patterns of dispersion sometimes depend on the scale of the observation. How might the dispersion of the penguins look to you if you were flying in an airplane over the ocean?*

by other individuals **(Figure 53.4b)**. Uniform patterns are not as common in populations as clumped patterns are.

In *random* dispersion (unpredictable spacing), the position of each individual is independent of other individuals. This pattern occurs in the absence of strong attractions or repulsions among individuals of a population or where key physical or chemical factors are relatively homogeneous across the study area. For example, plants established by windblown seeds, such as dandelions, may be randomly distributed in a fairly consistent habitat (Figure 53.4c). Random patterns are not as common in nature as one might expect; most populations show at least a tendency toward a clumped distribution.

Demographics

The factors that influence population density and dispersion patterns—ecological needs of a species, structure of the environment, and interactions between individuals within the population—also influence other characteristics of populations. **Demography** is the study of the vital statistics of populations and how they change over time. Of particular interest to demographers are birth rates and how they vary among individuals (specifically among females, as you'll read shortly) and death rates. A useful way of summarizing some of the vital statistics of a population is with a life table.

Life Tables

About a century ago, when life insurance first became available, insurance companies began to estimate how long, on average, individuals of a given age could be expected to live. To do this,

demographers developed **life tables**, age-specific summaries of the survival pattern of a population. Population ecologists adapted this approach to the study of nonhuman populations.

The best way to construct a life table is to follow the fate of a **cohort**, a group of individuals of the same age, from birth until all are dead. To build the life table, we need to determine the number of individuals that die in each age-group and calculate the proportion of the cohort surviving from one age to the next. Sherman and Morton's studies of the Belding's ground squirrels near Tioga Pass produced the life table in **Table 53.1**. The table reveals many things about the population. For instance, the third and eighth columns list, respectively, the proportions of females and males in the cohort that are still alive at each age. A comparison of the fifth and tenth columns reveals that males have higher death rates than females.

Survivorship Curves

A graphic method of representing the data in a life table is a **survivorship curve**, a plot of the proportion or numbers in a cohort still alive at each age. As an example, let's use the data for Belding's ground squirrels in Table 53.1 to construct a survivorship curve for this population. Generally, a survivorship curve is constructed beginning with a cohort of a specified size—say, 1,000 individuals. We can do this for the Belding's ground squirrel population by multiplying the proportion

Table 53.1 Life Table for Belding's Ground Squirrels (*Spermophilus beldingi*) at Tioga Pass, in the Sierra Nevada of California*

Age (years)	FEMALES					MALES				
	Number Alive at Start of Year	Proportion Alive at Start of Year	Number of Deaths During Year	Death Rate[†]	Average Additional Life Expectancy (years)	Number Alive at Start of Year	Proportion Alive at Start of Year	Number of Deaths During Year	Death Rate[†]	Average Additional Life Expectancy (years)
0–1	337	1.000	207	0.61	1.33	349	1.000	227	0.65	1.07
1–2	252[††]	0.386	125	0.50	1.56	248[††]	0.350	140	0.56	1.12
2–3	127	0.197	60	0.47	1.60	108	0.152	74	0.69	0.93
3–4	67	0.106	32	0.48	1.59	34	0.048	23	0.68	0.89
4–5	35	0.054	16	0.46	1.59	11	0.015	9	0.82	0.68
5–6	19	0.029	10	0.53	1.50	2	0.003	0	1.00	0.50
6–7	9	0.014	4	0.44	1.61	0				
7–8	5	0.008	1	0.20	1.50					
8–9	4	0.006	3	0.75	0.75					
9–10	1	0.002	1	1.00	0.50					

*Females and males have different mortality schedules, so they are tallied separately.
[†]The death rate is the proportion of individuals dying during the specific time interval.
[††]Includes 122 females and 126 males first captured as 1-year-olds and therefore not included in the count of squirrels age 0–1.

Source: P. W. Sherman and M. L. Morton, Demography of Belding's ground squirrel, *Ecology* 65:1617–1628 (1984).

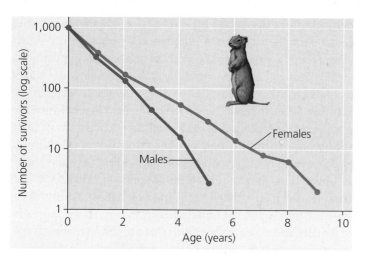

▲ **Figure 53.5 Survivorship curves for male and female Belding's ground squirrels.** The logarithmic scale on the *y*-axis allows the number of survivors to be visible across the entire range (2–1,000 individuals) on the graph.

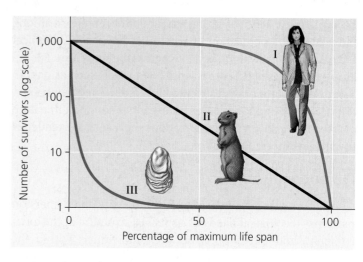

▲ **Figure 53.6 Idealized survivorship curves: Types I, II, and III.** The *y*-axis is logarithmic and the *x*-axis is on a relative scale, so that species with widely varying life spans can be presented together on the same graph.

alive at the start of each year (the third and eighth columns of Table 53.1) by 1,000 (the hypothetical beginning cohort). The result is the number alive at the start of each year. Plotting these numbers versus age for female and male Belding's ground squirrels yields **Figure 53.5**. The relatively straight lines of the plots indicate relatively constant rates of death; however, male Belding's ground squirrels have a lower survival rate overall than females have.

Figure 53.5 represents just one of many patterns of survivorship exhibited by natural populations. Though diverse, survivorship curves can be classified into three general types **(Figure 53.6)**. A Type I curve is flat at the start, reflecting low death rates during early and middle life, and then drops steeply as death rates increase among older age-groups. Many large mammals, including humans, that produce few offspring but provide them with good care exhibit this kind of curve. In contrast, a Type III curve drops sharply at the start, reflecting very high death rates for the young, but flattens out as death rates decline for those few individuals that survive the early period of die-off. This type of curve is usually associated with organisms that produce very large numbers of offspring but provide little or no care, such as long-lived plants, many fishes, and most marine invertebrates. An oyster, for example, may release millions of eggs, but most offspring die in the larval stage from predation or other causes. Those few that survive long enough to attach to a suitable substrate and begin growing a hard shell tend to survive for a relatively long time. Type II curves are intermediate, with a constant death rate over the organism's life span. This kind of survivorship occurs in Belding's ground squirrels (see Figure 53.5) and some other rodents, various invertebrates, some lizards, and some annual plants.

Many species fall somewhere between these basic types of survivorship or show more complex patterns. In birds, for example, mortality is often high among the youngest individuals

(as in a Type III curve) but fairly constant among adults (as in a Type II curve). Some invertebrates, such as crabs, may show a "stair-stepped" curve, with brief periods of increased mortality during molts, followed by periods of lower mortality when their protective exoskeleton is hard.

In populations not experiencing immigration or emigration, survivorship is one of the two key factors determining changes in population size. The other key factor determining population trends in such populations is reproductive rate.

Reproductive Rates

Demographers who study sexually reproducing species generally ignore the males and concentrate on the females in a population because only females produce offspring. Therefore, demographers view populations in terms of females giving rise to new females. The simplest way to describe the reproductive pattern of a population is to ask how reproductive output varies with the ages of females.

A **reproductive table**, or fertility schedule, is an age-specific summary of the reproductive rates in a population. It is constructed by measuring the reproductive output of a cohort from birth until death. For a sexual species, the reproductive table tallies the number of female offspring produced by each age-group. **Table 53.2** illustrates a reproductive table for Belding's ground squirrels. Reproductive output for sexual organisms such as birds and mammals is the product of the proportion of females of a given age that are breeding and the number of female offspring of those breeding females. Multiplying these numbers gives the average number of female offspring for each female in a given age-group (the last column in Table 53.2). For Belding's ground squirrels, which begin to reproduce at age 1 year, reproductive output rises to a peak at 4 years of age and then falls off in older females.

Age (years)	Proportion of Females Weaning a Litter	Mean Size of Litters (Males + Females)	Mean Number of Females in a Litter	Average Number of Female Offspring*
0–1	0.00	0.00	0.00	0.00
1–2	0.65	3.30	1.65	1.07
2–3	0.92	4.05	2.03	1.87
3–4	0.90	4.90	2.45	2.21
4–5	0.95	5.45	2.73	2.59
5–6	1.00	4.15	2.08	2.08
6–7	1.00	3.40	1.70	1.70
7–8	1.00	3.85	1.93	1.93
8–9	1.00	3.85	1.93	1.93
9–10	1.00	3.15	1.58	1.58

*The average number of female offspring is the proportion weaning a litter multiplied by the mean number of females in a litter.

Source: P. W. Sherman and M. L. Morton, Demography of Belding's ground squirrel, *Ecology* 65:1617–1628 (1984).

Reproductive tables vary greatly, depending on the species. Squirrels have a litter of two to six young once a year for less than a decade, whereas oak trees drop thousands of acorns each year for tens or hundreds of years. Mussels and other invertebrates may release hundreds of thousands of eggs in a spawning cycle. Why a particular type of reproductive pattern evolves in a particular population—one of many questions at the interface of population ecology and evolutionary biology—is the subject of life history studies, the topic of the next section.

CONCEPT CHECK 53.1

1. One species of forest bird is highly territorial, while a second lives in flocks. Predict each species' likely pattern of dispersion, and explain.
2. **DRAW IT** Each female of a particular fish species produces millions of eggs per year. Draw and label the most likely survivorship curve for this species, and explain your choice.
3. **WHAT IF?** As noted in Figure 53.2, an important assumption of the mark-recapture method is that marked individuals have the same probability of being recaptured as unmarked individuals. Describe a situation where this assumption might not be valid, and explain how the estimate of population size would be affected.

For suggested answers, see Appendix A.

CONCEPT 53.2
Life history traits are products of natural selection

Natural selection favors traits that improve an organism's chances of survival and reproductive success. In every species, there are trade-offs between survival and traits such as frequency of reproduction, number of offspring produced (number of seeds produced by plants; litter or clutch size for animals), and investment in parental care. The traits that affect an organism's schedule of reproduction and survival (from birth through reproduction to death) make up its **life history**. A life history entails three basic variables: when reproduction begins (the age at first reproduction or age at maturity), how often the organism reproduces, and how many offspring are produced during each reproductive episode.

With the important exception of humans, which we will consider later in the chapter, organisms do not choose consciously when to reproduce or how many offspring to have. Rather, organisms' life history traits are evolutionary outcomes reflected in their development, physiology, and behavior.

Evolution and Life History Diversity

The fundamental idea that evolution accounts for the diversity of life is manifest in a broad range of life histories found in nature. Pacific salmon, for example, hatch in the headwaters of a stream and then migrate to the open ocean, where they require one to four years to mature. The salmon eventually return to the freshwater stream to spawn, producing thousands of eggs in a single reproductive opportunity before they die. This "one-shot" pattern of **big-bang reproduction**, or **semelparity** (from the Latin *semel*, once, and *parere*, to beget), also occurs in some plants, such as the agave, or "century plant" (**Figure 53.7**).

▶ Figure 53.7 **An agave (*Agave americana*), an example of big-bang reproduction.** The leaves of the plant are visible at the base of the giant flowering stalk, which is produced only at the end of the agave's life.

Agaves generally grow in arid climates with unpredictable rainfall and poor soils. An agave grows for years, accumulating nutrients in its tissues, until there is an unusually wet year. It then sends up a large flowering stalk, produces seeds, and dies. This life history is an adaptation to the agave's harsh desert environment.

In contrast to semelparity is **iteroparity** (from the Latin *iterare*, to repeat), or **repeated reproduction**. Some lizards, for example, produce a few large eggs during their second year of life and then reproduce annually for several years.

What factors contribute to the evolution of semelparity versus iteroparity? A current hypothesis suggests that there are two critical factors: the survival rate of the offspring and the likelihood that the adult will survive to reproduce again. Where the survival rate of offspring is low, typically in highly variable or unpredictable environments, the prediction is that big-bang reproduction (semelparity) will be favored. Adults are also less likely to survive in such environments, so producing large numbers of offspring should increase the probability that at least some of those offspring will survive. Repeated reproduction (iteroparity) may be favored in more dependable environments where adults are more likely to survive to breed again and where competition for resources may be intense. In such cases, a few relatively large, well-provisioned offspring should have a better chance of surviving until they are capable of reproducing.

Nature abounds with life histories that are intermediate between the two extremes of semelparity and iteroparity. Oak trees and sea urchins are examples of organisms that can live a long time but repeatedly produce relatively large numbers of offspring.

"Trade-offs" and Life Histories

Natural selection cannot maximize all reproductive variables simultaneously. We might imagine an organism that could produce as many offspring as a semelparous species, provision them well like an iteroparous species, and do so repeatedly, but such organisms do not exist. Time, energy, and nutrients limit the reproductive capabilities of all organisms. In the broadest sense, there is a trade-off between reproduction and survival. A study of red deer in Scotland showed that females that reproduced in a given summer were more likely to die during the next winter than females that did not reproduce. A study of European kestrels also demonstrated the survival cost to parents of caring for young (**Figure 53.8**).

Selective pressures influence the trade-off between the number and size of offspring. Plants and animals whose young are subject to high mortality rates often produce large numbers of relatively small offspring. Plants that colonize disturbed environments, for example, usually produce many small seeds, only a few of which may reach a suitable habitat. Small size may also increase the chance of seedling establish-

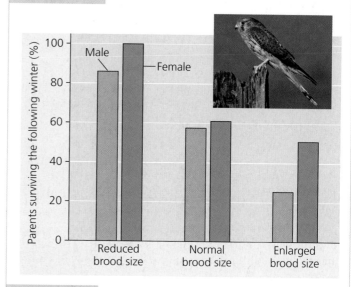

▼ **Figure 53.8** **Inquiry**

How does caring for offspring affect parental survival in kestrels?

EXPERIMENT Cor Dijkstra and colleagues in the Netherlands studied the effects of parental caregiving in European kestrels over five years. The researchers transferred chicks among nests to produce reduced broods (three or four chicks), normal broods (five or six), and enlarged broods (seven or eight). They then measured the percentage of male and female parent birds that survived the following winter. (Both males and females provide care for chicks.)

RESULTS

CONCLUSION The lower survival rates of kestrels with larger broods indicate that caring for more offspring negatively affects survival of the parents.

SOURCE C. Dijkstra et al., Brood size manipulations in the kestrel (*Falco tinnunculus*): effects on offspring and parent survival, *Journal of Animal Ecology* 59:269–285 (1990).

WHAT IF? The males of many bird species provide no parental care. If this were true for the European kestrel, how would the experimental results differ from those shown above?

ment by enabling the seeds to be carried longer distances to a broader range of habitats (**Figure 53.9a**). Animals that suffer high predation rates, such as quail, sardines, and mice, also tend to produce large numbers of offspring.

In other organisms, extra investment on the part of the parent greatly increases the offspring's chances of survival. Walnut trees and coconut palms both provision large seeds with energy and nutrients that help the seedlings become established (**Figure 53.9b**). In animals, parental investment in offspring does not always end after incubation or gestation. For instance, primates generally bear only one or two offspring at a time. Parental care and an extended period of learning in the first several years of life are very important to offspring fitness in these species.

(a) Most weedy plants, such as this dandelion, grow quickly and produce a large number of seeds, ensuring that at least some will grow into plants and eventually produce seeds themselves.

(b) Some plants, such as this coconut palm, produce a moderate number of very large seeds. Each seed's large endosperm provides nutrients for the embryo, an adaptation that helps ensure the success of a relatively large fraction of offspring.

▲ **Figure 53.9 Variation in the size of seed crops in plants.**

CONCEPT CHECK 53.2

1. Consider two rivers: One is spring fed and has a constant water volume and temperature year-round; the other drains a desert landscape and floods and dries out at unpredictable intervals. Which river would you predict is more likely to support many species of iteroparous animals? Why?

2. In the fish called the peacock wrasse (*Symphodus tinca*), females disperse some of their eggs widely and lay other eggs in a nest. Only the latter receive parental care. Explain the trade-offs in reproduction that this behavior illustrates.

3. **WHAT IF?** Mice that cannot find enough food or that experience other forms of stress will sometimes abandon their young. Explain how this behavior might have evolved in the context of reproductive trade-offs and life history.

For suggested answers, see Appendix A.

CONCEPT 53.3
The exponential model describes population growth in an idealized, unlimited environment

Populations of all species, regardless of their life histories, have the potential to expand greatly when resources are abundant. To appreciate the potential for population increase, consider a bacterium that can reproduce by fission every 20 minutes under ideal laboratory conditions. There would be 2 bacteria after 20 minutes, 4 after 40 minutes, and 8 after 60 minutes. If reproduction continued at this rate, with no mortality, for only a day and a half, there would be enough bacteria to form a layer a foot deep over the entire globe. At the other life history extreme, an elephant may produce only 6 offspring in a 100-year life span. Still, Charles Darwin once estimated that the descendants of a single pair of mating elephants would number 19 million within only 750 years. Darwin's estimate may not have been precisely correct, but such analyses led him to recognize the tremendous capacity for growth in all populations. Although unlimited growth does not occur for long in nature, studying population growth in an idealized, unlimited environment reveals the capacity of species for increase and the conditions under which that capacity may be expressed.

Per Capita Rate of Increase

Imagine a population consisting of a few individuals living in an ideal, unlimited environment. Under these conditions, there are no restrictions on the abilities of individuals to harvest energy, grow, and reproduce, aside from the inherent biological limitations of their life history traits. The population will increase in size with every birth and with the immigration of individuals from other populations, and it will decrease in size with every death and with the emigration of individuals out of the population. We can thus define a change in population size during a fixed time interval with the following verbal equation:

$$\begin{pmatrix} \text{Change in} \\ \text{population} \\ \text{size during} \\ \text{time} \\ \text{interval} \end{pmatrix} = \begin{pmatrix} \text{Births} \\ \text{during} \\ \text{time} \\ \text{interval} \end{pmatrix} + \begin{pmatrix} \text{Immigrants} \\ \text{entering} \\ \text{population} \\ \text{during time} \\ \text{interval} \end{pmatrix} - \begin{pmatrix} \text{Deaths} \\ \text{during} \\ \text{time} \\ \text{interval} \end{pmatrix} + \begin{pmatrix} \text{Emigrants} \\ \text{leaving} \\ \text{population} \\ \text{during time} \\ \text{interval} \end{pmatrix}$$

For simplicity here, we will ignore the effects of immigration and emigration, although a more complex formulation would certainly include these factors. We can also use mathematical notation to express this simplified relationship more concisely. If N represents population size and t represents time, then ΔN is the change in population size and Δt is the time interval (appropriate to the life span or generation time of the species) over which we are evaluating population growth. (The Greek letter delta, Δ, indicates change, such as change in time.) We can now rewrite the verbal equation as

$$\frac{\Delta N}{\Delta t} = B - D$$

where B is the number of births in the population during the time interval and D is the number of deaths.

Next, we can convert this simple model into one in which births and deaths are expressed as the average number of births and deaths per individual (per capita) during the specified time interval. The *per capita birth rate* is the number of offspring produced per unit time by an average member of the population. If, for example, there are 34 births per year in a population of 1,000 individuals, the annual per capita birth rate is 34/1,000, or 0.034. If we know the annual per capita birth rate (symbolized by b), we can use the formula $B = bN$ to calculate the expected number of births per year in a population of any size. For example, if the annual per capita birth rate is 0.034 and the population size is 500,

$$B = bN$$
$$B = 0.034 \times 500$$
$$B = 17 \text{ per year}$$

Similarly, the *per capita death rate* (symbolized by d) allows us to calculate the expected number of deaths per unit time in a population of any size, using the formula $D = dN$. If $d = 0.016$ per year, we would expect 16 deaths per year in a population of 1,000 individuals. For natural populations or those in the laboratory, the per capita birth and death rates can be calculated from estimates of population size and data in life tables and reproductive tables (for example, Tables 53.1 and 53.2).

Now we can revise the population growth equation again, this time using per capita birth and death rates rather than the numbers of births and deaths:

$$\frac{\Delta N}{\Delta t} = bN - dN$$

One final simplification is in order. Population ecologists are most interested in the *difference* between the per capita birth rate and per capita death rate. This difference is the *per capita rate of increase*, or r:

$$r = b - d$$

The value of r indicates whether a given population is growing ($r > 0$) or declining ($r < 0$). **Zero population growth (ZPG)** occurs when the per capita birth and death rates are equal ($r = 0$). Births and deaths still occur in such a population, of course, but they balance each other exactly.

Using the per capita rate of increase, we can now rewrite the equation for change in population size as

$$\frac{\Delta N}{\Delta t} = rN$$

Remember that this equation is for a discrete, or fixed, time interval (often one year, as in the previous example) and does not include immigration or emigration. Most ecologists prefer to use differential calculus to express population growth *instantaneously*, as growth rate at a particular instant in time:

$$\frac{dN}{dt} = r_{inst}N$$

In this case r_{inst} is simply the instantaneous per capita rate of increase. If you have not yet studied calculus, don't be intimidated by the form of the last equation; it is similar to the previous one, except that the time intervals Δt are very short and are expressed in the equation as dt. In fact, as Δt becomes shorter, the discrete r approaches the instantaneous r_{inst} in value.

Exponential Growth

Earlier we described a population whose members all have access to abundant food and are free to reproduce at their physiological capacity. Population increase under these ideal conditions is called **exponential population growth**, also known as geometric population growth. Under these conditions, the per capita rate of increase may assume the maximum rate for the species, denoted as r_{max}. The equation for exponential population growth is

$$\frac{dN}{dt} = r_{max}N$$

The size of a population that is growing exponentially increases at a constant rate, resulting eventually in a J-shaped growth curve when population size is plotted over time **(Figure 53.10)**. Although the maximum *rate* of increase is constant, the population accumulates more new individuals per unit of time when it is large than when it is small; thus, the

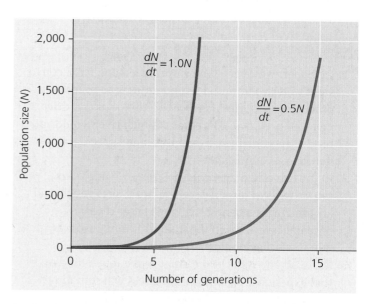

▲ **Figure 53.10 Population growth predicted by the exponential model.** This graph compares growth in two populations with different values of r_{max}. Increasing the value from 0.5 to 1.0 increases the rate of rise in population size over time, as reflected by the relative slopes of the curves at any given population size.

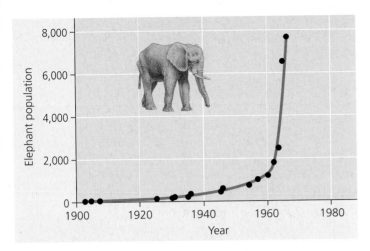

▲ Figure 53.11 Exponential growth in the African elephant population of Kruger National Park, South Africa.

curves in Figure 53.10 get progressively steeper over time. This occurs because population growth depends on N as well as r_{max}, and larger populations experience more births (and deaths) than small ones growing at the same per capita rate. It is also clear from Figure 53.10 that a population with a higher maximum rate of increase ($dN/dt = 1.0N$) will grow faster than one with a lower rate of increase ($dN/dt = 0.5N$).

The J-shaped curve of exponential growth is characteristic of some populations that are introduced into a new environment or whose numbers have been drastically reduced by a catastrophic event and are rebounding. For example, the population of elephants in Kruger National Park, South Africa, grew exponentially for approximately 60 years after they were first protected from hunting (Figure 53.11). The increasingly large number of elephants eventually caused enough damage to vegetation in the park that a collapse in their food supply was likely. To protect other species and the park ecosystem before that happened, park managers began limiting the elephant population by using birth control and exporting elephants to other countries.

CONCEPT CHECK 53.3

1. Explain why a constant rate of increase (r_{max}) for a population produces a growth graph that is J-shaped rather than a straight line.
2. Where is exponential growth by a plant population more likely—on a newly formed volcanic island or in a mature, undisturbed rain forest? Why?
3. **WHAT IF?** In 2006, the United States had a population of about 300 million people. If there were 14 births and 8 deaths per 1,000 people, what was the country's net population growth that year (ignoring immigration and emigration, which are substantial)? Do you think the United States is currently experiencing exponential population growth? Explain.

For suggested answers, see Appendix A.

The logistic model describes how a population grows more slowly as it nears its carrying capacity

The exponential growth model assumes that resources are unlimited, which is rarely the case in the real world. As population density increases, each individual has access to fewer resources. Ultimately, there is a limit to the number of individuals that can occupy a habitat. Ecologists define **carrying capacity**, symbolized as K, as the maximum population size that a particular environment can sustain. Carrying capacity varies over space and time with the abundance of limiting resources. Energy, shelter, refuge from predators, nutrient availability, water, and suitable nesting sites can all be limiting factors. For example, the carrying capacity for bats may be high in a habitat with abundant flying insects and roosting sites, but lower where there is abundant food but fewer suitable shelters.

Crowding and resource limitation can have a profound effect on population growth rate. If individuals cannot obtain sufficient resources to reproduce, the per capita birth rate (b) will decline. If they cannot consume enough energy to maintain themselves, or if disease or parasitism increases with density, the per capita death rate (d) may increase. A decrease in b or an increase in d results in a lower per capita rate of increase (r).

The Logistic Growth Model

We can modify our mathematical model to incorporate changes in growth rate as the population size nears the carrying capacity. In the **logistic population growth** model, the per capita rate of increase approaches zero as the carrying capacity is reached.

To construct the logistic model, we start with the exponential population growth model and add an expression that reduces the per capita rate of increase as N increases. If the maximum sustainable population size (carrying capacity) is K, then $K - N$ is the number of additional individuals the environment can support, and $(K - N)/K$ is the fraction of K that is still available for population growth. By multiplying the exponential rate of increase $r_{max}N$ by $(K - N)/K$, we modify the change in population size as N increases:

$$\frac{dN}{dt} = r_{max}N \frac{(K - N)}{K}$$

When N is small compared to K, the term $(K - N)/K$ is large, and the per capita rate of increase, $r_{max}(K - N)/K$, is close to the maximum rate of increase. But when N is large and resources are limiting, then $(K - N)/K$ is small, and so is the per capita rate of increase. When N equals K, the population stops

Popu-lation Size (N)	Intrinsic Rate of Increase (r_{max})	$\dfrac{K-N}{K}$	Per Capita Rate of Increase: $r_{max}\left(\dfrac{K-N}{K}\right)$	Population Growth Rate:* $r_{max}N\left(\dfrac{K-N}{K}\right)$
25	1.0	0.98	0.98	+25
100	1.0	0.93	0.93	+93
250	1.0	0.83	0.83	+208
500	1.0	0.67	0.67	+333
750	1.0	0.50	0.50	+375
1,000	1.0	0.33	0.33	+333
1,500	1.0	0.00	0.00	0

Table 53.3 Logistic Growth of a Hypothetical Population ($K = 1,500$)

*Rounded to the nearest whole number.

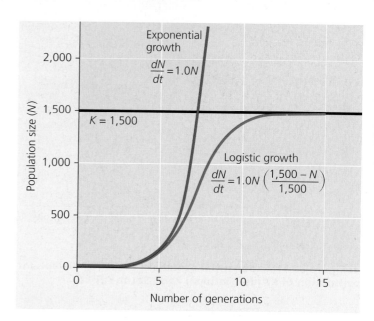

▲ **Figure 53.12 Population growth predicted by the logistic model.** The rate of population growth slows as population size (N) approaches the carrying capacity (K) of the environment. The red line shows logistic growth in a population where $r_{max} = 1.0$ and $K = 1,500$ individuals. For comparison, the blue line illustrates a population continuing to grow exponentially with the same r_{max}.

growing. **Table 53.3** shows calculations of population growth rate for a hypothetical population growing according to the logistic model, with $r_{max} = 1.0$ per individual per year. Notice that the overall population growth rate is highest, +375 individuals per year, when the population size is 750, or half the carrying capacity. At a population size of 750, the per capita rate of increase remains relatively high (one-half the maximum rate), but there are more reproducing individuals (N) in the population than at lower population sizes.

The logistic model of population growth produces a sigmoid (S-shaped) growth curve when N is plotted over time (the red line in **Figure 53.12**). New individuals are added to the population most rapidly at intermediate population sizes, when there is not only a breeding population of substantial size, but also lots of available space and other resources in the environment. The population growth rate slows dramatically as N approaches K.

Note that we haven't said anything yet about *why* the population growth rate slows as N approaches K. For a population's growth rate to decrease, either the birth rate b must decrease, the death rate d must increase, or both. Later in the chapter, we will consider some of the factors affecting these rates.

The Logistic Model and Real Populations

The growth of laboratory populations of some small animals, such as beetles and crustaceans, and of some microorganisms, such as paramecia, yeasts, and bacteria, fits an S-shaped curve fairly well under conditions of limited resources **(Figure 53.13a)**. These populations are grown in a constant environment lacking predators and competing species that may reduce growth of the populations, conditions that rarely occur in nature.

Some of the basic assumptions built into the logistic model clearly do not apply to all populations. The logistic model assumes that populations adjust instantaneously to growth and approach carrying capacity smoothly. In reality, there is often a lag time before the negative effects of an increasing population are realized. If food becomes limiting for a population, for instance, reproduction will decline eventually, but females may use their energy reserves to continue reproducing for a short time. This may cause the population to overshoot its carrying capacity temporarily, as shown for the water fleas in **Figure 53.13b**. If the population then drops below carrying capacity, there will be a delay in population growth until the increased number of offspring are actually born. Still other populations fluctuate greatly, making it difficult even to define carrying capacity. We will examine some possible reasons for such fluctuations later in the chapter.

The logistic model also incorporates the idea that regardless of population density, each individual added to a population has the same negative effect on population growth rate. However, some populations show an *Allee effect* (named after W. C. Allee, of the University of Chicago, who first described it), in which individuals may have a more difficult time surviving or reproducing if the population size is too small. For example, a single plant may be damaged by excessive wind if it is standing alone, but it would be protected in a clump of individuals.

The logistic model is a useful starting point for thinking about how populations grow and for constructing more complex models. The model is also important in conservation

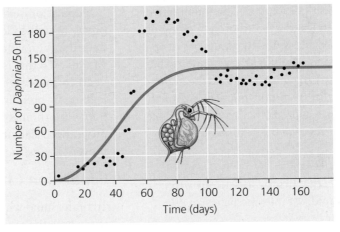

(a) A *Paramecium* population in the lab. The growth of *Paramecium aurelia* in small cultures (black dots) closely approximates logistic growth (red curve) if the researcher maintains a constant environment.

(b) A *Daphnia* population in the lab. The growth of a population of water fleas (*Daphnia*) in a small laboratory culture (black dots) does not correspond well to the logistic model (red curve). This population overshoots the carrying capacity of its artificial environment before it settles down to an approximately stable population size.

biology for predicting how rapidly a particular population might increase in numbers after it has been reduced to a small size and for estimating sustainable harvest rates for fish and wildlife populations. Conservation biologists can use the model to estimate the critical size below which populations of certain organisms, such as the northern subspecies of the white rhinoceros (*Ceratotherium simum*), may become extinct (**Figure 53.14**). Like any good starting hypothesis, the logistic model has stimulated research that has led to a better understanding of the factors affecting population growth.

The Logistic Model and Life Histories

The logistic model predicts different per capita growth rates for populations of low or high density relative to the carrying

▲ **Figure 53.14 White rhinoceros mother and calf.** The two animals pictured here are members of the southern subspecies, which has a population of more than 10,000 individuals. The northern subspecies is critically endangered, with a population of fewer than 25 individuals.

capacity of the environment. At high densities, each individual has few resources available, and the population grows slowly. At low densities, per capita resources are relatively abundant, and the population grows rapidly. Different life history features are favored under each condition. At high population density, selection favors adaptations that enable organisms to survive and reproduce with few resources. Competitive ability and efficient use of resources should be favored in populations that are at or near their carrying capacity. (Note that these are the traits we associated earlier with iteroparity.) At low population density, adaptations that promote rapid reproduction, such as the production of numerous, small offspring, should be favored.

Ecologists have attempted to connect these differences in favored traits at different population densities with the logistic growth model. Selection for life history traits that are sensitive to population density is known as *K*-selection, or density-dependent selection. In contrast, selection for life history traits that maximize reproductive success in uncrowded environments (low densities) is called *r*-selection, or density-independent selection. These names follow from the variables of the logistic equation. *K*-selection is said to operate in populations living at a density near the limit imposed by their resources (the carrying capacity, K), where competition among individuals is relatively strong. Mature trees growing in an old-growth forest are an example of *K*-selected organisms. In contrast, *r*-selection is said to maximize r, the per capita rate of increase, and occurs in environments in which population densities are well below carrying capacity or individuals face little competition. Such conditions are often found in disturbed habitats.

Like the concepts of semelparity and iteroparity, the concepts of *K*- and *r*-selection represent two extremes in a range of actual life histories. The framework of *K*- and *r*-selection, grounded in the idea of carrying capacity, has helped ecologists to propose alternative hypotheses of life history evolution. These alternative hypotheses, in turn, have stimulated more thorough study of how factors such as disturbance, stress, and the frequency of opportunities for successful reproduction affect the evolution of life histories. They have also forced ecologists to address the important question we alluded to earlier: Why does population growth rate decrease as population size approaches carrying capacity? Answering this question is the focus of the next section.

CONCEPT 53.5

Many factors that regulate population growth are density dependent

In this section, we will apply biology's unifying theme of *feedback regulation* (see Chapter 1) to populations. What environmental factors keep populations from growing indefinitely? Why are some populations fairly stable in size, while others, such as the Soay sheep on Hirta Island, are not (see Figure 53.1)?

Population regulation is an area of ecology that has many practical applications. In agriculture, a farmer may want to reduce the abundance of insect pests or stop the growth of an invasive weed that is spreading rapidly. Conservation ecologists need to know what environmental factors create favorable feeding or breeding habitats for endangered species, such as the white rhinoceros and the whooping crane. Management programs based on population-regulating factors have helped prevent the extinction of many endangered species.

Population Change and Population Density

To understand why a population stops growing, it is helpful to study how the rates of birth, death, immigration, and emigration change as population density rises. If immigration and emigration offset each other, then a population grows when the birth rate exceeds the death rate and declines when the death rate exceeds the birth rate.

A birth rate or death rate that does *not* change with population density is said to be **density independent**. In a classic study of population regulation, Andrew Watkinson and John Harper, of the University of Wales, found that the mortality of dune fescue grass (*Vulpia membranacea*) is mainly due to physical factors that kill similar proportions of a local population, regardless of its density. For example, drought stress that arises when the roots of the grass are uncovered by shifting sands is a density-independent factor. In contrast, a death rate that rises as population density rises is said to be **density dependent**, as is a birth rate that falls with rising density. Watkinson and Harper found that reproduction by dune fescue declines as population density increases, in part because water or nutrients become more scarce. Thus, in this grass population, the key factors regulating birth rate are density dependent, while death rate is largely regulated by density-independent factors. **Figure 53.15** models how a population may stop increasing and reach equilibrium as a result of various combinations of density-dependent and density-independent regulation.

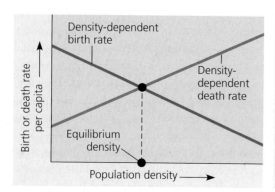

(a) Both birth rate and death rate change with population density.

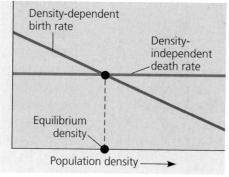

(b) Birth rate changes with population density while death rate is constant.

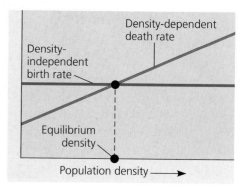

(c) Death rate changes with population density while birth rate is constant.

▲ **Figure 53.15 Determining equilibrium for population density.** This simple model considers only birth and death rates (immigration and emigration rates are assumed to be either zero or equal).

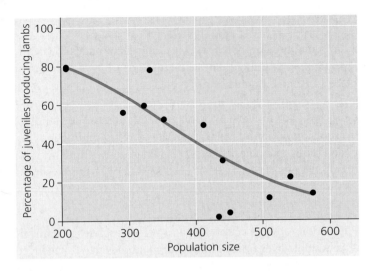

▲ Figure 53.16 Decreased reproduction at high population densities. Reproduction by juvenile Soay sheep on Hirta Island drops dramatically as population size increases.

Density-Dependent Population Regulation

Without some type of negative feedback between population density and the vital rates of birth and death, a population would never stop growing. Density-dependent regulation provides that feedback, operating through mechanisms that help to reduce birth rates and increase death rates, halting population growth.

Competition for Resources

In a crowded population, increasing population density intensifies competition for declining nutrients and other resources, resulting in a lower birth rate. Crowding can reduce reproduction by plants, as discussed earlier for dune fescue. Many animal populations also experience internal competition for food and other resources. On Hirta Island, ecologists have closely monitored the relationship between Soay sheep density and reproduction for many years. Their results show that the effects of increasing density on birth rate are strongest for the youngest sheep that reproduce, typically 1-year-old juveniles (Figure 53.16).

Territoriality

In many vertebrates and some invertebrates, territoriality can limit population density. In this case, territory space becomes the resource for which individuals compete. Cheetahs, for example, are highly territorial, using chemical communication to warn other cheetahs of their territorial boundaries (Figure 53.17a). Maintaining a territory increases the likelihood that a cheetah will capture enough food to reproduce. Oceanic birds, such as gannets, often nest on rocky islands to avoid predators (Figure 53.17b). Up to a certain population density, most gannets can find a suitable

(a) Cheetahs stake out their territories with a chemical marker in urine.

(b) Gannets nest virtually a peck apart and defend their territories by calling and pecking at one another.

▲ Figure 53.17 Territoriality. In some animals, defense of territories provides negative feedback on population density.

nest site, but beyond that threshold, few additional birds breed successfully. Birds that cannot obtain a nesting spot do not reproduce. The presence of surplus, or nonbreeding, individuals is a good indication that territoriality is restricting population growth, as it does in many bird populations.

Disease

Population density can also influence the health and thus the survival of organisms. If the transmission rate of a particular disease depends on a certain level of crowding in a population, the disease's impact may be density dependent. Among plants, the severity of infection by fungal pathogens is often greater in locations where the density of the host plant population is higher. Animals, too, can experience an increased rate of infection by pathogens at high population densities. Steven Kohler and Wade Hoiland, of the Illinois Natural History Survey, showed that in caddis flies (*Brachycentrus americanus*, a stream-dwelling insect), peaks in disease-related mortality followed years of high insect abundance, leading to cyclic fluctuations in the density of the caddis fly population. In humans, the lung disease tuberculosis, which is caused by bacteria that spread through the air when an infected person sneezes or coughs, strikes a greater percentage of people living in densely populated cities than those in rural areas.

Predation

Predation may be an important cause of density-dependent mortality if a predator encounters and captures more food as the population density of the prey increases. As a prey population builds up, predators may feed preferentially on that species, consuming a higher percentage of individuals. For example, trout may concentrate for a few days on a particular species of insect that is emerging from its aquatic larval stage and then switch to eating another insect species as it becomes more abundant.

Toxic Wastes

The accumulation of toxic wastes can contribute to density-dependent regulation of population size. In laboratory cultures of microorganisms, metabolic by-products accumulate as the populations grow, poisoning the organisms within this limited, artificial environment. For example, ethanol accumulates as a by-product of yeast fermentation. The alcohol content of wine is usually less than 13% because that is the maximum concentration of ethanol that most wine-producing yeast cells can tolerate.

Intrinsic Factors

For some animal species, intrinsic (physiological) factors, rather than the extrinsic (environmental) factors we've just discussed, appear to regulate population size. For instance, white-footed mice in a small field enclosure will multiply, but eventually their reproductive rate will decline until the population ceases to grow. This drop in reproduction is associated with aggressive interactions that increase with population density, and it occurs even when food and shelter are provided in abundance. High population densities in mice can induce a stress syndrome in which hormonal changes delay sexual maturation, cause reproductive organs to shrink, and depress the immune system. In this case, high densities cause an increase in mortality and a decrease in birth rates. Similar effects of crowding occur in other wild rodent populations.

These various examples of population regulation by negative feedback show how increased densities cause population growth rates to decline by affecting reproduction, growth, and survivorship. But although negative feedback helps explain why populations stop growing, it does not address why some populations fluctuate dramatically while others remain relatively stable. This is the topic we address next.

Population Dynamics

All populations for which we have long-term data show some fluctuation in numbers. These fluctuations from year to year or place to place influence the seasonal or annual harvest of fish and other commercially important species. They also give ecologists insight into what controls population size. The study of **population dynamics** focuses on the complex interactions between biotic and abiotic factors that cause variation in the size of populations.

Stability and Fluctuation

Populations of large mammals were once thought to remain relatively stable over time, but long-term studies have challenged that idea. The numbers of Soay sheep on Hirta Island fluctuate greatly, rising or falling by more than half from one year to the next (**Figure 53.18**). What causes the size of this population to change so dramatically? The most important factor appears to be the weather. Harsh weather, particularly cold, wet winters, weakens the sheep and decreases food availability, leading to a decrease in the size of the population. When sheep numbers are high, other factors, such as an increase in the density of parasites, also cause the population to shrink. Conversely, when sheep numbers are low and the weather is mild, food is readily available and the population grows quickly.

Like the Soay sheep population on Hirta, the moose population on Isle Royale in Lake Superior also fluctuates over time. In the case of the moose, predation is an additional factor that regulates the population. Moose from the mainland colonized the island around 1900 by walking across the frozen lake. Wolves, which rely on moose for most of their food, followed around 1950. Because the lake has not frozen over in recent years, both populations have been isolated from immigration and emigration. Despite this isolation, the moose population

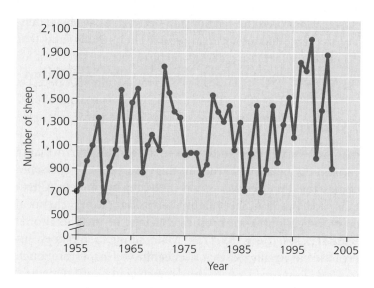

▲ Figure 53.18 **Variation in size of the Soay sheep population on Hirta Island, 1955–2002.**

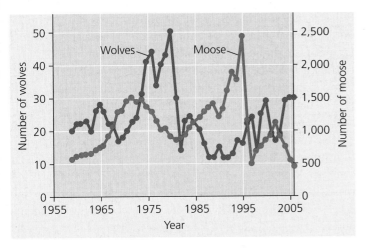

▲ **Figure 53.19 Fluctuations in moose and wolf populations on Isle Royale, 1959–2006.**

? *The first several moose reached Isle Royale in the early 1900s, and by 1925 the population on the island had grown to 2,000. Why do you think it was able to grow so quickly? What growth model best describes this initial growth?*

▲ **Figure 53.20 Population cycles in the snowshoe hare and lynx.** Population counts are based on the number of pelts sold by trappers to the Hudson Bay Company.

? *What do you observe about the relative timing of the peaks in lynx numbers and hare numbers? What might explain this observation?*

experienced two major increases and collapses during the last 45 years **(Figure 53.19)**. The first collapse coincided with a peak in the numbers of wolves from 1975 to 1980. The second collapse, around 1995, coincided with harsh winter weather, which increased the energy needs of the animals and made it harder for the moose to find food under the deep snow.

Population Cycles: Scientific Inquiry

While many populations fluctuate at unpredictable intervals, others undergo regular boom-and-bust cycles. Some small herbivorous mammals, such as voles and lemmings, tend to have 3- to 4-year cycles, and some birds, such as ruffed grouse and ptarmigans, have 9- to 11-year cycles.

One striking example of population cycles is the 10-year cycling of snowshoe hares (*Lepus americanus*) and lynx (*Lynx canadensis*) in the far northern forests of Canada and Alaska. Lynx are predators that specialize in preying on snowshoe hares, so it is not surprising that lynx numbers rise and fall with the numbers of hares **(Figure 53.20)**. But why do hare numbers rise and fall in 10-year cycles? Three main hypotheses have been proposed. First, the cycles may be caused by food shortage during winter. Hares eat the terminal twigs of small shrubs such as willow and birch in winter, although why this food supply might cycle in 10-year intervals is uncertain. Second, the cycles may be due to predator-prey interactions. Many predators other than lynx eat hares, and they may overexploit their prey. Third, the size of the hare population may vary with sunspot activity, which also undergoes cyclic changes. When sunspot activity is low, slightly less atmospheric ozone is produced, and slightly more UV radiation reaches Earth's surface. In response, plants produce more UV-blocking chemicals and fewer chemicals that deter herbivores, increasing the quality of the hares' food.

Let's consider the evidence for the hypotheses. If hare cycles are due to winter food shortage, then they should stop if extra food is provided to a field population. Researchers have conducted such experiments in the Yukon for 20 years—over two hare cycles. They have found that hare populations in the areas with extra food have increased about threefold in density but have continued to cycle in the same way as the unfed control populations. Thus, food supplies alone do not cause the hare cycle shown in Figure 53.20, so we can reject the first hypothesis.

Using radio collars, ecologists have tracked individual hares to determine why they died. Predators killed almost 90% of the hares in such studies, and none of the hares appeared to have died of starvation. These data support the second hypothesis. When ecologists excluded predators from one area with electric fences and excluded predators *and* provided food in another area, they found that the hare cycle is driven largely by excessive predation but that food availability also plays an important role, particularly in the winter. Perhaps better-fed hares are more likely to escape from predators.

To test the third hypothesis, ecologists compared the timing of hare cycles and sunspot activity. As predicted, periods of low sunspot activity were followed by peaks in the hare population. The results of all of these experiments suggest that both predation and sunspot activity may regulate the cycling of hare numbers and that food availability plays a less important role.

The availability of prey is the major factor influencing population changes for predators such as lynx, great-horned owls, and weasels, each of which depends heavily on a single prey species. When prey become scarce, predators often turn on one another. Coyotes kill both foxes and lynx, and great-horned owls kill smaller birds of prey as well as weasels, accelerating the collapse of the predator populations. Long-term experimental studies help to unravel the causes of such population cycles.

Immigration, Emigration, and Metapopulations

So far our discussion of population dynamics has focused mainly on the contributions of births and deaths. However, immigration and emigration also influence populations, particularly when a number of local populations are linked, forming a **metapopulation**. For example, immigration and emigration link the Belding's ground squirrel population we discussed earlier to other populations of the species, all of which make up a metapopulation.

Local populations in a metapopulation can be thought of as occupying discrete patches of suitable habitat in a sea of unsuitable habitat. The patches vary in size, quality, and isolation from other patches, factors that influence how many individuals move among the populations. Patches with many individuals, for instance, can supply more emigrants to other patches. If one population becomes extinct, the patch it occupied can be recolonized by immigrants from another population.

The Glanville fritillary (*Melitaea cinxia*) illustrates the movement of individuals between populations **(Figure 53.21)**. This

▲ **Figure 53.21 The Glanville fritillary: a metapopulation.** On the Åland Islands, local populations of this butterfly (filled circles) are found in only a fraction of the suitable habitat patches (open circles) at any given time. Individuals can move between local populations and colonize unoccupied patches.

butterfly is found in about 500 meadows across the Åland Islands of Finland, but its potential habitat in the islands is much larger, approximately 4,000 suitable patches. New populations of the butterfly regularly appear and existing populations become extinct, constantly shifting the locations of the 500 colonized patches. The species persists in a balance of extinctions and recolonizations.

The metapopulation concept underscores the significance of immigration and emigration in the butterfly populations. It also helps ecologists understand population dynamics and gene flow in patchy habitats, providing a framework for the conservation of species living in a network of habitat fragments and reserves.

CONCEPT CHECK 53.5

1. Identify three density-dependent factors that limit population size, and explain how each exerts negative feedback.
2. Describe three attributes of habitat patches that could affect population density and rates of immigration and emigration.
3. **WHAT IF?** If you were studying an endangered species that, like the snowshoe hare, has a 10-year population cycle, how long would you need to study the species to determine if its population size is declining? Explain.

For suggested answers, see Appendix A.

CONCEPT 53.6

The human population is no longer growing exponentially but is still increasing rapidly

In the last few centuries, the human population has grown at an unprecedented rate, more like the elephant population in Kruger National Park (see Figure 53.11) than the fluctuating populations we considered in Concept 53.5. No population can grow indefinitely, however, and humans are no exception. In this last section of the chapter, we'll apply the concepts of population dynamics to the specific case of the human population.

The Global Human Population

The exponential growth model in Figure 53.10 approximates the human population explosion since 1650. Ours is a singular case; it is unlikely that any other population of large animals has ever sustained so much growth for so long **(Figure 53.22)**. The human population increased relatively slowly until about 1650, at which time approximately 500 million people inhabited Earth. Our population doubled to 1 billion within the next two centuries, doubled again to 2 billion between 1850 and 1930, and

▲ **Figure 53.22 Human population growth (data as of 2006).** The global human population has grown almost continuously throughout history, but it skyrocketed after the Industrial Revolution. Though it is not apparent at this scale, the rate of population growth has slowed in recent decades, mainly as a result of decreased birth rates throughout the world.

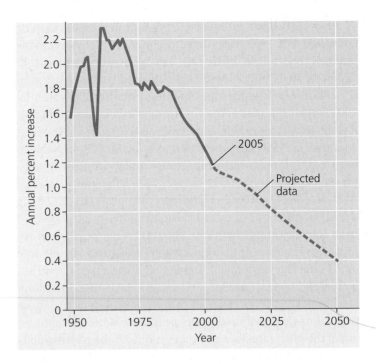

▲ **Figure 53.23 Annual percent increase in the global human population (data as of 2005).** The sharp dip in the 1960s is due mainly to a famine in China in which about 60 million people died.

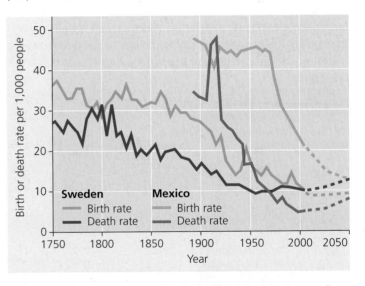

▲ **Figure 53.24 Demographic transition in Sweden and Mexico, 1750–2050 (data as of 2005).**

doubled still again by 1975 to more than 4 billion. The global population is now more than 6.6 billion people and is increasing by about 75 million each year. The population grows by approximately 200,000 people each day, the equivalent of adding a city the size of Amarillo, Texas, or Madison, Wisconsin. It takes only about four years for world population growth to add the equivalent of another United States. Population ecologists predict a population of 7.8–10.8 billion people on Earth by the year 2050.

Though the global population is still growing, the *rate* of growth began to slow during the 1960s **(Figure 53.23)**. The annual rate of increase in the global population peaked at 2.2% in 1962; by 2005, it had declined to 1.15%. Current models project a continued decline in the annual growth rate to just over 0.4% by 2050, a rate that would still add 36 million more people per year if the population climbs to a projected 9 billion. The reduction in growth rate over the past four decades shows that the human population has departed from true exponential growth, which assumes a constant rate. This departure is the result of fundamental changes in population dynamics due to diseases, including AIDS, and to voluntary population control.

Regional Patterns of Population Change

So far we have described changes in the global population, but population dynamics vary widely from region to region. In a stable regional human population, birth rate equals death rate (disregarding the effects of immigration and emigration). Two possible configurations for a stable population are

Zero population growth = High birth rate − High death rate

or

Zero population growth = Low birth rate − Low death rate

The movement toward the second configuration is called the **demographic transition**. **Figure 53.24** compares the demographic transition in one of the most industrialized countries, Sweden, and in a less industrialized country, Mexico. The demographic transition in Sweden took about 150 years, from 1810 to 1960, when birth rates finally approached death rates; in Mexico, the changes are projected to continue until sometime after 2050, almost the same length of time as they took in Sweden. Demographic transition is associated with an increase in the quality of health care and sanitation as well as improved access to education, especially for women.

After 1950, death rates declined rapidly in most developing countries, but birth rates have declined in a more variable manner. The fall in birth rate has been most dramatic in China. In 1970, the Chinese birth rate predicted an average of 5.9 children per woman per lifetime (total fertility rate); by 2004, largely because of the government's strict one-child policy, the expected total fertility rate was 1.7 children. In some countries of Africa, the transition to lower birth rates has also been rapid, though birth rates remain high in most of sub-Saharan Africa. In India, birth rates have fallen more slowly.

How do such variable birth rates affect the growth of the world's population? In industrialized nations, populations are near equilibrium (growth rate about 0.1% per year), with reproductive rates near the replacement level (total fertility rate = 2.1 children per female). In many industrialized countries, including Canada, Germany, Japan, and the United Kingdom, total reproductive rates are in fact *below* replacement. These populations will eventually decline if there is no immigration and if the birth rate does not change. In fact, the population is already declining in many eastern and central European countries. Most of the current global population growth (1.15% per year) is concentrated in less industrialized countries, where about 80% of the world's people now live.

A unique feature of human population growth is our potential ability to control it with family planning and voluntary contraception. Reduced family size is the key to the demographic transition. Social change and the rising educational and career aspirations of women in many cultures encourage women to delay marriage and postpone reproduction. Delayed reproduction helps to decrease population growth rates and to move a society toward zero population growth under conditions of low birth rates and low death rates. However, there is a great deal of disagreement among world leaders as to how much support should be provided for global family planning efforts.

Age Structure

One important demographic variable in present and future growth trends is a country's **age structure**, the relative number of individuals of each age in the population. Age structure is commonly graphed as "pyramids" like those in **Figure 53.25**. For Afghanistan, the pyramid is bottom-heavy, skewed toward young individuals who will grow up and may sustain the explosive growth with their own reproduction. The age structure for the United States is relatively even until the older, post-reproductive ages, except for a bulge that corresponds to the "baby boom" that lasted for about two decades after the end of World War II. Even though couples born during those years have had an average of fewer than two children, the nation's overall birth rate still exceeds the death rate because so many "boomers" and their offspring are still of reproductive age. Moreover, although the current total reproductive rate in the United States is 2.1 children per woman—approximately replacement rate—the population is projected to grow slowly

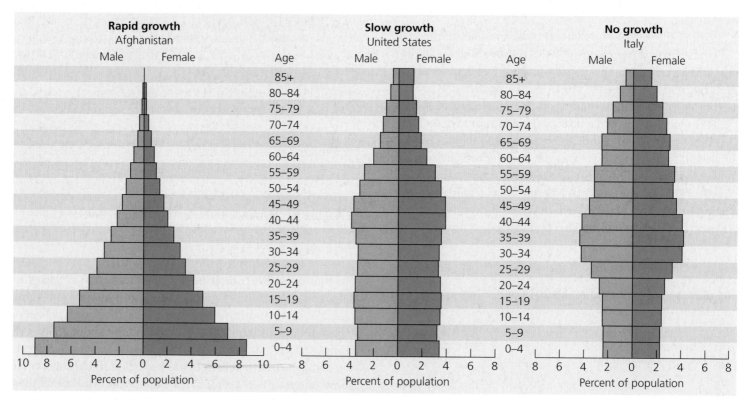

▲ **Figure 53.25 Age-structure pyramids for the human population of three countries (data as of 2005).** As of 2007, the annual rate of population growth was approximately 2.6% in Afghanistan, 0.9% in the United States, and 0.0% in Italy.

through 2050 as a result of immigration. For Italy, the pyramid has a small base, indicating that individuals younger than reproductive age are relatively underrepresented in the population. This situation contributes to the projection of a population decrease in Italy.

Age-structure diagrams not only predict a population's growth trends but can also illuminate social conditions. Based on the diagrams in Figure 53.25, we can predict, for instance, that employment and education opportunities will continue to be a significant problem for Afghanistan in the foreseeable future. The large number of young entering the Afghan population could also be a source of continuing social and political unrest, particularly if their needs and aspirations are not met. In Italy and the United States, a decreasing proportion of younger working-age people will soon be supporting an increasing population of retired "boomers." In the United States, this demographic feature has made the future of Social Security and Medicare a major political issue. Understanding age structures can help us plan for the future.

Infant Mortality and Life Expectancy

Infant mortality, the number of infant deaths per 1,000 live births, and *life expectancy at birth*, the predicted average length of life at birth, vary widely among different human populations. These differences reflect the quality of life faced by children at birth and influence the reproductive choices parents make. If infant mortality is high, then parents are likely to have more children to ensure that some of them reach adulthood. **Figure 53.26** contrasts average infant mortality and life expectancy in the industrialized and less industrialized countries of the world in 2005. While these averages are markedly different, they do not capture the broad range of the human condition. In 2005, for example, the infant mortality rate was 163 (16.3%) in Afghanistan

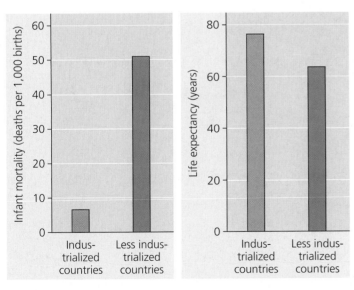

▲ **Figure 53.26 Infant mortality and life expectancy at birth in industrialized and less industrialized countries (data as of 2005).**

but only 3 (0.3%) in Japan, while life expectancy at birth was 43 years in Afghanistan and 81 years in Japan. Although global life expectancy has been increasing since about 1950, more recently it has dropped in a number of regions, including countries of the former Soviet Union and in sub-Saharan Africa. In these regions, the combination of social upheaval, decaying infrastructure, and infectious diseases such as AIDS and tuberculosis is reducing life expectancy. In the South African country of Angola, for instance, life expectancy in 2005 was approximately 39 years, about half that in Japan, Sweden, Italy, and Spain.

Global Carrying Capacity

No ecological question is more important than the future size of the human population. The projected worldwide population size depends on assumptions about future changes in birth and death rates. As we noted earlier, population ecologists project a global population of approximately 7.8–10.8 billion people in 2050. In other words, without some catastrophe, an estimated 1–4 billion people will be added to the population in the next four decades because of the momentum of population growth. But just how many humans can the biosphere support? Will the world be overpopulated in 2050? Is it *already* overpopulated?

Estimates of Carrying Capacity

For over three centuries, scientists have attempted to estimate the human carrying capacity of Earth. The first known estimate, 13.4 billion, was made in 1679 by Anton van Leeuwenhoek, the discoverer of protists (see Chapter 28). Since then, estimates have varied from less than 1 billion to more than 1,000 billion (1 trillion), with an average of 10–15 billion.

Carrying capacity is difficult to estimate, and the scientists who provide these estimates use different methods to get their answers. Some current researchers use curves like that produced by the logistic equation (see Figure 53.12) to predict the future maximum of the human population. Others generalize from existing "maximum" population density and multiply this number by the area of habitable land. Still others base their estimates on a single limiting factor, such as food, and consider many variables, including the amount of available farmland, the average yield of crops, the prevalent diet—vegetarian or meat-based—and the number of calories needed per person per day.

Limits on Human Population Size

A more comprehensive approach to estimating the carrying capacity of Earth is to recognize that humans have multiple constraints: We need food, water, fuel, building materials, and other resources, such as clothing and transportation. The **ecological footprint** concept summarizes the aggregate land and water area required by each person, city, or nation to produce all the resources it consumes and to absorb all the waste it generates.

One way to estimate the ecological footprint of the entire human population is to add up all the ecologically productive land on the planet and divide by the population. This calculation yields approximately 2 hectares (ha) per person (1 ha = 2.47 acres). Reserving some land for parks and conservation means reducing this allotment to 1.7 ha per person—the benchmark for comparing actual ecological footprints. Anyone who consumes resources that require more than 1.7 ha to produce is said to be using an unsustainable share of Earth's resources. A typical ecological footprint for a person in the United States is about 10 ha.

Ecologists sometimes calculate ecological footprints using other currencies besides land area. For instance, the amount of photosynthesis that occurs on Earth is finite, constrained by the amount of land and sea area and by the sun's radiation. Scientists recently studied the extent to which people around the world consume seven types of photosynthetic products: plant foods, wood for building and fuel, paper, fiber, meat, milk, and eggs (the last three based on estimates of how much plant material goes into their production). **Figure 53.27** shows that areas with high population densities, such as China and India, have high consumption rates. However, areas of much lower population density but higher *per capita* consumption, such as parts of the United States and Europe, have equally high rates, as much as 400 times the rate at which photosynthetic products are produced locally. The combination of population density *and* resource use per person determines our global ecological footprint.

We can only speculate about Earth's ultimate carrying capacity for the human population or about what factors will eventually limit our growth. Perhaps food will be the main fac-

tor. Malnutrition and famine are common in some regions, but they result mainly from unequal distribution of food rather than inadequate production. So far, technological improvements in agriculture have allowed food supplies to keep up with global population growth. However, the principles of energy flow through ecosystems (explained in Chapter 55) tell us that environments can support a larger number of herbivores than carnivores. If everyone ate as much meat as the wealthiest people in the world, less than half of the present world population could be fed by current food harvests.

Perhaps we humans will eventually be limited by suitable space, like the gannets on oceanic islands. Certainly, as our population grows, the conflict over how space is utilized will intensify, and agricultural land will be developed for housing. There seem to be few limits, however, on how closely humans can be crowded together, as long as adequate food and water are provided to them and space is available to dispose of their waste.

Humans could also run out of nonrenewable resources, such as certain metals and fossil fuels. The demands of many populations have already far exceeded the local and even regional supplies of one renewable resource—fresh water. More than 1 billion people do not have access to sufficient water to meet their basic sanitation needs. It is also possible that the human population will eventually be limited by the capacity of the environment to absorb its wastes. In such cases, Earth's current human occupants could lower the planet's long-term carrying capacity for future generations.

Some optimists have suggested that because of our ability to develop technology, human population growth has no practical limits. Technology has undoubtedly increased Earth's

Log (g carbon/year)

13.4

9.8

5.8

Not analyzed

▲ **Figure 53.27 The amount of photosynthetic products that humans use around the world.** The unit of measurement is the logarithm of the number of grams of photosynthetic products consumed each year. The greatest usage is in places where population density is high or where people consume the most resources individually (high per capita consumption).

carrying capacity for humans, but as we have emphasized, no population can continue to grow indefinitely. After reading this chapter, you should realize that there is no single carrying capacity for the human population on Earth. How many people our planet can sustain depends on the quality of life each of us enjoys and the distribution of wealth across people and nations, topics of great concern and political debate. Unlike other organisms, we can decide whether zero population growth will be attained through social changes based on human choices or through increased mortality due to resource limitation, plagues, war, and environmental degradation.

Chapter 53 Review

SUMMARY OF KEY CONCEPTS

CONCEPT 53.1

Dynamic biological processes influence population density, dispersion, and demographics (pp. 1174–1179)

▶ **Density and Dispersion** Population density—the number of individuals per unit area or volume—results from the interplay of births, deaths, immigration, and emigration. Environmental and social factors influence the dispersion of individuals.

Patterns of dispersion

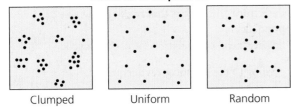

| Clumped | Uniform | Random |

▶ **Demographics** Populations increase from births and immigration and decrease from deaths and emigration. Life tables, survivorship curves, and reproductive tables summarize specific demographic trends.

MEDIA

Activity Techniques for Estimating Population Density and Size
Activity Investigating Survivorship Curves

CONCEPT 53.2

Life history traits are products of natural selection (pp. 1179–1181)

▶ Life history traits are evolutionary outcomes reflected in the development, physiology, and behavior of an organism.

▶ **Evolution and Life History Diversity** Big-bang, or semelparous, organisms reproduce once and die. Iteroparous organisms produce offspring repeatedly.

▶ **"Trade-offs" and Life Histories** Life history traits such as brood size, age at maturity, and parental caregiving represent trade-offs between conflicting demands for time, energy, and nutrients.

CONCEPT 53.3

The exponential model describes population growth in an idealized, unlimited environment (pp. 1181–1183)

▶ **Per Capita Rate of Increase** If immigration and emigration are ignored, a population's growth rate (the per capita rate of increase) equals birth rate minus death rate.

▶ **Exponential Growth** The exponential growth equation $dN/dt = r_{max}N$ represents a population's potential growth in an unlimited environment, where r_{max} is the maximum per capita, or intrinsic, rate of increase and N is the number of individuals in the population.

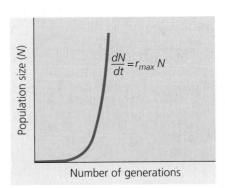

$$\frac{dN}{dt} = r_{max}N$$

CONCEPT 53.4

The logistic model describes how a population grows more slowly as it nears its carrying capacity (pp. 1183–1186)

▶ Exponential growth cannot be sustained for long in any population. A more realistic population model limits growth by incorporating carrying capacity (K), the maximum population size the environment can support.

▶ **The Logistic Growth Model** According to the logistic equation $dN/dt = r_{max}N(K - N)/K$, growth levels off as population size approaches the carrying capacity.

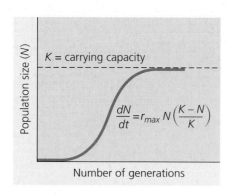

▶ **The Logistic Model and Real Populations** The logistic model fits few real populations perfectly, but it is useful for estimating possible growth.

▶ **The Logistic Model and Life Histories** Two hypothetical but controversial life history patterns are K-selection, or density-dependent selection, and r-selection, or density-independent selection.

CONCEPT 53.5

Many factors that regulate population growth are density dependent (pp. 1186–1190)

▶ **Population Change and Population Density** In density-dependent population regulation, death rates rise and birth rates fall with increasing density. In density-independent population regulation, birth and death rates do not change with increasing density.

▶ **Density-Dependent Population Regulation** Density-dependent changes in birth and death rates curb population increase through negative feedback and can eventually stabilize a population near its carrying capacity. Density-dependent limiting factors include intraspecific competition for limited food or space, increased predation, disease, stress due to crowding, and buildup of toxic substances.

▶ **Population Dynamics** Because changing environmental conditions periodically disrupt them, all populations exhibit some size fluctuations. Many populations undergo regular boom-and-bust cycles that are influenced by complex interactions between biotic and abiotic factors. A metapopulation is a group of populations linked by immigration and emigration.

MEDIA
Biology Labs On-Line PopulationEcologyLab

CONCEPT 53.6

The human population is no longer growing exponentially but is still increasing rapidly (pp. 1190–1195)

▶ **The Global Human Population** Since about 1650, the global human population has grown exponentially, but within the last 40 years, the rate of growth has fallen by nearly 50%. Differences in age structure show that while some nations' populations are growing rapidly, those of others are stable or declining in size. Infant mortality rates and life expectancy at birth differ markedly between industrialized and less industrialized countries.

▶ **Global Carrying Capacity** The carrying capacity of Earth for humans is uncertain. Ecological footprint is the aggregate land and water area needed to produce all the resources a person or group of people consume and to absorb all of their waste. It is one measure of how close we are to the carrying capacity of Earth. With a world population of more than 6.6 billion people, we are already using many resources in an unsustainable manner.

MEDIA
Activity Human Population Growth
Activity Analyzing Age-Structure Pyramids
GraphIt! Age Pyramids and Population Growth
Biology Labs On-Line DemographyLab

TESTING YOUR KNOWLEDGE

SELF-QUIZ

1. The observation that members of a population are uniformly distributed suggests that
   a. the size of the area occupied by the population is increasing.
   b. resources are distributed unevenly.
   c. the members of the population are competing for access to a resource.
   d. the members of the population are neither attracted to nor repelled by one another.
   e. the density of the population is low.

2. Population ecologists follow the fate of same-age cohorts to
   a. determine a population's carrying capacity.
   b. determine if a population is regulated by density-dependent processes.
   c. determine the birth rate and death rate of each group in a population.
   d. determine the factors that regulate the size of a population.
   e. determine if a population's growth is cyclic.

3. According to the logistic growth equation
$$\frac{dN}{dt} = r_{max}N\,\frac{(K - N)}{K}$$
   a. the number of individuals added per unit time is greatest when N is close to zero.
   b. the per capita growth rate (r) increases as N approaches K.
   c. population growth is zero when N equals K.
   d. the population grows exponentially when K is small.
   e. the birth rate (b) approaches zero as N approaches K.

4. A population's carrying capacity
   a. can be accurately calculated using the logistic growth model.
   b. generally remains constant over time.
   c. increases as the per capita growth rate (r) decreases.
   d. may change as environmental conditions change.
   e. can never be exceeded.

5. Which pair of terms most accurately describes life history traits for a stable population of wolves?
   a. semelparous; *r*-selected
   b. semelparous; *K*-selected
   c. iteroparous; *r*-selected
   d. iteroparous; *K*-selected
   e. iteroparous; *N*-selected

6. During exponential growth, a population always
   a. grows by thousands of individuals.
   b. grows at its maximum per capita rate.
   c. quickly reaches its carrying capacity.
   d. cycles through time.
   e. loses some individuals to emigration.

7. Scientific study of the population cycles of the snowshoe hare and its predator, the lynx, has revealed that
   a. the prey population is controlled by predators alone.
   b. hares and lynx are so mutually dependent that each species cannot survive without the other.
   c. multiple biotic and abiotic factors contribute to the cycling of the hare and lynx populations.
   d. both hare and lynx populations are regulated mainly by abiotic factors.
   e. the hare population is *r*-selected and the lynx population is *K*-selected.

8. Based on current growth rates, Earth's human population in 2010 will be closest to
   a. 2 million.   d. 7 billion.
   b. 3 billion.   e. 10 billion.
   c. 4 billion.

9. Which of the following statements about human population in industrialized countries is *incorrect*?
   a. Average family size is relatively small.
   b. The population has undergone the demographic transition.
   c. Life history is *r*-selected.
   d. The survivorship curve is Type I.
   e. Age distribution is relatively uniform.

10. A recent study of ecological footprints concluded that
    a. Earth's carrying capacity for humans is about 10 billion.
    b. Earth's carrying capacity would increase if per capita meat consumption increased.
    c. current demand by industrialized countries for resources is much smaller than the ecological footprint of those countries.
    d. the ecological footprint of the United States is large because per capita resource use is high.
    e. it is not possible for technological improvements to increase Earth's carrying capacity for humans.

11. **DRAW IT** To estimate which age cohort in a population of females produces the most female offspring, you need information about the number of offspring produced per capita within that cohort and the number of individuals alive in the cohort. Make this estimate for Belding's ground squirrels by multiplying the number of females alive at the start of the year (column 2 in Table 53.1) by the average number of female offspring produced per female (column 5 in Table 53.2). Draw a bar graph with female age in years on the *x*-axis (0–1, 1–2, and so on) and total number of female offspring produced for each age cohort on the *y*-axis. Which cohort of female Belding's ground squirrels produces the most female young?

For Self-Quiz answers, see Appendix A.

MEDIA Visit the Study Area at **www.masteringbio.com** for a Practice Test.

EVOLUTION CONNECTION

12. Write a paragraph contrasting the conditions that favor the evolution of semelparous (one-time) reproduction versus iteroparous (repeated) reproduction.

SCIENTIFIC INQUIRY

13. You are testing the hypothesis that the population density of a particular plant species influences the rate at which a pathogenic fungus infects the plant. Because the fungus causes visible scars on the leaves, you can easily determine whether a plant is infected. Design an experiment to test your hypothesis. Include your experimental treatments and control, the data you will collect, and the results expected if your hypothesis is correct.

SCIENCE, TECHNOLOGY, AND SOCIETY

14. Many people regard the rapid population growth of less industrialized countries as our most serious environmental problem. Others think that the population growth in industrialized countries, though smaller, is actually a greater environmental threat. What problems result from population growth in (a) less industrialized countries and (b) industrialized nations? Which do you think is a greater threat, and why?

Community Ecology 54

KEY CONCEPTS

54.1 Community interactions are classified by whether they help, harm, or have no effect on the species involved

54.2 Dominant and keystone species exert strong controls on community structure

54.3 Disturbance influences species diversity and composition

54.4 Biogeographic factors affect community biodiversity

54.5 Community ecology is useful for understanding pathogen life cycles and controlling human disease

OVERVIEW

A Sense of Community

On your next walk through a park or in the woods, or even across campus, look for evidence of interactions between different species. You may observe birds using trees as nesting sites, bees pollinating flowers, spiders trapping insects in their webs, or ferns growing in shade provided by trees—a tiny sample of the many interactions between species that exist in any ecological theater.

Some ecological interactions are more obvious than others. At first glance, **Figure 54.1** depicts a simple interaction between an herbivore, a hornworm caterpillar, and its preferred food, a tomato plant. But the white objects on the caterpillar's back are telltale signs of an interaction between the caterpillar and a third species, a parasitic wasp. The wasp lays its eggs inside the caterpillar, and the larvae that emerge from the eggs feed on the caterpillar's tissues. The larvae then develop into adult wasps inside the white cocoons on their host's back. This interaction will eventually kill the caterpillar.

In Chapter 53, you learned how individuals within a population can affect other individuals of the same species. This chapter will examine ecological interactions between populations of different species. A group of populations of different species living close enough to interact is called a biological **community**. Ecologists define the boundaries of a particular community to fit their research questions: They might study the community of decomposers and other organisms living on a rotting log, the benthic community in Lake Superior, or the community of trees and shrubs in Shenandoah National Park.

We begin this chapter by exploring the kinds of interactions that occur between species in a community. We then consider several of the factors that are most significant in structuring a community—in determining how many species there are, which particular species are present, and the relative abundance of these species. Finally, we will apply some of the principles of community ecology to the study of human disease.

CONCEPT 54.1

Community interactions are classified by whether they help, harm, or have no effect on the species involved

Some key relationships in the life of an organism are its interactions with individuals of other species in the community. These **interspecific interactions** include competition, predation, herbivory, and symbiosis (including parasitism, mutualism, and commensalism). In this section, we will define and describe each of these interactions, recognizing that ecologists do not always agree on the precise boundaries of each type of interaction.

We will use the symbols + and − to indicate how each interspecific interaction affects the survival and reproduction of the two species engaged in the interaction. For example, predation is a +/− interaction, with a positive effect on the survival and reproduction of the predator population and a negative effect on that of the prey population. Mutualism is a +/+ interaction because the survival and reproduction of each species is increased in the presence of the other. A 0 indicates that a population is not affected by the interaction in any known way.

Historically, most ecological research has focused on interactions that have a negative effect on at least one species, such as competition and predation. However, positive interactions are ubiquitous, and their contributions to community structure are the subject of considerable study today.

Competition

Interspecific competition is a −/− interaction that occurs when individuals of different species compete for a resource that limits their growth and survival. For instance, weeds growing in a garden compete with garden plants for soil nutrients and water. Grasshoppers and bison in the Great Plains compete for the grass they both eat. Lynx and foxes in the northern forests of Alaska and Canada compete for prey such as snowshoe hares. In contrast, some resources, such as oxygen, are rarely in short supply; thus, although most species use this resource, they do not usually compete for it.

Competitive Exclusion

What happens in a community over time when two species directly compete for limited resources? In 1934, the Russian ecologist G. F. Gause studied this question in laboratory experiments with two closely related species of ciliated protists, *Paramecium aurelia* and *Paramecium caudatum*. He cultured the species under stable conditions, adding a constant amount of food every day. When Gause grew the two species in separate cultures, each population grew rapidly and then leveled off at what was apparently the carrying capacity of the culture (see Figure 53.13a for an illustration of the logistic growth of *P. aurelia*). But when Gause cultured the two species together, *P. caudatum* was driven to extinction in the culture. Gause inferred that *P. aurelia* had a competitive edge in obtaining food, and he concluded that two species competing for the same limiting resources cannot coexist in the same place. In the absence of disturbance, one species will use the resources more efficiently and thus reproduce more rapidly than the other. Even a slight reproductive advantage will eventually lead to local elimination of the inferior competitor, an outcome called **competitive exclusion**.

Ecological Niches

The sum of a species' use of the biotic and abiotic resources in its environment is called the species' **ecological niche**. American ecologist Eugene Odum used the following analogy to explain the niche concept: If an organism's habitat is its "address," the niche is the organism's "profession." Put another way, an organism's niche is its ecological role—how it "fits into" an ecosystem. For example, the niche of a tropical tree lizard consists of, among many components, the temperature range it tolerates, the size of branches on which it perches, the time of day when it is active, and the sizes and kinds of insects it eats.

We can use the niche concept to restate the principle of competitive exclusion: Two species cannot coexist permanently in a community if their niches are identical. However, ecologically similar species *can* coexist in a community if there are one or more significant differences in their niches. When competition between species with identical niches does not lead to local extinction of either species, it is generally because one species' niche becomes modified. In other words, evolution by natural selection can result in one of the species using a different set of resources. The differentiation of niches that enables similar species to coexist in a community is called **resource partitioning (Figure 54.2)**. You can think of resource partitioning in a community as "the ghost of competition past"—the indirect evidence of earlier interspecific competition resolved by the evolution of niche differentiation.

As a result of competition, a species' *fundamental niche*, which is the niche potentially occupied by that species, is often different from its *realized niche*, the portion of its fundamental niche that it actually occupies in a particular environment.

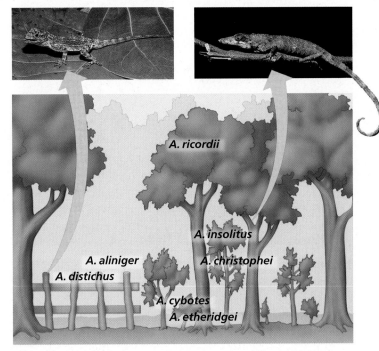

A. distichus perches on fence posts and other sunny surfaces.

A. insolitus usually perches on shady branches.

▲ **Figure 54.2 Resource partitioning among Dominican Republic lizards.** Seven species of *Anolis* lizards live in close proximity, and all feed on insects and other small arthropods. However, competition for food is reduced because each lizard species has a different preferred perch, thus occupying a distinct niche.

Ecologists can identify the fundamental niche of a species by testing the range of conditions in which it grows and reproduces in the absence of competitors. They can also test whether a potential competitor limits a species' realized niche by removing the competitor and seeing if the first species expands into the newly available space (**Figure 54.3**). The classic experiment depicted in the figure clearly showed that competition from one barnacle species kept a second barnacle species from occupying part of its fundamental niche.

Character Displacement

Closely related species whose populations are sometimes allopatric (geographically separate; see Chapter 24) and sometimes sympatric (geographically overlapping) provide more evidence for the importance of competition in structuring communities. In some cases, the allopatric populations of such species are morphologically similar and use similar resources. By contrast, sympatric populations, which would potentially compete for resources, show differences in body structures and in the resources they use. This tendency for characteristics to diverge more in sympatric populations of two species than in allopatric populations of the same two species is called **character displacement**. An example of character displacement is the variation in beak size between different populations of the Galápagos finches *Geospiza fuliginosa* and *Geospiza fortis* (**Figure 54.4**).

▼ **Figure 54.3** **Inquiry**

Can a species' niche be influenced by interspecific competition?

EXPERIMENT Ecologist Joseph Connell studied two barnacle species— *Chthamalus stellatus* and *Balanus balanoides*—that have a stratified distribution on rocks along the coast of Scotland. *Chthamalus* is usually found higher on the rocks than *Balanus*. To determine whether the distribution of *Chthamalus* is the result of interspecific competition with *Balanus*, Connell removed *Balanus* from the rocks at several sites.

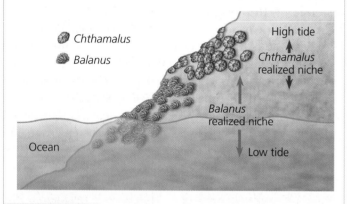

RESULTS *Chthamalus* spread into the region formerly occupied by *Balanus*.

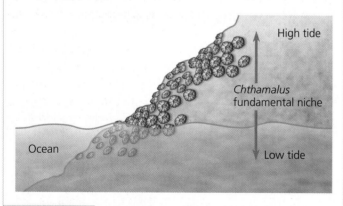

CONCLUSION Interspecific competition makes the realized niche of *Chthamalus* much smaller than its fundamental niche.

SOURCE J. H. Connell, The influence of interspecific competition and other factors on the distribution of the barnacle *Chthamalus stellatus*, *Ecology* 42:710–723 (1961).

WHAT IF? Other observations showed that *Balanus* cannot survive high on the rocks because it dries out during low tides. How would *Balanus*'s realized niche compare with its fundamental niche?

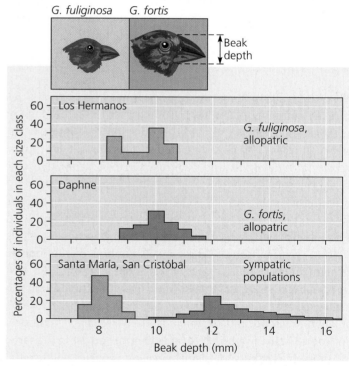

▲ **Figure 54.4** **Character displacement: indirect evidence of past competition.** Allopatric populations of *Geospiza fuliginosa* and *Geospiza fortis* on Los Hermanos and Daphne Islands have similar beak morphologies (top two graphs) and presumably eat similarly sized seeds. However, where the two species are sympatric on Santa María and San Cristóbal, *G. fuliginosa* has a shallower, smaller beak and *G. fortis* a deeper, larger one (bottom graph), adaptations that favor eating different sizes of seeds.

? *Suppose that the sympatric populations of both finch species colonized a new island that contained seeds of only one size. What would you expect to happen to the differences in beak size over time? Explain your reasoning.*

Predation

Predation refers to a +/− interaction between species in which one species, the predator, kills and eats the other, the prey. Though the term *predation* generally elicits such images as a lion attacking and eating an antelope, it applies to a wide range of interactions. An animal that kills a plant by eating the plant's tissues can also be considered a predator. Because eating and avoiding being eaten are prerequisite to reproductive success, the adaptations of both predators and prey tend to be refined through natural selection.

Many important feeding adaptations of predators are both obvious and familiar. Most predators have acute senses that enable them to locate and identify potential prey. In addition, many predators have adaptations such as claws, teeth, fangs, stingers, or poison that help them catch and subdue the or-

ganisms on which they feed. Rattlesnakes and other pit vipers, for example, find their prey with a pair of heat-sensing organs located between their eyes and nostrils (see Figure 50.5a), and they kill small birds and mammals by injecting them with toxins through their fangs. Predators that pursue their prey are generally fast and agile, whereas those that lie in ambush are often disguised in their environments.

Just as predators possess adaptations for capturing prey, prey animals have adaptations that help them avoid being eaten. Some common behavioral defenses are hiding, fleeing, and forming herds or schools. Active self-defense is less common, though some large grazing mammals vigorously defend their young from predators such as lions. Other behavioral defenses include alarm calls that summon many individuals of the prey species, which then mob the predator.

Animals also display a variety of morphological and physiological defensive adaptations. For example, **cryptic coloration**, or camouflage, makes prey difficult to spot **(Figure 54.5a)**. Other animals have mechanical or chemical defenses. For example, most predators are strongly discouraged by the familiar defenses of porcupines and skunks. Some animals, such as the European fire salamander, can synthesize toxins, whereas others passively acquire a chemical defense by accumulating toxins from the plants they eat. Animals with effective chemical defenses often exhibit bright **aposematic coloration**, or warning coloration, such as that of the poison dart frog **(Figure 54.5b)**. Aposematic coloration seems to be adaptive: There is evidence that predators are particularly cautious in dealing with potential prey having bright color patterns (see Chapter 1).

Some prey species gain significant protection by mimicking the appearance of other species. In **Batesian mimicry**, a palatable or harmless species mimics an unpalatable or harmful model. For example, the larva of the hawkmoth *Hemeroplanes ornatus* puffs up its head and thorax when disturbed, looking like the head of a small poisonous snake **(Figure 54.5c)**. In this case, the mimicry even involves behavior; the larva weaves its head back and forth and hisses like a snake. In **Müllerian mimicry**, two or more unpalatable species, such as the cuckoo bee and yellow jacket, resemble each other **(Figure 54.5d)**. Presumably, each species gains an additional

▼ **Figure 54.5 Examples of defensive coloration in animals.**

(a) Cryptic coloration

▶ Canyon tree frog

(b) Aposematic coloration

▶ Poison dart frog

(c) Batesian mimicry: A harmless species mimics a harmful one.

◀ Hawkmoth larva

▼ Green parrot snake

(d) Müllerian mimicry: Two unpalatable species mimic each other.

◀ Cuckoo bee

▼ Yellow jacket

advantage because the more unpalatable prey there are, the more quickly and effectively predators adapt, avoiding any prey with that particular appearance. The shared appearance thus becomes a kind of aposematic coloration. In an example of convergent evolution, unpalatable animals in several different taxa have similar patterns of coloration: Black and yellow or red stripes characterize unpalatable animals as diverse as yellow jackets and coral snakes (see Figure 1.25).

Predators also use mimicry. For example, some snapping turtles have tongues that resemble a wriggling worm, thus luring small fish. Any fish that tries to eat the "bait" is itself quickly consumed as the turtle's strong jaws snap closed. Anglerfish also lure prey with their own bait, in this case a modified bone of the dorsal fin that luminesces in some species.

Herbivory

Ecologists use the term **herbivory** to refer to a $+/-$ interaction in which an organism eats parts of a plant or alga. While large mammalian herbivores such as cattle, sheep, and water buffalo may be most familiar, most herbivores are actually invertebrates, such as grasshoppers and beetles. In the ocean, herbivores include snails, sea urchins, some tropical fishes, and certain mammals, such as the manatee **(Figure 54.6)**.

Like predators, herbivores have many specialized adaptations. Many herbivorous insects have chemical sensors on their feet that enable them to distinguish between toxic and nontoxic plants as well as between more nutritious and less nutritious plants. Some mammalian herbivores, such as goats, use their sense of smell to examine plants, rejecting some and eating others. They may also eat just a specific part of a plant, such as the flowers. Many herbivores also have specialized teeth or digestive systems adapted for processing vegetation (see Chapter 41).

Unlike prey animals, plants cannot run away to avoid being eaten. Instead, a plant's arsenal against herbivores may feature chemical toxins or structures such as spines and thorns.

▲ **Figure 54.6 A West Indies manatee (*Trichechus manatus*) in Florida.** The animal in this photo is feeding on water hyacinth, an introduced species.

Among the plant compounds that serve as chemical weapons are the poison strychnine, produced by the tropical vine *Strychnos toxifera*; nicotine, from the tobacco plant; and tannins, from a variety of plant species. Plants in the genus *Astragalus* accumulate selenium toxins; they are known as "locoweeds" because the cattle and sheep that eat them wander aimlessly in circles and may even die. Compounds that are not toxic to humans but may be distasteful to many herbivores are responsible for the familiar flavors of cinnamon, cloves, and peppermint. Certain plants produce chemicals that cause abnormal development in some insects that eat them.

Symbiosis

When individuals of two or more species live in direct and intimate contact with one another, their relationship is called **symbiosis**. This text adopts a general definition of symbiosis that includes all such interactions, whether harmful, helpful, or neutral. Some biologists define symbiosis more narrowly as a synonym for mutualism, in which both species benefit.

Parasitism

Parasitism is a $+/-$ symbiotic interaction in which one organism, the **parasite**, derives its nourishment from another organism, its **host**, which is harmed in the process. Parasites that live within the body of their host, such as tapeworms, are called **endoparasites**; parasites that feed on the external surface of a host, such as ticks and lice, are called **ectoparasites**. In one particular type of parasitism, parasitoid insects—usually small wasps—lay eggs on or in living hosts (see Figure 54.1). The larvae then feed on the body of the host, eventually killing it. Some ecologists have estimated that at least one-third of all species on Earth are parasites.

Many parasites have complex life cycles involving multiple hosts. The life cycle of the blood fluke, which currently infects approximately 200 million people around the world, involves two hosts: humans and freshwater snails (see Figure 33.11). Some parasites change the behavior of their hosts in a way that increases the probability of the parasite being transferred from one host to another. For instance, the presence of parasitic acanthocephalan (spiny-headed) worms leads their crustacean hosts to engage in a variety of atypical behaviors, including leaving protective cover and moving into the open. As a result of their modified behavior, the crustaceans have a greater chance of being eaten by the birds that are the second host in the parasitic worm's life cycle.

Parasites can significantly affect the survival, reproduction, and density of their host population, either directly or indirectly. For example, ticks that live as ectoparasites on moose weaken their hosts by withdrawing blood and causing hair breakage and loss, increasing the chance that the moose will die from cold stress or predation by wolves. Some of the declines of the moose population on Isle Royale, Michigan, have been attributed to tick outbreaks (see Figure 53.19).

Mutualism

Mutualistic symbiosis, or **mutualism**, is an interspecific interaction that benefits both species ($+/+$). We have described many examples of mutualism in previous chapters: nitrogen fixation by bacteria in the root nodules of legumes; the digestion of cellulose by microorganisms in the digestive systems of termites and ruminant mammals; the exchange of nutrients in mycorrhizae, associations of fungi and the roots of plants; and photosynthesis by unicellular algae in corals. The interaction between termites and the microorganisms in their digestive system is an example of *obligate mutualism*, in which at least one species has lost the ability to survive without its partner. In *facultative mutualism*, as in the acacia-ant example shown in **Figure 54.7**, both species can survive alone.

Mutualistic relationships sometimes involve the evolution of related adaptations in both species, with changes in either species likely to affect the survival and reproduction of the other. For example, most flowering plants have adaptations such as nectar or fruit that attract animals that function in pollination or seed dispersal (see Chapter 38). In turn, many animals have adaptations that help them find and consume nectar.

Commensalism

An interaction between species that benefits one of the species but neither harms nor helps the other ($+/0$) is called **commensalism**. Commensal interactions are difficult to document in nature because any close association between species likely affects both species, even if only slightly. For instance, "hitchhiking" species, such as algae that live on the shells of aquatic turtles or barnacles that attach to whales, are sometimes considered commensal. The hitchhikers gain a place to grow while having seemingly little effect on their ride. However, the hitchhikers may in fact slightly decrease the reproductive success of their hosts by reducing the hosts' efficiency of movement in searching for food or escaping from predators. Conversely, the hitchhikers may provide a benefit in the form of camouflage.

Some associations that are possibly commensal involve one species obtaining food that is inadvertently exposed by another. For instance, cowbirds and cattle egrets feed on insects flushed out of the grass by grazing bison, cattle, horses, and other herbivores. Because the birds increase their feeding rates when following the herbivores, they clearly benefit from the association. Much of the time, the herbivores may be unaffected by the relationship **(Figure 54.8)**. However, they, too, may sometimes derive some benefit; the birds tend to be opportunistic feeders that occasionally remove and eat ticks and other ectoparasites from the herbivores. They may also give warning to the herbivores of a predator's approach.

All four types of interactions that we have discussed so far—competition, predation, herbivory, and symbiosis—strongly influence the structure of communities. You will see other examples of these interactions throughout this chapter.

(a) Certain species of acacia trees in Central and South America have hollow thorns that house stinging ants of the genus *Pseudomyrmex*. The ants feed on nectar produced by the tree and on protein-rich swellings (orange in the photograph) at the tips of leaflets.

(b) The acacia benefits because the pugnacious ants, which attack anything that touches the tree, remove fungal spores, small herbivores, and debris, and clip vegetation that grows close to the acacia.

▲ **Figure 54.7 Mutualism between acacia trees and ants.**

▲ **Figure 54.8 A possible example of commensalism between cattle egrets and water buffalo.**

CONCEPT CHECK 54.1

1. Explain how interspecific competition, predation, and mutualism differ in their effects on the interacting populations of two species.
2. According to the principle of competitive exclusion, what outcome is expected when two species with identical niches compete for a resource? Why?
3. **WHAT IF?** Suppose you live in an agricultural area. What examples of the four types of community interactions (competition, predation, herbivory, and symbiosis) might you see in the growing or use of food?

For suggested answers, see Appendix A.

CONCEPT 54.2
Dominant and keystone species exert strong controls on community structure

Although the interactions of many species influence biological communities, sometimes a few species exert strong control on a community's structure, particularly on the composition, relative abundance, and diversity of its species. Before examining the effects of these particularly influential species, we first need to consider two fundamental features of community structure: species diversity and feeding relationships.

Species Diversity

The **species diversity** of a community—the variety of different kinds of organisms that make up the community—has two components. One is **species richness**, the number of different species in the community. The other is the **relative abundance** of the different species, the proportion each species represents of all individuals in the community. For example, imagine two small forest communities, each with 100 individuals distributed among four tree species (A, B, C, and D) as follows:

> Community 1: 25A, 25B, 25C, 25D
> Community 2: 80A, 5B, 5C, 10D

The species richness is the same for both communities because they both contain four species of trees, but the relative abundance is very different **(Figure 54.9)**. You would easily notice the four types of trees in community 1, but without looking carefully, you might see only the abundant species A in the second forest. Most observers would intuitively describe community 1 as the more diverse of the two communities.

Ecologists use many tools to quantitatively compare the diversity of different communities across time and space. They often calculate an index of diversity based on species richness

Community 1
A: 25% B: 25% C: 25% D: 25%

Community 2
A: 80% B: 5% C: 5% D: 10%

▲ **Figure 54.9 Which forest is more diverse?** Ecologists would say that community 1 has greater species diversity, a measure that includes both species richness and relative abundance.

and relative abundance. One widely used index is the **Shannon diversity** (H):

$$H = -[(p_A \ln p_A) + (p_B \ln p_B) + (p_C \ln p_C) + \ldots]$$

where A, B, C ... are the species in the community, p is the relative abundance of each species, and ln is the natural logarithm. Let's use this equation to calculate the Shannon diversity of the two communities in Figure 54.9. For community 1, $p = 0.25$ for each community, so $H = -4 \times (0.25 \ln 0.25) = 1.39$. For community 2, $H = -[(0.8 \ln 0.8) + (0.05 \ln 0.05) + (0.05 \ln 0.05) + (0.1 \ln 0.1)] = 0.71$. These calculations confirm our intuitive description of community 1 as more diverse.

Determining the number and relative abundance of species in a community is easier said than done. Many sampling techniques can be used, but since most species in a community are relatively rare, it may be hard to obtain a sample size large enough to be representative. It is also difficult to census the highly mobile or less visible members of communities, such as mites, nematodes, and microorganisms. The small size of microorganisms makes them particularly difficult to sample, so ecologists now use molecular tools to help determine microbial diversity **(Figure 54.10)**. Although measuring species diversity is often challenging, it is essential not only for understanding community structure but for conserving biodiversity, as you will read in Chapter 56.

Research Method

Determining Microbial Diversity Using Molecular Tools

APPLICATION Ecologists are increasingly using molecular techniques, such as the analysis of restriction fragment length polymorphisms (RFLPs), to determine microbial diversity and richness in environmental samples. As used in this application, RFLP analysis produces a DNA fingerprint for microbial taxa based on sequence variations in the DNA that encodes the small subunit of ribosomal RNA. Noah Fierer and Rob Jackson, of Duke University, used this method to compare the diversity of soil bacteria in 98 habitats across North and South America to help identify environmental variables associated with high bacterial diversity.

TECHNIQUE Researchers first extract and purify DNA from the microbial community in each sample. They use the polymerase chain reaction (PCR) to amplify the ribosomal DNA and label the DNA with a fluorescent dye (see Chapter 20). Restriction enzymes then cut the amplified, labeled DNA into fragments of different lengths, which are separated by gel electrophoresis. The number and abundance of these fragments characterize the DNA fingerprint of the sample.

Based on their RFLP analysis, Fierer and Jackson calculated the Shannon diversity (H) of each sample. They then looked for a correlation between H and several environmental variables, including vegetation type, mean annual temperature and rainfall, and acidity and quality of the soil at each site.

RESULTS The diversity of bacterial communities in soils across North and South America was related almost exclusively to soil pH, with the Shannon diversity being highest in neutral soils and lowest in acidic soils. Amazonian rain forests, which have extremely high plant and animal diversity, had the most acidic soils and the lowest bacterial diversity of the samples tested.

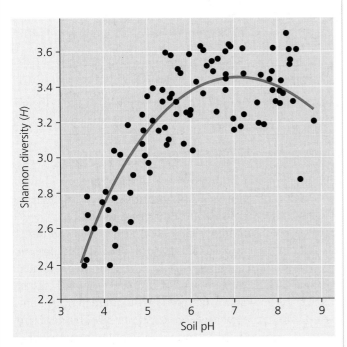

SOURCE N. Fierer and R. B. Jackson, The diversity and biogeography of soil bacterial communities, *Proceedings of the National Academy of Sciences USA* 103:626–631 (2006).

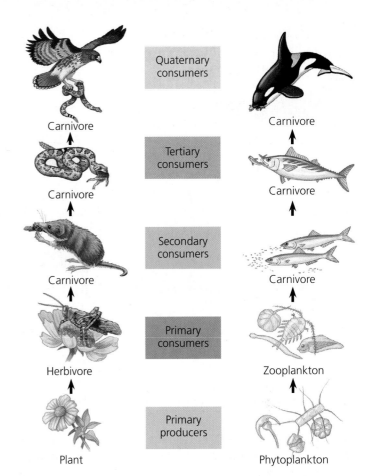

A terrestrial food chain   **A marine food chain**

▲ **Figure 54.11 Examples of terrestrial and marine food chains.** The arrows trace energy and nutrients that pass through the trophic levels of a community when organisms feed on one another. Decomposers, which "feed" on organisms from all trophic levels, are not shown here.

Trophic Structure

The structure and dynamics of a community depend to a large extent on the feeding relationships between organisms—the **trophic structure** of the community. The transfer of food energy up the trophic levels from its source in plants and other autotrophic organisms (primary producers) through herbivores (primary consumers) to carnivores (secondary, tertiary, and quaternary consumers) and eventually to decomposers is referred to as a **food chain** (**Figure 54.11**).

Food Webs

In the 1920s, Oxford University biologist Charles Elton recognized that food chains are not isolated units but are linked together in **food webs**. An ecologist can summarize the trophic relationships of a community by diagramming a food web with arrows linking species according to who eats whom. In an antarctic pelagic community, for example, the primary producers are phytoplankton, which serve as food for the dominant

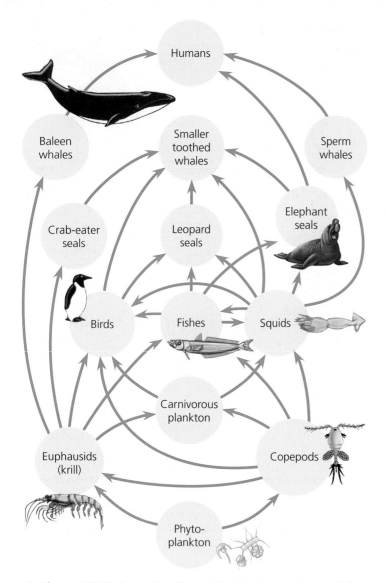

▲ **Figure 54.12 An antarctic marine food web.** Arrows follow the transfer of food from the producers (phytoplankton) up through the trophic levels. For simplicity, this diagram omits decomposers.

grazing zooplankton, especially euphausids (krill) and copepods, both of which are crustaceans **(Figure 54.12)**. These zooplankton species are in turn eaten by various carnivores, including other plankton, penguins, seals, fishes, and baleen whales. Squids, which are carnivores that feed on fishes as well as zooplankton, are another important link in these food webs, as they are in turn eaten by seals and toothed whales. During the time when whales were commonly hunted for food, humans became the top predator in this food web. Having hunted many whale species to low numbers, humans are now harvesting at lower trophic levels, catching krill as well as fishes for food.

How are food chains linked into food webs? First, a given species may weave into the web at more than one trophic level. In the food web shown in Figure 54.12, euphausids feed on phytoplankton as well as on other grazing zooplankton, such as copepods. Such "nonexclusive" consumers are also found in terrestrial communities. For instance, foxes are omnivores whose

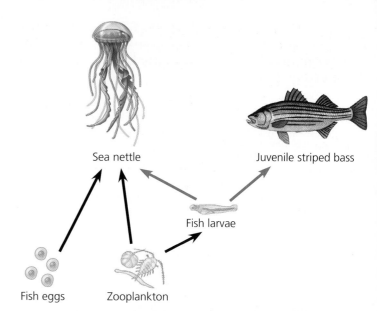

▲ **Figure 54.13 Partial food web for the Chesapeake Bay estuary on the U.S. Atlantic coast.** The sea nettle (*Chrysaora quinquecirrha*) and juvenile striped bass (*Morone saxatilis*) are the main predators of fish larvae (bay anchovy and several other species). Note that sea nettles are secondary consumers (black arrows) when they eat zooplankton, but tertiary consumers (red arrows) when they eat fish larvae, which are themselves secondary consumers of zooplankton.

diet includes berries and other plant materials, herbivores such as mice, and other predators, such as weasels. Humans are among the most versatile of omnivores.

Food webs can be very complicated, but we can simplify them for easier study in two ways. First, we can group species with similar trophic relationships in a given community into broad functional groups. For example, in Figure 54.12, more than 100 phytoplankton species are grouped as the primary producers in the food web. A second way to simplify a food web for closer study is to isolate a portion of the web that interacts very little with the rest of the community. **Figure 54.13** illustrates a partial food web for sea nettles (a type of cnidarian) and juvenile striped bass in Chesapeake Bay.

Limits on Food Chain Length

Each food chain within a food web is usually only a few links long. In the antarctic web of Figure 54.12, there are rarely more than seven links from the producers to any top-level predator, and most chains in this web have fewer links. In fact, most food webs studied to date have chains consisting of five or fewer links.

Why are food chains relatively short? There are two main hypotheses. One, the **energetic hypothesis**, suggests that the length of a food chain is limited by the inefficiency of energy transfer along the chain. As you will read in Chapter 55, only about 10% of the energy stored in the organic matter of each trophic level is converted to organic matter at the next trophic level. Thus, a producer level consisting of 100 kg of plant material can support about 10 kg of herbivore **biomass** (the total mass of all individuals in a population) and 1 kg of carnivore biomass. The energetic hypothesis predicts that food chains should be relatively longer in habitats of higher photosynthetic production, since the starting amount of energy is greater than in habitats with lower photosynthetic production.

A second hypothesis, the **dynamic stability hypothesis**, proposes that long food chains are less stable than short chains. Population fluctuations at lower trophic levels are magnified at higher levels, potentially causing the local extinction of top predators. In a variable environment, top predators must be able to recover from environmental shocks (such as extreme winters) that can reduce the food supply all the way up the food chain. The longer a food chain is, the more slowly top predators can recover from environmental setbacks. This hypothesis predicts that food chains should be shorter in unpredictable environments.

Most of the data available support the energetic hypothesis. For example, ecologists have used tree-hole communities in tropical forests as experimental models to test the energetic hypothesis. Many trees have small branch scars that rot, forming holes in the tree trunk. The tree holes hold water and provide a habitat for tiny communities consisting of microorganisms and insects that feed on leaf litter, as well as predatory insects. **Figure 54.14** shows the results of experiments in which researchers manipulated productivity (leaf litter falling into the tree holes). As predicted by the energetic hypothesis, holes with the most leaf litter, and hence the greatest total food supply at the producer level, supported the longest food chains.

Another factor that may limit food chain length is that carnivores in a food chain tend to be larger at successive trophic levels. The size of a carnivore and its feeding mechanism put some upper limit on the size of food it can take into its mouth. And except in a few cases, large carnivores cannot live on very small food items because they cannot procure enough food in a given time to meet their metabolic needs. Among the ex-

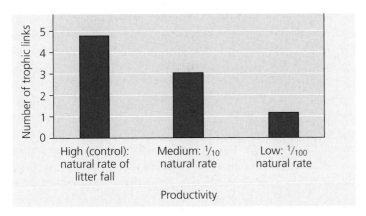

▲ **Figure 54.14 Test of the energetic hypothesis for the restriction of food chain length.** Researchers manipulated the productivity of tree-hole communities in Queensland, Australia, by providing leaf litter input at three levels. Reducing energy input reduced food chain length, a result consistent with the energetic hypothesis.

? *According to the dynamic stability hypothesis, which productivity treatment should have the most stable food chain? Explain.*

ceptions are baleen whales, huge suspension feeders with adaptations that enable them to consume enormous quantities of krill and other small organisms (see Figure 41.6).

Species with a Large Impact

Certain species have an especially large impact on the structure of entire communities either because they are highly abundant or because they play a pivotal role in community dynamics. The impact of these species can occur either through their trophic interactions or through their influences on the physical environment.

Dominant Species

Dominant species are those species in a community that are the most abundant or that collectively have the highest biomass. As a result, dominant species exert a powerful control over the occurrence and distribution of other species. For example, the abundance of sugar maples, the dominant plant species in many eastern North American forest communities, has a major impact on abiotic factors such as shading and soil, which in turn affect which other species live there.

There is no single explanation for why a species becomes dominant in a community. One hypothesis suggests that dominant species are competitively superior in exploiting limited resources such as water or nutrients. Another explanation is that dominant species are most successful at avoiding predation or the impact of disease. This latter idea could explain the high biomass attained in some environments by **invasive species**, organisms (typically introduced by humans) that take hold outside their native range. Such species may not face the natural predators and agents of disease that would otherwise hold their populations in check.

One way to discover the impact of a dominant species is to remove it from the community. This type of experiment has been carried out many times by accident. The American chestnut was a dominant tree in deciduous forests of eastern North America before 1910, making up more than 40% of mature trees. Then humans accidentally introduced the fungal disease chestnut blight to New York City via nursery stock imported from Asia. Between 1910 and 1950, this fungus killed all the chestnut trees in eastern North America. In this case, removing the dominant species had a relatively small impact on some species but severe effects on others. Oaks, hickories, beeches, and red maples that were already present in the forest increased in abundance and replaced the chestnuts. No mammals or birds seemed to have been harmed by the loss of the chestnut, but seven species of moths and butterflies that fed on the tree became extinct.

The American chestnut story is only one example of a community response to the loss of a dominant species. More research is needed before we can generalize about the overall effects of such losses.

Is *Pisaster ochraceus* a keystone predator?

EXPERIMENT In rocky intertidal communities of western North America, the relatively uncommon sea star *Pisaster ochraceus* preys on mussels such as *Mytilus californianus*, a dominant species and strong competitor for space. Robert Paine, of the University of Washington, removed *Pisaster* from an area in the intertidal zone and examined the effect on species richness.

RESULTS In the absence of *Pisaster*, species richness declined as mussels monopolized the rock face and eliminated most other invertebrates and algae. In a control area where *Pisaster* was not removed, species richness changed very little.

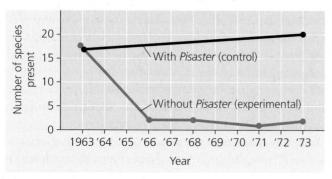

CONCLUSION *Pisaster* acts as a keystone species, exerting an influence on the community that is not reflected in its abundance.

SOURCE R. T. Paine, Food web complexity and species diversity, *American Naturalist* 100:65–75 (1966).

WHAT IF? Suppose that an invasive fungus killed most individuals of *Mytilus* at these sites. What do you think would happen to species richness if *Pisaster* were then removed?

Keystone Species

In contrast to dominant species, **keystone species** are not necessarily abundant in a community. They exert strong control on community structure not by numerical might but by their pivotal ecological roles, or niches. One way to identify keystone species is by removal experiments like the one described in **Figure 54.15**, which highlights the importance of a

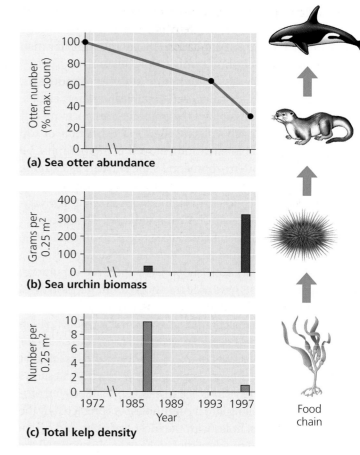

▲ **Figure 54.16 Sea otters as keystone predators in the North Pacific.** The graphs correlate changes over time in sea otter abundance **(a)** with changes in sea urchin biomass **(b)** and changes in kelp density **(c)** in kelp forests at Adak Island (part of the Aleutian Island chain). The vertical diagram on the right represents the food chain after orcas (top) entered the chain.

keystone species in maintaining the diversity of an intertidal community.

The sea otter, a keystone predator in the North Pacific, offers another example (**Figure 54.16**). Sea otters feed on sea urchins, and sea urchins feed mainly on kelp. In areas where sea otters are abundant, sea urchins are rare and kelp forests are well developed. Where sea otters are rare, sea urchins are common and kelp is almost absent. Over the last 20 years, orcas have been preying on sea otters as the whales' usual prey has declined. As a result, sea otter populations have declined precipitously in large areas off the coast of western Alaska, sometimes at rates as high as 25% per year. The loss of this keystone species has allowed sea urchin populations to increase, resulting in the loss of kelp forests.

Foundation Species (Ecosystem "Engineers")

Some organisms exert their influence on a community not through their trophic interactions but by causing physical changes in the environment. Such organisms may alter the environment through their behavior or their large collective biomass.

Species that dramatically alter their physical environment on a large scale are called ecosystem "engineers" or, to avoid implying conscious intent, "foundation species." A familiar foundation species is the beaver (Figure 54.17), which, through tree felling and dam building, can transform landscapes. The effects of foundation species on other species can be positive or negative, depending on the needs of the other species.

By altering the structure or dynamics of the environment, foundation species sometimes act as **facilitators**: They have positive effects on the survival and reproduction of other species in the community. For example, by modifying soils, the black rush *Juncus gerardi* increases the species richness in some zones of New England salt marshes. *Juncus* helps prevent salt buildup in the soil by shading the soil surface, which reduces evaporation (Figure 54.18a). *Juncus* also prevents the salt marsh soils from becoming oxygen depleted as it transports oxygen to its belowground tissues. Sally Hacker and Mark Bertness, of Brown University, uncovered some of *Juncus*'s facilitation effects by removing *Juncus* from study plots. Their experiment suggested that without *Juncus*, the up-

▲ **Figure 54.17 Beavers as ecosystem "engineers."** By felling trees, building dams, and creating ponds, beavers can transform large areas of forest into flooded wetlands.

(a) Salt marsh with *Juncus* (foreground)

(b)

▲ **Figure 54.18 Facilitation by black rush (*Juncus gerardi*) in New England salt marshes.** Black rush facilitates the occupation of the middle upper zone of the marsh, which increases local plant species richness.

per middle intertidal zone would support 50% fewer plant species (Figure 54.18b).

Bottom-Up and Top-Down Controls

Simplified models based on relationships between adjacent trophic levels are useful for discussing community organization. For example, let's consider the three possible relationships between plants (*V* for vegetation) and herbivores (*H*):

$$V \rightarrow H \qquad V \leftarrow H \qquad V \leftrightarrow H$$

The arrows indicate that a change in the biomass of one trophic level causes a change in the other trophic level. $V \rightarrow H$ means that an increase in vegetation will increase the numbers or biomass of herbivores, but not vice versa. In this situation, herbivores are limited by vegetation, but vegetation is not limited by herbivory. In contrast, $V \leftarrow H$ means that an increase in herbivore biomass will decrease the abundance of vegetation, but not vice versa. A double-headed arrow indicates that feedback flows in both directions, with each trophic level sensitive to changes in the biomass of the other.

Two models of community organization are common: the bottom-up model and the top-down model. The $V \rightarrow H$ linkage suggests a **bottom-up model**, which postulates a unidirectional influence from lower to higher trophic levels. In this case, the presence or absence of mineral nutrients (*N*) controls plant (*V*) numbers, which control herbivore (*H*) numbers, which in turn control predator (*P*) numbers. The simplified bottom-up model is thus $N \rightarrow V \rightarrow H \rightarrow P$. To change the community structure of a bottom-up community, you need to alter biomass at the lower trophic levels, allowing those changes to propagate up through the food web. For example, if you add mineral nutrients to stimulate growth of vegetation, then the higher trophic levels should also increase in biomass. If you add predators to or remove predators from a bottom-up community, however, the effect should not extend down to the lower trophic levels.

In contrast, the **top-down model** postulates the opposite: Predation mainly controls community organization because predators limit herbivores, herbivores limit plants, and plants limit nutrient levels through their uptake of nutrients during growth and reproduction. The simplified top-down model, $N \leftarrow V \leftarrow H \leftarrow P$, is also called the *trophic cascade model*. For example, in a lake community with four trophic levels, the model predicts that removing the top carnivores will increase the abundance of primary carnivores, in turn decreasing the number of herbivores, increasing phytoplankton abundance, and decreasing concentrations of mineral nutrients. If there were only three trophic levels in a lake, removing primary carnivores would increase the number of herbivores and decrease phytoplankton abundance, causing nutrient levels to rise. The effects of any manipulation thus move down the trophic structure as alternating $+/-$ effects.

Diana Wall (see interview on pages 1146–1147) and Ross Virginia investigated whether bottom-up or top-down factors are more important in a community of soil nematodes in the deserts of Antarctica. They chose this extreme environment because its nematode community contains only two or three species and is therefore easier to manipulate and study than other more species-rich communities. Their experiment, described in **Figure 54.19**, showed that top-down factors appear to control the organization of this simple community.

The top-down model has practical applications. For example, ecologists have applied the top-down model to improve water quality in polluted lakes. This approach, called **biomanipulation**, attempts to prevent algal blooms and eutrophication by altering the density of higher-level consumers in lakes instead of using chemical treatments. In lakes with three trophic levels, for example, removing fish should improve water quality by increasing zooplankton and thereby decreasing algal populations. In lakes with four trophic levels, adding top predators should have the same effect. We can summarize this scenario with the following diagram:

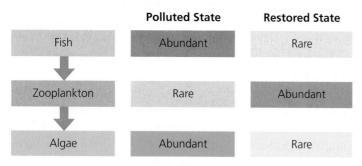

	Polluted State	**Restored State**
Fish	Abundant	Rare
Zooplankton	Rare	Abundant
Algae	Abundant	Rare

Ecologists used biomanipulation on a large scale in Lake Vesijärvi in southern Finland. Lake Vesijärvi is a large (110 km²), shallow lake that was polluted with city sewage and industrial wastewater until 1976. After pollution controls reduced these inputs, the water quality of the lake began to improve. By 1986, however, massive blooms of cyanobacteria started to occur in the lake. These blooms coincided with a dense population of roach, a fish that had benefited from the mineral nutrients that the pollution provided over many years. Roach eat zooplankton, which otherwise keep the cyanobacteria and algae in check. To reverse these changes, ecologists removed nearly a million kilograms of fish from Lake Vesijärvi between 1989 and 1993, reducing roach to about 20% of their former abundance. At the same time, the ecologists stocked the lake with pike perch, a predatory fish that eats roach. This added a fourth trophic level to the lake, which kept down the population of roach. Biomanipulation was a success in Lake Vesijärvi. The water became clear, and the last cyanobacterial bloom was in 1989. The lake remains clear even though roach removal ended in 1993.

As these examples show, communities vary in their degree of bottom-up and top-down control. To manage agricultural landscapes, parks, reservoirs, and fisheries, we need to understand each particular community's dynamics.

▼ Figure 54.19 **Inquiry**

Are soil nematode communities in Antarctica controlled by bottom-up or top-down factors?

EXPERIMENT   Previous research in the deserts of Antarctica had shown that the predatory nematode *Eudorylaimus antarcticus* becomes less abundant in drier soils, but its prey species, the nematode *Scottnema lindsayae*, does not. To determine whether bottom-up or top-down factors control interactions in these communities, Diana Wall and Ross Virginia, then both of Colorado State University, decreased the abundance of *E. antarcticus* in selected plots by warming and drying the soil. They placed clear plastic chambers over the ground for a year to trap the heat from sunlight and warm the soil by 5°C.

RESULTS   The density of *E. antarcticus* in the warmed plots dropped to one-quarter of the density in control plots. In contrast, the density of *S. lindsayae* increased by one-sixth.

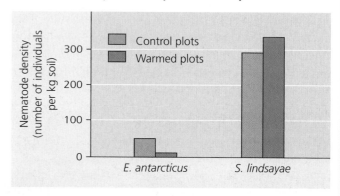

CONCLUSION   The prey species' increase in density as the predator density declined suggests that this soil nematode community is controlled by top-down factors.

SOURCE   D. Wall-Freckman and R. A. Virginia, Low-diversity Antarctic soil nematode communities: distribution and response to disturbance, *Ecology* 78:363–369 (1997).

WHAT IF?   Suppose a second predatory species existed in this community and that its abundance was unaffected by soil warming. How would you expect the density of *S. lindsayae* to change if the experiment were repeated under these conditions? Explain.

CONCEPT CHECK 54.2

1. What two components contribute to species diversity? Explain how two communities that contain the same number of species can differ in species diversity.
2. Describe two hypotheses that explain why food chains are usually short, and state a key prediction of each hypothesis.
3. **WHAT IF?**   Consider a grassland with five trophic levels: plants, grasshoppers, snakes, raccoons, and bobcats. If you released additional bobcats into the grassland, how would plant biomass change if the bottom-up model applied? If the top-down model applied?

For suggested answers, see Appendix A.

Disturbance influences species diversity and composition

Decades ago, most ecologists favored the traditional view that biological communities are in a state of equilibrium, a more or less stable balance, unless seriously disturbed by human activities. The "balance of nature" view focused on interspecific competition as a key factor determining community composition and maintaining stability in communities. *Stability* in this context refers to a community's tendency to reach and maintain a relatively constant composition of species.

One of the earliest proponents of this view, F. E. Clements, of the Carnegie Institution of Washington, argued in the early 1900s that the community of plants at a site had only one state of equilibrium, controlled solely by climate. According to Clements, biotic interactions caused the species in this *climax community* to function as an integrated unit—in effect, as a superorganism. His argument was based on the observation that certain species of plants are consistently found together, such as the oaks, maples, birches, and beeches in deciduous forests of the northeastern United States.

Other ecologists questioned whether most communities were at equilibrium or functioned as integrated units. A. G. Tansley, of Oxford University, challenged the concept of a climax community, arguing that differences in soils, topography, and other factors created many potential communities that were stable within a region. H. A. Gleason, of the University of Chicago, saw communities not as superorganisms but more as chance assemblages of species found in the same area simply because they happen to have similar abiotic requirements— for example, for temperature, rainfall, and soil type. Gleason and other ecologists also realized that disturbance keeps many communities from reaching a state of equilibrium in species diversity or composition. A **disturbance** is an event, such as a storm, fire, flood, drought, overgrazing, or human activity, that changes a community by removing organisms from it or altering resource availability.

This recent emphasis on change has produced the **nonequilibrium model**, which describes most communities as constantly changing after being affected by disturbances. Even where relatively stable communities do exist, they can be rapidly transformed into nonequilibrium communities. Let's now take a look at the ways disturbances influence community structure and composition.

Characterizing Disturbance

The types of disturbances and their frequency and severity vary from community to community. Storms disturb almost all communities, even those in the oceans, through the action of waves. Fire is a significant disturbance in most terrestrial communities; in fact, chaparral and some grassland biomes require regular burning to maintain their structure and species composition. Freezing is a frequent occurrence in many rivers, lakes, and ponds, and many streams and ponds are disturbed by spring flooding and seasonal drying. A high level of disturbance is generally the result of a high intensity *and* high frequency of disturbance, while low disturbance levels can result from either a low intensity or low frequency of disturbance.

The **intermediate disturbance hypothesis** states that moderate levels of disturbance can create conditions that foster greater species diversity than low or high levels of disturbance. High levels of disturbance reduce species diversity by creating environmental stresses that exceed the tolerances of many species or by subjecting the community to such a high frequency of disturbance that slow-growing or slow-colonizing species are excluded. At the other extreme, low levels of disturbance can reduce species diversity by allowing competitively dominant species to exclude less competitive species. Meanwhile, intermediate levels of disturbance can foster greater species diversity by opening up habitats for occupation by less competitive species. Such intermediate disturbance levels rarely create conditions so severe that they exceed the environmental tolerances of or rate of recovery by potential community members.

The intermediate disturbance hypothesis is supported by many terrestrial and aquatic studies. In one such study, ecologists in New Zealand compared the richness of invertebrate taxa living in the beds of streams exposed to different frequencies and intensities of flooding **(Figure 54.20)**. When floods occurred either very frequently or rarely, invertebrate richness was low. Frequent floods made it difficult for some species to become established in the streambed, while rare floods resulted in species being displaced by superior competitors. Invertebrate richness peaked in streams that had an intermediate frequency or intensity of flooding, as predicted by the intermediate disturbance hypothesis.

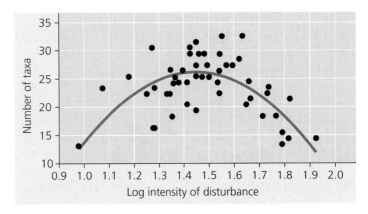

▲ **Figure 54.20 Testing the intermediate disturbance hypothesis.** Researchers identified the taxa (species or genera) of invertebrates at two locations in each of 27 New Zealand streams. They assessed the intensity of flooding at each location using an index of streambed disturbance. The number of invertebrate taxa peaked when the intensity of flooding was at intermediate levels.

Although moderate levels of disturbance appear to maximize species diversity, small and large disturbances can have important effects on community structure. Small-scale disturbances can create patches of different habitats across a landscape, which can be a key to maintaining diversity in a community. Large-scale disturbances are also a natural part of many communities. Much of Yellowstone National Park, for example, is dominated by lodgepole pine, a tree that requires the rejuvenating influence of periodic fires. Lodgepole cones remain closed until exposed to intense heat. When a forest fire burns the trees, the cones open and the seeds are released. The new generation of lodgepole pines can then thrive on nutrients released from the burned trees and in the sunlight that is no longer blocked by taller trees.

In the summer of 1988, extensive areas of Yellowstone burned during a severe drought. By 1989, burned areas in the park were largely covered with new vegetation, suggesting that the species in this community are adapted to rapid recovery after fire **(Figure 54.21)**. In fact, large-scale fires have periodically swept through the lodgepole pine forests of Yellowstone and other northern areas for thousands of years. In contrast, more southerly pine forests were historically affected by frequent but low-intensity fires. In these forests, a century of human intervention to suppress small fires has allowed an unnatural buildup of fuels and elevated the risk of large, severe fires to which the species are not adapted.

Studies of the Yellowstone forest community and many others indicate that they are nonequilibrium communities, changing continually because of natural disturbances and the internal processes of growth and reproduction. Mounting evidence suggests that nonequilibrium conditions resulting from disturbance are in fact the norm for most communities.

Ecological Succession

Changes in the composition and structure of terrestrial communities are most apparent after some severe disturbance, such as a volcanic eruption or a glacier, strips away all the existing vegetation. The disturbed area may be colonized by a variety of species, which are gradually replaced by other species, which are in turn replaced by still other species—a process called **ecological succession**.

When this process begins in a virtually lifeless area where soil has not yet formed, such as on a new volcanic island or on the rubble (moraine) left by a retreating glacier, it is called **primary succession**. Often the only life-forms initially present are autotrophic prokaryotes and heterotrophic prokaryotes and protists. Lichens and mosses, which grow from windblown spores, are commonly the first macroscopic photosynthesizers to colonize such areas. Soil develops gradually as rocks weather and organic matter accumulates from the decomposed remains of the early colonizers. Once soil is present, the lichens and mosses are usually overgrown by grasses, shrubs, and trees that sprout from seeds blown in from nearby areas or carried in by animals. Eventually, an area is colonized by plants that become the community's prevalent form of vegetation. Producing such a community through primary succession may take hundreds or thousands of years.

Secondary succession occurs when an existing community has been cleared by some disturbance that leaves the soil intact, as in Yellowstone following the 1988 fires (see Figure 54.21). Sometimes the area begins to return to something like its original state. For instance, in a forested area that has been cleared for farming and later abandoned, the earliest plants to recolonize are often herbaceous species that grow from windblown or animal-borne seeds. If the area has not been burned or

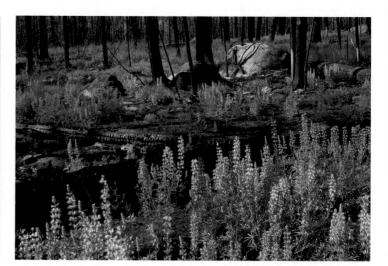

(a) Soon after fire. The burn left a patchy landscape. Note the unburned trees in the far distance.

(b) One year after fire. The community has begun to recover. A variety of herbaceous plants, different from those in the former forest, cover the ground.

▲ **Figure 54.21 Recovery following a large-scale disturbance.** The 1988 Yellowstone National Park fires burned large areas of forests dominated by lodgepole pines.

heavily grazed, woody shrubs may in time replace most of the herbaceous species, and forest trees may eventually replace most of the shrubs.

Early arrivals and later-arriving species may be linked in one of three key processes. The early arrivals may *facilitate* the appearance of the later species by making the environment more favorable—for example, by increasing the fertility of the soil. Alternatively, the early species may *inhibit* establishment of the later species, so that successful colonization by later species occurs in spite of, rather than because of, the activities of the early species. Finally, the early species may be completely independent of the later species, which *tolerate* conditions created early in succession but are neither helped nor hindered by early species.

Let's look at how these various processes contribute to primary succession on glacial moraines. Ecologists have conducted the most extensive research on moraine succession at Glacier Bay in southeastern Alaska, where glaciers have retreated more than 100 km since 1760 **(Figure 54.22)**. By studying the communities on moraines at different distances from the mouth of the bay, ecologists can examine different stages in succession. ❶ The exposed moraine is colonized first by pioneering species that include liverworts, mosses, fireweed, scat-

tered *Dryas* (a mat-forming shrub), willows, and cottonwood. ❷ After about three decades, *Dryas* dominates the plant community. ❸ A few decades later, the area is invaded by alder, which forms dense thickets up to 9 m tall. In the next two centuries, these alder stands are overgrown first by Sitka spruce ❹ and later by a combination of western hemlock and mountain hemlock. In areas of poor drainage, the forest floor of this spruce-hemlock forest is invaded by sphagnum moss, which holds large amounts of water and acidifies the soil, eventually killing the trees. Thus, by about 300 years after glacial retreat, the vegetation consists of sphagnum bogs on the poorly drained flat areas and spruce-hemlock forest on the well-drained slopes.

How is succession on glacial moraines related to the environmental changes caused by transitions in the vegetation? The bare soil exposed as the glacier retreats is quite basic, with a pH of 8.0–8.4 due to the carbonate compounds in the parent rocks. The soil pH falls rapidly as vegetation develops. Decomposition of acidic spruce needles in particular reduces the pH of the soil from 7.0 to approximately 4.0. The soil concentrations of mineral nutrients also change with time. Because the bare soil after glacial retreat is low in nitrogen content, almost all the pioneer plant species begin succession with poor

❶ **Pioneer stage, with fireweed dominant**

❷ *Dryas* **stage**

❹ **Spruce stage**

❸ **Alder stage**

▲ **Figure 54.22 Glacial retreat and primary succession at Glacier Bay, Alaska.** The different shades of blue on the map show retreat of the glacier since 1760, based on historical descriptions.

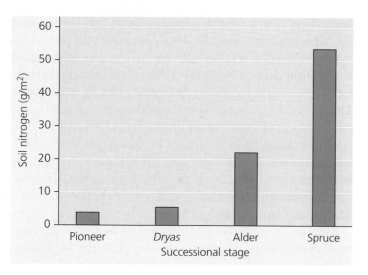

▲ Figure 54.23 **Changes in soil nitrogen content during succession at Glacier Bay.**

▲ Figure 54.24 **Disturbance of the ocean floor by trawling.** These photos show the seafloor off northwestern Australia before (top) and after (bottom) deep-sea trawlers have passed.

growth and yellow leaves due to inadequate nitrogen supply. The exceptions are *Dryas* and, particularly, alder; these species have symbiotic bacteria that fix atmospheric nitrogen (see Chapter 37). Soil nitrogen content increases rapidly during the alder stage of succession and continues to increase during the spruce stage **(Figure 54.23)**. By altering soil properties, pioneer plant species permit new plant species to grow, and the new plants in turn alter the environment in different ways, contributing to succession.

Human Disturbance

Ecological succession is a response to disturbance of the environment, and one of the strongest agents of disturbance today is human activity. Of all animals, humans have the greatest impact on biological communities worldwide. Agricultural development has disrupted what were once the vast grasslands of the North American prairie. Logging and clearing for urban development, mining, and farming have reduced large tracts of forests to small patches of disconnected woodlots in many parts of the United States and throughout Europe. After forests are clear-cut, weedy and shrubby vegetation often colonizes the area and dominates it for many years. This type of vegetation is also found in agricultural fields that are no longer under cultivation and in vacant lots and construction sites.

Human disturbance of communities is by no means limited to the United States and Europe; nor is it a recent problem. Tropical rain forests are quickly disappearing as a result of clear-cutting for lumber, cattle grazing, and farmland. Centuries of overgrazing and agricultural disturbance have contributed to famine in parts of Africa by turning seasonal grasslands into vast barren areas.

Humans disturb marine ecosystems just as extensively as terrestrial ones. The effects of ocean trawling, where boats drag weighted nets across the seafloor, are similar to those of clear-cutting a forest or plowing a field **(Figure 54.24)**. The trawls scrape and scour corals and other life on the seafloor and in its sediments. In a typical year, ships trawl 15 million km² of ocean floor, an area about the size of South America and 150 times larger than the area of forests that are clear-cut annually.

Because human disturbance is often severe, it reduces species diversity in many communities. In Chapter 56, we will take a closer look at how community disturbance by human activities is affecting the diversity of life.

CONCEPT CHECK **54.3**

1. Why do high and low levels of disturbance usually reduce species diversity? Why does an intermediate level of disturbance promote species diversity?
2. During succession, how might the early species facilitate the arrival of other species?
3. **WHAT IF?** Most prairies experience regular fires, typically every few years. How would the species diversity of a prairie likely be affected if no burning occurred for 100 years? Explain your answer.

For suggested answers, see Appendix A.

CONCEPT **54.4**
Biogeographic factors affect community biodiversity

So far we have examined relatively small-scale or local factors that influence the diversity of communities, including the effects of species interactions, dominant species, and many types of disturbances. Ecologists also recognize that large-scale biogeographic factors contribute to the tremendous range of diversity observed in biological communities. The contributions of two biogeographic factors in particular—the latitude of a community and the area it occupies—have been investigated for more than a century.

Latitudinal Gradients

In the 1850s, both Charles Darwin and Alfred Wallace pointed out that plant and animal life was generally more abundant and diverse in the tropics than in other parts of the globe. Since that time, many researchers around the world have confirmed this observation. For example, one study found that a 6.6-hectare (1 ha = 10,000 m^2) plot in tropical Malaysia contained 711 tree species, while a 2-ha plot of deciduous forest in Michigan typically contains just 10 to 15 tree species. Moreover, in all of western Europe north of the Alps there are only 50 tree species. Many groups of animals show similar latitudinal gradients. For instance, there are more than 200 species of ants in Brazil but only 7 in Alaska.

The two key factors in latitudinal gradients of species richness are probably evolutionary history and climate. Over the course of evolutionary time, species diversity may increase in a community as more speciation events occur. Tropical communities are generally older than temperate or polar communities. This age difference stems partly from the fact that the growing season is about five times as long in tropical forests as in the tundra communities of high latitudes. In effect, biological time, and hence intervals between speciation events, run about five times as fast in the tropics as near the poles. And many polar and temperate communities have repeatedly "started over" as a result of major disturbances in the form of glaciations.

Climate is likely the primary cause of the latitudinal gradient in biodiversity. In terrestrial communities, the two main climatic factors correlated with biodiversity are solar energy input and water availability, both of which are relatively high in the tropics. These factors can be considered together by measuring a community's rate of **evapotranspiration**, the evaporation of water from soil plus the transpiration of water from plants. Evapotranspiration, a function of solar radiation, temperature, and water availability, is much higher in hot areas with abundant rainfall than in areas with low temperatures or low precipitation. *Potential evapotranspiration*, a measure of potential water loss that assumes that water is readily available, is determined by the amount of solar radiation and temperature and is highest in regions where both are plentiful. The species richness of plants and animals correlates with both measures of evapotranspiration (**Figure 54.25**).

Area Effects

In 1807, naturalist and explorer Alexander von Humboldt described one of the first patterns of biodiversity to be recognized,

(a) Trees

(b) Vertebrates

▲ **Figure 54.25 Energy, water, and species richness. (a)** Species richness of North American trees increases most predictably with actual evapotranspiration, while **(b)** vertebrate species richness in North America increases most predictably with potential evapotranspiration. Evapotranspiration values are expressed as rainfall equivalents.

the **species-area curve**: All other factors being equal, the larger the geographic area of a community, the more species it has. The likely explanation for this pattern is that larger areas offer a greater diversity of habitats and microhabitats than smaller areas. In conservation biology, developing species-area curves for the key taxa in a community helps ecologists predict how the potential loss of a certain area of habitat is likely to affect the community's biodiversity.

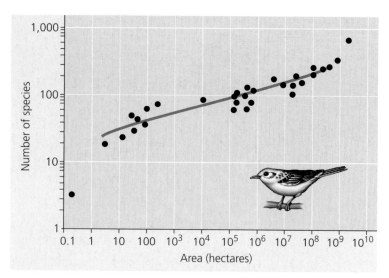

▲ **Figure 54.26 Species-area curve for North American breeding birds.** Both area and number of species are plotted on a logarithmic scale. The data points range from a 0.2-ha plot with 3 species in Pennsylvania to the whole United States and Canada (1.9 billion ha) with 625 species.

Figure 54.26 is a species-area curve for North American breeding birds (birds with breeding populations in the mapped area, as opposed to migrant populations). The slope indicates the extent to which species richness increases with community area. While the slopes of different species-area curves vary, the basic concept of diversity increasing with increasing area applies in a variety of situations, from surveys of ant diversity in New Guinea to the number of plant species on islands of different sizes. In fact, island biogeography provides some of the best examples of species-area curves, as we will discuss next.

Island Equilibrium Model

Because of their isolation and limited size, islands provide excellent opportunities for studying the biogeographic factors that affect the species diversity of communities. By "islands," we mean not only oceanic islands, but also habitat islands on land, such as lakes, mountain peaks separated by lowlands, or natural woodland fragments surrounded by areas disturbed by humans—in other words, any patch surrounded by an environment not suitable for the "island" species. In the 1960s, American ecologists Robert MacArthur and E. O. Wilson developed a general model of island biogeography identifying the key determinants of species diversity on an island with a given set of physical characteristics **(Figure 54.27)**.

Consider a newly formed oceanic island that receives colonizing species from a distant mainland. Two factors that determine the number of species on the island are the rate at which new species immigrate to the island and the rate at which species become extinct on the island. At any given time, an island's immigration and extinction rates are affected by the number of species already present. As the number of species on the island increases, the immigration rate of new species decreases, because any individual reaching the island is less likely to represent a species that is not already present. At the same time, as more species inhabit an island, extinction rates on the island increase because of the greater likelihood of competitive exclusion.

Two physical features of the island further affect immigration and extinction rates: its size and its distance from the mainland. Small islands generally have lower immigration rates because potential colonizers are less likely to reach a small island. For instance, birds blown out to sea by a storm

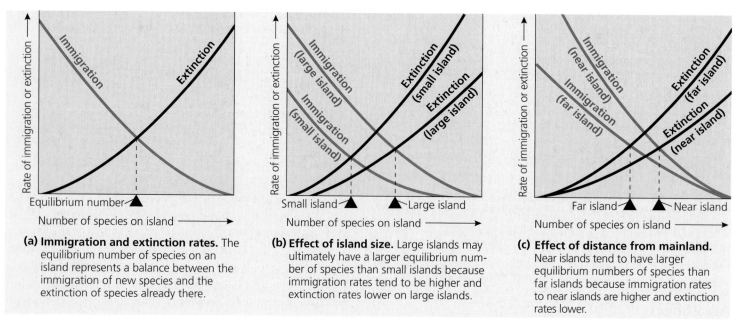

(a) Immigration and extinction rates. The equilibrium number of species on an island represents a balance between the immigration of new species and the extinction of species already there.

(b) Effect of island size. Large islands may ultimately have a larger equilibrium number of species than small islands because immigration rates tend to be higher and extinction rates lower on large islands.

(c) Effect of distance from mainland. Near islands tend to have larger equilibrium numbers of species than far islands because immigration rates to near islands are higher and extinction rates lower.

▲ **Figure 54.27 The equilibrium model of island biogeography.** Black triangles represent equilibrium numbers of species.

are more likely to land by chance on a larger island than on a small one. Small islands also have higher extinction rates, as they generally contain fewer resources and less diverse habitats for colonizing species to partition. Distance from the mainland is also important; for two islands of equal size, a closer island generally has a higher immigration rate than one farther away. Because of their higher immigration rates, closer islands also have lower extinction rates, as arriving colonists help sustain the presence of a species on a near island and prevent its extinction.

These relationships make up MacArthur and Wilson's model of island biogeography (see Figure 54.27). Immigration and extinction rates are plotted as a function of the number of species present on the island. This model is called the *island equilibrium model* because an equilibrium will eventually be reached where the rate of species immigration equals the rate of species extinction. The number of species at this equilibrium point is correlated with the island's size and distance from the mainland. Like any ecological equilibrium, this species equilibrium is dynamic; immigration and extinction continue, and the exact species composition may change over time.

MacArthur and Wilson's studies of the diversity of plants and animals on many island chains, including the Galápagos Islands, support the prediction that species richness increases with island size, in keeping with the island equilibrium model **(Figure 54.28)**. Species counts also fit the prediction that the number of species decreases with increasing remoteness of the island.

The island equilibrium model's predictions of equilibria in the species composition of communities may apply in only a limited number of cases and over relatively short periods, where colonization is the main process affecting species composition. Over longer periods, abiotic disturbances such as storms, adaptive evolutionary changes, and speciation generally alter the species composition and community structure on islands. Nonetheless, the model is widely applied in conservation biology, particularly for the design of habitat reserves and for providing a starting point for predicting the effects of habitat loss on species diversity.

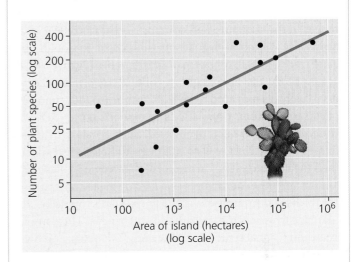

▼ Figure 54.28 **Inquiry**

How does species richness relate to area?

FIELD STUDY Ecologists Robert MacArthur and E. O. Wilson studied the number of plant species on the Galápagos Islands, which vary greatly in size, in relation to the area of each island.

RESULTS

CONCLUSION Plant species richness increases with island size, supporting the island equilibrium model.

SOURCE R. H. MacArthur and E. O. Wilson, *The Theory of Island Biogeography*, Princeton University Press, Princeton, NJ (1967).

WHAT IF? Four islands in this study ranging in area from about 40 to 10,000 ha all contained about 50 plant species. What does such variation tell you about the simple assumptions of the island equilibrium model?

CONCEPT CHECK 54.4

1. Describe two hypotheses that explain why species diversity is greater in tropical regions than in temperate and polar regions.
2. Describe how an island's size and distance from the mainland affect the island's species richness.
3. **WHAT IF?** Based on MacArthur and Wilson's model of island biogeography, how would you expect the richness of birds on islands to compare with the richness of snakes or mammals? Explain.

For suggested answers, see Appendix A.

CONCEPT **54.5**

Community ecology is useful for understanding pathogen life cycles and controlling human disease

Now that we have examined several important factors that structure ecological communities, let's finish the chapter by examining community interactions involving **pathogens**— disease-causing microorganisms, viruses, viroids, or prions (viroids and prions are infectious RNA molecules and proteins, respectively; see Chapter 19). Scientists have recently come to appreciate how universal the effects of pathogens are in ecological communities. Pathogens can alter community structure quickly and extensively, as you saw in the discussion of chestnut blight and the fungus that causes it (see Concept 54.2). Ecologists are also applying ecological knowledge to help track and control the pathogens that cause human diseases.

Pathogens and Community Structure

In spite of the potential of pathogens to limit populations, pathogens have until recently been the subject of relatively few ecological studies. This imbalance is now being addressed as dramatic events highlight the ecological importance of disease.

Coral reef communities are increasingly susceptible to the influence of newly discovered pathogens. White-band disease, caused by an unknown pathogen, has resulted in dramatic changes in the structure and composition of Caribbean reefs. The disease kills corals by causing their tissue to slough off in a band from the base to the tip of the branches (Figure 54.29). Because of the disease, staghorn coral (*Acropora cervicornis*) has virtually disappeared from the Caribbean since the 1980s. In the same region, populations of elkhorn coral (*Acropora palmata*) have also been decimated. Such corals provide key habitat for lobsters as well as snappers and other fish species. When the corals die, they are quickly overgrown by algae. Surgeonfish and other herbivores that feed on algae come to dominate the fish community. Eventually, the corals topple because of damage from storms and other disturbances. The complex, three-dimensional structure of the reef disappears, and diversity plummets.

Pathogens also influence community structure in terrestrial ecosystems. In the forests and savannas of California, trees of several species are dying from sudden oak death (SOD). This recently discovered disease is caused by the fungus-like protist *Phytophthora ramorum* (see Chapter 28). SOD was first described in California in 1995 when hikers noticed trees dying around San Francisco Bay. By 2007, it had spread more than 650 km. During that time, it killed more than a million oaks and other trees from the central California coast to southern Oregon. The loss of these oaks led to a decrease in the abundance of at least five bird species, including the acorn woodpecker and the oak titmouse, that rely on the oaks for food and habitat. Although there is currently no cure for SOD, scientists

▲ **Figure 54.29 White-band disease visible on a coral.**

recently sequenced the genome of *P. ramorum* in hopes of finding a way to fight the pathogen.

One reason ecologists now study pathogens is that human activities are transporting pathogens around the world at unprecedented rates. Genetic analyses using simple sequence DNA (see Chapter 21) suggest that the fungus that causes SOD likely came from Europe through the horticulture trade. Similarly, the pathogens that cause human diseases are spread by our global economy. A person traveling by airplane can quickly introduce a pathogen to a new location; this mechanism may have been how the West Nile virus arrived in North America in 1999. Many diseases are becoming more common, and community ecology is needed to help study and combat them.

Community Ecology and Zoonotic Diseases

Three-quarters of today's emerging human diseases, including hantavirus and mad cow disease (see Chapter 19), and many historically important ones, such as malaria (see Chapter 28), are caused by **zoonotic pathogens**. Zoonotic pathogens are defined as those that are transferred from other animals to humans, either through direct contact with an infected animal or by means of an intermediate species, called a **vector**. The vectors that spread zoonotic diseases are often parasites, including ticks, lice, and mosquitoes. Community ecologists can help prevent zoonotic diseases by identifying key species interactions involving pathogens and their vectors and by tracking pathogen spread.

Understanding parasite life cycles enables scientists to devise ways to control zoonotic diseases. The disease river blindness, for instance, is caused by a nematode transmitted by blackflies. When the World Health Organization began a global fight against river blindness, doctors had no medical treatments for the disease. Scientists focused instead on controlling the blackflies that spread the pathogenic nematodes. They used airplanes to spray biodegradable insecticides (which were monitored to minimize harm to aquatic communities). Ivermectin, a drug that kills the nematodes, was developed in 1987, and since then the combination of vector control and ivermectin use has saved the sight of an estimated 300,000 people. However, research published in 2007 suggests that the nematodes are developing resistance to ivermectin, so blackfly control remains a key part of the program to fight the disease.

Ecologists also use their knowledge of community interactions to track the spread of zoonotic diseases. A timely example is ecological research on the spread of avian flu. Avian flu is caused by highly contagious viruses transmitted through the saliva and feces of birds (see Chapter 19). Most of these viruses affect wild birds mildly, but they often cause stronger symptoms in domesticated birds, the most common source of human infections. Since 2003, one particular viral strain, called H5N1, has killed hundreds of millions of poultry and more than 150 people. Millions more people are at risk of infection.

the Americas. The most likely place for infected wild birds to enter the Americas is Alaska, the entry point for ducks, geese, and shorebirds that migrate across the Bering Sea from Asia each year. Ecologists are studying the potential spread of the virus by trapping and testing migrating and resident birds in Alaska (**Figure 54.30**). These ecological detectives are trying to catch the first wave of the disease entering North America.

Community ecology provides the foundation for understanding the life cycles of pathogens and their interactions with hosts. Pathogen interactions are also greatly influenced by changes in the environment. To control pathogens and the diseases they cause, scientists need an ecosystem perspective—an intimate knowledge of how the pathogens interact with other species and with their environment. Ecosystems are the subject of Chapter 55.

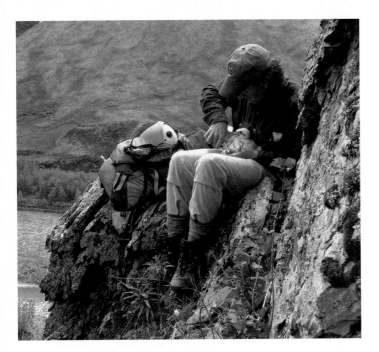

▲ **Figure 54.30 Tracking avian flu.** Graduate student Travis Booms, of the University of Alaska, Fairbanks, bands a young gyrfalcon (*Falco rusticolus*) as part of a project to monitor the spread of the disease.

Control programs that quarantine domestic birds or monitor their transport may be ineffective if avian flu spreads naturally through the movements of wild birds. From 2003 to 2006, the H5N1 strain spread rapidly from southeast Asia into Europe and Africa, but by late 2007 it had not appeared in Australia or

CONCEPT CHECK 54.5

1. What are pathogens?
2. Some parasites require contact with at least two host species to complete their life cycle. Why might this characteristic be important for the spread of certain zoonotic diseases?
3. **WHAT IF?** Suppose a new zoonotic disease emerges from a tropical rain forest. Doctors have no way yet to treat the disease, so preventing infections is particularly important. As a community ecologist, how might you help prevent the spread of the disease?

For suggested answers, see Appendix A.

Chapter 54 Review

SUMMARY OF KEY CONCEPTS

CONCEPT 54.1

Community interactions are classified by whether they help, harm, or have no effect on the species involved (pp. 1198–1204)

▶ Populations are linked by interspecific interactions that affect the survival and reproduction of the species that engage in them. These interactions include competition, predation, herbivory, and symbiosis. Parasitism, mutualism, and commensalism are types of symbiotic interactions.

MEDIA
Activity Interspecific Interactions
Biology Labs On-Line PopulationEcologyLab

Interspecific Interaction	Description
Competition (−/−)	Two or more species compete for a resource that is in short supply. The competitive exclusion principle states that two species cannot coexist in the same community if their niches (ecological roles) are identical.
Predation (+/−)	One species, the predator, kills and eats the other, the prey. Predation has led to diverse adaptations, including mimicry.
Herbivory (+/−)	An herbivore eats part of a plant or alga. Plants have various chemical and mechanical defenses against herbivory, and herbivores have specialized adaptations for feeding.
Symbiosis	Individuals of two or more species live in close contact with one another. Symbiosis includes parasitism, mutualism, and commensalism.
Parasitism (+/−)	The parasite derives its nourishment from a second organism, its host, which is harmed.
Mutualism (+/+)	Both species benefit from the interaction.
Commensalism (+/0)	One species benefits from the interaction, while the other is unaffected by it.

Dominant and keystone species exert strong controls on community structure (pp. 1204–1210)

▶ **Species Diversity** Species diversity measures the number of species in a community—its species richness—and their relative abundance. A community with similar abundances of species is more diverse than one in which one or two species are abundant and the remainder are rare.

▶ **Trophic Structure** Trophic structure is a key factor in community dynamics. Food chains link the trophic levels from producers to top carnivores. Branching food chains and complex trophic interactions form food webs. The energetic hypothesis suggests that the length of a food chain is limited by the inefficiency of energy transfer along the chain. The dynamic stability hypothesis proposes that long food chains are less stable than short chains.

▶ **Species with a Large Impact** Dominant species and keystone species exert strong controls on community structure. Dominant species are the most abundant species in a community, and their dominance is achieved by having high competitive ability. Keystone species are usually less abundant species that exert a disproportionate influence on community structure because of their ecological niche. Ecosystem "engineers," also called foundation species, exert influence on community structure through their effects on the physical environment.

▶ **Bottom-Up and Top-Down Controls** The bottom-up model proposes a unidirectional influence from lower to higher trophic levels, in which nutrients and other abiotic factors are the main determinants of community structure, including the abundance of primary producers. The top-down model proposes that control of each trophic level comes from the trophic level above, with the result that predators control herbivores, which in turn control primary producers.

MEDIA

Investigation How Are Impacts on Community Diversity Measured?
Activity Food Webs

Disturbance influences species diversity and composition (pp. 1211–1214)

▶ **Characterizing Disturbance** More and more evidence suggests that disturbance and lack of equilibrium, rather than stability and equilibrium, are the norm for most communities. According to the intermediate disturbance hypothesis, moderate levels of disturbance can foster higher species diversity than can low or high levels of disturbance.

▶ **Ecological Succession** Ecological succession is the sequence of community and ecosystem changes after a disturbance. Primary succession occurs where no soil exists when succession begins; secondary succession begins in an area where soil remains after a disturbance. Mechanisms that produce community change during succession include facilitation and inhibition.

▶ **Human Disturbance** Humans are the most widespread agents of disturbance, and their effects on communities often reduce species diversity. Humans also prevent some naturally occurring disturbances, such as fire, which can be important to community structure.

MEDIA

Activity Primary Succession

Biogeographic factors affect community biodiversity (pp. 1214–1217)

▶ **Latitudinal Gradients** Species richness generally declines along a latitudinal gradient from the tropics to the poles. The greater age of tropical environments may account for the greater species richness of the tropics. Climate also influences the biodiversity gradient through energy (heat and light) and water.

▶ **Area Effects** Species richness is directly related to a community's geographic size, a principle formalized in the species-area curve.

▶ **Island Equilibrium Model** Species richness on islands depends on island size and distance from the mainland. The island equilibrium model maintains that species richness on an ecological island reaches an equilibrium where new immigrations are balanced by extinctions. This model may not apply over long periods, during which abiotic disturbances, evolutionary changes, and speciation may alter community structure.

MEDIA

Activity Exploring Island Biogeography
GraphIt! Species-Area Effect and Island Biogeography

Community ecology is useful for understanding pathogen life cycles and controlling human disease (pp. 1217–1219)

▶ **Pathogens and Community Structure** Recent work has highlighted the role that pathogens play in structuring terrestrial and marine communities.

▶ **Community Ecology and Zoonotic Diseases** Zoonotic diseases, caused by pathogens transferred from other animals to humans, are the largest class of emerging human diseases. Community ecology provides the framework for understanding the species interactions associated with such pathogens and for our ability to track and control their spread.

TESTING YOUR KNOWLEDGE

SELF-QUIZ

1. The feeding relationships among the species in a community determine the community's
   a. secondary succession.
   b. ecological niche.
   c. trophic structure.
   d. species-area curve.
   e. species richness.

2. The principle of competitive exclusion states that
   a. two species cannot coexist in the same habitat.
   b. competition between two species always causes extinction or emigration of one species.
   c. competition in a population promotes survival of the best-adapted individuals.
   d. two species that have exactly the same niche cannot coexist in a community.
   e. two species will stop reproducing until one species leaves the habitat.

3. Keystone predators can maintain species diversity in a community if they
   a. competitively exclude other predators.
   b. prey on the community's dominant species.
   c. allow immigration of other predators.
   d. reduce the number of disruptions in the community.
   e. prey only on the least abundant species in the community.

4. Food chains are sometimes short because
   a. only a single species of herbivore feeds on each plant species.
   b. local extinction of a species causes extinction of the other species in its food chain.
   c. most of the energy in a trophic level is lost as it passes to the next higher level.
   d. predator species tend to be less diverse and less abundant than prey species.
   e. most producers are inedible.

5. Based on the intermediate disturbance hypothesis, a community's species diversity is
   a. increased by frequent massive disturbance.
   b. increased by stable conditions with no disturbance.
   c. increased by moderate levels of disturbance.
   d. increased when humans intervene to eliminate disturbance.
   e. increased by intensive disturbance by humans.

6. Which of the following could qualify as a top-down control on a grassland community?
   a. limitation of plant biomass by rainfall amount
   b. influence of temperature on competition among plants
   c. influence of soil nutrients on the abundance of grasses versus wildflowers
   d. effect of grazing intensity by bison on plant species diversity
   e. effect of humidity on plant growth rates

7. The most plausible hypothesis to explain why species richness is higher in tropical than in temperate regions is that
   a. tropical communities are younger.
   b. tropical regions generally have more available water and higher levels of solar radiation.
   c. higher temperatures cause more rapid speciation.
   d. biodiversity increases as evapotranspiration decreases.
   e. tropical regions have very high rates of immigration and very low rates of extinction.

8. According to the equilibrium model of island biogeography, species richness would be greatest on an island that is
   a. small and remote.
   b. large and remote.
   c. large and close to a mainland.
   d. small and close to a mainland.
   e. environmentally homogeneous.

9. Community 1 contains 100 individuals distributed among four species (A, B, C, and D). Community 2 contains 100 individuals distributed among three species (A, B, and C).
   Community 1: 5A, 5B, 85C, 5D
   Community 2: 30A, 40B, 30C
   Calculate the Shannon diversity (H) for each community. Which community is more diverse?

10. **DRAW IT**   Figure 54.13 presents a partial food web for the Chesapeake Bay estuary. Another important species in Chesapeake Bay is the blue crab (*Callinectes sapidus*). It is an omnivore, eating eelgrass and other primary producers as well as clams. Blue crabs are also cannibals. In turn, the crabs are a preferred food source for the endangered Kemp's Ridley sea turtle and, of course, for people. Based on this information, draw a food web that includes the blue crab. Assuming that the top-down model holds for this system, what would happen to the abundance of eelgrass if people were banned from catching crabs?

For Self-Quiz answers, see Appendix A.

MEDIA   Visit the Study Area at **www.masteringbio.com** for a Practice Test.

EVOLUTION CONNECTION

11. Explain why adaptations of particular organisms to interspecific competition may not necessarily represent instances of character displacement. What would a researcher have to demonstrate about two competing species to make a convincing case for character displacement?

SCIENTIFIC INQUIRY

12. An ecologist studying plants in the desert performed the following experiment. She staked out two identical plots, each of which included a few sagebrush plants and numerous small annual wildflowers. She found the same five wildflower species in roughly equal numbers on both plots. She then enclosed one of the plots with a fence to keep out kangaroo rats, the most common grain-eaters of the area. After two years, four of the wildflower species were no longer present in the fenced plot, but one species had increased drastically. The control plot had not changed in species diversity. Using the principles of community ecology, propose a hypothesis to explain her results. What additional evidence would support your hypothesis?

SCIENCE, TECHNOLOGY, AND SOCIETY

13. By 1935, hunting and trapping had eliminated wolves from the United States except for Alaska. Because wolves have since been protected as an endangered species, they have moved south from Canada and have become reestablished in the Rocky Mountains and northern Great Lakes region. Conservationists who would like to speed up wolf recovery have reintroduced wolves into Yellowstone National Park. Local ranchers are opposed to bringing back the wolves because they fear predation on their cattle and sheep. What are some reasons for reestablishing wolves in Yellowstone National Park? What effects might the reintroduction of wolves have on the ecological communities in the region? What might be done to mitigate the conflicts between ranchers and wolves?

Ecosystems 55

▲ Figure 55.1 **What makes this ecosystem dynamic?**

OVERVIEW

Observing Ecosystems

Sitting beside a mountain lake, you watch the last rays of the sun reflected on its surface (**Figure 55.1**). While enjoying the tranquil scene, you begin to sense that the lake is much more dynamic than you first thought. Small rings form where fish snatch insects that have fallen to the lake's surface. A stream flows into the lake, delivering a bounty of mineral nutrients and organic matter. A slight breeze carries the lake's scent, shaped by microorganisms whose activities affect the composition of Earth's atmosphere. More than just a body of water, the lake is an **ecosystem**, the sum of all the organisms living within its boundaries and all the abiotic factors with which they interact.

An ecosystem can encompass a vast area, such as a forest, or a microcosm, such as the space under a fallen log or a small pool (**Figure 55.2**). As with populations and communities, the boundaries of ecosystems sometimes are not discrete. Many ecologists view the entire biosphere as a global ecosystem, a composite of all the local ecosystems on Earth.

Regardless of an ecosystem's size, its dynamics involve two processes that cannot be fully described by population or community phenomena: energy flow and chemical cycling. Energy enters most ecosystems as sunlight. It is converted to chemical energy by autotrophs, passed to heterotrophs in the organic compounds of food, and dissipated as heat. Chemical elements, such as carbon and nitrogen, are cycled among abiotic and biotic components of the ecosystem. Photosynthetic organisms assimilate these elements in inorganic form from the air, soil, and water and incorporate them into their biomass, some of which is consumed by animals. The elements are returned in inorganic form to the environment by the metabolism of plants and animals and by other organisms, such as bacteria and fungi, that break down organic wastes and dead organisms.

Both energy and matter are transformed in ecosystems through photosynthesis and feeding relationships. Unlike matter, however, energy cannot be recycled. Therefore, an ecosystem must be powered by a continuous influx of energy from an external source—in most cases, the sun. Energy flows through ecosystems, whereas matter cycles within and through them.

▲ Figure 55.2 **A cave pool.** This small ecosystem is home to a complex microbial community.

Resources critical to human survival and welfare, ranging from the food we eat to the oxygen we breathe, are products of ecosystem processes. In this chapter, we will explore the dynamics of energy flow and chemical cycling, emphasizing the results of ecosystem experiments. One way to study ecosystem processes is to alter environmental factors, such as temperature or the abundance of nutrients, and study how ecosystems respond. We will also consider some of the impacts of human activities on energy flow and chemical cycling. Those impacts are evident not just in human-dominated ecosystems, such as cities and farms, but in the most remote ecosystems on Earth.

CONCEPT 55.1

Physical laws govern energy flow and chemical cycling in ecosystems

In Unit Two, we saw how cells transform energy and matter, subject to the laws of thermodynamics. Like cell biologists, ecosystem ecologists study the transformations of energy and matter within a system and measure the amounts of both that cross the system's boundaries. By grouping the species in a community into trophic levels of feeding relationships (see Chapter 54), we can follow the transformations of energy in an ecosystem and map the movements of chemical elements.

Conservation of Energy

Because ecosystem ecologists study the interactions of organisms with the physical environment, many ecosystem approaches are based on well-established laws of physics and chemistry. The first law of thermodynamics, which you studied in Chapter 8, states that energy cannot be created or destroyed but only transferred or transformed. Thus, we can potentially account for the transfer of energy through an ecosystem from its input as solar radiation to its release as heat from organisms. Plants and other photosynthetic organisms convert solar energy to chemical energy, but the total amount of energy does not change: The total amount of energy stored in organic molecules plus the amounts reflected and dissipated as heat must equal the total solar energy intercepted by the plant. One area of ecosystem ecology involves computing such energy budgets and tracing energy flow through ecosystems in order to understand the factors that control these energy transfers. Such transfers help determine how many organisms a habitat can support and the amount of food humans can harvest from a given site.

One implication of the second law of thermodynamics, which states that every exchange of energy increases the entropy of the universe, is that energy conversions cannot be completely efficient; some energy is always lost as heat (see Chapter 8). This idea suggests that we can measure the efficiency of ecological energy conversions in the same way we measure the efficiency of light bulbs and car engines. Energy flowing through ecosystems is ultimately dissipated into space as heat, so if the sun were not continuously providing energy to Earth, most ecosystems would vanish.

Conservation of Mass

Matter, like energy, cannot be created or destroyed. This **law of conservation of mass** is as important to ecosystem ecologists as the laws of thermodynamics are. Because mass is conserved, we can determine how much of a chemical element cycles within an ecosystem or is gained or lost by that ecosystem over time.

Unlike energy, chemical elements are continually recycled within ecosystems. A carbon atom in CO_2 is released from the soil by a decomposer, taken up by a grass through photosynthesis, consumed by a bison or other grazer, and returned to the soil in the bison's waste. The measurement and analysis of such chemical cycling within ecosystems and in the biosphere as a whole are an important aspect of ecosystem ecology.

Although elements are not lost on a global scale, they move between ecosystems as inputs and outputs. In a forest ecosystem, for example, most mineral nutrients—the essential elements that plants obtain from soil—enter as dust or as solutes dissolved in rainwater or leached from rocks in the ground. Nitrogen is also supplied through the biological process of nitrogen fixation (see Figure 37.9). On the output side, gases return elements to the atmosphere, and water carries materials away. Like organisms, ecosystems are open systems, absorbing energy and mass and releasing heat and waste products.

Most inputs and outputs are small compared to the amounts recycled within ecosystems. Still, the balance between inputs and outputs determines whether an ecosystem is a source or a sink for a given element. If a mineral nutrient's outputs exceed its inputs, it will eventually limit production in that system. Human activities often change the balance of inputs and outputs considerably, as we will see later in this chapter.

Energy, Mass, and Trophic Levels

As you read in Chapter 54, ecologists assign species to trophic levels on the basis of their main source of nutrition and energy. The trophic level that ultimately supports all others consists of autotrophs, also called the **primary producers** of the ecosystem. Most autotrophs are photosynthetic organisms that use light energy to synthesize sugars and other organic compounds, which they then use as fuel for cellular respiration and as building material for growth. Plants, algae, and photosynthetic prokaryotes are the biosphere's main autotrophs, although chemosynthetic prokaryotes are the primary producers in certain ecosystems, such as deep-sea hydrothermal vents (see Figure 52.18) and some spring-fed pools in caves (see Figure 55.2).

▲ Figure 55.3 **Fungi decomposing a dead tree.**

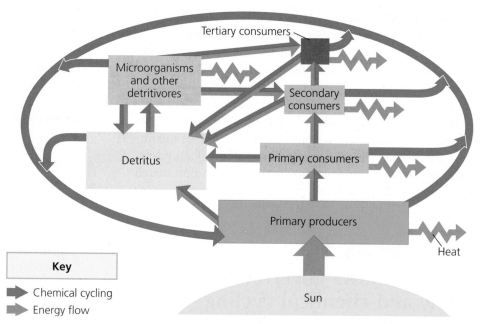

▲ Figure 55.4 **An overview of energy and nutrient dynamics in an ecosystem.** Energy enters, flows through, and exits an ecosystem, whereas chemical nutrients cycle primarily within it. In this generalized scheme, energy (dark orange arrows) enters from the sun as radiation, moves as chemical energy transfers through the food web, and exits as heat radiated into space. Most transfers of nutrients (blue arrows) through the trophic levels lead eventually to detritus; the nutrients then cycle back to the primary producers.

Organisms in trophic levels above the primary producers are heterotrophs, which directly or indirectly depend on the biosynthetic output of primary producers. Herbivores, which eat plants and other primary producers, are **primary consumers**. Carnivores that eat herbivores are **secondary consumers**, and carnivores that eat other carnivores are **tertiary consumers**.

Another important group of heterotrophs consists of the detritivores. **Detritivores**, or **decomposers**, are consumers that get their energy from **detritus**, which is nonliving organic material, such as the remains of dead organisms, feces, fallen leaves, and wood. Many detritivores are in turn eaten by secondary and tertiary consumers. Two important groups of detritivores are prokaryotes and fungi **(Figure 55.3)**. These organisms secrete enzymes that digest organic material; they then absorb the breakdown products, linking the consumers and primary producers in an ecosystem. In a forest, for example, birds eat earthworms that have been feeding on leaf litter and its associated prokaryotes and fungi.

Even more important than this channeling of resources from producers to consumers is the role that detritivores play in recycling chemical elements back to primary producers. Detritivores convert organic materials from all trophic levels to inorganic compounds usable by primary producers, closing the loop of an ecosystem's chemical cycling. Producers can then recycle these elements into organic compounds. If decomposition stopped, all life on Earth would cease as detritus piled up and the supply of chemical ingredients for the syn-

thesis of new organic matter was exhausted. **Figure 55.4** summarizes the trophic relationships in an ecosystem.

CONCEPT CHECK 55.1

1. Why is the transfer of energy in an ecosystem referred to as energy flow, not energy cycling?
2. How does the second law of thermodynamics explain why an ecosystem's energy supply must be continually replenished?
3. **WHAT IF?** You are studying nitrogen cycling on the Serengeti Plain in Africa. During your experiment, a herd of migrating wildebeests grazes through your study plot. What would you need to know to measure their effect on nitrogen balance in the plot?

For suggested answers, see Appendix A.

CONCEPT 55.2

Energy and other limiting factors control primary production in ecosystems

The amount of light energy converted to chemical energy (organic compounds) by autotrophs during a given time period is an ecosystem's **primary production**. This photosynthetic product is the starting point for studies of ecosystem metabolism and energy flow.

Ecosystem Energy Budgets

Most primary producers use light energy to synthesize energy-rich organic molecules, which are subsequently broken down to generate ATP (see Chapter 10). Consumers acquire their organic fuels secondhand (or even third- or fourthhand) through food webs such as those in Figures 54.12 and 54.13. Therefore, the amount of all photosynthetic production sets the spending limit for the entire ecosystem's energy budget.

The Global Energy Budget

Every day, Earth's atmosphere is bombarded by about 10^{22} joules of solar radiation (1 J = 0.239 cal). This is enough energy to supply the demands of the entire human population for approximately 25 years at 2006 consumption levels. As described in Chapter 52, the intensity of the solar energy striking Earth varies with latitude, with the tropics receiving the greatest input. Most incoming solar radiation is absorbed, scattered, or reflected by clouds and dust in the atmosphere. The amount of solar radiation that ultimately reaches Earth's surface limits the possible photosynthetic output of ecosystems.

Furthermore, only a small fraction of the solar radiation that makes it to Earth's surface is used in photosynthesis. Much of the radiation strikes materials that don't photosynthesize, such as ice and soil. Of the radiation that does reach photosynthetic organisms, only certain wavelengths are absorbed by photosynthetic pigments; the rest is transmitted, reflected, or lost as heat. As a result, only about 1% of the visible light that strikes photosynthetic organisms is converted to chemical energy by photosynthesis. Nevertheless, Earth's primary producers collectively create about 150 billion metric tons (150×10^{12} kg) of organic material each year.

Gross and Net Primary Production

Total primary production in an ecosystem is known as that ecosystem's **gross primary production (GPP)**—the amount of light energy that is converted to chemical energy by photosynthesis per unit time. Not all of this production is stored as organic material in the primary producers because they use some of the molecules as fuel in their own cellular respiration. **Net primary production (NPP)** is equal to gross primary production minus the energy used by the primary producers for respiration (R):

$$NPP = GPP - R$$

In many ecosystems, NPP is about one-half of GPP. To ecologists, net primary production is the key measurement because it represents the storage of chemical energy that will be available to consumers in the ecosystem.

Net primary production can be expressed as energy per unit area per unit time ($J/m^2 \cdot yr$) or as biomass (mass of vegetation) added to the ecosystem per unit area per unit time ($g/m^2 \cdot yr$). (Note that biomass is usually expressed in terms of the dry mass of organic material.) An ecosystem's net primary production should not be confused with the *total* biomass of photosynthetic autotrophs present at a given time, a measure called the *standing crop*. Net primary production is the amount of *new* biomass added in a given period of time. Although a forest has a very large standing crop, its net primary production may actually be less than that of some grasslands, which do not accumulate much vegetation because animals consume the plants rapidly and because grasses and herbs decompose more quickly than trees do.

Satellites provide a powerful tool for studying global patterns of primary production (**Figure 55.5**). Images produced from satellite data show that different ecosystems vary considerably in

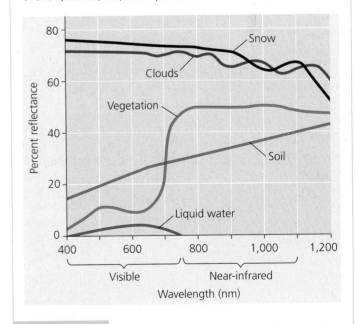

▼ **Figure 55.5** **Research Method**

Determining Primary Production with Satellites

APPLICATION   Because chlorophyll captures visible light (see Figure 10.9), photosynthetic organisms absorb more visible wavelengths (about 380–750 nm) than near-infrared wavelengths (750–1,100 nm). Scientists use this difference in absorption to estimate the rate of photosynthesis in different regions of the globe using satellites.

TECHNIQUE   Most satellites determine what they "see" by comparing the ratios of wavelengths reflected back to them. Vegetation reflects much more near-infrared radiation than visible radiation, producing a reflectance pattern very different from that of snow, clouds, soil, and liquid water.

RESULTS   Scientists use the satellite data to help produce maps of primary production like that in Figure 55.6.

Net primary production (kg carbon/m²·yr)

0   1   2   3

▲ **Figure 55.6 Global net primary production in 2002.** The map is based on data, such as chlorophyll activity, collected by satellites. Note that tropical areas on land have the highest rates of production (yellow and red on the map).

? *Does this global map accurately reflect the importance of some highly productive habitats, such as wetlands, coral reefs, and coastal zones? Explain.*

their net primary production **(Figure 55.6)**. Tropical rain forests are among the most productive terrestrial ecosystems and contribute a large portion of the planet's overall net primary production. Estuaries and coral reefs also have very high net primary production, but their contribution to the global total is relatively small because these ecosystems cover only about one-tenth the area covered by tropical rain forests. One striking aspect of Figure 55.6 is how unproductive the oceans are per unit area compared to tropical forests and some other ecosystems. Because of their vast size, however, the oceans altogether contribute as much global net primary production as terrestrial systems do.

What limits primary production in ecosystems? To ask this question another way, what factors could we change to increase or decrease primary production for a given ecosystem? We'll address this question first for aquatic ecosystems.

Primary Production in Aquatic Ecosystems

In aquatic (marine and freshwater) ecosystems, both light and nutrients are important in controlling primary production.

Light Limitation

Because solar radiation drives photosynthesis, you might expect that light is a key variable in controlling primary production in oceans. Indeed, the depth of light penetration affects primary production throughout the photic zone of an ocean or lake (see Figure 52.16). About half of the solar radiation is absorbed in the first 15 m of water. Even in "clear" water, only 5–10% of the radiation may reach a depth of 75 m.

If light were the main variable limiting primary production in the ocean, we would expect production to increase along a gradient from the poles toward the equator, which receives the greatest intensity of light. However, you can see in Figure 55.6 that there is no such gradient. Another factor must influence primary production in the ocean.

Nutrient Limitation

More than light, nutrients limit primary production in different geographic regions of the ocean and in lakes. A **limiting nutrient** is the element that must be added for production to increase. The nutrient most often limiting marine production is either nitrogen or phosphorus. Concentrations of these nutrients are very low in the photic zone because they are rapidly taken up by phytoplankton and because detritus tends to sink.

As detailed in **Figure 55.7**, nutrient enrichment experiments confirmed that nitrogen was limiting phytoplankton growth off the south shore of Long Island, New York. Practical applications of this work include preventing algal "blooms" caused by nitrogen pollution that fertilizes the phytoplankton. Eliminating phosphates from sewage, once thought to be the cause of the problem, will not help prevent algal blooms unless nitrogen pollution is also controlled.

Several large areas of the ocean, however, have low phytoplankton densities in spite of relatively high nitrogen concentrations. For example, the Sargasso Sea, a subtropical region of the Atlantic Ocean, has some of the clearest water in the world because of its very low density of phytoplankton. A series of nutrient enrichment experiments revealed that the availability of the micronutrient iron can limit primary production there **(Table 55.1)**. Windblown dust from the land is the main input of iron to the ocean, but relatively little windblown dust reaches the center of oceans.

The finding that iron limits production in some oceanic ecosystems encouraged marine ecologists to carry out recent large-scale experiments in the Pacific Ocean. In one study, researchers spread low concentrations of dissolved iron over 72 km² of ocean and then measured the change in phytoplankton density over a seven-day period. A massive phytoplankton bloom occurred, as indicated by increased chlorophyll concentration in the water. Adding iron stimulates growth of cyanobacteria that fix atmospheric nitrogen (see Chapter 27), and the extra nitrogen stimulates proliferation of phytoplankton.

Areas of upwelling, where nutrient-rich deep waters circulate to the ocean surface, have exceptionally high primary production, which supports the hypothesis that nutrient availability

Which nutrient limits phytoplankton production along the coast of Long Island?

EXPERIMENT   Pollution from duck farms concentrated near Moriches Bay adds both nitrogen and phosphorus to the coastal water off Long Island, New York. To determine which nutrient limits phytoplankton growth in this area, John Ryther and William Dunstan, of the Woods Hole Oceanographic Institution, cultured the phytoplankton *Nannochloris atomus* with water collected from several sites (labeled A–G on the map below). They added either ammonium (NH_4^+) or phosphate (PO_4^{3-}) to some of the cultures.

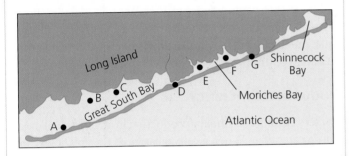

RESULTS   The addition of ammonium caused heavy phytoplankton growth in the cultures, but the addition of phosphate did not.

CONCLUSION   Since adding phosphorus, which was already in rich supply, had no effect on *Nannochloris* growth, whereas adding nitrogen increased phytoplankton density dramatically, the researchers concluded that nitrogen is the nutrient that limits phytoplankton growth in this ecosystem.

SOURCE   J. H. Ryther and W. M. Dunstan, Nitrogen, phosphorus, and eutrophication in the coastal marine environment, *Science* 171:1008–1013 (1971).

WHAT IF?   How would you expect the results of this experiment to change if new duck farms substantially increased the amount of pollution in the water? Explain your reasoning.

Table 55.1 Nutrient Enrichment Experiment for Sargasso Sea Samples

Nutrients Added to Experimental Culture	Relative Uptake of ^{14}C by Cultures*
None (controls)	1.00
Nitrogen (N) + phosphorus (P) only	1.10
N + P + metals (excluding iron)	1.08
N + P + metals (including iron)	12.90
N + P + iron	12.00

*^{14}C uptake by cultures measures primary production.

Source: D. W. Menzel and J. H. Ryther, Nutrients limiting the production of phytoplankton in the Sargasso Sea, with special reference to iron, *Deep Sea Research* 7:276–281 (1961).

determines marine primary production. Because the steady supply of nutrients stimulates growth of the phytoplankton populations that form the base of marine food webs, upwelling areas are prime fishing locations. The largest areas of upwelling occur in the Southern Ocean (also called the Antarctic Ocean) and the coastal waters off Peru, California, and parts of western Africa.

Nutrient limitation is also common in freshwater lakes. During the 1970s, scientists showed that sewage and fertilizer runoff from farms and yards added large amounts of nutrients to lakes. Cyanobacteria and algae grow rapidly in response to these added nutrients, ultimately reducing the oxygen concentration and clarity of the water. This process, known as **eutrophication** (from the Greek *eutrophos*, well nourished), has many ecological impacts, including the eventual loss of all but the most tolerant fish species from the lakes (see Figure 52.18). Controlling eutrophication requires knowing which polluting nutrient is responsible; nitrogen is rarely the limiting factor for primary production in lakes. A series of whole-lake experiments conducted by ecologists showed that phosphorus availability limited cyanobacterial growth. This and other research led to the use of phosphate-free detergents and other important water quality reforms.

Primary Production in Terrestrial Ecosystems

On a large geographic scale, temperature and moisture are the main factors controlling primary production in terrestrial ecosystems. Note again in Figure 55.6 that tropical rain forests, with their warm, wet conditions that promote plant growth, are the most productive of all terrestrial ecosystems. In contrast, low-productivity terrestrial ecosystems are generally dry—for example, deserts—or cold and dry—for example, the arctic tundra. Between these extremes lie the temperate forest and grassland ecosystems, which have moderate climates and intermediate productivity. These contrasts in climate can be represented by a measure called **actual evapotranspiration**,

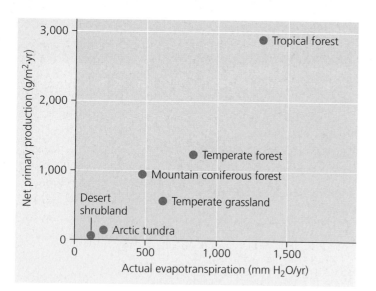

▲ Figure 55.8 **Relationship between net primary production and actual evapotranspiration in six terrestrial ecosystems.**

which is the annual amount of water transpired by plants and evaporated from a landscape, usually measured in millimeters. Actual evapotranspiration increases with the amount of precipitation in a region and the amount of solar energy available to drive evaporation and transpiration. **Figure 55.8** shows the positive relationship between net primary production and actual evapotranspiration in selected ecosystems.

On a more local scale, mineral nutrients in the soil can limit primary production in terrestrial ecosystems. As in aquatic ecosystems, nitrogen and phosphorus are most often the nutrients limiting terrestrial production. Adding a nonlimiting nutrient, even one that is scarce, will not stimulate production. Conversely, adding more of the limiting nutrient will increase production until some other nutrient becomes limiting.

Studies relating nutrients to terrestrial primary production have practical applications in agriculture. Farmers maximize their crop yields by using fertilizers with the right balance of nutrients for the local soil and the type of crop.

CONCEPT CHECK 55.2

1. Why is only a small portion of the solar energy that strikes Earth's atmosphere stored by primary producers?
2. How can ecologists experimentally determine the factor that limits primary production in an ecosystem?
3. **WHAT IF?** As part of a science project, a student is trying to estimate total primary production of plants in a prairie ecosystem for a year. Once each quarter, the student cuts a plot of grass with a lawnmower and then collects and weighs the cuttings to estimate plant production. What components of plant primary production is the student missing with this approach?

For suggested answers, see Appendix A.

CONCEPT 55.3
Energy transfer between trophic levels is typically only 10% efficient

The amount of chemical energy in consumers' food that is converted to their own new biomass during a given time period is called the **secondary production** of the ecosystem. Consider the transfer of organic matter from primary producers to herbivores, the primary consumers. In most ecosystems, herbivores eat only a small fraction of plant material produced. Moreover, they cannot digest all the plant material that they *do* eat, as anyone who has walked through a dairy farm will attest. Thus, much of primary production is not used by consumers. Let's analyze this process of energy transfer more closely.

Production Efficiency

First let's examine secondary production in an individual organism—a caterpillar. When a caterpillar feeds on a plant leaf, only about 33 J out of 200 J (48 cal), or one-sixth of the energy in the leaf, is used for secondary production, or growth **(Figure 55.9)**. The caterpillar uses some of the remaining energy for cellular respiration and passes the rest in its feces. The energy contained in the feces remains in the ecosystem temporarily, but most of it is lost as heat after the feces are consumed by detritivores. The energy used for the caterpillar's respiration is also lost from the ecosystem as heat. This is why energy is said to flow through, not cycle within, ecosystems. Only the chemical energy stored by

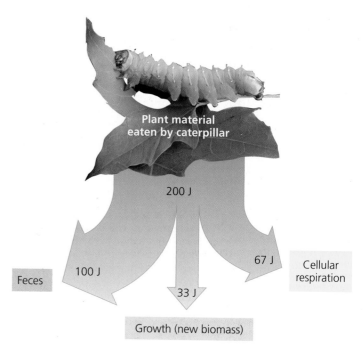

▲ Figure 55.9 **Energy partitioning within a link of the food chain.** Less than 17% of the caterpillar's food is actually used for secondary production (growth).

herbivores as biomass (through growth or the production of off-spring) is available as food to secondary consumers.

We can measure the efficiency of animals as energy transformers using the following equation:

$$\text{Production efficiency} = \frac{\text{Net secondary production} \times 100\%}{\text{Assimilation of primary production}}$$

Net secondary production is the energy stored in biomass represented by growth and reproduction. Assimilation consists of the total energy taken in and used for growth, reproduction, and respiration. **Production efficiency**, therefore, is the percentage of energy stored in assimilated food that is *not* used for respiration. For the caterpillar in Figure 55.9, production efficiency is 33%; 67 J of the 100 J of assimilated energy is used for respiration. (Note that the energy lost as undigested material in feces does not count toward assimilation.) Birds and mammals typically have low production efficiencies, in the range of 1–3%, because they use so much energy in maintaining a constant, high body temperature. Fishes, which are ectotherms (see Chapter 40), have production efficiencies around 10%. Insects and microorganisms are even more efficient, with production efficiencies averaging 40% or more.

Trophic Efficiency and Ecological Pyramids

Let's scale up now from the production efficiencies of individual consumers to the flow of energy through trophic levels.

Trophic efficiency is the percentage of production transferred from one trophic level to the next. Trophic efficiencies must always be less than production efficiencies because they take into account not only the energy lost through respiration and contained in feces, but also the energy in organic material in a lower trophic level that is not consumed by the next trophic level. Trophic efficiencies are generally about 10% and range from approximately 5% to 20%, depending on the type of ecosystem. In other words, 90% of the energy available at one trophic level typically is *not* transferred to the next. This loss is multiplied over the length of a food chain. For example, if 10% of available energy is transferred from primary producers to primary consumers, and 10% of that energy is transferred to secondary consumers, then only 1% of net primary production is available to secondary consumers (10% of 10%).

The progressive loss of energy along a food chain severely limits the abundance of top-level carnivores that an ecosystem can support. Only about 0.1% of the chemical energy fixed by photosynthesis can flow all the way through a food web to a tertiary consumer, such as a snake or a shark. This explains why most food webs include only about four or five trophic levels (see Chapter 54).

The loss of energy with each transfer in a food chain can be represented by a *pyramid of net production*, in which the trophic levels are arranged in tiers **(Figure 55.10)**. The width of each tier is proportional to the net production, expressed in joules, of each trophic level. The highest level, which represents top-level pred-

ators, contains relatively few individuals. Because populations of top predators are typically small and the animals may be widely spaced within their habitats, many predator species are highly susceptible to extinction (as well as to the evolutionary consequences of small population size, discussed in Chapter 23).

One important ecological consequence of low trophic efficiencies is represented in a *biomass pyramid*, in which each tier represents the standing crop (the total dry mass of all organisms) in one trophic level. Most biomass pyramids narrow sharply from primary producers at the base to top-level carnivores at the apex because energy transfers between trophic levels are so inefficient **(Figure 55.11a)**. Certain aquatic ecosystems, however,

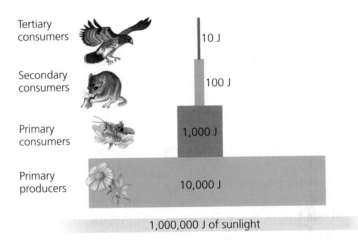

▲ **Figure 55.10 An idealized pyramid of net production.** This example assumes a trophic efficiency of 10% for each link in the food chain. Notice that primary producers convert only about 1% of the energy available to them to net primary production.

(a) Most biomass pyramids show a sharp decrease in biomass at successively higher trophic levels, as illustrated by data from a Florida bog.

(b) In some aquatic ecosystems, such as the English Channel, a small standing crop of primary producers (phytoplankton) supports a larger standing crop of primary consumers (zooplankton).

▲ **Figure 55.11 Pyramids of biomass (standing crop).** Numbers denote the dry mass of all organisms at each trophic level.

have inverted biomass pyramids: Primary consumers outweigh the producers (**Figure 55.11b**). Such inverted biomass pyramids occur because the producers—phytoplankton—grow, reproduce, and are consumed so quickly by the zooplankton that they never develop a large population size, or standing crop. In other words, the phytoplankton have a short **turnover time**, which means they have a small standing crop compared to their production:

$$\text{Turnover time} = \frac{\text{Standing crop (g/m}^2)}{\text{Production (g/m}^2 \cdot \text{day)}}$$

Because the phytoplankton continually replace their biomass at such a rapid rate, they can support a biomass of zooplankton bigger than their own biomass. Nevertheless, because phytoplankton have much higher production than zooplankton, the pyramid of *production* for this ecosystem is still bottom-heavy, like the one in Figure 55.10.

The dynamics of energy flow through ecosystems have important implications for the human population. Eating meat is a relatively inefficient way of tapping photosynthetic production. A person obtains far more calories by eating grains directly as a primary consumer than by eating the same amount of grain fed to an animal. Worldwide agriculture could, in fact, successfully feed many more people and require less cultivated land if humans all fed more efficiently—as primary consumers, eating only plant material. Consequently, estimates of Earth's human carrying capacity (see Chapter 53) depend greatly on our diet and on the amount of resources each of us consumes.

The Green World Hypothesis

Earlier in this book, you learned why the world is green: Plants reflect more green light than red or blue light (see Figure 10.9). Land plants store approximately 70×10^{10} metric tons of carbon, and global terrestrial primary production is about 6×10^{10} metric tons per year. However, herbivores annually consume less than one-sixth the global NPP by plants (**Figure 55.12**).

Most of the rest is eventually consumed by detritivores. Thus, despite occasional outbreaks of pests, herbivores are generally only a minor nuisance to plants.

Why do herbivores consume such a small fraction of plants' net primary production? According to the **green world hypothesis**, terrestrial herbivores are held in check by a variety of factors. Plant defenses, such as spines or noxious chemicals (see Chapter 39), limit the success of herbivores. Low nutrient concentrations in plant tissues mean that large quantities of biomass are needed to support each herbivore. Other factors also limit the number of herbivores, including abiotic pressures, such as temperature and moisture extremes; intraspecific competition, including territorial behavior; and interspecific competition, particularly from predators, parasites, and pathogens (as in the top-down model of community structure, which you learned about in Chapter 54).

In the next section, we will look at how the transfer of nutrients along with energy through food webs is part of a larger picture of chemical cycling in ecosystems.

CONCEPT CHECK 55.3

1. If an insect that eats plant seeds containing 100 J of energy uses 30 J of that energy for respiration and excretes 50 J in its feces, what is the insect's net secondary production? What is its production efficiency?
2. Tobacco leaves contain nicotine, a poisonous compound that is energetically expensive for the plant to make. What advantage might the plant gain by using some of its resources to produce nicotine?
3. **WHAT IF?** As part of a new reality show on television, a group of overweight people are trying to safely lose in one month as much weight as possible. In addition to eating less, what could they do to decrease their production efficiency for the food they eat?

For suggested answers, see Appendix A.

▶ **Figure 55.12 A green ecosystem.** Most terrestrial ecosystems have large standing crops of vegetation despite the large number of resident herbivores. The green world hypothesis offers possible explanations for this observation.

CONCEPT 55.4

Biological and geochemical processes cycle nutrients between organic and inorganic parts of an ecosystem

Although most ecosystems receive an abundant supply of solar energy, chemical elements are available only in limited amounts. (The meteorites that occasionally strike Earth are the only extraterrestrial source of new matter.) Life on Earth therefore depends on the recycling of essential chemical elements. While an organism is alive, much of its chemical stock is replaced continuously as nutrients are assimilated and waste products released. When the organism dies, the atoms in its complex molecules are returned in simpler compounds to the atmosphere, water, or soil by the action of decomposers. Decomposition replenishes the pools of inorganic nutrients that plants and other autotrophs use to build new organic matter. Because nutrient cycles involve both biotic and abiotic components, they are called **biogeochemical cycles**.

Biogeochemical Cycles

An element's specific route through a biogeochemical cycle depends on the element and the trophic structure of the ecosystem. We can, however, recognize two general categories of biogeochemical cycles: global and local. Gaseous forms of carbon, oxygen, sulfur, and nitrogen occur in the atmosphere, and cycles of these elements are essentially global. For example, some of the carbon and oxygen atoms a plant acquires from the air as CO_2 may have been released into the atmosphere by the respiration of an organism in a distant locale. Other elements, including phosphorus, potassium, and calcium, are too heavy to occur as gases at Earth's surface. In terrestrial ecosystems, these elements cycle more locally, absorbed from the soil by plant roots and eventually returned to the soil by decomposers. In aquatic systems, however, they cycle more broadly as dissolved forms carried in currents.

Before examining the details of individual cycles, let's look at a general model of nutrient cycling that includes the main reservoirs of elements and the processes that transfer elements between reservoirs **(Figure 55.13)**. Each reservoir is defined by two characteristics: whether it contains organic or inorganic materials and whether or not the materials are directly available for use by organisms.

The nutrients in living organisms themselves and in detritus (reservoir A in Figure 55.13) are available to other organisms when consumers feed and when detritivores consume nonliving organic matter. Some material moved from the living organic reservoir to the fossilized organic reservoir (reservoir B) long ago, when dead organisms were converted to coal, oil, or peat (fossil fuels). Nutrients in these deposits generally cannot be assimilated directly.

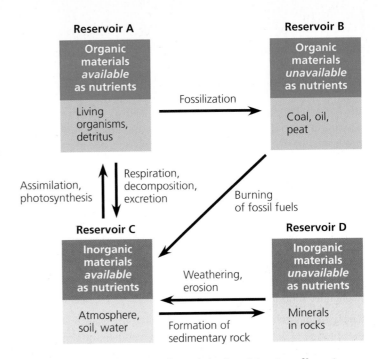

▲ **Figure 55.13 A general model of nutrient cycling.** Arrows indicate the processes that move nutrients between reservoirs.

? *Recent evidence suggests that mycorrhizal fungi can release acids that dissolve some minerals, including calcium phosphate. Where does this fungal activity fit into the model?*

Inorganic materials (elements and compounds) that are dissolved in water or present in soil or air (reservoir C) are available for use. Organisms assimilate materials from this reservoir directly and return chemicals to it through the relatively rapid processes of cellular respiration, excretion, and decomposition. Although most organisms cannot directly tap into the inorganic elements tied up in rocks (reservoir D), these nutrients may slowly become available through weathering and erosion. Similarly, unavailable organic materials move into the available reservoir of inorganic nutrients when fossil fuels are burned, releasing exhaust into the atmosphere.

How have ecologists worked out the details of chemical cycling in various ecosystems? Two common methods use isotopes—either by adding tiny amounts of radioactive isotopes of specific elements and tracking their progress or by following the movement of naturally occurring, nonradioactive isotopes through the biotic and abiotic components of an ecosystem. For example, scientists have been able to trace the flow into ecosystems of radioactive carbon (^{14}C) released into the atmosphere during atom bomb testing in the 1950s and early 1960s. This "spike" of ^{14}C can be used to date the age of bones and teeth, to measure the turnover rate of soil organic matter, and to follow changes in many other carbon pools in the environment.

Figure 55.14, on the next two pages, provides a detailed look at the cycling of water, carbon, nitrogen, and phosphorus. Examine these four biogeochemical cycles closely, considering the major reservoirs of each chemical and the processes that drive the movement of each chemical through its cycle.

Exploring Nutrient Cycles

The Water Cycle

Biological importance Water is essential to all organisms (see Chapter 3), and its availability influences the rates of ecosystem processes, particularly primary production and decomposition in terrestrial ecosystems.

Forms available to life Liquid water is the primary physical phase in which water is used, though some organisms can harvest water vapor. Freezing of soil water can limit water availability to terrestrial plants.

Reservoirs The oceans contain 97% of the water in the biosphere. Approximately 2% is bound in glaciers and polar ice caps, and the remaining 1% is in lakes, rivers, and groundwater, with a negligible amount in the atmosphere.

Key processes The main processes driving the water cycle are evaporation of liquid water by solar energy, condensation of water vapor into clouds, and precipitation. Transpiration by terrestrial plants also moves significant volumes of water into the atmosphere. Surface and groundwater flow can return water to the oceans, completing the water cycle. The widths of the arrows in the diagram reflect the relative contribution of each process to the movement of water in the biosphere.

The Carbon Cycle

Biological importance Carbon forms the framework of the organic molecules essential to all organisms.

Forms available to life Photosynthetic organisms utilize CO_2 during photosynthesis and convert the carbon to organic forms that are used by consumers, including animals, fungi, and heterotrophic protists and prokaryotes.

Reservoirs The major reservoirs of carbon include fossil fuels, soils, the sediments of aquatic ecosystems, the oceans (dissolved carbon compounds), plant and animal biomass, and the atmosphere (CO_2). The largest reservoir is sedimentary rocks such as limestone; however, this pool turns over very slowly.

Key processes Photosynthesis by plants and phytoplankton removes substantial amounts of atmospheric CO_2 each year. This quantity is approximately equaled by CO_2 added to the atmosphere through cellular respiration by producers and consumers. Over geologic time, volcanoes are also a substantial source of CO_2. The burning of fossil fuels is adding significant amounts of additional CO_2 to the atmosphere. The widths of the arrows reflect the relative contribution of each process.

The Terrestrial Nitrogen Cycle

Biological importance Nitrogen is part of amino acids, proteins, and nucleic acids and is often a limiting plant nutrient.

Forms available to life Plants can use two inorganic forms of nitrogen—ammonium (NH_4^+) and nitrate (NO_3^-)—and some organic forms, such as amino acids. Various bacteria can use all of these forms as well as nitrite (NO_2^-). Animals can use only organic forms of nitrogen.

Reservoirs The main reservoir of nitrogen is the atmosphere, which is 80% nitrogen gas (N_2). The other reservoirs are soils and the sediments of lakes, rivers, and oceans (bound nitrogen); surface water and groundwater (dissolved nitrogen); and the biomass of living organisms.

Key processes The major pathway for nitrogen to enter an ecosystem is via *nitrogen fixation*, the conversion of N_2 by bacteria to forms that can be used to synthesize nitrogenous organic compounds (see Chapter 37). Some nitrogen is also fixed by lightning. Nitrogen fertilizer, precipitation, and blowing dust can also provide substantial inputs of NH_4^+ and NO_3^- to ecosystems. *Ammonification* decomposes organic nitrogen to NH_4^+. In *nitrification*, NH_4^+ is converted to NO_3^- by nitrifying bacteria. Under anaerobic conditions, denitrifying bacteria use NO_3^- in their metabolism instead of O_2, releasing N_2 in a process known as *denitrification*. The widths of the arrows reflect the relative contribution of each process.

The Phosphorus Cycle

Biological importance Organisms require phosphorus as a major constituent of nucleic acids, phospholipids, and ATP and other energy-storing molecules and as a mineral constituent of bones and teeth.

Forms available to life The most biologically important inorganic form of phosphorus is phosphate (PO_4^{3-}), which plants absorb and use in the synthesis of organic compounds.

Reservoirs The largest accumulations of phosphorus are in sedimentary rocks of marine origin. There are also large quantities of phosphorus in soils, in the oceans (in dissolved form), and in organisms. Because humus and soil particles bind phosphate, the recycling of phosphorus tends to be quite localized in ecosystems.

Key processes Weathering of rocks gradually adds PO_4^{3-} to soil; some leaches into groundwater and surface water and may eventually reach the sea. Phosphate taken up by producers and incorporated into biological molecules may be eaten by consumers and distributed through the food web. Phosphate is returned to soil or water through either decomposition of biomass or excretion by consumers. Because there are no significant phosphorus-containing gases, only relatively small amounts of phosphorus move through the atmosphere, usually in the forms of dust and sea spray. The widths of the arrows reflect the relative contribution of each process.

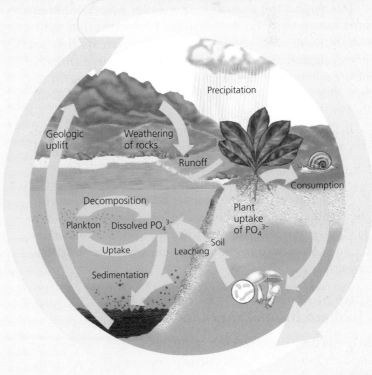

Decomposition and Nutrient Cycling Rates

The diagrams in Figure 55.14 illustrate the essential role that decomposers (detritivores) play in recycling carbon, nitrogen, and phosphorus. The rates at which these nutrients cycle in different ecosystems are extremely variable, mostly as a result of differences in rates of decomposition.

Decomposition is controlled by the same factors that limit primary production in aquatic and terrestrial ecosystems (see Concept 55.2). Those factors include temperature, moisture, and nutrient availability. Decomposers usually grow faster and decompose material more quickly in warmer ecosystems (Figure 55.15). In tropical rain forests, for instance, most organic material decomposes in a few months to a few years, while in temperate forests, decomposition takes four to six years, on average. The difference is largely the result of the higher temperatures and more abundant precipitation in tropical rain forests.

Because decomposition in a tropical rain forest is rapid, relatively little organic material accumulates as leaf litter on the forest floor; about 75% of the nutrients in the ecosystem is present in the woody trunks of trees, and about 10% is contained in the soil. Thus, the relatively low concentrations of some nutrients in the soil of tropical rain forests result from a short cycling time, not from a lack of these elements in the ecosystem. In temperate forests, where decomposition is much slower, the soil may contain as much as 50% of all the organic material in the ecosystem. The nutrients that are present in temperate forest detritus and soil may remain there for fairly long periods before plants assimilate them.

Decomposition on land is also slower when conditions are either too dry for decomposers to thrive or too wet to supply them with enough oxygen. Ecosystems that are both cold and wet, such as peatlands, store large amounts of organic matter; decomposers grow poorly most of the year there, and net primary production greatly exceeds decomposition.

In aquatic ecosystems, decomposition in anaerobic muds can take 50 years or more. Bottom sediments are comparable to the detritus layer in terrestrial ecosystems; however, algae and aquatic plants usually assimilate nutrients directly from the water. Thus, the sediments often constitute a nutrient sink, and aquatic ecosystems are very productive only when there is interchange between the bottom layers of water and the surface (as in the upwelling regions described earlier).

Case Study: Nutrient Cycling in the Hubbard Brook Experimental Forest

In one of the longest-running ecological research experiments in North America, ecologists Herbert Bormann, Eugene Likens, and their colleagues have been studying nutrient cycling in a

▼ Figure 55.15 **Inquiry**

How does temperature affect litter decomposition in an ecosystem?

EXPERIMENT Researchers with the Canadian Forest Service placed identical samples of organic material on the ground in 21 sites across Canada (marked by letters on the map below). Three years later, they returned to see how much of each sample had decomposed.

RESULTS Litter mass decreased four times faster in warmer ecosystems than in colder ones.

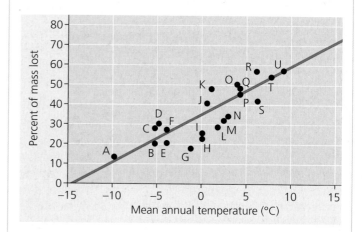

CONCLUSION Decomposition increases with temperature across much of Canada.

SOURCE T. R. Moore et al., Litter decomposition rates in Canadian forests, *Global Change Biology* 5:75–82 (1999).

WHAT IF? What factors other than temperature might also have varied across these 21 sites? How might this variation have affected the interpretation of the results?

forest ecosystem since 1963. Their study site, the Hubbard Brook Experimental Forest in the White Mountains of New Hampshire, is a deciduous forest with several valleys, each drained by a small creek that is a tributary of Hubbard Brook. Bedrock impenetrable to water is close to the surface of the soil, and each valley constitutes a watershed that can drain only through its creek.

The research team first determined the mineral budget for each of six valleys by measuring the input and outflow of several key nutrients. They collected rainfall at several sites to measure the amount of water and dissolved minerals added to the ecosystem. To monitor the loss of water and minerals, they constructed a small concrete dam with a V-shaped spillway across the creek at the bottom of each valley **(Figure 55.16a)**. About 60% of the water added to the ecosystem as rainfall and snow exits through the stream, and the remaining 40% is lost by evapotranspiration.

Preliminary studies confirmed that internal cycling within a terrestrial ecosystem conserves most of the mineral nutrients. For example, only about 0.3% more calcium (Ca^{2+}) left a valley via its creek than was added by rainwater, and this small net loss was probably replaced by chemical decomposition of the bedrock. During most years, the forest actually registered small net gains of a few mineral nutrients, including nitrogen.

In one experiment, the trees in one valley were cut down and then the valley was sprayed with herbicides for three years to prevent regrowth of plants **(Figure 55.16b)**. All the original plant material was left in place to decompose. The inflow and outflow of water and minerals in this experimentally altered watershed were compared with those in a control watershed. Over the three years, water runoff from the altered watershed increased by 30–40%, apparently because there were no plants to absorb and transpire water from the soil. Net losses of minerals from the altered watershed were huge. The concentration of Ca^{2+} in the creek increased 4-fold, for example, and the concentration of K^+ increased by a factor of 15. Most remarkable was the loss of nitrate, whose concentration in the creek increased 60-fold, reaching levels considered unsafe for drinking water **(Figure 55.16c)**.

This study demonstrated that the amount of nutrients leaving an intact forest ecosystem is controlled mainly by the plants. The effects of deforestation occur within a few months and continue as long as living plants are absent.

The 45 years of data from Hubbard Brook reveal some other trends. For instance, in the last half century, acid rain and snow have dissolved most of the Ca^{2+} in the forest soil, and the streams have carried it away. By the 1990s, the forest biomass at Hubbard Brook had stopped increasing, apparently because of a lack of Ca^{2+}. To test this idea, ecologists at Hubbard Brook began a massive experiment in 1998. They first established a control and an experimental watershed, which they monitored over two years before using a helicopter to add Ca^{2+} to the experimental watershed. By 2006, sugar maple trees growing in the Ca^{2+}-enriched location had higher Ca^{2+} concentrations in their foliage, healthier crowns, and

(a) Concrete dams and weirs built across streams at the bottom of watersheds enabled researchers to monitor the outflow of water and nutrients from the ecosystem.

(b) One watershed was clear-cut to study the effects of the loss of vegetation on drainage and nutrient cycling.

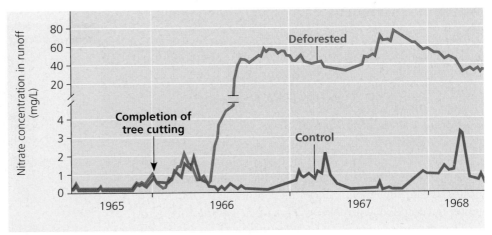

(c) The concentration of nitrate in runoff from the deforested watershed was 60 times greater than in a control (unlogged) watershed.

▲ **Figure 55.16 Nutrient cycling in the Hubbard Brook Experimental Forest: an example of long-term ecological research.**

greater seedling establishment than those growing in the control watershed. These data suggest that sugar maple declines in the northeastern United States and southern Canada are attributable at least in part to the consequences of soil acidification.

The Hubbard Brook studies, as well as many other long-term ecological research projects funded by the National Science Foundation, assess natural ecosystem processes and provide important insight into the mechanisms by which human activities affect these processes.

CONCEPT CHECK 55.4

1. **DRAW IT** For each of the four biogeochemical cycles detailed in Figure 55.14, draw a simple diagram that shows one possible path for an atom or molecule of that chemical from abiotic to biotic reservoirs and back.
2. Why does deforestation of a watershed increase the concentration of nitrates in streams draining the watershed?
3. **WHAT IF?** Why is nutrient availability in a tropical rain forest particularly vulnerable to logging?

For suggested answers, see Appendix A.

CONCEPT 55.5
Human activities now dominate most chemical cycles on Earth

As the human population has grown rapidly in size (see Concept 53.6), our activities and technological capabilities have disrupted the trophic structure, energy flow, and chemical cycling of ecosystems. In fact, most chemical cycles are now influenced more by human activities than by natural processes.

Nutrient Enrichment

Human activity often removes nutrients from one part of the biosphere and adds them to another. On the simplest level, someone eating a piece of broccoli in Washington, DC, consumes nutrients that only days before were in the soil in California; a short time later, some of these nutrients will be in the Potomac River, having passed through the person's digestive system and a local sewage treatment facility. On a larger scale, nutrients in farm soil may run off into streams and lakes, depleting nutrients in one area, increasing them in another, and altering chemical cycles in both. Furthermore, humans have added entirely novel materials—some of them toxic—to ecosystems.

Humans have altered nutrient cycles so much that we can no longer understand any cycle without taking these effects into account. Let's examine a few specific examples of how humans are impacting the biosphere's chemical dynamics.

Agriculture and Nitrogen Cycling

After natural vegetation is cleared from an area, the existing reserve of nutrients in the soil is sufficient to grow crops for some time. In agricultural ecosystems, however, a substantial fraction of these nutrients is exported from the area in crop biomass. The "free" period for crop production—when there is no need to add nutrients to the soil—varies greatly. When some of the early North American prairie lands were first tilled, good crops could be produced for decades because the large store of organic materials in the soil continued to decompose and provide nutrients. By contrast, some cleared land in the tropics can be farmed for only one or two years because so little of the ecosystems' nutrient load is contained in the soil. Despite such variations, in any area under intensive agriculture, the natural store of nutrients eventually becomes exhausted.

Nitrogen is the main nutrient lost through agriculture; thus, agriculture has a great impact on the nitrogen cycle. Plowing mixes the soil and speeds up decomposition of organic matter, releasing nitrogen that is then removed when crops are harvested. Applied fertilizers make up for the loss of usable nitrogen from agricultural ecosystems (**Figure 55.17**). In addition, as we saw in the case of Hubbard Brook, without plants to take up nitrates from the soil, the nitrates are likely to be leached from the ecosystem.

Recent studies indicate that human activities have more than doubled Earth's supply of fixed nitrogen available to primary producers. Industrial fertilizers provide the largest additional nitrogen source. Fossil fuel combustion also releases nitrogen oxides, which enter the atmosphere and dissolve in rainwater; the nitrogen ultimately enters ecosystems as nitrate. Increased cultivation of legumes, with their nitrogen-fixing symbionts, is a third way in which humans increase the amount of fixed nitrogen in the soil.

▲ **Figure 55.17 Fertilization of a corn (maize) crop.** To replace the nutrients removed in crops, farmers must apply fertilizers—either organic, such as manure or mulch, or synthetic, as shown here.

Winter

Summer

◄ **Figure 55.18 The dead zone arising from nitrogen pollution in the Mississippi basin.** In these satellite images from 2004, red and orange represent high concentrations of phytoplankton and river sediment in the Gulf of Mexico. This dead zone extends much farther from land in summer than in winter.

Contamination of Aquatic Ecosystems

The key problem with excess nutrients is the **critical load**, the amount of added nutrient, usually nitrogen or phosphorus, that can be absorbed by plants without damaging ecosystem integrity. For example, nitrogenous minerals in the soil that exceed the critical load eventually leach into groundwater or run off into freshwater and marine ecosystems, contaminating water supplies and killing fish. Nitrate concentrations in groundwater are increasing in most agricultural regions, sometimes exceeding safe levels for drinking.

Many rivers contaminated with nitrates and ammonium from agricultural runoff and sewage drain into the Atlantic Ocean, with the highest inputs coming from northern Europe and the central United States. The Mississippi River carries nitrogen pollution to the Gulf of Mexico, fueling a phytoplankton bloom each summer. When the phytoplankton die, their decomposition creates an extensive "dead zone" of low oxygen availability along the coast **(Figure 55.18)**. Fish, shrimp, and other marine animals disappear from some of the most economically important waters in the country. To reduce the size of the dead zone, farmers have begun using fertilizers more efficiently, and managers are restoring wetlands in the Mississippi watershed, two changes stimulated by the results of ecosystem experiments.

Nutrient runoff can also lead to the eutrophication of lakes, as you learned in Concept 55.2. The bloom and subsequent die-off of algae and cyanobacteria and the ensuing depletion of oxygen are similar to what occurs in a marine dead zone. Such conditions threaten the survival of organisms. For example, eutrophication of Lake Erie coupled with overfishing wiped out commercially important fishes such as blue pike, whitefish, and lake trout by the 1960s. Since then, tighter regulations on waste dumping into the lake have enabled some fish populations to rebound, but many native species of fishes and invertebrates have not recovered.

Acid Precipitation

The burning of wood and of fossil fuels, including coal and oil, releases oxides of sulfur and nitrogen that react with water in the atmosphere, forming sulfuric and nitric acid, respectively.

The acids eventually fall to Earth's surface as acid precipitation—rain, snow, sleet, or fog that has a pH less than 5.2. Acid precipitation lowers the pH of streams and lakes and affects soil chemistry and nutrient availability. Although acid precipitation has been occurring since the Industrial Revolution, the emissions that cause it have increased during the past century, mainly from ore smelters and electrical generating plants.

Acid precipitation is a regional problem arising from local emissions. Smelters and generating plants are built with exhaust stacks more than 300 m high that reduce pollution at ground level but export it far downwind. Sulfur and nitrogen pollutants may drift hundreds of kilometers before falling as acid precipitation.

In the 1960s, ecologists determined that lake-dwelling organisms in eastern Canada were dying because of air pollution from factories in the midwestern United States. Lakes and streams in southern Norway and Sweden were losing fish because of acid rain from pollutants generated in Great Britain and central Europe. By 1980, the pH of precipitation in large areas of North America and Europe averaged 4.0–4.5 and occasionally dropped as low as 3.0.

In terrestrial ecosystems, such as the deciduous forests of New England, the change in soil pH due to acid precipitation causes calcium and other nutrients to leach from the soil (see the Hubbard Brook studies in Concept 55.4). The nutrient deficiencies affect the health of plants and limit their growth. Acid precipitation can also damage plants directly, mainly by leaching nutrients from leaves.

Freshwater ecosystems are particularly sensitive to acid precipitation. The lakes in North America and northern Europe that are most readily damaged by acid precipitation are those that have a low concentration of bicarbonate, an important buffer (see Chapter 3). Fish populations have declined in thousands of such lakes in Norway and Sweden, where the pH of the water has dropped below 5.0. In Canada, newly hatched lake trout, a keystone predator, die when the pH drops below 5.4. When the trout are replaced by acid-tolerant fish, the dynamics of food webs change dramatically.

Several large ecosystem experiments have been carried out to test the feasibility of reversing the effects of acid precipitation. One is the Ca^{2+} addition experiment at Hubbard Brook discussed earlier in this chapter. Another is a 17-year experiment

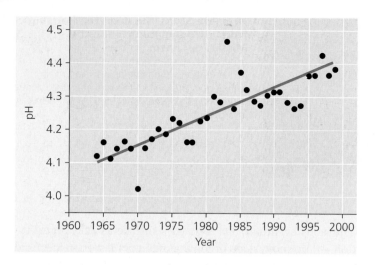

▲ **Figure 55.19 Changes in the pH of precipitation at Hubbard Brook.** Although still very acidic, the precipitation in this northeastern U.S. forest has been increasing in pH for more than three decades.

in Norway in which scientists built a glass roof over a forest and then showered the forest with precipitation from which acids had been removed. This "clean" precipitation quickly increased the pH and decreased the nitrate, ammonium, and sulfate concentrations in stream water in the forest. Results from this and other experiments helped convince leaders of more than 40 European nations to sign a treaty to reduce air pollution.

Environmental regulations and new industrial technologies have enabled many developed countries to reduce sulfur dioxide emissions during the past 40 years. In the United States, for example, sulfur dioxide emissions decreased 31% between 1993 and 2002. As a result, precipitation in the northeastern United States is gradually becoming less acidic **(Figure 55.19)**. However, ecologists estimate that it will take decades for aquatic ecosystems in this region to recover, even if sulfur dioxide emissions continue to decrease. Meanwhile, emissions of nitrogen oxides are increasing in the United States, and emissions of sulfur dioxide and acid precipitation continue to damage forests in central and eastern Europe.

Toxins in the Environment

Humans release an immense variety of toxic chemicals, including thousands of synthetic compounds previously unknown in nature, with little regard for the ecological consequences. Organisms acquire toxic substances from the environment along with nutrients and water. Some of the poisons are metabolized and excreted, but others accumulate in specific tissues, especially fat. One of the reasons accumulated toxins are particularly harmful is that they become more concentrated in successive trophic levels of a food web, a process called **biological magnification**. Magnification occurs because the biomass at any given trophic level is produced from a much larger biomass ingested from the level

below (see Concept 55.3). Thus, top-level carnivores tend to be the organisms most severely affected by toxic compounds in the environment.

One class of industrially synthesized compounds that have demonstrated biological magnification are the chlorinated hydrocarbons, which include the industrial chemicals called PCBs (polychlorinated biphenyls) and many pesticides, such as DDT. Current research implicates many of these compounds in endocrine system disruption in a large number of animal species, including humans. Biological magnification of PCBs has been found in the food web of the Great Lakes, where the concentration of PCBs in herring gull eggs, at the top of the food web, is nearly 5,000 times that in phytoplankton, at the base of the food web **(Figure 55.20)**.

An infamous case of biological magnification that harmed top-level carnivores involved DDT, a chemical used to control insects such as mosquitoes and agricultural pests. In the decade after World War II, the use of DDT grew rapidly; its ecological consequences were not yet fully understood. By the 1950s, scientists were learning that DDT persists in the environment and is transported by water to areas far from where it is applied. One of the first signs that DDT was a serious en-

Herring gull eggs 124 ppm

Lake trout 4.83 ppm

Smelt 1.04 ppm

Zooplankton 0.123 ppm

Phytoplankton 0.025 ppm

Concentration of PCBs

▲ **Figure 55.20 Biological magnification of PCBs in a Great Lakes food web.**

vironmental problem was a decline in the populations of pelicans, ospreys, and eagles, birds that feed at the top of food webs. The accumulation of DDT (and DDE, a product of its breakdown) in the tissues of these birds interfered with the deposition of calcium in their eggshells. When the birds tried to incubate their eggs, the weight of the parents broke the shells of affected eggs, resulting in catastrophic declines in the birds' reproduction rates. Rachel Carson's book *Silent Spring* helped bring the problem to public attention in the 1960s (see Chapter 52), and DDT was banned in the United States in 1971. A dramatic recovery in populations of the affected bird species followed.

In much of the tropics, DDT is still used to control the mosquitoes that spread malaria and other diseases. Societies there face a trade-off between saving human lives and protecting other species. The best approach seems to be to apply DDT sparingly and to couple its use with mosquito netting and other low-technology solutions. The complicated history of DDT illustrates the importance of understanding the ecological connections between diseases and communities (see Concept 54.5).

Many toxins cannot be degraded by microorganisms and persist in the environment for years or even decades. In other cases, chemicals released into the environment may be relatively harmless but are converted to more toxic products by reaction with other substances, by exposure to light, or by the metabolism of microorganisms. For example, mercury, a by-product of plastic production and coal-fired power generation, has been routinely expelled into rivers and the sea in an insoluble form. Bacteria in the bottom mud convert the waste to methylmercury (CH_3Hg^+), an extremely toxic soluble compound that accumulates in the tissues of organisms, including humans who consume fish from the contaminated waters.

Greenhouse Gases and Global Warming

Human activities release a variety of gaseous waste products. People once thought that the vast atmosphere could absorb these materials indefinitely, but we now know that such additions can cause fundamental changes to the atmosphere and to its interactions with the rest of the biosphere. In this section, we will examine how increasing atmospheric carbon dioxide concentration and global warming af-

fect ecosystems. Although global warming will likely bring some benefits to people, it will also bring enormous costs to humans and to many other species on Earth.

Rising Atmospheric CO₂ Levels

Since the Industrial Revolution, the concentration of CO_2 in the atmosphere has been increasing as a result of the burning of fossil fuels and deforestation. Scientists estimate that the average CO_2 concentration in the atmosphere before 1850 was about 274 ppm. In 1958, a monitoring station began taking very accurate measurements on Hawaii's Mauna Loa peak, a location far from cities and high enough for the atmosphere to be well mixed. At that time, the CO_2 concentration was 316 ppm **(Figure 55.21)**. Today, it exceeds 380 ppm, an increase of about 40% since the mid-19th century. If CO_2 emissions continue to increase at the present rate, by the year 2075 the atmospheric concentration of this gas will be more than double what it was at the start of the Industrial Revolution.

Increased productivity by plants is one predictable consequence of increasing CO_2 levels. In fact, when CO_2 concentrations are raised in experimental chambers such as greenhouses, most plants grow faster. Because C_3 plants are more limited than C_4 plants by CO_2 availability (see Chapter 10), one effect of

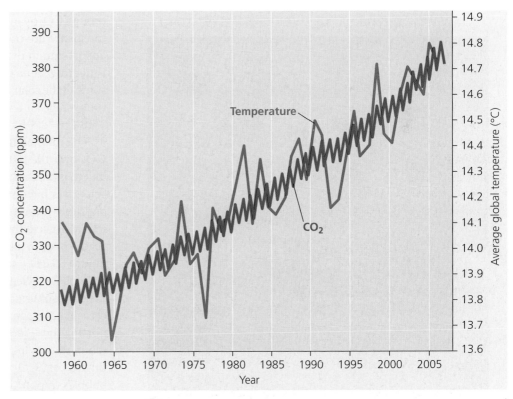

▲ **Figure 55.21 Increase in atmospheric carbon dioxide concentration at Mauna Loa, Hawaii, and average global temperatures.** Aside from normal seasonal fluctuations, the CO_2 concentration (blue curve) has increased steadily from 1958 to 2007. Though average global temperatures (red curve) fluctuated a great deal over the same period, there is a clear warming trend.

increasing global CO_2 concentration may be the spread of C_3 species into terrestrial habitats that currently favor C_4 plants. Such changes could influence whether corn (maize), a C_4 plant and the most important grain crop in the United States, will be replaced by wheat and soybeans, C_3 crops that could outproduce corn in a CO_2-enriched environment. To predict the gradual and complex effects of rising CO_2 levels on productivity and species composition, scientists are turning to long-term field experiments.

How Elevated CO_2 Levels Affect Forest Ecology: The FACTS-I Experiment

To assess how the increasing atmospheric concentration of CO_2 might affect temperate forests, scientists at Duke University began the Forest-Atmosphere Carbon Transfer and Storage (FACTS-I) experiment in 1995. The researchers are manipulating the concentration of CO_2 to which trees are exposed. The FACTS-I experiment includes six plots in an 80-hectare (200-acre) tract of loblolly pine within the university's experimental forest. Each plot consists of a circular area, approximately 30 m in diameter, ringed by 16 towers **(Figure 55.22)**. In three of the six plots, the towers produce air containing about 1½ times present-day CO_2 concentrations. Instruments on a tall tower in the center of each plot measure the direction and speed of the wind, adjusting the distribution of CO_2 to maintain a

▲ **Figure 55.22 Large-scale experiment on the effects of elevated CO_2 concentration.** Rings of towers in the Duke University Experimental Forest emit enough carbon dioxide to raise and maintain CO_2 levels 200 ppm above present-day concentrations in half of the experimental plots.

stable CO_2 concentration. All other factors, such as temperature, precipitation, and wind speed and direction, vary normally for both experimental plots and adjacent control plots exposed to atmospheric CO_2.

The FACTS-I study is testing how elevated CO_2 levels influence tree growth, carbon concentration in soils, insect populations, soil moisture, the growth of plants in the forest understory, and other factors. After ten years, trees in the experimental plots produced about 15% more wood each year than those in the control plots. This increased growth is important for timber production and carbon storage but is far lower than predicted from the results of greenhouse experiments. The availability of nitrogen and other nutrients apparently limits the ability of the trees to use the extra CO_2. Researchers at FACTS-I began removing this limitation in 2005 by fertilizing half of each plot with ammonium nitrate.

In most of the world's ecosystems, nutrients limit ecosystem productivity and fertilizers are unavailable. The results of FACTS-I and other experiments suggest that increased atmospheric CO_2 levels will increase plant production somewhat, but far less than scientists predicted even a decade ago.

The Greenhouse Effect and Climate

Rising concentrations of long-lived greenhouse gases such as CO_2 are also changing Earth's heat budget. Much of the solar radiation that strikes the planet is reflected back into space. Although CO_2, water vapor, and other greenhouse gases in the atmosphere are transparent to visible light, they intercept and absorb much of the infrared radiation the Earth emits, re-reflecting some of it back toward Earth. This process retains some of the solar heat. If it were not for this **greenhouse effect**, the average air temperature at Earth's surface would be a frigid $-18°C$ $(-2.4°F)$, and most life as we know it could not exist.

The marked increase in the concentration of atmospheric CO_2 over the last 150 years concerns scientists because of its link to increased global temperature. For more than a century, scientists have studied how greenhouse gases warm Earth and how fossil fuel burning could contribute to the warming. Most scientists are convinced that such warming has already begun and will increase rapidly this century (see Figure 55.21).

Global models predict that by the end of the 21st century, the atmospheric CO_2 concentration will more than double, increasing average global temperature by about $3°C$ $(5°F)$. Supporting these models is a correlation between CO_2 levels and temperatures in prehistoric times. One way climatologists estimate past CO_2 concentrations is to measure CO_2 levels in bubbles trapped in glacial ice, some of which are half a million years old. Prehistoric temperatures are inferred by several methods, including analysis of past vegetation based on fossils and the chemical isotopes in sediments and corals. An increase of only $1.3°C$ would make the world warmer than at any time in the past 100,000 years.

The ecosystems where the largest warming has *already* occurred are those in the far north, particularly northern coniferous forests and tundra. As snow and ice melt and uncover darker, more absorptive surfaces, these systems reflect less radiation back to the atmosphere and warm further. Arctic sea ice in the summer of 2007 covered the smallest area on record. Climate models suggest that there may be no summer ice there by the end of this century, decreasing habitat for polar bears, seals, and seabirds. Higher temperatures also increase the likelihood of fires. In boreal forests of western North America and Russia, fires have burned twice the usual area in recent decades.

A warming trend would also alter the geographic distribution of precipitation, making major agricultural areas of the central United States much drier, for example. However, the various mathematical models disagree about the details of how climate in each region will be affected. By studying how past periods of global warming and cooling affected plant communities, ecologists are trying to predict the consequences of future temperature changes. Analysis of fossilized pollen indicates that plant communities change dramatically with changes in temperature. Past climate changes occurred gradually, though, and plant and animal populations had time to migrate into areas where abiotic conditions allowed them to survive. Many organisms, especially plants that cannot disperse rapidly over long distances, may not be able to survive the high rates of climate change projected to result from global warming. Furthermore, many habitats today are much more fragmented than they were in the past (see Chapter 56), further limiting the ability of many organisms to migrate.

We will need many tools to slow global warming. Quick progress can be made in using energy more efficiently and in replacing fossil fuels with renewable solar and wind power and, more controversially, with nuclear power. Today, coal, gasoline, wood, and other organic fuels remain central to industrialized societies and cannot be burned without releasing CO_2. Stabilizing CO_2 emissions will require concerted international effort and the acceptance of changes in both personal lifestyles and industrial processes. Many ecologists think that effort suffered a major setback in 2001, when the United States pulled out of the Kyoto Protocol, a 1997 pledge by industrialized nations to reduce their CO_2 output by about 5%. Such a reduction would be a first step in the journey to stabilize atmospheric CO_2 concentrations.

Depletion of Atmospheric Ozone

Life on Earth is protected from the damaging effects of ultraviolet (UV) radiation by a layer of ozone molecules (O_3) located in the stratosphere 17–25 km above Earth's surface. However, satellite studies of the atmosphere show that the ozone layer has been gradually thinning since the mid-1970s **(Figure 55.23)**. The destruction of atmospheric ozone results mainly

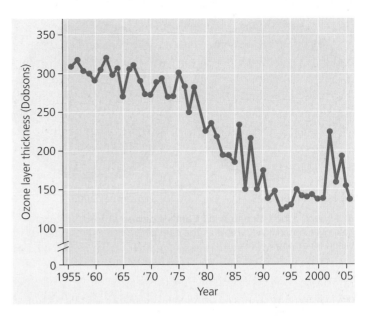

▲ **Figure 55.23 Thickness of the ozone layer over Antarctica in units called Dobsons.**

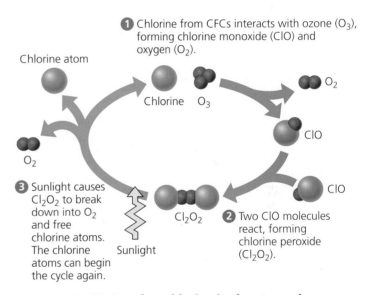

① Chlorine from CFCs interacts with ozone (O_3), forming chlorine monoxide (ClO) and oxygen (O_2).

② Two ClO molecules react, forming chlorine peroxide (Cl_2O_2).

③ Sunlight causes Cl_2O_2 to break down into O_2 and free chlorine atoms. The chlorine atoms can begin the cycle again.

▲ **Figure 55.24 How free chlorine in the atmosphere destroys ozone.**

from the accumulation of chlorofluorocarbons (CFCs), chemicals used in refrigeration and in manufacturing. When the breakdown products from these chemicals rise to the stratosphere, the chlorine they contain reacts with ozone, reducing it to molecular O_2 **(Figure 55.24)**. Subsequent chemical reactions liberate the chlorine, allowing it to react with other ozone molecules in a catalytic chain reaction.

The thinning of the ozone layer is most apparent over Antarctica in spring, where cold, stable air allows the chain reaction to continue. The magnitude of ozone depletion and the size of the ozone hole have generally increased in recent years, and the hole sometimes extends as far as the southernmost portions of Australia, New Zealand, and South America

(a) September 1979   **(b) September 2006**

▲ **Figure 55.25 Erosion of Earth's ozone shield.** The ozone hole over Antarctica is visible as the dark blue patch in these images based on atmospheric data.

(Figure 55.25). At the more heavily populated middle latitudes, ozone levels have decreased 2–10% during the past 20 years.

Decreased ozone levels in the stratosphere increase the intensity of UV rays reaching Earth's surface. The consequences of ozone depletion for life on Earth may be severe for plants, animals, and microorganisms. Some scientists expect increases in both lethal and nonlethal forms of skin cancer and in cataracts among humans, as well as unpredictable effects on crops and natural communities, especially the phytoplankton that are responsible for a large proportion of Earth's primary production.

To study the consequences of ozone depletion, ecologists have conducted field experiments in which they use filters to decrease or block the UV radiation in sunlight. One such experiment, performed on a scrub ecosystem near the tip of South America, showed that when the ozone hole passed over the area, the amount of UV radiation reaching the ground increased sharply, causing more DNA damage in plants that were not protected by filters. Scientists have shown similar DNA damage and a reduction in phytoplank-

ton growth when the ozone hole opens over the Southern Ocean each year.

The good news about the ozone hole is how quickly many countries have responded to it. Since 1987, approximately 190 nations, including the United States, have signed the Montreal Protocol, a treaty that regulates the use of ozone-depleting chemicals. Many nations, again including the United States, have ended the production of CFCs. As a consequence of these actions, chlorine concentrations in the stratosphere have stabilized and ozone depletion is slowing. Even if all CFCs were globally banned today, however, chlorine molecules that are already in the atmosphere would continue to influence stratospheric ozone levels for at least 50 years.

The partial destruction of Earth's ozone shield is one more example of how much humans have been able to disrupt the dynamics of ecosystems and the biosphere. It also highlights our ability to solve environmental problems when we set our minds to it. In this book's final chapter, we will explore how scientists in the fields of conservation biology and restoration ecology are studying the effects of human activities on Earth's biodiversity and are using ecological knowledge to reduce those effects.

CONCEPT CHECK 55.5

1. How can the addition of excess nutrients to a lake threaten its fish population?
2. In the face of biological magnification of toxins, is it healthier to feed at a lower or higher trophic level? Explain.
3. **WHAT IF?**   There are vast stores of organic matter in the soils of northern coniferous forests and tundra around the world. Based on what you learned about decomposition from Figure 55.15, suggest an explanation for why scientists who study global warming are closely monitoring these stores.

For suggested answers, see Appendix A.

Chapter 55 Review

SUMMARY OF KEY CONCEPTS

CONCEPT 55.1

Physical laws govern energy flow and chemical cycling in ecosystems (pp. 1223–1224)

▶ **Conservation of Energy** An ecosystem consists of all the organisms in a community and all the abiotic factors with which

they interact. The laws of physics and chemistry apply to ecosystems, particularly in regard to the flow of energy. Energy is conserved but degraded to heat during ecosystem processes.

▶ **Conservation of Mass** Ecologists study how much of a chemical element enters and leaves an ecosystem and cycles within it. Inputs and outputs are generally small compared to recycled amounts, but their balance determines whether the ecosystem gains or loses an element over time.

► **Energy, Mass, and Trophic Levels**

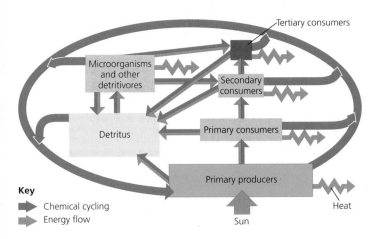

Key
→ Chemical cycling
→ Energy flow

CONCEPT 55.2

Energy and other limiting factors control primary production in ecosystems (pp. 1224–1228)

► **Ecosystem Energy Budgets** Primary production sets the spending limit for the global energy budget. Gross primary production is the total energy assimilated by an ecosystem in a given period. Net primary production, the energy accumulated in autotroph biomass, equals gross primary production minus the energy used by the primary producers for respiration. Only net primary production is available to consumers.

► **Primary Production in Aquatic Ecosystems** In marine and freshwater ecosystems, light and nutrients limit primary production. Within the photic zone, the factor that most often limits primary production is a nutrient such as nitrogen, phosphorus, or iron.

► **Primary Production in Terrestrial Ecosystems** In terrestrial ecosystems, climatic factors such as temperature and moisture affect primary production on a large geographic scale. More locally, a soil nutrient is often the limiting factor in primary production.

> **MEDIA**
> **Investigation** How Do Temperature and Light Affect Primary Production?

CONCEPT 55.3

Energy transfer between trophic levels is typically only 10% efficient (pp. 1228–1230)

► **Production Efficiency** The amount of energy available to each trophic level is determined by the net primary production and the efficiency with which food energy is converted to biomass at each link in the food chain. The percentage of energy transferred from one trophic level to the next, called trophic efficiency, is generally 5–20%, with 10% being the typical value. Pyramids of net production and biomass reflect low trophic efficiency.

► **The Green World Hypothesis** According to the green world hypothesis, herbivores consume only a small percentage of vegetation because predators, pathogens, competition, nutrient limitations, and other factors keep their populations in check.

> **MEDIA**
> **Activity** Pyramids of Production
> **GraphIt!** Animal Food Production Efficiency and Food Policy
> **MP3 Tutor** Energy Flow in Ecosystems

CONCEPT 55.4

Biological and geochemical processes cycle nutrients between organic and inorganic parts of an ecosystem (pp. 1231–1236)

► **Biogeochemical Cycles**

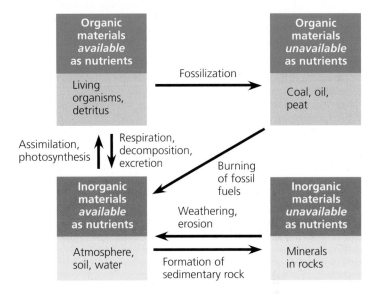

Water moves in a global cycle driven by solar energy. The carbon cycle primarily reflects the reciprocal processes of photosynthesis and cellular respiration. Nitrogen enters ecosystems through atmospheric deposition and nitrogen fixation by prokaryotes, but most of the nitrogen cycling in natural ecosystems involves local cycles between organisms and soil or water. The phosphorus cycle is relatively localized.

► **Decomposition and Nutrient Cycling Rates** The proportion of a nutrient in a particular form and its cycling time in that form vary among ecosystems, largely because of differences in the rate of decomposition.

► **Case Study: Nutrient Cycling in the Hubbard Brook Experimental Forest** Nutrient cycling is strongly regulated by vegetation. The Hubbard Brook study showed that logging increases water runoff and can cause large losses of minerals. It also demonstrated the importance of long-term ecological measurements in documenting the occurrence of and recovery from environmental problems.

> **MEDIA**
> **Activity** Energy Flow and Chemical Cycling
> **Activity** The Carbon Cycle
> **Activity** The Nitrogen Cycle

CONCEPT 55.5

Human activities now dominate most chemical cycles on Earth (pp. 1236–1242)

► **Nutrient Enrichment** Agriculture removes nutrients from ecosystems, so large supplements are usually required. The nutrients in fertilizer can pollute groundwater and surface-water aquatic ecosystems, where they can stimulate excess algal growth (eutrophication).

► **Acid Precipitation** Burning of fossil fuels is the main cause of acid precipitation. North American and European ecosystems downwind from industrial regions have been damaged by rain and snow containing nitric acid and sulfuric acid.

▶ **Toxins in the Environment** Toxins can become concentrated in successive trophic levels of food webs. The release of toxic wastes has polluted the environment with harmful substances that often persist for long periods and become concentrated along the food chain by biological magnification.

▶ **Greenhouse Gases and Global Warming** Because of the burning of wood and fossil fuels and other human activities, the atmospheric concentration of CO_2 has been steadily increasing. The ultimate effects include significant global warming and other climate changes.

▶ **Depletion of Atmospheric Ozone** The ozone layer reduces the penetration of UV radiation through the atmosphere. Human activities, including release of chlorine-containing pollutants, are eroding the ozone layer, but government policies are helping to solve the problem.

TESTING YOUR KNOWLEDGE

SELF-QUIZ

1. Which of the following organisms is *incorrectly* paired with its trophic level?
   a. cyanobacterium—primary producer
   b. grasshopper—primary consumer
   c. zooplankton—primary producer
   d. eagle—tertiary consumer
   e. fungus—detritivore

2. Which of these ecosystems has the *lowest* net primary production per square meter?
   a. a salt marsh   d. a grassland
   b. an open ocean   e. a tropical rain forest
   c. a coral reef

3. Nitrifying bacteria participate in the nitrogen cycle mainly by
   a. converting nitrogen gas to ammonia.
   b. releasing ammonium from organic compounds, thus returning it to the soil.
   c. converting ammonia to nitrogen gas, which returns to the atmosphere.
   d. converting ammonium to nitrate, which plants absorb.
   e. incorporating nitrogen into amino acids and organic compounds.

4. Which of the following has the greatest effect on the rate of chemical cycling in an ecosystem?
   a. the ecosystem's rate of primary production
   b. the production efficiency of the ecosystem's consumers
   c. the rate of decomposition in the ecosystem
   d. the trophic efficiency of the ecosystem
   e. the location of the nutrient reservoirs in the ecosystem

5. The Hubbard Brook watershed deforestation experiment yielded all of the following results *except* that
   a. most minerals were recycled within a forest ecosystem.
   b. the flow of minerals out of a natural watershed was offset by minerals flowing in.

   c. deforestation increased water runoff.
   d. the nitrate concentration in waters draining the deforested area became dangerously high.
   e. calcium levels remained high in the soil of deforested areas.

6. Which of the following is a consequence of biological magnification?
   a. Toxic chemicals in the environment pose greater risk to top-level predators than to primary consumers.
   b. Populations of top-level predators are generally smaller than populations of primary consumers.
   c. The biomass of producers in an ecosystem is generally higher than the biomass of primary consumers.
   d. Only a small portion of the energy captured by producers is transferred to consumers.
   e. The amount of biomass in the producer level of an ecosystem decreases if the producer turnover time increases.

7. The main cause of the increase in the amount of CO_2 in Earth's atmosphere over the past 150 years is
   a. increased worldwide primary production.
   b. increased worldwide standing crop.
   c. an increase in the amount of infrared radiation absorbed by the atmosphere.
   d. the burning of larger amounts of wood and fossil fuels.
   e. additional respiration by the rapidly growing human population.

8. **DRAW IT** Using Figure 55.21 as a starting point, extend the x-axis to the year 2100. Then extend the CO_2 curve, assuming that the CO_2 concentration continues to rise as fast as it did from 1974 to 2007. What will be the approximate CO_2 concentration in 2100? What ecological factors and human decisions will influence the actual rise in CO_2 concentration? How might additional scientific data help societies predict this value?

For Self-Quiz answers, see Appendix A.

EVOLUTION CONNECTION

9. Some biologists have suggested that ecosystems are emergent, "living" systems capable of evolving. One manifestation of this idea is environmentalist James Lovelock's Gaia hypothesis, which views Earth itself as a living, homeostatic entity—a kind of superorganism. Use the principles of evolution you have learned in this book to critique the idea that ecosystems and the biosphere can evolve. If ecosystems are capable of evolving, is this a form of Darwinian evolution? Why or why not?

SCIENTIFIC INQUIRY

10. Using two neighboring ponds in a forest as your study site, design a controlled experiment to measure the effect of falling leaves on net primary production in a pond.

Biological Inquiry: A Workbook of Investigative Cases Explore how changes to the Chesapeake affect shellfishing with the case "Back to the Bay."

Conservation Biology and Restoration Ecology

56

OVERVIEW

Striking Gold

Tucking its wings, a bird lands on a branch deep inside a tropical jungle. Sensing the motion, a conservation biologist scans the branch through binoculars, a glimpse of golden orange stopping her short. Staring back is a smoky honeyeater, a species that had never been described before (**Figure 56.1**). In 2005, a team of American, Indonesian, and Australian biologists experienced many moments like this as they spent a month cataloging the living riches hidden in a remote mountain range in Indonesia. In addition to the honeyeater, they discovered dozens of new frog, butterfly, and plant species, including five new palms.

To date, scientists have described and formally named about 1.8 million species of organisms. Some biologists think that about 10 million more species currently exist; others estimate the number to be as high as 100 million. Some of the greatest concentrations of species are found in the tropics. Unfortunately, tropical forests are being cleared at an alarming rate to make room for and support a burgeoning human population. Rates of deforestation in Indonesia are among the highest in the world (**Figure 56.2**). What will become of the smoky honeyeater and other newly discovered species in Indonesia if such deforestation continues unchecked?

▲ **Figure 56.1 What will be the fate of this newly described bird species?**

Throughout the biosphere, human activities are altering trophic structures, energy flow, chemical cycling, and natural disturbance—ecosystem processes on which we and all other species depend (see Chapter 55). We have physically altered nearly half of Earth's land surface, and we use over half of all accessible surface fresh water. In the oceans, stocks of most major fisheries are shrinking because of overharvesting. By some estimates, we are pushing more species toward extinction than the large asteroid or comet that triggered the mass extinctions at the close of the Cretaceous period 65.5 million years ago (see Figure 25.16).

Biology is the science of life. Thus, it is fitting that our final chapter focuses on two disciplines that seek to preserve life. **Conservation biology** integrates ecology, physiology, molecular biology, genetics, and evolutionary biology to conserve biological diversity at all levels. Efforts to sustain ecosystem processes and stem the loss of biodiversity also connect the life sciences with the social sciences, economics, and humanities.

▲ **Figure 56.2 Tropical deforestation in West Kalimantan, an Indonesian province.**

Restoration ecology applies ecological principles to return ecosystems that have been disturbed by human activity to a condition as similar as possible to their natural state.

In this chapter, we will take a closer look at the biodiversity crisis and examine some of the conservation and restoration strategies being adopted to slow the rate of species loss.

CONCEPT 56.1
Human activities threaten Earth's biodiversity

Extinction is a natural phenomenon that has been occurring since life first evolved; it is the *rate* of extinction that is responsible for today's biodiversity crisis (see Chapter 25). Because we can only estimate the number of species currently existing, we cannot determine the exact rate of species loss. However, we do know for certain that the extinction rate is high and that human activities threaten Earth's biodiversity at all levels.

Three Levels of Biodiversity

Biodiversity—short for biological diversity—can be considered at three main levels: genetic diversity, species diversity, and ecosystem diversity **(Figure 56.3)**.

Genetic Diversity

Genetic diversity comprises not only the individual genetic variation *within* a population, but also the genetic variation *between* populations that is often associated with adaptations to local conditions (see Chapter 23). If one population becomes extinct, then a species may have lost some of the genetic diversity that makes microevolution possible. This erosion of genetic diversity in turn reduces the adaptive prospects of the species.

The loss of genetic diversity throughout the biosphere also affects human welfare. If we lose wild populations of plants closely related to agricultural species, we lose genetic resources that could be used to improve crop qualities, such as disease resistance, through plant breeding. For example, plant breeders responded to devastating outbreaks of the grassy stunt virus in rice (*Oryza sativa*) by screening 7,000 populations of this species and its close relatives for resistance to the virus. One population of a single relative, Indian rice (*Oryza nivara*), demonstrated resistance to the virus, and scientists succeeded in breeding the resistant trait into commercial rice varieties. Today, the original disease-resistant population has apparently become extinct in the wild.

Species Diversity

Public awareness of the biodiversity crisis centers on species diversity—the variety of species in an ecosystem or throughout the biosphere (see Chapter 54). As more species are lost to extinction, species diversity decreases. The U.S. Endangered

Genetic diversity in a vole population

Species diversity in a coastal redwood ecosystem

Community and ecosystem diversity across the landscape of an entire region

▲ **Figure 56.3 Three levels of biodiversity.** The oversized chromosomes in the top diagram symbolize the genetic variation within the population.

Species Act (ESA) defines an **endangered species** as one that is "in danger of extinction throughout all or a significant portion of its range." Also defined for protection by the ESA, **threatened species** are those that are considered likely to become endangered in the foreseeable future. The following are just a few statistics that illustrate the problem of species loss:

▶ According to the International Union for Conservation of Nature and Natural Resources (IUCN), 12% of the nearly 10,000 known species of birds and at least 20% of the nearly 5,000 known species of mammals are threatened.

▶ A survey by the Center for Plant Conservation showed that of the nearly 20,000 known plant species in the United States, 200 have become extinct since such records have been kept, and 730 are endangered or threatened.

- About 20% of the known species of freshwater fishes in the world have either become extinct during historical times or are seriously threatened. In North America, 123 freshwater animal species have become extinct since 1900, and hundreds more species are threatened. The extinction rate for North American freshwater fauna is about five times as high as that for terrestrial animals.
- According to a 2004 report in the journal *Science* that was based on a global assessment of amphibians by more than 500 scientists, 32% of all known amphibian species are either very near extinction or endangered.

Extinction of species may be local; for example, a species may be lost in one river system but survive in an adjacent one. Global extinction of a species means that it is lost from *all* the ecosystems in which it lived, leaving them permanently impoverished **(Figure 56.4)**.

(a) Philippine eagle

(b) Yangtze River dolphin

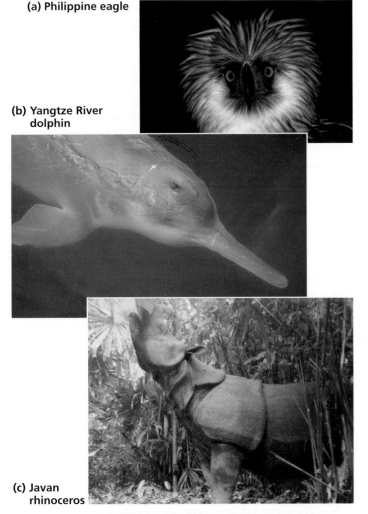

(c) Javan rhinoceros

▲ **Figure 56.4 A hundred heartbeats from extinction.** These are just three members of what E. O. Wilson calls the Hundred Heartbeat Club, species with fewer than 100 individuals remaining on Earth. The Yangtze River dolphin was even thought to be extinct, but a few individuals were reportedly sighted in 2007.

? *To document that a species has actually become extinct, what spatial and temporal factors would you need to consider?*

Ecosystem Diversity

The variety of the biosphere's ecosystems is a third level of biological diversity. Because of the network of community interactions among populations of different species within an ecosystem, the local extinction of one species can have a negative impact on the overall species richness of the community (see Figure 54.15). For instance, bats called "flying foxes" are important pollinators and seed dispersers in the Pacific Islands, where they have been subject to increasing pressure from hunters, who sell them as luxury foods **(Figure 56.5)**. Conservation biologists fear that the extinction of flying foxes would also harm the native plants of the Samoan islands, where more than 79% of the trees depend on flying foxes for pollination or seed dispersal.

Some ecosystems have already been heavily impacted by humans, and others are being altered at a rapid pace. For example, since European colonization, more than 50% of wetlands in the contiguous United States have been drained and converted to other ecosystems, primarily agricultural ones. In California, Arizona, and New Mexico, approximately 90% of native riparian communities have been affected by overgrazing, flood control, water diversions, lowering of water tables, and invasion by non-native plants.

Biodiversity and Human Welfare

Why should we care about the loss of biodiversity? Perhaps the purest reason is what E. O. Wilson calls *biophilia*, our sense of connection to nature and other forms of life. The belief that other species are entitled to life is a pervasive theme of many religions and the basis of a moral argument that we should protect biodiversity. There is also a concern for future human generations: Is it fair to deprive them of Earth's species richness? Paraphrasing an old proverb, G. H. Brundtland, a former prime minister of Norway, said: "We must consider our planet to be on

▲ **Figure 56.5 The endangered Marianas "flying fox" bat (*Pteropus mariannus*), an important pollinator.**

loan from our children, rather than being a gift from our ancestors." In addition to such philosophical and moral justifications, species and genetic diversity bring us many practical benefits.

Benefits of Species and Genetic Diversity

Many species that are threatened could potentially provide crops, fibers, and medicines for human use, making biodiversity a crucial natural resource. In the United States, about 25% of the prescriptions dispensed from pharmacies contain substances originally derived from plants. In the 1970s, researchers discovered that the rosy periwinkle, which grows on the island of Madagascar, off the coast of Africa, contains alkaloids that inhibit cancer cell growth (Figure 56.6). This discovery led to treatments for two deadly forms of cancer, Hodgkin's disease and a form of childhood leukemia, resulting in remission in most cases. Madagascar is also home to five other species of periwinkles, one of which is approaching extinction. The loss of these species would mean the loss of any possible medicinal benefits they might offer.

Each loss of a species means the loss of unique genes, some of which may code for enormously useful proteins. Consider the example of Taq polymerase, a DNA polymerase first extracted from the bacterium *Thermus aquaticus* in hot springs at Yellowstone National Park. This enzyme is an essential part of the polymerase chain reaction (PCR) because it is stable at the high temperatures required for PCR (see Figure 20.8). DNA from many other species of prokaryotes in a variety of environments is used in the mass production of proteins for new medicines, foods, petroleum substitutes, industrial chemicals, and other products. However, because millions of species may become extinct before we even know about them, we stand to lose irretrievably the valuable genetic potential held in their unique libraries of genes.

Ecosystem Services

The benefits that individual species provide to humans are often substantial, but saving individual species is only part of the rationale for saving ecosystems. Humans evolved in Earth's ecosystems, and we rely on these systems and their inhabitants for our survival. **Ecosystem services** encompass all the processes through which natural ecosystems help sustain human life on Earth. Ecosystems purify our air and water. They detoxify and decompose our wastes and reduce the impacts of extreme weather and flooding. The organisms in ecosystems pollinate our crops, control pests, and create and preserve our soils. Moreover, ecosystems provide all these services and countless others for free.

Perhaps because we don't attach a monetary value to the services of natural ecosystems, we generally undervalue them. In a controversial 1997 article, ecologist Robert Costanza and his colleagues estimated the value of Earth's ecosystem services at $33 trillion per year, nearly twice the gross national product of all the countries on Earth at that time ($18 trillion). It may be more realistic, and more meaningful, to do the accounting on a smaller scale. In 1996, New York City invested more than $1 billion to buy land and restore habitat in the Catskill Mountains, the source of much of the city's fresh water. This investment was spurred by increasing pollution of the water by sewage, pesticides, and fertilizers. By harnessing ecosystem services to purify its water naturally, the city saved $8 billion it would have otherwise spent to build a new filtration plant and $300 million a year to run the plant.

There is growing evidence that the functioning of ecosystems, and hence their capacity to perform services, is linked to biodiversity. As human activities reduce biodiversity, we are reducing the capacity of the planet's ecosystems to perform processes critical to our own survival.

Three Threats to Biodiversity

Many different human activities threaten biodiversity on local, regional, and global scales. The threats posed by these activities are of three major types: habitat loss, introduced species, and overexploitation.

Habitat Loss

Human alteration of habitat is the single greatest threat to biodiversity throughout the biosphere. Habitat loss has been brought about by agriculture, urban development, forestry, mining, and pollution. Global warming is already altering habitats today and will have an even larger effect later this century (see Chapter 55). When no alternative habitat is available or a species is unable to move, habitat loss may mean extinction. The IUCN implicates destruction of physical habitat for 73% of the species that have become extinct, endangered, vulnerable, or rare in the last few hundred years.

Habitat loss and fragmentation may occur over immense regions. For instance, approximately 98% of the tropical dry forests of Central America and Mexico have been cleared (cut down). Clearing of tropical rain forest in the state of Veracruz,

▶ Figure 56.6
The rosy periwinkle (*Catharanthus roseus*), a plant that saves lives.

▲ **Figure 56.7 Habitat fragmentation in the foothills of Los Angeles.** Development in the valleys may confine the organisms that inhabit the narrow strips of hillside.

Mexico, mostly for cattle ranching, has resulted in the loss of approximately 91% of the original forest, leaving a fragmented archipelago of small forest islands. Other natural habitats have also been fragmented by human activities **(Figure 56.7)**.

In almost all cases, habitat fragmentation leads to species loss, since the smaller populations in habitat fragments have a higher probability of local extinction. The prairies of North America are an example: Prairie covered about 800,000 hectares of southern Wisconsin when Europeans first arrived, but now occupies less than 0.1% of its original area. Plant diversity surveys of 54 Wisconsin prairie remnants were conducted in 1948–1954 and then repeated in 1987–1988. During the three decades between the surveys, the various prairie fragments lost between 8% and 60% of their plant species.

Though most studies have focused on terrestrial ecosystems, habitat loss is also a major threat to aquatic biodiversity, especially along continental coasts and around coral reefs. About 93% of coral reefs, among Earth's most species-rich aquatic communities, have been damaged by human activities. At the current rate of destruction, 40–50% of the reefs, home to one-third of marine fish species, could disappear in the next 30 to 40 years. Freshwater habitats are also being lost, often as a result of the dams, reservoirs, channel modification, and flow regulation now affecting most of the world's rivers. For example, the more than 30 dams and locks built along the Mobile River basin, in the southeastern United States, changed river depth and flow and thereby helped drive more than 40 species of endemic mussels and snails to extinction.

Introduced Species

Introduced species, also called non-native or exotic species, are those that humans move, either intentionally or accidentally, from the species' native locations to new geographic regions. Rapid human travel by ship and airplane has accelerated the transplant of species. Free from the predators, parasites, and pathogens that limit their populations in their native habitats, such transplanted species may spread very rapidly through a new region.

Some introduced species that gain a foothold disrupt their adopted community, often by preying on native organisms or outcompeting them for resources. The brown tree snake was accidentally introduced to the island of Guam as a "stowaway" in military cargo after World War II **(Figure 56.8a)**. Since then, 12 species of birds and 6 species of lizards on which the snakes prey have become extinct on Guam. The devastating zebra mussel was introduced into the Great Lakes of North America in 1988, most likely in the ballast water of ships arriving from Europe. Efficient suspension-feeding molluscs that form dense colonies, zebra mussels have extensively disrupted freshwater ecosystems, threatening native aquatic species. Zebra mussels have also clogged water intake structures, disrupting domestic and industrial water supplies and causing billions of dollars in damage.

Humans have deliberately introduced many species with good intentions but disastrous effects. For example, an Asian plant called kudzu, which the U.S. Department of Agriculture once introduced in the southern United States to help control erosion, has taken over large areas of the landscape there **(Figure 56.8b)**. The European starling, brought intentionally into New York's Central Park in 1890 by a citizens' group intent on introducing all the plants and animals mentioned in Shakespeare's plays, quickly spread across North America, increasing to a population of more than 100 million and displacing many native songbirds.

Introduced species are a worldwide problem, contributing to approximately 40% of the extinctions recorded since 1750

(a) Brown tree snake, introduced to Guam in cargo

(b) Introduced kudzu thriving in South Carolina

▲ **Figure 56.8 Two introduced species.**

and costing billions of dollars annually in damage and control efforts. There are more than 50,000 introduced species in the United States alone.

Overexploitation

The term *overexploitation* refers generally to the human harvesting of wild organisms at rates exceeding the ability of populations of those species to rebound. Species with restricted habitats, such as small islands, are particularly vulnerable to overexploitation. One such species was the great auk, a large, flightless seabird found on islands in the North Atlantic Ocean. By the 1840s, humans had hunted the great auk to extinction to satisfy demand for its feathers, eggs, and meat.

Also susceptible to overexploitation are large organisms with low intrinsic reproductive rates, such as elephants, whales, and rhinoceroses. The decline of Earth's largest extant terrestrial animals, the African elephants, is a classic example of the impact of overhunting. Largely because of the trade in ivory, elephant populations have been declining in most of Africa during the last 50 years. An international ban on the sale of new ivory resulted in increased poaching (illegal hunting), so the ban had little effect in much of central and eastern Africa. Only in South Africa, where once-decimated herds have been well protected for nearly a century, have elephant populations been stable or increasing (see Chapter 53).

Conservation biologists increasingly use the tools of molecular genetics to track the origins of tissues harvested from threatened and endangered species. For instance, Samuel Wasser and colleagues, at the University of Washington, created a DNA reference map for the African elephant using DNA isolated from elephant dung. By comparing this reference map with DNA isolated from a small sample of ivory harvested either legally or by poachers, they can determine where the elephant was killed to within a few hundred kilometers. Similarly, biologists using phylogenetic analyses of mitochondrial DNA (mtDNA) showed that some whale meat sold in Japanese fish markets came from illegally harvested species, including fin and humpback whales, which are endangered (see Figure 26.6).

Many populations of commercially important marine fishes, once thought to be inexhaustible, have been dramatically reduced by overfishing. The exploding human population's increasing demand for protein, coupled with new harvesting technologies, such as long-line fishing and modern trawlers, have reduced these fish populations to levels that cannot sustain further exploitation. The fate of the North Atlantic bluefin tuna is just one example. Until the past few decades, this big tuna was considered a sport fish of little commercial value—just a few cents per pound for cat food. Then, in the 1980s, wholesalers began airfreighting fresh, iced bluefin to Japan for sushi and sashimi. In that market, the fish now brings up to $100 per pound (Figure 56.9). With the in-

▲ Figure 56.9 **Overexploitation.** North Atlantic bluefin tuna are auctioned in a Japanese fish market.

creased harvesting spurred by such high prices, it took just ten years to reduce the western North Atlantic bluefin population to less than 20% of its 1980 size. The collapse of the northern cod fishery off Newfoundland in the 1990s is a more recent example of how it is possible to overharvest what was formerly a very common species.

CONCEPT CHECK 56.1

1. Explain why it is too narrow to define the biodiversity crisis as simply a loss of species.
2. Identify the three main threats to biodiversity and explain how each damages diversity.
3. **WHAT IF?** Imagine two populations of a fish species, one in the Mediterranean Sea and one in the Caribbean Sea. Now imagine two scenarios: (1) The populations breed separately, and (2) adults of both populations migrate to the North Atlantic to interbreed. Which scenario would result in a greater loss of genetic diversity if the Mediterranean population were harvested to extinction? Explain your answer.

For suggested answers, see Appendix A.

CONCEPT 56.2
Population conservation focuses on population size, genetic diversity, and critical habitat

Biologists focusing on conservation at the population and species levels follow two main approaches: the small-population approach and the declining-population approach.

Small-Population Approach

A species is designated as endangered when its populations are very small. Small populations are particularly vulnerable to overexploitation, habitat loss, and the other threats to biodiversity that you read about in Concept 56.1. After such factors have taken their toll on population size, a population's smallness itself can drive it to extinction. Conservation biologists who adopt the small-population approach study the processes that cause extinctions once population sizes have been severely reduced.

The Extinction Vortex

A small population is prone to positive-feedback loops of inbreeding and genetic drift that draw the population down an **extinction vortex** toward smaller and smaller population size until no individuals exist **(Figure 56.10)**. One key factor driving the extinction vortex is the loss of the genetic variation necessary to enable evolutionary responses to environmental change, such as the appearance of new strains of pathogens. Both inbreeding and genetic drift can cause a loss of genetic variation (see Chapter 23), and the effects of both processes become more significant as a population shrinks. Inbreeding often reduces fitness because offspring are more likely to be homozygous for harmful recessive traits.

Not all small populations are doomed by low genetic diversity, and low genetic variability does not automatically lead to permanently small populations. For instance, over-

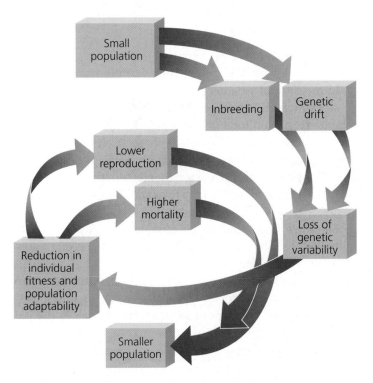

▲ **Figure 56.10 Processes culminating in an extinction vortex.**

hunting of northern elephant seals in the 1890s reduced the species to only 20 individuals—clearly a bottleneck with reduced genetic variation. Since that time, however, the northern elephant seal populations have rebounded to about 150,000 individuals today, though their genetic variation remains relatively low. Furthermore, a number of plant species seem to have inherently low genetic variability. For example, many populations of cord grass (*Spartina anglica*), which thrives in salt marshes, are genetically uniform at many loci. *S. anglica* arose from a few parent plants only about a century ago by hybridization and allopolyploidy (see Figure 24.11). Having spread by cloning, this species now dominates large areas of tidal mudflats in Europe and Asia. Thus, in rare cases, low genetic diversity has not impeded population growth.

Case Study: *The Greater Prairie Chicken and the Extinction Vortex*

When Europeans arrived in North America, the greater prairie chicken (*Tympanuchus cupido*) was common from New England to Virginia and all across the western prairies of the continent. As you read in Chapter 23, land cultivation for agriculture fragmented the populations of this species, and its abundance decreased drastically. In Illinois, there were millions of greater prairie chickens in the 19th century, but fewer than 50 were left by 1993. Researchers found that the decline in the Illinois population was associated with a decrease in fertility. As a test of the extinction vortex hypothesis, the scientists imported genetic variation by transplanting 271 birds from larger populations elsewhere (**Figure 56.11**, on the next page). The Illinois population rebounded, confirming that it had been on its way down the extinction vortex until rescued by the transfusion of genetic variation.

Minimum Viable Population Size

How small does a population have to be before it starts down an extinction vortex? The answer depends on the type of organism and other factors. For example, large predators that feed high on the food chain usually require very large individual ranges, resulting in very low population densities. Therefore, not all rare species concern conservation biologists. All populations, however, require some minimum size in order to remain viable.

The minimal population size at which a species is able to sustain its numbers and survive is known as the **minimum viable population (MVP)**. MVP is usually estimated for a given species using computer models that integrate many factors. The calculation may include, for example, an estimate of how many individuals in a small population are likely to be killed by some natural catastrophe such as a storm. Once in the extinction vortex, two or three years in a row of bad weather could finish off a population that is already below MVP.

▼ Figure 56.11 Inquiry

What caused the drastic decline of the Illinois greater prairie chicken population?

EXPERIMENT Researchers had observed that the population collapse of the greater prairie chicken was mirrored in a reduction in fertility, as measured by the hatching rate of eggs. Comparison of DNA samples from the Jasper County, Illinois, population with DNA from feathers in museum specimens showed that genetic variation had declined in the study population (see Figure 23.10). In 1992, Ronald Westemeier, Jeffrey Brawn, and colleagues began transplanting prairie chickens from Minnesota, Kansas, and Nebraska in an attempt to increase genetic variation.

RESULTS After translocation (blue arrow), the viability of eggs rapidly increased, and the population rebounded.

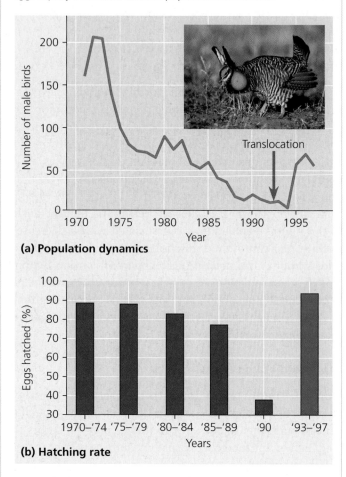

(a) Population dynamics

(b) Hatching rate

CONCLUSION Reduced genetic variation had started the Jasper County population of prairie chickens down the extinction vortex.

SOURCE R. L. Westemeier et al., Tracking the long-term decline and recovery of an isolated population, *Science* 282:1695–1698 (1998).

Inquiry in Action Read and analyze the original paper in *Inquiry in Action: Interpreting Scientific Papers.*

WHAT IF? Given the success of using transplanted birds as a tool for increasing the percentage of hatched eggs in Illinois, why wouldn't you transplant *additional* birds immediately to Illinois?

Effective Population Size

Genetic variation is the key issue in the small-population approach. The *total* size of a population may be misleading because only certain members of the population breed successfully and pass their alleles on to offspring. Therefore, a meaningful estimate of MVP requires the researcher to determine the **effective population size**, which is based on the breeding potential of the population.

The following formula incorporates the sex ratio of breeding individuals into the estimate of effective population size, abbreviated N_e:

$$N_e = \frac{4N_f N_m}{N_f + N_m}$$

where N_f and N_m are, respectively, the number of females and the number of males that successfully breed. If we apply this formula to an idealized population whose total size is 1,000 individuals, N_e will also be 1,000 if every individual breeds and the sex ratio is 500 females to 500 males. In this case, $N_e = (4 \times 500 \times 500)/(500 + 500) = 1,000$. Any deviation from these conditions (not all individuals breed or there is not a 1:1 sex ratio) reduces N_e. For instance, if the total population size is 1,000 but only 400 females and 400 males breed, then $N_e = (4 \times 400 \times 400)/(400 + 400) = 800$, or 80% of the total population size. Numerous life history traits can influence N_e, and alternative formulas for estimating N_e take into account family size, age at maturation, genetic relatedness among population members, the effects of gene flow between geographically separated populations, and population fluctuations.

In actual study populations, N_e is always some fraction of the total population. Thus, simply determining the total number of individuals in a small population does not provide a good measure of whether the population is large enough to avoid extinction. Whenever possible, conservation programs attempt to sustain total population sizes that include at least the minimum viable number of *reproductively active* individuals. The conservation goal of sustaining effective population size (N_e) above MVP stems from the concern that populations retain enough genetic diversity to adapt as their environment changes.

The MVP of a population is often used in population viability analysis. The objective of this analysis is to predict a population's chances for survival, usually expressed as a specific probability of survival (for example, a 95% chance) over a particular time interval (for instance, 100 years). Such modeling approaches allow conservation biologists to explore the potential consequences of alternative management plans. Because modeling depends on reliable information about the populations under study, conservation biology is most robust when theoretical modeling is combined with field studies of the managed populations.

Case Study: *Analysis of Grizzly Bear Populations*

One of the first population viability analyses was conducted in 1978 by Mark Shaffer, of Duke University, as part of a long-term study of grizzly bears in Yellowstone National Park and its surrounding areas (**Figure 56.12**). A threatened species in the United States, the grizzly bear (*Ursus arctos horribilis*) is currently found in only 4 of the 48 contiguous states. Its populations in those states have been drastically reduced and fragmented: In 1800, an estimated 100,000 grizzlies ranged over about 500 million hectares of mostly continuous habitat, while today only about 1,000 individuals in six relatively isolated populations range over less than 5 million hectares.

Shaffer attempted to determine viable sizes for the Yellowstone grizzly populations. Using life history data obtained for individual Yellowstone bears over a 12-year period, he simulated the effects of environmental factors on survival and reproduction. His models predicted that, given a suitable habitat, a Yellowstone grizzly bear population of 70 to 90 individuals would have about a 95% chance of surviving for 100 years, whereas a population of 100 bears would have a 95% chance of surviving for twice as long, about 200 years.

How does the actual size of the Yellowstone grizzly population compare with Shaffer's estimates of MVP? A current estimate puts the total grizzly bear population in the greater Yellowstone ecosystem at about 400 individuals. The relationship of this estimate to the effective population size, N_e, depends on several factors. Usually, only a few dominant males breed, and it may be difficult for them to locate females, since individuals inhabit such extensive areas. Moreover, females may reproduce only when there is abundant food. As a result, N_e is only about 25% of the total population size, or about 100 bears.

Because small populations tend to lose genetic variation over time, a number of research teams have analyzed proteins,

mtDNA, and short tandem repeats (see Chapter 21) to assess genetic variability in the Yellowstone grizzly bear population. All results to date indicate that the Yellowstone population has less genetic variability than other grizzly bear populations in North America. However, the isolation and decline in genetic variability in the Yellowstone grizzly bear population were gradual during the 20th century and not as severe as feared: Museum specimens collected in the early 1900s demonstrate that genetic variability among the Yellowstone grizzly bears was low even then.

How might conservation biologists increase the effective size and genetic variation of the Yellowstone grizzly bear population? Migration between isolated populations of grizzlies could increase both effective and total population sizes. Computer models predict that introducing only two unrelated bears each decade into a population of 100 individuals would reduce the loss of genetic variation by about half. For the grizzly bear, and probably for many other species whose populations are very small, finding ways to promote dispersal among populations may be one of the most urgent conservation needs.

This case study and that of the greater prairie chicken bridge small-population models to practical applications in conservation. Next, we look at an alternative approach to understanding the biology of extinction.

Declining-Population Approach

The declining-population approach focuses on threatened and endangered populations that show a downward trend, even if the population is far above MVP. The distinction between a declining population (which is not always small) and a small population (which is not always declining) is less important than the different priorities of the two basic conservation approaches. The small-population approach emphasizes smallness itself as an ultimate cause of a population's extinction, especially through loss of genetic diversity. In contrast, the declining-population approach emphasizes the environmental factors that caused a population decline in the first place. If, for example, an area is deforested, then species that depend on trees will decline in number and become locally extinct, whether or not they retain genetic variation.

Steps for Analysis and Intervention

The declining-population approach requires that population declines be evaluated on a case-by-case basis, with researchers carefully dissecting the causes of a decline before taking steps to correct it. If, for example, the biological magnification of a toxic pollutant is harming some top-level consumer such as a predatory bird (see Chapter 55), then managers need to reduce or eliminate the pollutant in the environment to restore vulnerable populations of the bird. Although most situations are

▲ **Figure 56.12 Long-term monitoring of a grizzly bear population.** The ecologist is fitting this tranquilized bear with a radio collar so that the bear's movements can be compared with those of other individuals in the Yellowstone National Park population.

more complex, we can use the following steps for analyzing declining populations:

1. Confirm, using population data, that the species is presently in decline or that it was formerly more widely distributed or more abundant.
2. Study the natural history of this and related species, including reviewing the research literature, to determine the species' environmental requirements.
3. Develop hypotheses for all possible causes of the decline, including human activities and natural events, and list the predictions of each hypothesis.
4. Because many factors may be correlated with the decline, test the most likely hypothesis first. For example, remove the suspected agent of decline to see if the experimental population rebounds compared to a control population.
5. Apply the results of the diagnosis to manage the threatened species and monitor recovery.

The following case study is an example of how the declining-population approach has been applied in recent years to one endangered species.

Case Study: *Decline of the Red-Cockaded Woodpecker*

The red-cockaded woodpecker (*Picoides borealis*) is an endangered species endemic to the southeastern United States. This species requires mature pine forests, preferably ones dominated by the longleaf pine, for its habitat. Most woodpeckers nest in dead trees, but the red-cockaded woodpecker drills its nest holes in mature, living pine trees. Red-cockaded woodpeckers also drill small holes around the entrance to their nest cavity, which causes resin from the tree to ooze down the trunk. The resin seems to repel certain predators, such as corn snakes, that eat bird eggs and nestlings.

Another critical habitat factor for this woodpecker species is that the understory of plants around the pine trunks must be low **(Figure 56.13a)**. Breeding birds tend to abandon nests when vegetation among the pines is thick and higher than about 4.5 m **(Figure 56.13b)**. Apparently, the birds require a clear flight path between their home trees and the neighboring feeding grounds. Periodic fires have historically swept through longleaf pine forests, keeping the undergrowth low.

One factor leading to decline of the red-cockaded woodpecker is the destruction or fragmentation of suitable habitats by logging and agriculture. By recognizing key habitat factors, protecting some longleaf pine forests, and using controlled fires to reduce forest undergrowth, conservation managers have helped restore habitat that can support viable populations. However, designing a recovery program was complicated by the birds' social organization. Red-cockaded woodpeckers live in groups of one breeding pair and up to four "helpers," mostly males (an example of altruism; see Chapter 51). Helpers are offspring that do not disperse and breed but remain behind to help incubate eggs and feed nestlings. They may eventually attain breeding status within the flock when older birds die, but the wait may take years, and even then, helpers must compete to breed. Young birds that do disperse as members of new groups also have a tough path to reproductive success. New groups usually occupy abandoned territories or start at a new site and excavate nesting cavities, which

Red-cockaded woodpecker

(a) Forests that can sustain red-cockaded woodpeckers have low undergrowth.

(b) Forests that cannot sustain red-cockaded woodpeckers have high, dense undergrowth that impacts the woodpeckers' access to feeding grounds.

▲ **Figure 56.13 Habitat requirements of the red-cockaded woodpecker.**
? *How is habitat disturbance absolutely necessary for the long-term survival of the woodpecker?*

can take several years. Individuals generally have a better chance of reproducing by remaining behind than by dispersing and expending the effort to excavate homes in new territories.

To test the hypothesis that this social behavior contributes to the decline of the red-cockaded woodpecker, Carole Copeyon, Jeffrey Walters, and Jay Carter, of North Carolina State University, constructed cavities in pine trees at 20 sites. The results were dramatic: Cavities in 18 of the 20 sites were colonized by red-cockaded woodpeckers, and new breeding groups formed only in these sites. The experiment supported the hypothesis that this woodpecker species had been leaving much suitable habitat unoccupied because of a lack of breeding cavities. Based on this experiment, conservationists initiated a habitat maintenance program that included controlled burning and excavation of new breeding cavities, enabling this endangered species to begin to recover.

Weighing Conflicting Demands

Determining population numbers and habitat needs is only part of the effort to save species. Scientists also need to weigh a species' biological and ecological needs against other conflicting demands. Conservation biology often highlights the relationship between science, technology, and society. For example, an ongoing, sometimes bitter debate in the U.S. Pacific Northwest pits habitat preservation for northern spotted owl, timber wolf, grizzly bear, and bull trout populations against job opportunities in the timber, mining, and other resource extraction industries. Programs to restock wolves in Yellowstone National Park were opposed by some recreationists concerned for human safety and by many ranchers concerned with potential loss of livestock.

Large, high-profile vertebrates are not always the focal point in such conflicts, but habitat use is almost always the issue. Should work proceed on a new highway bridge if it destroys the only remaining habitat of a species of freshwater mussel? If you were the owner of a coffee plantation growing varieties that thrive in bright sunlight, would you be willing to change to shade-tolerant varieties that produce less coffee per area but can grow beneath trees that support large numbers of songbirds?

Another important consideration is the ecological role of a species. Because we will not be able to save every endangered species, we must determine which species are most important for conserving biodiversity as a whole. Identifying keystone species and finding ways to sustain their populations can be central to maintaining communities and ecosystems.

Management aimed at conserving a single species carries with it the possibility of negatively affecting populations of other species. For example, management of open pine forests for the red-cockaded woodpecker might impact migratory birds that use later-successional broadleaf forests. To test for such impacts, ecologists compared bird communities near clusters of nest cavities in managed pine forests with communities in forests not managed for the woodpeckers. Contrary to expectations, the managed sites supported higher numbers and a higher diversity of other birds than the control forests. In this case, managing for one bird species increased the diversity of an entire community of birds. In most situations, conservation must look beyond single species and consider the whole community and ecosystem as an important unit of biodiversity.

CONCEPT CHECK 56.2

1. Why does the reduced genetic diversity of small populations make them more vulnerable to extinction?
2. Consider a hypothetical population of 100 greater prairie chickens, a species in which females choose a mate from a group of displaying males. What is the effective population size if 35 females and 10 males of this species breed?
3. **WHAT IF?** In 2005, at least ten grizzly bears in the greater Yellowstone ecosystem were killed through contact with people. Three things caused most of these deaths: collisions with automobiles, hunters (not of grizzly bears) shooting when charged by a female with cubs nearby, and conservation managers killing bears that attacked livestock repeatedly. If you were a conservation manager, what steps might you take to minimize such encounters in Yellowstone?

For suggested answers, see Appendix A.

CONCEPT 56.3
Landscape and regional conservation aim to sustain entire biotas

Preservation efforts historically focused on saving individual species, but efforts today often aim to sustain the biodiversity of entire communities, ecosystems, and landscapes. Such a broad view requires understanding and applying the principles of community, ecosystem, and landscape ecology as well as the principles of human population dynamics and economics. The goals of landscape ecology (see Chapter 52), of which ecosystem management is a part, include understanding past, present, and future patterns of landscape use and making biodiversity conservation part of land-use planning.

Landscape Structure and Biodiversity

The biodiversity of a given landscape is in large part a function of the structure of the landscape. Understanding landscape structure is critically important in conservation because many species use more than one kind of ecosystem, and many live on the borders between ecosystems.

Fragmentation and Edges

The boundaries, or *edges*, between ecosystems—such as between a lake and the surrounding forest or between cropland and suburban housing tracts—are defining features of landscapes (Figure 56.14). An edge has its own set of physical conditions, which differ from those on either side of it. The soil surface of an edge between a forest patch and a burned area receives more sunlight and is usually hotter and drier than the forest interior, but it is cooler and wetter than the soil surface in the burned area.

(a) Natural edges. Grasslands give way to forest ecosystems in Yellowstone National Park.

(b) Edges created by human activity. Pronounced edges (roads) surround clear-cuts in this photograph of a heavily logged rain forest in Malaysia.

▲ **Figure 56.14 Edges between ecosystems.**

Some organisms thrive in edge communities because they gain resources from both adjacent areas. The ruffed grouse (*Bonasa umbellatus*) is a bird that needs forest habitat for nesting, winter food, and shelter, but it also needs forest openings with dense shrubs and herbs for summer food. White-tailed deer also thrive in edge habitats, where they can browse on woody shrubs; deer populations often expand when forests are logged and more edges are exposed.

The proliferation of edge species can have positive or negative effects on biodiversity. A 1997 study in Cameroon comparing edge and interior populations of the little greenbul (a tropical rain forest bird) suggested that forest edges may be important sites of speciation. On the other hand, communities in which edges arise from human alterations often have reduced biodiversity because the relatively large percentage of edge habitat leads to a preponderance of edge-adapted species. For example, the brown-headed cowbird (*Molothrus ater*) is an edge-adapted species that lays its eggs in the nests of other birds, particularly migratory songbirds. Cowbirds need forests, where they can parasitize the nests of other birds, and also open fields, where they forage on insects. Thus, their populations are growing where forests are being cut and fragmented, creating more edge habitat and open land. Increasing cowbird parasitism and loss of habitat are correlated with declining populations of several of the cowbird's host species.

The influence of fragmentation on the structure of communities has been explored since 1979 in the long-term Biological Dynamics of Forest Fragments Project. Located in the heart of the Amazon River basin, the study area consists of isolated fragments of forest separated from surrounding continuous tropical rain forest by distances of 80–1,000 m (Figure 56.15). Researchers from all over the world have clearly documented

▲ **Figure 56.15 Amazon rain forest fragments created as part of the Biological Dynamics of Forest Fragments Project.**

the physical and biological effects of this fragmentation in organisms ranging from bryophytes to beetles to birds. They have consistently found that species adapted to forest interiors show the greatest declines in the smallest fragments, suggesting that landscapes dominated by small fragments will support fewer species, mainly due to loss of interior-adapted species.

Corridors That Connect Habitat Fragments

In fragmented habitats, the presence of a **movement corridor**, a narrow strip or series of small clumps of habitat connecting otherwise isolated patches, can be extremely important for conserving biodiversity. Streamside habitats often serve as corridors, and in some nations, government policy prohibits altering these riparian areas. In areas of heavy human use, artificial corridors are sometimes constructed. Bridges or tunnels, for instance, can reduce the number of animals killed trying to cross highways **(Figure 56.16)**.

Movement corridors also can promote dispersal and reduce inbreeding in declining populations. Corridors have been shown to increase the exchange of individuals in many organisms, including butterflies, voles, and aquatic plants. Corridors are especially important to species that migrate between different habitats seasonally. However, a corridor can also be harmful—as, for example, in the spread of disease. In a 2003 study, Agustin Estrada-Peña, of the University of Zaragoza, Spain, showed that habitat corridors facilitate the movement of disease-carrying ticks among forest patches in northern Spain. All the effects of corridors are not yet understood, and their impact is an area of active research in conservation biology and restoration ecology.

Establishing Protected Areas

Conservation biologists are applying their understanding of community, ecosystem, and landscape dynamics in establishing protected areas to slow biodiversity loss. Currently, governments have set aside about 7% of the world's land in various forms of reserves. Choosing where to place and how to design nature reserves poses many challenges. Should the reserve be managed to minimize the risks of fire and predation to a threatened species? Or should the reserve be left as natural as possible, with such processes as fires ignited by lightning allowed to play out on their own? This is just one of the debates that arise among people who share an interest in the health of national parks and other protected areas. In deciding which areas are of highest conservation priority, biologists often focus on hot spots of biological diversity.

Finding Biodiversity Hot Spots

A **biodiversity hot spot** is a relatively small area with an exceptional concentration of endemic species and a large number of endangered and threatened species **(Figure 56.17)**. Nearly 30% of all bird species are confined to only about 2% of Earth's land area. Approximately 50,000 plant species, or about one-sixth of all known plant species, inhabit just 18 hot

▲ **Figure 56.16 An artificial corridor.** This bridge in Banff National Park, Canada, helps animals cross a human-created barrier.

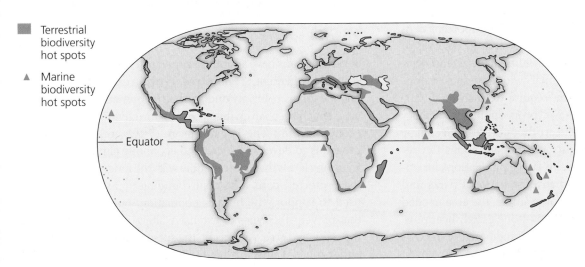

■ Terrestrial biodiversity hot spots

▲ Marine biodiversity hot spots

Equator

◀ **Figure 56.17 Earth's terrestrial and marine biodiversity hot spots.**

spots covering 0.5% of the global land surface. Together, the "hottest" of the terrestrial biodiversity hot spots total less than 1.5% of Earth's land but are home to more than a third of all species of plants, amphibians, reptiles (including birds), and mammals. Hot spots also include aquatic ecosystems, such as coral reefs and certain river systems.

Biodiversity hot spots are obviously good choices for nature reserves, but identifying them is not always simple. One problem is that a hot spot for one taxonomic group, such as butterflies, may not be a hot spot for some other taxonomic group, such as birds. Designating an area as a biodiversity hot spot is often biased toward saving vertebrates and plants, with less attention paid to invertebrates and microorganisms. Some biologists are also concerned that the hot-spot strategy places too much emphasis on such a small fraction of Earth's surface.

Philosophy of Nature Reserves

Nature reserves are biodiversity islands in a sea of habitat degraded to varying degrees by human activity. Protected "islands" are not isolated from their surroundings, however, and the nonequilibrium model we described in Chapter 54 applies to nature reserves as well as to the larger landscapes in which they are embedded.

An earlier policy—that protected areas should be set aside to remain unchanged forever—was based on the concept that ecosystems are balanced, self-regulating units. As we saw in Chapter 54, however, disturbance is a functional component of all ecosystems, and management policies that ignore natural disturbances or attempt to prevent them have generally failed. For instance, setting aside an area of a fire-dependent community, such as a portion of a tallgrass prairie, chaparral, or dry pine forest, with the intention of saving it is unrealistic if periodic burning is excluded. Without the dominant disturbance, the fire-adapted species are usually outcompeted and biodiversity is reduced.

Because human disturbance and fragmentation are increasingly common landscape features, the dynamics of disturbances, populations, edges, and corridors are all important for designing and managing protected areas. An important conservation question is whether to create fewer large reserves or more numerous small reserves. One argument for extensive reserves is that large, far-ranging animals with low-density populations, such as the grizzly bear, require extensive habitats. More extensive areas also have proportionately smaller perimeters than smaller areas and are therefore less affected by edges. As conservation biologists learn more about the requirements for achieving minimum viable populations for endangered species, they realize that most national parks and other reserves are far too small. For example, the area needed for the long-term survival of the Yellowstone grizzly bear population is more than ten times the combined area of Yellowstone and Grand Teton National Parks **(Figure 56.18)**. Given

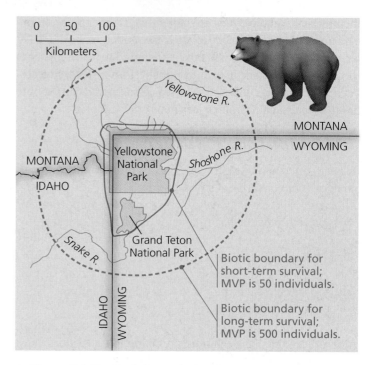

▲ **Figure 56.18 Biotic boundaries for grizzly bears in Yellowstone and Grand Teton National Parks.** The biotic boundaries (solid and dashed red lines) surround the areas needed to support minimum viable populations of 50 and 500 bears. Even the smaller of these areas is larger than the two parks.

political and economic realities, many existing parks will not be enlarged, and most newly created reserves will also be too small. Areas of private and public land surrounding reserves will likely have to contribute to biodiversity conservation. On the other side of the argument, smaller, unconnected reserves may slow the spread of disease throughout a population.

In practical terms, land use by humans may outweigh all other considerations and ultimately dictate the size and shape of protected areas. Much of the land left for conservation efforts is useless for exploitation by agriculture or forestry. But in some cases, as when reserve land is surrounded by commercially viable property, the use of land for agriculture or forestry must be integrated into conservation strategies.

Zoned Reserves

Several nations have adopted a zoned reserve approach to landscape management. A **zoned reserve** is an extensive region that includes areas relatively undisturbed by humans surrounded by areas that have been changed by human activity and are used for economic gain. The key challenge of the zoned reserve approach is to develop a social and economic climate in the surrounding lands that is compatible with the long-term viability of the protected core. These surrounding areas continue to be used to support the human population, but with regulations that prevent the types of extensive alterations likely to impact the protected area. As a result, the surrounding habitats serve as buffer zones against further intrusion into the undisturbed area.

The small Central American nation of Costa Rica has become a world leader in establishing zoned reserves (Figure 56.19). An agreement initiated in 1987 reduced Costa Rica's international debt in return for land preservation there. The agreement resulted in eight zoned reserves, called "conservation areas," that contain designated national park land. Costa Rica is making progress toward managing its zoned reserves, and the buffer zones provide a steady, lasting supply of forest products, water, and hydroelectric power and also support sustainable agriculture and tourism. An important goal is providing a stable economic base for people living there. As University of Pennsylvania ecologist Daniel Janzen, a leader in tropical conservation, has said, "The likelihood of long-term survival of a conserved wildland area is directly proportional to the economic health and stability of the society in which that wildland is embedded."

(a) Boundaries of the zoned reserves are indicated by black outlines.

(b) Local schoolchildren marvel at the diversity of life in one of Costa Rica's reserves.

▲ **Figure 56.19 Zoned reserves in Costa Rica.**

Destructive practices that are not compatible with long-term ecosystem conservation and from which there is often little local profit, such as massive logging, large-scale single-crop agriculture, and extensive mining, are ideally confined to the outermost fringes of the buffer zones and are gradually being discouraged.

Costa Rica relies on its zoned reserve system to maintain at least 80% of its native species, but the system is not without problems. A 2003 analysis of land cover change between 1960 and 1997 showed negligible deforestation within Costa Rica's national parks and a gain in forest cover in the 1-km buffer around the parks. However, significant losses in forest cover were discovered in the 10-km buffer zones around all national parks, which threaten to turn the parks into isolated habitat islands.

Although marine ecosystems have also been heavily impacted by human exploitation, reserves in the ocean are far less common than reserves on land. Many fish populations around the world have collapsed as increasingly sophisticated equipment puts nearly all potential fishing grounds within human reach. In response, Fiona Gell and Callum Roberts, of the University of York, England, have proposed establishing marine reserves around the world that would be off limits to fishing. Gell and Roberts present strong evidence that a patchwork of marine reserves can serve as a means of both increasing fish populations within the reserves and improving fishing success in nearby areas. Their proposed system is a modern application of a centuries-old practice in the Fiji Islands in which some areas have historically remained closed to fishing—a traditional example of the zoned reserve concept.

The United States adopted such a system in establishing the Florida Keys National Marine Sanctuary in 1990 (Figure 56.20). Populations of marine organisms, including fishes and lobsters, recovered quickly after harvests were banned in the 9,500-km^2 reserve. Larger and more abundant fish now produce larvae that

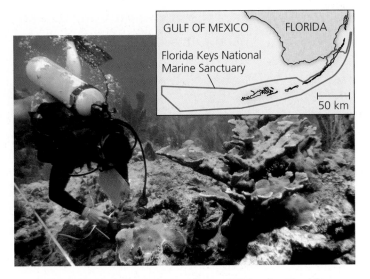

▲ **Figure 56.20 A diver measuring coral in the Florida Keys National Marine Sanctuary.**

help repopulate reefs and improve fishing outside the sanctuary. The increased marine life within the sanctuary also makes it a favorite for recreational divers, increasing the economic value of this zoned reserve.

CONCEPT CHECK 56.3

1. What is a biodiversity hot spot?
2. How do zoned reserves provide economic incentives for long-term conservation of protected areas?
3. **WHAT IF?** Suppose a developer proposes to clear-cut a forest that serves as a corridor between two parks. To compensate, the developer also proposes to add the same area of forest to one of the parks. As a professional ecologist, how might you argue for retaining the corridor?

For suggested answers, see Appendix A.

CONCEPT 56.4

Restoration ecology attempts to restore degraded ecosystems to a more natural state

Given enough time, biological communities can recover naturally from most disturbances through the stages of ecological succession that we discussed in Chapter 54. Sometimes that recovery takes centuries, though, particularly when humans degrade the environment. Degraded habitats are increasing in area because the natural rate of recovery by successional processes is often slower than the rate of degradation by human activities. The soils of many tropical areas quickly become unproductive and are soon abandoned after being cleared for farming. Mining activities may last for several decades, but the lands are then abandoned in a degraded state. Many ecosystems are also damaged inadvertently by the dumping of toxic chemicals or such mishaps as oil spills.

Restoration ecology seeks to initiate or speed up the recovery of degraded ecosystems. One of its basic assumptions is that environmental damage is at least partly reversible. This optimistic view must be balanced by a second assumption—that ecosystems are not infinitely resilient. Restoration ecologists therefore work to identify and manipulate the processes that most limit the speed of recovery of ecosystems from disturbances. Where disturbance is so severe that restoring all of a habitat is impractical, ecologists try to reclaim as much of a habitat or ecological process as possible, within the limits of the time and money available to them.

In extreme cases, the structure of a site may first need to be restored before biological restoration can occur. If a stream was straightened to channel water quickly through a suburb, restoration ecologists may reconstruct a meandering channel to slow down the flow of water eroding the stream bank. To restore an open-pit mine, engineers may first grade the site with heavy equipment to reestablish a gentle slope, spreading topsoil when the slope is in place (Figure 56.21). Once such physical reconstruction is complete—or when it is not needed—biological restoration is the next step.

Two key strategies in restoration ecology are bioremediation and biological augmentation.

Bioremediation

The use of organisms, usually prokaryotes, fungi, or plants, to detoxify polluted ecosystems is known as **bioremediation** (see Chapter 27). Some plants adapted to soils containing heavy metals can accumulate high concentrations of potentially toxic metals such as zinc, nickel, lead, and cadmium in

(a) In 1991, before restoration

(b) In 2000, near the completion of restoration

▲ **Figure 56.21 A gravel and clay mine site in New Jersey before and after restoration.**

(a) Wastes containing uranium were dumped in these four unlined pits for more than 30 years, contaminating soils and groundwater.

(b) After ethanol was added, microbial activity decreased the concentration of soluble uranium in groundwater near the pits.

▲ **Figure 56.22 Bioremediation of groundwater contaminated with uranium at Oak Ridge National Laboratory, Tennessee.**

their tissues. Restoration ecologists can use such plants to revegetate sites polluted by mining and other human activities and then harvest the plants to remove the metals from the ecosystem. Researchers in the United Kingdom discovered a lichen species that grows on soil polluted with uranium dust left over from mining. The lichen concentrates uranium in a dark pigment, making it useful as a biological monitor and potentially as a remediator.

Ecologists are examining the abilities of many prokaryotes to carry out bioremediation of soils and water. Scientists have sequenced the genomes of at least seven prokaryotic species specifically for their bioremediation potential. One of the species, the bacterium *Shewanella oneidensis*, appears particularly promising. It can metabolize more than ten elements under aerobic and anaerobic conditions to generate its energy. For instance, it converts soluble uranium, chromium, and nitrogen to insoluble forms that are less likely to leach into streams or groundwater. Wei-Min Wu and colleagues, at Oak Ridge National Laboratory, in Tennessee, stimulated the growth of *Shewanella* and other uranium-reducing bacteria by adding ethanol to groundwater contaminated with uranium; over five months, the concentration of soluble uranium dropped by 80% **(Figure 56.22)**. In the future, genetic engineering may become increasingly useful as a tool for improving the performance of prokaryotes and other organisms as bioremediators.

Biological Augmentation

In contrast to bioremediation, which is a strategy for removing harmful substances, **biological augmentation** uses organisms to add essential materials to a degraded ecosystem. Augmenting ecosystem processes requires determining what factors, such as chemical nutrients, have been removed from an area and thus limit its rate of recovery. Encouraging the growth of plants that thrive in nutrient-poor soils often speeds up the rate of successional changes that can lead to recovery of damaged sites. In alpine ecosystems of the western United States, nitrogen-fixing herbs such as lupines are often planted to bolster nitrogen concentrations in soils disturbed by mining and other uses. Once these nitrogen-fixing plants become established, other native species are better able to obtain enough nitrogen from the soil to survive. In other systems where the soil has been severely disturbed or where topsoil is missing entirely, plant roots may lack the mycorrhizal symbionts that help them meet their nutritional needs (see Chapter 31). Ecologists restoring a tallgrass prairie in Minnesota recognized this limitation and significantly accelerated the recovery of native species by adding mycorrhizal symbionts to the soil they seeded.

Exploring Restoration

Because restoration ecology is a relatively new discipline and because ecosystems are complex, restoration ecologists generally learn as they go. Many restoration ecologists advocate adaptive management: experimenting with several promising types of management to learn what works best.

The long-term objective of restoration is to speed the reestablishment of an ecosystem as similar as possible to the predisturbance ecosystem. **Figure 56.23**, on the next two pages, identifies several ambitious and successful restoration projects around the world. The great number of such projects, the dedication of the people engaged in them, and the successes that have been achieved suggest that restoration ecology will continue to grow as a discipline for many years.

Exploring Restoration Ecology Worldwide

The examples highlighted on these pages are just a few of the many restoration ecology projects taking place around the world. The color-coded dots on the map indicate the locations of the projects.

Truckee River, Nevada. Damming and water diversions during the 20th century reduced flow in the Truckee River, Nevada, leading to declines in riparian forests. Restoration ecologists worked with water managers to ensure that sufficient water would be released during the short season of seed release by the native cottonwood and willow trees for seedlings to become established. Nine years of controlled-flow release led to the result shown here: a dramatic recovery of cottonwood-willow riparian forest.

Kissimmee River, Florida. The Kissimmee River was converted from a meandering river to a 90-km canal, threatening many fish and wetland bird populations. Kissimmee River restoration has filled 12 km of drainage canal and reestablished 24 km of the original 167 km of natural river channel. Pictured here is a section of the Kissimmee canal that has been plugged (wide, light strip on the right side of the photo), diverting flow into remnant river channels in the center of the photo. The project will also restore the natural flow regime, which will foster self-sustaining populations of wetland birds and fishes.

Tropical dry forest, Costa Rica. Clearing for agriculture, mainly for livestock grazing, eliminated approximately 98% of tropical dry forest in Central America and Mexico. Reversing this trend, tropical dry forest restoration in Costa Rica has used domestic livestock to disperse the seeds of native trees into open grasslands. The photo shows one of the first trees (right center), dispersed as seed by livestock, to colonize former pastureland. This project is a model for joining restoration ecology with the local economy and educational institutions.

Rhine River, Europe. Centuries of dredging and channeling for navigation (see the barges in the wide, main channel on the right side of the photo) have straightened the once-meandering Rhine River and disconnected it from its floodplain and associated wetlands. The countries along the Rhine, particularly France, Germany, Luxembourg, the Netherlands, and Switzerland, are cooperating to reconnect the river to side channels, such as the one shown on the left side of the photo. Such side channels increase the diversity of habitats available to aquatic biota, improve water quality, and provide flood protection.

Coastal Japan. Seaweed and seagrass beds are important nursery grounds for a wide variety of fishes and shellfish. Once extensive but now reduced by development, these beds are being restored in the coastal areas of Japan. Techniques include constructing suitable seafloor habitat, transplanting from natural beds using artificial substrates, and hand seeding (shown in this photograph).

Succulent Karoo, South Africa. In this desert region of southern Africa, as in many arid regions, overgrazing by livestock has damaged vast areas. Reversing this trend, private landowners and government agencies in South Africa are restoring large areas of this unique region, revegetating the land and employing more sustainable resource management. The photo shows a small sample of the exceptional plant diversity of the Succulent Karoo; its 5,000 plant species include the highest diversity of succulent plants in the world.

Maungatautari, New Zealand. Weasels, rats, pigs, and other introduced species pose a serious threat to New Zealand's native plants and animals, including the kiwi, a flightless, ground-dwelling bird. The goal of the Maungatautari restoration project is to exclude all exotic mammals from a 3,400-ha reserve located on a forested volcanic cone. A specialized fence around the reserve eliminates the need to continue setting traps and using poisons that can harm native wildlife. In 2006, a pair of critically endangered takahe (a species of flightless rail) were released into the reserve in hopes of reestablishing a breeding population of this colorful bird on New Zealand's north island.

1. Identify the main goal of restoration ecology.

2. How do bioremediation and biological augmentation differ?

3. **WHAT IF?** In what way is the Kissimmee River project a more complete ecological restoration than the Maungatautari project (see Figure 56.23)?

For suggested answers, see Appendix A.

CONCEPT 56.5

Sustainable development seeks to improve the human condition while conserving biodiversity

With the increasing loss and fragmentation of habitats, we face difficult trade-offs in how to manage Earth's resources. Preserving all habitat patches isn't feasible, so biologists must help societies set conservation priorities by identifying which habitat patches are most crucial. Ideally, implementing these priorities should also improve the quality of life for local people. Ecologists use the concept of *sustainability* as a tool to establish long-term conservation priorities.

Sustainable Biosphere Initiative

We must understand the complex interconnections of the biosphere to protect species from extinction and to improve the quality of human life. To this end, many nations, scientific societies, and other groups have embraced the concept of **sustainable development**, development that meets the needs of people today without limiting the ability of future generations to meet their needs. The forward-looking Ecological Society of America, the world's largest organization of professional ecologists, endorses a research agenda called the Sustainable Biosphere Initiative. The goal of this initiative is to define and acquire the basic ecological information needed to develop, manage, and conserve Earth's resources as responsibly as possible. The research agenda includes studies of global change, including interactions between climate and ecological processes; biological diversity and its role in maintaining ecological processes; and the ways in which the productivity of natural and artificial ecosystems can be sustained. This initiative requires a strong commitment of human and economic resources.

Achieving sustainable development is an ambitious goal. To sustain ecosystem processes and stem the loss of biodiversity, we must connect life science with the social sciences, economics, and humanities. We must also reassess our personal values. Those of us living in wealthier nations have a larger ecological footprint than do people living in developing na-

tions (see Chapter 53). By reducing our orientation toward short-term gain, we can learn to value the natural processes that sustain us. The following case study illustrates how the combination of scientific and personal efforts can make a significant difference in creating a truly sustainable world.

Case Study: Sustainable Development in Costa Rica

The success of conservation in Costa Rica that we discussed in Concept 56.3 has involved an essential partnership between the national government, nongovernment organizations (NGOs), and private citizens. Many nature reserves established by individuals have been recognized by the government as national wildlife reserves and given significant tax benefits. However, conservation and restoration of biodiversity make up only one facet of sustainable development; the other key facet is improving the human condition.

How have the living conditions of the Costa Rican people changed as the country has pursued its conservation goals? As we discussed in Chapter 53, two of the most fundamental indicators of living conditions are infant mortality rate and life expectancy. From 1930 to 2007, the infant mortality rate in Costa Rica declined from 170 to 9 per 1,000 live births; over the same period, life expectancy increased from about 43 years to 77 years (Figure 56.24). Another indicator of living conditions is literacy rate. The 2004 literacy rate in Costa Rica was 96%, compared to 97% in the United States. Such statistics show that living conditions in Costa Rica have improved greatly over the period in which the country has dedicated itself to conservation and restoration. While this result does not prove that conservation *causes* an increase in human welfare, we can say with certainty that development in Costa Rica has attended to both nature *and* people.

▲ **Figure 56.24 Infant mortality and life expectancy at birth in Costa Rica.**

Despite the successes in Costa Rica, many problems remain. One of the challenges that the country faces is maintaining its commitment to conservation while its population grows. Costa Rica is in the middle of a rapid demographic transition (see Chapter 53), and even though birth rates are dropping rapidly, its population is growing at about 1.5% annually (compared to 0.9% growth in the United States). Costa Rica's population, which is currently about 4 million, is predicted to continue to grow until the middle of this century, when it is projected to level off at approximately 6 million. If recent success is any guide, the people of Costa Rica will overcome the challenge of population growth in their quest for sustainable development.

The Future of the Biosphere

Our modern lives are very different from those of early humans, who hunted and gathered to survive. Their reverence for the natural world is evident in the early murals of wildlife they painted on cave walls **(Figure 56.25a)** and in the stylized visions of life they sculpted from bone and ivory **(Figure 56.25b)**.

Our lives reflect remnants of our ancestral attachment to nature and the diversity of life—the concept of *biophilia* that we introduced early in this chapter. We evolved in natural environments rich in biodiversity, and we still have an affinity for such settings **(Figure 56.25c)**. E. O. Wilson makes the case that our biophilia is innate, an evolutionary product of natural selection acting on a brainy species whose survival depended on a close connection to the environment and a practical appreciation of plants and animals.

Our appreciation of life guides the field of biology today. We celebrate life by deciphering the genetic code that makes each species unique. We embrace life by using fossils and DNA to chronicle the march of evolution through time. We preserve life through our efforts to classify and protect the millions of species on Earth. We respect life by using nature responsibly and reverently to improve human welfare.

Biology is the scientific expression of our desire to know nature. We are most likely to protect what we appreciate, and we are most likely to appreciate what we understand. By learning about the processes and diversity of life, we also become more aware of ourselves and our place in the biosphere. We hope this book serves you well in this lifelong adventure.

(a) Detail of animals in a 36,000-year-old cave painting, Lascaux, France

---

CONCEPT CHECK **56.5**

1. What is meant by the term *sustainable development*?
2. How might biophilia influence us to conserve species and restore ecosystems?
3. **WHAT IF?** Suppose a new fishery is discovered, and you are put in charge of developing it sustainably. What ecological data might you want on the fish population? What criteria would you apply for the fishery's development?

For suggested answers, see Appendix A.

(b) A 30,000-year-old ivory carving of a water bird, found in Germany

(c) Biologist Carlos Rivera Gonzales examining a tiny tree frog in Peru

▲ **Figure 56.25 Biophilia, past and present.**

SUMMARY OF KEY CONCEPTS

CONCEPT 56.1

Human activities threaten Earth's biodiversity (pp. 1246–1250)

▶ **Three Levels of Biodiversity**

Genetic diversity: source of variations that enable populations to adapt to environmental changes

Species diversity: important in maintaining structure of communities and food webs

Ecosystem diversity: provides life-sustaining services such as nutrient cycling and waste decomposition

▶ **Biodiversity and Human Welfare** Our biophilia enables us to recognize the value of biodiversity for its own sake. Other species also provide humans with food, fiber, medicines, and ecosystem services.

▶ **Three Threats to Biodiversity** Three major threats to biodiversity are habitat loss, introduced species, and overexploitation.

CONCEPT 56.2

Population conservation focuses on population size, genetic diversity, and critical habitat (pp. 1250–1255)

▶ **Small-Population Approach** When a population drops below a minimum viable population (MVP) size, its loss of genetic variation due to nonrandom mating and genetic drift can trap it in an extinction vortex.

▶ **Declining-Population Approach** The declining-population approach focuses on the environmental factors that cause decline, regardless of absolute population size. It follows a step-by-step proactive conservation strategy.

▶ **Weighing Conflicting Demands** Conserving species often requires resolving conflicts between the habitat needs of endangered species and human demands.

CONCEPT 56.3

Landscape and regional conservation aim to sustain entire biotas (pp. 1255–1260)

▶ **Landscape Structure and Biodiversity** The structure of a landscape can strongly influence biodiversity. As habitat fragmentation increases and edges become more extensive, biodiversity tends to decrease. Movement corridors can promote dispersal and help sustain populations.

▶ **Establishing Protected Areas** Biodiversity hot spots are also hot spots of extinction and thus prime candidates for protection. Sustaining biodiversity in parks and reserves requires management to ensure that human activities in the surrounding landscape do not harm the protected habitats. The zoned reserve model recognizes that conservation efforts often involve working in landscapes that are greatly affected by human activity.

CONCEPT 56.4

Restoration ecology attempts to restore degraded ecosystems to a more natural state (pp. 1260–1264)

▶ **Bioremediation** Restoration ecologists harness organisms to detoxify polluted ecosystems.

▶ **Biological Augmentation** Ecologists also use organisms to add essential materials to ecosystems.

▶ **Exploring Restoration** The newness and complexity of restoration ecology require scientists to consider alternative solutions and adjust approaches based on experience.

CONCEPT 56.5

Sustainable development seeks to improve the human condition while conserving biodiversity (pp. 1264–1265)

▶ **Sustainable Biosphere Initiative** The goal of the Sustainable Biosphere Initiative is to acquire the ecological information needed for the development, management, and conservation of Earth's resources.

▶ *Case Study:* **Sustainable Development in Costa Rica** Costa Rica's success in conserving tropical biodiversity has involved partnerships between the government, other organizations, and private citizens. Human living conditions in Costa Rica have improved along with ecological conservation.

▶ **The Future of the Biosphere** By learning about biological processes and the diversity of life, we become more aware of our close connection to the environment and the value of other organisms in it.

MEDIA
Activity Conservation Biology Review
GraphIt! Global Freshwater Resources
GraphIt! Prospects for Renewable Energy

TESTING YOUR KNOWLEDGE

SELF-QUIZ

1. Ecologists conclude there is a biodiversity crisis because
   a. biophilia causes humans to feel ethically responsible for protecting other species.
   b. scientists have at last discovered and counted most of Earth's species and can now accurately calculate the current extinction rate.
   c. current extinction rates are very high and many species are threatened or endangered.
   d. many potential life-saving medicines are being lost as species evolve.
   e. there are too few biodiversity hot spots.

2. Which of the following would be considered an example of bioremediation?
   a. adding nitrogen-fixing microorganisms to a degraded ecosystem to increase nitrogen availability
   b. using a bulldozer to regrade a strip mine
   c. identifying a new biodiversity hot spot
   d. reconfiguring the channel of a river
   e. adding seeds of a chromium-accumulating plant to soil contaminated by chromium

3. What is the effective population size (N_e) of a population of 50 strictly monogamous swans (40 males and 10 females) if every female breeds successfully?
   a. 50 b. 40 c. 30 d. 20 e. 10

4. One characteristic that distinguishes a population in an extinction vortex from most other populations is that
   a. its habitat is fragmented.
   b. it is a rare, top-level predator.
   c. its effective population size is much lower than its total population size.
   d. its genetic diversity is very low.
   e. it is not well adapted to edge conditions.

5. The discipline that applies ecological principles to returning degraded ecosystems to more natural states is known as
   a. population viability analysis.
   b. landscape ecology.
   c. conservation ecology.
   d. restoration ecology.
   e. resource conservation.

6. What is the single greatest threat to biodiversity?
   a. overexploitation of commercially important species
   b. introduced species that compete with or prey on native species
   c. pollution of Earth's air, water, and soil
   d. disruption of trophic relationships as more and more prey species become extinct
   e. habitat alteration, fragmentation, and destruction

7. Which of the following strategies would most rapidly increase the genetic diversity of a population in an extinction vortex?
   a. Capture all remaining individuals in the population for captive breeding followed by reintroduction to the wild.
   b. Establish a reserve that protects the population's habitat.
   c. Introduce new individuals transported from other populations of the same species.
   d. Sterilize the least fit individuals in the population.
   e. Control populations of the endangered population's predators and competitors.

8. Of the following statements about protected areas that have been established to preserve biodiversity, which one is *not* correct?
   a. About 25% of Earth's land area is now protected.
   b. National parks are one of many types of protected areas.
   c. Most protected areas are too small to protect species.
   d. Management of a protected area should be coordinated with management of the land surrounding the area.
   e. It is especially important to protect biodiversity hot spots.

For Self-Quiz answers, see Appendix A.

MEDIA Visit the Study Area at **www.masteringbio.com** for a Practice Test.

EVOLUTION CONNECTION

9. One factor favoring rapid population growth by an introduced species is the absence of the predators, parasites, and pathogens that controlled its population in the region where it evolved. Over the long term, how should evolution by natural selection influence the rate at which the native predators, parasites, and pathogens in a region of introduction attack an introduced species?

SCIENTIFIC INQUIRY

10. **DRAW IT** Suppose that you are in charge of planning a forest reserve, and one of your goals is to help sustain local populations of woodland birds suffering from parasitism by the brown-headed cowbird. Reading research reports, you note that female cowbirds are usually reluctant to penetrate more than about 100 m into a forest and that nest parasitism is reduced for woodland birds nesting in denser, more central forest regions. The forested area you have to work with extends about 6,000 m from east to west and 1,000 m from north to south. Intact forest surrounds the reserve everywhere but on the west side, where the reserve borders deforested pastureland, and in the southwest corner, where it borders an agricultural field for 500 m. Your plan must include space for a small maintenance building, which you estimate to take up about 100 m². It will also be necessary to build a road, 10 m by 1,000 m, from the north to the south side of the reserve. Draw a map of the reserve, showing where you would construct the road and the building to minimize cowbird intrusion along edges. Explain your reasoning.

Answers

CHAPTER 1

Figure Questions

Figure 1.3 Of the properties shown in this figure, the lawn mower shows only order, regulation, and energy processing. **Figure 1.6** The arrangement of fingers and opposable thumb in the human hand, combined with fingernails and a complex system of nerves and muscles, allows the hand to grasp and manipulate objects with great dexterity. **Figure 1.13** Substance B would be made continuously and would accumulate in large amounts. Neither C nor D would be made. **Figure 1.27** The percentage of brown artificial snakes attacked would probably be higher than the percentage of artificial kingsnakes attacked in all areas (whether or not inhabited by coral snakes). **Figure 1.28** The hole would allow some mixing of blood between the two ventricles. As a result, some of the blood pumped from the left ventricle to the body would not have received oxygen in the lungs, and some of the blood pumped to the lungs would already carry oxygen.

Concept Check 1.1

1. Examples: A molecule consists of *atoms* bonded together. Each organelle has an orderly arrangement of *molecules*. Photosynthetic plant cells contain *organelles* called chloroplasts. A tissue consists of a group of similar *cells*. Organs such as the heart are constructed from several *tissues*. A complex multicellular organism, such as a plant, has several types of *organs*, such as leaves and roots. A population is a set of *organisms* of the same species. A community consists of *populations* of the various species inhabiting a specific area. An ecosystem consists of a biological *community* along with the nonliving factors important to life, such as air, soil, and water. The biosphere is made up of all of Earth's *ecosystems*. **2.** (a) Structure and function are correlated. (b) Cells are an organism's basic units, *and* the continuity of life is based on heritable information in the form of DNA. (c) Organisms interact with their environments, exchanging matter and energy. **3.** Some possible answers: *Evolution:* All plants have chloroplasts, indicating their descent from a common ancestor. *Emergent properties:* The ability of a human heart to pump blood requires an intact heart; it is not a capability of any of the heart's tissues or cells working alone. *Exchange of matter and energy with the environment:* A mouse eats food, then uses the nutrients for growth and the generation of energy for its activities; some of the food material is expelled in urine and feces, and some of the energy returns to the environment as heat. *Structure and function:* The strong, sharp teeth of a wolf are well suited to grasping and dismembering its prey. *Cells:* The digestion of food is made possible by chemicals (chiefly enzymes) made by cells of the digestive tract. *DNA:* Human eye color is determined by the combination of genes inherited from the two parents. *Feedback regulation:* When your stomach is full, it signals your brain to decrease your appetite.

Concept Check 1.2

1. An address pinpoints a location by tracking from broader to narrower categories—a state, city, zip, street, and building number. This is analogous to the groups-subordinate-to-groups structure of biological taxonomy. **2.** Natural selection starts with the naturally occurring heritable variation in a population and then "edits" the population as individuals with heritable traits better suited to the environment survive and reproduce more successfully than others.
3.

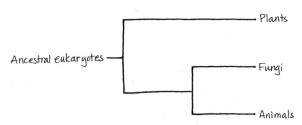

Concept Check 1.3

1. Inductive reasoning derives generalizations from specific cases; deductive reasoning predicts specific outcomes from general premises. **2.** Compared to a hypothesis, a scientific theory is usually more general and substantiated by a much greater amount of evidence. Natural selection is an explanatory idea that applies to all kinds of organisms and is supported by vast amounts of evidence of various kinds. **3.** Based on the results shown in Figure 1.27, you might predict that the colorful artificial snakes would be attacked more often than the brown ones, simply because they are easier to see. This prediction assumes that the area in Virginia where you are working has predators that attack snakes but no poisonous snakes that resemble the colorful artificial snakes.

Self-Quiz

1. b **2.** d **3.** a **4.** c **5.** c **6.** c **7.** c **8.** d **9.** b **10.** c
11. Your figure should show: (1) For the biosphere, the Earth with an arrow coming out of a tropical ocean; (2) for the ecosystem, a distant view of a coral reef; (3) for the community, a collection of reef animals and algae, with corals, fish, some seaweed, and any other organisms you can think of; (4) for the population, a group of fish of the same species; (5) for the organism, one fish from your population; (6) for the organ, the fish's stomach, and for the organ system, the whole digestive tract (see Chapter 41 for help); (7) for a tissue, a group of similar cells from the stomach; (8) for a cell, one cell from the tissue, showing its nucleus and a few other organelles; (9) for an organelle, the nucleus, where most of the cell's DNA is located; and (10) for a molecule, a DNA double helix. Your sketches can be very rough!

CHAPTER 2

Figure Questions

Figure 2.2 The most significant difference in the results would be that the two *Cedrela* saplings inside each garden would show similar amounts of dying leaf tissue because a poisonous chemical released from the *Duroia* trees would presumably reach the saplings via the air or soil and would not be blocked by the insect barrier. The *Cedrela* saplings planted outside the gardens would not show damage unless *Duroia* trees were nearby. Also, any ants present on the unprotected *Cedrela* saplings inside the gardens would probably not be observed making injections into the leaves. However, formic acid would likely still be found in the ants' glands, as for most species of ants.
Figure 2.9 Atomic number = 12; 12 protons, 12 electrons; three electron shells; 2 electrons in the valence shell
Figure 2.16

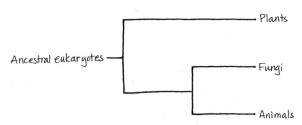

Figure 2.19 The plant is submerged in water (H_2O), in which the CO_2 is dissolved. The sun's energy is used to make sugar, which is found in the plant and can act as food for the plant itself, as well as for animals that eat the plant. The oxygen (O_2) is present in the bubbles.

Concept Check 2.1

1. Table salt is made up of sodium and chlorine. We are able to eat the compound, showing that it has different properties from those of a metal and a poisonous gas. **2.** Yes, because an organism requires trace elements, even though only in small amounts. **3.** A person with an iron deficiency will probably show effects of low oxygen in the blood, such as fatigue. (The condition is called anemia and can also result from too few red blood cells or abnormal hemoglobin.)

Concept Check 2.2
1. 7 **2.** $^{15}_{7}N$ **3.** 9 electrons; two electron shells; $1s$, $2s$, $2p$ (three orbitals); 1 electron is needed to fill the valence shell. **4.** The elements in a row all have the same number of electron shells. In a column, all the elements have the same number of electrons in their valence shells.

Concept Check 2.3
1. Each carbon atom has only three covalent bonds instead of the required four. **2.** The attractions between oppositely charged ions form ionic bonds. **3.** If researchers can synthesize molecules that mimic these shapes, they may be able to treat diseases or conditions caused by the inability of affected individuals to synthesize such molecules.

Concept Check 2.4
1.

2. At equilibrium, the forward and reverse reactions occur at the same rate. **3.** $C_6H_{12}O_6 + 6\,O_2 \rightarrow 6\,CO_2 + 6\,H_2O$ + Energy. Glucose and oxygen react to form carbon dioxide, water, and energy. We breathe in oxygen because we need it for this reaction to occur, and we breathe out carbon dioxide because it is a by-product of this reaction. By the way, this reaction is called cellular respiration, and you will learn more about it in Chapter 9.

Self-Quiz
1. a **2.** b **3.** b **4.** c **5.** b **6.** a **7.** b **8.** b

9.

a. This structure doesn't make sense because the valence shell of carbon is incomplete; carbon can form 4 bonds.

b. This structure makes sense because all valence shells are complete, and all bonds have the correct number of electrons.

c. This structure doesn't make sense because H has only 1 electron to share, so it cannot form bonds with 2 atoms.

d. This structure doesn't make sense for several reasons: The valence shell of oxygen is incomplete; oxygen can form 2 bonds. H has only 1 electron to share, so it cannot form a double bond. Nitrogen usually makes only 3 bonds. It does not have enough electrons to make 2 single bonds, make a double bond, and complete its valence shell.

CHAPTER 3

Figure Questions
Figure 3.6 Without hydrogen bonds, water would behave like other small molecules, and the solid phase (ice) would be denser than liquid water. The ice would sink to the bottom, and because it would no longer insulate the whole body of water, it could freeze. Freezing would take a longer time because the Antarctic is an ocean (the Southern Ocean), not a pond or lake, but the average annual temperature at the South Pole is $-50°C$, so eventually it would freeze. The krill could not survive. **Figure 3.7** Heating the solution would cause the water to evaporate faster than it is evaporating at room temperature. At a certain point, there wouldn't be enough water molecules to solubilize the salt ions. The salt would start coming out of solution and re-forming crystals. Eventually, all the water would evaporate, leaving behind a pile of salt like the original pile. **Figure 3.11** Given that Ca^{2+} and CO_3^{2-} must interact to form $CaCO_3$, you would predict that $[Ca^{2+}]$ would also have an effect on the calcification rate, and this result is observed in the current study. Under natural conditions in the oceans, the $[Ca^{2+}]$ remains relatively constant, so the $[CO_3^{2-}]$ has a much more important effect on calcification rate.

Concept Check 3.1
1. Electronegativity is the attraction of an atom for the electrons of a covalent bond. Because oxygen is more electronegative than hydrogen, the oxygen atom in H_2O pulls electrons toward itself, resulting in a partial negative charge on the oxygen atom and partial positive charges on the hydrogen atoms. Oppositely charged ends of water molecules are attracted to each other, forming a hydrogen bond. **2.** The hydrogen atoms of one molecule, with their partial positive charges, would repel the hydrogen atoms of the adjacent molecule. **3.** Water molecules would not be polar, and they would not form hydrogen bonds with each other.

Concept Check 3.2
1. Hydrogen bonds hold neighboring water molecules together. This cohesion helps the molecules resist gravity. Adhesion between water molecules and the walls of water-conducting cells also counters gravity. As water evaporates from leaves, the chain of water molecules in water-conducting cells moves upward. **2.** High humidity hampers cooling by suppressing the evaporation of sweat. **3.** As water freezes, it expands because water molecules move farther apart in forming ice crystals. When there is water in a crevice of a boulder, expansion due to freezing may crack the rock. **4.** The molecular mass of NaCl is 58.5 daltons. A mole would have a mass of 58.5 g, so you would measure out 0.5 mol, or 29.3 g, of NaCl and gradually add water, stirring until it is dissolved. You would add water to bring the final volume to 1 L. **5.** The hydrophobic substance repels water, perhaps helping to keep the ends of the legs from becoming coated with water and breaking through the surface. If the legs were coated with a hydrophilic substance, water would be drawn up them, possibly making it more difficult for the water strider to walk on water.

Concept Check 3.3
1. 10^5, or 100,000 **2.** $[H^+] = 0.01\ M = 10^{-2}\ M$, so pH = 2 **3.** $CH_3COOH \rightleftharpoons CH_3COO^- + H^+$. CH_3COOH is the acid (the H^+ donor) and CH_3COO^- is the base (the H^+ acceptor). **4.** The pH of the water should go from 7 to about 2; the pH of the acetic acid solution will only decrease a small amount, because the reaction shown for question 3 will shift to the left, with CH_3COO^- accepting the influx of H^+ and becoming CH_3COOH molecules.

Self-Quiz
1. d **2.** c **3.** b **4.** c **5.** c **6.** d **7.** c **8.** c
9.

CHAPTER 4

Figure Questions
Figure 4.2 Because the concentration of the reactants influences the equilibrium (as discussed in Chapter 2), there might be more HCN relative to CH_2O, since there would be a higher concentration of the reactant gas that contains nitrogen.

Figure 4.4

Figure 4.7

H–C–H (structure)

Figure 4.10 Molecule b, because there are not only the two electronegative oxygens of the carboxyl group, but also an oxygen on the next (carbonyl) carbon. All of these oxygens help make the bond between the O and H of the —OH group more polar, thus making the dissociation of H$^+$ more likely.

Concept Check 4.1

1. Amino acids are essential molecules for living organisms. Their synthesis from gases of the primitive atmosphere on Earth demonstrated that life's molecules could initially have been synthesized from nonliving molecules. **2.** The spark provides energy needed for the inorganic molecules in the atmosphere to react with each other. (You'll learn more about energy and chemical reactions in Chapter 8.)

Concept Check 4.2

1. (structure of C=C with H's)

2. The forms of C$_4$H$_{10}$ in (b) are structural isomers, as are the butenes in (c). **3.** Both consist largely of hydrocarbon chains. **4.** No. There is not enough diversity in the atoms. It can't form structural isomers because there is only one way for three carbons to attach to each other (in a line). There are no double bonds, so geometric isomers are not possible. Each carbon has at least two hydrogens attached to it, so the molecule is symmetrical and cannot have enantiomeric isomers.

Concept Check 4.3

1. It has both an amino group (—NH$_2$), which makes it an amine, and a carboxyl group (—COOH), which makes it a carboxylic acid. **2.** The ATP molecule loses a phosphate, becoming ADP.

3. (structure) A chemical group that can act as a base has been replaced with a group that can act as an acid, increasing the acidic properties of the molecule. The shape of the molecule would also change, likely changing the molecules with which it can interact.

Self-Quiz

1. b **2.** d **3.** a **4.** b **5.** b **6.** a **7.** d
8. (·Si· symbol) Si has four valence electrons, the same number as carbon. Therefore, silicon would be able to form long chains, including branches, that could act as skeletons for organic molecules. It would clearly do this much better than neon (with no valence electrons) or aluminum (with three valence electrons).

CHAPTER 5

Figure Questions
Figure 5.4

Linear form → Ring forming → Ring form (structures)

Four carbons are in the fructose ring, and two are not. (The latter two carbons are hanging off carbons 2 and 5, which are in the ring.) This form differs from glucose, which has five carbons in the ring and one that is not. (Note that the orientation of this fructose molecule is flipped relative to the one in Figure 5.5b.)

Figure 5.18

Figure 5.25 The green spiral is an α helix.

Concept Check 5.1

1. Proteins, carbohydrates, lipids, and nucleic acids **2.** Nine, with one water required to hydrolyze each connected pair of monomers **3.** The amino acids in the green bean protein are released in hydrolysis reactions and incorporated into other proteins in dehydration reactions.

Concept Check 5.2

1. C$_3$H$_6$O$_3$ **2.** C$_{12}$H$_{22}$O$_{11}$ **3.** The absence of these prokaryotes would hamper the cow's ability to obtain energy from food and could lead to weight loss and possibly death.

Concept Check 5.3

1. Both have a glycerol molecule attached to fatty acids. The glycerol of a fat has three fatty acids attached, whereas the glycerol of a phospholipid is attached to two fatty acids and one phosphate group. **2.** Human sex hormones are steroids, a type of hydrophobic compound. **3.** The oil droplet membrane could consist of a single layer of phospholipids rather than a bilayer, because an arrangement in which the hydrophobic tails of the membrane phospholipids were in contact with the hydrocarbon regions of the oil molecules would be more stable.

Concept Check 5.4

1. The function of a protein is a consequence of its specific shape, which is lost when a protein becomes denatured. **2.** Secondary structure involves hydrogen bonds between atoms of the polypeptide backbone. Tertiary structure involves bonding between atoms of the R groups of the amino acid subunits. **3.** Primary structure, the amino acid sequence, affects the secondary structure, which affects the tertiary structure, which affects the quaternary structure (if any). In short, the amino acid sequence affects the shape of the protein. Because the function of a protein depends on its shape, a change in primary structure can destroy a protein's function.

Concept Check 5.5
1. (structure showing 5' end to 3' end)

2. 5'–TAGGCCT–3'
3'–ATCCGGA–5'

3. (a)

Mismatch

5'–T A (A) G C C T–3'
3'–A T (C) C G G A–5'

(b)

3'–A T T C G G A–5'

Self-Quiz
1. d **2.** c **3.** a **4.** b **5.** a **6.** d **7.** b
8.

	Monomers or Components	Polymer or larger molecule	Type of linkage
Sugars	Monosaccharides	Polysaccharides	Glycosidic linkages
Lipids	Fatty acids	Triacylglycerols	Ester linkages
Proteins	Amino acids	Polypeptides	Peptide bonds
Nucleic acids	Nucleotides	Polynucleotides	Phosphodiester linkages

9.

Original Strand   Complementary strand

CHAPTER 6

Figure Questions
Figure 6.7 A phospholipid is a lipid, consisting of a glycerol molecule joined to two fatty acids and one phosphate group. Together, the glycerol and phosphate end of the phospholipid form is the "head," which is hydrophilic, while the hydrocarbon chains on the fatty acids form hydrophobic "tails." The presence in a single molecule of both a hydrophilic and a hydrophobic region makes the molecule ideal as the main building block of a membrane.
Figure 6.22 Each centriole has 9 sets of 3 microtubules, so the entire centrosome has 54. Each microtubule consists of a helical array of tubulin dimers (as shown in Table 6.1).

1 microtubule

Figure 6.29 The microtubules would reorient, and based on the earlier results, the cellulose synthase proteins would also change their path, orienting along the repositioned microtubules. (This is, in fact, what was observed.)

Concept Check 6.1
1. Stains used for light microscopy are colored molecules that bind to cell components, affecting the light passing through, while stains used for electron microscopy involve heavy metals that affect the beams of electrons passing through.
2. (a) Light microscope, (b) scanning electron microscope, (c) transmission electron microscope

Concept Check 6.2
1. See Figure 6.9.
2.

125

1

1

This cell would have the same volume as the cells in columns 2 and 3 but proportionally more surface area than that in column 2 and less than that in column 3. Thus, the surface-to-volume ratio should be greater than 1.2 but less than 6. To obtain the surface area, you'd have to add the area of the six sides (the top, bottom, sides, and ends): 125 + 125 + 125 + 125 + 1 + 1 = 502. The surface-to-volume ratio equals 502 divided by a volume of 125, or 4.0.

Concept Check 6.3
1. Ribosomes in the cytoplasm translate the genetic message, carried from the DNA in the nucleus by mRNA, into a polypeptide chain.   **2.** Nucleoli consist of DNA and the ribosomal RNA (rRNA) made according to its instructions, as well as proteins imported from the cytoplasm. Together, the rRNA and proteins are assembled into large and small ribosomal subunits. (These are exported through nuclear pores to the cytoplasm, where they will participate in polypeptide synthesis.)   **3.** The information in a gene (on a chromosome in the nucleus) is used to synthesize an mRNA that is then transported through a nuclear pore to the cytoplasm. There it is translated into protein, which is transported back through a nuclear pore into the nucleus, where it joins other proteins and DNA, forming chromatin.

Concept Check 6.4
1. The primary distinction between rough and smooth ER is the presence of bound ribosomes on the rough ER. While both types of ER make phospholipids, membrane proteins and secretory proteins are all produced on the ribosomes of the rough ER. The smooth ER also functions in detoxification, carbohydrate metabolism, and storage of calcium ions.   **2.** Transport vesicles move membranes and substances they enclose between other components of the endomembrane system.   **3.** The mRNA is synthesized in the nucleus and then passes out through a nuclear pore to be translated on a bound ribosome, attached to the rough ER. The protein is synthesized into the lumen of the ER and perhaps modified there. A transport vesicle carries the protein to the Golgi apparatus. After further modification in the Golgi, another transport vesicle carries it back to the ER, where it will perform its cellular function.

Concept Check 6.5
1. Both organelles are involved in energy transformation, mitochondria in cellular respiration and chloroplasts in photosynthesis. They both have multiple membranes that separate their interiors into compartments. In both organelles, the innermost membranes—cristae, or infoldings of the inner membrane, in mitochondria, and the thylakoid membranes in chloroplasts—have large surface areas with embedded enzymes that carry out their main functions.   **2.** Mitochondria, chloroplasts, and peroxisomes are not derived from the ER, nor are they connected physically or via transport vesicles to organelles of the endomembrane system. Mitochondria and chloroplasts are structurally quite different from vesicles derived from the ER, which are bounded by a single membrane.

Concept Check 6.6
1. Both systems of movement involve long filaments that are moved in relation to each other by motor proteins that grip, release, and grip again adjacent polymers.   **2.** Dynein arms, powered by ATP, move neighboring doublets of microtubules relative to one another. Because they are anchored within the organelle and with respect to each other, the doublets bend instead of sliding past one another.   **3.** Such individuals have defects in the microtubule-based movement of cilia and flagella. Thus, the sperm can't move because of malfunctioning flagella; the airways are compromised; and signaling events during embryogenesis do not occur correctly due to malfunctioning cilia.

Concept Check 6.7

1. The most obvious difference is the presence of direct cytoplasmic connections between cells of plants (plasmodesmata) and animals (gap junctions). These connections result in the cytoplasm being continuous between adjacent cells.   **2.** The cell would not be able to function properly and would probably soon die, as the cell wall or ECM must be permeable to allow the exchange of matter between the cell and its external environment. Molecules involved with energy production and use must be allowed entry, as well as those that provide information about the cell's environment. Other molecules, such as products synthesized by the cell for export and the by-products of cellular respiration, must be allowed to exit.

Self-Quiz
   1. c   **2.** b   **3.** d   **4.** d   **5.** b   **6.** c   **7.** e   **8.** a
   9. See Figure 6.9.

CHAPTER 7

Figure Questions
Figure 7.6 You couldn't rule out movement of proteins within the cell membrane of the same species. You might speculate that the membrane lipids and proteins from one species weren't able to mingle with those from the other species because of some incompatibility.   **Figure 7.9** A transmembrane protein like the integrin dimer in (f) might change its shape upon binding to a particular ECM molecule. The new shape might enable the interior portion of the protein to bind to a second, cytoplasmic protein that would relay the message to the inside of the cell, as shown in (c).   **Figure 7.12** The orange solute would be evenly distributed throughout the solution on both sides of the membrane. The solution levels would not be affected because the orange solute can diffuse through the membrane and equalize its concentration. Thus, no additional osmosis of water would take place in either direction.

Concept Check 7.1
1. They are on the inner side of the transport vesicle membrane.   **2.** Plants adapted to cold environments would be expected to have more unsaturated fatty acids in their membranes because those remain fluid at lower temperatures. Plants adapted to hot environments would be expected to have more saturated fatty acids, which would allow the fatty acids to "stack" more closely, making the membranes less fluid and therefore helping them to stay intact at higher temperatures.

Concept Check 7.2
1. O_2 and CO_2 are both small nonpolar molecules that can easily pass through the hydrophobic core of a membrane.   **2.** Water is a polar molecule, so it cannot pass very rapidly through the hydrophobic region in the middle of a phospholipid bilayer.   **3.** The hydronium ion is charged, while glycerol is not. Charge is probably more significant than size as a basis for exclusion by the aquaporin channel.

Concept Check 7.3
1. CO_2 is a small nonpolar molecule that can diffuse through the plasma membrane. As long as it diffuses away so the concentration remains low outside the cell, it will continue to exit the cell in this way. (This is the opposite of the case for O_2, described in this section.)   **2.** The water is hypotonic to the plant cells, so they take up water and the cells of the vegetable remain turgid, rather than plasmolyzing. The vegetable (for example, lettuce or spinach) remains crisp and not wilted.   **3.** The activity of the *Paramecium's* contractile vacuole will decrease. The vacuole pumps out excess water that flows into the cell; this flow occurs only in a hypotonic environment.

Concept Check 7.4
1. The pump uses ATP. To establish a voltage, ions have to be pumped against their gradients, which requires energy.   **2.** Each ion is being transported against its electrochemical gradient. If either ion were flowing down its electrochemical gradient, this *would* be considered cotransport.   **3.** Even if proton pumps were still using ATP and moving protons, no proton gradient would become established. This would have serious consequences for the cells, because processes like the cotransport of sucrose (as well as synthesis of ATP) depend on establishment of a proton gradient.

Concept Check 7.5
1. Exocytosis. When a transport vesicle fuses with the plasma membrane, the vesicle membrane becomes part of the plasma membrane.   **2.** Receptor-mediated endocytosis. In this case, one specific kind of molecule needs to be

taken up at a particular time; pinocytosis takes up substances in a nonspecific manner.

Self-Quiz
   1. b   **2.** c   **3.** a   **4.** d   **5.** b
   6. a.

b. The solution outside is hypotonic. It has less sucrose, which is a nonpenetrating solute.
c. See answer for (a).
d. The artificial cell will become more turgid.
e. Eventually, the two solutions will have the same solute concentrations. Even though sucrose can't move through the membrane, water flow (osmosis) will lead to isotonic conditions.

CHAPTER 8

Figure Questions
Figure 8.14   **Figure 8.18**

Figure 8.21 Because the affinity of the caspase for the inhibitor is very low (as is expected of an allosterically inhibited enzyme), the inhibitor is likely to diffuse away. Because no additional source of the inhibitory compound is present (the concentration of inhibitor is very low), the inhibitor is unlikely to bind again to the enzyme once the covalent linkage is broken. Thus, normal activity of the enzyme would most likely not be affected. (This test was performed by the researchers, and enzyme activity was observed to be normal upon release of the inhibitor.)

Concept Check 8.1
1. The second law is the trend toward randomness. Equal concentrations of a substance on both sides of a membrane is a more random distribution than unequal concentrations. Diffusion of a substance to a region where it is initially less concentrated increases entropy, as described by the second law.   **2.** The apple has potential energy in its position hanging on the tree, and the sugars and other nutrients it contains have chemical energy. The apple has kinetic energy as it falls from the tree to the ground. Finally, when the apple is digested and its molecules broken down, some of the chemical energy is used to do work, and the rest is lost as thermal energy.   **3.** The sugar crystals become less ordered (entropy increases) as they dissolve and become randomly spread out in the water. Over time, the water evaporates, and the crystals form again because the water volume is insufficient to keep them in solution. While the reappearance of sugar crystals may represent a "spontaneous" increase in order (decrease in entropy), it is balanced by the decrease in order (increase in entropy) of the water molecules, which changed from a relatively compact arrangement in liquid water to a much more dispersed and disordered form in water vapor.

Concept Check 8.2
1. Cellular respiration is a spontaneous and exergonic process. The energy released from glucose is used to do work in the cell or is lost as heat.   **2.** Hydrogen ions can

perform work only if their concentrations on each side of a membrane differ. When the H^+ concentrations are the same, the system is at equilibrium and can do no work. **3.** The reaction is exergonic because it releases energy—in this case, in the form of light. (This is a chemical version of the bioluminescence seen in Figure 8.1.)

Concept Check 8.3
1. ATP transfers energy to endergonic processes by phosphorylating (adding phosphate groups to) other molecules. (Exergonic processes phosphorylate ADP to regenerate ATP.) **2.** A set of coupled reactions can transform the first combination into the second. Since, overall, this is an exergonic process, ΔG is negative and the first group must have more free energy. (See Figure 8.10.)

Concept Check 8.4
1. A spontaneous reaction is a reaction that is exergonic. However, if it has a high activation energy that is rarely attained, the rate of the reaction may be low. **2.** Only the specific substrate(s) will fit properly into the active site of an enzyme, the part of the enzyme that carries out catalysis. **3.** Increase the concentration of the normal substrate (succinate) and see whether the rate of reaction increases. If it does, malonate is a competitive inhibitor.

Concept Check 8.5
1. The activator binds in such a way that it stabilizes the active form of an enzyme, whereas the inhibitor stabilizes the inactive form. **2.** You might choose to screen chemical compounds that bind allosterically to the enzyme, because allosteric regulatory sites are less likely to share similarity between different enzymes.

Self-Quiz
1. b **2.** c **3.** b **4.** a **5.** e **6.** c **7.** c

Scientific Inquiry
9.

A: The substrate molecules are entering the cells, so no product is made yet.
B: There is sufficient substrate, so the reaction is proceeding at a maximum rate.
C: As the substrate is used up, the rate falls.
D: The line is flat because no new substrate remains and thus no new product appears.

CHAPTER 9

Figure Questions
Figure 9.7 Because an enzyme is catalyzing this reaction and there is no external source of energy, it must be exergonic, and the reactants must be at a higher energy level than the products. **Figure 9.9** It would probably stop glycolysis, or at least slow it down, since this would tend to push the equilibrium for this step toward the left. If less (or no) glyceraldehyde-3-phosphate were made, step 6 would slow down (or be unable to occur). **Figure 9.15** Rotation in the opposite direction (blue bars) would be expected to hydrolyze some of the ATP present, lowering ATP concentration below the background level. Thus, the blue bars would be expected to be lower than the gray bars, which is not what the researchers observed. (A possible explanation: In the article, the researchers explained that when they enclosed ATP synthases in a chamber for this assay, a number of the complexes adhered to the chamber ceiling instead of the nickel plate. The enzymes adhering to the chamber ceiling would be expected to spin in an opposite direction to those on the nickel plate on the floor. When the floor-based enzymes produce ATP during a particular spin (yellow bars), those on the ceiling would be expected to consume ATP, which would make the yellow bars lower than they would have been if all enzymes were floor-based. The opposite is also true: When the floor-based enzymes hydrolyze ATP (blue bars), the ceiling-based enzymes would be synthesizing ATP, which would make the blue bars higher than if all enzymes were floor-based. Evidence of this phenomenon is shown in the graph: The spins expected to hydrolyze ATP (blue bars) result in higher ATP levels than those with no rotation (gray bars), suggesting that there are probably some "upside-down" ceiling-based complexes generating ATP while the rest are floor-based and are hydrolyzing ATP.) **Figure 9.16** At first, some ATP could be made, since electron transport could proceed as far as complex III, and a small H^+ gradient could be built up. Soon, however, no more electrons could be passed to complex III because it could not be reoxidized by passing its electrons to complex IV.

Concept Check 9.1
1. Both processes include glycolysis, the citric acid cycle, and oxidative phosphorylation. In aerobic respiration, the final electron acceptor is molecular oxygen (O_2), whereas in anaerobic respiration, the final electron acceptor is a different substance. **2.** $C_4H_6O_5$ would be oxidized and NAD^+ would be reduced.

Concept Check 9.2
1. NAD^+ acts as the oxidizing agent in step 6, accepting electrons from glyceraldehyde-3-phosphate, which thus acts as the reducing agent. **2.** Since the overall process of glycolysis results in net production of ATP, it would make sense for the process to slow down when ATP levels have increased substantially. Thus we would expect ATP to allosterically inhibit phosphofructokinase.

Concept Check 9.3
1. NADH and $FADH_2$; they will donate electrons to the electron transport chain. **2.** CO_2 is released from the pyruvate that is formed during glycolysis, and CO_2 is also released during the citric acid cycle. **3.** In both cases, the precursor molecule loses a CO_2 molecule and then donates electrons to an electron carrier in an oxidation step. Also, the product has been activated due to the attachment of a CoA group.

Concept Check 9.4
1. Oxidative phosphorylation would stop entirely, resulting in no ATP production by this process. Without oxygen to "pull" electrons down the electron transport chain, H^+ would not be pumped into the mitochondrion's intermembrane space and chemiosmosis would not occur. **2.** Decreasing the pH is the addition of H^+. It would establish a proton gradient even without the function of the electron transport chain, and we would expect ATP synthase to function and synthesize ATP. (In fact, it was experiments like this that provided support for chemiosmosis as an energy-coupling mechanism.)

Concept Check 9.5
1. A derivative of pyruvate—such as acetaldehyde during alcohol fermentation—or pyruvate itself during lactic acid fermentation; oxygen. **2.** The cell would need to consume glucose at a rate about 19 times the consumption rate in the aerobic environment (2 ATP are generated by fermentation versus up to 38 ATP by cellular respiration).

Concept Check 9.6
1. The fat is much more reduced; it has many —CH_2— units, and in all these bonds the electrons are equally shared. The electrons present in a carbohydrate molecule are already somewhat oxidized (shared unequally in bonds), as quite a few of them are bound to oxygen. **2.** When we consume more food than necessary for metabolic processes, our body synthesizes fat as a way of storing energy for later use. **3.** AMP will accumulate, stimulating phosphofructokinase, which increases the rate of glycolysis. Since oxygen is not present, the cell will convert pyruvate to lactate in lactic acid fermentation, providing a supply of ATP.

Self-Quiz
1. b **2.** d **3.** c **4.** c **5.** a **6.** a **7.** d **8.** b **9.** b
10.

CHAPTER 10

Figure Questions
Figure 10.9 Red, but not violet-blue, wavelengths would pass through the filter, so the bacteria would not congregate where the violet-blue light normally comes through. Therefore, the left "peak" of bacteria would not be present, but the right peak would be observed because the red wavelengths passing through the filter would be used for photosynthesis. **Figure 10.11** In the leaf, most of the chlorophyll electrons excited by photon absorption are used to power the reactions of photosynthesis.

Figure 10.18

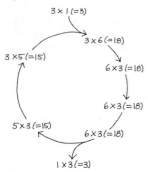

Three carbon atoms enter the cycle, one by one, as individual CO_2 molecules, and leave the cycle in one three-carbon molecule (G3P) per three turns of the cycle.

Concept Check 10.1

1. CO_2 enters leaves via stomata, and water enters via roots and is carried to leaves through veins. **2.** Using ^{18}O, a heavy isotope of oxygen, as a label, van Niel was able to show that the oxygen produced during photosynthesis originates in water, not in carbon dioxide. **3.** The light reactions could *not* keep producing NADPH and ATP without the $NADP^+$, ADP, and Ⓟ$_i$ that the Calvin cycle generates. The two cycles are interdependent.

Concept Check 10.2

1. Green, because green light is mostly transmitted and reflected—not absorbed—by photosynthetic pigments **2.** In chloroplasts, light-excited electrons are trapped by a primary electron acceptor, which prevents them from dropping back to the ground state. In isolated chlorophyll, there is no electron acceptor, so the photoexcited electrons immediately drop back down to the ground state, with the emission of light and heat. **3.** Water (H_2O) is the initial electron donor; $NADP^+$ accepts electrons at the end of the electron transport chain, becoming reduced to NADPH. **4.** In this experiment, the rate of ATP synthesis would slow and eventually stop. Because the added compound would not allow a proton gradient to build up across the membrane, ATP synthase could not catalyze ATP production.

Concept Check 10.3

1. 6, 18, 12 **2.** The more potential energy a molecule stores, the more energy and reducing power is required for the formation of that molecule. Glucose is a valuable energy source because it is highly reduced, storing lots of potential energy in its electrons. To reduce CO_2 to glucose, much energy and reducing power are required in the form of large numbers of ATP and NADPH molecules, respectively. **3.** The light reactions require ADP and $NADP^+$, which would not be formed in sufficient quantities from ATP and NADPH if the Calvin cycle stopped.

Concept Check 10.4

1. Photorespiration decreases photosynthetic output by adding oxygen, instead of carbon dioxide, to the Calvin cycle. As a result, no sugar is generated (no carbon is fixed), and O_2 is used rather than generated. **2.** Without PS II, no O_2 is generated in bundle-sheath cells. This avoids the problem of O_2 competing with CO_2 for binding to rubisco in these cells. **3.** C_4 and CAM species would replace many of the C_3 species.

Self-Quiz

1. d **2.** b **3.** b **4.** c **5.** d **6.** d **7.** c

Scientific Inquiry

9.

The ATP would end up outside the thylakoid. The chloroplasts were able to make ATP in the dark because the researchers set up an artificial proton concentration gradient across the thylakoid membrane; thus, the light reactions were not necessary to establish the H^+ gradient required for ATP synthesis by ATP synthase.

CHAPTER 11

Figure Questions

Figure 11.6 Epinephrine is a signaling molecule; presumably it binds to a cell-surface receptor protein. **Figure 11.8** The testosterone molecule is hydrophobic and can therefore pass directly through the lipid bilayer of the plasma membrane into the cell. (Hydrophilic molecules cannot do this.) **Figure 11.9** The active form of protein kinase 2 **Figure 11.10** The signaling molecule (cAMP) would remain in its active form and would continue to signal. **Figure 11.16** In the model, the directionality of growth is determined by the association of Fus3 with the membrane near the site of receptor activation. Thus, the development of shmoos would be severely compromised, and the affected cell would likely resemble the ΔFus3 and Δformin cells.

Concept Check 11.1

1. The two cells of opposite mating type (**a** and **α**) each secrete a certain signaling molecule, which can only be bound by receptors carried on cells of the opposite mating type. Thus, the **a** mating factor cannot bind to another **a** cell and cause it to grow toward the first **a** cell. Only an **α** cell can "receive" the signaling molecule and respond by directed growth (see Figure 11.16 for more information). **2.** The secretion of neurotransmitter molecules at a synapse is an example of local signaling. The electrical signal that travels along a very long nerve cell and is passed to the next nerve cell can be considered an example of long-distance signaling. (Note, however, that local signaling at the synapse between two cells is necessary for the signal to pass from one cell to the next.) **3.** Glucose-1-phosphate is not generated, because the activation of the enzyme requires an intact cell, with an intact receptor in the membrane and an intact signal transduction pathway. The enzyme cannot be activated directly by interaction with the signaling molecule in the test tube. **4.** Glycogen phosphorylase acts in the third stage, the response to epinephrine signaling.

Concept Check 11.2

1. The water-soluble NGF molecule cannot pass through the lipid membrane to reach intracellular receptors, as steroid hormones can. Therefore, you'd expect the NGF receptor to be in the plasma membrane—which is, in fact, the case. **2.** The cell with the faulty receptor would not be able to respond appropriately to the signaling molecule when it was present. This would most likely have dire consequences for the cell, since regulation of the cell's activities by this receptor would not occur appropriately.

Concept Check 11.3

1. A protein kinase is an enzyme that transfers a phosphate group from ATP to a protein, usually activating that protein (often a second type of protein kinase). Many signal transduction pathways include a series of such interactions, in which each phosphorylated protein kinase in turn phosphorylates the next protein kinase in the series. Such phosphorylation cascades carry a signal from outside the cell to the cellular protein(s) that will carry out the response. **2.** Protein phosphatases reverse the effects of the kinases. **3.** Information is transduced by way of sequential protein-protein interactions that change protein shapes, causing them to function in a way that passes the signal along. **4.** The IP_3-gated channel opens, allowing calcium ions to flow out of the ER, which raises the cytosolic Ca^{2+} concentration.

Concept Check 11.4

1. At each step in a cascade of sequential activations, one molecule or ion may activate numerous molecules functioning in the next step. **2.** Scaffolding proteins hold molecular components of signaling pathways in a complex with each other. Different scaffolding proteins would assemble different collections of proteins, leading to different cellular responses in the two cells.

Concept Check 11.5

1. In formation of the hand or paw in mammals, cells in the regions between the digits are programmed to undergo apoptosis. This serves to shape the digits of the hand or paw so that they are not webbed. **2.** If a receptor protein for a death-signaling molecule was defective so that it was activated for signaling even in the absence of the death signal, this would lead to apoptosis when it wouldn't normally occur. Similar defects in any of the proteins in the signaling pathway, which would activate these relay or response proteins in the absence of interaction with the previous protein or second messenger in the pathway, would have the same effect. Conversely, if any protein in the pathway were defective in its ability to respond to an interaction with an early protein or other molecule or ion, apoptosis would not occur when it normally should. For example, a receptor protein for a death-signaling ligand might not be able to be activated, even when ligand was bound. This would stop the signal from being transduced into the cell.

Self-Quiz
1. c **2.** d **3.** a **4.** c **5.** c **6.** b **7.** a **8.** d
9. This is one possible drawing of the pathway. (Similar drawings would also be correct.)

CHAPTER 12

Figure Questions
Figure 12.4

Circling the other chromatid instead would also be correct. The chromosome has four arms. **Figure 12.6** 12; 2; 2; 1
Figure 12.7

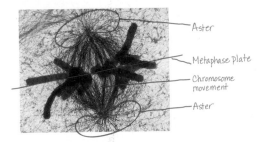

Figure 12.8 The mark would have moved toward the nearer pole. The lengths of fluorescent microtubules between that pole and the mark would have decreased, while the lengths between the chromosomes and the mark would have remained the same. **Figure 12.13** In both cases, the G_1 nucleus would have remained in G_1 until the time it normally would have entered the S phase. Chromosome condensation and spindle formation would not have occurred until the S and G_2 phases had been completed. **Figure 12.15** The cell would divide under conditions where it was inappropriate to do so. If the daughter cells and their descendants also ignored the checkpoint and divided, there would soon be an abnormal mass of cells. (This type of inappropriate cell division can contribute to the development of cancer.) **Figure 12.16** Given that control experiments showed that the *cdc2* protein kinase was the primary source of kinase activity detected in this experiment, there would be virtually no kinase activity. The percentage of cells dividing would be zero because the cells would be unable to undergo mitosis without the *cdc2* kinase. **Figure 12.18** The cells in the vessel with PDGF would not be able to respond to the growth factor signal and thus would not divide. The culture would resemble that without the added PDGF.

Concept Check 12.1
1. 32 cells **2.** 2 **3.** 39; 39; 78

Concept Check 12.2
1. 6; 12 **2.** Cytokinesis results in two genetically identical daughter cells in both plant cells and animal cells, but the mechanism of dividing the cytoplasm is different in animals and plants. In an animal cell, cytokinesis occurs by cleavage, which divides the parent cell in two with a contractile ring of actin filaments. In a plant cell, a cell plate forms in the middle of the cell and grows until its membrane fuses with the plasma membrane of the parent cell. A new cell wall grows inside the cell plate. **3.** They elongate the cell during anaphase. **4.** Sample answer: Each type of chromosome consists of a single molecule of DNA with attached proteins. If stretched out, the molecules of DNA would be many times longer than the cells in which they reside. During cell division, the two copies of each type of chromosome actively move apart, and one copy ends up in each of the two daughter cells. Chromosome movement in both types of cells may involve similar cytoskeletal proteins. **5.** During eukaryotic cell division, tubulin is involved in spindle formation and chromosome movement, while actin functions during cytokinesis. In bacterial binary fission, it's the opposite: Tubulin-like molecules are thought to act in daughter cell separation, and actin-like molecules are thought to move the daughter bacterial chromosomes to opposite ends of the cell. **6.** From the end of S phase in interphase through the end of metaphase in mitosis

Concept Check 12.3
1. The nucleus on the right was originally in the G_1 phase; therefore, it had not yet duplicated its chromosome. The nucleus on the left was in the M phase, so it had already duplicated its chromosome. **2.** A sufficient amount of MPF has to build up for a cell to pass the G_2 checkpoint. **3.** Most body cells are in a nondividing state called G_0. **4.** Both types of tumors consist of abnormal cells. A benign tumor stays at the original site and can usually be surgically removed. Cancer cells from a malignant tumor spread from the original site by metastasis and may impair the functions of one or more organs. **5.** The cells might divide even in the absence of PDGF, in which case they would not stop when the surface of the culture vessel was covered; they would continue to divide, piling on top of one another.

Self-Quiz
1. b **2.** a **3.** a **4.** c **5.** c **6.** e **7.** a **8.** b
9. See Figure 12.6 for a description of major events.

10.

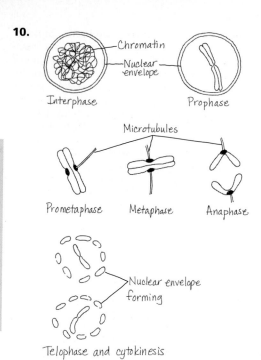

Interphase

Prophase

Microtubules

Prometaphase   Metaphase   Anaphase

Nuclear envelope forming

Telophase and cytokinesis

CHAPTER 13

Figure Questions

Figure 13.4 The haploid number, *n*, is 3. A set is always haploid.   **Figure 13.7** A short strand of DNA is shown here for simplicity, but each chromosome or chromatid contains a very long coiled and folded DNA molecule.

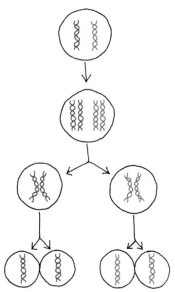

Figure 13.9 Yes. Each of the chromosomes shown in telophase I has one nonrecombinant chromatid and one recombinant chromatid. Therefore, eight possible sets of chromosomes can be generated for the cell on the left and eight for the cell on the right.   **Figure 13.10** The chromosomes arising from chromatids of the unlabeled chromosome would be expected to behave exactly like those of the labeled chromosome. Therefore, the graph would look identical to the one shown in the figure.

Concept Check 13.1

1. Parents pass genes to their offspring; the genes program cells to make specific enzymes and other proteins, whose cumulative action produces an individual's inherited traits.   **2.** Such organisms reproduce by mitosis, which generates offspring whose genomes are exact copies of the parent's

genome (in the absence of mutation).   **3.** She should clone it. Breeding it would generate offspring that have additional variation, which she no longer desires now that she has obtained her ideal orchid.

Concept Check 13.2

1. A female has two X chromosomes; a male has an X and a Y.   **2.** In meiosis, the chromosome count is reduced from diploid to haploid; the union of two haploid gametes in fertilization restores the diploid chromosome count.   **3.** The haploid number (*n*) is 7; the diploid number (2*n*) is 14.   **4.** This organism has the life cycle shown in Figure 13.6c. Therefore, it must be a fungus or a protist, perhaps an alga.

Concept Check 13.3

1. The chromosomes are similar in that each is composed of two sister chromatids, and the individual chromosomes are positioned similarly on the metaphase plate. The chromosomes differ in that in a mitotically dividing cell, sister chromatids of each chromosome are genetically identical, but in a meiotically dividing cell, sister chromatids are genetically distinct because of crossing over in meiosis I. Moreover, the chromosomes in metaphase of mitosis can be a diploid set or a haploid set, but the chromosomes in metaphase of meiosis II always consist of a haploid set.   **2.** If crossing over did not occur, the two homologs would not be associated in any way. This might result in incorrect arrangement of homologs during metaphase I and ultimately in formation of gametes with an abnormal number of chromosomes.

Concept Check 13.4

1. Mutations in a gene lead to the different versions (alleles) of that gene.   **2.** Without crossing over, independent assortment of chromosomes during meiosis I theoretically can generate 2^n possible haploid gametes, and random fertilization can produce $2^n \times 2^n$ possible diploid zygotes. Because the haploid number (*n*) of grasshoppers is 23 and that of fruit flies is 4, two grasshoppers would be expected to produce a greater variety of zygotes than would two fruit flies.   **3.** If the segments of the maternal and paternal chromatids that undergo crossing over are genetically identical and thus have the same two alleles for every gene, then the recombinant chromosomes will be genetically equivalent to the parental chromosomes. Crossing over contributes to genetic variation only when it involves the rearrangement of different alleles.

Self-Quiz

1. a   **2.** d   **3.** b   **4.** a   **5.** d   **6.** c   **7.** d   **8.** This cell must be undergoing meiosis because homologous chromosomes are associated with each other; this does not occur in mitosis.   **9.** Metaphase I
10.

The chromosomes of one color make up a haploid set.
All red and blue chromosomes together make up a diploid set.

CHAPTER 14

Figure Questions

Figure 14.3 All offspring would have purple flowers. (The ratio would be one purple to zero white.) The P generation plants are true-breeding, so mating two purple-flowered plants produces the same result as self-pollination: All the offspring have the same trait.

Figure 14.8

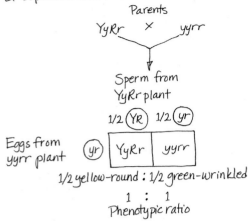

If dependent assortment:

Parents

YyRr × yyrr

Sperm from YyRr plant

1/2 (YR) 1/2 (yr)

Eggs from yyrr plant

	YyRr	yyrr
(yr)	YyRr	yyrr

1/2 yellow-round : 1/2 green-wrinkled

1 : 1
Phenotypic ratio

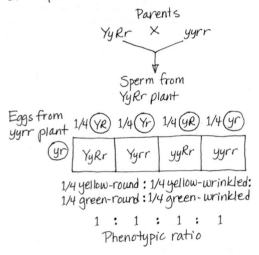

If independent assortment:

Parents

YyRr × yyrr

Sperm from YyRr plant

Eggs from yyrr plant

1/4 (YR) 1/4 (Yr) 1/4 (yR) 1/4 (yr)

(yr)	YyRr	Yyrr	yyRr	yyrr

1/4 yellow-round : 1/4 yellow-wrinkled:
1/4 green-round : 1/4 green-wrinkled

1 : 1 : 1 : 1
Phenotypic ratio

Yes, this cross would also have allowed Mendel to make different predictions for the two hypotheses, thereby allowing him to distinguish the correct one. **Figure 14.10** Your classmate would probably point out that the F₁ generation hybrids show an intermediate phenotype between those of the homozygous parents, which supports the blending hypothesis. You could respond that crossing the F₁ hybrids results in the reappearance of the white phenotype, rather than identical pink offspring, which fails to support the idea of blending traits during inheritance. **Figure 14.11** Both the I^A and I^B alleles are dominant to the i allele, which results in no attached carbohydrate. The I^A and I^B alleles are codominant; both are expressed in the phenotype of $I^A I^B$ heterozygotes, who have type AB blood.
Figure 14.13

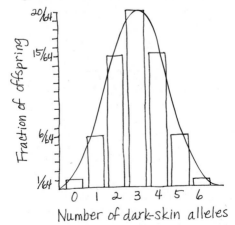

The majority of individuals have intermediate phenotypes (skin color in the middle range), while fewer individuals have phenotypes at either end (very dark or very light skin). (As you may know, this is called a "bell curve" and represents a "normal distribution.") **Figure 14.16** In the Punnett square, two of the three individuals with normal coloration are carriers, so the probability is ⅔.

Concept Check 14.1

1. A cross of $Ii \times ii$ would yield offspring with a genotypic ratio of 1 Ii : 1 ii (2:2 is an equivalent answer) and a phenotypic ratio of 1 inflated : 1 constricted (2:2 is equivalent).

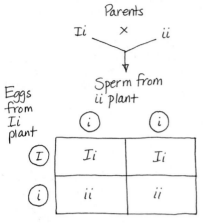

Parents

Ii × ii

Sperm from ii plant

Eggs from Ii plant

(i) (i)

	(i)	(i)
(I)	Ii	Ii
(i)	ii	ii

Genotypic ratio 1 Ii : 1 ii
(2:2 is equivalent)

Phenotypic ratio 1 inflated : 1 constricted
(2:2 is equivalent)

2. According to the law of independent assortment, 25 plants (¹⁄₁₆ of the offspring) are predicted to be *aatt*, or recessive for both characters. The actual result is likely to differ slightly from this value.

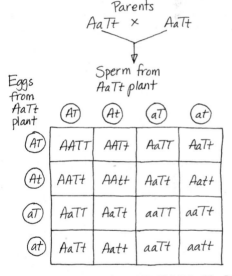

Parents

AaTt × AaTt

Sperm from AaTt plant

Eggs from AaTt plant

(AT) (At) (aT) (at)

	(AT)	(At)	(aT)	(at)
(AT)	AATT	AATt	AaTT	AaTt
(At)	AATt	AAtt	AaTt	Aatt
(aT)	AaTT	AaTt	aaTT	aaTt
(at)	AaTt	Aatt	aaTt	aatt

3. The plant could make eight different gametes (*YRI, YRi, YrI, Yri, yRI, yRi, yrI,* and *yri*). To fit all the possible gametes in a self-pollination, a Punnett square would need 8 rows and 8 columns. It would have spaces for the 64 possible unions of gametes in the offspring.

Concept Check 14.2

1. ½ homozygous dominant (*CC*), 0 homozygous recessive (*cc*), and ½ heterozygous (*Cc*) **2.** ¼ *BBDD*; ¼ *BbDD*; ¼ *BBDd*; ¼ *BbDd* **3.** The genotypes that fulfill this condition are *ppyyIi, ppYyii, Ppyyii, ppYYii,* and *ppyyii*. Use the multiplication rule to find the probability of getting each genotype, and then use the addition rule to find the overall probability of meeting the conditions of this problem:

ppyy Ii	½ (probability of *pp*) × ¼ (*yy*) × ½ (*Ii*)	= $\frac{1}{16}$
pp Yy ii	½ (*pp*) × ½ (*Yy*) × ½ (*ii*)	= $\frac{2}{16}$
Pp yy ii	½ (*Pp*) × ¼ (*yy*) × ½ (*ii*)	= $\frac{1}{16}$
pp YY ii	½ (*pp*) × ¼ (*YY*) × ½ (*ii*)	= $\frac{1}{16}$
pp yy ii	½ (*pp*) × ¼ (*yy*) × ½ (*ii*)	= $\frac{1}{16}$

Fraction predicted to have at least two recessive traits = $\frac{6}{16}$ or ⅜

Concept Check 14.3

1. Incomplete dominance describes the relationship between two alleles of a single gene, whereas epistasis relates to the genetic relationship between two genes (and the respective alleles of each). **2.** Half of the children would be expected to have type A blood and half type B blood. **3.** The black and white alleles are incompletely dominant, with heterozygotes being gray in color. A cross between a gray rooster and a black hen should yield approximately equal numbers of gray and black offspring.

Concept Check 14.4

1. ⅙ (Since cystic fibrosis is caused by a recessive allele, Beth and Tom's siblings who have CF must be homozygous recessive. Therefore, each parent must be a carrier of the recessive allele. Since neither Beth nor Tom has CF, this means they each have a ⅔ chance of being a carrier. If they are both carriers, there is a ¼ chance that they will have a child with CF. ⅔ × ⅔ × ¼ = ⅑); 0 (Both Beth and Tom would have to be carriers to produce a child with the disease.) **2.** Joan's genotype is Dd. Because the allele for polydactyly (D) is dominant to the allele for five digits per appendage (d), the trait is expressed in people with either the DD or Dd genotype. But because Joan's father does not have polydactyly, his genotype must be dd, which means Joan inherited a d allele from him. Therefore Joan, who does have the trait, must be heterozygous. **3.** Since polydactyly is a dominant trait, one of the parents of an affected individual should show the trait. Therefore, this must be an extremely rare case of a mutation that occurred during formation of one of the gametes involved in the fertilization that created Peter.

Genetics Problems

1. Gene, l. Allele, e. Character, g. Trait, b. Dominant allele, j. Recessive allele, a. Genotype, k. Phenotype, h. Homozygous, c. Heterozygous, f. Testcross, i. Monohybrid cross, d.

2.

Parents
$GgIi$ × $GgIi$

Sperm

	GI	Gi	gI	gi
GI	GGII	GGIi	GgII	GgIi
Gi	GGIi	GGii	GgIi	Ggii
gI	GgII	GgIi	ggII	ggIi
gi	GgIi	Ggii	ggIi	ggii

9 green-inflated : 3 green-constricted : 3 yellow-inflated : 1 yellow-constricted

3. Parental cross is $AAC^R C^R \times aaC^W C^W$. F_1 genotype is $AaC^R C^W$, phenotype is all axial-pink. F_2 genotypes are 1 $AAC^R C^R$: 2 $AAC^R C^W$: 1 $AAC^W C^W$: 2 $AaC^R C^R$: 4 $AaC^R C^W$: 2 $AaC^W C^W$: 1 $aaC^R C^R$: 2 $aaC^R C^W$: 1 $aaC^W C^W$. F_2 phenotypes are 3 axial-red : 6 axial-pink : 3 axial-white : 1 terminal-red : 2 terminal-pink : 1 terminal-white.

4. a. $^1/_{64}$
b. $^1/_{64}$
c. $^1/_8$
d. $^1/_{32}$

5. Albino (b) is a recessive trait; black (B) is dominant. First cross: parents $BB \times bb$; gametes B and b; offspring all Bb (black coat). Second cross: parents $Bb \times bb$; gametes ½ B and ½ b (heterozygous parent) and b; offspring ½ Bb and ½ bb.

6. a. $PPLl \times PPLl$, $PPLl \times PpLl$, or $PPLl \times ppLl$.
b. $ppLl \times ppLl$.
c. $PPLL \times$ any of the 9 possible genotypes or $PPll \times ppLL$.
d. $PpLl \times Ppll$.
e. $PpLl \times PpLl$.

7. Man $I^A i$; woman $I^B i$; child ii. Other genotypes for children are ¼ $I^A I^B$, ¼ $I^A i$, ¼ $I^B i$.

8. a. ¾ × ¾ × ¾ = $^{27}/_{64}$
b. $1 - ^{27}/_{64} = ^{37}/_{64}$
c. ¼ × ¼ × ¼ = $^1/_{64}$
d. $1 - ^1/_{64} = ^{63}/_{64}$

9. a. $^1/_{256}$
b. $^1/_{16}$
c. $^1/_{256}$
d. $^1/_{64}$
e. $^1/_{128}$

10. a. 1
b. $^1/_{32}$
c. $^1/_8$
d. $^1/_2$

11. $^1/_9$

12. Matings of the original mutant cat with true-breeding noncurl cats will produce both curl and noncurl F_1 offspring if the curl allele is dominant, but only noncurl offspring if the curl allele is recessive. You would obtain some true-breeding offspring homozygous for the curl allele from matings between the F_1 cats resulting from the original curl × noncurl crosses whether the curl trait is dominant or recessive. You know that cats are true-breeding when curl × curl matings produce only curl offspring. As it turns out, the allele that causes curled ears is dominant. **13.** $^1/_{16}$ **14.** 25% will be cross-eyed; all of the cross-eyed offspring will also be white. **15.** The dominant allele I is epistatic to the P/p locus, and thus the genotypic ratio for the F_1 generation will be 9 $I\_P\_$ (colorless) : 3 I_pp (colorless) : 3 $iiP\_$ (purple) : 1 $iipp$ (red). Overall, the phenotypic ratio is 12 colorless : 3 purple : 1 red. **16.** Recessive. All affected individuals (Arlene, Tom, Wilma, and Carla) are homozygous recessive aa. George is Aa, since some of his children with Arlene are affected. Sam, Ann, Daniel, and Alan are each Aa, since they are all unaffected children with one affected parent. Michael also is Aa, since he has an affected child (Carla) with his heterozygous wife Ann. Sandra, Tina, and Christopher can each have the AA or Aa genotype. **17.** $^1/_2$ **18.** $^1/_6$ **19.** 9 $B\_A\_$ (agouti) : 3 B_aa (black) : 3 $bbA\_$ (white) : 1 $bbaa$ (white). Overall, 9 agouti : 3 black : 4 white.

CHAPTER 15

Figure Questions

Figure 15.2 The ratio would be 1 yellow-round : 1 green-round : 1 yellow-wrinkled : 1 green-wrinkled. **Figure 15.4** About ¾ of the F_2 offspring would have red eyes and about ¼ would have white eyes. About half of the white-eyed flies would be female and half would be male; about half of the red-eyed flies would be female. **Figure 15.7** All the males would be color-blind, and all the females would be carriers. **Figure 15.9** The two largest classes would still be the parental-type offspring, but now they would be gray-vestigial and black-normal because those were the specific allele combinations in the P generation. **Figure 15.10** The two chromosomes below, left are like the two chromosomes inherited by the F_1 female, one from each P generation fly. They are passed by the F_1 female intact to the offspring and thus could be called "parental" chromosomes. The other two chromosomes result from crossing over during meiosis in the F_1 female. Because they have combinations of alleles not seen in either of the F_1 female's chromosomes, they can be called "recombinant" chromosomes.

Parental chromosomes   Recombinant chromosomes

Concept Check 15.1

1. The law of segregation relates to the inheritance of alleles for a single character. The law of independent assortment of alleles relates to the inheritance of alleles for two characters. **2.** The physical basis for the law of segregation is the separation of homologs in anaphase I. The physical basis for the law of independent assortment is the alternative arrangements of homologous chromosome pairs in metaphase I. **3.** To show the mutant phenotype, a male needs to possess only one mutant allele. If this gene had been on a pair of autosomes, *two* mutant alleles would have had to be present for an individual to show the mutant phenotype, a much less probable situation.

Concept Check 15.2

1. Because the gene for this eye-color character is located on the X chromosome, all female offspring will be red-eyed and heterozygous ($X^{w+} X^w$); all male offspring will inherit a Y chromosome from the father and be white-eyed (X^wY). **2.** ¼; ½ chance that the child will inherit a Y chromosome from the father and be male × ½ chance that he will inherit the X carrying the disease allele from his mother. If the child is a boy, there is a ½ chance he will have the disease; a female would have zero chance (but ½ chance of being a carrier). **3.** The cells in the eye responsible for color vision must come from multiple cells in the early embryo. The descendants of half of those cells express the allele for normal color vision and half the allele for color blindness. Having half the number of mature eye cells expressing the normal allele must be sufficient for normal color vision.

Concept Check 15.3

1. Crossing over during meiosis I in the heterozygous parent produces some gametes with recombinant genotypes for the two genes. Offspring with a recombinant phenotype arise from fertilization of the recombinant gametes by homozygous recessive gametes from the double-mutant parent. **2.** In each case, the alleles contributed by the female parent determine the phenotype of the offspring because the male contributes only recessive alleles in this cross. **3.** No. The order could be *A-C-B* or *C-A-B*. To determine which possibility is correct, you need to know the recombination frequency between *B* and *C*.

Concept Check 15.4

1. At some point during development, one of the embryo's cells may have failed to carry out mitosis after duplicating its chromosomes. Subsequent normal cell cycles would produce genetic copies of this tetraploid cell. **2.** In meiosis, a combined 14-21 chromosome will behave as one chromosome. If a gamete receives the combined 14-21 chromosome and a normal copy of chromosome 21, trisomy 21 will result when this gamete combines with a normal gamete during fertilization. **3.** No. The child can be either $I^A I^A i$ or $I^A ii$. A sperm of genotype $I^A I^A$ could result from nondisjunction in the father during meiosis II, while an egg with the genotype *ii* could result from nondisjunction in the mother during either meiosis I or meiosis II.

Concept Check 15.5

1. Inactivation of an X chromosome in females and genomic imprinting. Because of X inactivation, the effective dose of genes on the X chromosome is the same in males and females. As a result of genomic imprinting, only one allele of certain genes is phenotypically expressed. **2.** The genes for leaf coloration are located in plastids within the cytoplasm. Normally, only the maternal parent transmits plastid genes to offspring. Since variegated offspring are produced only when the female parent is of the B variety, we can conclude that variety B contains both the wild-type and mutant alleles of pigment genes, producing variegated leaves. **3.** The situation is similar to that for chloroplasts. Each cell contains numerous mitochondria, and in affected individuals, most cells contain a variable mixture of normal and mutant mitochondria. The normal mitochondria carry out enough cellular respiration for survival.

Genetics Problems

1. 0; ½; ¹⁄₁₆ **2.** Recessive; if the disorder were dominant, it would affect at least one parent of a child born with the disorder. The disorder's inheritance is sex-linked because it is seen only in boys. For a girl to have the disorder, she would have to inherit recessive alleles from *both* parents. This would be very rare, since males with the recessive allele on their X chromosome die in their early teens. **3.** ¼ for each daughter (½ chance that child will be female × ½ chance of a homozygous recessive genotype); ½ for first son. **4.** 17% **5.** 6%. Wild type (heterozygous for normal wings and red eyes) × recessive homozygote with vestigial wings and purple eyes

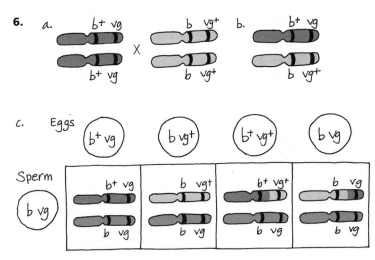

d. 41.5% gray body, vestigial wings
41.5% black body, normal wings
8.5% gray body, normal wings
8.5% black body, vestigial wings

7. The disorder would always be inherited from the mother. **8.** The inactivation of two X chromosomes in XXX women would leave them with one genetically active X, as in women with the normal number of chromosomes. Microscopy should reveal two Barr bodies in XXX women. **9.** *D–A–B–C* **10.** Fifty percent of the offspring would show phenotypes that resulted from crossovers. These results would be the same as those from a cross where *A* and *B* were not linked. Further crosses involving other genes on the same chromosome would reveal the linkage and map distances. **11.** Between *T* and *A*, 12%; between *A* and *S*, 5% **12.** Between *T* and *S*, 18%; sequence of genes is *T-A-S* **13.** 450 each of blue-oval and white-round (parentals) and 50 each of blue-round and white-oval (recombinants) **14.** About one-third of the distance from the vestigial-wing locus to the brown-eye locus **15.** Because bananas are triploid, homologous pairs cannot line up during meiosis. Therefore, it is not possible to generate gametes that can fuse to produce a zygote with the triploid number of chromosomes.

CHAPTER 16

Figure Questions

Figure 16.2 The living S cells found in the blood sample were able to reproduce to yield more S cells, indicating that the S trait is a permanent, heritable change, rather than just a one-time use of the dead S cells' capsules. **Figure 16.4** The radioactivity would have been found in the pellet when proteins were labeled (batch 1) because proteins would have had to enter the bacterial cells to program them with genetic instructions. It's hard for us to imagine now, but the DNA might have played a structural role that allowed some of the proteins to be injected while it remained outside the bacterial cell (thus no radioactivity in the pellet in batch 2). **Figure 16.11** The tube from the first replication would look the same, with a middle band of hybrid ^{15}N-^{14}N DNA, but the second tube would not have the upper band of two light blue strands. Instead it would have a bottom band of two dark blue strands, like the bottom band in the result predicted after one replication in the conservative model. **Figure 16.12** In the bubble at the top in (b), arrows should be drawn pointing left and right to indicate the two replication forks. **Figure 16.14** Looking at any of the DNA strands, we see that one end is called the 5′ end and the other the 3′ end. If we proceed from the 5′ end to the 3′ end on the left-most strand, for example, we list the components in this order: phosphate group → 5′ C of the sugar → 3′ C → phosphate → 5′ C → 3′ C. Going in the opposite direction on the same strand, the components proceed in the reverse order: 3′ C → 5′ C → phosphate. Thus, the two directions are distinguishable, which is what we mean when we say that the strands have directionality. (Review Figure 16.5 if necessary.) **Figure 16.22** The cells in the mutant would probably have the same defects in meiosis that were seen in this experiment, such as the failure of condensin to be concentrated in a small region in the nucleus. The defect in the two mutants is essentially the same: In the mutant described in the experiment, the kinase doesn't function properly; in the newly discovered mutant, the kinase could not phosphorylate the correct amino acid because that amino acid is missing.

Concept Check 16.1

1. Chargaff's rules state that in DNA, the percentages of A and T and of G and C are essentially the same, and the fly data are consistent with those rules. (Slight variations are most likely due to limitations of analytical technique.) **2.** In the Watson-Crick model, each A hydrogen-bonds to a T, so in a DNA double helix, their numbers are equal; the same is true for G and C. **3.** The mouse injected with the mixture of heat-killed S cells and living R cells would have survived, since neither type of cell alone could have killed the mouse.

Concept Check 16.2

1. Complementary base pairing ensures that the two daughter molecules are exact copies of the parent molecule. When the two strands of the parent molecule separate, each serves as a template on which nucleotides are arranged, by the base-pairing rules, into new complementary strands. **2.** DNA pol III covalently adds nucleotides to new DNA strands and proofreads each added nucleotide for correct base pairing. **3.** Synthesis of the leading strand is initiated by an RNA primer, which must be removed and replaced with DNA, a task that could not be performed if the cell's DNA pol I were nonfunctional. In the overview box in Figure 16.17, just to the left of the top origin of replication, a functional DNA pol I would replace the RNA primer of the leading strand (shown in red) with DNA nucleotides (blue).

Concept Check 16.3

1. A nucleosome is made up of eight histone proteins, two each of four different types, around which DNA is wound. Linker DNA runs from one nucleosome to the next. **2.** Euchromatin is chromatin that becomes less compacted during interphase and is accessible to the cellular machinery responsible for gene activity. Heterochromatin, on the other hand, remains quite condensed during interphase and contains genes that are largely inaccessible to this machinery. **3.** Like histones, the *E. coli* proteins would be expected to contain many basic (positively charged) amino acids, such as lysine and arginine, which can form weak bonds with the negatively charged phosphate groups on the sugar-phosphate backbone of the DNA molecule.

Self-Quiz

1. c **2.** d **3.** b **4.** c **5.** b **6.** d **7.** a **8.** c
10.

New DNA strand (olive)
Parental DNA strand (purple)
Sliding clamp
DNA pol III
Single-strand binding protein
Direction of replication

CHAPTER 17

Figure Questions

Figure 17.2 The previously presumed pathway would have been wrong. The new results would support this pathway: precursor → citrulline → ornithine → arginine. They would also indicate that class I mutants have a defect in the second step and class II mutants have a defect in the first step. **Figure 17.8** The RNA polymerase would bind directly to the promoter, rather than depending on the previous binding of other factors. **Figure 17.24** The mRNA on the right (the longest one) started transcription first. The ribosome at the top, closest to the DNA, started translating first and thus has the longest polypeptide.

Concept Check 17.1

1. A polypeptide made up of 10 Gly (glycine) amino acids

2.
Template sequence
(from problem):   3'-TTCAGTCGT-5'

Nontemplate sequence: 5'-AAGTCAGCA-3'

mRNA sequence: 5'-AAGUCAGCA-3'

The nontemplate and mRNA base sequences are the same, except there is T in the nontemplate strand of DNA wherever there is U in the mRNA.

3. "Template sequence" (from nontemplate sequence in problem, written 3' → 5'):   3'-ACGACTGAA-5'

mRNA sequence: 5'-UGCUGACUU-3'

Translated: Cys-STOP-Leu

(Remember that the mRNA is antiparallel to the DNA strand.) A protein translated from the nontemplate sequence would have a completely different amino acid sequence and would surely be nonfunctional. (It would also be shorter because of the stop signal shown in the mRNA sequence above—and possibly others earlier in the mRNA sequence.)

Concept Check 17.2

1. Both assemble nucleic acid chains from monomer nucleotides whose order is determined by complementary base pairing to a template strand. Both synthesize in the 5' → 3' direction, antiparallel to the template. DNA polymerase requires a primer, but RNA polymerase can start a nucleotide chain from scratch. DNA polymerase uses nucleotides with the sugar deoxyribose and the base T, whereas RNA polymerase uses nucleotides with the sugar ribose and the base U. **2.** The promoter is the region of DNA to which RNA polymerase binds to begin transcription, and it is at the upstream end of the gene (transcription unit). **3.** In a bacterial cell, RNA polymerase recognizes the gene's promoter and binds to it. In a eukaryotic cell, transcription factors mediate the binding of RNA polymerase to the promoter. **4.** The transcription factor that recognizes the TATA sequence would be unable to bind, so RNA polymerase could not bind and transcription of that gene probably would not occur.

Concept Check 17.3

1. The 5' cap and poly-A tail facilitate mRNA export from the nucleus, prevent the mRNA from being degraded by hydrolytic enzymes, and facilitate ribosome attachment. **2.** In editing a video, segments are cut out and discarded (like introns), and the remaining segments are joined together (like exons) so that the regions of joining ("splicing") are not noticeable. **3.** Six different forms could be made because alternative splicing could generate six different mRNAs (two possibilities for exon 4 × three possibilities for exon 7).

Concept Check 17.4

1. First, each aminoacyl-tRNA synthetase specifically recognizes a single amino acid and attaches it only to an appropriate tRNA. Second, a tRNA charged with its specific amino acid binds only to an mRNA codon for that amino acid. **2.** Polyribosomes enable the cell to produce multiple copies of a polypeptide very quickly. **3.** A signal peptide on the leading end of the polypeptide being synthesized is recognized by a signal-recognition particle that brings the ribosome to the ER membrane. There the ribosome attaches and continues to synthesize the polypeptide, depositing it in the ER lumen. **4.** The structure and function of the ribosome seem to depend more on the rRNAs than on the ribosomal proteins. Because it is single-stranded, an RNA molecule can hydrogen-bond with itself and with other RNA molecules. RNA molecules make up the interface between the two ribosomal subunits, so presumably RNA-RNA binding helps hold the ribosome together. The binding site for mRNA in the ribosome could include rRNA that can bind the mRNA. (In fact, this turns out to be the case.) Also, complementary bonding within an RNA molecule allows it to assume a particular three-dimensional shape, and, along with the RNA's functional groups, presumably enables rRNA to catalyze peptide bond formation during translation.

Concept Check 17.5

1. In the mRNA, the reading frame downstream from the deletion is shifted, leading to a long string of incorrect amino acids in the polypeptide and, in most cases, a stop codon will arise, leading to premature termination. The polypeptide will most likely be nonfunctional.

2. Normal DNA sequence
(template strand is on top): 3′–TACTTGTCCGATATC–5′
                              5′–ATGAACAGGCTATAG–3′

mRNA sequence: 5′–AUGAACAGGCUAUAG–3′

Amino acid sequence: Met-Asn-Arg-Leu-STOP

―――――――――――――――――――――――――――――――――――――――

Mutated DNA sequence
(template strand is on top): 3′–TACTTGTCCAATATC–5′
                              5′–ATGAACAGGTTATAG–3′

mRNA sequence: 5′–AUGAACAGGUUAUAG–3′

Amino acid sequence: Met-Asn-Arg-Leu-STOP

The amino acid sequence is Met-Asn-Arg-Leu both before and after the mutation because the mRNA codons 5′-CUA-3′ and 5′-UUA-3′ both code for Leu. (The fifth codon is a stop codon.)

Concept Check 17.6

1. No, transcription and translation are separated in space and time in a eukaryotic cell, a result of the eukaryotic cell's nuclear compartment. **2.** When one ribosome terminates translation and dissociates, the two subunits would be very close to the cap. This could facilitate their rebinding and initiating synthesis of a new polypeptide, thus increasing the efficiency of translation.

Self-Quiz

1. b **2.** d **3.** a **4.** a **5.** d **6.** e **7.** b

8.

Type of RNA	Functions
Messenger RNA (mRNA)	Carries information specifying amino acid sequences of proteins from DNA to ribosomes.
Transfer RNA (tRNA)	Serves as adapter molecule in protein synthesis; translates mRNA codons into amino acids.
Ribosomal RNA (rRNA)	Plays catalytic (ribozyme) roles and structural roles in ribosomes.
Primary transcript	Is a precursor to mRNA, rRNA, or tRNA, before being processed. Some intron RNA acts as a ribozyme, catalyzing its own splicing.
Small nuclear RNA (snRNA)	Plays structural and catalytic roles in spliceosomes, the complexes of protein and RNA that splice pre-mRNA.

CHAPTER 18

Figure Questions

Figure 18.3 As the concentration of tryptophan in the cell falls, eventually there will be none bound to repressor molecules. These will then take on their inactive shapes and dissociate from the operator, allowing transcription of the operon to resume. The enzymes for tryptophan synthesis will be made, and they will begin to synthesize tryptophan again in the cell. **Figure 18.10** The albumin gene enhancer has the three control elements colored yellow, gray, and red. The sequences in the two cells would be identical, since the cells are in the same organism. **Figure 18.16** Even if the mutant MyoD protein couldn't activate the *myoD* gene, it could still turn on genes for the other proteins in the pathway (other transcription factors, which would turn on the genes for muscle-specific proteins, for example). Therefore, some differentiation would occur. But unless

there were other activators that could compensate for the loss of the MyoD protein's activation of the *myoD* gene, the cell would not be able to maintain its differentiated state. **Figure 18.19** Normal Bicoid protein would be made in the anterior end and compensate for the presence of mutant *bicoid* mRNA put into the egg by the mother. Development should be normal, with a head present. **Figure 18.21** The mutation is likely to be recessive because it is more likely to have an effect if both copies of the gene are mutated and code for nonfunctional proteins. If one normal copy of the gene is present, its product could inhibit the cell cycle. (However, there are also known cases of dominant *p53* mutations.)

Concept Check 18.1

1. Binding by the *trp* corepressor (tryptophan) activates the *trp* repressor, shutting off transcription of the *trp* operon; binding by the *lac* inducer (allolactose) inactivates the *lac* repressor, leading to transcription of the *lac* operon. **2.** The cell would continuously produce β-galactosidase and the two other enzymes for lactose utilization, even in the absence of lactose, thus wasting cell resources. **3.** With glucose scarce, cAMP would be bound to CAP and CAP would be bound to the promoter, favoring the binding of RNA polymerase. However, in the absence of lactose, the repressor would be bound to the operator, blocking RNA polymerase binding to the promoter. The operon genes would therefore not be transcribed. If another sugar were present and the genes encoding enzymes for its breakdown were in an operon regulated like the *lac* operon, we might expect to find active transcription of those genes.

Concept Check 18.2

1. Histone acetylation is generally associated with gene expression, while DNA methylation is generally associated with lack of expression. **2.** General transcription factors function in assembling the transcription initiation complex at the promoters for all genes. Specific transcription factors bind to control elements associated with a particular gene and, once bound, either increase (activators) or decrease (repressors) transcription of that gene. **3.** The three genes should have some similar or identical sequences in the control elements of their enhancers. Because of this similarity, the same specific transcription factors could bind to the enhancers of all three genes and stimulate their expression coordinately. **4.** Degradation of the mRNA, regulation of translation, activation of the protein (by chemical modification, for example), and protein degradation **5.** Expression of the gene encoding the yellow activator (YA) must be regulated at one of the steps shown in Figure 18.6. The YA gene might be transcribed only in liver cells because the necessary activators for the enhancer of the YA gene are found only in liver cells.

Concept Check 18.3

1. Both miRNAs and siRNAs are small, single-stranded RNAs that associate with a complex of proteins and then can base-pair with mRNAs that have a complementary sequence. This base pairing leads to either degradation of the mRNA or blockage of its translation. Some siRNAs, in association with other proteins, can bind back to the chromatin in a certain region, causing chromatin changes that affect transcription. Both miRNAs and siRNAs are processed from double-stranded RNA precursors by the enzyme Dicer. However, miRNAs are encoded by genes in the cell's genome, and the single transcript folds back on itself to form one or more double-stranded hairpins, each of which is processed into an miRNA. In contrast, siRNAs arise from a longer stretch of double-stranded RNA, which may be introduced into the cell by a virus or an experimenter. In some cases, a cellular gene codes for one RNA strand of the precursor molecule, and an enzyme then synthesizes the complementary strand. **2.** The mRNA would persist and be translated into the cell division–promoting protein, and the cell would probably divide. If the intact miRNA is necessary for inhibition of cell division, then division of this cell might be inappropriate. Uncontrolled cell division could lead to formation of a mass of cells (tumor) that prevents proper functioning of the organism.

Concept Check 18.4

1. Cells undergo differentiation during embryonic development, becoming different from each other; in the adult organism, there are many highly specialized cell types. **2.** By binding to a receptor on the receiving cell's surface and triggering a signal transduction pathway that affects gene expression **3.** Because their products, made and deposited into the egg by the mother, determine the head and tail ends, as well as the back and belly, of the embryo (and eventually the adult fly) **4.** The lower cell is synthesizing signaling molecules because the gene encoding them is activated, meaning that the appropriate specific transcription factors are binding to the gene's enhancer. The genes encoding these specific transcription factors are also being expressed in this cell because the transcriptional activators that can turn them on were expressed in the precursor to this cell. A similar explanation also applies to the cells expressing the receptor proteins. This scenario began with specific cytoplasmic determinants localized in specific regions of the egg. These cytoplasmic determinants were distributed unevenly to daughter cells, resulting in cells going down different developmental pathways.

Concept Check 18.5

1. The protein product of a proto-oncogene is usually involved in a pathway that stimulates cell division. The protein product of a tumor-suppressor gene is usually involved in a pathway that inhibits cell division. **2.** When an individual has inherited an oncogene or a mutant allele of a tumor-suppressor gene **3.** A cancer-causing mutation in a proto-oncogene usually makes the gene product overactive, whereas a cancer-causing mutation in a tumor-suppressor gene usually makes the gene product nonfunctional.

Self-Quiz

1. d **2.** a **3.** d **4.** a **5.** c **6.** e **7.** a **8.** c **9.** b **10.** b **11.** a.

The purple, blue, and red activator proteins would be present.

b.

Only gene 4 would be transcribed.

c. In nerve cells, the orange, blue, green, and black activators would have to be present, thus activating transcription of genes 1, 2, and 4. In skin cells, the red, black, purple, and blue activators would have to be present, thus activating genes 3 and 5.

CHAPTER 19

Figure Questions

Figure 19.2 Beijerinck might have concluded that the agent was a toxin produced by the plant that was able to pass through a filter but that became more and more dilute. In this case, he would have concluded that the infectious agent could not reproduce. **Figure 19.4** Top vertical arrow: Infection. Left upper arrow: Replication. Right upper arrow: Transcription. Right middle arrow: Translation. Lower left and right arrows: Self-assembly. Bottom middle arrow: Exit. **Figure 19.7** Any class V virus, including the viruses that cause influenza (flu), measles, and mumps.

Concept Check 19.1

1. TMV consists of one molecule of RNA surrounded by a helical array of proteins. The influenza virus has eight molecules of RNA, each surrounded by a helical array of proteins, similar to the arrangement of the single RNA molecule in TMV. Another difference is that the influenza virus has an outer envelope. **2.** One of the arguments for regarding viruses as nonliving is that they cannot perform any activity characteristic of living organisms unless they are inside a host cell. This virus challenges that generalization because the virus can change its shape without having access to host cell proteins. (Further analysis suggested that the projections contain proteins related to intermediate filaments that may polymerize spontaneously under certain conditions.)

Concept Check 19.2

1. Lytic phages can only carry out lysis of the host cell, whereas lysogenic phages may either lyse the host cell or integrate into the host chromosome. In the latter case, the viral DNA (prophage) is simply replicated along with the host chromosome. Under certain conditions, a prophage may exit the host chromosome and initiate a lytic cycle. **2.** The genetic material of these viruses is RNA, which is replicated inside the infected cell by enzymes encoded by the virus. The viral genome (or a complementary copy of it) serves as mRNA for the synthesis of viral proteins. **3.** Because it synthesizes DNA from its RNA genome. This is the reverse ("retro") of the usual DNA → RNA information flow. **4.** There are many steps that could be interfered with: binding of the virus to the cell, reverse transcriptase function, integration into the host cell chromosome, genome synthesis (in this case, transcription of RNA from the integrated provirus), assembly of the virus inside the cell, and budding of the virus. (Many, if not all, of these are targets of actual medical strategies to block progress of the infection in HIV-infected people.)

Concept Check 19.3

1. Mutations can lead to a new strain of a virus that can no longer be effectively fought by the immune system, even if an animal had been exposed to the original strain; a virus can jump from one species to a new host; and a rare virus can spread if a host population becomes less isolated. **2.** In horizontal transmission, a plant is infected from an external source of virus, which could enter through a break in the plant's epidermis due to damage by herbivores. In vertical transmission, a plant inherits viruses from its parent either via infected seeds (sexual reproduction) or via an infected cutting (asexual reproduction). **3.** Humans are not within the host range of TMV, so they can't be infected by the virus. **4.** It is unlikely that human air travel could have spread the virus, since existing strains of the virus do not seem to be transmissible from human to human. It is conceivable but unlikely that an infected human traveling from Asia passed the virus to birds in Africa and Europe. It is possible that domestic birds carried the virus, perhaps in shipments of poultry. The likeliest scenario of all may be that migratory wild birds carried the virus during their migrations and passed it to domestic and wild birds in the new locations. To test these latter hypotheses, the timing of the outbreaks should be analyzed to see if they correlate with recent poultry shipments or known wild bird migrations. Any such migratory birds should be tested for the presence of the African or European strain of the virus, based on the nucleotide sequences of their genomes.

Self-Quiz

1. d **2.** b **3.** c **4.** d **5.** c
6. As shown below, the viral genome would be translated into capsid proteins and envelope glycoproteins directly, rather than after a complementary RNA copy was made. A complementary RNA strand would still be made, however, that could be used as a template for many new copies of the viral genome.

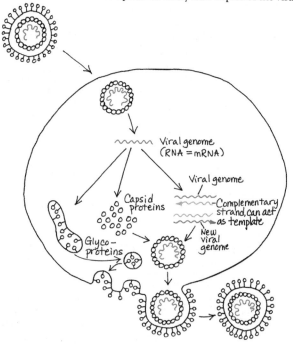

CHAPTER 20

Figure Questions
Figure 20.3

Figure 20.4 Cells containing no plasmid at all would be able to grow; these colonies would be white because they would lack functional *lacZ* genes. **Figure 20.10** Grow each clone of cells in culture. Isolate the plasmids from each and cut them with the restriction enzyme originally used to make the clone (see Figure 20.4). Run each sample on an electrophoretic gel, and recover the DNA of the insert from the gel band. **Figure 20.16** The researchers might have concluded that differentiated cells are irreversibly changed so that they can make only one type of tissue in the plant. (This result would support the idea that cloning isn't possible.) **Figure 20.17** None of the eggs with the transplanted nuclei would have developed into a tadpole. Also, the result might include only some of the tissues of a tadpole which might differ depending on which nucleus was transplanted. (This assumes that there was some way to tell the four cells apart, as one can in some frog species.)

Concept Check 20.1
1. The covalent sugar-phosphate bonds of the DNA strands **2.** Yes, *Pvu*I will cut the molecule

3. Some human genes are too large to be incorporated into bacterial plasmids. Bacterial cells lack the means to process RNA transcripts into mRNA, and even if the need for RNA processing is avoided by using cDNA, bacteria lack enzymes to catalyze the post-translational processing that many human proteins require to function properly. **4.** 5'-CGGT-3' and 5'-CCTT-3'

Concept Check 20.2
1. Any restriction enzyme will cut genomic DNA in many places, generating such a large number of fragments that they would appear as a smear rather than distinct bands when the gel is stained after electrophoresis. **2.** In Southern blotting, Northern blotting, and microarray analysis, the labeled probe binds only to the specific target sequence owing to complementary nucleic acid hybridization (DNA-DNA hybridization in Southern blotting and microarray analysis, DNA-RNA hybridization in Northern blotting). In DNA sequencing, primers base-pair to the template, allowing DNA synthesis to start. In RT-PCR, the primers must base-pair with their target sequences in the DNA mixture. **3.** If a spot is green, the gene represented on that spot is expressed only in normal tissue. If red, the gene is expressed only in cancerous tissue. If yellow, the gene is expressed in both. And if black, the gene is expressed in neither type of tissue. As a researcher interested in cancer development, you would want to study genes represented by spots that are green or red because these are genes for which the expression level differs between the two types of tissues. Some of these genes may be expressed differently as a result of cancer, but others might play a role in causing cancer.

Concept Check 20.3
1. No, primarily because of subtle (and perhaps not so subtle) differences in their environments **2.** The state of chromatin modification in the nucleus from the intestinal cell was undoubtedly less similar to that of a nucleus from a fertilized egg, explaining why many fewer of these nuclei were able to be reprogrammed. In contrast, the chromatin in a nucleus from a cell at the four-cell stage would have been much more like that of a nucleus in a fertilized egg and therefore much more easily programmed to direct development. **3.** A technique would have to be worked out for turning a human iPS cell into a pancre-

atic cell (probably by inducing expression of pancreas-specific regulatory genes in the cell).

Concept Check 20.4
1. Stem cells continue to reproduce themselves. **2.** Herbicide resistance, pest resistance, disease resistance, salinity resistance, delayed ripening, and improved nutritional value **3.** Because hepatitis A is an RNA virus, you could isolate RNA from the blood and try to detect copies of hepatitis A RNA by one of three methods. First, you could run the RNA on a gel and then do a Northern blot using probes complementary to hepatitis A genome sequences. A second approach would be to use reverse transcriptase to make cDNA from the RNA in the blood, run the cDNA on a gel, and do a Southern blot using the same probe. However, neither of these methods would be as sensitive as RT-PCR, in which you would reverse transcribe the blood RNA into cDNA and then use PCR to amplify the cDNA, using primers specific to hepatitis A sequences. If you then ran the products on an electrophoretic gel, the presence of a band would support your hypothesis.

Self-Quiz
1. b **2.** b **3.** c **4.** b **5.** a **6.** c **7.** c **8.** d
9.

10. A cDNA library, made using mRNA from human lens cells, which would be expected to contain many copies of crystallin mRNAs

CHAPTER 21

Figure Questions
Figure 21.3 The fragments in stage 2 of this figure are like those in stage 2 of Figure 21.2, but in this figure their order relative to each other is not known and will be determined later by computer. The order of the fragments in Figure 21.2 is completely known before sequencing begins. (Determining the order takes longer but makes the eventual sequence assembly much easier.) **Figure 21.9** The transposon would be cut out of the DNA at the original site rather than copied, so part (a) would show the original stretch of DNA without the transposon after the mobile transposon had been cut out. **Figure 21.10** The RNA transcripts extending from the DNA in each transcription unit are shorter on the left and longer on the right. This means that RNA polymerase must be starting on the left end of the unit and moving toward the right. **Figure 21.13** Pseudogenes are nonfunctional. They could have arisen by any mutations in the second copy that made the gene product unable to function. Examples would be base changes that introduce stop codons in the sequence, alter amino acids, or change a region of the gene promoter so that the gene can no longer be expressed. **Figure 21.14** Let's say a transposable element (TE) existed in the intron to the left of the indicated EGF exon in the *EGF* gene, and the same TE was present in the intron to the left of the indicated F exon

in the fibronectin gene. During meiotic recombination, these TEs could cause nonsister chromatids on the same chromosome to pair up incorrectly, as seen in Figure 21.12. One gene might end up with an F exon next to an EGF exon. Further mistakes in pairing over many generations might result in these two exons being separated from the rest of the gene and placed next to a single or duplicated K exon. In general, the presence of repeated sequences in introns and between genes facilitates these processes because it allows incorrect pairing of nonsister chromatids, leading to novel exon combinations.

Figure 21.16 Since you know that chimpanzees do not speak but humans do, you'd probably want to know how many amino acid differences there are between the human wild-type FOXP2 protein and that of the chimpanzee and whether these changes affect the function of the protein. (As we explain later in the text, there are two amino acid differences.) You know that humans with mutations in this gene have severe language impairment. You would want to learn more about the human mutations by checking whether they affect the same amino acids in the gene product that the chimpanzee sequence differences affect. If so, those amino acids might play an important role in the function of the protein in language. Going further, you could analyze the differences between the chimpanzee and mouse FOXP2 proteins. You might ask: Are they more similar than the chimpanzee and human proteins? (It turns out that the chimpanzee and mouse proteins have only one amino acid difference and thus are more similar than the chimpanzee and human proteins, which have two differences, and than the human and mouse proteins, which have three differences.)

Concept Check 21.1

1. In a linkage map, genes and other markers are ordered with respect to each other, but only the relative distances between them are known. In a physical map, the actual distances between markers, expressed in base pairs, are known. **2.** The three-stage approach employed in the Human Genome Project involves linkage mapping, physical mapping, and then sequencing of short, overlapping fragments that previously have been ordered relative to each other (see Figure 21.2). The whole-genome shotgun approach eliminates the linkage mapping and physical mapping stages; instead, short fragments generated by multiple restriction enzymes are sequenced and then ordered by computer programs that identify overlapping regions (see Figure 21.3). **3.** Because the two mouse species are very closely related, their genome sequences are expected to be very similar. This means that the field mouse genome fragments could be compared with the assembled lab mouse genome, providing valuable information to use in placing the field mouse genome fragments in the correct order. In a sense, the lab mouse genome could be used as a rough map for the field mouse genome, removing the necessity to carry out complete genetic and physical mapping for the field mouse.

Concept Check 21.2

1. The Internet allows centralization of databases such as GenBank and software resources such as BLAST, making them freely accessible. Having all the data in a central database, easily accessible on the Internet, minimizes the possibility of errors and of researchers working with different data. It streamlines the process of science, since all researchers are able to use the same software programs, rather than each having to obtain their own software. It speeds up dissemination of data and ensures as much as possible that errors are corrected in a timely fashion. These are just a few answers; you can probably think of more. **2.** Cancer is a disease caused by multiple factors. To focus on a single gene or a single defect would ignore other factors that may influence the cancer and even the behavior of the single gene being studied. The systems approach, because it takes into account many factors at the same time, is more likely to lead to an understanding of the causes and most useful treatments for cancer. **3.** The DNA would first be sequenced and analyzed for whether the mutation is in the coding region for a gene or in a promoter or enhancer, affecting the expression of a gene. In either case, the nature of the gene product could be explored by searching the protein database for similar proteins. If similar proteins have known functions, that would provide a clue about the function of your protein. Otherwise, biochemical and other methods could provide some ideas about possible function. Software could be used to compare what is known about your protein and similar proteins.

Concept Check 21.3

1. Alternative splicing of RNA transcripts from a gene and post-translational processing of polypeptides **2.** The total number of completed genomes is found by clicking on "Published Complete Genomes." Add the figures for bacterial, archaeal, and eukaryotic "ongoing genomes" to get the number "in progress." Finally, look at the top of the Published Complete Genomes page to get numbers of completed genomes for each domain. (*Note:* You can click on the "Size" column and the table will be re-sorted by genome size. Scroll down to get an idea of relative sizes of genomes in the three domains. Remember, though, that most of the sequenced genomes are bacterial.) **3.** Prokaryotes are generally smaller cells than eukaryotic cells, and they reproduce by binary fission. The evolutionary process involved is natural selection for more quickly reproducing cells: The faster they can replicate their DNA and divide, the more likely they will be able to dominate a population of prokaryotes. The less DNA they have to replicate, then, the faster they will reproduce.

Concept Check 21.4

1. The number of genes is higher in mammals, and the amount of noncoding DNA is greater. Also, the presence of introns in mammalian genes makes them longer, on average, than prokaryotic genes. **2.** Introns are interspersed within the coding sequences of genes. Many copies of each transposable element are scattered throughout the genome. Simple sequence DNA is concentrated at the centromeres and telomeres and is clustered in other locations. **3.** In the rRNA gene family, identical transcription units for the three different RNA products are present in long, tandemly repeated arrays. The large number of copies of the rRNA genes enable organisms to produce the rRNA for enough ribosomes to carry out active protein synthesis, and the single transcription unit ensures that the relative amounts of the different rRNA molecules produced are correct. Each globin gene family consists of a relatively small number of nonidentical genes. The differences in the globin proteins encoded by these genes result in production of hemoglobin molecules adapted to particular developmental stages of the organism. **4.** First, you could check the sequence by translating it into a predicted amino acid sequence and see if there are multiple stop codons. If there aren't, the next step would be to see whether the gene is expressed, probably by carrying out a Northern blot or *in situ* hybridization to look for the mRNA in the cells that express the gene.

Concept Check 21.5

1. If meiosis is faulty, two copies of the entire genome can end up in a single cell. Errors in crossing over during meiosis can lead to one segment being duplicated while another is deleted. During DNA replication, slippage backward along the template strand can result in a duplication. **2.** For either gene, a mistake in crossing over during meiosis could have occurred between the two copies of that gene, such that one ended up with a duplicated exon. This could have happened several times, resulting in the multiple copies of a particular exon in each gene. **3.** Homologous transposable elements scattered throughout the genome provide sites where recombination can occur between different chromosomes. Movement of these elements into coding or regulatory sequences may change expression of genes. Transposable elements also can carry genes with them, leading to dispersion of genes and in some cases different patterns of expression. Transport of an exon during transposition and its insertion into a gene may add a new functional domain to the originally encoded protein, a type of exon shuffling. **4.** Because more offspring are born to women who have this inversion, it must provide some advantage. It would be expected to persist and spread in the population. (In fact, evidence in the study allowed the researchers to conclude that it has been increasing in proportion in the population. You'll learn more about population genetics in the next unit.)

Concept Check 21.6

1. Because both humans and macaques are primates, their genomes are expected to be more similar than the macaque and mouse genomes are. The mouse lineage diverged from the primate lineage before the human and macaque lineages diverged. **2.** Homeotic genes differ in their *non*homeobox sequences, which determine the interactions of homeotic gene products with other transcription factors and hence which genes are regulated by the homeotic genes. These nonhomeobox sequences differ in the two organisms, as do the expression patterns of the homeobox genes. **3.** *Alu* elements must have undergone transposition more actively in the human genome for some reason. Their increased numbers may have then allowed more recombination errors in the human genome, resulting in more or different duplications. The divergence of the organization and content of the two genomes presumably accelerated divergence of the two species by making matings less and less likely to result in fertile offspring.

Self-Quiz

1. c **2.** e **3.** a **4.** e **5.** c **6.** a

7.
1. ATETI...PKSSD...TSSTT...NARRD
2. ATETI...PKSSE...TSSTT...NARRD
3. ATETI...PKSSD...TSSTT...NARRD
4. ATETI...PKSSD...TSSNT...SARRD
5. ATETI...PKSSD...TSSTT...NARRD
6. VTETI...PKSSD...TSSTT...NARRD

a. Lines 1, 3, and 5 are the C, G, R species.

b. Line 4 is the human sequence.

c. Line 6 is the orangutan sequence.

d. There is one amino acid difference between the mouse (line 2) and the C, G, R species; there are three amino acid differences between the mouse and the human.

e. Because only one amino acid difference arose during the 60–100 million years since the mouse and C, G, R species diverged, it is somewhat surprising that two additional amino acid differences resulted during the 6 million years since chimpanzees and humans diverged. This indicates that the *FOXP2* gene has been evolving faster in the human lineage than in the lineages of other primates.

CHAPTER 22

Figure Questions

Figure 22.8 More than 5.5 million years ago. **Figure 22.13** The original pool of the transplanted guppy population contains pike-cichlids, a potent predator of adult guppies. Brightly colored adult males would be at a disadvantage in this pool. Thus, it is likely that color patterns in the guppy population would become more drab if they were returned to their original pool. **Figure 22.19** Based on this evolutionary tree, crocodiles are more closely related to birds than to lizards because they share a more recent common ancestor with birds (ancestor ⑤) than with lizards (ancestor ④).

Concept Check 22.1

1. Hutton and Lyell proposed that events in the past were caused by the same processes operating today. This principle suggested that Earth must be much older than a few thousand years, the age that was widely accepted at that time. Hutton and Lyell also thought that geologic change occurs gradually, stimulating Darwin to reason that the slow accumulation of small changes could ultimately produce the profound changes documented in the fossil record. In this context, the age of Earth was important to Darwin, because unless Earth was very old, he could not envision how there would have been enough time for evolution to occur. **2.** By these criteria, Cuvier's explanation of the fossil record and Lamarck's hypothesis of evolution are both scientific. Cuvier suggested that catastrophes and the resulting extinctions were usually confined to local regions, and that such regions were later repopulated by a different set of species that immigrated from other areas. These assertions can be tested against the fossil record (they have been found to be false). With respect to Lamarck, his principle of use and disuse can be used to make testable predictions for fossils of groups such as whale ancestors as they adapt to a new habitat. Lamarck's principle of the inheritance of acquired characteristics can be tested directly in living organisms (it has been found to be false).

Concept Check 22.2

1. Organisms share characteristics (the unity of life) because they share common ancestors; the great diversity of life occurs because new species have repeatedly formed when descendant organisms gradually adapted to different environments, becoming different from their ancestors. **2.** All species have the potential to produce more offspring (overreproduce) than can be supported by the environment. This ensures there will be what Darwin called a "struggle for existence" in which many of the offspring are eaten, starved, diseased, or unable to reproduce for a variety of other reasons. Members of a

population exhibit a range of heritable variations, some of which make it likely that their bearers will leave more offspring than other individuals (for example, the bearer may escape predators more effectively or be more tolerant of the physical conditions of the environment). Over time, natural selection imposed by factors such as predators, lack of food, or the physical conditions of the environment can increase the proportion of individuals with favorable traits in a population (evolutionary adaptation). **3.** The fossil mammal species (or its ancestors) would most likely have colonized the Andes from within South America, whereas ancestors of mammals currently found in African mountains would most likely have colonized those mountains from other parts of Africa. As a result, the Andes fossil species would share a more recent common ancestor with South American mammals than with mammals in Africa. Thus, for many of its traits, the fossil mammal species would probably more closely resemble mammals that live in South American jungles than mammals that live on African mountains.

Concept Check 22.3

1. An environmental factor such as a drug does not create new traits such as drug resistance, but rather selects for traits among those that are already present in the population. **2.** (a) Despite their different functions, the forelimbs of different mammals are structurally similar because they all represent modifications of a structure found in the common ancestor. (b) Convergent evolution: The similarities between the sugar glider and flying squirrel indicate that similar environments selected for similar adaptations despite different ancestry.

3. At the time that dinosaurs originated, Earth's landmasses formed a single large continent, Pangaea. Because many dinosaurs were large and mobile, it is likely that early members of these groups lived on many different parts of Pangaea. When Pangaea broke apart, fossils of these organisms would have moved with the rocks in which they were deposited. As a result, we would predict that fossils of early dinosaurs would have a broad geographic distribution (this prediction has been upheld).

Self-Quiz

1. b **2.** c **3.** d **4.** d **5.** a **6.** d

8. (a)

(b) The rapid rise in the percentage of mosquitoes resistant to DDT was most likely caused by natural selection in which mosquitoes resistant to DDT could survive and reproduce while other mosquitoes could not. (c) In India—where DDT resistance first appeared—natural selection would have caused the frequency of resistant mosquitoes to increase over time. If resistant mosquitoes then migrated from India (for example, transported by wind or in planes, trains, or ships) to other parts of the world, the frequency of DDT resistance would increase there as well.

CHAPTER 23

Figure Questions

Figure 23.7 The predicted frequencies are 36% $C^R C^R$, 48% $C^R C^W$, and 16% $C^W C^W$. **Figure 23.12** Because such a shift in prevailing winds would increase the transfer of alleles (gene flow) from plants living on mine soils to plants living at the location marked by the arrow, the change would probably lead to an increase in the index of copper tolerance of plants at that location. **Figure 23.16** Crossing a single female's eggs with both an SC and an LC male's sperm allowed the researchers to directly compare the effects of the males' contribution to the next generation, since both batches of offspring had the same maternal contribution. This isolation of the male's impact enabled researchers to draw conclusions about differences in genetic "quality" between the SC and LC males. **Figure 23.18** The researchers measured the percentages of successfully reproducing adults out of the breeding adult population that had each phenotype. This approach of determining which phenotype was favored by selection assumes that reproduction was a sufficient indicator of relative fitness (as opposed to counting the number of eggs laid or offspring hatched, for example) and that mouth phenotype was the driving factor determining the fishes' ability to reproduce.

Concept Check 23.1

1. (a) Within a population, genetic differences among individuals provide the raw material on which natural selection and other mechanisms can act. Without such differences, allele frequencies could not change over time—and hence the population could not evolve. (b) Genetic variation among populations can arise by natural selection if selection favors different alleles in different populations; this might occur, for example, if the different populations experienced different environmental conditions. Genetic variation among populations can also arise by genetic drift when the genetic differences between populations are selectively neutral. **2.** Many mutations occur in somatic cells that do not produce gametes and so are lost when the organism dies. Of mutations that do occur in cell lines that produce gametes, many do not have a phenotypic effect on which natural selection can act. Others have a harmful effect and are thus unlikely to increase in frequency because they decrease the reproductive success of their bearers. **3.** Its genetic variation (whether measured at the level of the gene or at the level of nucleotide sequences) would probably drop over time. During meiosis, crossing over and the independent assortment of chromosomes produce many new combinations of alleles. In addition, a population contains a vast number of possible mating combinations, and fertilization brings together the gametes of individuals with different genetic backgrounds. Thus, via crossing over, independent assortment of chromosomes, and fertilization, sexual reproduction reshuffles alleles into fresh combinations each generation. Without sexual reproduction, new sources of genetic variation would be reduced, causing the overall amount of genetic variation to drop.

Concept Check 23.2

1. 750. Half the loci (250) are fixed, meaning only one allele exists for each locus: $250 \times 1 = 250$. There are two alleles each for the other loci: $250 \times 2 = 500$. $250 + 500 = 750$. **2.** $p^2 + 2pq$; p^2 represents homozygotes with two A alleles, and $2pq$ represents heterozygotes with one A allele. **3.** There are 120 individuals in the population, so there are 240 alleles. Of these, there are 124 A alleles—32 from the 16 AA individuals and 92 from the 92 Aa individuals. Thus, the frequency of the A allele is $p = 124/240 = 0.52$; hence, the frequency of the a allele is $q = 0.48$. Based on the Hardy-Weinberg equation, if the population were not evolving, the frequency of genotype AA should be $p^2 = 0.52 \times 0.52 = 0.27$; the frequency of genotype Aa should be $2pq = 2 \times 0.52 \times 0.48 = 0.5$; and the frequency of genotype aa should be $q^2 = 0.48 \times 0.48 = 0.23$. In a population of 120 individuals, these expected genotype frequencies lead us to predict that there would be 32 AA individuals (0.27×120), 60 Aa individuals (0.5×120), and 28 aa individuals (0.23×120). The actual numbers for the population (16 AA, 92 Aa, 12 aa) deviate from these expectations (fewer homozygotes and more heterozygotes than expected). This suggests that the population is not in Hardy-Weinberg equilibrium and hence is evolving.

Concept Check 23.3

1. Natural selection is more "predictable" in that it alters allele frequencies in a nonrandom way: It tends to increase the frequency of alleles that increase the organism's reproductive success in its environment and decrease the frequency of alleles that decrease the organism's reproductive success. Alleles subject to genetic drift increase or decrease in frequency by chance alone, whether or not they are advantageous. **2.** Genetic drift results from chance events that cause allele frequencies to fluctuate at random from generation to generation; within a population, this process tends to decrease genetic variation over time. Gene flow is the exchange of alleles between populations; a process that can introduce new alleles to a population and hence may increase its genetic variation (albeit slightly, since rates of gene flow are often low). **3.** Selection is not important at this locus; furthermore, the populations are reasonably large, and hence the effects of genetic drift should not be pronounced. Gene flow is occurring via the movement of pollen and seeds. Thus, allele and genotype frequencies in these populations should become more similar over time as a result of gene flow.

Concept Check 23.4

1. Zero, because fitness includes reproductive contribution to the next generation, and a sterile mule cannot produce offspring. **2.** Although both gene flow and genetic drift can increase the frequency of advantageous alleles in a population, they can also decrease the frequency of advantageous alleles or increase the frequency of harmful alleles. Only natural selection *consistently* results in an increase in the frequency of alleles that enhance survival or reproduction. Thus, natural selection is the only mechanism that consistently causes adaptive evolution. **3.** The three modes of natural selection (directional, stabilizing, and disruptive) are defined in terms of the selective advantage of different *phenotypes*, not different genotypes. Thus, the type of selection represented by heterozygote advantage depends on the phenotype of the heterozygotes. In this question, because heterozygous individuals have a more extreme phenotype than either homozygote, heterozygote advantage represents directional selection.

Self-Quiz

1. d **2.** a **3.** e
4. b **5.** b
7. The frequency of the lap^{94} allele forms a cline, decreasing as one moves from southwest to northeast across Long Island Sound.

A hypothesis that explains the cline and accounts for the observations stated in the question is that the cline is maintained by an interaction between selection and gene flow. Under this hypothesis, in the southwest portion of the Sound, salinity is relatively low, and selection against the lap^{94} allele is strong. Moving toward the northeast and into the open ocean, where salinity is relatively high, selection favors a high frequency of the lap^{94} allele. However, because mussel larvae disperse long distances, gene flow prevents the lap^{94} allele from becoming fixed in the open ocean or from declining to zero in the southwestern portion of Long Island Sound.

CHAPTER 24

Figure Questions

Figure 24.3 Allele 1 (found in some birds in Population B) is more closely related to alleles found in Population A than to other alleles found in Population B. This implies that the ancestral allele from which allele 1 descended existed in Population A. Hence, the direction of gene flow was from Population A to Population B. **Figure 24.9** This change would have the effect of increasing gene flow between the populations, which would make the evolution of reproductive isolation more difficult. **Figure 24.12** Such results would suggest that mate choice based on coloration does not provide a reproductive barrier between these two cichlid species. **Figure 24.14** Because the populations had only just begun to diverge from one another at this point in the process, it is likely that any existing barriers to reproduction would weaken over time. **Figure 24.20** The presence of *M. cardinalis* plants that carry the *M. lewisii yup* allele would make it more likely that bumblebees would transfer pollen between the two monkey flower species. As a result, we would expect the number of hybrid offspring to increase.

Concept Check 24.1

1. (a) All except the biological species concept can be applied to both asexual and sexual species because they define species on the basis of characteristics other than ability to reproduce. In contrast, the biological species concept can be applied only to sexual species. (b) The easiest species concept to apply in the field would be the morphological species concept because it is based only on the appearance of the organism. Additional information about its ecological habits, evolutionary history, and reproduction are not required. **2.** Because these birds live in fairly similar environments and can breed successfully in captivity, the reproductive barrier in nature is probably prezygotic; given the species differences in habitat preference, this barrier could result from habitat isolation.

Concept Check 24.2

1. In allopatric speciation, a new species forms while in geographic isolation from its parent species; in sympatric speciation, a new species forms in the absence of geographic isolation. Geographic isolation greatly reduces gene flow between populations, whereas ongoing gene flow is more likely in sympatry. As a result, sympatric speciation is less common than allopatric speciation. **2.** Gene flow between subsets of a population that live in the same area can be reduced in a variety of ways. In some species—especially plants—changes in chromosome number can block gene flow and establish reproductive isolation in a single generation. Gene flow can also be reduced in sympatric populations by habitat differentiation (as seen in the apple maggot fly, *Rhagoletis*) and sexual selection (as seen in Lake Victoria cichlids). **3.** Allopatric speciation would be less likely to occur on a nearby island than on an isolated island of the same size. The reason we expect this result is that continued gene flow between mainland populations and those on a nearby island reduces the chance that enough genetic divergence will take place for allopatric speciation to occur.

Concept Check 24.3

1. Hybrid zones are regions in which members of different species meet and mate, producing some offspring of mixed ancestry. Such regions are "natural laboratories" in which to study speciation because scientists can directly observe factors that cause (or fail to cause) reproductive isolation. **2.** (a) If hybrids consistently survive and reproduce poorly compared to the offspring of intraspecific matings, it is possible that reinforcement would occur. If it did, natural selection would cause prezygotic barriers to reproduction between the parent species to strengthen over time, decreasing the production of unfit hybrids and leading to a completion of the speciation process. (b) If hybrid offspring survive and reproduce as well as the offspring of intraspecific matings, indiscriminate mating between the parent species would lead to the production of large numbers of hybrid offspring. As these hybrids mated with each other and with members of both parent species, the gene pools of the parent species could fuse over time, reversing the speciation process.

Concept Check 24.4

1. The time between speciation events includes (1) the length of time that it takes for populations of a newly formed species to begin diverging reproductively from one another and (2) the time it takes for speciation to be complete once this divergence begins. Although speciation can occur rapidly once populations have begun to diverge from one another, it may take millions of years for that divergence to begin. **2.** Investigators transferred alleles at the *yup* locus (which influences flower color) from each parent species to the other. *M. lewisii* plants with an *M. cardinalis yup* allele received many more visits from hummingbirds than usual; hummingbirds usually pollinate *M. cardinalis* but avoid *M. lewisii*. Similarly, *M. cardinalis* plants with an *M. lewisii yup* allele received many more visits from bumblebees than usual; bumblebees usually pollinate *M. lewisii* and avoid *M. cardinalis*. Thus, alleles at the *yup* locus can influence pollinator choice, which in these species provides the primary barrier to interspecific mating. Nevertheless, the experiment does not prove that the *yup* locus alone controls barriers to reproduction between *M. lewisii* and *M. cardinalis*; other genes

might enhance the effect of the *yup* locus (by modifying flower color) or cause entirely different barriers to reproduction (for example, gametic isolation or a postzygotic barrier).

Self-Quiz

1. b   **2.** a   **3.** c   **4.** e   **5.** d   **6.** c
8. One possible process is

CHAPTER 25

Figure Questions

Figure 25.5 Because uranium-238 has a half-life of 4.5 billion years, the *x*-axis would be relabeled (in billions of years) as: 4.5, 9, 13.5, and 18.   **Figure 25.23** The coding sequence of the *Pitx1* gene would differ between the marine and lake populations, but patterns of gene expression would not.

Concept Check 25.1

1. The hypothesis that conditions on early Earth could have permitted the synthesis of organic molecules from inorganic ingredients   **2.** In contrast to random mingling of molecules in an open solution, segregation of molecular systems by membranes could concentrate organic molecules, assisting biochemical reactions.   **3.** No. Such a result would only show that life *could* have begun as in the experiment.

Concept Check 25.2

1. 22,920 years (four half-lives: $5,730 \times 4$)   **2.** The fossil record shows that different groups of organisms dominated life on Earth at different points in time and that many organisms once alive are now extinct; specific examples of these points can be found in Figure 25.4. The fossil record also indicates that new groups of organisms can arise via the gradual modification of previously existing organisms, as illustrated by fossils that document the origin of mammals from cynodont ancestors.   **3.** The discovery of such a (hypothetical) fossil organism would indicate that aspects of our current understanding of the origin of mammals are not correct because mammals are thought to have originated much more recently (see Figure 25.6). For example, such a discovery could suggest that the dates of previous fossil discoveries are not correct or that the lineages shown in Figure 25.6 shared features with mammals but were not their direct ancestors. Such a discovery would also suggest that radical changes in multiple aspects of the skeletal structure of organisms could arise suddenly—an idea that is not supported by the known fossil record.

Concept Check 25.3

1. Free oxygen attacks chemical bonds and can inhibit enzymes and damage cells.   **2.** All eukaryotes have mitochondria or remnants of these organelles, but not all eukaryotes have plastids.   **3.** A fossil record of life today would include many organisms with hard body parts (such as vertebrates and many marine invertebrates), but might not include some species we are very familiar with, such as those that have small geographic ranges and/or small population sizes (for example, all five rhinoceros species).

Concept Check 25.4

1. Continental drift alters the physical geography and climate of Earth, as well as the extent to which organisms are geographically isolated. Because these factors affect extinction and speciation rates, continental drift has a major impact on life on Earth. **2.** Mass extinctions; major evolutionary innovations; the diversification of another group of organisms (which can provide new sources of food); migration to new locations where few competitor species exist **3.** Their fossils should be present right up to the time of the catastrophic event, then disappear. Reality is a bit more complicated because the fossil record is not perfect. So the most recent fossil for a species might be a million years before the mass extinction, even if the species did not become extinct until the mass extinction.

Concept Check 25.5

1. Heterochrony can cause a variety of morphological changes. For example, if the onset of sexual maturity changes, a retention of juvenile characteristics (paedomorphosis) may result. Paedomorphosis can be caused by small genetic changes that result in large changes in morphology, as seen in the axolotl salamander. **2.** In animal embryos, *Hox* genes influence the development of structures such as limbs or feeding appendages. As a result, changes in these genes—or in the regulation of these genes—are likely to have major effects on morphology. **3.** From genetics, we know that gene regulation is altered by how well transcription factors bind to noncoding DNA sequences called control elements. Thus, if changes in morphology are often caused by changes in gene regulation, portions of noncoding DNA that contain control elements are likely to be strongly affected by natural selection.

Concept Check 25.6

1. Complex structures do not evolve all at once, but in increments, with natural selection selecting for adaptive variants of the earlier versions. **2.** Although the myxoma virus is highly lethal, initially some of the rabbits are resistant (0.2% of infected rabbits are not killed). Thus, assuming resistance is an inherited trait, we would expect the rabbit population to show a trend for increased resistance to the virus. We would also expect the virus to show an evolutionary trend toward reduced lethality. We would expect this trend because a rabbit infected with a less lethal virus would be more likely to live long enough for a mosquito to bite it and hence potentially transmit the virus to another rabbit. (A virus that kills its rabbit host before a mosquito transmits it to another rabbit dies with its host.)

Self-Quiz

1. c **2.** a **3.** e **4.** b **5.** c **6.** d **7.** b
8.

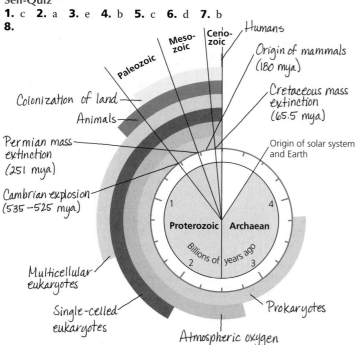

CHAPTER 26

Figure Questions

Figure 26.5 This new version does not alter any of the evolutionary relationships shown in Figure 26.5. For example, B and C remain sister taxa, taxon A is still as closely related to taxon B as it is to taxon C, and so on.

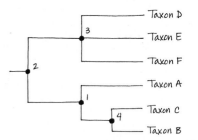

Figure 26.6 Mistakes can occur while performing the experiment (such as errors in DNA sequencing) and analyzing the results (such as misaligning the DNA sequences of different species). But an erroneous conclusion—such as concluding that a sample was from a humpback whale when in fact it came from a gray whale—could be reached even if no such errors were made. A particular humpback whale might, for example, happen to have a DNA sequence that was rare for its species, yet common for another species. To reduce the chance that such events could lead to an erroneous conclusion, gene trees could be constructed for multiple genes; if similar results emerged from all of these gene trees, there would be little reason to doubt the conclusions. **Figure 26.9** There are four possible bases (A, C, G, T) at each nucleotide position. If the base at each position depends on chance, not common descent, we would expect roughly one out of four (25%) of them to be the same. **Figure 26.12** The zebrafish lineage; of the five vertebrate lineages shown, its branch length is the longest. **Figure 26.19** The molecular clock indicates that the divergence time is roughly 45–50 million years. **Figure 26.21** Bacteria was the first to emerge. Archaea is the sister domain to Eukarya.

Concept Check 26.1

1. We are classified the same down to the class level; both the leopard and human are mammals. Leopards belong to order Carnivora, whereas humans do not. **2.** The branching pattern of the tree indicates that the badger and the wolf share a common ancestor that is more recent than the ancestor that these two animals share with the leopard. **3.** The tree in (c) shows a different pattern of evolutionary relationships. In (c), C and B are sister taxa, whereas C and D are sister taxa in (a) and (b).
4.

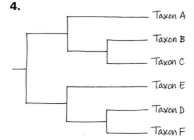

Concept Check 26.2

1. (a) Analogy, since porcupines and cacti are not closely related and since most other animals and plants do not have similar structures; (b) homology, since cats and humans are both mammals and have homologous forelimbs, of which the hand and paw are the lower part; (c) analogy, since owls and hornets are not closely related and since the structure of their wings is very different. **2.** Species 2 and 3 are more likely to be closely related. Small genetic changes (as between species 2 and 3) can produce divergent physical appearances, whereas if genes have diverged greatly (as in species 1 and 2), that suggests that the lineages have been separate for a long time.

Concept Check 26.3

1. No; hair is a shared ancestral character common to all mammals and thus is not helpful in distinguishing different mammalian subgroups. **2.** The principle of maximum parsimony states that the hypothesis about nature we investigate first should be the simplest explanation found to be consistent with the facts. Actual evolutionary relationships may differ from those inferred by parsimony owing to complicating factors such as convergent evolution. **3.** The traditional classification provides a poor match to evolutionary history, thus violating the basic principle of cladistics—that classification should be based on common descent. Both birds and mammals originated from groups traditionally designated as reptiles, making reptiles as traditionally delineated a paraphyletic group. These problems can be addressed by removing *Dimetrodon* and cynodonts from the reptiles, and by considering birds as a group of reptiles (specifically, as a group of dinosaurs).

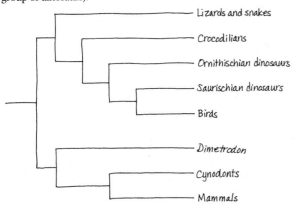

Concept Check 26.4

1. Proteins are gene products. Their amino acid sequences are determined by the nucleotide sequences of the DNA that codes for them. Thus, differences between comparable proteins in two species reflect underlying genetic differences. **2.** These observations suggest that the evolutionary lineages leading to species 1 and species 2 diverged from one another before a gene duplication event in species 1 produced gene B from gene A.

Concept Check 26.5

1. A molecular clock is a method of estimating the actual time of evolutionary events based on numbers of base changes in orthologous genes. It is based on the assumption that the regions of genomes being compared evolve at constant rates. **2.** There are many portions of the genome that do not code for genes; many base changes in these regions could accumulate through drift without affecting an organism's fitness. Even in coding regions of the genome, some mutations may not have a critical effect on genes or proteins. **3.** The gene (or genes) used for the molecular clock may have evolved more slowly in these two taxa than in the species used to calibrate the clock; as a result, the clock would underestimate the time at which the taxa diverged from one another.

Concept Check 26.6

1. The kingdom Monera included bacteria and archaea, but we now know that these organisms are in separate domains. Kingdoms are subsets of domains, so a single kingdom (like Monera) that includes taxa from different domains is not valid (it is polyphyletic). **2.** Because of horizontal gene transfer, some genes in eukaryotes are more closely related to bacteria, while others are more closely related to archaea; thus, depending on which genes are used, phylogenetic trees constructed from DNA data can yield conflicting results.

3.

The third tree, in which the eukaryotic lineage diverged first, is not likely to receive support from genetic data because the fossil record shows that prokaryotes originated long before eukaryotes.

Self-Quiz

1. b **2.** d **3.** a **4.** d **5.** c **6.** d **7.** d

9. (a)

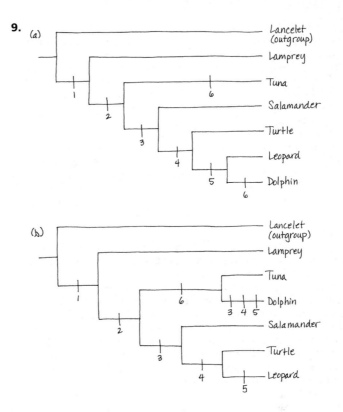

(b)

(c) The tree in (a) requires seven evolutionary changes, while the tree in (b) requires nine evolutionary changes. Thus, the tree in (a) is the most parsimonious, since it requires fewer evolutionary changes.

CHAPTER 27

Figure Questions

Figure 27.10 It is likely that the expression or sequence of genes that affect glucose metabolism may have changed; genes for metabolic processes no longer needed by the cell also may have changed. **Figure 27.12** The population that included individuals capable of conjugation would probably be more successful, since some of its members could form recombinant cells whose new gene combinations might be advantageous in a novel environment. **Figure 27.17** Thermophiles live in very hot environments, so it is likely that their enzymes can continue to function normally at much higher temperatures than do the enzymes of other organisms. At low temperatures, however, the enzymes of thermophiles may not function as well as the enzymes of other organisms. **Figure 27.19** From the graph, plant uptake can be estimated as 0.7, 0.6, and 0.95 (mg K) for strains 1, 2, and 3, respectively. These values average to 0.75 mg K. If bacteria had no effect, the average plant uptake of potassium for strains 1, 2, and 3 should be close to 0.5 mg K, the value observed for plants grown in bacteria-free soil.

Concept Check 27.1

1. Adaptations include the capsule (shields prokaryotes from host's immune system) and endospores (enable cells to survive harsh conditions and to revive when the environment becomes favorable). **2.** Prokaryotic cells generally lack the internal compartmentalization of eukaryotic cells. Prokaryotic genomes have much less DNA than eukaryotic genomes, and most of this DNA is contained in a single ring-shaped chromosome located in the nucleoid rather than within a true membrane-bounded nucleus. In addition, many prokaryotes also have plasmids, small ring-shaped DNA molecules containing a few genes. **3.** Because prokaryotic populations evolve rapidly in response to their environment, it is likely that bacteria from endospores that formed 40 years ago would already be adapted to the polluted conditions. Hence, at least initially, these bacteria would probably grow better than bacteria from endospores that formed 150 years ago, when the lake was not polluted.

Concept Check 27.2

1. Prokaryotes have extremely large population sizes, in part because they have short generation times. The large number of individuals in prokaryotic populations makes it likely that in each generation there will be thousands of individuals that have new mutations at any particular gene, thereby adding considerable genetic diversity to the population. **2.** In transformation, naked, foreign DNA from the environment is taken up by a bacterial cell. In transduction, phages carry bacterial genes from one bacterial cell to another. In conjugation, a bacterial cell directly transfers plasmid or chromosomal DNA to another cell via a mating bridge that temporarily connects the two cells. **3.** Yes. Genes for antibiotic resistance could be transferred (by transformation, transduction, or conjugation) from the nonpathogenic bacterium to a pathogenic bacterium; this could make the pathogen an even greater threat to human health. In general, transformation, transduction, and conjugation tend to increase the spread of resistance genes.

Concept Check 27.3

1. A phototroph derives its energy from light, while a chemotroph gets its energy from chemical sources. An autotroph derives its carbon from inorganic sources (often CO_2), while a heterotroph gets its carbon from organic sources. Thus, there are four nutritional modes: photoautotrophic, photoheterotrophic (unique to prokaryotes), chemoautotrophic (unique to prokaryotes), and chemoheterotrophic. **2.** Chemoheterotrophy; the bacterium must rely on chemical sources of energy, since it is not exposed to light, and it must be a heterotroph if it requires an organic source of carbon rather than CO_2 (or another inorganic source, like bicarbonate). **3.** If humans could fix nitrogen, we could build proteins using atmospheric N_2 and hence would not need to eat high-protein foods such as meat or fish. Our diet would, however, need to include a source of carbon, along with minerals and water. Thus, a typical meal might consist of carbohydrates as a carbon source, along with fruits and vegetables to provide essential minerals (and additional carbon).

Concept Check 27.4

1. Before molecular systematics, taxonomists classified prokaryotes according to phenotypic characters that did not clarify evolutionary relationships. Molecular comparisons—of DNA in particular—indicate key divergences in prokaryotic lineages. **2.** By not requiring that organisms be cultured in the laboratory, genetic prospecting has revealed an immense diversity of previously unknown prokaryotic species. Over time, the ongoing discovery of new species by genetic prospecting is likely to alter our understanding of prokaryotic phylogeny greatly. **3.** At present, all known methanogens are archaea in the clade Euryarchaeota; this suggests that this unique metabolic pathway arose in ancestral species within Euryarchaeota. Since Bacteria and Archaea have been separate evolutionary lineages for billions of years, the discovery of a methanogen from the domain Bacteria would suggest that adaptations that enabled the use of CO_2 to oxidize H_2 evolved at least twice—once in Archaea (within Euryarchaeota) and once in Bacteria.

Concept Check 27.5

1. Although prokaryotes are small, their large numbers and metabolic abilities enable them to play key roles in ecosystems by decomposing wastes, recycling chemicals, and affecting the concentrations of nutrients available to other organisms. **2.** *Bacteroides thetaiotaomicron*, which lives inside the human intestine, benefits by obtaining nutrients from the digestive system and by receiving protection from competing bacteria from host-produced antimicrobial compounds to which it is not sensitive. The human host benefits because the bacterium manufactures carbohydrates, vitamins, and other nutrients. **3.** Some of the many different species of prokaryotes that live in the human gut compete with one another for resources (in the food you eat). Because different prokaryotic species have different adaptations, a change in diet may alter which species can grow most rapidly, thus altering species abundance.

Concept Check 27.6

1. Sample answers: eating fermented foods such as yogurt, sourdough bread, or cheese; receiving clean water from sewage treatment; taking medicines produced by bacteria. **2.** No. If the poison is secreted as an exotoxin, live bacteria could be transmitted to another person. But the same is true if the poison is an endotoxin—only in this case, the live bacteria that are transmitted may be descendants of the (now-dead) bacteria that produced the poison. **3.** Strain K-12 may have lost genes by deletion mutations. A phylogenetic analysis would help distinguish between these hypotheses—if some of the genes found in O157:H7 but not in K-12 are present in the common ancestor of the two strains, that would suggest that strain K-12 lost these genes over the course of its evolution.

Self-Quiz

1. e **2.** a **3.** d **4.** d **5.** b **6.** a
8. (a)

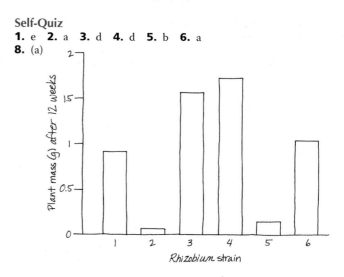

(b) Some *Rhizobium* strains are much more effective at promoting plant growth than are other *Rhizobium* strains; the most ineffective strains have little positive effect (plant growth with these strains differs little from plant growth in the absence of *Rhizobium*). The ineffective strains may transfer relatively little nitrogen to their plant host, hence limiting plant growth.

CHAPTER 28

Figure Questions

Figure 28.10 Merozoites are produced by the asexual (mitotic) cell division of haploid sporozoites; similarly, gametocytes are produced by the asexual cell division of merozoites. Hence, it is likely that individuals in these three stages have the same complement of genes and that morphological differences between them result from changes in gene expression. **Figure 28.22** The following stage should be circled: step 6, where a mature cell undergoes mitosis and forms four or more daughter cells. In step 7, the zoospores eventually grow into mature haploid cells, but they do not produce new daughter cells. Likewise, in step 2, a mature cell develops into a gamete, but it does not produce new daughter cells. **Figure 28.23** If the assumption is correct, then their results indicate that the DHFR-TS gene fusion may be a derived trait shared by members of four supergroups of eukaryotes (Excavata, Chromalveolata, Rhizaria, and Archaeplastida). However, if the assumption is not correct, the presence or absence of the gene fusion may tell little about phylogenetic history. For example, if the genes fused multiple times, groups could share the trait because of convergent evolution rather than common descent. If the genes were secondarily split, a group with such a split could be placed (incorrectly) in Unikonta rather than its correct placement in one of the other four supergroups.

Concept Check 28.1

1. Sample response: Protists include unicellular, colonial, and multicellular organisms; photoautotrophs, heterotrophs, and mixotrophs; species that reproduce asexually, sexually, or both ways; and organisms with diverse physical forms and adaptations. **2.** Strong evidence shows that eukaryotes acquired mitochondria after an early eukaryote first engulfed and then formed an endosymbiotic association with an alpha proteobacterium. Similarly, chloroplasts in red and green algae appear to have descended from a photosynthetic cyanobacterium that was engulfed by an ancient heterotrophic eukaryote. Secondary endosymbiosis also played an important role: Various protist lineages acquired plastids by engulfing unicellular red or green algae. **3.** The modified tree would look as follows:

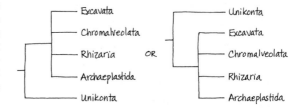

and the placenta completely takes over progesterone production.   **2.** Both tubal ligation and vasectomy block the movement of gametes from the gonads to a site where fertilization could take place.   **3.** By introducing a spermatid nucleus directly into an oocyte, ICSI bypasses the sperm's acquisition of motility in the epididymis, its swimming to meet the egg in the oviduct, and its fusion with the egg.

Self-Quiz
1. d   **2.** b   **3.** a   **4.** b   **5.** c   **6.** c   **7.** a   **8.** d
9.

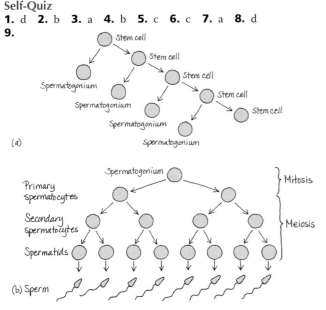

(c) The supply of stem cells would be used up and spermatogenesis would not be able to continue.

CHAPTER 47

Figure Questions
Figure 47.4 You could inject the compound into an unfertilized egg, expose the egg to sperm, and see whether the fertilization envelope forms. **Figure 47.7** The researchers allowed normal cortical rotation to occur, resulting in activation of the "back-forming" determinants. Then they forced the opposite rotation to occur, which established the back on the opposite side as well. Because the molecules on the normal side were already activated, forcing the opposite rotation apparently did not "cancel out" the establishment of the back side by the first rotation.   **Figure 47.14** Given that these regions form from ectoderm but are just inside the body, you might propose that they form by an inpocketing of the ectoderm that then meets and fuses with the endoderm. And you would be right!   **Figure 47.19** Cadherin is required to hold the cells of the blastula together, and extracellular calcium is required for cadherin function, so in the absence of calcium in the water, you'd expect to see a disorganized embryo like the one shown in the experimental SEM.   **Figure 47.20** You could cut out the same tissues from control and injected embryos as was done in experiment 2 and place them between cover slips coated with the artificial fibronectin (FN) matrix. If convergent extension occurred in the tissues from both injected and control embryos, that would support the hypothesis that convergent extension can occur on a preexisting FN matrix in the embryo.   **Figure 47.23** In Spemann's control, the two blastomeres were physically separated, and each grew into a whole embryo. In Roux's experiment, remnants of the dead blastomere were still contacting the live blastomere, which developed into a half-embryo. Therefore, molecules present in the dead cell's remnants may have been signaling to the live cell, inhibiting it from making all the embryonic structures.   **Figure 47.24** You could inject the isolated protein or an mRNA encoding it into ventral cells of an earlier gastrula. If dorsal structures formed on the ventral side, that would support the idea that the protein is the signaling molecule secreted or presented by the dorsal lip. You should also do a control experiment to make sure the injection process alone did not cause dorsal structures to form.   **Figure 47.26** You could remove the AER and look for Sonic

hedgehog mRNA or protein as a marker of the ZPA. If either was absent, that would support your hypothesis. You could also block FGF function and see whether the ZPA formed (by looking for Sonic hedgehog).

Concept Check 47.1
1. The fertilization envelope forms after cortical granules release their contents outside the egg, causing the vitelline membrane to rise and harden. The fertilization envelope serves as a barrier to fertilization by more than one sperm.   **2.** During cleavage in frogs and many other animals, the cell cycle is modified so that it virtually skips G_1 and G_2, the growth phases. As a result, the early cleavage divisions divide the zygote's cytoplasm into smaller and smaller cells as the embryo's size remains nearly the same.   **3.** Cleavage transforms the single-celled zygote into an embryo consisting of many cells; cleavage does not involve cell or tissue movement. During gastrulation, the cells and tissues of a blastula are extensively rearranged, so that by the late gastrula stage there are three tissue layers positioned in new relationships to each other.   **4.** The neural tube forms when a band of ectodermal tissue on the dorsal side along the anterior-posterior axis, called the neural plate, rolls into a tube and pinches off from the rest of the ectoderm. Neural crest cells arise as groups of cells in the regions between the edges of the neural tube and the surrounding ectoderm migrate away from the neural tube.   **5.** The increased Ca^{2+} concentration in the egg would cause the cortical granules to fuse with the plasma membrane, releasing their contents and causing a fertilization envelope to form, even though no sperm had entered. This would prevent fertilization.   **6.** Conjoined twins develop from monozygotic twins that separate quite late, after part of the embryo has already formed. (This part is shared by the twins.) By this time, both the chorion and amnion have formed, so there is only one of each.

Concept Check 47.2
1. Microtubules elongate, lengthening the cell along one axis, while microfilaments oriented crosswise at one end of the cell contract, making that end smaller and the whole cell wedge-shaped.   **2.** The cells of the notochord migrate toward the midline of the embryo (converge), rearranging themselves so there are fewer cells across the notochord, which thus becomes longer overall (extends; see Figure 47.18).   **3.** Because microfilaments would not be able to contract and decrease the size of one end of the cell, both the inward bending in the middle of the neural tube and the outward bending of the hinge regions at the edges would be blocked. Therefore, the neural tube probably would not form.

Concept Check 47.3
1. Once the first two axes are specified, the third one is automatically determined. (Think of your own body: If you know where your anterior and posterior ends are and where your left and right sides are, you automatically know which sides are your front and back.) Of course, there still must be a mechanism for determining where asymmetrically placed organs must go, such as the vertebrate stomach or appendix.   **2.** Yes, a second embryo could develop because inhibiting BMP-4 activity would have the same effect as transplanting an organizer.   **3.** The limb that developed probably would have a mirror-image duplication, with the most posterior digits in the middle and the most anterior digits at either end.

Self-Quiz
1. a   **2.** b   **3.** e   **4.** c   **5.** a   **6.** c   **7.** e
8.

CHAPTER 48

Figure Questions

Figure 48.7 Adding chloride channels makes the membrane potential less negative. Adding sodium or potassium channels would have no effect, because sodium movement is already at equilibrium and there are no potassium ions present. **Figure 48.15** The production and transmission of action potentials would be unaffected. However, action potentials arriving at chemical synapses would be unable to trigger release of neurotransmitter. Signaling at such synapses would thus be blocked. **Figure 48.17** In theory, the results would be similar because the binding studies indicate that both opiates and naloxone, an opiate antagonist, bind directly to the receptor.

Concept Check 48.1

1. Sensors in your ear transmit information to your brain. There the activity of interneurons in processing centers enables you to recognize your name. In response, signals transmitted via motor neurons cause contraction of muscles that turn your neck. **2.** The nervous system is required for control of vital functions, such as circulation and gas exchange, and the transmission of information occurs on a very short time scale. **3.** It would prevent information from being transmitted away from the cell body along the axon.

Concept Check 48.2

1. Ions can flow against a chemical concentration gradient if there is an opposing electrical gradient of greater magnitude. **2.** A decrease in permeability to K^+, an increase in permeability to Na^+, or both. **3.** The activity of the sodium-potassium pump is essential to maintain the resting potential. With the pump inactivated, the sodium and potassium concentration gradients would gradually disappear, and so would the resting potential.

Concept Check 48.3

1. A graded potential has a magnitude that varies with stimulus strength, whereas an action potential has an all-or-none magnitude that is independent of stimulus strength. **2.** Loss of the insulation provided by myelin sheaths leads to a disruption of action potential propagation along axons. Voltage-gated sodium channels are restricted to the nodes of Ranvier, and without the insulating effect of myelin, the inward current produced at one node during an action potential cannot depolarize the membrane to the threshold at the next node. **3.** The maximum frequency would decrease because the refractory period would be extended.

Concept Check 48.4

1. It can bind to different types of receptors, each triggering a specific response in postsynaptic cells. **2.** These toxins would prolong the EPSPs that acetylcholine produces because the neurotransmitter would remain longer in the synaptic cleft. **3.** Such a drug might act as a sedative, decreasing the general level of activity in the brain and hence in the person.

Self-Quiz

1. c **2.** b **3.** c **4.** a **5.** c **6.** e

7. As shown in this pair of drawings, a pair of action potentials would move outward in both directions from each electrode. (Action potentials are unidirectional only if they begin at one end of an axon.) However, because of the refractory period, the two action potentials between the electrodes both stop where they meet. Thus, only one action potential reaches the synaptic terminals.

CHAPTER 49

Figure Questions

Figure 49.8 Neurosecretory cells of the adrenal medulla secrete epinephrine in response to preganglionic input from sympathetic neurons. Epinephrine travels in the circulation to reach target tissues throughout the body. Thus, the rapid changes in body tissues required for the "fight-or-flight" response rely on direct input from the nervous system as well as indirect input via neurohormone products of the adrenal medulla. **Figure 49.12** If the new mutation disrupted only pacemaker function, you should be able to restore rhythmic activity by removing the SCN and replacing it with an SCN transplant from either a wild-type or τ mutant hamster. Using the new mutant as the donor would not be as informative, since both failed transplants and successful ones would result in a lack of rhythmic activity. **Figure 49.22** The depolarization should mimic natural stimulation of the brain reward system, resulting in positive and perhaps pleasurable sensations.

Concept Check 49.1

1. The sympathetic division, which mediates the "fight-or-flight" response in stressful situations **2.** The preganglionic neurons use the same neurotransmitter and function similarly in each division (to activate postganglionic neurons). The postganglionic neurons generally have opposing functions and use different neurotransmitters. **3.** Nerves contain bundles of axons, some of which belong to motor neurons that send signals outward from the CNS, and some that belong to sensory neurons that bring signals into the CNS. Therefore, you would expect effects on both motor control and sensation.

Concept Check 49.2

1. The cerebral cortex on the left side of the brain control initiates voluntary movement of the right side of the body. **2.** Alcohol diminishes function of the cerebellum. **3.** Paralysis reflects an inability to carry out motor functions transmitted from the cerebrum to the spinal cord. You would expect these patients to have injuries below the reticular formation. A coma reflects a disruption in the cycles of sleep and arousal regulated by communication between the reticular formation and the cerebrum. You would expect these patients to have injuries at or above the reticular formation.

Concept Check 49.3

1. Brain lesions that disrupt behavior, cognition, memory, or other functions provide evidence that the portion of the brain affected by the damage is important for the normal activity that is blocked or altered. **2.** Broca's area, which is active during the generation of speech, is located near the part of the primary motor cortex that controls muscles in the face. Wernicke's area, which is active when speech is heard, is located near the part of the temporal lobe that is involved in hearing. **3.** Each cerebral hemisphere is specialized for different parts of this task—the right for face recognition and the left for language. Without an intact corpus callosum, neither hemisphere can take advantage of the other's processing abilities.

Concept Check 49.4

1. There can be an increase in the number of synapses between the neurons or an increase in the strength of existing synaptic connections. **2.** If consciousness is an emergent property resulting from the interaction of many different regions of the brain, then it is unlikely that localized brain damage will have a discrete effect on consciousness. **3.** The hippocampus is responsible for organizing newly acquired information. Without hippocampal function, the links necessary to retrieve information from the neocortex will be lacking and no functional memory, short- or long-term, will be formed.

Concept Check 49.5

1. Both are progressive brain diseases whose risk increases with advancing age. Both result from the death of brain neurons and are associated with the accumulation of peptide or protein aggregates. **2.** The symptoms of schizophrenia can be mimicked by a drug that stimulates dopamine-releasing neurons. The brain reward system, which is involved in addiction, is comprised of dopamine-releasing neurons that connect the ventral tegmental area to regions in the cerebrum. Parkinson's disease results from the death of dopamine-releasing neurons. **3.** Not necessarily. It might be that the plaques, tangles, and missing regions of the brain seen at death reflect secondary effects, the consequence of other unseen changes that are actually responsible for the alterations in brain function.

Self-Quiz

1. c **2.** a **3.** d **4.** d **5.** e **6.** c

7. (a)

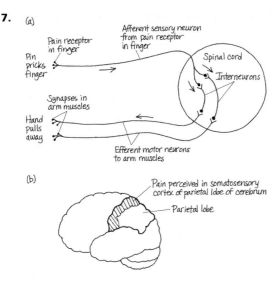

(b)

CHAPTER 50

Figure Questions

Figure 50.10 In the brain. Each note is detected separately in the ear, with each causing vibration of the basilar membrane and deflection of hair cells in a distinct location. Sensory neurons in each location provide output in the form of action potentials that travel along distinct axons in the auditory nerve. It is not until the information reaches the brain that the individual notes are detected and the perception of the chord is generated. **Figure 50.14** The results of the experiment would have been identical. What matters is the activation of particular sets of neurons, not the manner in which they are activated. Any signal from a bitter cell will be interpreted by the brain as a bitter taste, regardless of the nature of the compound and the receptor involved. **Figure 50.15** Only perception. Binding of an odorant to its receptor will cause action potentials to be sent to the brain. Although an excess of that odorant might cause a diminished response through adaptation, another odorant can mask the first only at the level of perception in the brain. **Figure 50.22** Each of the three types of cones is most sensitive to a distinct wavelength of light. A cone might be fully depolarized when there is light present if the light is of a wavelength far from its optimum. **Figure 50.27** Hundreds of myosin heads participate in sliding each pair of thick and thin filaments past each other. Because cross-bridge formation and breakdown are not synchronized, many myosin heads are exerting force on the thin filaments at all times during muscle contraction. **Figure 50.37** Since a duck is more specialized for flying than for swimming, you might expect that it would consume more energy per unit body mass and distance in swimming than would, for example, a fish. (In fact, if the value for a 10^3 g swimming duck were plotted on this graph, it would appear well above the line for swimmers and just above the line for runners.)

Concept Check 50.1

1. Electromagnetic receptors in general detect only external stimuli. Non-electromagnetic receptors, such as chemoreceptors or mechanoreceptors, can act as either internal or external sensors. **2.** The capsaicin present in the spice mix activates the thermoreceptor for high temperatures. In response to the perceived high temperature, the nervous system triggers sweating to achieve evaporative cooling. **3.** You would perceive the electrical stimulus as if the sensory receptors that regulate that neuron had been activated. For example, electrical stimulation of the sensory neuron controlled by the thermoreceptor activated by menthol would likely be perceived as a local cooling.

Concept Check 50.2

1. Statocysts detect the animal's orientation with respect to gravity, providing information that is essential in environments such as these, where light cues are absent. **2.** As a sound that changes gradually from a very low to a very high pitch **3.** The stapes and the other middle ear bones transmit vibrations from the tympanic membrane to the oval window. Fusion of these bones, as occurs in otosclerosis, would block this transmission and result in hearing loss.

Concept Check 50.3

1. Both taste cells and olfactory cells have receptor proteins in their plasma membrane that bind certain substances, leading to membrane depolarization through a signal transduction pathway involving a G protein. However, olfactory cells are sensory neurons, whereas taste cells are not. **2.** Since animals rely on chemical signals for behaviors that include finding mates, marking territories, and avoiding dangerous substances, it is adaptive for the olfactory system to have a robust response to a very small number of molecules of a particular odorant. **3.** Because the sweet, bitter, and umami tastes involve GPCR proteins but the sour taste does not, you might predict that the mutation is in a molecule that acts in the signal transduction pathway common to the different GPCR receptors.

Concept Check 50.4

1. Planarians have ocelli that cannot form images but can sense the intensity and direction of light, providing enough information to enable the animals to find protection in shaded places. Flies have compound eyes that form images and excel at detecting movement. **2.** The person can focus on distant objects but not close objects (without glasses) because close focusing requires the lens to become almost spherical. This problem is common after age 50. **3.** Close each eye in turn. An object floating on the surface of an eyeball will appear only when that eye is open.

Concept Check 50.5

1. By causing all of the motor neurons that control the muscle to generate action potentials at a rate high enough to produce tetanus in all of the muscle fibers **2.** In a skeletal muscle fiber, Ca^{2+} binds to the troponin complex, which moves tropomyosin away from the myosin-binding sites on actin and allows cross-bridges to form. In a smooth muscle cell, Ca^{2+} binds to calmodulin, which activates an enzyme that phosphorylates the myosin head and thus enables cross-bridge formation. **3.** *Rigor mortis*, a Latin phrase meaning "stiffness of death," results from the complete depletion of ATP in skeletal muscle. Since ATP is required for release of myosin from actin and to pump Ca^{2+} out of the cytosol, muscles become chronically contracted beginning about 3 or 4 hours after death.

Concept Check 50.6

1. Septa provide the divisions of the coelom that allow for peristalsis, a form of locomotion requiring independent control of different body segments. **2.** The main problem in swimming is drag; a fusiform body minimizes drag. The main problem in flying is overcoming gravity; wings shaped like airfoils provide lift, and adaptations such as air-filled bones reduce body mass. **3.** You could start by standing with your upper arm against your side and your lower arm extended out at a ninety degree angle from your hip. You could then slowly lower your hand toward the ground. Because you are holding the weight of your hand and lower arm against gravity, you need to maintain tetanus in the biceps muscle. As you lower your hand, you are gradually decreasing the number of motor units in the biceps that are contracted. The triceps is not involved because gravity is providing the force for arm extension.

Self Quiz

1. e **2.** d **3.** b **4.** a **5.** c **6.** b
7.

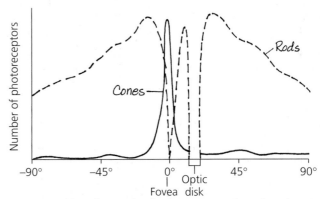

The answer shows the actual distribution of rods and cones in the human eye. Your graph may differ but should have the following properties: Only cones at the fovea; fewer cones and more rods at both ends of the *x*-axis; no photoreceptors in the optic disk.

CHAPTER 51

Figure Questions

Figure 51.3 The fixed action pattern based on the sign stimulus of a red belly ensures that the male will chase away any invading males of his species. By chasing away such males, the defender decreases the chance that eggs laid in his nesting territory will be fertilized by another male. **Figure 51.10** There should be no effect. Imprinting is an innate behavior that is carried out anew in each generation. Assuming the nest was not disturbed, the offspring of the Lorenz followers would imprint on the mother goose. **Figure 51.11** Perhaps the wasp doesn't use visual cues. It might also be that wasps recognize objects native to their environment, but not foreign objects, such as the pinecones. Tinbergen addressed these ideas before carrying out the pinecone study. When he swept away the pebbles and sticks around the nest, the wasps could no longer find their nests. If he shifted the natural objects in their natural arrangement, the shift in the landmarks caused a shift in the site to which the wasps returned. Finally, if the natural objects around the nest site were replaced with pinecones while the wasp was in the burrow, the wasp nevertheless found her way back to the nest site. **Figure 51.14** Courtship song generation must be coupled to courtship song recognition. Unless the genes that control generation of particular song elements also control recognition, the hybrids might be unlikely to find mating partners, depending on what aspects of the songs are important for mate recognition and acceptance. **Figure 51.15** It might be that the birds require stimuli during flight to exhibit their migratory preference. If this were true, the birds would show the same orientation in the funnel experiment despite their distinct genetic programming. **Figure 51.28** It holds true for some, but not all individuals. If a parent has more than one reproductive partner, the offspring of different partners will have a coefficient of relatedness less than 0.5.

Concept Check 51.1

1. It is an example of a fixed action pattern. The proximate explanation might be that nudging and rolling are released by the sign stimulus of an object outside the nest, and the behavior is carried to completion once initiated. The ultimate explanation might be that ensuring that eggs remain in the nest increases the chance of producing healthy offspring. **2.** Circannual rhythms are typically based on the cycles of light and dark in the environment. As the global climate changes, animals that migrate in response to these rhythms may shift to a location before or after local environmental conditions are optimal for reproduction and survival. **3.** There might be selective pressure for other prey fish to detect an injured fish because the source of the injury might threaten them as well. There might be selection for predators to be attracted to the alarm substance because they would be more likely to encounter crippled prey than would be predators that can't respond. Fish with adequate defenses might show no change because they have a selective advantage if they do not waste energy responding to the alarm substance.

Concept Check 51.2

1. Natural selection would tend to favor convergence in color pattern because a predator learning to associate a pattern with a sting or bad taste would avoid all other individuals with that same color pattern, regardless of species. **2.** Forgetting the location of some caches, which consist of pine seeds buried in the ground, might benefit the nutcracker by increasing the number of pines growing in its habitat. This example points out one of the difficulties in making simplistic assumptions about the purpose of a behavior. **3.** You might move objects around to establish an abstract rule, such as "past landmark A, the same distance as A is from the starting point," while maintaining a minimum of fixed metric relationships, that is, avoiding having the food directly adjacent to or a set distance from a landmark. As you might surmise, designing an informative experiment of this kind is not easy.

Concept Check 51.3

1. Because this geographic variation corresponds to differences in prey availability between two garter snake habitats, it seems likely that snakes with characteristics enabling them to feed on the abundant prey in their locale would have had increased survival and reproductive success, and thus natural selection would have resulted in the divergent foraging behaviors. **2.** Courtship is easier to study because it is essential for reproduction, but

not for growth, development, and survival. Mutations disrupting many other behaviors would be lethal. **3.** You would need to know the percentage of time that unrelated individuals behave identically when performing this behavior.

Concept Check 51.4

1. Certainty of paternity is higher with external fertilization. **2.** Natural selection acts on genetic variation in the population. **3.** Because females would now be present in much larger numbers than males, all three types of males should have some reproductive success. Nevertheless, since the advantage that the blue-throats rely on—a limited number of females in their territory—will be absent, the yellow-throats are likely to increase in frequency in the short term.

Concept Check 51.5

1. Reciprocal altruism, the exchange of helpful behaviors for future similar behaviors, can explain cooperative behaviors between unrelated animals, though often the behavior has some potential benefit to the benefactor as well. **2.** Yes. Kin selection does not require any recognition or awareness of relatedness. **3.** The older individual cannot be the beneficiary because he or she cannot have extra offspring. However, the cost is low for an older individual performing the altruistic act because that person has already reproduced (but perhaps is still caring for a child or grandchild). There can therefore be selection for an altruistic act by a postreproductive individual that benefits a young relative.

Self-Quiz

1. d **2.** a **3.** c **4.** a **5.** c **6.** b **7.** c
8.

You could measure the size of mussels that oystercatchers successfully open and compare that with the size distribution in the habitat.

CHAPTER 52

Figure Questions

Figure 52.6 Some factors, such as fire, are relevant only for terrestrial systems. At first glance, water availability is primarily a terrestrial factor, too. However, species living along the intertidal zone of oceans or along the edge of lakes suffer desiccation as well. Salinity stress is important for species in some aquatic and terrestrial systems. Oxygen availability is an important factor primarily for species in some aquatic systems and in soils and sediments. **Figure 52.8** When only urchins were removed, limpets may have increased in abundance and reduced seaweed cover somewhat (the difference between the purple and blue lines on the graph). **Figure 52.14** Dispersal limitations, the activities of people (such as a broad-scale conversion of forests to agriculture or selective harvesting), or other factors listed in Figure 52.6.

Concept Check 52.1

1. *Ecology* is the scientific study of the interactions between organisms and their environment; *environmentalism* is advocacy for the environment. Ecology provides scientific understanding that can inform decision making about environmental issues. **2.** Interactions in ecological time that affect the survival or reproduction of organisms can result in changes to the population's gene pool and ultimately result in a change in the population on an evolutionary time scale. **3.** If the fungicides are used together, fungi will likely evolve resistance to all four much more quickly than if the fungicides are used individually at different times.

Concept Check 52.2

1. a. Humans could transplant a species to a new area that it could not previously reach because of a geographic barrier (dispersal change). b. Humans could change a species' biotic interactions by eliminating a predator or herbivore species, such as sea urchins, from an area. **2.** The sun's unequal heating of Earth's surface produces temperature variations between the warmer tropics and colder polar regions, and it influences the movement of air masses and thus the distribution of moisture at different latitudes. **3.** One test would be to build a fence around a plot of land in an area that has trees of that species, excluding all deer from the plot. You could then compare the abundance of tree seedlings inside and outside the fenced plot over time.

Concept Check 52.3
1. Rapid changes in salinity can cause salt stress in many organisms. **2.** In the oceanic pelagic zone, the ocean bottom lies below the photic zone, so there is too little light to support benthic algae or rooted plants. **3.** In a river below a dam, the fish are more likely to be species that prefer colder water. In summer, the deep layers of a reservoir are colder than the surface layers, so a river below a dam will be colder than an undammed river.

Concept Check 52.4
1. Higher average temperature in deserts **2.** Answers will vary by location but should be based on the information and maps in Figure 52.21. How much your local area has been altered from its natural state will influence how much it reflects the expected characteristics of your biome, particularly the expected plants and animals. **3.** Northern coniferous forest is likely to replace tundra along the boundary between these biomes. To see why, note that northern coniferous forest is adjacent to tundra throughout North America, northern Europe, and Asia (see Figure 52.19) and that the temperature range for northern coniferous forest is just above that for tundra (see Figure 52.20).

Self-Quiz
1. c **2.** d **3.** a **4.** d **5.** b **6.** d **7.** d **8.** e **9.** a
10.

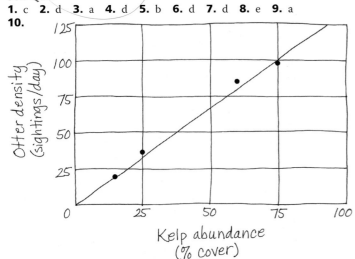

Based on what you learned from Figure 52.8 and on the positive relationship you observed in the field between kelp abundance and otter density, you could hypothesize that otters lower sea urchin density, reducing feeding of the urchins on kelp.

CHAPTER 53

Figure Questions
Figure 53.4 The dispersion of the penguins would likely appear clumped as you flew over densely populated islands and sparsely populated ocean. **Figure 53.8** If male European kestrels provided no parental care, brood size should not affect their survival. Therefore, the three bars representing male survival in Figure 53.8 should have similar heights. In contrast, female survival should still decline with increasing brood size, as shown in the current figure. **Figure 53.19** The moose population grew quickly because food was abundant and predators were absent. During this period, the population experienced exponential growth. **Figure 53.20** Hare numbers typically peaked slightly before lynx numbers did. The lynx depend on the hares for food, but there is a delay between increased food availability and increased reproduction by the lynx.

Concept Check 53.1
1. The territorial species likely has a uniform pattern of dispersion, since the interactions between individuals will maintain constant space between

them. The flocking species is probably clumped, since most individuals probably live in one of the clumps (flocks).
2.

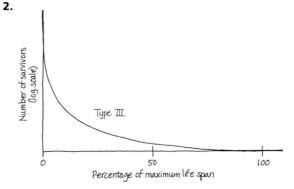

A type III survivorship curve is most likely because very few of the young probably survive. **3.** If an animal is captured by attracting it with food, it may be more likely to be recaptured if it seeks the same food. The number of marked animals recaptured (x) would be an overestimate, and because the population size $(N) = mn/x$, N would be an underestimate. Alternatively, if an animal has a negative experience during capture and learns from that experience, it may be less likely to be recaptured. In this case, x would be an underestimate and N would be an overestimate.

Concept Check 53.2
1. The constant, spring-fed stream. In more constant physical conditions, where populations are more stable and competition for resources is more likely, larger well-provisioned young, which are more typical of iteroparous species, have a better chance of surviving. **2.** By preferentially investing in the eggs it lays in the nest, the peacock wrasse increases their probability of survival. The eggs it disperses widely and does not provide care for are less likely to survive, at least some of the time, but require a lower investment by the adults. (In this sense, the adults avoid the risk of placing all their eggs in one basket.) **3.** If a parent's survival is compromised greatly by bearing young during times of stress, the animal's fitness may increase if it abandons its current young and survives to produce healthier young at a later time.

Concept Check 53.3
1. Though r_{max} is constant, N, the population size, is increasing. As r_{max} is applied to an increasingly large N, population growth $(r_{max}N)$ accelerates, producing the J-shaped curve. **2.** On the new island. The first plants that found suitable habitat on the island would encounter an abundance of space, nutrients, and light. In the rain forest, competition among plants for these resources is intense. **3.** The net population growth is $\Delta N/\Delta t = bN - dN$. The annual per capita birth rate, b, equals 14/1,000, or 0.014, and the per capita death rate, d, equals 8/1,000, or 0.008. Therefore, the net population growth in 2006 is

$$\frac{\Delta N}{\Delta t} = (0.014 \times 300,000,000) - (0.008 \times 300,000,000)$$

or 1.8 million people. A population is growing exponentially only if its per capita rate of increase equals its maximum rate. That is not the case for the United States currently.

Concept Check 53.4
1. When N (population size) is small, there are relatively few individuals producing offspring. When N is large, near the carrying capacity, per capita growth is relatively small because it is limited by available resources. The steepest part of the logistic growth curve corresponds to a population with a number of reproducing individuals that is substantial but not yet near carrying capacity. **2.** r-selected. Weeds that colonize an abandoned field face little competition, and their initial populations are well below carrying capacity. These are characteristics of environments that favor r-selected species. **3.** Using a population size of 1,600 as an example,

$$\frac{dN}{dt} = r_{max}N \frac{(K-N)}{K} = \frac{1(1,600)(1,500 - 1,600)}{1,500}$$

and the population "growth" rate is –107 individuals per year. The population shrinks even faster when N is farther from the carrying capacity; when N equals 1,750 and 2,000 individuals, the population shrinks by 292 and 667 individuals per year, respectively. These negative growth rates correspond most closely to the time when the *Daphnia* population has overshot its carrying capacity and is shrinking, about days 65–100 in Figure 53.13b.

Concept Check 53.5

1. Competition for resources and space can negatively impact population growth by limiting reproductive output. Diseases that are transmitted more easily in crowded populations can exert negative feedback on increasing population size. Some predators feed preferentially on species at higher population densities, since those prey are easier to find than are prey in less dense populations. In crowded populations, toxic metabolic wastes can build up and poison the organisms. **2.** Three attributes are the size, quality, and isolation of patches. A patch that is larger or of higher quality is more likely to attract individuals and to be a source of individuals for other patches. A patch that is relatively isolated will undergo less exchange of individuals with other patches. **3.** You would need to study the population for more than one cycle (longer than 10 years and probably at least 20) before having sufficient data to examine changes through time. Otherwise, it would be impossible to know whether an observed decrease in the population size reflected a long-term trend or was part of the normal cycle.

Concept Check 53.6

1. A bottom-heavy age structure, with a disproportionate number of young people, portends continuing growth of the population as these young people begin reproducing. In contrast, a more evenly distributed age structure predicts a more stable population size. **2.** The growth rate of Earth's human population has dropped by half since the 1960s, from 2.2% in 1962 to 1.15% today. Nonetheless, growth has not slowed much because the smaller growth rate is counterbalanced by increased population size; the number of extra people on Earth each year remains enormous—approximately 75 million. **3.** Each of us influences our ecological footprint by how we live—what we eat, how much energy we use, and the amount of waste we generate—as well as by how many children we have. Making choices that reduce our demand for resources makes our ecological footprint smaller.

Self-Quiz

1. c **2.** c **3.** c **4.** d **5.** d **6.** b **7.** c **8.** d **9.** c **10.** d
11.

The total number of female offspring produced is greatest in females 1–2 years of age. Sample calculation for females of this age group: 252 indiv. × 1.07 female offspring/indiv. = 270 female offspring.

CHAPTER 54

Figure Questions

Figure 54.3 Its realized and fundamental niches would be similar. **Figure 54.4** If both species were feeding on seeds of the same size, you would expect differences in beak size to disappear over evolutionary time. The species could not specialize on seeds of different sizes. **Figure 54.14** The low-productivity treatment had the shortest food chain, so that food chain should be the most stable. **Figure 54.15** The death of individuals

of *Mytilus*, a dominant species, should open up space for other species and increase species richness even in the absence of *Pisaster*. **Figure 54.19** Because the abundance of the second predatory species is unaffected by soil warming, there would be a less dramatic decrease in total predator numbers. Therefore, if the top-down model applies in this community, you would expect a smaller increase in *S. lindsayae* density than was actually observed. **Figure 54.28** Other factors not included in the model must contribute to the unexplained variation in the results.

Concept Check 54.1

1. Interspecific competition has negative effects on both species ($-/-$). In predation, the predator population benefits at the expense of the prey population ($+/-$). Mutualism is a symbiosis in which both species benefit ($+/+$). **2.** One of the competing species will become locally extinct because of the greater reproductive success of the more efficient competitor. **3.** Examples of relevant interactions include competition between weeds and food crops; predation by humans on herbivores, such as cattle; herbivory by humans on leafy vegetables, such as lettuce or spinach; and the planting of symbiotic nitrogen-fixing plants, such as beans or peas.

Concept Check 54.2

1. Species richness, the number of species in the community, and relative abundance, the proportions of the community represented by the various species, both contribute to species diversity. Compared to a community with a very high proportion of one species, one with a more even proportion of species is considered to be more diverse. **2.** The energetic hypothesis suggests that the length of a food chain is limited by the inefficiency of energy transfer along the chain, while the dynamic stability hypothesis proposes that long food chains are less stable than short chains. The energetic hypothesis predicts that food chains will be longer in habitats with higher primary productivity. The dynamic stability hypothesis predicts that food chains will be longer in more predictable environments. **3.** According to the bottom-up model, adding extra predators would have little effect on lower trophic levels, particularly vegetation. If the top-down model applied, increased bobcat numbers would decrease raccoon numbers, increase snake numbers, decrease grasshopper numbers, and increase plant biomass.

Concept Check 54.3

1. High levels of disturbance are generally so disruptive that they eliminate many species from communities, leaving the community dominated by a few tolerant species. Low levels of disturbance permit competitively dominant species to exclude other species from the community. In contrast, moderate levels of disturbance can facilitate coexistence of a greater number of species in a community by preventing competitively dominant species from becoming abundant enough to eliminate other species from the community. **2.** Early successional species can facilitate the arrival of other species in many ways, including increasing the fertility or water-holding capacity of soils or providing shelter to seedlings from wind and intense sunlight. **3.** The absence of fire for 100 years would represent a change to a low level of disturbance. According to the intermediate disturbance hypothesis, this change should cause diversity to decline as competitively dominant species gain sufficient time to exclude less competitive species.

Concept Check 54.4

1. Ecologists propose that the greater species richness of tropical regions is the result of their longer evolutionary history and the greater solar energy input and water availability in tropical regions. **2.** Immigration of species to islands declines with distance from the mainland and increases with island area. Extinction of species is lower on larger islands and on less isolated islands. Since the number of species on islands is largely determined by the difference between rates of immigration and extinction, the number of species will be highest on large islands near the mainland and lowest on small islands far from the mainland. **3.** Because of their greater mobility, birds disperse to islands more often than snakes or mammals, so birds should have greater richness.

Concept Check 54.5

1. Pathogens are microorganisms, viruses, viroids, or prions that cause disease. **2.** If the parasite requires contact with a human and another animal, the parasite might be an especially likely vector for the pathogens that cause zoonotic diseases. **3.** If you can identify the host or hosts of the disease as well as any intermediate vectors, such as mosquitoes or fleas, you can reduce the rate of infection by decreasing the abundance of the host and vector or by reducing their contact with people.

Self-Quiz
1. c **2.** d **3.** b **4.** c **5.** c **6.** d **7.** b **8.** c
9. Community 1: $H = -[(0.05)(\ln 0.05) + (0.05)(\ln 0.05) + (0.85)(\ln 0.85) + (0.05)(\ln 0.05)] = 0.59$. Community 2: $H = -[(0.30)(\ln 0.30) + (0.40)(\ln 0.40) + (0.30)(\ln 0.30)] = 1.1$. Community 2 is more diverse.
10.

Crab numbers should increase, reducing the abundance of eelgrass.

CHAPTER 55

Figure Questions
Figure 55.6 Wetlands, coral reefs, and coastal zones cover areas too small to show up clearly on global maps. **Figure 55.7** If the new duck farms made nitrogen available in rich supply, as phosphorus already is, then adding extra nitrogen in the experiment would not increase phytoplankton density. **Figure 55.13** By dissolving minerals, the fungi move nutrients from reservoir D (inorganic materials unavailable as nutrients) to reservoir C (inorganic materials available as nutrients). **Figure 55.15** Water availability is probably another factor that varied across the sites. Such factors not included in the experimental design could make the results more difficult to interpret. Multiple factors can also covary in nature, so ecologists must be careful that the factor they are studying is actually causing the observed response and is not just correlated with it.

Concept Check 55.1
1. Energy passes through an ecosystem, entering as sunlight and leaving as heat. It is not recycled within the ecosystem. **2.** The second law states that in any energy transfer or transformation, some of the energy is dissipated to the surroundings as heat. This "escape" of energy from an ecosystem is offset by the continuous influx of solar radiation. **3.** You would need to know how much biomass the wildebeests ate from your plot and how much nitrogen was contained in that biomass. You would also need to know how much nitrogen they deposited in urine or feces.

Concept Check 55.2
1. Only a fraction of solar radiation strikes plants or algae, only a portion of that fraction is of wavelengths suitable for photosynthesis, and much energy is lost as a result of reflection or heating of plant tissue. **2.** By manipulating the level of the factors of interest, such as phosphorus availability or soil moisture, and measuring responses by primary producers **3.** The student is missing the plant biomass eaten by herbivores and the production allocated to plant roots and other belowground tissues.

Concept Check 55.3
1. 20 J; 40% **2.** Nicotine protects the plant from herbivores. **3.** There are many things they could do to reduce their production efficiency. For example, exercising vigorously will use energy that might otherwise go to biomass, and keeping the house cool will force their bodies to use energy to stay warm.

Concept Check 55.4
1. For example, for the carbon cycle:

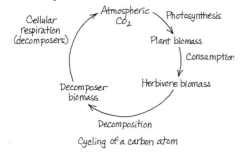

2. Removal of the trees stops nitrogen uptake from the soil, allowing nitrate to accumulate there. The nitrate is washed away by precipitation and enters the streams. **3.** Most of the nutrients in a tropical rain forest are contained in the trees, so removing the trees by logging rapidly depletes nutrients from the ecosystem. The nutrients that remain in the soil are quickly carried away into streams and groundwater by the abundant precipitation.

Concept Check 55.5
1. Adding nutrients causes population explosions of algae and the organisms that feed on them. Increased respiration by algae and consumers, including detritivores, depletes the lake's oxygen, which the fish require. **2.** At a lower trophic level, because biological magnification increases the concentration of toxins up the food chain **3.** Because higher temperatures lead to faster decomposition, organic matter in these soils could be quickly decomposed to CO_2, speeding up global warming.

Self-Quiz
1. c **2.** b **3.** d **4.** c **5.** e **6.** a **7.** d
8.

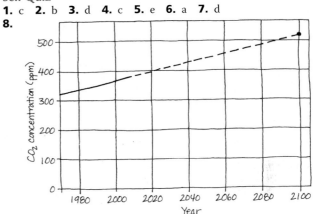

Between 1974 and 2007, Earth's atmospheric CO_2 concentration increased from approximately 330 ppm to 385 ppm. If this rate of increase of 1.7 ppm/yr continues, the concentration in 2100 will be about 540 ppm. The actual rise in CO_2 concentration could be larger or smaller, depending on Earth's human population, per capita energy use, and the extent to which societies take steps to reduce CO_2 emissions, including replacing fossil fuels with renewable or nuclear fuels. Additional scientific data will be important for many reasons, including determining how quickly greenhouse gases such as CO_2 are removed from the atmosphere by the biosphere.

CHAPTER 56

Figure Questions
Figure 56.4 You would need to know the complete range of the species and that it is missing across all of that range. You would also need to be certain that the species isn't hidden, as might be the case for an animal that is hibernating underground or a plant that is present in the form of seeds or spores. **Figure 56.11** Because the population of Illinois birds has a different genetic makeup than birds in other regions, you would want to maintain to the greatest extent possible the frequency of beneficial genes or alleles found only in that population. In restoration, preserving genetic diversity in a species is as important as increasing organism numbers. **Figure 56.13** The natural disturbance regime in this habitat included frequent fires that cleared undergrowth but did not kill mature pine trees. Without these fires, the undergrowth quickly fills in and the habitat becomes unsuitable for red-cockaded woodpeckers.

Concept Check 56.1
1. In addition to species loss, the biodiversity crisis includes the loss of genetic diversity within populations and species and the degradation of entire ecosystems. **2.** Habitat destruction, such as deforestation, channelizing of rivers, or conversion of natural ecosystems to agriculture or cities, deprives species of places to live. Introduced species, which are transported by humans to regions outside their native range, where they are not controlled by their natural pathogens or predators, often reduce the population sizes of native species through competition or predation. Overexploitation has reduced populations of plants and animals or driven them to extinction. **3.** If both

populations breed separately, then gene flow between the populations would not occur and genetic differences between them would be greater. As a result, the loss of genetic diversity would be greater than if the populations interbreed.

Concept Check 56.2

1. Reduced genetic variation decreases the capacity of a population to evolve in the face of change. **2.** The effective population size, N_e, is $4(35 \times 10)/(35 + 10) = 31$ birds. **3.** Because millions of people use the greater Yellowstone ecosystem each year, it would be impossible to eliminate all contact between people and bears. Instead, you might try to reduce the kinds of encounters where bears are killed. You might recommend lower speed limits on roads in the park, adjust the timing or location of hunting seasons (where hunting is allowed outside the park) to minimize contact with mother bears and cubs, and provide financial incentives for livestock owners to try alternative means (such as guard dogs) of protecting livestock.

Concept Check 56.3

1. A small area supporting an exceptionally large number of endemic species as well as a disproportionate number of endangered and threatened species **2.** Zoned reserves may provide sustained supplies of forest products, water, hydroelectric power, educational opportunities, and income from ecotourism. **3.** Habitat corridors can increase the rate of movement or dispersal of organisms between habitat patches and thus the rate of gene flow between subpopulations. They thus help prevent a decrease in fitness attributable to inbreeding. They can also minimize interactions between organisms and humans as the organisms disperse; in cases involving potential predators, such as bears or large cats, minimizing such interactions is desirable.

Concept Check 56.4

1. The main goal is to restore degraded ecosystems to a more natural state. **2.** Bioremediation uses organisms, generally prokaryotes, fungi, or plants, to detoxify or remove pollutants from ecosystems. Biological augmentation uses organisms, such as nitrogen-fixing plants, to add essential materials to degraded ecosystems. **3.** The Kissimmee River project returns the flow of water to the original channel and restores natural flow, a self-sustaining outcome. Ecologists at the Maungatautari reserve will need to maintain the integrity of the fence indefinitely, an outcome that is not self-sustaining in the long term.

Concept Check 56.5

1. Sustainable development is an approach to development that works toward the long-term prosperity of human societies and the ecosystems that support them, which requires linking the biological sciences with the social sciences, economics, and humanities. **2.** Biophilia, our sense of connection to nature and other forms of life, may act as a significant motivation for the development of an environmental ethic that resolves not to allow species to become extinct or ecosystems to be destroyed. Such an ethic is necessary if we are to become more attentive and effective custodians of the environment. **3.** At a minimum, you would want to know the size of the population and the average reproductive rate of individuals in it. To develop the fishery sustainably, you would seek a harvest rate that maintains the population near its original size and maximizes its harvest in the long term rather than the short term.

Self-Quiz

1. c **2.** e **3.** d **4.** d **5.** d **6.** e **7.** c **8.** a
10.

To minimize the area of forest into which the cowbirds penetrate, you should locate the road along one edge of the reserve. Any other location would increase the area of affected habitat. Similarly, the maintenance building should be in a corner of the reserve to minimize the area susceptible to cowbirds.

APPENDIX B Periodic Table of the Elements

Representative elements

Alkali metals | Alkaline earth metals | Halogens | Noble gases

Period number	1 Group 1A	2 Group 2A	Transition elements										13 Group 3A	14 Group 4A	15 Group 5A	16 Group 6A	17 Group 7A	18 Group 8A
1	1 H 1.008																	2 He 4.003
2	3 Li 6.941	4 Be 9.012											5 B 10.81	6 C 12.01	7 N 14.01	8 O 16.00	9 F 19.00	10 Ne 20.18
3	11 Na 22.99	12 Mg 24.31	3 3B	4 4B	5 5B	6 6B	7 7B	8	9 8B	10	11 1B	12 2B	13 Al 26.98	14 Si 28.09	15 P 30.97	16 S 32.07	17 Cl 35.45	18 Ar 39.95
4	19 K 39.10	20 Ca 40.08	21 Sc 44.96	22 Ti 47.87	23 V 50.94	24 Cr 52.00	25 Mn 54.94	26 Fe 55.85	27 Co 58.93	28 Ni 58.69	29 Cu 63.55	30 Zn 65.41	31 Ga 69.72	32 Ge 72.64	33 As 74.92	34 Se 78.96	35 Br 79.90	36 Kr 83.80
5	37 Rb 85.47	38 Sr 87.62	39 Y 88.91	40 Zr 91.22	41 Nb 92.91	42 Mo 95.94	43 Tc (98)	44 Ru 101.1	45 Rh 102.9	46 Pd 106.4	47 Ag 107.9	48 Cd 112.4	49 In 114.8	50 Sn 118.7	51 Sb 121.8	52 Te 127.6	53 I 126.9	54 Xe 131.3
6	55 Cs 132.9	56 Ba 137.3	57* La 138.9	72 Hf 178.5	73 Ta 180.9	74 W 183.8	75 Re 186.2	76 Os 190.2	77 Ir 192.2	78 Pt 195.1	79 Au 197.0	80 Hg 200.6	81 Tl 204.4	82 Pb 207.2	83 Bi 209.0	84 Po (209)	85 At (210)	86 Rn (222)
7	87 Fr (223)	88 Ra (226)	89† Ac (227)	104 Rf (261)	105 Db (262)	106 Sg (266)	107 Bh (264)	108 Hs (269)	109 Mt (268)	110 Ds (271)	111 — (272)	112 — (285)	113 (284)	114 (289)	115 (288)			

*Lanthanides	58 Ce 140.1	59 Pr 140.9	60 Nd 144.2	61 Pm (145)	62 Sm 150.4	63 Eu 152.0	64 Gd 157.3	65 Tb 158.9	66 Dy 162.5	67 Ho 164.9	68 Er 167.3	69 Tm 168.9	70 Yb 173.0	71 Lu 175.0
†Actinides	90 Th 232.0	91 Pa 231.0	92 U 238.0	93 Np (237)	94 Pu (244)	95 Am (243)	96 Cm (247)	97 Bk (247)	98 Cf (251)	99 Es 252	100 Fm 257	101 Md 258	102 No 259	103 Lr 260

Metals | Metalloids | Nonmetals

Name (Symbol)	Atomic Number
Actinium (Ac)	89
Aluminum (Al)	13
Americium (Am)	95
Antimony (Sb)	51
Argon (Ar)	18
Arsenic (As)	33
Astatine (At)	85
Barium (Ba)	56
Berkelium (Bk)	97
Beryllium (Be)	4
Bismuth (Bi)	83
Bohrium (Bh)	107
Boron (B)	5
Bromine (Br)	35
Cadmium (Cd)	48
Calcium (Ca)	20
Californium (Cf)	98
Carbon (C)	6
Cerium (Ce)	58
Cesium (Cs)	55
Chlorine (Cl)	17
Chromium (Cr)	24
Cobalt (Co)	27
Copper (Cu)	29
Curium (Cm)	96
Darmstadtium (Ds)	110
Dubnium (Db)	105
Dysprosium (Dy)	66
Einsteinium (Es)	99
Erbium (Er)	68
Europium (Eu)	63
Fermium (Fm)	100
Fluorine (F)	9
Francium (Fr)	87
Gadolinium (Gd)	64
Gallium (Ga)	31
Germanium (Ge)	32
Gold (Au)	79
Hafnium (Hf)	72
Hassium (Hs)	108
Helium (He)	2
Holmium (Ho)	67
Hydrogen (H)	1
Indium (In)	49
Iodine (I)	53
Iridium (Ir)	77
Iron (Fe)	26
Krypton (Kr)	36
Lanthanum (La)	57
Lawrencium (Lr)	103
Lead (Pb)	82
Lithium (Li)	3
Lutetium (Lu)	71
Magnesium (Mg)	12
Manganese (Mn)	25
Meitnerium (Mt)	109
Mendelevium (Md)	101
Mercury (Hg)	80
Molybdenum (Mo)	42
Neodymium (Nd)	60
Neon (Ne)	10
Neptunium (Np)	93
Nickel (Ni)	28
Niobium (Nb)	41
Nitrogen (N)	7
Nobelium (No)	102
Osmium (Os)	76
Oxygen (O)	8
Palladium (Pd)	46
Phosphorus (P)	15
Platinum (Pt)	78
Plutonium (Pu)	94
Polonium (Po)	84
Potassium (K)	19
Praseodymium (Pr)	59
Promethium (Pm)	61
Protactinium (Pa)	91
Radium (Ra)	88
Radon (Rn)	86
Rhenium (Re)	75
Rhodium (Rh)	45
Rubidium (Rb)	37
Ruthenium (Ru)	44
Rutherfordium (Rf)	104
Samarium (Sm)	62
Scandium (Sc)	21
Seaborgium (Sg)	106
Selenium (Se)	34
Silicon (Si)	14
Silver (Ag)	47
Sodium (Na)	11
Strontium (Sr)	38
Sulfur (S)	16
Tantalum (Ta)	73
Technetium (Tc)	43
Tellurium (Te)	52
Terbium (Tb)	65
Thallium (Tl)	81
Thorium (Th)	90
Thulium (Tm)	69
Tin (Sn)	50
Titanium (Ti)	22
Tungsten (W)	74
Uranium (U)	92
Vanadium (V)	23
Xenon (Xe)	54
Ytterbium (Yb)	70
Yttrium (Y)	39
Zinc (Zn)	30
Zirconium (Zr)	40

The Metric System

Measurement	Unit and Abbreviation	Metric Equivalent	Metric-to-English Conversion Factor	English-to-Metric Conversion Factor
Length	1 kilometer (km) 1 meter (m)	= 1000 (10^3) meters = 100 (10^2) centimeters = 1000 millimeters	1 km = 0.62 mile 1 m = 1.09 yards 1 m = 3.28 feet 1 m = 39.37 inches	1 mile = 1.61 km 1 yard = 0.914 m 1 foot = 0.305 m
	1 centimeter (cm)	= 0.01 (10^{-2}) meter	1 cm = 0.394 inch	1 foot = 30.5 cm 1 inch = 2.54 cm
	1 millimeter (mm) 1 micrometer (µm) (formerly micron, µ) 1 nanometer (nm) (formerly millimicron, mµ) 1 angstrom (Å)	= 0.001 (10^{-3}) meter = 10^{-6} meter (10^{-3} mm) = 10^{-9} meter (10^{-3} µm) = 10^{-10} meter (10^{-4} µm)	1 mm = 0.039 inch	
Area	1 hectare (ha) 1 square meter (m^2)	= 10,000 square meters = 10,000 square centimeters	1 ha = 2.47 acres 1 m^2 = 1.196 square yards 1 m^2 = 10.764 square feet	1 acre = 0.405 ha 1 square yard = 0.8361 m^2 1 square foot = 0.0929 m^2
	1 square centimeter (cm^2)	= 100 square millimeters	1 cm^2 = 0.155 square inch	1 square inch = 6.4516 cm^2
Mass	1 metric ton (t) 1 kilogram (kg) 1 gram (g)	= 1000 kilograms = 1000 grams = 1000 milligrams	1 t = 1.103 tons 1 kg = 2.205 pounds 1 g = 0.0353 ounce 1 g = 15.432 grains	1 ton = 0.907 t 1 pound = 0.4536 kg 1 ounce = 28.35 g
	1 milligram (mg) 1 microgram (µg)	= 10^{-3} gram = 10^{-6} gram	1 mg = approx. 0.015 grain	
Volume (solids)	1 cubic meter (m^3)	= 1,000,000 cubic centimeters	1 m^3 = 1.308 cubic yards 1 m^3 = 35.315 cubic feet	1 cubic yard = 0.7646 m^3 1 cubic foot = 0.0283 m^3
	1 cubic centimeter (cm^3 or cc) 1 cubic millimeter (mm^3)	= 10^{-6} cubic meter = 10^{-9} cubic meter (10^{-3} cubic centimeter)	1 cm^3 = 0.061 cubic inch	1 cubic inch = 16.387 cm^3
Volume (liquids and gases)	1 kiloliter (kl or kL) 1 liter (l or L)	= 1000 liters = 1000 milliliters	1 kL = 264.17 gallons 1 L = 0.264 gallons 1 L = 1.057 quarts	1 gallon = 3.785 L 1 quart = 0.946 L
	1 milliliter (ml or mL)	= 10^{-3} liter = 1 cubic centimeter	1 mL = 0.034 fluid ounce 1 mL = approx. 1/4 teaspoon 1 mL = approx. 15-16 drops (gtt.)	1 quart = 946 mL 1 pint = 473 mL 1 fluid ounce = 29.57 mL 1 teaspoon = approx. 5 mL
	1 microliter (µl or µL)	= 10^{-6} liter (10^{-3} milliliters)		
Time	1 second (s) 1 millisecond (ms)	= 1/60 minute = 10^{-3} second		
Temperature	Degrees Celsius (°C) (Absolute zero, when all molecular motion ceases, is − 273°C. The Kelvin [K] scale, which has the same size degrees as Celsius, has its zero point at absolute zero. Thus, 0°K = −273°C.)		°F = 9/5°C + 32	°C = 5/9 (°F − 32)

D A Comparison of the Light Microscope and the Electron Microscope

Eye
Ocular lens
Objective lens
Specimen
Condenser lens
Light source

Electron source
Condenser lens
Specimen
Objective lens
Intermediate image
Projector lens
Eye
Binoculars
Final image on digital detector, fluorescent screen, or photographic film

Light Microscope

In light microscopy, light is focused on a specimen by a glass condenser lens; the image is then magnified by an objective lens and an ocular lens, for projection on the eye, digital camera, digital video camera, or photographic film.

Electron Microscope

In electron microscopy, a beam of electrons (top of the microscope) is used instead of light, and electromagnets are used instead of glass lenses. The electron beam is focused on the specimen by a condenser lens; the image is magnified by an objective lens and a projector lens for projection on a digital detector, fluorescent screen, or photographic film.

E Classification of Life

Classification of Life

This appendix presents a taxonomic classification for the major extant groups of organisms discussed in this text; not all phyla are included. The classification presented here is based on the three-domain system, which assigns the two major groups of prokaryotes, bacteria and archaea, to separate domains (with eukaryotes making up the third domain). This classification contrasts with the traditional five-kingdom system, which groups all prokaryotes in a single kingdom, Monera. Systematists no longer recognize the kingdom Monera because it would have members in two different domains (see Chapter 26).

Various alternative classification schemes are discussed in Unit Five of the text. The taxonomic turmoil includes debates about the number and boundaries of kingdoms and about the alignment of the Linnaean classification hierarchy with the findings of modern cladistic analysis. In this review, asterisks (*) indicate currently recognized phyla thought by some systematists to be paraphyletic.

DOMAIN BACTERIA

▶ **Proteobacteria**

▶ **Chlamydia**

▶ **Spirochetes**

▶ **Gram-positive Bacteria**

▶ **Cyanobacteria**

DOMAIN ARCHAEA

▶ **Korarchaeota**

▶ **Euryarchaeota**

▶ **Crenarchaeota**

▶ **Nanoarchaeota**

DOMAIN EUKARYA

In the phylogenetic hypothesis we present in Chapter 28, major clades of eukaryotes are grouped together in the five "supergroups" listed below in bold type. The traditional five-kingdom classification scheme united all the eukaryotes generally called protists in a single kingdom, Protista. However, advances in systematics have made it clear that Protista is in fact polyphyletic: Some protists are more closely related to plants, fungi, or animals than they are to other protists. As a result, the kingdom Protista has been abandoned. In contrast, the kingdoms Plantae (land plants), Fungi, and Animalia (animals) have survived from the five-kingdom system.

Excavata
▶ Diplomonadida (diplomonads)
▶ Parabasala (parabasalids)
▶ Euglenozoa (euglenozoans)
    Euglenophyta (euglenids)
    Kinetoplastida (kinetoplastids)

Chromalveolata
▶ Alveolata (alveolates)
    Dinoflagellata (dinoflagellates)
    Apicomplexa (apicomplexans)
    Ciliophora (ciliates)
▶ Stramenopila (stramenopiles)
    Bacillariophyta (diatoms)
    Chrysophyta (golden algae)
    Phaeophyta (brown algae)
    Oomycota (water molds)

Archaeplastida
▶ Rhodophyta (red algae)
▶ Chlorophyta (green algae: chlorophytes)
▶ Charophyceae (green algae: charophyceans)
▶ Plantae

Phylum Hepatophyta (liverworts) ⎫
Phylum Anthocerophyta (hornworts) ⎬ Bryophytes (nonvascular plants)
Phylum Bryophyta (mosses) ⎭

Phylum Lycophyta (lycophytes) ⎫
Phylum Pterophyta (ferns, horsetails, whisk ferns) ⎬ Seedless vascular plants

Phylum Ginkgophyta (ginkgo) ⎫
Phylum Cycadophyta (cycads) ⎪
Phylum Gnetophyta (gnetophytes) ⎬ Gymnosperms ⎫
Phylum Coniferophyta (conifers) ⎭ ⎬ Seed plants

Phylum Anthophyta (flowering plants) ⎬ Angiosperms ⎭

Rhizaria
▶ Chlorarachniophyta (chlorarachniophytes)
▶ Foraminifera (forams)
▶ Radiolaria (radiolarians)

Unikonta
▶ Amoebozoa (amoebozoans)
      Myxogastrida (plasmodial slime molds)
      Dictyostelida (cellular slime molds)
      Gymnamoeba (gymnamoebas)
      Entamoeba (entamoebas)
      Nucleariida (nucleariids)

▶ Fungi
    *Phylum Chytridiomycota (chytrids)
    Phylum Zygomycota (zygomycetes)
    Phylum Glomeromycota (glomeromycetes)
    Phylum Ascomycota (sac fungi)
    Phylum Basidiomycota (club fungi)

▶ Choanoflagellata (choanoflagellates)

▶ Animalia
    Phylum Calcarea ⎤
    Phylum Silicea ⎦ (sponges)
    Phylum Cnidaria (cnidarians)
      Class Hydrozoa (hydrozoans)
      Class Scyphozoa (jellies)
      Class Cubozoa (box jellies and sea wasps)
      Class Anthozoa (sea anemones and most corals)
    Phylum Ctenophora (comb jellies)
    Phylum Acoela (acoel flatworms)
    Lophotrochozoa (lophotrochozoans)
    Phylum Placozoa (placozoans)
    Phylum Kinorhyncha (kinorhynchs)
    Phylum Platyhelminthes (flatworms)
      Class Turbellaria (free-living flatworms)
      Class Trematoda (flukes)
      Class Monogenea (monogeneans)
      Class Cestoda (tapeworms)
    Phylum Nemertea (proboscis worms)
    Phylum Ectoprocta (ectoprocts)
    Phylum Phoronida (phoronids)
    Phylum Brachiopoda (brachiopods)
    Phylum Rotifera (rotifers)
    Phylum Cycliophora (cycliophorans)
    Phylum Mollusca (molluscs)
      Class Polyplacophora (chitons)
      Class Gastropoda (gastropods)
      Class Bivalvia (bivalves)
      Class Cephalopoda (cephalopods)

Ecdysozoa (ecdysozoans)
    Phylum Annelida (segmented worms)
      Class Oligochaeta (oligochaetes)
      Class Polychaeta (polychaetes)
      Class Hirudinea (leeches)
    Phylum Acanthocephala (spiny-headed worms)
    Phylum Loricifera (loriciferans)
    Phylum Priapula (priapulans)
    Phylum Nematoda (roundworms)
    Phylum Arthropoda (This survey groups arthropods into
      a single phylum, but some zoologists now split the
      arthropods into multiple phyla.)
      Subphylum Cheliceriformes (horseshoe crabs, arachnids)
      Subphylum Myriapoda (millipedes, centipedes)
      Subphylum Hexapoda (insects, springtails)
      Subphylum Crustacea (crustaceans)
    Phylum Tardigrada (tardigrades)
    Phylum Onychophora (velvet worms)
Deuterostomia (deuterostomes)
    Phylum Hemichordata (hemichordates)
    Phylum Echinodermata (echinoderms)
      Class Asteroidea (sea stars)
      Class Ophiuroidea (brittle stars)
      Class Echinoidea (sea urchins and sand dollars)
      Class Crinoidea (see lilies)
      Class Concentricycloidea (sea daisies)
      Class Holothuroidea (sea cucumbers)
    Phylum Chordata (chordates)
      Subphylum Cephalochordata (cephalochordates: lancelets)
      Subphylum Urochrodata (urochordates: tunicates)
      Subphylum Craniata (craniates)
        Class Myxini (hagfishes)
        Class Cephalaspidomorphi (lampreys) ⎤
        Class Chondrichthyes (sharks, rays, ⎟
          chimaeras) ⎟
        Class Acinopterygii (ray-finned fishes) ⎟
        Class Actinistia (coelacanths) ⎬ Vertebrates
        Class Dipnoi (lungfishes) ⎟
        Class Amphibia (amphibians) ⎟
        Class Reptilia (tuataras, lizards, snakes, ⎟
          turtles, crocodilians, birds) ⎟
        Class Mammalia (mammals) ⎦

Credits

PHOTO CREDITS

Cover Image Chris Fox/Corbis

Unit Opening Interviews Unit One Stuart Brinin; **Unit Two** Zach Veilleux, Rockefeller University; **Unit Three** Maria Nemchuk; **Unit Four** Justin Ide; **Unit Five** Brent Nicastro; **Unit Six** Noah Berger Photography; **Unit Seven** Skeeter Hagler; **Unit Eight** William A. Cotton, Colorado State University.

Detailed Contents Unit One David A. Bushnell. **Unit Two** Albert Tousson, High Resolution Imaging Facility, University of Alabama at Birmingham. **Unit Three** Kosman D, Mizutani CM, Lemons D, Cox WG, McGinnis W, Bier E. Multiplex detection of RNA expression in Drosophila embryos. Science. 2004 Aug 6;305(5685):846; Fig 1. **Unit Four** Olivier Grunewald. **Unit Five** Ray Watson, canadianphotography.ca. **Unit Six** Pierre-Michel Blais, orchidees.provence.free.fr. **Unit Seven** Michael Nichols/National Geographic/Getty Images. **Unit Eight** Galen Rowell/Corbis.

Chapter 1 1.1 Chris Fox/Corbis; **1.2** Henri and Käthi Oertli; **1.3.1** Fred Bavendam/Minden Pictures; **1.3.2** Kim Taylor and Jane Burton/Dorling Kindersley; **1.3.3** Frans Lanting/Minden Pictures; **1.3.4** Frans Lanting/Minden Pictures; **1.3.5** Michael & Patricia Fogden/Corbis; **1.3.6** Joe McDonald/Corbis; **1.3.7** ImageState/International Stock Photography Ltd.; **1.4.1** WorldSat International/Photo Researchers, Inc.; **1.4.2** Bill Brooks/Alamy; **1.4.3** Mark Raycroft/Minden Pictures, and Dave McShaffrey, Marietta College, Ohio; **1.4.4** Michael Orton/Photographer's Choice/Getty Images; **1.4.5** Ross M. Horowitz/Iconica/Getty Images; **1.4.6** Photodisc/Getty Images; **1.4.7** Jeremy Burgess/SPL/Photo Researchers; **1.4.8** Manfred Kage/Peter Arnold, Inc.; **1.4.9** E.H. Newcomb & W.P. Wergin/Biological Photo Service; **1.5** Shin Yoshino/Minden Pictures; **1.6a** PhotoLink/Photodisc/Getty Images; **1.6b** Janice Sheldon; **1.6c** T. D. Parsons, D. Kleinfeld, F. Raccuia-Behling and B. Salzberg. Biophysical Journal, July 1989. Photo courtesy of Brian Salzberg; **1.7** Conly L. Rieder, Ph.D.; **1.8.1** S. C. Holt/Biological Photo Service; **1.8.2** Visuals Unlimited; **1.9** Camille Tokerud/Stone/Getty Images; **1.10a** Photodisc/Getty Images; **1.11** Roy Kaltschmidt, Lawrence Berkeley National Laboratory; **1.12** Giot L, Bader JS, Brouwer C, Chaudhuri A, Kuang B, Li Y, Hao YL, Ooi CE, Godwin B, Vitols E, Vijayadamodar G, Pochart P, Machineni H, Welsh M, Kong Y, Zerhusen B, Malcolm R, Varrone Z, Collis A, Minto M, Burgess S, McDaniel L, Stimpson E, Spriggs F, Williams J, Neurath K, Ioime N, Agee M, Voss E, Furtak K, Renzulli R, Aanensen N, Carrolla S, Bickelhaupt E, Lazovatsky Y, DaSilva A, Zhong J, Stanyon CA, Finley RL Jr, White KP, Braverman M, Jarvie T, Gold S, Leach M, Knight J, Shimkets RA, McKenna MP, Chant J, Rothberg JM. A protein interaction map of Drosophila melanogaster. Science. 2003 Dec 5; 302 (5651): 1727-36; Fig. 4b. Image supplied by Joel S. Bader; **1.15a** Oliver Meckes/Nicole Ottawa/Photo Researchers; **1.15b** Ralph Robinson/Visuals Unlimited; **1.15c left to right** D. P. Wilson/Photo Researchers; Peter Lilja/Taxi/Getty Images; Kunst & Scheidulin/AGE Fotostock; Anup Shah/Nature Picture Library; **1.16.1** VVG/SPL/Photo Researchers; **1.16.2** Omikron/Photo Researchers; **1.16.3** W. L. Dentler, University of Kansas/Biological Photo Services; **1.17** Mike Hettwer/Project Exploration; **1.18** Archiv/Photo Researchers; **1.19.1** Michael P. Fogden/Bruce Coleman Inc./Alamy; **1.19.2** Michael & Patricia Fogden/Minden Pictures **1.19.3** Hal Horwitz/Corbis; **1.21** Frank Greenaway/Dorling Kindersley; **1.23.1** Karl Ammann/Corbis; **1.23.2** Tim Ridley/Dorling Kindersley; **1.25.1** Breck P. Kent; **1.25.2** E R Degginger; **1.26** David Pfennig; **1.29** Gloria M. Coruzzi, Professor of Biology, New York University; **1.30** Stone/Getty Images. **Chapter 2 2.1** Martin Dohrn/BBC Natural History Unit; **2.2** Martin Dohrn/BBC Natural History Unit; **2.3** Chip Clark; **2.4a** Grant Heilman/Grant Heilman Photography; **2.4b** Ivan Polunin/Bruce Coleman Inc.; **2.6** Clayton T Hamilton, Stanford University; **2.7** CTI Molecular Imaging, Inc.; **p. 41** Jerry Young/Dorling Kindersley; **2.19** Runk/Schoenberg/Grant Heilman, Inc.; **p. 45** E. R. Degginger/Color-Pic, Inc. **Chapter 3 3.1** NASA/Johnson Space Center; **3.3** R. Kessel-Shih/Visuals Unlimited; **3.4** Charles S. Lewallen; **3.6** Flip Nicklin/Minden Pictures; **3.10** Oliver Strewe/Stone Allstock/Getty Images; **3.11** Raena M. Cota; **inset** DeLois Galleciez; **p. 57** Kargel JS. Planetary science. Proof for water, hints of life? Science. 2004 Dec 3; 306(5702):1689-91; Fig. E and O. **Chapter 4 4.1** Mark Moffett/Minden Pictures; **4.6a** Manfred Kage/Peter Arnold, Inc. **Chapter 5 5.1** Lester Lefkowitz/Corbis; **5.6a** John N. A. Lott/Biological Photo Service; **5.6b** H. Shio and P. B. Lazarow; **5.8.1** Photodisc/Getty Images; **5.8.2** Manfred Kage/

Peter Arnold, Inc.; **5.8.3** J. Litray/Visuals Unlimited; **5.9.1** Photodisc/Getty Images **5.9.2** T. J. Beveridge/Visuals Unlimited; **5.10b** F. Collet/Photo Researchers; **5.10c** Corbis; **5.12a** Dorling Kindersley; **5.12b** Corbis; **5.20** Tulip WR, Varghese JN, Laver WG, Webster RG, Colman PM. Refined crystal structure of the influenza virus N9 neuraminidase-NC41 Fab complex. J Mol Biol. 1992 Sep 5;227(1):122-48; **5.21** Wolfgang Kaehler; **5.22** Eye of Science/Photo Researchers; **5.24** Reprinted by permission from Nature. P. B. Sigler from Z. Xu, A. L. Horwich, and P. B. Sigler. 388:741-750 Copyright (c) 1997 Macmillan Magazines Limited; **5.25.1** Cramer P, Bushnell DA, Fu J, Gnatt AL, Maier-Davis B, Thompson NE, Burgess RR, Edwards AM, David PR, Kornberg RD. Architecture of RNA polymerase II and implications for the transcription mechanism.Science. 2000 Apr 28;288(5466):640-9; Fig. 3. Image supplied by David Bushnell; **5.25.2** David A. Bushnell. **Chapter 6 6.1** Albert Tousson, High Resolution Imaging Facility, University of Alabama at Birmingham; **6.3.1** Biophoto Associates/Photo Researchers; **6.3.2** Ed Reschke; **6.3.3** David M. Phillips/Visuals Unlimited; **6.3.4** David M. Phillips/Visuals Unlimited; **6.3.5** Molecular Probes, Inc.; **6.3.6** Karl Garsha; **6.3.7** Karl Garsha; **6.4** William Dentler/Biological Photo Service; **6.6b** S. C. Holt, University of Texas Health Center/Biological Photo Service; **6.7a** Daniel S. Friend; **6.10.1** Reproduced by permission from L.Orci and A.Perelet, Freeze-Etch Histology. (Heidelberg: Springer-Veerlag, 1975). Copyright (c)1975 by Springer-Verlag GmbH & Co KG; **6.10.2** Reproduced by permission from A. C. Faberge, Cell Tiss. Res. 151 Copyright (c) 1974 by Springer-Verlag GmbH & Co KG; **6.10.3** Reprinted by permission from Nature 323. U. Aebi et al. Copyright (c) 1996: 560-564, figure 1a. Used with permission. Macmillan Magazines Limited; **6.11** D. W. Fawcett/Photo Researchers; **6.12** R. Bolender, D. Fawcett/Photo Researchers; **6.13** Don Fawcett/Visuals Unlimited; **6.14** Daniel S. Friend; **6.15** E. H. Newcomb; **6.17** Daniel S. Friend; **6.18** E.H. Newcomb & W.P. Wergin/Biological Photo Service; **6.19** From S. E. Fredrick and E. H. Newcomb, The Journal of Cell Biology 43 (1969): 343; **6.20** John E. Heuser, M.D., Washington University School of Medicine, St. Louis, Missouri; **6.21b** B. J. Schapp et al., 1985, Cell 40:455; p. 113 **left to right** Dr. Mary Osborn, Dr. Frank Solomon, Mark S. Ladinsky, and J. Richard McIntosh, University of Colorado; **6.22** Kent L. McDonald; **6.23a** Biophoto Associates/Photo Researchers; **6.23b** Meckes/Ottawa/Eye of Science/Photo Researchers, Inc.; **6.24.1** Omikron/Science Source/Photo Researchers; **6.24.2** W. L. Dentler/Biological Photo Service; **6.24.3** Linck RW, Stephens RE. Functional protofilament numbering of ciliary, flagellar, and centriolar microtubules. Cell Motil Cytoskeleton. 2007 Jul;64(7):489-95; cover. Micrograph by D. Woodrum Hensley; **6.26** From Hirokawa Nobutaka, The Journal of Cell Biology 94 (1982): 425. Fig.1. Reproduced by copyright permission of The Rockefeller University Press; **6.28** G. F. Leedale/Photo Researchers; **6.29** Paredez AR, Somerville CR, Ehrhardt DW. Visualization of Cellulose Synthase Demonstrates Functional Association with Microtubules. Science. 2006 Jun 9; 312 (5779): 1491-5; Fig. 2; **6.31** Micrograph by W. P. Wergin, provided by E. H. Newcomb; **6.32.1** From Douglas J. Kelly, The Journal of Cell Biology 28 (1966): 51. Fig.17. Reproduced by copyright permission of The Rockefeller University Press; **6.32.2** Reproduced by permission from L. Orci and A. Perelet, Freeze-Etch Histology. (Heidelberg: Springer-Verlag). Copyright (c) 1975 by Springer-Verlag GmbH & Co KG; **6.32.3** From C. Peracchia and A. F. Dulhunty, The Journal of Cell Biology 70 (1976): 419. Fig. 6 Reproduced by copyright permission of The Rockefeller University Press; **6.33** Lennart Nilsson/Albert Bonniers Forlag; **p 123** E. H. Newcomb; p. 123 From S. E. Fredrick and E. H. Newcomb, The Journal of Cell Biology 43 (1969): 343. **Chapter 7 7.1** Long SB, Campbell EB, Mackinnon R. Crystal structure of a mammalian voltage-dependent Shaker family K^+ channel. Science. 2005 Aug 5;309 (5736):897-903; cover; **7.4** D. W. Fawcett/Photo Researchers, Inc.; **7.14** Cabisco/Visuals Unlimited; **7.20.1** H. S. Pankratz, T.C. Beaman & P. Gerhardt/Biological Photo Service; **7.20.2** D. W. Fawcett/Photo Researchers, Inc.; **7.20.3** M. M. Perry J. Cell Science 39(1979):257 (c) 1979 by the Company of Biologists Ltd; **7.20.4** M. M. Perry & A. B. Gilbert, J. Cell Science 39 (1979):257 (c) 1979 by the Company of Biologists Ltd. **Chapter 8 8.1** Jean-Marie Bassot/Photo Researchers, Inc.; **8.2** David W. Hamilton/Getty Images, Inc.; **8.3a** Joe McDonald/Corbis; **8.3b** Manoj Shah/Getty Images, Inc.; **8.4** Brian Capon; **8.16** Thomas A. Steitz, Yale University; **8.21** Scheer JM, Romanowski MJ, Wells JA. A common allosteric site and mechanism in caspases. Proc Natl Acad Sci U S A. 2006 May 16;103(20): 7595-600; Fig. 4a; **8.23** Nicolae Simionescu. **Chapter 9 9.1** Frans Lanting/Minden Pictures. **Chapter 10 10.1** Bob Rowan, Progressive Image/Corbis;

10.2a Jim Brandenburg/Minden Pictures; 10.2b Bob Evans/Peter Arnold, Inc.; 10.2c Michael Abbey/Visuals Unlimited; 10.2d Susan M. Barns, Ph.D.; 10.2e National Library of Medicine; 10.3.1 M. Eichelberger/Visuals Unlimited; 10.3.2 Courtesy of W.P. Wergin and E.H. Newcomb, University of Wisconsin/BPS; 10.11 Christine Case, Skyline College; 10.20a David Muench/Corbis; 10.20b Dave Bartruff/Corbis. **Chapter 11** 11.1 CrystalGenomics, Inc.; 11.3.1 Dale Kaiser; 11.3.2 Kuner JM, Kaiser D. Fruiting body morphogenesis in submerged cultures of Myxococcus xanthus. J Bacteriol. 1982 Jul;151(1):458-61. By permission of ASM; 11.16 Matheos D, Metodiev M, Muller E, Stone D, Rose MD.Pheromone-induced polarization is dependent on the Fus3p MAPK acting through the formin Bni1p. J Cell Biol. 2004 Apr;165(1):99-109; Fig. 9; 11.19 Dr. Gopal Murti/Visuals Unlimited; 11.21 Development 127, 5245-5252 (2000). Mesenchymal cells engulf and clear apoptotic footplate cells in macrophageless PU. 1 null mouse embryos. William Wood, Mark Turmaine, Roberta Weber, Victoria Camp, Richard A. Maki, Scott R. McKercher and Paul Martin. **Chapter 12** 12.1 Jan-Michael Peters/Silke Hauf; 12.2a Biophoto Associates/Photo Researchers, Inc.; 12.2b C.R. Wyttenback/Biological Photo Service; 12.2c Biophoto/Science Source/Photo Researchers, Inc.; 12.3 John Murray; 12.4 Biophoto/Photo Researchers, Inc.; 12.6 Conly L. Rieder; 12.7.1 J. Richard McIntosh, University of Colorado at Boulder; 12.7.2 Reproduced by permission from Matthew Schibler, from Protoplasma 137. Copyright (c) 1987: 29-44 by Springer-Verlag GmbH & Co KG; 12.9a David M. Phillips/Visuals Unlimited; 12.9b B. A. Palevitz, Courtesy of E. H. Newcomb, University of Wisconsin; 12.10 Carolina Biological Supply/Phototake NYC; 12.18 Guenter Albrecht-Buehler, Ph.D.; 12.19 Lan Bo Chen; p. 245 Carolina Biological Supply/Phototake NYC. **Chapter 13** 13.1 Steve Granitz/WireImage; 13.2a Roland Birke/OKAPIA/Photo Researchers; 13.2b Robert Nessler; 13.3.1 Veronique Burger/Phanie Agency/Photo Researchers; 13.3.2 CNRI/Photo Researchers; 13.12 Petronczki M, Siomos MF, Nasmyth K. Un menage a quatre: the molecular biology of chromosome segregation in meiosis. Cell. 2003 Feb 21;112(4):423-40; Fig. 5a. **Chapter 14** 14.1 Mendel Museum, Augustinian Abbey, Brno; 14.14.1 altrendo nature/Getty Images; 14.14.2 Corbis; 14.15 top Photodisc/Getty Images; 14.15 bottom Anthony Loveday; 14.16 Rick Guidotti for Positive Exposure; 14.17 Dick Zimmerman/Shooting Star; p 285 Norma Jubinville. **Chapter 15** 15.1 Peter Lichter and David Ward, Science 247 (1990). Copyright 1990 American Association for the Advancemcnt of Science; 15.3 Cabisco/Visuals Unlimited; 15.5 Andrew Syred/Photo Researchers; 15.8 Dave King/Dorling Kindersley; 15.14 Milton H. Gallardo; 15.16.1 Lauren Shear/SPL/Photo Researchers; 15.16.2 CNRI/SPL/Photo Researchers; p 301 Koichi Kamoshida/Getty Images; 15.19 Ken Wagner/Phototake NYC. p 304 James K. Adams, Biology, Dalton State College, Dalton, Georgia. **Chapter 16** 16.1 National Institute of Health; 16.3 Oliver Meckes/Photo Researchers; 16.6a Courtesy of the Library of Congress; 16.6b From the Double Helix: by James D. Watson, Atheneum Press, N. Y., 1968, p. 215. (c) 1968. Courtesy CSHL Archive; 16.7c Richard Wagner; 16.12a Jerome Vinograd; 16.12b From D. J. Burks and P. J. Stambrook, The Journal of Cell Biology 77 (1978). 762, fig.6 by copyright permission of The Rockefeller University Press. Photo provided by P. J. Stambrook; 16.20 Peter Lansdorp/Terry Fox Laboratory; 16.21.1 S. C. Holt. University of Texas, Health Science Center, San Antonio/Biological Photo Service; 16.21.2 Dr. Victoria E. Foe; 16.21.3 Barbara Hamkalo; 16.21.4 From J. R. Paulsen and U. K. Laemmli, Cell 12 (1977):817-828; 16.21.5 National Museum of Health and Medicine/Armed Forces Institute of Pathology; 16.22 Ivanovska I, Khandan T, Ito K and Orr-Weaver TL. A histone code in meiosis: the histone kinase, NHK-1, is required for proper chromosomal architecture in Drosophila oocytes. Genes & Development. 2005; 192571-2582; p 324 Courtesy of J. Wang and T. A. Steitz, modified from J. Wang et al., Cell (1997) 89:1087-1099. (c)Cell Press. **Chapter 17** 17.1 DDP; 17.6a Keith V. Wood, University of California, San Diego; 17.6b Associated Press; 17.15 M. A. Rould, J.J. Perona, P. Vogt, and T.A. Steitz, Science 246 (1 December 1989): cover. Copyright 1989 by the American Association for the Advancement of Science. Thomas A. Steitz, Yale University; 17.16a Joachim Frank; 17.20 B. Hamkalo and O. Miller, Jr; 17.24 Reproduced with permission from O. L. Miller, Jr., B. A. Hamkalo, and C. A. Thomas, Jr., Science 169 (1970): 392. Copyright (c)1970 American Association for the Advancement of Science. Fig# 3. **Chapter 18** 18.1 Cook O, Biehs B, Bier E. Brinker and optomotor-blind act coordinately to initiate development of the L5 wing vein primordium in Drosophila. Development. 2004 May;131(9):2113-24; 18.14a Carolina Biological/Visuals Unlimited; 18.14b Hans Pfletschinger/Peter Arnold, Inc.; 18.18 F. Rudolf Turner, Indiana University; 18.19.1 Wolfgang Driever, University of Freiburg, Freiburg, Germany; 18.19.2 Wolfgang Driever, University of Freiburg, Freiburg, Germany; 18.19.3 Dr. Ruth Lahmann, The Whitehead Institution; 18.19.4 Dr. Ruth Lahmann, The Whitehead Institution; 18.23 University of Washington. **Chapter 19** 19.1 Science Photo Library/Photo Researchers; 19.2 Peter von Sengbusch/Botanik; 19.3.1 Robley C. Williams/Biological Photo Service; 19.3.2 R.C. Valentine and H.G. Pereira, J. Mol. Biol/Biological Photo Service; 19.3.3 K.G. Murti/Visuals Unlimited; 19.3.4 Robley C. Williams/Biological Photo Service; 19.8 C. Dauguet/Institute Pasteur/Photo Researchers; 19.9.1 National Museum of Health and Medicine, Armed Forces Institute of Pathology, Washington, DC (NCP 1603); 19.9.2 Eye of Science/Photo Researchers, Inc.; 19.9.3 Ryan Pyle/Corbis; 19.10.1 Thomas A. Zitter; 19.10.2 Dennis E. Mayhew; 19.10.3 Science VU/Wayside/Visuals Unlimited. **Chapter 20** 20.1 Reproduced with permission from R.F. Service, Science (1998) 282:396-3999. Copyright 1998 American Association for the Advancement of Science. Incyte Pharmaceuticals, Inc., Palo Alto, CA; 20.5c L. Brent Selinger, Department of Biological Sciences, University of Lethbridge, Alberta, Canada; 20.9 Repligen Corporation; 20.14 Kosman D, Mizutani CM, Lemons D, Cox WG, McGinnis W, Bier E. Multiplex detection of RNA expression in Drosophila embryos. Science. 2004 Aug 6;305(5685):846; Fig 1; 20.15 Reproduced with permission from R.F. Service, Science (1998) 282:396-3999. Copyright 1998 American Association for the Advancement of Science. Incyte Pharmaceuticals, Inc., Palo Alto, CA; 20.19 Pat Sullivan/Associated Press; 20.23 Brad DeCecco; 20.24a Steve Helber/Associated Press. **Chapter 21** 21.1 Yann Arthus-Bertrand/Corbis; 21.5 Giot L, Bader JS, Brouwer C, Chaudhuri A, Kuang B, Li Y, Hao YL, Ooi CE, Godwin B, Vitols E, Vijayadamodar G, Pochart P, Machineni H, Welsh M, Kong Y, Zerhusen B, Malcolm R, Varrone Z, Collis A, Minto M, Burgess S, McDaniel L, Stimpson E, Spriggs F, Williams J, Neurath K, Ioime N, Agee M, Voss E, Furtak K, Renzulli R, Aanensen N, Carrolla S, Bickelhaupt E, Lazovatsky Y, DaSilva A, Zhong J, Stanyon CA, Finley RL Jr, White KP, Braverman M, Jarvie T, Gold S, Leach M, Knight J, Shimkets RA, McKenna MP, Chant J, Rothberg JM. A protein interaction map of Drosophila melanogaster. Science. 2003 Dec 5; 302 (5651): 1727-36, Fig. 4b. Image supplied by Joel S. Bader; 21.6 Affymetrix; 21.8.1 AP Wide World Photos; 21.8.2 Courtesy of Virginia Walbot, Stanford University; 21.10a Courtesy of O. L. Miller Jr., Dept. of Biology, University of Virginia; 21.16 Shu W, Cho JY, Jiang Y, Zhang M, Weisz D, Elder GA, Schmeidler J, De Gasperi R, Sosa MA, Rabidou D, Santucci AC, Perl D, Morrisey E, Buxbaum JD. Altered ultrasonic vocalization in mice with a disruption in the Foxp2 gene. : Proc Natl Acad Sci U S A. 2005 Jul 5;102(27):9643-8; Fig. 3. Image supplied by Joseph Buxbaum. **Chapter 22** 22.1 Olivier Grunewald; 22.4 Michael S. Yamashita/Corbis; 22.5.1 Archiv/Photo Researchers; 22.5.2 National Maritime Museum Picture Library, London, England; 22.6 Tui De Roy/Minden Pictures; 22.7 Darwin's Tree of life sketch, MS.DAR.121:p.36. Reproduced with the permission of the Cambridge University Library; 22.9 Jack Wilburn/Animals Animals/Earth Scenes; 22.10 Wil Meinderts/FOTO NATURA/Minden Pictures; 22.11 Richard Packwood/Oxfor Scientific/Jupiter Images; 22.12a Edward S. Ross, California Academy of Sciences; 22.12b Michael & Patricia Fogden/Minden Pictures; 22.15 Mark Webster, Department of the Geophysical Sciences. University of Chicago; 22.18.1 Dwight R. Kuhn Photography; 22.18.2 Lennart Nilsson/Albert Bonniers Forlag AB. **Chapter 23** 23.1 Grant PR, Grant BR. Evolution of character displacement in Darwin's finches. Science 2006 Jul 14;313(5784):224-6; Fig. 1a; 23.2a Greene, E. A diet-induced developmental polymorphism in a caterpillar. Science. 1989. 243:643-646. Photo by Erick Greene; 23.2b Erick Greene; 23.3a Steve Gorton/Dorling Kindersley; 23.3b Janice Britton-Davidian, ISEM, UMR 5554 CNRS, Universite Montpellier II. Reprinted by permission from Nature, Vol.403, 13 January 2000, p. 158 Copyright (c) 2000 Macmillan Magazines Limited; 23.4 New York State Department of Environmental Conservation; 23.5.1 Michio Hosino/Minden Pictures; 23.5.2 James L. Davis/ProWildlife; 23.10a William Ervin/Photo Researchers, Inc.; 23.11 1993 Time Magazine cover/TimePix; 23.12 J. Antonovics/Visuals Unlimited; 23.14a Fred Bavendam/Minden Pictures; 23.14b John Visser/Bruce Coleman USA; 23.15 Frans Lanting/Minden Pictures; 23.16a Allison M. Welch, College of Charleston, South Carolina; 23.18 Dr. Michio Hori, Kyoto University; 23.19 Merlin D. Tuttle, Bat Conservation International. **Chapter 24** 24.1 George Harrison/Grant Heilman Photography, Inc.; 24.2a1 John Shaw/Tom Stack & Associates, Inc.; 24.2a2 Don & Pat Valenti/Tom Stack & Associates, Inc.; 24.2b1 Zefa/Corbis; 24.2b2 Photodisc/Getty Images; 24.2b3 Photodisc/Getty Images; 24.2b4 Photodisc/Getty Images; 24.2b5 Photodisc/Getty Images; 24.2b6 Masterfile; 24.3 Graeme Chapman; 24.4a Joe McDonald/Bruce Coleman Inc.; 24.4b Joe McDonald/Corbis; 24.4c USDA/APHIS/Animal and Plant Health Inspection Service; 24.4d Stephen Krasemann/Photo Researchers; 24.4e Barbara Gerlach/Tom Stack & Associates, Inc.; 24.4f Ueshima R, Asami T. Evolution: single-gene speciation by left-right reversal. Nature. 2003 Oct 16;425(6959):679; Fig. 1; 24.4g William E. Ferguson; 24.4h Charles W. Brown; 24.4i Photodisc/Getty Images; 24.4j Ralph A. Reinhold/Animals Animals/Earth Scenes; 24.4k Grant Heilman/Grant Heilman Photography, Inc.; 24.4l Kazutoshi Okuno; 24.6.1 Corbis; 24.6.2 John Shaw/Bruce Coleman, Inc.; 24.12 Ole Seehausen; 24.13.1 Stephen Dalton/Animals Animals - Earth Scenes; 24.13.2 ChristopheCorteau/naturepl.com; 24.15.1 Juan Martín Simón; 24.15.2 Melvin Grey/NHPA; 24.16 Ole Seehausen; 24.18a Jason Rick; 24.19 Ueshima R, Asami T. Evolution: single-gene speciation by left-right reversal. Nature. 2003 Oct 16;425(6959):679; Fig. 1 24.20 Bradshaw HD, Schemske DW. Allele substitution at a flower colour locus produces a pollinator shift in monkeyflowers. Nature. 2003 Nov 13;426(6963):176-8. **Chapter 25** 25.1 Gerhard Boeggemann; p 507 William R. Hammer and

ILLUSTRATION CREDITS

Jurassic and evolution of mammalian characteristics. *Science* 292: 1535; **25.7** Adapted from D. J. Des Marais. September 8, 2000. When did photosynthesis emerge on Earth? *Science* 289: 1703—1705; **25.10** Data from A. H. Knoll and S. B. Carroll, June 25, 1995. *Science* 284: 2129—2137; **25.12** Map adapted from http://gelology.er.usgs.gov/eastern/plates.html; **25.14** Graph created from D. M. Raup and J. J. Sepkoski, Jr. 1982. Mass extinctions in the marine fossil record. *Science*. 215: 1501-1503 and J. J. Sepkoski, Jr. 1984. A kinetic model of Phanerozoic taxonomic diversity. III. Post-Paleozoic families and mass extinctions. *Paleobiology.* Vol 10, No. 2, pp. 246-267 in D. J. Futuyma, fig. 7.3a, p. 143 and fig. 7.6, p. 145, Sunderland, MA: Sinauer Associates; **25.16** Graph from R. K. Bambach et al. 2002. Anatomical and ecological constraints on Phanerozoic animal diversity in the marien realm. *PNAS* 99: 6854-6859; **25.17** Adapted from Hickman, Roberts, and Larson.1997, *Zoology*, 10th ed, Wm. C. Brown, fig. 31.1; **25.22** Adapted from M. Ronshaugen et al. Feb. 21, 2002. Hox protein mutation and macroevolution of the insect body plan. *Nature* 415: 914-917, fig. 1a; **25.24** Adapted from M. Strickberger, 1990. *Evolution*, Boston: Jones & Bartlett. **Chapter 26 26.6** Adapted from C. S. Baker and S. R. Palumbi. 1994. Which whales are hunted? A molecular genetic approach to monitoring whaling. *Science* 265: 1538-1539, fig. 1. Copyright © 1994. Reprinted with permission from AAAS; **26.12** Adapted from S. M. Shimeld. 1999. The evolution of the hedgehog gene family in chordates: Insights from amphioxus hedgehog. *Development Genes and Evolution* 209: 40-47, fig. 3; **26.19** Adapted from J. C. Avise, 2004. *Molecular Markers, Natural History, and Evolution*, 2/e, fig. 4.3c. Copyright © Sinauer Associates, Inc. Used with permission; **26.20a** Graph adapted from B. Korber et al. Timing the ancestor of the HIV-1 pandemic strains. *Science* 288: 1789-1796. June 9, 2000. Copyright © 2000. Reprinted with permission from AAAS. **26.21** Adapted from S. L. Baldauf et al. 2004. The Tree of Life: An Overview. In *Assembling the Tree of Life* by J. Cracraft and MJ Donoghue (eds), Oxford University Press, NY; **26.22** Adapted from S. Blair Hedges. The origin and evolution of model organisms. *Nature Reviews Genetics* 3: 838-848, fig. 1, p. 840; **26.23** Adapted from M. C. Rivera and J. A. Lake. 2004. The ring of life provides evidence for a genome fusion origin of eukaryotes. *Nature* 431: 152-155, fig. 3. Copyright © 2004. Reprinted by permission of Macmillan Publishers, Ltd. **Chapter 27 27.10b** Graph adapted from V. S. Cooper and R. E. Lenski. 2000. The population genetics of ecological specialization in evolving *E. coli* populations. *Nature* 407: 736-739; **27.19** Graph created from data in C. Calvaruso et al. 2006. Root-associated bacteria contribute to mineral weathering and to mineral nutrition in trees: A budgeting analysis. *Applied and Environmental Microbiology* 72: 1258-1266. **Chapter 28 28.2** From Archibald and Keeling, "Recycled Plastids," *Trends in Genetics*, Vol. 18, No. 11, 2002. Copyright © 2002, with permission from Elsevier; **28.11** Adapted from R. W. Bauman. 2004. *Microbiology*, fig. 12.7, p. 350. Copyright © 2004 Pearson Education, Inc., publishing as Pearson Benjamin Cummings; **28.23** Data from A. Stechman and T. Cavalier-Smith. 2002. Rooting the eukaryote tree by using a derived gene fusion, *Science* 297: 89-91; **28.27** Copyright © 2004 The Nature Conservancy. Map produced by N. Law – Global Priorities Group – 08/14/2004. **Chapter 29 29.10** Source: R. D. Bowden. 1991. Inputs, outputs and accumulation of nitrogen in an early successional moss *(Polytrichum)* ecosystem. *Ecological Monographs* 61: 207-223; **29.14** Adapted from Raven et al. *Biology of Plants*, 6th ed., fig. 19.7. **Chapter 30 30.12a** Adapted from Soltis et al., 2005. *Phylogeny and Evolution of Angiosperms*, Sinauer Associates, pp. 17, fig. 1.11 from Crane 1985, which is based on Harris, 1964; **30.12b** Adapted from Soltis et al., *Phylogeny and Evolution of Angiosperms*, p. 28, fig. 2.3. Copyright © 2005. Reprinted by permission of Sinauer Associates, Inc.; **Table 30.1** Adapted from Randy Moore et al., *Botany*, 2nd ed. Dubuque, IA: Brown, 1998, Table 2.2, p. 37. **Chapter 31 31.21** Graphs adapted from A. E. Arnold et al. 2003. Fungal endophytes limit pathogen damage in a tropical tree. *PNAS* 100: 15649-15654, figs. 4 and 5. **Chapter 33 33.28a** From J. K. Grenier et al. 1997. Evolution of the entire arthropod *Hox* gene set predated the origin and radiation of the onychophoran/arthropod clade, *Current Biology* 7: 547-553, fig. 3c, p. 551. Copyright © 1997, with permission from Elsevier, Inc. **Chapter 34 34.8b** Adapted from J. Mallatt and J. Chen. 2003. Fossil sister group of craniates: Predicted and found. *Journal of Morphology* 258: 1-31, fig. 1, 5/15/03. Copyright © 2003. Reprinted with permission of Wiley-Liss, Inc., a subsidiary of John Wiley & Sons, Inc.; **34.12** Adapted from K. Kardong. 2001. *Vertebrates: Comparative Anatomy, Function, and Evolution,* 3/e. © 2001 McGraw-Hill Science/Engineering/Mathematics.; **34.19 and 34.20** From C. Zimmer. *At the Water's Edge.* Copyright © 1999 by Carl Zimmer. Reprinted by permission of Jankow & Nesbit; **34.31a** Adapted from D. J. Futuyma. 2005. *Evolution*, 1/e, fig. 4.10. Sunderland, MA: Sinauer Associates; **34.40** Drawn from photos of fossils: *O. tugenensis* photo in Michael Balter, Early hominid sows division, *ScienceNow*, Feb. 22, 2001, © 2001 American Association for the Advancement of Science. *A. ramidus kadabba* photo by Timothy White, 1999/Brill Atlanta. *A. anamensis, A. garhi,* and *H. neanderthalensis* adapted from *The Human Evolution Coloring Book. K platyops* drawn from photo in Meave Leakey et al., New hominid genus from eastern Africa shows diverse middle Pliocene lineages, *Nature*, March 22, 2001, 410: 433. *P. boisei* drawn from a photo

by David Bill. *H. ergaster* drawn from a photo at www.inhandmuseum.com. *S. tchadensis* drawn from a photo in Michel Brunet et al., A new hominid from the Upper Miocene of Chad, Central Africa, *Nature*, July 11, 2002, 418: 147, fig. 1b.; **34.43a** and **b** Adapted from I. V. Ovchinnikov et al. 2000. Molecular analysis of Neanderthal DNA from the northern Caucasus. *Nature* 404: 492, fig.3a and b. **Chapter 35 35.24 (right)** Pie chart adapted from *Nature*, Dec. 14, 2000, 408: 799. New data from The Arabidopsis Information Resource (TAIR). **Chapter 39 39.16 (top)** Adapted from M. Wilkins. 1988. *Plant Watching*, Facts of File Publ.; **39.28** Reprinted with permission from Edward Farmer, 1997, *Science* 279: 912. Copyright © 1997 American Association for the Advancement of Science. **Chapter 40 40.14** Adapted from fig. 2 in V. H. Hutchinson et al. Thermoregulation in a brooding female Indian python, *Python molurus bivittatus. Science* 151: 694-695, fig. 2. Copyright © 1966. Reprinted with permission from AAAS; **40.15** Adapted with permission from B. Heinrich. 1974. Thermoregulation in endothermic insects. *Science* 185: 747-756, fig. 7. © 1974 American Association for the Advancement of Science. **Chapter 41 41.5** Source: R. W. Smithells et al. 1980. Possible prevention of neural-tube defects by periconceptual vitamins supplementation. *Lancet* 315: 339-340; **41.10** Adapted from R. A. Rhoades and R.G. Pflanzer, *Human Physiology*, 3/e, fig. 22-1, p. 666. Copyright © 1996. Reprinted by permission of Brooks/Cole, a division of Thomson Learning. www.thomsonrights.comFax 800 732-2215; **41.23** Adapted from J. Marx, "Cellular Warriors at the Battle of the Bulge," *Science*, Vol. 299, p. 846. Copyright © 2003 American Association for the Advancement of Science. Illustration: Katharine Sutliff. **Chapter 42 42.31** Adapted from S. L. Lindstedt et al. 1991. Running energetics in the pronghorn antelope. *Nature* 353: 748–750. Copyright © 1991. Reprinted by permission of Macmillan Publishers, Ltd. **Chapter 43 43.5** Adapted from Phoebe Tzou et al, "Constitutive expression of a single antimicrobial peptide can restore wild-type resistance to infection in immuno-deficient *Drosophila* mutants," *PNAS*, 99: 2152-2157, figs. 2a and 4a. Copyright © 2002 National Academy of Sciences, U.S.A. Used with permission. **Chapter 44 44.6** Kangaroo rat data adapted from K. B. Schmidt-Nielson. 1990. *Animal Physiology: Adaptation and Environment*, 4th ed., p. 339. Cambridge: Cambridge University Press; **44.7** Adapted from K. B. Schmidt-Nielsen et al. 1958. Extrarenal salt excretion in birds. *American Journal of Physiology* 193: 101-107; **44.20** Table adapted from P. M. T. Deen et al. 1994. Requirement of human renal water channel aquaporin-2 for vasopressin-dependent concentration in urine. *Science* 264: 92-95, table 1. Copyright © 1994. Reprinted with permission from AAAS; **44 EOC** (visual summary) Adapted from W. S. Beck et al. 1991. *Life: An Introduction to Biology*, p. 649. Copyright © 1991 HarperCollins. Reprinted by permission of Pearson Education. **Chapter 45 45.4** J. M. Horowitz, et al. 1980. The Response of Single Melanophores to Extracellular and Intracellular Iontophoretic Injection of Melanocyte-Stimulating Hormone. *Endocrinology* 106: 771, fig. B. © 1980 by The Endocrine Society; **45.22** A. Jost, Recherches sur la differenciation sexuelle de l'embryon de lapin (Studies on the sexual differentiation of the rabbit embryo). *Arch. Anat. Microsc. Morphol. Exp (Archives d'anatomie microscopique et de morphologie expérimentale*). 36: 271-316, 1947. **Chapter 46 46.9** Figure adapted from R. R. Snook and D. J. Hosken. 2004. Sperm death and dumping in *Drosophila.. Nature* 428: 939—941, fig. 2. Copyright © 2004. Reprinted by permission of Macmillan Publishers, Ltd. **Chapter 47 47.18** From Wolpert, et al. 1998. *Principles of Development*, fig. 8.25, p. 251 (right). Oxford: Oxford University Press. By permission of Oxford University Press; **47.21a** Copyright © 1989 from *Molecular Biology of the Cell,* 2nd ed. by Bruce Alberts et al. Reproduced by permission of Garland Science/Taylor & Francis Books, Inc.; **47.21b** From Hiroki Nishida, "Cell lineage analysis in ascidian embryos by intracellular injection of a tracer enzyme: III. Up to the tissue restricted stage," *Developmental Biology*, Vol. 121, p. 526, June, 1987. Copyright © 1987 with permission from Elsevier, Inc.; **47.22** Copyright © 2002 from *Molecular Biology of the Cell*, 4th ed. by Bruce Alberts et al., fig. 21.17, p. 1172. Reproduced by permission of Garland Science/Taylor & Francis Books, Inc.; **47.24 experiment** and **left side of results** From Wolpert et al. 1998. *Principles of Development*, fig. 1.10, Oxford: Oxford University Press. By permission of Oxford University Press; **47.24 right side of results** Figure 15.12, p. 604 from *Developmental Biology*, 5th ed. by Gilbert et al. Copyright © 1997 Sinauer Associates. Used with permission. **Chapter 48 48.10** Adapted from G. Matthews, 1986. *Cellular Physiology of Nerve and Muscle*, Cambridge, MA: Blackwell Scientific Publications. © 1986 Blackwell Science. Used with permission of Blackwell Science, Inc.; **48.17** Adapted from C. B. Pert and S. H. Snyder. 1973. Opiate receptor: Demonstration in nervous tissue. *Science* 179: 1011-1014, Table 1. **Chapter 49 49.11** Adapted from L. M. Mukhametov. 1984. Sleep in marine mammals. In *Sleep Mechanisms*, by A. A. Borbéley and J. L. Valatx (eds.). Munich: Springer-Verlag, pp 227-238; **49.12** Adapted from M. R. Ralph et al. 1990. Transplanted suprachiasmatic nucleus determines circadian period. *Science* 247: 975-978, fig. 2; **49.14** Adapted from E. D. Jarvis et al. 2005. Avian brains and a new understanding of vertebrate brain evolution. *Nature Reviews Neuroscience* 6: 151-159, fig. 1c. **Chapter 50 50.14** Adapted from K. L. Mueller et al. 1975. The receptors and coding logic for bitter taste. *Nature* 434: 225-229;

50.19 Adapted from Bear et al. 2001. *Neuroscience: Exploring the Brain*, 2nd ed., figs. 11.8 and 11.9, pp. 281 and 283. Hagerstown,MD: Lippincott Williams & Wilkins. © 2001 Lippincott Williams and Wilkins; **50.22** Adapted from Shepherd. 1988. *Neurobiology*, 2nd ed., fig. 11.4, p. 227. Oxford University Press. (From V. G. Dethier. 1976. *The Hungry Fly*. Cambridge, MA: Harvard University Press.); **50.23** Adapted from Bear et al. 2001, Neuroscience: Exploring the Brain, 2nd ed., fig. 8.7, p. 196. Hagerstown,MD: Lippincott Williams & Wilkins. © 2001 Lippincott Williams and Wilkins; **50.32** Grasshopper adapted from Hickman et al. 1993. *Integrated Principles of Zoology*, 9th ed., Fig. 22.6, p. 518. New York: McGraw-Hill Higher Education. © 1993 The McGraw-Hill Companies; **50.37** K. Schmidt-Nielsen. 1972. Locomotion: Energy cost of swimming, flying, and running. *Science* 177: 222-228. **Chapter 51 51.3b** Adapted from N. Tinbergen. 1951. *The Study of Instinct*. Oxford: Oxford University Press. By permission of Oxford University Press; **51.7** Adapted from M. B. Sokolowski, 2001. *Drosophila*: Genetics meets behavior. *Nature Reviews: Genetics* 2: 881, fig. 1. Copyright © 2001 McMillan Publishing. Used with permission; **51.14 (left)** Adapted from C. S. Henry et al. 2002. The inheritance of mating songs in two cryptic, sibling lacewings species (Neuroptera: Chrysopidae: *Chrysoperla*). *Genetica* 116: 269-289, fig. 2. Copyright © 2002. Reprinted by permission of Springer Verlag; **51.15 (top)** Adapted from a photograph by Jonathan Blair in Alcock, 2002. *Animal Behavior*, 7th ed. Sinauer Associates, Inc., Publiishers. **51.15 (bottom)** Adapted from P. Berthold et al. 1992. Rapid microevolution of migratory behaviour in a wild bird species. *Nature* 360, 12/17,/92, p. 668, fig. 1. Copyright © 1992 Nature Publishing, Inc., used with permission; **51.18** Adapted from M. B. Sokolowski et al. 1997. Evolution of foraging behavior in *Drosophila* by density-dependent selection. Proceedings of the National Academy of Sciences of the United States of America. 94: 7373-7377. Copyright © 1997 National Academy of Sciences, U.S.A.; **51.24** K. Witte and N. Sawka. 2003. Sexual imprinting on a novel trait in the dimorphic zebra finch: sexes differ. *Animal Behaviour* 65: 195-203. Art adapted from http://www.uni-bielefeld.de/biologue/vhf/KW/Forschungsprojekte2.html. **Chapter 52 52.3** Adapted from figure at http://tde.ornl.gov. Project supported by the U.S. Dept. of Energy's Office of Science (BER); **52.5** Map adapted from G. Caughly et al. 1987. *Kangaroos: Their Ecology and Management in the Sheep Rangelands of Australia*, p. 12, fig. 1.2, Cambridge: Cambridge University Press. Copyright © 1987 Cambridge University Press. Used with permission; **52.7** Map adapted from R. L. Smith. 1974. *Ecology and Field Biology*, fig. 11.19, p. 353. Harper and Row Publishers. Map updated from D. A. Sibley. 2000. National Audubon Society *The Sibley Guide to Birds*, Alfred A. Knopf: New York; **52.8** Data from W. J. Fletcher. 1987. Interactions among subtidal Australian sea urchins, gastropods and algae: effects of experimental removals. *Ecological Monographs* 57: 89–109; **52.11** Map adapted from Physicists track great ocean conveyor belt. http://www.anl.gov/Media_Center/Frontiers/2003/d8ee.html; **52.14** Adapted from L. Roberts. 1989. How fast can trees migrate? *Science* 243: 736, fig. 2. © 1989 by the American Association for the Advancement of Science; **52.19** Adapted from Heinrich Walter and Siegmar-Walter Breckle. 2003. *Walter's Vegetation of the Earth*, fig. 16, p. 36. Springer-Verlag, © 2003; **Un. 52.2** Data from J. Clausen, D. D. Keck, and W. M. Hiesey. 1948. Experimental studies on the nature of species. III. Environmental responses of climatic races of *Achillea*. Carnegie Institution of Washington Publication 581. **Chapter 53 53.5** Adapted from P. W. Sherman and M. L. Morton, "Demography of Belding's ground squirrels," *Ecology*, Vol. 65, No. 5, p. 1622, fig. 1a, 1984. Copyright © 1984 Ecological Society of America. Used by pemission. **53.15** Adapted from J. T. Enright. 1976. Climate and population regulation: The biogeographer's dilemma. *Oecologia* 24: 295-310; **53.16** and **53.18** Adapted from T. Clutton-Brock and J. Pemberton. 2004. Soay Sheep: Dynamics and selection in an island population. Cambridge University Press. Used with permission; **53.19** Data courtesy of Rolf O. Peterson, Michigan Technological University; **53.23** Data from U. S. Census Bureau International Data Base; **53.24** Data from Population Reference Bureau 2000 and U. S. Census Bureau International Data Base, 2003; **53.25** Data from U. S. Census Bureau International Data Base; **53.26** Data from U. S. Census Bureau International Data Base 2003; **53.27** Adapted from M. L. Imhoff et al. 2004. Global patterns in human consumption of net primary production. *Nature* 429: 870-873, fig. 1a; **Tables 53.1** and **53.2** Data from P. W. Sherman and M. L. Morton, "Demography of Belding's ground squirrels," *Ecology*, Vol. 65, No. 5, p. 1622, fig. 1a, 1984. Copyright © 1984 Ecological Society of America. **Chapter 54 54.2** A. S. Rand and E. E. Williams. 1969. The anoles of La Palma: Aspects of their ecological relationships. *Breviora* 327. Museum of Comparative Zoology, Harvard University. Copyright © 1969 by the President and Fellows of Harvard College. Reprinted with permission from the Museum of Comparative Zoology; **54.10** Adapted from N. Fierer and R. B. Jackson. 2006. The diversity and biogeography of soil bacterial communities. *Proceedings of the National Academy of Sciences USA* 103: 626–631 fig. 1a. Copyright © 2006 National Academy of Sciences, U.S.A. Used with permission; **54.12** Adapted from E. A, Knox. 1970. Antarctic marine ecosystems. In *Antarctic Ecology*, ed. M. W. Holdgate, 69-96. London: Academic Press; **54.13** Adapted from D. L. Breitburg et al. 1997. Varying effects of low dissolved oxygen on trophic interactions in an estuarine food web. *Ecological Monographs* 67: 490. Copyright © 1997 Ecological Society of America; **54.14** Adapted from B. Jenkins. 1992. Productivity, disturbance and food web structure at a local spatial scale in experimental container habitats. *Oikos* 65: 252. Copyright © 1992 Oikos, Sweden, **54.15** Adapted from R. T. Paine. 1966. Food web complexity and species diversity. *American Naturalist* 100: 65-75; **54.16** Adapted from J. A. Estes et al. 1998. Killer whale predation on sea otters linking oceanic and nearshore ecosystems. *Science* 282: 474. Copyright © 1998 by the American Association for the Advancement of Science. Reprinted with permission from AAAS; **54.18** Data for graph from S. D. Hacker and M. D. Bertness. 1999. Experimental evidence for factors maintaining plant species diversity in a New England salt marsh. *Ecology* 80: 2064-2073; **54.19** Data from D. Wall Freckman and R. A. Virginia 1997. Low-diversity Antarctic soil nematode communities: distribution and response to disturbance. *Ecology* 78: 363-369; **54.20** Graph adapted from A. R. Townsend et al. 1997. The intermediate disturbance hypothesis, refugia, and diversity in streams. *Limnology and Oceanography* 42: 938-949. Copyright © 1997 by the American Society of Limnology and Oceanography, Inc. Used with permission; **54.22** Adapted from R. L. Crocker and J. Major. 1955. Soil Development in relation to vegetation and surface age at Glacier Bay, Alaska. *Journal of Ecology* 43: 427-448; **54.23** Data from F. S. Chapin, III, et al. 1994. Mechanisms of primary succession following deglaciation at Glacier Bay, Alaska. *Ecological Monographs* 64: 149-175; **54.25** Adapted from D. J. Currie. 1991. Energy and large-scale patterns of animal- and plant-species richness. *American Naturalist* 137: 27-49; **54.26** Adapted from F. W. Preston. 1960. Time and space and the variation of species. *Ecology* 41: 611-627; **54.28** Adapted from F. W. Preston. 1962. The canonical distribution of commonness and rarity. *Ecology* 43: 185-215, 410-432. **Chapter 55 55.4** and **Un 55.1** Adapted from D. L. DeAngelis. 1992. *Dynamics of Nutrient Cycling and Food Webs*. New York: Chapman & Hall; **55.7** Adapted from J. H. Ryther and W. M. Dunstan. 1971. Nitrogen, phosphorus, and eutrophication in the coastal marine environment. *Science* 171: 1008-1013. Copyright © 1971. Reprinted with permission from AAAS; **55.8** Data from M. L. Rosenzweig. 1968. New primary productivity of terrestrial environments: Predictions from climatologic data, *American Naturalist* 102: 67-74; **55.14a** Adapted from R. E. Ricklefs. 1997. *The Economy of Nature*, 4th ed. © 1997 by W. H. Freeman and Company. Used with permission; **55.15** Map adapted from Moore et al. 1999. Litter decomposition rates in Canadian forests, Global Change Biology 5: 75-82. Trofymow et al. 1998. Canadian Intersite Decomposition Experiment (CIDET): Project and site establishment. Information Report BC-X-378. NRCAN CFS Victoria. 126pp. Produced under license from Her Majesty the Queen in Right of Canada, with permission of Natural Resources Canada. The Canadian Intersite Decomposition Experiment (CIDET) - http://cfs.nrcan.gc.ca/subsite/cidet; **55.21** CO$_2$ data from C. D. Keeling and T. P. Whorf, Scripps Institution of Oceanography. Temperature data from www.earth-policy.org/Indicators/Temp/Temp_data.htm. **55.23** Data from ozonewatch.gsfc.nasa.gov/facts/history/htmml; **Table 55.1** Data from Menzel and Ryther. 1961. *Deep Sea Ranch* 7: 276-281. **Chapter 56 56.10** Adapted from C. J. Krebs. 2001. *Ecology*, 5th ed., fig. 19.1. Copyright © 2001 Pearson Education, Inc., publishing as Pearson Benjamin Cummings; **56.11** Adapted from R. L. Westemeiier et al. 1998. Tracking the long-term decline and recovery of an isolated population. *Science* 282: 1696. © 1998 by the American Association for the Advancement of Science; **56.17** Adapted from N. Myers et al., "Biodiversity hotspots for conservation priorities," *Nature*, Vol. 403, p. 853, 2/24/2000. Copyright © 2000 Nature Publishing, Inc. Used with permission. Updated with data from C. H. Roberts et al. 2002. Marine biodiversity hotspots and conservation priorities for tropical reefs. *Science* 295: 1280-1284; **56.18** Adapted from W.D. Newmark, "Legal and biotic boundaries of western North American national parks: A problem of congruence." *Biological Conservation* 33: 199, 1985. © 1985 Elsevier, with kind permission; **56.19a** Map adapted from W. Purves and G. Orians, *Life, The Science of Biology*, 5th ed., fig. 55.23, p. 1239. © 1998 by Sinauer Associates, Inc. Used with permission; **56.22b** Graph adapted from http://news-service.standford.edu/news/2006/may24/gcriddle_ponds.jpg; **56.24** Data from Instituto Nacional de Estadistica y Censos de Costa Rica and Centro Centroamericano de Poblacion, Universidad de Costa Rica.

Glossary

Pronunciation Key

Pronounce

$\bar{a}$	as in	ace
a		ash
ch		chose
$\bar{e}$		meet
e/eh		bet
g		game
$\bar{i}$		ice
i		hit
ks		box
kw		quick
ng		song
$\bar{o}$		robe
o		ox
oy		boy
s		say
sh		shell
th		thin
$\bar{u}$		boot
u/uh		up
z		zoo

′ = primary accent

′ = secondary accent

5′ cap A modified form of guanine nucleotide added onto the nucleotide at the 5′ end of a pre-mRNA molecule.

A site One of a ribosome's three binding sites for tRNA during translation. The A site holds the tRNA carrying the next amino acid to be added to the polypeptide chain. (A stands for aminoacyl tRNA.)

ABC model A model of flower formation identifying three classes of organ identity genes that direct formation of the four types of floral organs.

abiotic ($\bar{a}$′-b$\bar{i}$-ot′-ik) Nonliving; referring to physical and chemical properties of an environment.

abortion The termination of a pregnancy in progress.

abscisic acid (ABA) (ab-sis′-ik) A plant hormone that slows growth, often antagonizing actions of growth hormones. Two of its many effects are to promote seed dormancy and facilitate drought tolerance.

absorption The third stage of food processing in animals: the uptake of small nutrient molecules by an organism's body.

absorption spectrum The range of a pigment's ability to absorb various wavelengths of light; also a graph of such a range.

abyssal zone (uh-bis′-ul) The part of the ocean's benthic zone between 2,000 and 6,000 m deep.

acanthodian (ak′-an-th$\bar{o}$′-d $\bar{e}$-un) Any of a group of ancient jawed aquatic vertebrates from the Devonian period.

accessory fruit A fruit, or assemblage of fruits, in which the fleshy parts are derived largely or entirely from tissues other than the ovary.

acclimatization (uh-kl$\bar{i}$′-muh-t$\bar{i}$-z$\bar{a}$′-shun) Physiological adjustment to a change in an environmental factor.

acetyl CoA Acetyl coenzyme A; the entry compound for the citric acid cycle in cellular respiration, formed from a fragment of pyruvate attached to a coenzyme.

acetylcholine (as′-uh-til-k$\bar{o}$′-l$\bar{e}$n) One of the most common neurotransmitters; functions by binding to receptors and altering the permeability of the postsynaptic membrane to specific ions, either depolarizing or hyperpolarizing the membrane.

acid A substance that increases the hydrogen ion concentration of a solution.

acid precipitation Rain, snow, or fog that is more acidic than pH 5.2.

acoelomate (uh-s$\bar{e}$′-l$\bar{o}$-m$\bar{a}$t) A solid-bodied animal lacking a cavity between the gut and outer body wall.

acquired immunity A vertebrate-specific defense that is mediated by B lymphocytes (B cells) and T lymphocytes (T cells). It exhibits specificity, memory, and self-nonself recognition. Also called adaptive immunity.

acrosomal reaction (ak′-ruh-s$\bar{o}$m′-ul) The discharge of hydrolytic enzymes from the acrosome, a vesicle in the tip of a sperm, when the sperm approaches or contacts an egg.

acrosome (ak′-ruh-s$\bar{o}$m) A vesicle in the tip of a sperm containing hydrolytic enzymes and other proteins that help the sperm reach the egg.

actin (ak′-tin) A globular protein that links into chains, two of which twist helically about each other, forming microfilaments (actin filaments) in muscle and other kinds of cells.

action potential A rapid change in the membrane potential of an excitable cell, caused by stimulus-triggered, selective opening and closing of voltage-sensitive gates in sodium and potassium ion channels.

action spectrum A graph that profiles the relative effectiveness of different wavelengths of radiation in driving a particular process.

activation energy The amount of energy that reactants must absorb before a chemical reaction will start; also called free energy of activation.

activator A protein that binds to DNA and stimulates gene transcription. In prokaryotes, activators bind in or near the promoter; in eukaryotes, activators bind to control elements in enhancers.

active immunity Long-lasting immunity conferred by the action of B cells and T cells and the resulting B and T memory cells specific for a pathogen. Active immunity can develop as a result of natural infection or immunization.

active site The specific portion of an enzyme that binds the substrate by means of multiple weak interactions and that forms the pocket in which catalysis occurs.

active transport The movement of a substance across a cell membrane, with an expenditure of energy, against its concentration or electrochemical gradient; mediated by specific transport proteins.

actual evapotranspiration The amount of water transpired by plants and evaporated from a landscape over a given period of time, usually measured in millimeters and estimated for a year.

adaptation Inherited characteristic of an organism that enhances its survival and reproduction in specific environments.

adaptive radiation Period of evolutionary change in which groups of organisms form many new species whose adaptations allow them to fill vacant ecological roles in their communities.

adenylyl cyclase (uh-den′-uh-lil) An enzyme that converts ATP to cyclic AMP in response to a signal.

adhesion The attraction between different kinds of molecules.

adipose tissue A connective tissue that insulates the body and serves as a fuel reserve; contains fat-storing cells called adipose cells.

adrenal gland (uh-dr$\bar{e}$′-nul) One of two endocrine glands located adjacent to the kidneys in mammals. Endocrine cells in the outer portion (cortex) respond to ACTH by secreting steroid hormones that help maintain homeostasis during long-term stress. Neurosecretory cells in the central portion (medulla) secrete epinephrine and norepinephrine in response to nervous inputs triggered by short-term stress.

adrenocorticotropic hormone (ACTH) A tropic hormone that is produced and secreted by the anterior pituitary and that stimulates the production and secretion of steroid hormones by the adrenal cortex.

aerobic respiration A catabolic pathway that consumes oxygen (O_2) and organic molecules, producing ATP. This is the most efficient catabolic pathway and is carried out in most eukaryotic cells and many prokaryotic organisms.

afferent arteriole (af′-er-ent) In the kidney, the blood vessel supplying a nephron.

age structure The relative number of individuals of each age in a population.

aggregate fruit A fruit derived from a single flower that has more than one carpel.

agonistic behavior (a'-gō-nis'-tik) In animals, an often ritualized contest that determines which competitor gains access to a resource, such as food or mates.

AIDS (acquired immunodeficiency syndrome) The symptoms and signs present during the late stages of HIV infection, defined by a specified reduction in the number of T cells and the appearance of characteristic secondary infections.

alcohol fermentation Glycolysis followed by the conversion of pyruvate to carbon dioxide and ethyl alcohol.

aldosterone (al-dos'-tuh-rōn) A steroid hormone that acts on tubules of the kidney to regulate the transport of sodium ions (Na^+) and potassium ions (K^+).

alimentary canal (al'-uh-men'-tuh-rē) A digestive tract consisting of a tube running between a mouth and an anus; also called a complete digestive tract.

allantois (al-an'-tō'-is) One of four extraembryonic membranes; serves as a repository for the embryo's nitrogenous waste and functions in gas exchange.

allele (uh-lē'-ul) Any of the alternative versions of a gene that produce distinguishable phenotypic effects.

allopatric speciation (al'-uh-pat'-rik) The formation of new species in populations that are geographically isolated from one another.

allopolyploid (al'-ō-pol'-ē-ployd) A fertile individual that has more than two chromosome sets as a result of two different species interbreeding and combining their chromosomes.

allosteric regulation The binding of a regulatory molecule to a protein at one site that affects the function of the protein at a different site.

alpha (α) helix (al'-fuh hē'-liks) A spiral shape constituting one form of the secondary structure of proteins, arising from a specific pattern of hydrogen bonding.

alternation of generations A life cycle in which there is both a multicellular diploid form, the sporophyte, and a multicellular haploid form, the gametophyte; characteristic of plants and some algae.

alternative RNA splicing A type of eukaryotic gene regulation at the RNA-processing level in which different mRNA molecules are produced from the same primary transcript, depending on which RNA segments are treated as exons and which as introns.

altruism (al'-trū-iz-um) Selflessness; behavior that reduces an individual's fitness while increasing the fitness of another individual.

alveolate (al-vē'-uh-let) A protist with membrane-bounded sacs (alveoli) located just under the plasma membrane.

alveolus (al-vē'-uh-lus) (plural, **alveoli**) One of the dead-end, multilobed air sacs where gas exchange occurs in a mammalian lung.

Alzheimer's disease (alts'-hī-merz) An age-related dementia (mental deterioration) characterized by confusion, memory loss, and other symptoms.

amacrine cell (am'-uh-krin) A neuron of the retina that helps integrate information before it is sent to the brain.

amino acid (uh-mēn'-ō) An organic molecule possessing both carboxyl and amino groups. Amino acids serve as the monomers of polypeptides.

amino group A chemical group consisting of a nitrogen atom bonded to two hydrogen atoms; can act as a base in solution, accepting a hydrogen ion and acquiring a charge of 1+.

aminoacyl-tRNA synthetase An enzyme that joins each amino acid to the appropriate tRNA.

ammonia A small, very toxic molecule (NH_3) produced by nitrogen fixation or as a metabolic waste product of protein and nucleic acid metabolism.

ammonite A member of a group of shelled cephalopods that were important marine predators for hundreds of millions of years until their extinction at the end of the Cretaceous period (65.5 mya).

amniocentesis (am'-nē-ō-sen-tē'-sis) A technique of prenatal diagnosis in which amniotic fluid, obtained by aspiration from a needle inserted into the uterus, is analyzed to detect certain genetic and congenital defects in the fetus.

amnion (am'-nē-on) One of four extraembryonic membranes. It surrounds a fluid-filled cavity that cushions the embryo.

amniote (am'-nē-ōt) Member of a clade of tetrapods named for a key derived character, the amniotic egg, which contains specialized membranes, including the fluid-filled amnion, that protect the embryo. Amniotes include mammals as well as birds and other reptiles.

amniotic egg A shelled egg in which an embryo develops within a fluid-filled amniotic sac and is nourished by yolk. Produced by reptiles (including birds) and egg-laying mammals, it enables them to complete their life cycles on dry land.

amoeba (uh-mē'-buh) A protist grade characterized by the presence of pseudopodia.

amoebocyte (uh-mē'-buh-sīt') An amoeba-like cell that moves by pseudopodia and is found in most animals. Depending on the species, it may digest and distribute food, dispose of wastes, form skeletal fibers, fight infections, and change into other cell types.

amoebozoan (uh-mē'-buh-zō'-an) A protist in a clade that includes many species with lobe- or tube-shaped pseudopodia.

amphibian Member of the tetrapod class Amphibia, including salamanders, frogs, and caecilians.

amphipathic (am'-fē-path'-ik) Having both a hydrophilic region and a hydrophobic region.

amplification The strengthening of stimulus energy during transduction.

amygdala (uh-mig'-duh-luh) A structure in the temporal lobe of the vertebrate brain that has a major role in the processing of emotions.

amylase (am'-uh-lās') An enzyme in saliva that hydrolyzes starch (a glucose polymer from plants) and glycogen (a glucose polymer from animals) into smaller polysaccharides and the disaccharide maltose.

anabolic pathway (an'-uh-bol'-ik) A metabolic pathway that consumes energy to synthesize a complex molecule from simpler compounds.

anaerobic respiration (an-er-ō'-bik) The use of inorganic molecules other than oxygen to accept electrons at the "downhill" end of electron transport chains.

analogous Having characteristics that are similar because of convergent evolution, not homology.

analogy (an-al'-uh-jē) Similarity between two species that is due to convergent evolution rather than to descent from a common ancestor with the same trait.

anaphase The fourth stage of mitosis, in which the chromatids of each chromosome have separated and the daughter chromosomes are moving to the poles of the cell.

anatomy The structure of an organism and its study.

anchorage dependence The requirement that a cell must be attached to a substratum in order to divide.

androgen (an'-drō-jen) Any steroid hormone, such as testosterone, that stimulates the development and maintenance of the male reproductive system and secondary sex characteristics.

aneuploidy (an'-yū-ploy'-dē) A chromosomal aberration in which one or more chromosomes are present in extra copies or are deficient in number.

angiosperm (an'-jē-ō-sperm) A flowering plant, which forms seeds inside a protective chamber called an ovary.

angiotensin II A peptide hormone that stimulates constriction of precapillary arterioles and increases reabsorption of NaCl and water by the proximal tubules of the kidney, increasing blood pressure and volume.

anhydrobiosis (an-hī'-drō-bī-ō'-sis) A dormant state involving loss of almost all body water.

animal pole The point at the end of an egg in the hemisphere where the least yolk is concentrated; opposite of vegetal pole.

Animalia The kingdom that consists of multicellular eukaryotes that ingest their food.

anion (an'-ī-on) A negatively charged ion.

annual A flowering plant that completes its entire life cycle in a single year or growing season.

anterior Pertaining to the front, or head, of a bilaterally symmetrical animal.

anterior pituitary Also called the adenohypophysis; portion of the pituitary that develops from nonneural tissue; consists of endocrine cells that synthesize and secrete several tropic and nontropic hormones.

anther In an angiosperm, the terminal pollen sac of a stamen, where pollen grains containing sperm-producing male gametophytes form.

antheridium (an-thuh-rid'-ē-um) (plural, **antheridia**) In plants, the male gametangium, a moist chamber in which gametes develop.

anthropoid (an´-thruh-poyd) Member of a primate group made up of the monkeys and the apes (gibbons, orangutans, gorillas, chimpanzees, bonobos, and humans).

antibody A protein secreted by plasma cells (differentiated B cells) that binds to a particular antigen; also called immunoglobulin. All antibody molecules have the same Y-shaped structure and in their monomer form consist of two identical heavy chains and two identical light chains.

anticodon (an´-tī-kō´-don) A nucleotide triplet at one end of a tRNA molecule that recognizes a particular complementary codon on an mRNA molecule.

antidiuretic hormone (ADH) (an´-tī-dī-yū-ret´-ik) A peptide hormone, also known as vasopressin, that promotes water retention by the kidneys. Produced in the hypothalamus and released from the posterior pituitary, ADH also has activities in the brain.

antigen (an´-ti-jen) A macromolecule that elicits an immune response by binding to receptors of B cells or T cells.

antigen presentation The process by which an MHC molecule binds to a fragment of an intracellular protein antigen and carries it to the cell surface, where it is displayed and can be recognized by a T cell.

antigen receptor The general term for a surface protein, located on B cells and T cells, that binds to antigens, initiating acquired immune responses. The antigen receptors on B cells are called B cell receptors, and the antigen receptors on T cells are called T cell receptors.

antigen-presenting cell A cell that upon ingesting pathogens or internalizing pathogen proteins generates peptide fragments that are bound by class II MHC molecules and subsequently displayed on the cell surface to T cells. Macrophages, dendritic cells, and B cells are the primary antigen-presenting cells.

antiparallel The opposite arrangement of the sugar-phosphate backbones in a DNA double helix.

aphotic zone (ā´-fō´-tik) The part of an ocean or lake beneath the photic zone, where light does not penetrate sufficiently for photosynthesis to occur.

apical bud (ā´-pik-ul) A bud at the tip of a plant stem; also called a terminal bud.

apical dominance Concentration of growth at the tip of a plant shoot, where a terminal bud partially inhibits axillary bud growth.

apical ectodermal ridge (AER) A thickened area of ectoderm at the tip of a limb bud that promotes outgrowth of the limb bud.

apical meristem (mār´-uh-stem) Embryonic plant tissue in the tips of roots and the buds of shoots. The dividing cells of an apical meristem enable the plant to grow in length.

apicomplexan (ap´-ē-kom-pleks´-un) A protist in a clade that includes many species that parasitize animals. Some apicomplexans cause human disease.

apomixis (ap´-uh-mik´-sis) The ability of some plant species to reproduce asexually through seeds without fertilization by a male gamete.

apoplast (ap´-ō-plast) In plants, the continuum of cell walls plus the extracellular spaces.

apoptosis (ā-puh-tō´-sus) A program of controlled cell suicide, which is brought about by signals that trigger the activation of a cascade of suicide proteins in the cell destined to die.

aposematic coloration (ap´-ō-si-mat´-ik) The bright coloration of animals with effective physical or chemical defenses that acts as a warning to predators.

appendix A small, finger-like extension of the vertebrate cecum; contains a mass of white blood cells that contribute to immunity.

aquaporin A channel protein in the plasma membrane of a plant, animal, or microorganism cell that specifically facilitates osmosis, the diffusion of water across the membrane.

aqueous humor Plasma-like liquid in the space between the lens and the cornea in the vertebrate eye; helps maintain the shape of the eye, supplies nutrients and oxygen to its tissues, and disposes of its wastes.

aqueous solution (ā´-kwē-us) A solution in which water is the solvent.

arachnid A member of a major arthropod group, the cheliceriforms. Arachnids include spiders, scorpions, ticks, and mites.

arbuscular mycorrhiza (ar-bus´-kyū-lur mī´-kō-rī´-zuh) Association of a fungus with a plant root system in which the fungus causes the invagination of the host (plant) cells' plasma membranes.

arbuscular mycorrhizal fungus A symbiotic fungus whose hyphae grow through the cell wall of plant roots and extend into the root cell (enclosed in tubes formed by invagination of the root cell plasma membrane).

Archaea (ar´-kē´-uh) One of two prokaryotic domains, the other being Bacteria.

archaean Member of the prokaryotic domain Archaea.

Archaeplastida (ar´-kē-plas´-tid-uh) One of five supergroups of eukaryotes proposed in a current hypothesis of the evolutionary history of eukaryotes. This monophyletic group, which includes red algae, green alage, and land plants, descended from an ancient protist ancestor that engulfed a cyanobacterium. *See also* Excavata, Chromalveolata, Rhizaria, and Unikonta.

archegonium (ar-ki-gō´-nē-um) (plural, **archegonia**) In plants, the female gametangium, a moist chamber in which gametes develop.

archenteron (ar-ken´-tuh-ron) The endoderm-lined cavity, formed during gastrulation, that develops into the digestive tract of an animal.

archosaur (ar´-kō-sōr) Member of the reptilian group that includes crocodiles, alligators, dinosaurs, and birds.

arteriole (ar-ter´-ē-ōl) A vessel that conveys blood between an artery and a capillary bed.

artery A vessel that carries blood away from the heart to organs throughout the body.

arthropod A segmented ecdysozoan with a hard exoskeleton and jointed appendages. Familiar examples include insects, spiders, millipedes, and crabs.

artificial selection The selective breeding of domesticated plants and animals to encourage the occurrence of desirable traits.

ascocarp The fruiting body of a sac fungus (ascomycete).

ascomycete (as´-kuh-mī´-sēt) Member of the fungal phylum Ascomycota, commonly called sac fungus. The name comes from the saclike structure in which the spores develop.

ascus (plural, **asci**) A saclike spore capsule located at the tip of a dikaryotic hypha of a sac fungus.

asexual reproduction The generation of offspring from a single parent that occurs without the fusion of gametes (by budding, division of a single cell, or division of the entire organism into two or more parts). In most cases, the offspring are genetically identical to the parent.

assisted reproductive technology A fertilization procedure that generally involves surgically removing eggs (secondary oocytes) from a woman's ovaries after hormonal stimulation, fertilizing the eggs, and returning them to the woman's body.

associative learning The acquired ability to associate one environmental feature (such as a color) with another (such as danger).

aster A radial array of short microtubules that extends from each centrosome toward the plasma membrane in an animal cell undergoing mitosis.

astrocyte A glial cell with diverse functions, including providing structural support for neurons, regulating the interstitial environment, facilitating synaptic transmission, and assisting in regulating the blood supply to the brain.

atherosclerosis A cardiovascular disease in which fatty deposits called plaques develop in the inner walls of the arteries, obstructing the arteries and causing them to harden.

atom The smallest unit of matter that retains the properties of an element.

atomic mass The total mass of an atom, which is the mass in grams of 1 mole of the atom.

atomic nucleus An atom's dense central core, containing protons and neutrons.

atomic number The number of protons in the nucleus of an atom, unique for each element and designated by a subscript to the left of the elemental symbol.

ATP (adenosine triphosphate) (a-den´-ō-sēn trī-fos´-fāt) An adenine-containing nucleoside triphosphate that releases free energy when its phosphate bonds are hydrolyzed. This energy is used to drive endergonic reactions in cells.

ATP synthase A complex of several membrane proteins that provide a port through which protons diffuse. This complex functions in chemiosmosis with adjacent electron transport chains, using the energy of a hydrogen ion (proton) concentration gradient to make ATP. ATP synthases are found in the inner mitochondrial membrane of eukaryotic cells and in the plasma membrane of prokaryotes.

atrial natriuretic peptide (ANP) (ā´-trē-ul na´-trē-yū-ret´-ik) A peptide hormone secreted by cells of the atria of the heart in response to high blood pressure. ANP's effects on the kidney alter ion and water movement and thereby reduce blood pressure.

atrioventricular (AV) node A region of specialized heart muscle tissue between the left and right atria where electrical impulses are delayed for about 0.1 second before spreading to both ventricles and causing them to contract.

atrioventricular (AV) valve A heart valve located between each atrium and ventricle that prevents a backflow of blood when the ventricle contracts.

atrium (ā´-trē-um) (plural, **atria**) A chamber of the vertebrate heart that receives blood from the veins and transfers blood to a ventricle.

autocrine Referring to a secreted molecule that acts on the cell that secreted it.

autoimmune disease An immunological disorder in which the immune system turns against self.

autonomic nervous system (ot´-ō-nom´-ik) An efferent branch of the vertebrate peripheral nervous system that regulates the internal environment; consists of the sympathetic, parasympathetic, and enteric divisions.

autopolyploid (ot´-ō-pol´-ē-ployd) An individual that has more than two chromosome sets that are all derived from a single species.

autosome (ot´-ō-sōm) A chromosome that is not directly involved in determining sex; not a sex chromosome.

autotroph (ot´-ō-trōf) An organism that obtains organic food molecules without eating other organisms or substances derived from other organisms. Autotrophs use energy from the sun or from the oxidation of inorganic substances to make organic molecules from inorganic ones.

auxin (ok´-sin) A term that primarily refers to indoleacetic acid (IAA), a natural plant hormone that has a variety of effects, including cell elongation, root formation, secondary growth, and fruit growth.

average heterozygosity (het´-er-ō-zī-gō´-si-tē) The percent, on average, of a population's loci that are heterozygous in members of the population.

avirulent Describing a pathogen that can only mildly harm, but not kill, the host.

axillary bud (ak´-sil-ār-ē) A structure that has the potential to form a lateral shoot, or branch. The bud appears in the angle formed between a leaf and a stem.

axon (ak´-son) A typically long extension, or process, of a neuron that carries nerve impulses away from the cell body toward target cells.

axon hillock The conical region of a neuron's axon where it joins the cell body; typically the region where nerve impulses are generated.

B cell receptor The antigen receptor on B cells: a Y-shaped, membrane-bound molecule consisting of two identical heavy chains and two identical light chains linked by disulfide bridges and containing two antigen-binding sites.

B cells The lymphocytes that complete their development in the bone marrow and become effector cells for the humoral immune response.

Bacteria One of two prokaryotic domains, the other being Archaea.

bacterial artificial chromosome (BAC) A large plasmid that acts as a bacterial chromosome and can carry inserts of 100,000 to 300,000 base pairs.

bacteriophage (bak-tēr´-ē-ō-fāj) A virus that infects bacteria; also called a phage.

bacterium Member of the prokaryotic domain Bacteria.

bacteroid A form of the bacterium *Rhizobium* contained within the vesicles formed by the root cells of a root nodule.

balancing selection Natural selection that maintains two or more phenotypic forms in a population.

bark All tissues external to the vascular cambium, consisting mainly of the secondary phloem and layers of periderm.

Barr body A dense object lying along the inside of the nuclear envelope in cells of female mammals, representing a highly condensed, inactivated X chromosome.

barrier method Contraception that relies on a physical barrier to block the passage of sperm. Examples include condoms and diaphragms.

basal angiosperm Member of a clade of three early-diverging lineages of flowering plants. Examples are *Amborella*, water lilies, and star anise and its relatives.

basal body (bā´-sul) A eukaryotic cell structure consisting of a 9 + 0 arrangement of microtubule triplets. The basal body may organize the microtubule assembly of a cilium or flagellum and is structurally very similar to a centriole.

basal metabolic rate (BMR) The metabolic rate of a resting, fasting, and non-stressed endotherm at a comfortable temperature.

base A substance that reduces the hydrogen ion concentration of a solution.

base-pair substitution A type of point mutation; the replacement of one nucleotide and its partner in the complementary DNA strand by another pair of nucleotides.

basidiocarp Elaborate fruiting body of a dikaryotic mycelium of a club fungus.

basidiomycete (buh-sid´-ē-ō-mī´-sēt) Member of the fungal phylum Basidiomycota, commonly called club fungus. The name comes from the club-like shape of the basidium.

basidium (plural, **basidia**) (buh-sid´-ē-um, buh-sid´-ē-ah) A reproductive appendage that produces sexual spores on the gills of mushrooms (club fungi).

Batesian mimicry (bāt´-zē-un mim´-uh-krē) A type of mimicry in which a harmless species looks like a species that is poisonous or otherwise harmful to predators.

behavior (in animals) Individually, an action carried out by muscles or glands under control of the nervous system in response to a stimulus; collectively, the sum of an animal's responses to external and internal stimuli.

behavioral ecology The study of the evolution of and ecological basis for animal behavior.

benign tumor A mass of abnormal cells that remains at the site of its origin.

benthic zone The bottom surface of an aquatic environment.

benthos (ben´-thōz) The communities of organisms living in the benthic zone of an aquatic biome.

beta (β) pleated sheet One form of the secondary structure of proteins in which the polypeptide chain folds back and forth. Two regions of the chain lie parallel to each other and are held together by hydrogen bonds.

beta oxidation A metabolic sequence that breaks fatty acids down to two-carbon fragments that enter the citric acid cycle as acetyl CoA.

bicoid A maternal effect gene that codes for a protein responsible for specifying the anterior end in *Drosophila*.

biennial (bī-en´-ē-ul) A flowering plant that requires two years to complete its life cycle.

big-bang reproduction Reproduction in which an organism produces all of its offspring in a single event; also known as semelparity.

bilateral symmetry Body symmetry in which a central longitudinal plane divides the body into two equal but opposite halves.

bilaterian (bī´-luh-ter´-ē-uhn) Member of a clade of animals with bilateral symmetry and three germ layers.

bile A mixture of substances that is produced in the liver but stored in the gallbladder and that enables formation of fat droplets in water as an aid in the digestion and absorption of fats.

binary fission A method of asexual reproduction by "division in half." In prokaryotes, binary fission does not involve mitosis; but in single-celled eukaryotes that undergo binary fission, mitosis is part of the process.

binomial The two-part latinized name of a species, consisting of the genus and specific epithet.

biodiversity hot spot A relatively small area with an exceptional concentration of endemic species and often a large number of endangered and threatened species.

bioenergetics (1) The overall flow and transformation of energy in an organism. (2) The study of how energy flows through organisms.

biofilm A surface-coating colony of one or more species of prokaryotes that engage in metabolic cooperation.

biofuel A fuel produced from dry organic matter or combustible oils produced by plants.

biogenic amine A neurotransmitter derived from an amino acid.

biogeochemical cycle Any of the various chemical cycles, which involve both biotic and abiotic components of ecosystems.

biogeography The study of the past and present distribution of species.

bioinformatics The use of computers, software, and mathematical models to process and integrate biological information from large data sets.

biological augmentation An approach to restoration ecology that uses organisms to add essential materials to a degraded ecosystem.

biological clock An internal timekeeper that controls an organism's biological rhythms. The biological clock marks time with or without environmental cues but often requires signals from the environment to remain tuned to an appropriate period. *See also* circadian rhythm.

biological magnification A process in which retained substances become more concentrated at each higher trophic level in a food chain.

biological species concept Definition of a species as a population or group of populations whose members have the potential to interbreed in nature and produce viable, fertile offspring, but do not produce viable, fertile offspring with members of other such groups.

biology The scientific study of life.

biomanipulation An approach that applies the top-down model of community organization to alter ecosystem characteristics. For example, ecologists can prevent algal blooms and eutrophication by altering the density of higher-level consumers in lakes instead of by using chemical treatments.

biomass The total mass of organic matter comprising a group of organisms in a particular habitat.

biome (bī'-ōm) Any of the world's major ecosystems, often classified according to the predominant vegetation and characterized by adaptations of organisms to that particular environment.

bioremediation The use of organisms to detoxify and restore polluted and degraded ecosystems.

biosphere The entire portion of Earth inhabited by life; the sum of all the planet's ecosystems.

biotechnology The manipulation of organisms or their components to produce useful products.

biotic (bī-ot'-ik) Pertaining to the living organisms in the environment.

bipolar cell A neuron that relays information between photoreceptors and ganglion cells in the retina.

bipolar disorder Depressive mental illness characterized by swings of mood from high to low; also called manic-depressive disorder.

birth control pill A chemical contraceptive that inhibits ovulation, retards follicular development, or alters a woman's cervical mucus to prevent sperm from entering the uterus.

blade (1) A leaflike structure of a seaweed that provides most of the surface area for photosynthesis. (2) The flattened portion of a typical leaf.

blastocoel (blas'-tuh-sēl) The fluid-filled cavity that forms in the center of a blastula.

blastocyst (blas'-tuh-sist) The blastula stage of mammalian embryonic development, consisting of an inner cell mass, a cavity, and an outer layer, the trophoblast. In humans, the blastocyst forms one week after fertilization.

blastomere An early embryonic cell arising during the cleavage stage of an early embryo.

blastopore (blas'-tō-pōr) In a gastrula, the opening of the archenteron that typically develops into the anus in deuterostomes and the mouth in protostomes.

blastula (blas'-tyū-luh) A hollow ball of cells that marks the end of the cleavage stage during early embryonic development in animals.

blood A connective tissue with a fluid matrix called plasma in which red blood cells, white blood cells, and cell fragments called platelets are suspended.

blood-brain barrier A specialized capillary arrangement in the brain that restricts the passage of most substances into the brain, thereby preventing dramatic fluctuations in the brain's environment.

blue-light photoreceptor A type of light receptor in plants that initiates a variety of responses, such as phototropism and slowing of hypocotyl elongation.

body cavity A fluid- or air-filled space between the digestive tract and the body wall.

body plan In animals, a set of morphological and developmental traits that are integrated into a functional whole—the living animal.

Bohr shift A lowering of the affinity of hemoglobin for oxygen, caused by a drop in pH. It facilitates the release of oxygen from hemoglobin in the vicinity of active tissues.

bolus A lubricated ball of chewed food.

bone A connective tissue consisting of living cells held in a rigid matrix of collagen fibers embedded in calcium salts.

book lung An organ of gas exchange in spiders, consisting of stacked plates contained in an internal chamber.

bottleneck effect Genetic drift that occurs when the size of a population is reduced, as by a natural disaster or human actions. Typically, the surviving population is no longer genetically representative of the original population.

bottom-up model A model of community organization in which mineral nutrients influence community organization by controlling plant or phytoplankton numbers, which in turn control herbivore numbers, which in turn control predator numbers.

Bowman's capsule (bō'-munz) A cup-shaped receptacle in the vertebrate kidney that is the initial, expanded segment of the nephron where filtrate enters from the blood.

brachiopod (bra'-kē-uh-pod') A marine lophophorate with a shell divided into dorsal and ventral halves. Brachiopods are also called lamp shells.

brain Organ of the central nervous system where information is processed and integrated.

brainstem Collection of structures in the vertebrate brain, including the midbrain, the pons, and the medulla oblongata; functions in homeostasis, coordination of movement, and conduction of information to higher brain centers.

branch point The representation on a phylogenetic tree of the divergence of two or more taxa from a common ancestor. Most branch points are shown as dichotomies, in which a branch representing the ancestral lineage splits (at the branch point) into two branches, one for each of the two descendant taxa.

brassinosteroid A steroid hormone in plants that has a variety of effects, including cell elongation, retarding leaf abscission, and promoting xylem differentiation.

breathing Ventilation of the lungs through alternating inhalation and exhalation.

breathing control center A brain center that directs the activity of organs involved in breathing.

bronchiole (brong'-kē-ōl') A fine branch of the bronchi that transports air to alveoli.

bronchus (brong'-kus) (plural, **bronchi**) One of a pair of breathing tubes that branch from the trachea into the lungs.

brown alga A multicellular, photosynthetic protist with a characteristic brown or olive color that results from carotenoids in its plastids. Most brown algae are marine, and some have a plantlike body (thallus).

bryophyte (brī'-uh-fīt) An informal name for a moss, liverwort, or hornwort; a nonvascular plant that lives on land but lacks some of the terrestrial adaptations of vascular plants.

budding Asexual reproduction in which outgrowths from the parent form and pinch off to live independently or else remain attached to eventually form extensive colonies.

buffer A substance that consists of acid and base forms in a solution and that minimizes changes in pH when extraneous acids or bases are added to the solution.

bulk feeder An animal that eats relatively large pieces of food.

bulk flow The movement of a fluid due to a difference in pressure between two locations.

bundle-sheath cell In C_4 plants, a type of photosynthetic cell arranged into tightly packed sheaths around the veins of a leaf.

C_3 plant A plant that uses the Calvin cycle for the initial steps that incorporate CO_2 into organic material, forming a three-carbon compound as the first stable intermediate.

C_4 plant A plant in which the Calvin cycle is preceded by reactions that incorporate CO_2 into a four-carbon compound, the end product of which supplies CO_2 for the Calvin cycle.

cadherin (kad-hēr'-in) A member of an important class of cell adhesion molecules that requires extracellular calcium ions for its function.

calcitonin (kal'-si-tō'-nin) A hormone secreted by the thyroid gland that lowers blood calcium levels by promoting calcium deposition in bone and calcium excretion from the kidneys; nonessential in adult humans.

callus A mass of dividing, undifferentiated cells at the cut end of a shoot.

calorie (cal) The amount of heat energy required to raise the temperature of 1 g of water by 1°C; also the amount of heat energy that 1 g of water releases when it cools by 1°C. The Calorie (with a capital C), usually used to indicate the energy content of food, is a kilocalorie.

Calvin cycle The second of two major stages in photosynthesis (following the light reactions), involving fixation of atmospheric CO_2 and reduction of the fixed carbon into carbohydrate.

CAM plant A plant that uses crassulacean acid metabolism, an adaptation for photosynthesis in arid conditions. In this process, carbon dioxide entering open stomata during the night is converted to organic acids, which release CO_2 for the Calvin cycle during the day, when stomata are closed.

Cambrian explosion A relatively brief time in geologic history when large, hard-bodied forms of animals with most of the major body plans known today appeared in the fossil record. This burst of evolutionary change occurred about 535–525 million years ago.

canopy The uppermost layer of vegetation in a terrestrial biome.

capillary (kap'-il-ār'-ē) A microscopic blood vessel that penetrates the tissues and consists of a single layer of endothelial cells that allows exchange between the blood and interstitial fluid.

capillary bed A network of capillaries in a tissue or organ.

capsid The protein shell that encloses a viral genome. It may be rod-shaped, polyhedral, or more complex in shape.

capsule (1) A sticky layer that surrounds the cell wall of some prokaryotes, protecting the cell surface and sometimes helping to glue the cell to surfaces. (2) The sporangium of a bryophyte (moss, liverwort, or hornwort).

carbohydrate (kar'-bō-hī'-drāt) A sugar (monosaccharide) or one of its dimers (disaccharides) or polymers (polysaccharides).

carbon fixation The initial incorporation of carbon from CO_2 into an organic compound by an autotrophic organism (a plant, another photosynthetic organism, or a chemoautotrophic prokaryote).

carbonyl group (kar'-buh-nēl') A chemical group present in aldehydes and ketones and consisting of a carbon atom double-bonded to an oxygen atom.

carboxyl group (kar-bok'-sil) A chemical group present in organic acids and consisting of a single carbon atom double-bonded to an oxygen atom and also bonded to a hydroxyl group.

cardiac cycle (kar'-dē-ak) The alternating contractions and relaxations of the heart.

cardiac muscle A type of muscle that forms the contractile wall of the heart. Its cells are joined by intercalated disks that relay each heartbeat.

cardiac output The volume of blood pumped per minute by each ventricle of the heart.

cardiovascular system A closed circulatory system with a heart and branching network of arteries, capillaries, and veins. The system is characteristic of vertebrates.

carnivore An animal that mainly eats other animals.

carotenoid (kuh-rot'-uh-noyd') An accessory pigment, either yellow or orange, in the chloroplasts of plants and in some prokaryotes. By absorbing wavelengths of light that chlorophyll cannot, carotenoids broaden the spectrum of colors that can drive photosynthesis.

carpel (kar'-pul) The ovule-producing reproductive organ of a flower, consisting of the stigma, style, and ovary.

carrier In genetics, an individual who is heterozygous at a given genetic locus, with one normal allele and one recessive allele. The heterozygote is phenotypically dominant for the character determined by the gene but can pass on the recessive allele to offspring.

carrying capacity The maximum population size that can be supported by the available resources, symbolized as K.

cartilage (kar'-til-ij) A flexible connective tissue with an abundance of collagenous fibers embedded in chondroitin sulfate.

Casparian strip (kas-pār'-ē-un) A water-impermeable ring of wax in the endodermal cells of plants that blocks the passive flow of water and solutes into the stele by way of cell walls.

catabolic pathway (kat'-uh-bol'-ik) A metabolic pathway that releases energy by breaking down complex molecules to simpler compounds.

catalyst (kat'-uh-list) A chemical agent that increases the rate of a reaction without being consumed by the reaction.

catastrophism (kuh-tas'-truh-fiz'-um) The principle that events in the past occurred suddenly and were caused by different mechanisms than those operating today. *See* uniformitarianism.

catecholamine (kat'-uh-kōl'-uh-mēn) Any of a class of neurotransmitters and hormones, including the hormones epinephrine and norepinephrine, that are synthesized from the amino acid tyrosine.

cation (cat'-ī-on) A positively charged ion.

cation exchange A process in which positively charged minerals are made available to a plant when hydrogen ions in the soil displace mineral ions from the clay particles.

CD4 A surface protein, present on most helper T cells, that binds to class II MHC molecules, enhancing the interaction between the T cell and an antigen-presenting cell.

CD8 A surface protein, present on most cytotoxic T cells, that binds to class I MHC molecules, enhancing the interaction between the T cell and a target cell.

cDNA library A gene library containing clones that carry complementary DNA (cDNA) inserts. The library includes only the genes that were transcribed in the cells whose mRNA was isolated to make the cDNA.

cecum (sē'-kum) (plural, **ceca**) The blind pouch at the beginning of the large intestine.

cell adhesion molecule (CAM) A transmembrane, cell-surface glycoprotein that binds to CAMs on other cells. The resulting cell-to-cell attachments contribute to stable tissue structure.

cell body The part of a neuron that houses the nucleus and most other organelles.

cell cycle An ordered sequence of events in the life of a cell, from its origin in the division of a parent cell until its own division into two; the eukaryotic cell cycle is composed of interphase (including G_1, S, and G_2 subphases) and M phase (including mitosis and cytokinesis).

cell cycle control system A cyclically operating set of molecules in the eukaryotic cell that both triggers and coordinates key events in the cell cycle.

cell differentiation The structural and functional divergence of cells as they become specialized during a multicellular organism's development. Cell differentiation depends on the control of gene expression.

cell division The reproduction of cells.

cell fractionation The disruption of a cell and separation of its parts by centrifugation.

cell plate A double membrane across the midline of a dividing plant cell, between which the new cell wall forms during cytokinesis.

cell wall A protective layer external to the plasma membrane in the cells of plants, prokaryotes, fungi, and some protists. Polysaccharides such as cellulose (in plants and some protists), chitin (in fungi), and peptidoglycan (in bacteria) are an important structural component of cell walls.

cell-mediated immune response The branch of acquired immunity that involves the activation of cytotoxic T cells, which defend against infected cells.

cellular respiration The catabolic pathways of aerobic and anaerobic respiration, which break down organic molecules for the production of ATP.

cellular slime mold A type of protist that has unicellular amoeboid cells and aggregated reproductive bodies in its life cycle.

cellulose (sel'-yū-lōs) A structural polysaccharide of plant cell walls, consisting of glucose monomers joined by β glycosidic linkages.

Celsius scale (sel'-sē-us) A temperature scale (°C) equal to $\frac{5}{9}$(°F − 32) that measures the freezing point of water at 0°C and the boiling point of water at 100°C.

central canal The narrow cavity in the center of the spinal cord that is continuous with the fluid-filled ventricles of the brain.

central vacuole A membranous sac in a mature plant cell with diverse roles in reproduction, growth, and development.

centriole (sen'-trē-ōl) A structure in the centrosome of an animal cell composed of a cylinder of microtubule triplets arranged in a 9 + 0 pattern. A centrosome has a pair of centrioles.

centromere (sen'-trō-mēr) The specialized region of the chromosome where two sister chromatids are most closely attached.

centrosome (sen'-trō-sōm) Structure present in the cytoplasm of animal cells, important during cell division; functions as a microtubule-organizing center. A centrosome has two centrioles.

cephalization (sef'-uh-luh-zā'-shun) An evolutionary trend toward the concentration of sensory equipment at the anterior end of the body.

cerebellum (sār'-ruh-bel'-um) Part of the vertebrate hindbrain located dorsally; functions in unconscious coordination of movement and balance.

cerebral cortex (suh-rē'-brul) The surface of the cerebrum; the largest and most complex part of the mammalian brain, containing nerve cell bodies of the cerebrum; the part of the vertebrate brain most changed through evolution.

cerebral hemisphere The right or left side of the cerebrum.

cerebrospinal fluid (suh-rē'-brō-spī'-nul) Blood-derived fluid that surrounds, protects against infection, nourishes, and cushions the brain and spinal cord.

cerebrum (suh-rē'-brum) The dorsal portion of the vertebrate forebrain, composed of right and left hemispheres; the integrating center for memory, learning, emotions, and other highly complex functions of the central nervous system.

cervix (ser'-viks) The neck of the uterus, which opens into the vagina.

chaparral A scrubland biome of dense, spiny evergreen shrubs found at midlatitudes along coasts where cold ocean currents circulate offshore; characterized by mild, rainy winters and long, hot, dry summers.

chaperonin (shap'-er-ō'-nin) A protein molecule that assists in the proper folding of other proteins.

character An observable heritable feature.

character displacement The tendency for characteristics to be more divergent in sympatric populations of two species than in allopatric populations of the same two species.

checkpoint A control point in the cell cycle where stop and go-ahead signals can regulate the cycle.

chelicera (kē-lih'-suh-ruh) (plural, **chelicerae**) One of a pair of clawlike feeding appendages characteristic of cheliceriforms.

cheliceriform (kē-lih-suh'-ri-form) An arthropod that has chelicerae and a body divided into a cephalothorax and an abdomen. Living cheliceriforms include sea spiders, horseshoe crabs, scorpions, ticks, and spiders.

chemical bond An attraction between two atoms, resulting from a sharing of outer-shell electrons or the presence of opposite charges on the atoms. The bonded atoms gain complete outer electron shells.

chemical energy Energy available in molecules for release in a chemical reaction; a form of potential energy.

chemical equilibrium In a chemical reaction, the state in which the rate of the forward reaction equals the rate of the reverse reaction, so that the relative concentrations of the reactants and products do not change with time.

chemical reaction The making and breaking of chemical bonds, leading to changes in the composition of matter.

chemiosmosis (kem'-ē-oz-mō'-sis) An energy-coupling mechanism that uses energy stored in the form of a hydrogen ion gradient across a membrane to drive cellular work, such as the synthesis of ATP. Most ATP synthesis in cells occurs by chemiosmosis.

chemoautotroph (kē'-mō-ot'-ō-trōf) An organism that needs only carbon dioxide as a carbon source but obtains energy by oxidizing inorganic substances.

chemoheterotroph (kē'-mō-het'-er-ō-trōf) An organism that must consume organic molecules for both energy and carbon.

chemoreceptor A sensory receptor that responds to a chemical stimulus, such as a solute or an odorant.

chiasma (plural, **chiasmata**) (kī-az'-muh, kī-az'-muh-tuh) The X-shaped, microscopically visible region where homologous nonsister chromatids have exchanged genetic material through crossing over during meiosis, the two homologs remaining associated due to sister chromatid cohesion.

chitin (kī'-tin) A structural polysaccharide, consisting of amino sugar monomers, found in many fungal cell walls and in the exoskeletons of all arthropods.

chlorophyll (klōr'-ō-fil) A green pigment located within the chloroplasts of plants and algae and in the membranes of certain prokaryotes. Chlorophyll *a* participates directly in the light reactions, which convert solar energy to chemical energy.

chlorophyll *a* A photosynthetic pigment that participates directly in the light reactions, which convert solar energy to chemical energy.

chlorophyll *b* An accessory photosynthetic pigment that transfers energy to chlorophyll *a*.

chloroplast (klōr'-ō-plast) An organelle found in plants and photosynthetic protists that absorbs sunlight and uses it to drive the synthesis of organic compounds from carbon dioxide and water.

choanocyte (kō-an'-uh-sīt) A flagellated feeding cell found in sponges. Also called a collar cell, it has a collar-like ring that traps food particles around the base of its flagellum.

cholesterol (kō-les'-tuh-rol) A steroid that forms an essential component of animal cell membranes and acts as a precursor molecule for the synthesis of other biologically important steroids, such as hormones.

chondrichthyan (kon-drik'-thē-an) Member of the class Chondrichthyes, vertebrates with skeletons made mostly of cartilage, such as sharks and rays.

chordate Member of the phylum Chordata, animals that at some point during their development have a notochord; a dorsal, hollow nerve cord; pharyngeal slits or clefts; and a muscular, post-anal tail.

chorion (kōr'-ē-on) The outermost of four extraembryonic membranes. It functions in gas exchange and contributes to the formation of the mammalian placenta.

chorionic villus sampling (CVS) (kōr'-ē-on'-ik vil'-us) A technique of prenatal diagnosis in which a small sample of the fetal portion of the placenta is removed and analyzed to detect certain genetic and congenital defects in the fetus.

choroid (kor'-oyd) A thin, pigmented inner layer of the vertebrate eye.

Chromalveolata One of five supergroups of eukaryotes proposed in a current hypothesis of the evolutionary history of eukaryotes. Chromalveolates may have originated by secondary endosymbiosis and include two large protist clades, the alveolates and the stramenopiles. *See also* Excavata, Rhizaria, Archaeplastida, and Unikonta.

chromatin (krō'-muh-tin) The complex of DNA and proteins that makes up a eukaryotic chromosome. When the cell is not dividing, chromatin exists in its dispersed form, as a mass of very long, thin fibers that are not visible with a light microscope.

chromosome (krō'-muh-sōm) A cellular structure carrying genetic material, found in the nucleus of eukaryotic cells. Each chromosome consists of one very long DNA molecule and associated proteins. (A bacterial chromosome usually consists of a single circular DNA molecule and associated proteins. It is found in the nucleoid region, which is not membrane bounded.) *See also* chromatin.

chromosome theory of inheritance A basic principle in biology stating that genes are located on chromosomes and that the behavior of chromosomes during meiosis accounts for inheritance patterns.

chylomicron (kī'-lō-mī'-kron) A small globule that transports lipids. Chylomicrons are composed of fats mixed with cholesterol and coated with proteins.

chyme (kīm) The mixture of partially digested food and digestive juices formed in the stomach.

chytrid (kī'-trid) Member of the fungal phylum Chytridiomycota, mostly aquatic fungi with flagellated zoospores that represent an early-diverging fungal lineage.

ciliary body A portion of the vertebrate eye associated with the lens. It produces the clear, watery aqueous humor that fills the anterior cavity of the eye.

ciliate (sil'-ē-it) A type of protist that moves by means of cilia.

cilium (sil'-ē-um) (plural, **cilia**) A short cellular appendage containing microtubules. A motile cilium is specialized for locomotion and is formed from a core of nine outer doublet microtubules and two inner single microtubules (the "9 + 2" arrangement) ensheathed in an extension of the plasma membrane. A primary cilium is usually nonmotile and plays a sensory and signaling role; it lacks the two inner microtubules (the "9 + 0" arrangement).

circadian rhythm (ser-kā′-dē-un) A physiological cycle of about 24 hours that is present in all eukaryotic organisms and that persists even in the absence of external cues.

citric acid cycle A chemical cycle involving eight steps that completes the metabolic breakdown of glucose molecules begun in glycolysis by oxidizing pyruvate to carbon dioxide; occurs within the mitochondrion in eukaryotic cells and in the cytosol of prokaryotes; the second major stage in cellular respiration.

clade (klayd) A group of species that includes an ancestral species and all its descendants.

cladistics (kluh-dis′-tiks) An approach to systematics in which organisms are placed into groups called clades based primarily on common descent.

class In classification, the taxonomic category above the level of order.

class I MHC molecule A type of MHC molecule found on the surface of nearly all nucleated cells and that functions in identification of infected cells by cytotoxic T cells.

class II MHC molecule A type of MHC molecule restricted to a few specialized immune cell types (dendritic cells, macrophages, and B cells) that serve as antigen-presenting cells.

classical conditioning A type of associative learning in which an arbitrary stimulus becomes associated with a particular outcome.

cleavage (1) The process of cytokinesis in animal cells, characterized by pinching of the plasma membrane. (2) The succession of rapid cell divisions without significant growth during early embryonic development that converts the zygote to a ball of cells.

cleavage furrow The first sign of cleavage in an animal cell; a shallow groove in the cell surface near the old metaphase plate.

climate The long-term prevailing weather conditions at a locality.

climograph A plot of the temperature and precipitation in a particular region.

cline A graded change in a character along a geographic axis.

clitoris (klit′-uh-ris) An organ at the upper intersection of the labia minora that engorges with blood and becomes erect during sexual arousal.

cloaca (klō-ā′-kuh) A common opening for the digestive, urinary, and reproductive tracts found in many nonmammalian vertebrates but in few mammals.

clonal selection The process by which an antigen selectively binds to and activates only those lymphocytes bearing receptors specific for the antigen. The selected lymphocytes proliferate and differentiate into a clone of effector cells and a clone of memory cells specific for the stimulating antigen.

clone (1) A lineage of genetically identical individuals or cells. (2) In popular usage, a single individual organism that is genetically identical to another individual. (3) As a verb, to make one or more genetic replicas of an individual or cell. *See also* gene cloning.

cloning vector In genetic engineering, a DNA molecule that can carry foreign DNA into a host cell and replicate there. Cloning vectors include plasmids that move recombinant DNA from a test tube back into a cell and viruses that transfer recombinant DNA by infection.

closed circulatory system A circulatory system in which blood is confined to vessels and is kept separate from the interstitial fluid.

club fungus *See* basidiomycete.

cnidocyte (nī′-duh-sīt) A specialized cell unique to the phylum Cnidaria; contains a capsule-like organelle housing a coiled thread that, when discharged, explodes outward and functions in prey capture or defense.

cochlea (kok′-lē-uh) The complex, coiled organ of hearing that contains the organ of Corti.

codominance The situation in which the phenotypes of both alleles are exhibited in the heterozygote because both alleles affect the phenotype in separate, distinguishable ways.

codon (kō′-don) A three-nucleotide sequence of DNA or mRNA that specifies a particular amino acid or termination signal; the basic unit of the genetic code.

coefficient of relatedness The fraction of genes that, on average, are shared by two individuals.

coelom (sē′-lōm) A body cavity lined by tissue derived only from mesoderm.

coelomate (sē′-lō-māt) An animal that possesses a true coelom (a body cavity lined by tissue completely derived from mesoderm).

coenocytic fungus (sē′-no-si′-tic) A fungus that lacks septa and hence whose body is made up of a continuous cytoplasmic mass that may contain hundreds or thousands of nuclei.

coenzyme (kō-en′-zīm) An organic molecule serving as a cofactor. Most vitamins function as coenzymes in metabolic reactions.

cofactor Any nonprotein molecule or ion that is required for the proper functioning of an enzyme. Cofactors can be permanently bound to the active site or may bind loosely with the substrate during catalysis.

cognition The process of knowing that may include awareness, reasoning, recollection, and judgment.

cognitive map A neural representation of the abstract spatial relationships between objects in an animal's surroundings.

cohesion The binding together of like molecules, often by hydrogen bonds.

cohort A group of individuals of the same age in a population.

coitus (kō′-uh-tus) The insertion of a penis into a vagina; also called sexual intercourse.

coleoptile (kō′-lē-op′-tul) The covering of the young shoot of the embryo of a grass seed.

coleorhiza (kō′-lē-uh-rī′-zuh) The covering of the young root of the embryo of a grass seed.

collagen A glycoprotein in the extracellular matrix of animal cells that forms strong fibers, found extensively in connective tissue and bone; the most abundant protein in the animal kingdom.

collecting duct The location in the kidney where processed filtrate, called urine, is collected from the renal tubules.

collenchyma cell (kō-len′-kim-uh) A flexible plant cell type that occurs in strands or cylinders that support young parts of the plant without restraining growth.

colloid A mixture made up of a liquid and particles that (because of their large size) remain suspended rather than dissolved in that liquid.

colon (kō′-len) The largest section of the vertebrate large intestine; functions in water absorption and formation of feces.

commensalism (kuh-men′-suh-lizm) A symbiotic relationship in which one organism benefits but the other is neither helped nor harmed.

communication In animal behavior, a process involving transmission of, reception of, and response to signals. The term is also used in connection with other organisms, as well as individual cells of multicellular organisms.

community All the organisms that inhabit a particular area; an assemblage of populations of different species living close enough together for potential interaction.

community ecology The study of how interactions between species affect community structure and organization.

companion cell A type of plant cell that is connected to a sieve-tube element by many plasmodesmata and whose nucleus and ribosomes may serve one or more adjacent sieve-tube elements.

competitive exclusion The concept that when populations of two similar species compete for the same limited resources, one population will use the resources more efficiently and have a reproductive advantage that will eventually lead to the elimination of the other population.

competitive inhibitor A substance that reduces the activity of an enzyme by entering the active site in place of the substrate whose structure it mimics.

complement system A group of about 30 blood proteins that may amplify the inflammatory response, enhance phagocytosis, or directly lyse extracellular pathogens.

complementary DNA (cDNA) A double-stranded DNA molecule made *in vitro* using mRNA as a template and the enzymes reverse transcriptase and DNA polymerase. A cDNA molecule corresponds to the exons of a gene.

complete digestive tract A digestive tube that runs between a mouth and an anus; also called an alimentary canal.

complete dominance The situation in which the phenotypes of the heterozygote and dominant homozygote are indistinguishable.

complete flower A flower that has all four basic floral organs: sepals, petals, stamens, and carpels.

complete metamorphosis The transformation of a larva into an adult that looks very different, and often functions very differently in its environment, than the larva.

compound A substance consisting of two or more different elements combined in a fixed ratio.

compound eye A type of multifaceted eye in insects and crustaceans consisting of up to several thousand light-detecting, focusing ommatidia; especially good at detecting movement.

concentration gradient A region along which the density of a chemical substance increases or decreases.

conception The fertilization of an egg by a sperm in humans.

condensation reaction A reaction in which two molecules become covalently bonded to each other through the loss of a small molecule, usually water, in which case it is also called a dehydration reaction.

condom A thin, latex rubber or natural membrane sheath that fits over the penis to collect semen.

conduction The direct transfer of thermal motion (heat) between molecules of objects in direct contact with each other.

cone A cone-shaped cell in the retina of the vertebrate eye, sensitive to color.

conformer An animal for which an internal condition conforms with a change in an environmental variable.

conidium (plural, **conidia**) A haploid spore produced at the tip of a specialized hypha in ascomycetes during asexual reproduction.

conifer Member of the largest gymnosperm phylum. Most conifers are cone-bearing trees, such as pines and firs.

conjugation (kon′-jū-gā′-shun) In prokaryotes, the direct transfer of DNA between two cells (of the same or different species) that are temporarily joined. In ciliates, a sexual process in which two cells exchange haploid micronuclei.

connective tissue Animal tissue that functions mainly to bind and support other tissues, having a sparse population of cells scattered through an extracellular matrix.

conodont An early, soft-bodied vertebrate with prominent eyes and dental elements.

conservation biology The integrated study of ecology, evolutionary biology, physiology, molecular biology, and genetics to sustain biological diversity at all levels.

continental drift The slow movement of the continental plates across Earth's surface.

contraception The deliberate prevention of pregnancy.

contractile vacuole A membranous sac that helps move excess water out of certain freshwater protists.

control element A segment of noncoding DNA that helps regulate transcription of a gene by binding a transcription factor. Multiple control elements are present in a eukaryotic gene's enhancer.

controlled experiment An experiment in which an experimental group is compared with a control group that varies only in the factor being tested.

convection The mass movement of warmed air or liquid to or from the surface of a body or object.

convergent evolution The evolution of similar features in independent evolutionary lineages.

convergent extension A process in which the cells of a tissue layer rearrange themselves, so that the sheet of cells becomes narrower (converges) and longer (extends).

cooperativity A kind of allosteric regulation whereby a shape change in one subunit of a protein caused by substrate binding is transmitted to all the others, facilitating binding of subsequent substrate molecules.

copepod (cō′-puh-pod) Any of a group of small crustaceans that are important members of marine and freshwater plankton communities.

coral reef Typically a warm-water, tropical ecosystem dominated by the hard skeletal structures secreted primarily by the resident cnidarians. Some reefs also exist in cold, deep waters.

corepressor A small molecule that binds to a bacterial repressor protein and changes its shape, allowing it to switch an operon off.

cork cambium (kam′-bē-um) A cylinder of meristematic tissue in woody plants that replaces the epidermis with thicker, tougher cork cells.

cornea (kor′-nē-uh) The transparent frontal portion of the sclera, which admits light into the vertebrate eye.

corpus callosum (kor′-pus kuh-lō′-sum) The thick band of nerve fibers that connects the right and left cerebral hemispheres in mammals, enabling the hemispheres to process information together.

corpus luteum (kor′-pus lū′-tē-um) A secreting tissue in the ovary that forms from the collapsed follicle after ovulation and produces progesterone.

cortex (1) The outer region of cytoplasm in a eukaryotic cell, lying just under the plasma membrane, that has a more gel-like consistency than the inner regions, due to the presence of multiple microfilaments. (2) In plants, ground tissue that is between the vascular tissue and dermal tissue in a root or eudicot stem.

cortical granule A vesicle containing enzymes and other macromolecules located in the cortex (the region just under the plasma membrane) of an egg. Cortical granules undergo exocytosis during the cortical reaction.

cortical nephron In mammals and birds, a nephron with a loop of Henle located almost entirely in the renal cortex.

cortical reaction Exocytosis of enzymes and other macromolecules from cortical granules in the egg cytoplasm during fertilization, leading to the formation of a fertilization envelope.

corticosteroid Any steroid hormone produced and secreted by the adrenal cortex.

cotransport The coupling of the "downhill" diffusion of one substance to the "uphill" transport of another against its own concentration gradient.

cotyledon (kot′-uh-lē′-dun) A seed leaf of an angiosperm embryo. Some species have one cotyledon, others two.

countercurrent exchange The exchange of a substance or heat between two fluids flowing in opposite directions. For example, blood in a fish gill flows in the opposite direction of water passing over the gill, maximizing diffusion of oxygen into and carbon dioxide out of the blood.

countercurrent multiplier system A countercurrent system in which energy is expended in active transport to facilitate exchange of materials and generate concentration gradients.

covalent bond (kō-vā′-lent) A type of strong chemical bond in which two atoms share one or more pairs of valence electrons.

cranial nerve A nerve that originates in the brain and terminates in an organ of the head or upper body.

craniate A chordate with a head.

crassulacean acid metabolism (CAM) An adaptation for photosynthesis in arid conditions, first discovered in the family Crassulaceae. In this process, a plant takes up CO_2 and incorporates it into a variety of organic acids at night; during the day, CO_2 is released from organic acids for use in the Calvin cycle.

crista (plural, **cristae**) (kris′-tuh, kris′-tē) An infolding of the inner membrane of a mitochondrion that houses electron transport chains and molecules of the enzyme catalyzing the synthesis of ATP (ATP synthase).

critical load The amount of added nutrient, usually nitrogen or phosphorus, that can be absorbed by plants without damaging ecosystem integrity.

crop rotation The practice of planting nonlegumes one year and legumes in alternating years to restore concentrations of fixed nitrogen in the soil.

cross-fostering study A behavioral study in which the young of one species are placed in the care of adults from another species.

crossing over The reciprocal exchange of genetic material between nonsister chromatids during prophase I of meiosis.

cross-pollination In angiosperms, the transfer of pollen from an anther of a flower on one plant to the stigma of a flower on another plant of the same species.

crustacean (kruh-stā′-shun) A member of a subphylum of mostly aquatic arthropods that includes lobsters, crayfishes, crabs, shrimps, and barnacles.

cryptic coloration Camouflage that makes a potential prey difficult to spot against its background.

culture A system of information transfer through social learning or teaching that influences the behavior of individuals in a population.

cuticle (kyū′-tuh-kul) (1) A waxy covering on the surface of stems and leaves that acts as an adaptation that prevents desiccation in terrestrial plants. (2) The exoskeleton of an arthropod, consisting of layers of protein and chitin that are variously modified for different functions. (3) A tough coat that covers the body of a nematode.

cyclic AMP (cAMP) Cyclic adenosine monophosphate, a ring-shaped molecule made from ATP that is a common intracellular signaling molecule (second messenger) in eukaryotic cells. It is also a regulator of some bacterial operons.

cyclic electron flow A route of electron flow during the light reactions of photosynthesis that involves only photosystem I and that produces ATP but not NADPH or O_2.

cyclin (sī′-klin) A cellular protein that occurs in a cyclically fluctuating concentration and that plays an important role in regulating the cell cycle.

cyclin-dependent kinase (Cdk) A protein kinase that is active only when attached to a particular cyclin.

cystic fibrosis (sis′-tik fī-brō′-sis) A human genetic disorder caused by a recessive allele for a chloride channel protein; characterized by an excessive secretion of mucus and consequent vulnerability to infection; fatal if untreated.

cytochrome (sī′-tō-krōm) An iron-containing protein that is a component of electron transport chains in the mitochondria and chloroplasts of eukaryotic cells and the plasma membranes of prokaryotic cells.

cytogenetic map A chart of a chromosome that locates genes with respect to chromosomal features distinguishable in a microscope.

cytokine (sī′-tō-kīn′) Any of a group of proteins secreted by a number of cell types, including macrophages and helper T cells, that regulate the function of lymphocytes and other cells of the immune system.

cytokinesis (sī′-tō-kuh-nē′-sis) The division of the cytoplasm to form two separate daughter cells immediately after mitosis, meiosis I, or meiosis II.

cytokinin (sī′-tō-kī′-nin) Any of a class of related plant hormones that retard aging and act in concert with auxin to stimulate cell division, influence the pathway of differentiation, and control apical dominance.

cytoplasm (sī′-tō-plaz′-um) The contents of the cell, exclusive of the nucleus and bounded by the plasma membrane.

cytoplasmic determinant A maternal substance, such as a protein or RNA, placed into an egg that influences the course of early development by regulating the expression of genes that affect the developmental fate of cells.

cytoplasmic streaming A circular flow of cytoplasm, involving myosin and actin filaments, that speeds the distribution of materials within cells.

cytoskeleton A network of microtubules, microfilaments, and intermediate filaments that branch throughout the cytoplasm and serve a variety of mechanical, transport, and signaling functions.

cytosol (sī′-tō-sol) The semifluid portion of the cytoplasm.

cytotoxic T cell A type of lymphocyte that, when activated, kills infected cells as well as certain cancer cells and transplanted cells.

dalton A measure of mass for atoms and subatomic particles; the same as the atomic mass unit, or amu.

data Recorded observations.

day-neutral plant A plant in which flower formation is not controlled by photoperiod or day length.

decapod A member of the group of crustaceans that includes lobsters, crayfishes, crabs, and shrimps.

decomposer An organism that absorbs nutrients from nonliving organic material such as corpses, fallen plant material, and the wastes of living organisms and converts them to inorganic forms; a detritivore.

deductive reasoning A type of logic in which specific results are predicted from a general premise.

deep-sea hydrothermal vent A dark, hot, oxygen-deficient environment associated with volcanic activity on or near the seafloor. The producers in a vent community are chemoautotrophic prokaryotes.

de-etiolation The changes a plant shoot undergoes in response to sunlight; also known informally as greening.

dehydration reaction A chemical reaction in which two molecules covalently bond to each other with the removal of a water molecule.

deletion (1) A deficiency in a chromosome resulting from the loss of a fragment through breakage. (2) A mutational loss of one or more nucleotide pairs from a gene.

demographic transition A shift from rapid population growth in which birth rate outpaces death rate to zero population growth characterized by low birth and death rates.

demography The study of statistics relating to births and deaths in populations.

denaturation (dē-nā′-chur-ā′-shun) In proteins, a process in which a protein unravels and loses its native shape, thereby becoming biologically inactive; in DNA, the separation of the two strands of the double helix. Denaturation occurs under extreme (noncellular) conditions of pH, salt concentration, and temperature.

dendrite (den′-drīt) One of usually numerous, short, highly branched extensions of a neuron that receive signals from other neurons.

dendritic cell An antigen-presenting cell, located mainly in lymphatic tissues and skin, that is particularly efficient in presenting antigens to helper T cells, thereby initiating a primary immune response.

density The number of individuals per unit area or volume.

density dependent Referring to any characteristic that varies according to an increase in population density.

density independent Referring to any characteristic that is not affected by population density.

density-dependent inhibition The phenomenon observed in normal animal cells that causes them to stop dividing when they come into contact with one another.

deoxyribonucleic acid (DNA) (dē-ok′-sē-rī′-bō-nū-klā′-ik) A double-stranded, helical nucleic acid molecule consisting of nucleotide monomers with a deoxyribose sugar and the nitrogenous bases adenine (A), cytosine (C), guanine (G), and thymine (T); capable of replicating and determining the inherited structure of a cell's proteins.

deoxyribose (dē-ok′-si-rī′-bōs) The sugar component of DNA nucleotides, having one fewer hydroxyl group than ribose, the sugar component of RNA nucleotides.

depolarization A change in a cell's membrane potential such that the inside of the membrane is made less negative relative to the outside. For example, a neuron membrane is depolarized if a stimulus decreases its voltage from the resting potential of −70 mV in the direction of zero voltage.

dermal tissue system The outer protective covering of plants.

desert A terrestrial biome characterized by very low precipitation.

desmosome A type of intercellular junction in animal cells that functions as a rivet.

determinate cleavage A type of embryonic development in protostomes that rigidly casts the developmental fate of each embryonic cell very early.

determinate growth A type of growth characteristic of most animals and some plant organs, in which growth stops after a certain size is reached.

determination The progressive restriction of developmental potential in which the possible fate of each cell becomes more limited as an embryo develops. At the end of determination, a cell is committed to its fate.

detritivore (deh-trī′-tuh-vōr) A consumer that derives its energy and nutrients from nonliving organic material such as corpses, fallen plant material, and the wastes of living organisms; a decomposer.

detritus (di-trī′-tus) Dead organic matter.

deuteromycete (dū′-tuh-rō-mī′-sēt) Traditional classification for a fungus with no known sexual stage. When a sexual stage for a so-called deuteromycete is discovered, the species is assigned to a phylum.

deuterostome development (dū′-tuh-rō-stōm′) In animals, a developmental mode distinguished by the development of the anus from the blastopore; often also characterized by radial cleavage and by the body cavity forming as outpockets of mesodermal tissue.

diabetes mellitus (dī′-uh-bē′-tis mel′-uh-tus) An endocrine disorder marked by inability to maintain glucose homeostasis. The type 1 form results from autoimmune destruction of insulin-secreting cells; treatment usually requires daily insulin injections. The type 2 form most commonly results from reduced responsiveness of target cells to insulin; obesity and lack of exercise are risk factors.

diacylglycerol (DAG) (dī-a′-sil-glis′-er-ol) A second messenger produced by the cleavage of a certain kind of phospholipid in the plasma membrane.

diaphragm (dī′-uh-fram′) (1) A sheet of muscle that forms the bottom wall of the thoracic cavity in mammals. Contraction of the diaphragm pulls air into the lungs. (2) A dome-shaped rubber cup fitted into the upper portion of the vagina before sexual intercourse. It serves as a physical barrier to the passage of sperm into the uterus.

diapsid (dī-ap′-sid) Member of an amniote clade distinguished by a pair of holes on each side of the skull. Diapsids include the lepidosaurs and archosaurs.

diastole (dī-as′-tō-lē) The stage of the cardiac cycle in which a heart chamber is relaxed and fills with blood.

diastolic pressure Blood pressure in the arteries when the ventricles are relaxed.

diatom (dī′-uh-tom) A unicellular photosynthetic alga with a unique glassy cell wall containing silica.

dicot A term traditionally used to refer to flowering plants that have two embryonic seed leaves, or cotyledons. Recent molecular evidence indicates that dicots do not form a clade; species once classified as dicots are now grouped into eudicots, magnoliids, and several lineages of basal angiosperms.

differential gene expression The expression of different sets of genes by cells with the same genome.

diffusion The spontaneous movement of a substance down its concentration gradient, from a region where it is more concentrated to a region where it is less concentrated.

digestion The second stage of food processing in animals: the breaking down of food into molecules small enough for the body to absorb.

dihybrid (dī′-hī′-brid) An organism that is heterozygous with respect to two genes of interest. All the offspring from a cross between parents doubly homozygous for different alleles are dihybrids. For example, parents of genotypes *AABB* and *aabb* produce a dihybrid of genotype *AaBb*.

dikaryotic (dī′-kār-ē-ot′-ik) Referring to a fungal mycelium with two haploid nuclei per cell, one from each parent.

dinoflagellate (dī′-nō-flaj′-uh-let) Member of a group of mostly unicellular photosynthetic algae with two flagella situated in perpendicular grooves in cellulose plates covering the cell.

dinosaur Member of an extremely diverse clade of reptiles varying in body shape, size, and habitat. Birds are the only extant dinosaurs.

dioecious (dī-ē′-shus) In plant biology, having the male and female reproductive parts on different individuals of the same species.

diploblastic Having two germ layers.

diploid cell (dip′-loyd) A cell containing two sets of chromosomes (*2n*), one set inherited from each parent.

diplomonad A protist that has modified mitochondria, two equal-sized nuclei, and multiple flagella.

directional selection Natural selection in which individuals at one end of the phenotypic range survive or reproduce more successfully than do other individuals.

disaccharide (dī-sak′-uh-rī d) A double sugar, consisting of two monosaccharides joined by a glycosidic linkage formed during dehydration synthesis.

discovery science The process of scientific inquiry that focuses on describing nature.

dispersal The movement of individuals (or gametes) away from their parent location. This movement sometimes expands the geographic range of a population or species.

dispersion The pattern of spacing among individuals within the boundaries of the geographic population.

disruptive selection Natural selection in which individuals on both extremes of a phenotypic range survive or reproduce more successfully than do individuals with intermediate phenotypes.

distal tubule In the vertebrate kidney, the portion of a nephron that helps refine filtrate and empties it into a collecting duct.

disturbance A natural or human-caused event that changes a biological community and usually removes organisms from it. Disturbances, such as fires and storms, play a pivotal role in structuring many communities.

disulfide bridge A strong covalent bond formed when the sulfur of one cysteine monomer bonds to the sulfur of another cysteine monomer.

DNA (deoxyribonucleic acid) (dē-ok′-sē-rī′-bō-nū-klā′-ik) A double-stranded, helical nucleic acid molecule, consisting of nucleotide monomers with a deoxyribose sugar and the nitrogenous bases adenine (A), cytosine (C), guanine (G), and thymine (T); capable of being replicated and determining the inherited structure of a cell's proteins.

DNA ligase (lī′-gās) A linking enzyme essential for DNA replication; catalyzes the covalent bonding of the 3′ end of one DNA fragment (such as an Okazaki fragment) to the 5′ end of another DNA fragment (such as a growing DNA chain).

DNA microarray assay A method to detect and measure the expression of thousands of genes at one time. Tiny amounts of a large number of single-stranded DNA fragments representing different genes are fixed to a glass slide and tested for hybridization with samples of labeled cDNA.

DNA polymerase (puh-lim′-er-ās) An enzyme that catalyzes the elongation of new DNA (for example, at a replication fork) by the addition of nucleotides to the 3′ end of an existing chain. There are several different DNA polymerases; DNA polymerase III and DNA polymerase I play major roles in DNA replication in prokaryotes.

domain (1) A taxonomic category above the kingdom level. The three domains are Archaea, Bacteria, and Eukarya. (2) An independently folding part of a protein.

dominant allele An allele that is fully expressed in the phenotype of a heterozygote.

dominant species A species with substantially higher abundance or biomass than other species in a community. Dominant species exert a powerful control over the occurrence and distribution of other species.

dopamine A neurotransmitter that is a catecholamine, like epinephrine and norepinephrine.

dormancy A condition typified by extremely low metabolic rate and a suspension of growth and development.

dorsal Pertaining to the top of an animal with radial or bilateral symmetry.

dorsal lip The region above the blastopore on the dorsal side of the amphibian embryo.

double bond A double covalent bond; the sharing of two pairs of valence electrons by two atoms.

double circulation A circulatory system consisting of separate pulmonary and systemic circuits, in which blood passes through the heart after completing each circuit.

double fertilization A mechanism of fertilization in angiosperms in which two sperm cells unite with two cells in the female gametophyte (embryo sac) to form the zygote and endosperm.

double helix The form of native DNA, referring to its two adjacent antiparallel polynucleotide strands wound around an imaginary axis into a spiral shape.

Down syndrome A human genetic disease caused by the presence of an extra chromosome 21; characterized by mental retardation and heart and respiratory defects.

Duchenne muscular dystrophy (duh-shen′) A human genetic disease caused by a sex-linked recessive allele; characterized by progressive weakening and a loss of muscle tissue.

duodenum (dū′-uh-dēn′-um) The first section of the small intestine, where chyme from the stomach mixes with digestive juices from the pancreas, liver, and gallbladder as well as from gland cells of the intestinal wall.

duplication An aberration in chromosome structure due to fusion with a fragment from a homologous chromosome, such that a portion of a chromosome is duplicated.

dynamic stability hypothesis The idea that long food chains are less stable than short chains.

dynein (dī′-nē-un) In cilia and flagella, a large contractile protein extending from one microtubule doublet to the adjacent doublet. ATP hydrolysis drives changes in dynein shape that lead to bending of cilia and flagella.

E site One of a ribosome's three binding sites for tRNA during translation. The E site is the place where discharged tRNAs leave the ribosome. (E stands for exit.)

ecdysone (ek′-duh-sōn) A steroid hormone, secreted by the prothoracic glands, that triggers molting in arthropods.

ecdysozoan Member of a group of animal phyla identified as a clade by molecular evidence. Many ecdysozoans are molting animals.

echinoderm (i-kī′-nō-derm) A slow-moving or sessile marine deuterostome with a water vascular system and, in larvae, bilateral symmetry. Echinoderms include sea stars, brittle stars, sea urchins, feather stars, and sea cucumbers.

ecological footprint The aggregate land and water area required by a person, city, or nation to produce all of the resources it consumes and to absorb all of the waste it generates.

ecological niche (nich) The sum of a species' use of the biotic and abiotic resources in its environment.

ecological species concept A definition of species in terms of ecological niche, the sum of how members of the species interact with the nonliving and living parts of their environment.

ecological succession Transition in the species composition of a community following a disturbance; the establishment of a community in an area virtually barren of life.

ecology The study of how organisms interact with each other and their environment.

ecosystem All the organisms in a given area as well as the abiotic factors with which they interact; one or more communities and the physical environment around them.

ecosystem ecology The study of energy flow and the cycling of chemicals among the various biotic and abiotic components in an ecosystem.

ecosystem service A function performed by an ecosystem that directly or indirectly benefits humans.

ecotone The transition from one type of habitat or ecosystem to another, such as the transition from a forest to a grassland.

ectoderm (ek′-tō-durm) The outermost of the three primary germ layers in animal embryos; gives rise to the outer covering and, in some phyla, the nervous system, inner ear, and lens of the eye.

ectomycorrhiza (ek′-tō-mī′-kō-rī′-zuh) Association of a fungus with a plant root system in which the fungus surrounds the roots but does not cause invagination of the host (plant) cells' plasma membranes.

ectomycorrhizal fungus A symbiotic fungus that forms sheaths of hyphae over the surface of plant roots and also grows into extracellular spaces of the root cortex.

ectoparasite A parasite that feeds on the external surface of a host.

ectopic Occurring in an abnormal location.

ectoproct A sessile, colonial lophophorate commonly called a bryozoan.

ectothermic Referring to organisms for which external sources provide most of the heat for temperature regulation.

Ediacaran biota (ē′-dē-uh-keh′-run bī-ō′-tuh) An early group of soft-bodied, multicellular eukaryotes known from fossils that range in age from 565 million to 545 million years old.

effective population size An estimate of the size of a population based on the numbers of females and males that successfully breed; generally smaller than the total population.

effector cell (1) A muscle cell or gland cell that performs the body's response to stimuli as directed by signals from the brain or other processing center of the nervous system. (2) A lymphocyte that has undergone clonal selection and is capable of mediating an acquired immune response.

efferent arteriole In the kidney, the blood vessel draining a nephron.

egg The female gamete.

egg-polarity gene A gene that helps control the orientation (polarity) of the egg; also called a maternal effect gene.

ejaculation The propulsion of sperm from the epididymis through the muscular vas deferens, ejaculatory duct, and urethra.

ejaculatory duct In mammals, the short section of the ejaculatory route formed by the convergence of the vas deferens and a duct from the seminal vesicle. The ejaculatory duct transports sperm from the vas deferens to the urethra.

electrocardiogram (ECG or EKG) A record of the electrical impulses that travel through heart muscle during the cardiac cycle.

electrochemical gradient The diffusion gradient of an ion, which is affected by both the concentration difference of the ion across a membrane (a chemical force) and the ion's tendency to move relative to the membrane potential (an electrical force).

electrogenic pump An ion transport protein that generates voltage across a membrane.

electromagnetic receptor A receptor of electromagnetic energy, such as visible light, electricity, or magnetism.

electromagnetic spectrum The entire spectrum of electromagnetic radiation ranging in wavelength from less than a nanometer to more than a kilometer.

electron A subatomic particle with a single negative electrical charge and a mass about $1/_{2,000}$ that of a neutron or proton. One or more electrons move around the nucleus of an atom.

electron microscope (EM) A microscope that uses magnets to focus an electron beam on or through a specimen, resulting in resolving power a thousandfold greater than that of a light microscope. A transmission electron microscope (TEM) is used to study the internal structure of thin sections of cells. A scanning electron microscope (SEM) is used to study the fine details of cell surfaces.

electron shell An energy level of electrons at a characteristic average distance from the nucleus of an atom.

electron transport chain A sequence of electron carrier molecules (membrane proteins) that shuttle electrons during the redox reactions that release energy used to make ATP.

electronegativity The attraction of a given atom for the electrons of a covalent bond.

electroporation A technique to introduce recombinant DNA into cells by applying a brief electrical pulse to a solution containing the cells. The pulse creates temporary holes in the cells' plasma membranes, through which DNA can enter.

element Any substance that cannot be broken down to any other substance by chemical reactions.

elimination The fourth and final stage of food processing in animals: the passing of undigested material out of the digestive system.

embryo sac (em′-brē-ō) The female gametophyte of angiosperms, formed from the growth and division of the megaspore into a multicellular structure that typically has eight haploid nuclei.

embryonic lethal A mutation with a phenotype leading to death of an embryo or larva.

embryophyte Alternate name for land plants that refers to their shared derived trait of multicellular, dependent embryos.

emergent properties New properties that arise with each step upward in the hierarchy of life, owing to the arrangement and interactions of parts as complexity increases.

emigration The movement of individuals out of a population.

enantiomer (en-an′-tē-ō-mer) One of two compounds that are mirror images of each other.

endangered species A species that is in danger of extinction throughout all or a significant portion of its range.

endemic (en-dem′-ik) Referring to a species that is confined to a specific, relatively small geographic area.

endergonic reaction (en′-der-gon′-ik) A nonspontaneous chemical reaction, in which free energy is absorbed from the surroundings.

endocrine gland (en′-dō-krin) A ductless gland that secretes hormones directly into the interstitial fluid, from which they diffuse into the bloodstream.

endocrine system The internal system of communication involving hormones, the ductless glands that secrete hormones, and the molecular receptors on or in target cells that respond to hormones; functions in concert with the nervous system to effect internal regulation and maintain homeostasis.

endocytosis (en′-dō-sī-tō′-sis) Cellular uptake of biological molecules and particulate matter via formation of new vesicles from the plasma membrane.

endoderm (en′-dō-durm) The innermost of the three primary germ layers in animal embryos; lines the archenteron and gives rise to the liver, pancreas, lungs, and the lining of the digestive tract in species that have these structures.

endodermis The innermost layer of the cortex in plant roots; a cylinder one cell thick that forms the boundary between the cortex and the vascular cylinder.

endomembrane system The collection of membranes inside and around a eukaryotic cell, related either through direct physical contact or by the transfer of membranous vesicles; includes the smooth and rough endoplasmic reticulum, the Golgi apparatus, lysosomes, and vacuoles.

endometriosis (en'-dō-mē-trē-ō'-sis) The condition resulting from the presence of endometrial tissue outside of the uterus.

endometrium (en'-dō-mē'-trē-um) The inner lining of the uterus, which is richly supplied with blood vessels.

endoparasite A parasite that lives within a host.

endophyte A fungus that lives inside a leaf or other plant part without causing harm to the plant.

endoplasmic reticulum (ER) (en'-dō-plaz'-mik ruh-tik'-yū-lum) An extensive membranous network in eukaryotic cells, continuous with the outer nuclear membrane and composed of ribosome-studded (rough) and ribosome-free (smooth) regions.

endorphin (en-dōr'-fin) Any of several hormones produced in the brain and anterior pituitary that inhibits pain perception.

endoskeleton A hard skeleton buried within the soft tissues of an animal, such as the spicules of sponges, the plates of echinoderms, and the bony skeletons of vertebrates.

endosperm In angiosperms, a nutrient-rich tissue formed by the union of a sperm with two polar nuclei during double fertilization. The endosperm provides nourishment to the developing embryo in angiosperm seeds.

endospore A thick-coated, resistant cell produced by a bacterial cell exposed to harsh conditions.

endosymbiosis A process in which a unicellular organism (the "host") engulfs another cell, which lives within the host cell and ultimately becomes an organelle in the host cell; also refers to the hypothesis that mitochondria and plastids were formerly small prokaryotes that began living within larger cells.

endothelin A peptide produced by a blood vessel's endothelium that causes the vessel to constrict.

endothelium (en'-dō-thē'-lē-um) The simple squamous layer of cells lining the lumen of blood vessels.

endothermic Referring to organisms with bodies that are warmed by heat generated by metabolism. This heat is usually used to maintain a relatively stable body temperature higher than that of the external environment.

endotoxin A toxic component of the outer membrane of certain gram-negative bacteria that is released only when the bacteria die.

energetic hypothesis The concept that the length of a food chain is limited by the inefficiency of energy transfer along the chain.

energy The capacity to cause change, especially to do work (to move matter against an opposing force).

energy coupling In cellular metabolism, the use of energy released from an exergonic reaction to drive an endergonic reaction.

enhancer A segment of eukaryotic DNA containing multiple control elements, usually located far from the gene whose transcription it regulates.

enteric division Networks of neurons in the digestive tract, pancreas, and gallbladder; normally regulated by the sympathetic and parasympathetic divisions of the autonomic nervous system.

entropy A measure of disorder, or randomness.

enzymatic hydrolysis The process in digestion that splits macromolecules from food by the enzymatic addition of water.

enzyme (en'-zīm) A macromolecule serving as a catalyst, a chemical agent that changes the rate of a reaction without being consumed by the reaction.

enzyme-substrate complex A temporary complex formed when an enzyme binds its substrate molecule(s).

eosinophil (ē'-ō-sin'-ō-fil) A type of white blood cell with low phagocytic activity that is thought to play a role in defense against parasitic worms by releasing enzymes toxic to these invaders.

epicotyl (ep'-uh-kot'-ul) In an angiosperm embryo, the embryonic axis above the point of attachment of the cotyledon(s) and below the first pair of miniature leaves.

epidemic A general outbreak of a disease.

epidermis (1) The dermal tissue system of nonwoody plants, usually consisting of a single layer of tightly packed cells. (2) The outermost layer of cells in an animal.

epididymis (ep'-uh-did'-uh-mus) A coiled tubule located adjacent to the mammalian testis where sperm are stored.

epigenetic inheritance Inheritance of traits transmitted by mechanisms not directly involving the nucleotide sequence of a genome.

epinephrine (ep'-i-nef'-rin) A catecholamine that, when secreted as a hormone by the adrenal medulla, mediates "fight-or-flight" responses to short-term stresses; also released by some neurons as a neurotransmitter; also known as adrenaline.

epiphyte (ep'-uh-fīt) A plant that nourishes itself but grows on the surface of another plant for support, usually on the branches or trunks of tropical trees.

epistasis (ep'-i-stā'-sis) A type of gene interaction in which one gene alters the phenotypic effects of another gene that is independently inherited.

epithelial tissue (ep'-uh-thē'-lē-ul) Sheets of tightly packed cells that line organs and body cavities as well as external surfaces.

epithelium An epithelial tissue.

epitope A small, accessible region of an antigen to which an antigen receptor or antibody binds; also called an antigenic determinant.

EPSP See excitatory postsynaptic potential.

equilibrium potential (E_{ion}) The magnitude of a cell's membrane voltage at equilibrium; calculated using the Nernst equation.

erythrocyte (eh-rith'-ruh-sīt) A blood cell that contains hemoglobin, which transports oxygen; also called a red blood cell.

erythropoietin (EPO) (eh-rith'-rō-poy'-uh-tin) A hormone that stimulates the production of erythrocytes. It is secreted by the kidney when body tissues do not receive enough oxygen.

esophagus (eh-sof'-uh-gus) A channel that conducts food, by peristalsis, from the pharynx to the stomach.

essential amino acid An amino acid that an animal cannot synthesize itself and must be obtained from food in prefabricated form. Eight amino acids are essential in the human adult.

essential element In plants, a chemical element required for the plant to grow from a seed and complete its life cycle, producing another generation in the form of seeds.

essential fatty acid An unsaturated fatty acid that an animal needs but cannot make.

essential nutrient A substance that an organism must absorb in preassembled form because it cannot be synthesized from any other material. In humans, there are essential vitamins, minerals, amino acids, and fatty acids.

estradiol (es'-truh-dī'-ol) A steroid hormone that stimulates the development and maintenance of the female reproductive system and secondary sex characteristics; the major estrogen in mammals.

estrogen (es'-trō-jen) Any steroid hormone, such as estradiol, that stimulates the development and maintenance of the female reproductive system and secondary sex characteristics.

estrous cycle (es'-trus) A reproductive cycle characteristic of female mammals except humans and certain other primates, in which the nonpregnant endometrium is reabsorbed rather than shed, and sexual response occurs only during mid-cycle at estrus.

estuary The area where a freshwater stream or river merges with the ocean.

ethology The scientific study of how animals behave, particularly in their natural environments.

ethylene (eth'-uh-lēn) The only gaseous plant hormone. Among its many effects are response to mechanical stress, programmed cell death, leaf abscission, and fruit ripening.

etiolation Plant morphological adaptations for growing in darkness.

euchromatin (yū-krō'-muh-tin) The less condensed form of eukaryotic chromatin that is available for transcription.

eudicot (yū-dī'-kot) Member of a clade consisting of the vast majority of flowering plants that have two embryonic seed leaves, or cotyledons.

euglenid (yū′-glen-id) A protist, such as *Euglena* or its relatives, characterized by an anterior pocket from which one or two flagella emerge.

euglenozoan Member of a diverse clade of flagellated protists that includes predatory heterotrophs, photosynthetic autotrophs, and pathogenic parasites.

Eukarya (yū-kar′-ē-uh) The domain that includes all eukaryotic organisms.

eukaryotic cell (yū′-ker-ē-ot′-ik) A type of cell with a membrane-enclosed nucleus and membrane-enclosed organelles. Organisms with eukaryotic cells (protists, plants, fungi, and animals) are called eukaryotes.

eumetazoan (yū′-met-uh-zō′-un) Member of a clade of animals with true tissues. All animals except sponges and a few other groups are eumetazoans.

euryhaline (yur′-i-hā′-līn) Referring to organisms that tolerate substantial changes in external osmolarity.

eurypterid (yur-ip′-tuh-rid) An extinct carnivorous cheliceriform also called a water scorpion.

Eustachian tube (yū-stā′-shun) The tube that connects the middle ear to the pharynx.

eutherian (yū-thēr′-ē-un) Placental mammal; mammal whose young complete their embryonic development within the uterus, joined to the mother by the placenta.

eutrophic lake (yū-trōf′-ik) A lake that has a high rate of biological productivity supported by a high rate of nutrient cycling.

eutrophication A process by which nutrients, particularly phosphorus and nitrogen, become highly concentrated in a body of water, leading to increased growth of organisms such as algae or cyanobacteria.

evaporation The process by which a liquid changes to a gas.

evaporative cooling The process in which the surface of an object becomes cooler during evaporation, owing to a change of the molecules with the greatest kinetic energy from the liquid to the gaseous state.

evapotranspiration The total evaporation of water from an ecosystem, including evaporation from soil and the outside of plants, as well as the transpiration of water from within plants through stomata.

evo-devo Evolutionary developmental biology; a field of biology that compares developmental processes of different multicellular organisms to understand how these processes have evolved and how changes can modify existing organismal features or lead to new ones.

evolution Descent with modification; the idea that living species are descendants of ancestral species that were different from the present-day ones; also defined more narrowly as the change in the genetic composition of a population from generation to generation.

evolutionary tree A branching diagram that reflects a hypothesis about evolutionary relationships among groups of organisms.

Excavata One of five supergroups of eukaryotes proposed in a current hypothesis of the evolutionary history of eukaryotes. Excavates have unique cytoskeletal features, and some species have an "excavated" feeding groove on one side of the cell body. *See also* Chromalveolata, Rhizaria, Archaeplastida, and Unikonta.

excitatory postsynaptic potential (EPSP) An electrical change (depolarization) in the membrane of a postsynaptic cell caused by the binding of an excitatory neurotransmitter from a presynaptic cell to a postsynaptic receptor; makes it more likely for a postsynaptic cell to generate an action potential.

excretion The disposal of nitrogen-containing metabolites and other waste products.

exergonic reaction (ek′-ser-gon′-ik) A spontaneous chemical reaction, in which there is a net release of free energy.

exocytosis (ek′-sō-sī-tō′-sis) The cellular secretion of biological molecules by the fusion of vesicles containing them with the plasma membrane.

exon A sequence within a primary transcript that remains in the RNA after RNA processing; also refers to the region of DNA from which this sequence was transcribed.

exoskeleton A hard encasement on the surface of an animal, such as the shell of a mollusc or the cuticle of an arthropod, that provides protection and points of attachment for muscles.

exotoxin (ek′-sō-tok′-sin) A toxic protein that is secreted by a prokaryote or other pathogen and that produces specific symptoms, even if the pathogen is no longer present.

expansin Plant enzyme that breaks the cross-links (hydrogen bonds) between cellulose microfibrils and other cell wall constituents, loosening the wall's fabric.

exponential population growth Growth of a population in an ideal, unlimited environment, represented by a J-shaped curve when population size is plotted over time.

expression vector A cloning vector that contains the requisite bacterial promoter just upstream of a restriction site where a eukaryotic gene can be inserted, allowing the gene to be expressed in a bacterial cell.

external fertilization The fusion of gametes that parents have discharged into the environment.

extinction vortex A downward population spiral in which inbreeding and genetic drift combine to cause a small population to shrink and, unless the spiral is reversed, to become extinct.

extracellular digestion The breakdown of food in compartments that are continuous with the outside of an animal's body.

extracellular matrix (ECM) The substance in which animal cells are embedded, consisting of protein and polysaccharides synthesized and secreted by cells.

extraembryonic membrane One of four membranes (yolk sac, amnion, chorion, and allantois) located outside the embryo that support the developing embryo in reptiles and mammals.

extreme halophile An organism that lives in a highly saline environment, such as the Great Salt Lake or the Dead Sea.

extreme thermophile An organism that thrives in hot environments (often 60–80°C or hotter).

extremophile An organism that lives in an environment whose conditions are so extreme that few other species can survive there. Extremophiles include extreme halophiles and extreme thermophiles.

F factor In bacteria, the DNA segment that confers the ability to form pili for conjugation and associated functions required for the transfer of DNA from donor to recipient. The F factor may exist as a plasmid or be integrated into the bacterial chromosome.

F plasmid The plasmid form of the F factor.

F_1 generation The first filial, or hybrid, offspring in a series of genetic crosses.

F_2 generation Offspring resulting from interbreeding of the hybrid F_1 generation.

facilitated diffusion The spontaneous passage of molecules or ions across a biological membrane with the assistance of specific transmembrane transport proteins.

facilitator A species that has a positive effect on the survival and reproduction of other species in a community and that influences community structure.

facultative anaerobe (fak′-ul-tā′-tiv an′-uh-rōb) An organism that makes ATP by aerobic respiration if oxygen is present but that switches to anaerobic respiration or fermentation if oxygen is not present.

family In classification, the taxonomic category above genus.

fast block to polyspermy The depolarization of the egg plasma membrane that begins within 1–3 seconds after a sperm binds to an egg membrane protein. The depolarization lasts about 1 minute and prevents additional sperm from fusing with the egg during that time.

fast-twitch fiber A muscle fiber used for rapid, powerful contractions.

fat A lipid consisting of three fatty acids linked to one glycerol molecule; also called a triacylglycerol or triglyceride.

fate map A territorial diagram of embryonic development that displays the future derivatives of individual cells and tissues.

fatty acid A long carbon chain carboxylic acid. Fatty acids vary in length and in the number and location of double bonds; three fatty acids linked to a glycerol molecule form a fat molecule, also known as a triacylglycerol or triglyceride.

feces (fē′-sēz) The wastes of the digestive tract.

feedback inhibition A method of metabolic control in which the end product of a metabolic pathway acts as an inhibitor of an enzyme within that pathway.

fermentation A catabolic process that makes a limited amount of ATP from glucose without an electron transport chain and that produces a characteristic end product, such as ethyl alcohol or lactic acid.

fertilization (1) The union of haploid gametes to produce a diploid zygote. (2) The addition of mineral nutrients to the soil.

fertilization envelope The protective layer formed when the vitelline layer of an egg is pushed away from the plasma membrane and hardened after fertilization by molecules exocytosed during the cortical reaction.

fetus (fē′-tus) A developing mammal that has all the major structures of an adult. In humans, the fetal stage lasts from the 9th week of gestation until birth.

fiber A lignified cell type that reinforces the xylem of angiosperms and functions in mechanical support; a slender, tapered sclerenchyma cell that usually occurs in bundles.

fibrin (fī′-brin) The activated form of the blood-clotting protein fibrinogen. Fibrin aggregates into threads that form the fabric of the clot.

fibroblast (fī′-brō-blast) A type of cell in loose connective tissue that secretes the protein ingredients of the extracellular fibers.

fibronectin A glycoprotein that helps animal cells attach to the extracellular matrix.

filament In an angiosperm, the stalk portion of the stamen, the pollen-producing reproductive organ of a flower.

filtrate Cell-free fluid extracted from the body fluid by the excretory system.

filtration In excretory systems, the extraction of water and small solutes, including metabolic wastes, from the body fluid.

fimbria (plural, **fimbriae**) A short, hairlike appendage of a prokaryotic cell that helps it adhere to the substrate or to other cells; also known as an attachment pilus.

first law of thermodynamics The principle of conservation of energy: Energy can be transferred and transformed, but it cannot be created or destroyed.

fission The separation of an organism into two or more individuals of approximately equal size.

fixed action pattern In animal behavior, a sequence of unlearned acts that is essentially unchangeable and, once initiated, usually carried to completion.

flaccid (flas′-id) Limp. Lacking in stiffness or firmness, as in a plant cell in surroundings where there is no tendency for water to enter the cell.

flagellum (fluh-jel′-um) (plural, **flagella**) A long cellular appendage specialized for locomotion. Like motile cilia, eukaryotic flagella have a core with nine outer doublet microtubules and two inner single microtubules ensheathed in an extension of the plasma membrane. Prokaryotic flagella have a different structure.

florigen A flowering signal, not yet chemically identified, that may be a hormone or may be a change in relative concentrations of multiple hormones.

flower In an angiosperm, a short stem with up to four sets of modified leaves, bearing structures that function in sexual reproduction.

fluid feeder An animal that lives by sucking nutrient-rich fluids from another living organism.

fluid mosaic model The currently accepted model of cell membrane structure, which envisions the membrane as a mosaic of protein molecules drifting laterally in a fluid bilayer of phospholipids.

follicle (fol′-uh-kul) A microscopic structure in the ovary that contains the developing oocyte and secretes estrogens.

follicle-stimulating hormone (FSH) A tropic hormone that is produced and secreted by the anterior pituitary and that stimulates the production of eggs by the ovaries and sperm by the testes.

follicular phase That part of the ovarian cycle during which follicles are growing and oocytes maturing.

food chain The pathway along which food energy is transferred from trophic level to trophic level, beginning with producers.

food vacuole A membranous sac formed by phagocytosis of microorganisms or particles to be used as food by the cell.

food web The interconnected feeding relationships in an ecosystem.

foot (1) The portion of a bryophyte sporophyte that gathers sugars, amino acids, water, and minerals from the parent gametophyte via transfer cells. (2) One of the three main parts of a mollusc; a muscular structure usually used for movement. *See also* mantle, visceral mass.

foraging The seeking and obtaining of food.

foram (foraminiferan) An aquatic protist that secretes a hardened shell containing calcium carbonate and extends pseudopodia through pores in the shell.

foraminiferan *See* foram.

forebrain One of three ancestral and embryonic regions of the vertebrate brain; develops into the thalamus, hypothalamus, and cerebrum.

fossil A preserved remnant or impression of an organism that lived in the past.

founder effect Genetic drift that occurs when a few individuals become isolated from a larger population and form a new population whose gene pool composition is not reflective of that of the original population.

fovea (fō′-vē-uh) The place on the retina at the eye's center of focus, where cones are highly concentrated.

fragmentation A means of asexual reproduction whereby a single parent breaks into parts that regenerate into whole new individuals.

frameshift mutation A mutation occurring when the number of nucleotides inserted or deleted is not a multiple of three, resulting in the improper grouping of the subsequent nucleotides into codons.

free energy The portion of a biological system's energy that can perform work when temperature and pressure are uniform throughout the system. (The change in free energy of a system is calculated by the equation $\Delta G = \Delta H -$

$T\Delta S$, where H is enthalpy [in biological systems, equivalent to total energy], T is absolute temperature, and S is entropy.)

frequency-dependent selection A decline in the reproductive success of individuals that have a phenotype that has become too common in a population.

fruit A mature ovary of a flower. The fruit protects dormant seeds and often aids in their dispersal.

functional group A specific configuration of atoms commonly attached to the carbon skeletons of organic molecules and usually involved in chemical reactions.

Fungi (fun′-jē) The eukaryotic kingdom that includes organisms that absorb nutrients after decomposing organic material.

G₀ phase A nondividing state occupied by cells that have left the cell cycle.

G₁ phase The first gap, or growth phase, of the cell cycle, consisting of the portion of interphase before DNA synthesis begins.

G₂ phase The second gap, or growth phase, of the cell cycle, consisting of the portion of interphase after DNA synthesis occurs.

gallbladder An organ that stores bile and releases it as needed into the small intestine.

game theory An approach to evaluating alternative strategies in situations where the outcome of a particular strategy depends on the strategies used by other individuals.

gametangium (gam′-uh-tan′-jē-um) (plural, **gametangia**) Multicellular plant structure in which gametes are formed. Female gametangia are called archegonia, and male gametangia are called antheridia.

gamete (gam′-ēt) A haploid reproductive cell, such as an egg or sperm. Gametes unite during sexual reproduction to produce a diploid zygote.

gametogenesis The process by which gametes are produced.

gametophore (guh-mē′-tō-fōr) The mature gamete-producing structure of a moss gametophyte.

gametophyte (guh-mē′-tō-fīt) In organisms (plants and some algae) that have alternation of generations, the multicellular haploid form that produces haploid gametes by mitosis. The haploid gametes unite and develop into sporophytes.

gamma-aminobutyric acid (GABA) An amino acid that functions as a CNS neurotransmitter in the central nervous system of vertebrates.

ganglion (gang′-glē-un) (plural, **ganglia**) A cluster (functional group) of nerve cell bodies in a centralized nervous system.

ganglion cell A type of neuron in the retina that synapses with bipolar cells and transmits action potentials to the brain via axons in the optic nerve.

gap junction A type of intercellular junction in animals that allows the passage of materials between cells.

gas exchange The uptake of molecular oxygen from the environment and the discharge of carbon dioxide to the environment.

Glossary

gastric juice A digestive fluid secreted by the stomach.

gastrovascular cavity A central cavity with a single opening in the body of certain animals that functions in both the digestion and distribution of nutrients.

gastrula (gas'-trū-luh) An embryonic stage in animal development encompassing the formation of three layers: ectoderm, mesoderm, and endoderm.

gastrulation (gas'-trū-lā'-shun) In animal development, a series of cell and tissue movements in which the blastula-stage embryo folds inward, producing a three-layered embryo, the gastrula.

gated channel A transmembrane protein channel that opens or closes in response to a particular stimulus.

gated ion channel A gated channel for a specific ion. The opening or closing of such channels may alter the membrane potential.

gel electrophoresis (ē-lek'-trō-fōr-ē'-sis) A technique for separating nucleic acids or proteins on the basis of their size and electrical charge, both of which affect their rate of movement through an electric field in a gel.

gene A discrete unit of hereditary information consisting of a specific nucleotide sequence in DNA (or RNA, in some viruses).

gene cloning The production of multiple copies of a gene.

gene expression The process by which DNA directs the synthesis of proteins or, in some cases, just RNAs.

gene flow The transfer of alleles from one population to another, resulting from the movement of fertile individuals or their gametes.

gene pool The aggregate of all of the alleles for all of the loci in all individuals in a population. The term is also used in a more restricted sense as the aggregate of alleles for just one or a few loci in a population.

gene therapy The introduction of genes into an afflicted individual for therapeutic purposes.

gene-for-gene recognition A widespread form of plant disease resistance involving recognition of pathogen-derived molecules by the protein products of specific plant disease resistance genes.

genetic drift A process in which chance events cause unpredictable fluctuations in allele frequencies from one generation to the next. Effects of genetic drift are most pronounced in small populations.

genetic engineering The direct manipulation of genes for practical purposes.

genetic map An ordered list of genetic loci (genes or other genetic markers) along a chromosome.

genetic profile An individual's unique set of genetic markers, detected most often today by PCR or, previously, by electrophoresis and nucleic acid probes.

genetic recombination General term for the production of offspring with combinations of traits that differ from those found in either parent.

genetically modified (GM) organism An organism that has acquired one or more genes by artificial means; also known as a transgenic organism.

genetics The scientific study of heredity and hereditary variation.

genome (jē'-nōm) The genetic material of an organism or virus; the complete complement of an organism's or virus's genes along with its noncoding nucleic acid sequences.

genomic imprinting A phenomenon in which expression of an allele in offspring depends on whether the allele is inherited from the male or female parent.

genomic library A set of cell clones containing all the DNA segments from a genome, each within a plasmid, phage, or other cloning vector.

genomics (juh-nō'-miks) The study of whole sets of genes and their interactions.

genotype (jē'-nō-tīp) The genetic makeup, or set of alleles, of an organism.

genus (jē'-nus) (*plural,* **genera**) A taxonomic category above the species level, designated by the first word of a species' two-part scientific name.

geographic variation Differences between the gene pools of geographically separate populations or population subgroups.

geologic record The division of Earth's history into time periods, grouped into three eons—Archaean, Proterozoic, and Phanerozoic—and further subdivided into eras, periods, and epochs.

geometric isomer One of several compounds that have the same molecular formula and covalent arrangements but differ in the spatial arrangements of their atoms owing to the inflexibility of double bonds.

germ layer One of the three main layers in a gastrula that will form the various tissues and organs of an animal body.

gestation (jes-tā'-shun) Pregnancy; the state of carrying developing young within the female reproductive tract.

gibberellin (jib'-uh-rel'-in) Any of a class of related plant hormones that stimulate growth in the stem and leaves, trigger the germination of seeds and breaking of bud dormancy, and (with auxin) stimulate fruit development.

glans The rounded structure at the tip of the clitoris or penis that is involved in sexual arousal.

glial cells (glia) Supporting cells that are essential for the structural integrity of the nervous system and for the normal functioning of neurons.

global ecology The study of the functioning and distribution of organisms across the biosphere and how the regional exchange of energy and materials affects them.

glomeromycete (glō'-mer-ō-mī'-sēt) Member of the fungal phylum Glomeromycota, characterized by a distinct branching form of mycorrhizae (mutualistic relationships with plant roots) called arbuscular mycorrhizae.

glomerulus (glō-mār'-yū-lus) A ball of capillaries surrounded by Bowman's capsule in the nephron and serving as the site of filtration in the vertebrate kidney.

glucagon (glū'-kuh-gon) A hormone secreted by pancreatic alpha cells that raises blood glucose levels. It promotes glycogen breakdown and release of glucose by the liver.

glucocorticoid A steroid hormone that is secreted by the adrenal cortex and that influences glucose metabolism and immune function.

glutamate An amino acid that functions as a neurotransmitter in the central nervous system.

glyceraldehyde-3-phosphate (G3P) (glis'-er-al'-de-hīd) A three-carbon carbohydrate that is the direct product of the Calvin cycle; it is also an intermediate in glycolysis.

glycogen (glī'-kō-jen) An extensively branched glucose storage polysaccharide found in the liver and muscle of animals; the animal equivalent of starch.

glycolipid A lipid with covalently attached carbohydrate(s).

glycolysis (glī-kol'-uh-sis) The splitting of glucose into pyruvate. Glycolysis occurs in almost all living cells, serving as the starting point for fermentation or cellular respiration.

glycoprotein A protein with one or more carbohydrates covalently attached to it.

glycosidic linkage A covalent bond formed between two monosaccharides by a dehydration reaction.

gnathostome (na'-thu-stōm) Member of the vertebrate subgroup possessing jaws.

golden alga A biflagellated, photosynthetic protist named for its color, which results from its yellow and brown carotenoids.

Golgi apparatus (gol'-jē) An organelle in eukaryotic cells consisting of stacks of flat membranous sacs that modify, store, and route products of the endoplasmic reticulum and synthesize some products, notably noncellulose carbohydrates.

gonads (gō'-nadz) The male and female sex organs; the gamete-producing organs in most animals.

G protein A GTP-binding protein that relays signals from a plasma membrane signal receptor, known as a G protein-coupled receptor, to other signal transduction proteins inside the cell.

G protein-coupled receptor A signal receptor protein in the plasma membrane that responds to the binding of a signaling molecule by activating a G protein. Also called a G protein-linked receptor.

grade A group of organisms that share the same level of organizational complexity or share a key adaptation.

Gram stain A staining method that distinguishes between two different kinds of bacterial cell walls.

gram-negative Describing the group of bacteria that have a cell wall that is structurally more complex and contains less peptidoglycan than the cell wall of gram-positive bacteria. Gram-negative bacteria are often more toxic than gram-positive bacteria.

gram-positive Describing the group of bacteria that have a cell wall that is structurally less complex and contains more peptidoglycan than the cell wall of gram-negative bacteria. Gram-positive bacteria are usually less toxic than gram-negative bacteria.

granum (gran'-um) (plural, **grana**) A stack of membrane-bounded thylakoids in the chloroplast. Grana function in the light reactions of photosynthesis.

gravitropism (grav'-uh-trō'-pizm) A response of a plant or animal to gravity.

gray crescent A light gray, crescent-shaped region of cytoplasm that becomes exposed after cortical rotation, located near the equator of an egg on the side opposite sperm entry, marking the future dorsal side of the embryo.

gray matter Regions of dendrites and clustered neuron cell bodies within the CNS.

green alga A photosynthetic protist, named for green chloroplasts that are similar in structure and pigment composition to those of land plants. Green algae are a paraphyletic group, some of whose members are more closely related to land plants than they are to other green algae.

green world hypothesis The conjecture that terrestrial herbivores consume relatively little plant biomass because they are held in check by a variety of factors, including predators, parasites, and disease.

greenhouse effect The warming of Earth due to the atmospheric accumulation of carbon dioxide and certain other gases, which absorb reflected infrared radiation and reradiate some of it back toward Earth.

gross primary production (GPP) The total primary production of an ecosystem.

ground tissue system Plant tissues that are neither vascular nor dermal, fulfilling a variety of functions, such as storage, photosynthesis, and support.

growth factor (1) A protein that must be present in the extracellular environment (culture medium or animal body) for the growth and normal development of certain types of cells. (2) A local regulator that acts on nearby cells to stimulate cell proliferation and differentiation.

growth hormone (GH) A hormone that is produced and secreted by the anterior pituitary and that has both direct (nontropic) and tropic effects on a wide variety of tissues.

guard cells The two cells that flank the stomatal pore and regulate the opening and closing of the pore.

gustation The sense of taste.

guttation The exudation of water droplets, caused by root pressure in certain plants.

gymnosperm (jim'-nō-sperm) A vascular plant that bears naked seeds—seeds not enclosed in specialized chambers.

habituation A simple type of learning that involves a loss of responsiveness to stimuli that convey little or no new information.

half-life The amount of time it takes for 50% of a sample of a radioactive isotope to decay.

Hamilton's rule The principle that for natural selection to favor an altruistic act, the benefit to the recipient, devalued by the coefficient of relatedness, must exceed the cost to the altruist.

haploid cell (hap'-loyd) A cell containing only one set of chromosomes (*n*).

Hardy-Weinberg equilibrium The condition describing a nonevolving population (one that is in genetic equilibrium).

Hardy-Weinberg principle The principle that frequencies of alleles and genotypes in a population remain constant from generation to generation, provided that only Mendelian segregation and recombination of alleles are at work.

haustorium (plural, **haustoria**) (ho-stōr'-ē-um, ho-stōr'-ē-uh) In certain symbiotic fungi, a specialized hypha that can penetrate the tissues of host organisms.

heart A muscular pump that uses metabolic energy to elevate the hydrostatic pressure of the circulatory fluid (blood or hemolymph). The fluid then flows down a pressure gradient through the body and eventually returns to the heart.

heart attack The damage or death of cardiac muscle tissue resulting from prolonged blockage of one or more coronary arteries.

heart murmur A hissing sound that most often results from blood squirting backward through a leaky valve in the heart.

heart rate The frequency of heart contraction.

heat The total amount of kinetic energy due to the random motion of atoms or molecules in a body of matter; also called thermal energy. Heat is energy in its most random form.

heat of vaporization The quantity of heat a liquid must absorb for 1 g of it to be converted from the liquid to the gaseous state.

heat-shock protein A protein that helps protect other proteins during heat stress. Heat-shock proteins are found in plants, animals, and microorganisms.

heavy chain One of the two types of polypeptide chains that make up an antibody molecule and B cell receptor; consists of a variable region, which contributes to the antigen-binding site, and a constant region.

helicase An enzyme that untwists the double helix of DNA at the replication forks, separating the two strands and making them available as template strands.

helper T cell A type of T cell that, when activated, secretes cytokines that promote the response of B cells (humoral response) and cytotoxic T cells (cell-mediated response) to antigens.

hemoglobin (hē'-mō-glō'-bin) An iron-containing protein in red blood cells that reversibly binds oxygen.

hemolymph (hē'-mō-limf') In invertebrates with an open circulatory system, the body fluid that bathes tissues.

hemophilia (hē'-muh-fil'-ē-uh) A human genetic disease caused by a sex-linked recessive allele resulting in the absence of one or more blood-clotting proteins; characterized by excessive bleeding following injury.

hepatic portal vein A large circulatory channel that conveys nutrient-laden blood from the small intestine to the liver, which regulates the blood's nutrient content.

herbivore (hur'-bi-vōr') An animal that mainly eats plants or algae.

herbivory An interaction in which an organism eats parts of a plant or alga.

heredity The transmission of traits from one generation to the next.

hermaphrodite (hur-maf'-ruh-dīt') An individual that functions as both male and female in sexual reproduction by producing both sperm and eggs.

hermaphroditism (hur-maf'-rō-dī-tizm) A condition in which an individual has both female and male gonads and functions as both a male and female in sexual reproduction by producing both sperm and eggs.

heterochromatin (het'-er-ō-krō'-muh-tin) Eukaryotic chromatin that remains highly compacted during interphase and is generally not transcribed.

heterochrony (het'-uh-rok'-ruh-nē) Evolutionary change in the timing or rate of an organism's development.

heterocyte (het'-er-ō-sīt) A specialized cell that engages in nitrogen fixation in some filamentous cyanobacteria; formerly called heterocyst.

heterokaryon (het'-er-ō-kār'-ē-un) A fungal mycelium that contains two or more haploid nuclei per cell.

heteromorphic (het'-er-ō-mōr'-fik) Referring to a condition in the life cycle of plants and certain algae in which the sporophyte and gametophyte generations differ in morphology.

heterosporous (het-er-os'-pōr-us) Referring to a plant species that has two kinds of spores: microspores, which develop into male gametophytes, and megaspores, which develop into female gametophytes.

heterotroph (het'-er-ō-trōf) An organism that obtains organic food molecules by eating other organisms or substances derived from them.

heterozygote advantage Greater reproductive success of heterozygous individuals compared with homozygotes; tends to preserve variation in a gene pool.

heterozygous (het'-er-ō-zī'-gus) Having two different alleles for a given gene.

hexapod An insect or closely related wingless, six-legged arthropod.

hibernation A physiological state in which metabolism decreases, the heart and respiratory system slow down, and body temperature is maintained at a lower level than normal.

high-density lipoprotein (HDL) A particle in the blood made up of cholesterol and other lipids surrounded by a single layer of phospholipids in which proteins are embedded. HDL carries less cholesterol than a related lipoprotein, LDL, and high HDL levels in the blood may be correlated with a decreased risk of blood vessel blockage.

hindbrain One of three ancestral and embryonic regions of the vertebrate brain; develops into the medulla oblongata, pons, and cerebellum.

histamine (his´-tuh-mēn) A substance released by mast cells that causes blood vessels to dilate and become more permeable in inflammatory and allergic responses.

histone (his´-tōn) A small protein with a high proportion of positively charged amino acids that binds to the negatively charged DNA and plays a key role in chromatin structure.

histone acetylation The attachment of acetyl groups to certain amino acids of histone proteins.

HIV (human immunodeficiency virus) The infectious agent that causes AIDS. HIV is a retrovirus.

holdfast A rootlike structure that anchors a seaweed.

holoblastic cleavage (hō´-lō-blas´-tik) A type of cleavage in which there is complete division of the egg; occurs in eggs that have little yolk (such as those of the sea urchin) or a moderate amount of yolk (such as those of the frog).

homeobox (hō´-mē-ō-boks´) A 180-nucleotide sequence within homeotic genes and some other developmental genes that is widely conserved in animals. Related sequences occur in plants and yeasts.

homeostasis (hō´-mē-ō-stā´-sis) The steady-state physiological condition of the body.

homeotic gene (ho´-mē-o´-tik) Any of the master regulatory genes that control placement and spatial organization of body parts in animals, plants, and fungi by controlling the developmental fate of groups of cells.

hominin (ho´-mi-nin) A species on the human branch of the evolutionary tree. Hominins include *Homo sapiens* and our ancestors, a group of extinct species that are more closely related to us than to chimpanzees.

homologous chromosomes (hō-mol´-uh-gus) A pair of chromosomes of the same length, centromere position, and staining pattern that possess genes for the same characters at corresponding loci. One homologous chromosome is inherited from the organism's father, the other from the mother. Also called homologs, or a homologous pair.

homologous structures Structures in different species that are similar because of common ancestry.

homology (hō-mol´-uh-jē) Similarity in characteristics resulting from a shared ancestry.

homoplasy (hō´-muh-play´-zē) Similar (analogous) structure or molecular sequence that has evolved independently in two species.

homosporous (hō-mos´-puh-rus) Referring to a plant species that has a single kind of spore, which typically develops into a bisexual gametophyte.

homozygous (hō´-mō-zī´-gus) Having two identical alleles for a given gene.

horizontal cell A neuron of the retina that helps integrate information before it is sent to the brain.

horizontal gene transfer The transfer of genes from one genome to another through

mechanisms such as transposable elements, plasmid exchange, viral activity, and perhaps fusions of different organisms.

hormone In multicellular organisms, one of many types of secreted chemicals that are formed in specialized cells, travel in body fluids, and act on specific target cells in other parts of the body to change their functioning.

hornwort A small, herbaceous nonvascular plant that is a member of the phylum Anthocerophyta.

host The larger participant in a symbiotic relationship, serving as home and food source for the smaller symbiont.

host range The limited range of host cells that each type of virus can infect.

human chorionic gonadotropin (hCG) (kōr´-ē-on´-ik gō-na´-dō-trō´-pin) A hormone secreted by the chorion that maintains the corpus luteum of the ovary during the first three months of pregnancy.

Human Genome Project An international collaborative effort to map and sequence the DNA of the entire human genome.

humoral immune response (hyū´-mer-ul) The branch of acquired immunity that involves the activation of B cells and that leads to the production of antibodies, which defend against bacteria and viruses in body fluids.

humus (hyū´-mus) Decomposing organic material that is a component of topsoil.

Huntington's disease A human genetic disease caused by a dominant allele; characterized by uncontrollable body movements and degeneration of the nervous system; usually fatal 10 to 20 years after the onset of symptoms.

hybrid Offspring that results from the mating of individuals from two different species or two true-breeding varieties of the same species.

hybrid zone A geographic region in which members of different species meet and mate, producing at least some offspring of mixed ancestry.

hybridization In genetics, the mating, or crossing, of two true-breeding varieties.

hydration shell The sphere of water molecules around a dissolved ion.

hydrocarbon An organic molecule consisting only of carbon and hydrogen.

hydrogen bond A type of weak chemical bond that is formed when the slightly positive hydrogen atom of a polar covalent bond in one molecule is attracted to the slightly negative atom of a polar covalent bond in another molecule.

hydrogen ion A single proton with a charge of $1+$. The dissociation of a water molecule (H_2O) leads to the generation of a hydroxide ion (OH^-) and a hydrogen ion (H^+).

hydrolysis (hī-drol´-uh-sis) A chemical process that lyses, or splits, molecules by the addition of water, functioning in disassembly of polymers to monomers.

hydronium ion A water molecule that has an extra proton bound to it; H_3O^+.

hydrophilic (hī´-drō-fil´-ik) Having an affinity for water.

hydrophobic (hī´-drō-fō´-bik) Having an aversion to water; tending to coalesce and form droplets in water.

hydrophobic interaction A type of weak chemical bond formed when molecules that do not mix with water coalesce to exclude water.

hydroponic culture A method in which plants are grown in mineral solutions rather than in soil.

hydrostatic skeleton A skeletal system composed of fluid held under pressure in a closed body compartment; the main skeleton of most cnidarians, flatworms, nematodes, and annelids.

hydroxide ion A water molecule that has lost a proton; OH^-.

hydroxyl group (hī-drok´-sil) A chemical group consisting of an oxygen atom joined to a hydrogen atom. Molecules possessing this group are soluble in water and are called alcohols.

hymen A thin membrane that partly covers the vaginal opening in the human female. The hymen is ruptured by sexual intercourse or other vigorous activity.

hyperpolarization A change in a cell's membrane potential such that the inside of the membrane becomes more negative relative to the outside. Hyperpolarization reduces the chance that a neuron will transmit a nerve impulse.

hypersensitive response A plant's localized defense response to a pathogen, involving the death of cells around the site of infection.

hypertension A disorder in which blood pressure remains abnormally high.

hypertonic Referring to a solution that, when surrounding a cell, will cause the cell to lose water.

hypha (plural, **hyphae**) (hī´-fuh, hī´-fē) One of many connected filaments that collectively make up the mycelium of a fungus.

hypocotyl (hī´-puh-cot´-ul) In an angiosperm embryo, the embryonic axis below the point of attachment of the cotyledon(s) and above the radicle.

hypothalamus (hī´-pō-thal´-uh-mus) The ventral part of the vertebrate forebrain; functions in maintaining homeostasis, especially in coordinating the endocrine and nervous systems; secretes hormones of the posterior pituitary and releasing factors that regulate the anterior pituitary.

hypothesis (hī-poth´-uh-sis) A tentative answer to a well-framed question, narrower in scope than a theory and subject to testing.

hypotonic Referring to a solution that, when surrounding a cell, will cause the cell to take up water.

imbibition The physical adsorption of water onto the internal surfaces of structures.

immigration The influx of new individuals into a population from other areas.

immune system An animal body's system of defenses against agents that cause disease.

immunization The process of generating a state of immunity by artificial means. In active immunization, also called vaccination, an inactive or weakened form of a pathogen is administered, inducing B and T cell responses and immunological memory. In passive immunization, antibodies specific for a particular microbe are administered, conferring immediate but temporary protection.

immunodeficiency A disorder in which the ability of an immune system to protect against pathogens is defective or absent.

immunoglobulin (Ig) (im′-yū-nō-glob′-yū-lin) Any of the class of proteins that function as antibodies. Immunoglobulins are divided into five major classes that differ in their distribution in the body and antigen disposal activities.

imprinting In animal behavior, the formation at a specific stage in life of a long-lasting behavioral response to a specific individual or object. (*See also* genomic imprinting.)

in situ **hybridization** A technique used to detect the location of a specific mRNA using nucleic acid hybridization with a labeled probe in an intact organism.

in vitro **fertilization (IVF)** (vē′-trō) Fertilization of oocytes in laboratory containers followed by artificial implantation of the early embryo in the mother's uterus.

in vitro **mutagenesis** A technique used to discover the function of a gene by cloning it, introducing specific changes into the cloned gene's sequence, reinserting the mutated gene into a cell, and studying the phenotype of the mutant.

inclusive fitness The total effect an individual has on proliferating its genes by producing its own offspring and by providing aid that enables other close relatives to increase the production of their offspring.

incomplete dominance The situation in which the phenotype of heterozygotes is intermediate between the phenotypes of individuals homozygous for either allele.

incomplete flower A flower in which one or more of the four basic floral organs (sepals, petals, stamens, or carpels) are either absent or nonfunctional.

incomplete metamorphosis A type of development in certain insects, such as grasshoppers, in which the young (called nymphs) resemble adults but are smaller and have different body proportions. The nymph goes through a series of molts, each time looking more like an adult, until it reaches full size.

incus The second of three bones in the middle ear of mammals; also called the anvil.

indeterminate cleavage A type of embryonic development in deuterostomes in which each cell produced by early cleavage divisions retains the capacity to develop into a complete embryo.

indeterminate growth A type of growth characteristic of plants, in which the organism continues to grow as long as it lives.

induced fit Induced by entry of the substrate, the change in shape of the active site of an enzyme so that it binds more snugly to the substrate.

inducer A specific small molecule that binds to a bacterial repressor protein and changes the repressor's shape so that it cannot bind to an operator, thus switching an operon on.

induction The process in which one group of embryonic cells influences the development of another, usually by causing changes in gene expression.

inductive reasoning A type of logic in which generalizations are based on a large number of specific observations.

inflammatory response An innate immune defense triggered by physical injury or infection of tissue involving the release of substances that promote swelling, enhance the infiltration of white blood cells, and aid in tissue repair and destruction of invading pathogens.

inflorescence A group of flowers tightly clustered together.

ingestion The first stage of food processing in animals: the act of eating.

ingroup A species or group of species whose evolutionary relationships we seek to determine.

inhibin A hormone produced in the male and female gonads that functions in part by regulating the function of the anterior pituitary by negative feedback.

inhibitory postsynaptic potential (IPSP) An electrical change (usually hyperpolarization) in the membrane of a postsynaptic neuron caused by the binding of an inhibitory neurotransmitter from a presynaptic cell to a postsynaptic receptor; makes it more difficult for a postsynaptic neuron to generate an action potential.

innate behavior Animal behavior that is developmentally fixed and under strong genetic control. Innate behavior is exhibited in virtually the same form by all individuals in a population despite internal and external environmental differences during development and throughout their lifetimes.

innate immunity A form of defense common to all animals that is active immediately upon exposure to pathogens and that is the same whether or not the pathogen has been encountered previously.

inner cell mass An inner cluster of cells at one end of a mammalian blastocyst that subsequently develops into the embryo proper and some of the extraembryonic membranes.

inner ear One of three main regions of the vertebrate ear; includes the cochlea (which in turn contains the organ of Corti) and the semicircular canals.

inositol trisphosphate (IP₃) (in-ō′-suh-tol) A second messenger that functions as an intermediate between certain nonsteroid hormones and a third messenger, a rise in cytoplasmic Ca^{2+} concentration.

inquiry The search for information and explanation, often focused by specific questions.

insertion A mutation involving the addition of one or more nucleotide pairs to a gene.

insulin (in′-suh-lin) A hormone secreted by pancreatic beta cells that lowers blood glucose levels. It promotes the uptake of glucose by most body cells and the synthesis and storage of glycogen in the liver and also stimulates protein and fat synthesis.

integral protein Typically a transmembrane protein with hydrophobic regions that extend into and often completely span the hydrophobic interior of the membrane and with hydrophilic regions in contact with the aqueous solution on either side of the membrane (or lining the channel in the case of a channel protein).

integrin In animal cells, a transmembrane receptor protein that interconnects the extracellular matrix and the cytoskeleton.

integument (in-teg′-yū-ment) Layer of sporophyte tissue that contributes to the structure of an ovule of a seed plant.

integumentary system The outer covering of a mammal's body, including skin, hair, and nails.

intercalated disk (in-ter′-kuh-lā′-ted) A special junction between cardiac muscle cells that provides direct electrical coupling between the cells.

interferon (in′-ter-fēr′-on) A protein that has antiviral or immune regulatory functions. Interferon-α and interferon-β, secreted by virus-infected cells, help nearby cells resist viral infection; interferon-γ, secreted by T cells, helps activate macrophages.

intermediate disturbance hypothesis The concept that moderate levels of disturbance can foster greater species diversity than low or high levels of disturbance.

intermediate filament A component of the cytoskeleton that includes filaments intermediate in size between microtubules and microfilaments.

internal fertilization The fusion of eggs and sperm within the female reproductive tract. The sperm are typically deposited in or near the tract.

interneuron An association neuron; a nerve cell within the central nervous system that forms synapses with sensory and/or motor neurons and integrates sensory input and motor output.

internode A segment of a plant stem between the points where leaves are attached.

interphase The period in the cell cycle when the cell is not dividing. During interphase, cellular metabolic activity is high, chromosomes and organelles are duplicated, and cell size may increase. Interphase accounts for 90% of the cell cycle.

intersexual selection Selection whereby individuals of one sex (usually females) are choosy in selecting their mates from individuals of the other sex; also called mate choice.

interspecific competition Competition for resources between individuals of two or more species when resources are in short supply.

interspecific interaction A relationship between individuals of two or more species in a community.

interstitial fluid The fluid filling the spaces between cells in an animal.

intertidal zone The shallow zone of the ocean adjacent to land and between the high- and low-tide lines.

intracellular digestion The hydrolysis of food inside vacuoles.

intracytoplasmic sperm injection (ICSI) The fertilization of an egg in the laboratory by the direct injection of a single sperm.

intrasexual selection A direct competition among individuals of one sex (usually the males in vertebrates) for mates of the opposite sex.

introduced species A species moved by humans, either intentionally or accidentally, from its native location to a new geographic region; also called non-native or exotic species.

intron (in′-tron) A noncoding, intervening sequence within a primary transcript that is removed from the transcript during RNA processing; also refers to the region of DNA from which this sequence was transcribed.

invagination The infolding, or pushing inward, of cells due to changes in cell shape.

invasive species A species, often introduced by humans, that takes hold outside its native range.

inversion An aberration in chromosome structure resulting from reattachment of a chromosomal fragment in a reverse orientation to the chromosome from which it originated.

invertebrate An animal without a backbone. Invertebrates make up 95% of animal species.

involution The process by which sheets of cells roll over the edge of the lip of the blastopore into the interior of the embryo during gastrulation.

ion (ī′-on) An atom or group of atoms that has gained or lost one or more electrons, thus acquiring a charge.

ion channel A transmembrane protein channel that allows a specific ion to flow across the membrane down its concentration gradient.

ionic bond (ī-on′-ik) A chemical bond resulting from the attraction between oppositely charged ions.

ionic compound A compound resulting from the formation of an ionic bond; also called a salt.

IPSP *See* inhibitory postsynaptic potential.

iris The colored part of the vertebrate eye, formed by the anterior portion of the choroid.

islets of Langerhans Clusters of endocrine cells within the pancreas that produce and secrete the hormones glucagon (from alpha cells) and insulin (from beta cells).

isomer (ī′-sō-mer) One of several compounds with the same molecular formula but different structures and therefore different properties. The three types of isomers are structural isomers, geometric isomers, and enantiomers.

isomorphic Referring to alternating generations in plants and certain algae in which the sporophytes and gametophytes look alike, although they differ in chromosome number.

isopod A member of one of the largest groups of crustaceans, which includes terrestrial, freshwater, and marine species. Among the terrestrial isopods are the pill bugs, or wood lice.

isotonic (ī′-sō-ton′-ik) Referring to a solution that, when surrounding a cell, has no effect on the passage of water into or out of the cell.

isotope (ī′-sō-tōp′) One of several atomic forms of an element, each with the same number of protons but a different number of neutrons, thus differing in atomic mass.

iteroparity Reproduction in which adults produce offspring over many years; also known as repeated reproduction.

joule (J) A unit of energy: 1 J = 0.239 cal; 1 cal = 4.184 J.

juvenile hormone A hormone in arthropods, secreted by the corpora allata (a pair of glands), that promotes the retention of larval characteristics.

juxtaglomerular apparatus (JGA) (juks′-tuh-gluh-mār′-yū-ler) A specialized tissue in nephrons that releases the enzyme renin in response to a drop in blood pressure or volume.

juxtamedullary nephron In mammals and birds, a nephron with a loop of Henle that extends far into the renal medulla.

karyogamy (kār′-ē-og′-uh-mē) The fusion of two nuclei, as part of syngamy (fertilization).

karyotype (kār′-ē-ō-tīp) A display of the chromosome pairs of a cell arranged by size and shape.

keystone species A species that is not necessarily abundant in a community yet exerts strong control on community structure by the nature of its ecological role or niche.

kilocalorie (kcal) A thousand calories; the amount of heat energy required to raise the temperature of 1 kg of water by 1°C.

kin selection Natural selection that favors altruistic behavior by enhancing the reproductive success of relatives.

kinesis (kuh-nē′-sis) A change in activity or turning rate in response to a stimulus.

kinetic energy (kuh-net′-ik) The energy associated with the relative motion of objects. Moving matter can perform work by imparting motion to other matter.

kinetochore (kuh-net′-uh-kōr) A structure of proteins attached to the centromere that links each sister chromatid to the mitotic spindle.

kinetoplastid A protist, such as a trypanosome, that has a single large mitochondrion that houses an organized mass of DNA.

kingdom A taxonomic category, the second broadest after domain.

K-selection Selection for life history traits that are sensitive to population density; also called density-dependent selection.

labia majora A pair of thick, fatty ridges that encloses and protects the rest of the vulva.

labia minora A pair of slender skin folds that surrounds the openings of the vagina and urethra.

labor A series of strong, rhythmic contractions of the uterus that expel a baby out of the uterus and vagina during childbirth.

lactation The continued production of milk from the mammary glands.

lacteal (lak′-tē-ul) A tiny lymph vessel extending into the core of an intestinal villus and serving as the destination for absorbed chylomicrons.

lactic acid fermentation Glycolysis followed by the conversion of pyruvate to lactate, with no release of carbon dioxide.

lagging strand A discontinuously synthesized DNA strand that elongates by means of Okazaki fragments, each synthesized in a 5′→3′ direction away from the replication fork.

lancelet Member of the subphylum Cephalochordata, small blade-shaped marine chordates that lack a backbone.

landmark A location indicator—a point of reference for orientation during navigation.

landscape An area containing several different ecosystems linked by exchanges of energy, materials, and organisms.

landscape ecology The study of how the spatial arrangement of habitat types affects the distribution and abundance of organisms and ecosystem processes.

large intestine The tubular portion of the vertebrate alimentary canal between the small intestine and the anus; functions mainly in water absorption and the formation of feces.

larva (lar′-vuh) (plural, **larvae**) A free-living, sexually immature form in some animal life cycles that may differ from the adult animal in morphology, nutrition, and habitat.

larynx (lār′-inks) The portion of the respiratory tract containing the vocal cords; also called the voice box.

lateral geniculate nucleus One of a pair of structures in the brain that are the destination for most of the ganglion cell axons that form the optic nerves.

lateral inhibition A process that sharpens the edges and enhances the contrast of a perceived image by inhibiting receptors lateral to those that have responded to light.

lateral line system A mechanoreceptor system consisting of a series of pores and receptor units along the sides of the body in fishes and aquatic amphibians; detects water movements made by the animal itself and by other moving objects.

lateral meristem (mār′-uh-stem) A meristem that thickens the roots and shoots of woody plants. The vascular cambium and cork cambium are lateral meristems.

lateral root A root that arises from the pericycle of an established root.

lateralization Segregation of functions in the cortex of the left and right hemispheres of the brain.

law of conservation of mass A physical law stating that matter can change form but cannot be created or destroyed. In a closed system, the mass of the system is constant.

law of independent assortment Mendel's second law, stating that each pair of alleles segregates, or assorts, independently of each other pair during gamete formation; applies when genes for two characters are located on different pairs of homologous chromosomes.

law of segregation Mendel's first law, stating that the two alleles in a pair segregate (separate) into different gametes during gamete formation.

leading strand The new complementary DNA strand synthesized continuously along the template strand toward the replication fork in the mandatory 5'→3' direction.

leaf The main photosynthetic organ of vascular plants.

leaf primordium A finger-like projection along the flank of a shoot apical meristem, from which a leaf arises.

learning The modification of behavior based on specific experiences.

lens The structure in an eye that focuses light rays onto the photoreceptors.

lenticel (len'-ti-sel) A small raised area in the bark of stems and roots that enables gas exchange between living cells and the outside air.

lepidosaur (leh-pid'-uh-sōr) Member of the reptilian group that includes lizards, snakes, and two species of New Zealand animals called tuataras.

leukocyte (lū'-kō-sīt') A blood cell that functions in fighting infections; also called a white blood cell.

Leydig cell (lī'-dig) A cell that produces testosterone and other androgens and is located between the seminiferous tubules of the testes.

lichen The symbiotic collective formed by the mutualistic association between a fungus and a photosynthetic alga or cyanobacterium.

life cycle The generation-to-generation sequence of stages in the reproductive history of an organism.

life history The traits that affect an organism's schedule of reproduction and survival.

life table A table of data summarizing mortality in a population.

ligament A fibrous connective tissue that joins bones together at joints.

ligand (lig'-und) A molecule that binds specifically to another molecule, usually a larger one.

ligand-gated ion channel A protein pore in cellular membranes that opens or closes in response to a signaling chemical (its ligand), allowing or blocking the flow of specific ions.

light chain One of the two types of polypeptide chains that make up an antibody molecule and B cell receptor; consists of a variable region, which contributes to the antigen-binding site, and a constant region.

light microscope (LM) An optical instrument with lenses that refract (bend) visible light to magnify images of specimens.

light reactions The first of two major stages in photosynthesis (preceding the Calvin cycle). These reactions, which occur on the thylakoid membranes of the chloroplast or on membranes of certain prokaryotes, convert solar energy to the chemical energy of ATP and NADPH, releasing oxygen in the process.

light-harvesting complex A complex of proteins associated with pigment molecules (including chlorophyll *a*, chlorophyll *b*, and carotenoids) that captures light energy and

transfers it to reaction-center pigments in a photosystem.

lignin (lig'-nin) A hard material embedded in the cellulose matrix of vascular plant cell walls that provides structural support in terrestrial species.

limiting nutrient An element that must be added for production to increase in a particular area.

limnetic zone In a lake, the well-lit, open surface waters farther from shore.

linear electron flow A route of electron flow during the light reactions of photosynthesis that involves both photosystems (I and II) and produces ATP, NADPH, and O_2. The net electron flow is from H_2O to $NADP^+$.

linkage map A genetic map based on the frequencies of recombination between markers during crossing over of homologous chromosomes.

linked genes Genes located close enough together on a chromosome that they tend to be inherited together.

lipid (lip'-id) One of a group of compounds, including fats, phospholipids, and steroids, that mix poorly, if at all, with water.

littoral zone In a lake, the shallow, well-lit waters close to shore.

liver The largest internal organ in the vertebrate body. The liver performs diverse functions, such as producing bile, preparing nitrogenous wastes for disposal, and detoxifying poisonous chemicals in the blood.

liverwort A small, herbaceous nonvascular plant that is a member of the phylum Hepatophyta.

loam The most fertile soil type, made up of roughly equal amounts of sand, silt, and clay.

lobe-fin Member of the vertebrate subgroup Sarcopterygii, osteichthyans with rod-shaped muscular fins, including coelacanths and lungfishes as well as the lineage that gave rise to tetrapods.

local regulator A secreted molecule that influences cells near where it is secreted.

locomotion Active motion from place to place.

locus (lō'-kus) (plural, **loci**) A specific place along the length of a chromosome where a given gene is located.

logistic population growth Population growth that levels off as population size approaches carrying capacity.

long-day plant A plant that flowers (usually in late spring or early summer) only when the light period is longer than a critical length.

long-term memory The ability to hold, associate, and recall information over one's lifetime.

long-term potentiation (LTP) An enhanced responsiveness to an action potential (nerve signal) by a receiving neuron.

loop of Henle The hairpin turn, with a descending and ascending limb, between the proximal and distal tubules of the vertebrate kidney; functions in water and salt reabsorption.

lophophore (lof'-uh-fōr) In some lophotrochozoan animals, including brachiopods, a crown of ciliated tentacles that surround the mouth and function in feeding.

lophotrochozoan Member of a group of animal phyla identified as a clade by molecular evidence. Lophotrochozoans include organisms that have lophophores or trochophore larvae.

low-density lipoprotein (LDL) A particle in the blood made up of cholesterol and other lipids surrounded by a single layer of phospholipids in which proteins are embedded. LDL carries more cholesterol than a related lipoprotein, HDL, and high LDL levels in the blood correlate with a tendency to develop blocked blood vessels and heart disease.

lung An infolded respiratory surface of a terrestrial vertebrate, land snail, or spider that connects to the atmosphere by narrow tubes.

luteal phase That portion of the ovarian cycle during which endocrine cells of the corpus luteum secrete female hormones.

luteinizing hormone (LH) (lū'-tē-uh-nī'-zing) A tropic hormone that is produced and secreted by the anterior pituitary and that stimulates ovulation in females and androgen production in males.

lycophyte (lī'-kuh-fīt) An informal name for a member of the phylum Lycophyta, which includes club mosses, spike mosses, and quillworts.

lymph The colorless fluid, derived from interstitial fluid, in the lymphatic system of vertebrates.

lymph node An organ located along a lymph vessel. Lymph nodes filter lymph and contain cells that attack viruses and bacteria.

lymphatic system A system of vessels and nodes, separate from the circulatory system, that returns fluid, proteins, and cells to the blood.

lymphocyte A type of white blood cell that mediates acquired immunity. The two main classes are B cells and T cells.

lysogenic cycle (lī'-sō-jen'-ik) A type of phage reproductive cycle in which the viral genome becomes incorporated into the bacterial host chromosome as a prophage and does not kill the host.

lysosome (lī'-suh-sōm) A membrane-enclosed sac of hydrolytic enzymes found in the cytoplasm of animal cells and some protists.

lysozyme (lī'-sō-zīm) An enzyme that destroys bacterial cell walls; in mammals, found in sweat, tears, and saliva.

lytic cycle (lit'-ik) A type of phage reproductive cycle resulting in the release of new phages by lysis (and death) of the host cell.

macroclimate Large-scale patterns in climate; the climate of an entire region.

macroevolution Evolutionary change above the species level, including the origin of a new group of organisms or a shift in the broad pattern of evolutionary change over a long period of time. Examples of macroevolutionary change include the appearance of major new features of organisms and the impact of mass extinctions on the diversity of life and its subsequent recovery.

macromolecule A giant molecule formed by the joining of smaller molecules, usually by a condensation reaction. Polysaccharides, proteins, and nucleic acids are macromolecules.

macronutrient A chemical substance that an organism must obtain in relatively large amounts. *See also* micronutrient.

macrophage (mak′-rō-fāj) A phagocytic cell present in many tissues that functions in innate immunity by destroying microbes and in acquired immunity as an antigen-presenting cell.

magnoliid Member of the angiosperm clade most closely related to eudicots. Extant examples are magnolias, laurels, and black pepper plants.

major depressive disorder A mood disorder characterized by feelings of sadness, lack of self-worth, emptiness, or loss of interest in nearly all things.

major histocompatibility complex (MHC) A family of genes that encode a large set of cell-surface proteins that function in antigen presentation. Foreign MHC molecules on transplanted tissue can trigger T cell responses that may lead to rejection of the transplant.

malignant tumor A cancerous tumor that is invasive enough to impair the functions of one or more organs.

malleus The first of three bones in the middle ear of mammals; also called the hammer.

malnourishment The long-term absence from the diet of one or more essential nutrients.

Malpighian tubule (mal-pig′-ē-un) A unique excretory organ of insects that empties into the digestive tract, removes nitrogenous wastes from the hemolymph, and functions in osmoregulation.

mammal Member of the class Mammalia, amniotes with mammary glands—glands that produce milk.

mammary glands Exocrine glands that secrete milk to nourish the young. These glands are characteristic of mammals.

mandible One of a pair of jaw-like feeding appendages found in myriapods, hexapods, and crustaceans.

mantle One of the three main parts of a mollusc; a fold of tissue that drapes over the mollusc's visceral mass and may secrete a shell. *See also* foot, visceral mass.

mantle cavity A water-filled chamber that houses the gills, anus, and excretory pores of a mollusc.

map unit A unit of measurement of the distance between genes. One map unit is equivalent to a 1% recombination frequency.

marine benthic zone The ocean floor.

mark-recapture method A sampling technique used to estimate the size of animal populations.

marsupial (mar-sū′-pē-ul) A mammal, such as a koala, kangaroo, or opossum, whose young complete their embryonic development inside a maternal pouch called the marsupium.

mass extinction Period of time when global environmental changes lead to the elimination of a large number of species throughout Earth.

mass number The sum of the number of protons and neutrons in an atom's nucleus.

mast cell A vertebrate body cell that produces histamine and other molecules that trigger inflammation in response to infection and in allergic reactions.

mate choice copying Behavior in which individuals in a population copy the mate choice of others, apparently as a result of social learning.

maternal effect gene A gene that, when mutant in the mother, results in a mutant phenotype in the offspring, regardless of the offspring's genotype. Maternal effect genes were first identified in *Drosophila*.

matter Anything that takes up space and has mass.

maximum likelihood As applied to systematics, a principle that states that when considering multiple phylogenetic hypotheses, one should take into account the hypothesis that reflects the most likely sequence of evolutionary events, given certain rules about how DNA changes over time.

maximum parsimony A principle that states that when considering multiple explanations for an observation, one should first investigate the simplest explanation that is consistent with the facts.

mechanoreceptor A sensory receptor that detects physical deformation in the body's environment associated with pressure, touch, stretch, motion, or sound.

medulla oblongata (meh-dul′-uh ob′-long-go′-tuh) The lowest part of the vertebrate brain, commonly called the medulla; a swelling of the hindbrain anterior to the spinal cord that controls autonomic, homeostatic functions, including breathing, heart and blood vessel activity, swallowing, digestion, and vomiting.

medusa (muh-dū′-suh) The floating, flattened, mouth-down version of the cnidarian body plan. The alternate form is the polyp.

megapascal (MPa) (meg′-uh-pas-kal′) A unit of pressure equivalent to about 10 atmospheres of pressure.

megaphyll (meh′-guh-fil) A leaf with a highly branched vascular system, characteristic of the vast majority of vascular plants.

megaspore A spore from a heterosporous plant species that develops into a female gametophyte.

meiosis (mī-ō′-sis) A modified type of cell division in sexually reproducing organisms consisting of two rounds of cell division but only one round of DNA replication. It results in cells with half the number of chromosome sets as the original cell.

meiosis I The first division of a two-stage process of cell division in sexually reproducing organisms that results in cells with half the number of chromosome sets as the original cell.

meiosis II The second division of a two-stage process of cell division in sexually reproducing organisms that results in cells with half the number of chromosome sets as the original cell.

melanocyte-stimulating hormone (MSH) A hormone produced and secreted by the anterior pituitary that regulates the activity of pigment-containing cells in the skin of some vertebrates.

melatonin A hormone secreted by the pineal gland that regulates body functions related to seasonal day length.

membrane potential The difference in electrical charge (voltage) across a cell's plasma membrane, due to the differential distribution of ions. Membrane potential affects the activity of excitable cells and the transmembrane movement of all charged substances.

memory cell One of a clone of long-lived lymphocytes, formed during the primary immune response, that remains in a lymphoid organ until activated by exposure to the same antigen that triggered its formation. Activated memory cells mount the secondary immune response.

menopause The cessation of ovulation and menstruation marking the end of a human female's reproductive years.

menstrual cycle (men′-strū-ul) In humans and certain other primates, a type of reproductive cycle in which the nonpregnant endometrium is shed through the cervix into the vagina.

menstrual flow phase That portion of the uterine (menstrual) cycle when menstrual bleeding occurs.

menstruation The shedding of portions of the endometrium during a uterine (menstrual) cycle.

meristem (mār′-uh-stem) Plant tissue that remains embryonic as long as the plant lives, allowing for indeterminate growth.

meristem identity gene A plant gene that promotes the switch from vegetative growth to flowering.

meroblastic cleavage (mār′-ō-blas′-tik) A type of cleavage in which there is incomplete division of a yolk-rich egg, characteristic of avian development.

mesoderm (mez′-ō-derm) The middle primary germ layer in an animal embryo; develops into the notochord, the lining of the coelom, muscles, skeleton, gonads, kidneys, and most of the circulatory system in species that have these structures.

mesohyl (mez′-ō-hīl) A gelatinous region between the two layers of cells of a sponge.

mesophyll (mez′-ō-fil) The ground tissue of a leaf, sandwiched between the upper and lower epidermis and specialized for photosynthesis.

mesophyll cell In C_4 plants, a type of loosely arranged photosynthetic cell located between the bundle sheath and the leaf surface.

messenger RNA (mRNA) A type of RNA, synthesized using a DNA template, that attaches to ribosomes in the cytoplasm and specifies the primary structure of a protein.

metabolic pathway A series of chemical reactions that either builds a complex molecule (anabolic pathway) or breaks down a complex molecule into simpler compounds (catabolic pathway).

metabolic rate The total amount of energy an animal uses in a unit of time.

metabolism (muh-tab′-uh-lizm) The totality of an organism's chemical reactions, consisting of catabolic and anabolic pathways, which manage the material and energy resources of the organism.

Glossary

metamorphosis (met′-uh-mōr′-fuh-sis) A developmental transformation that turns an animal larva into either an adult or an adult-like stage that is not yet sexually mature.

metanephridium (met′-uh-nuh-frid′-ē-um) (plural, **metanephridia**) An excretory organ found in many invertebrates that typically consists of tubules connecting ciliated internal openings to external openings.

metaphase The third stage of mitosis, in which the spindle is complete and the chromosomes, attached to microtubules at their kinetochores, are all aligned at the metaphase plate.

metaphase plate An imaginary plane midway between the two poles of a cell in metaphase on which the centromeres of all the duplicated chromosomes are located.

metapopulation A group of spatially separated populations of one species that interact through immigration and emigration.

metastasis (muh-tas′-tuh-sis) The spread of cancer cells to locations distant from their original site.

methanogen (meth-an′-ō-jen) An organism that obtains energy by using carbon dioxide to oxidize hydrogen, producing methane as a waste product; all known methanogens are in domain Archaea.

methyl group A chemical group consisting of a carbon bonded to three hydrogen atoms. The methyl group may be attached to a carbon or to a different atom.

microclimate Very fine scale patterns of climate, such as the specific climatic conditions underneath a log.

microevolution Evolutionary change below the species level; change in the allele frequencies in a population over generations.

microfilament A cable composed of actin proteins in the cytoplasm of almost every eukaryotic cell, making up part of the cytoskeleton and acting alone or with myosin to cause cell contraction; also known as an actin filament.

micronutrient An element that an organism needs in very small amounts and that functions as a component or cofactor of enzymes. *See also* macronutrient.

microphyll (mī′-krō-fil) In lycophytes, a small leaf with a single unbranched vein.

micropyle A pore in the integument(s) of an ovule.

microRNA (miRNA) A small, single-stranded RNA molecule, generated from a hairpin structure on a precursor RNA transcribed from a particular gene. The miRNA associates with one or more proteins in a complex that can degrade or prevent translation of an mRNA with a complementary sequence.

microspore A spore from a heterosporous plant species that develops into a male gametophyte.

microtubule A hollow rod composed of tubulin proteins that make up part of the cytoskeleton in all eukaryotic cells and is found in cilia and flagella.

microvillus (plural, **microvilli**) One of many fine, finger-like projections of the epithelial cells in the lumen of the small intestine that increase its surface area.

midbrain One of three ancestral and embryonic regions of the vertebrate brain; develops into sensory integrating and relay centers that send sensory information to the cerebrum.

middle ear One of three main regions of the vertebrate ear; in mammals, a chamber containing three small bones (the malleus, incus, and stapes) that convey vibrations from the eardrum to the oval window.

middle lamella (luh-mel′-uh) In plants, a thin layer of adhesive extracellular material, primarily pectins, found between the primary walls of adjacent young cells.

migration A regular, long-distance change in location.

mineral In nutrition, a simple nutrient that is inorganic and therefore cannot be synthesized.

mineralocorticoid A steroid hormone secreted by the adrenal cortex that regulates salt and water homeostasis.

minimum viable population (MVP) The smallest population size at which a species is able to sustain its numbers and survive.

mismatch repair The cellular process that uses specific enzymes to remove and replace incorrectly paired nucleotides.

missense mutation A base-pair substitution that results in a codon that codes for a different amino acid.

mitochondrial matrix The compartment of the mitochondrion enclosed by the inner membrane and containing enzymes and substrates for the citric acid cycle.

mitochondrion (mī′-tō-kon′-drē-un) (plural, **mitochondria**) An organelle in eukaryotic cells that serves as the site of cellular respiration.

mitosis (mī-tō′-sis) A process of nuclear division in eukaryotic cells conventionally divided into five stages: prophase, prometaphase, metaphase, anaphase, and telophase. Mitosis conserves chromosome number by allocating replicated chromosomes equally to each of the daughter nuclei.

mitotic (M) phase The phase of the cell cycle that includes mitosis and cytokinesis.

mitotic spindle An assemblage of microtubules and associated proteins that is involved in the movements of chromosomes during mitosis.

mixotroph An organism that is capable of both photosynthesis and heterotrophy.

model A representation of a theory or process.

model organism A particular species chosen for research into broad biological principles because it is representative of a larger group and usually easy to grow in a lab.

molarity A common measure of solute concentration, referring to the number of moles of solute per liter of solution.

mold Informal term for a fungus that grows as a filamentous fungus, producing haploid spores by mitosis and forming a visible mycelium.

mole (mol) The number of grams of a substance that equals its molecular weight in daltons and contains Avogadro's number of molecules.

molecular clock A method for estimating the time required for a given amount of evolutionary change, based on the observation that some regions of genomes appear to evolve at constant rates.

molecular formula A type of molecular notation representing the quantity of constituent atoms, but not the nature of the bonds that join them.

molecular mass The sum of the masses of all the atoms in a molecule; sometimes called molecular weight.

molecular systematics A scientific discipline that uses nucleic acids or other molecules in different species to infer evolutionary relationships.

molecule Two or more atoms held together by covalent bonds.

molting A process in ecdysozoans in which the exoskeleton is shed at intervals, allowing growth by the production of a larger exoskeleton.

monoclonal antibody (mon′-ō-klōn′-ul) Any of a preparation of antibodies that have been produced by a single clone of cultured cells and thus are all specific for the same epitope.

monocot Member of a clade consisting of flowering plants that have one embryonic seed leaf, or cotyledon.

monogamous (muh-nog′-uh-mus) Referring to a type of relationship in which one male mates with just one female.

monohybrid An organism that is heterozygous with respect to a single gene of interest. All the offspring from a cross between parents homozygous for different alleles are monohybrids. For example, parents of genotypes *AA* and *aa* produce a monohybrid of genotype *Aa*.

monomer (mon′-uh-mer) The subunit that serves as the building block of a polymer.

monophyletic (mon′-ō-fī-let′-ik) Pertaining to a group of taxa that consists of a common ancestor and all its descendants. A monophyletic taxon is equivalent to a clade.

monosaccharide (mon′-ō-sak′-uh-rīd) The simplest carbohydrate, active alone or serving as a monomer for disaccharides and polysaccharides. Also known as simple sugars, monosaccharides have molecular formulas that are generally some multiple of CH_2O.

monosomic Referring to a cell that has only one copy of a particular chromosome instead of the normal two.

morphogen A substance, such as Bicoid protein in *Drosophila*, that provides positional information in the form of a concentration gradient along an embryonic axis.

morphogenesis (mōr′-fō-jen′-uh-sis) The development of body shape and organization.

morphological species concept A definition of species in terms of measurable anatomical criteria.

morphology An organism's external form.

moss A small, herbaceous nonvascular plant that is a member of the phylum Bryophyta.

motor neuron A nerve cell that transmits signals from the brain or spinal cord to muscles or glands.

motor protein A protein that interacts with cytoskeletal elements and other cell components, producing movement of the whole cell or parts of the cell.

motor system An efferent branch of the vertebrate peripheral nervous system composed of motor neurons that carry signals to skeletal muscles in response to external stimuli.

motor unit A single motor neuron and all the muscle fibers it controls.

movement corridor A series of small clumps or a narrow strip of quality habitat (usable by organisms) that connects otherwise isolated patches of quality habitat.

MPF Maturation-promoting factor (M-phase-promoting factor); a protein complex required for a cell to progress from late interphase to mitosis. The active form consists of cyclin and a protein kinase.

mucus A viscous and slippery mixture of glycoproteins, cells, salts, and water that moistens and protects the membranes lining body cavities that open to the exterior.

Müllerian mimicry (myū-lār′-ē-un) A mutual mimicry by two unpalatable species.

multifactorial Referring to a phenotypic character that is influenced by multiple genes and environmental factors.

multigene family A collection of genes with similar or identical sequences, presumably of common origin.

multiple fruit A fruit derived from an inflorescence, a group of flowers tightly clustered together.

muscle tissue Tissue consisting of long muscle cells that can contract, either on its own or when stimulated by nerve impulses.

mutagen (myū′-tuh-jen) A chemical or physical agent that interacts with DNA and causes a mutation.

mutation (myū-tā′-shun) A change in the nucleotide sequence of an organism's DNA, ultimately creating genetic diversity. Mutations also can occur in the DNA or RNA of a virus.

mutualism (myū′-chū-ul-izm) A symbiotic relationship in which both participants benefit.

mycelium (mī-sē′-lē-um) The densely branched network of hyphae in a fungus.

mycorrhiza (mī′-kō-rī′-zuh) (plural, **mycorrhizae**) A mutualistic association of plant roots and fungus.

mycosis (mī-kō′-sis) General term for a fungal infection.

myelin sheath (mī′-uh-lin) Around the axon of a neuron, an insulating coat of cell membranes from Schwann cells or oligodendrocytes. It is interrupted by nodes of Ranvier, where action potentials are generated.

myofibril (mī′-ō-fī′-bril) A fibril collectively arranged in longitudinal bundles in muscle cells (fibers); composed of thin filaments of actin and a regulatory protein and thick filaments of myosin.

myoglobin (mī′-uh-glō′-bin) An oxygen-storing, pigmented protein in muscle cells.

myosin (mī′-uh-sin) A type of protein filament that acts as a motor protein with actin filaments to cause cell contraction.

myotonia (mī′-uh-tō′-nī-uh) Increased muscle tension, characteristic of sexual arousal in certain human tissues.

myriapod (mir′-ē-uh-pod′) A terrestrial arthropod with many body segments and one or two pairs of legs per segment. Millipedes and centipedes comprise the two classes of living myriapods.

NAD$^+$ Nicotinamide adenine dinucleotide, a coenzyme that can accept an electron and acts as an electron carrier in the electron transport chain.

NADP$^+$ Nicotinamide adenine dinucleotide phosphate, an electron acceptor that, as NADPH, temporarily stores energized electrons produced during the light reactions.

natural family planning A form of contraception that relies on refraining from sexual intercourse when conception is most likely to occur; also called the rhythm method.

natural killer (NK) cell A type of white blood cell that can kill tumor cells and virus-infected cells as part of innate immunity.

natural selection A process in which organisms with certain inherited characteristics are more likely to survive and reproduce than are organisms with other characteristics.

negative feedback A primary mechanism of homeostasis, whereby a change in a physiological variable triggers a response that counteracts the initial change.

negative pressure breathing A breathing system in which air is pulled into the lungs.

nematocyst (nem′-uh-tuh-sist′) In a cnidocyte of a cnidarian, a specialized capsule-like organelle containing a coiled thread that when discharged can penetrate the body wall of the prey.

nephron (nef′-ron) The tubular excretory unit of the vertebrate kidney.

neritic zone The shallow region of the ocean overlying the continental shelf.

nerve A ropelike bundle of neuron fibers (axons) tightly wrapped in connective tissue.

nerve net A weblike system of neurons, characteristic of radially symmetrical animals, such as hydra.

nervous system The fast-acting internal system of communication involving sensory receptors, networks of nerve cells, and connections to muscles and glands that respond to nerve signals; functions in concert with the endocrine system to effect internal regulation and maintain homeostasis.

nervous tissue Tissue made up of neurons and supportive cells.

net primary production (NPP) The gross primary production of an ecosystem minus the energy used by the producers for respiration.

neural crest cells In vertebrates, groups of cells along the sides of the neural tube where it pinches off from the ectoderm. The cells migrate to various parts of the embryo and form pigment cells in the skin and parts of the skull, teeth, adrenal glands, and peripheral nervous system.

neural plasticity The capacity of a nervous system to change with experience.

neural tube A tube of infolded ectodermal cells that runs along the anterior-posterior axis of a vertebrate, just dorsal to the notochord. It will give rise to the central nervous system.

neurohormone A molecule that is secreted by a neuron, travels in body fluids, and acts on specific target cells to change their functioning.

neuron (nyūr′-on) A nerve cell; the fundamental unit of the nervous system, having structure and properties that allow it to conduct signals by taking advantage of the electrical charge across its plasma membrane.

neuropeptide A relatively short chain of amino acids that serves as a neurotransmitter.

neurotransmitter A molecule that is released from the synaptic terminal of a neuron at a chemical synapse, diffuses across the synaptic cleft, and binds to the postsynaptic cell, triggering a response.

neutral theory The hypothesis that much evolutionary change in genes and proteins has no effect on fitness and therefore is not influenced by Darwinian natural selection.

neutral variation Genetic variation that does not appear to provide a selective advantage or disadvantage.

neutron A subatomic particle having no electrical charge (electrically neutral), with a mass of about 1.7×10^{-24} g, found in the nucleus of an atom.

neutrophil The most abundant type of white blood cell. Neutrophils are phagocytic and tend to self-destruct as they destroy foreign invaders, limiting their life span to a few days.

nitric oxide (NO) A gas produced by many types of cells that functions as a local regulator and as a neurotransmitter.

nitrogen cycle The natural process by which nitrogen, either from the atmosphere or from decomposed organic material, is converted by soil bacteria to compounds that can be assimilated by plants. This incorporated nitrogen is then taken in by other organisms and subsequently released, acted on by bacteria, and made available again to the nonliving environment.

nitrogen fixation The conversion of atmospheric nitrogen (N_2) to ammonia (NH_3). Biological nitrogen fixation is carried out by certain prokaryotes, some of which have mutualistic relationships with plants.

nociceptor (nō′-si-sep′-tur) A sensory receptor that responds to noxious or painful stimuli; also called a pain receptor.

node A point along the stem of a plant at which leaves are attached.

node of Ranvier (ron′-vē-ā′) Gap in the myelin sheath of certain axons where an action potential may be generated. In saltatory conduction, an action potential is regenerated at each node, appearing to "jump" along the axon from node to node.

nodule A swelling on the root of a legume. Nodules are composed of plant cells that contain nitrogen-fixing bacteria of the genus *Rhizobium*.

noncompetitive inhibitor A substance that reduces the activity of an enzyme by binding to a location remote from the active site, changing the enzyme's shape so that the active site no longer functions effectively.

nondisjunction An error in meiosis or mitosis in which members of a pair of homologous chromosomes or a pair of sister chromatids fail to separate properly from each other.

nonequilibrium model A model that maintains that communities change constantly after being buffeted by disturbances.

nonpolar covalent bond A type of covalent bond in which electrons are shared equally between two atoms of similar electronegativity.

nonsense mutation A mutation that changes an amino acid codon to one of the three stop codons, resulting in a shorter and usually nonfunctional protein.

norepinephrine A catecholamine that is chemically and functionally similar to epinephrine and acts as a hormone or neurotransmitter; also known as noradrenaline.

norm of reaction The range of phenotypes produced by a single genotype, due to environmental influences.

normal range An upper and lower limit of a variable.

Northern blotting A technique that enables specific nucleotide sequences to be detected in a sample of mRNA. It involves gel electrophoresis of RNA molecules and their transfer to a membrane (blotting), followed by nucleic acid hybridization with a labeled probe.

northern coniferous forest A terrestrial biome characterized by long, cold winters and dominated by cone-bearing trees.

no-till agriculture A plowing technique that involves creating furrows, resulting in minimal disturbance of the soil.

notochord (nō'-tuh-kord') A longitudinal, flexible rod made of tightly packed mesodermal cells that runs along the anterior-posterior axis of a chordate in the dorsal part of the body.

nuclear envelope The double membrane in a eukaryotic cell that encloses the nucleus, separating it from the cytoplasm.

nuclear lamina A netlike array of protein filaments lining the inner surface of the nuclear envelope; it helps maintain the shape of the nucleus.

nucleariid Member of a group of unicellular, amoeboid protists that are more closely related to fungi than they are to other protists.

nuclease An enzyme that cuts DNA or RNA, either removing one or a few bases or hydrolyzing the DNA or RNA completely into its component nucleotides.

nucleic acid (nū-klā'-ik) A polymer (polynucleotide) consisting of many nucleotide monomers; serves as a blueprint for proteins and, through the actions of proteins, for all cellular activities. The two types are DNA and RNA.

nucleic acid hybridization The process of base pairing between a gene and a complementary sequence on another nucleic acid molecule.

nucleic acid probe In DNA technology, a labeled single-stranded nucleic acid molecule used to locate a specific nucleotide sequence in a nucleic acid sample. Molecules of the probe hydrogen-bond to the complementary sequence wherever it occurs; radioactive or other labeling of the probe allows its location to be detected.

nucleoid (nū'-klē-oyd) A dense region of DNA in a prokaryotic cell.

nucleolus (nū-klē'-ō-lus) (plural, **nucleoli**) A specialized structure in the nucleus, consisting of chromatin regions containing ribosomal RNA genes along with ribosomal proteins imported from the cytoplasmic site of rRNA synthesis and ribosomal subunit assembly. *See also* ribosome.

nucleosome (nū'-klē-ō-sōm') The basic, bead-like unit of DNA packing in eukaryotes, consisting of a segment of DNA wound around a protein core composed of two copies of each of four types of histone.

nucleotide (nū'-klē-ō-tīd') The building block of a nucleic acid, consisting of a five-carbon sugar covalently bonded to a nitrogenous base and a phosphate group.

nucleotide excision repair A repair system that removes and then correctly replaces a damaged segment of DNA using the undamaged strand as a guide.

nucleus (1) An atom's central core, containing protons and neutrons. (2) The chromosome-containing organelle of a eukaryotic cell. (3) A cluster of neurons.

nutrition The process by which an organism takes in and makes use of food substances.

obligate aerobe (ob'-lig-et ār'-ōb) An organism that requires oxygen for cellular respiration and cannot live without it.

obligate anaerobe (ob'-lig-et an'-uh-rōb) An organism that only carries out fermentation or anaerobic respiration. Such organisms cannot use oxygen and in fact may be poisoned by it.

oceanic pelagic zone Most of the ocean's waters far from shore, constantly mixed by ocean currents.

odorant A molecule that can be detected by sensory receptors of the olfactory system.

Okazaki fragment (ō'-kah-zah'-kē) A short segment of DNA synthesized away from the replication fork on a template strand during DNA replication, many of which are joined together to make up the lagging strand of newly synthesized DNA.

olfaction The sense of smell.

oligodendrocyte A type of glial cell that forms insulating myelin sheaths around the axons of neurons in the central nervous system.

oligotrophic lake A nutrient-poor, clear lake with few phytoplankton.

ommatidium (ōm'-uh-tid'-ē-um) (plural, **ommatidia**) One of the facets of the compound eye of arthropods and some polychaete worms.

omnivore An animal that regularly eats animals as well as plants or algae.

oncogene (on'-kō-jēn) A gene found in viral or cellular genomes that is involved in triggering molecular events that can lead to cancer.

oocyte A cell in the female reproductive system that differentiates to form an egg.

oogenesis (ō'-uh-jen'-uh-sis) The process in the ovary that results in the production of female gametes.

oogonium (ō'-uh- gō'-nē-em) A cell that divides mitotically to form oocytes.

oomycete (ō'-uh-mī'- sēt) A protist with flagellated cells, such as a water mold, white rust, or downy mildew, that acquires nutrition mainly as a decomposer or plant parasite.

open circulatory system A circulatory system in which fluid called hemolymph bathes the tissues and organs directly and there is no distinction between the circulating fluid and the interstitial fluid.

operant conditioning (op'-er-ent) A type of associative learning in which an animal learns to associate one of its own behaviors with a reward or punishment and then tends to repeat or avoid that behavior; also called trial-and-error learning.

operator In bacterial DNA, a sequence of nucleotides near the start of an operon to which an active repressor can attach. The binding of the repressor prevents RNA polymerase from attaching to the promoter and transcribing the genes of the operon.

operculum (ō-per'-kyuh-lum) In aquatic osteichthyans, a protective bony flap that covers and protects the gills.

operon (op'-er-on) A unit of genetic function found in bacteria and phages, consisting of a promoter, an operator, and a coordinately regulated cluster of genes whose products function in a common pathway.

opisthokont (uh-pis'-thuh-kont') Member of the diverse clade Opisthokonta, organisms that descended from an ancestor with a posterior flagellum, including fungi, animals, and certain protists.

opposable thumb A thumb that can touch the ventral surface of the fingertips of all four fingers.

opsin A membrane protein bound to a light-absorbing pigment molecule.

optic chiasm The place where the two optic nerves meet and where the sensations from the left visual field of both eyes are transmitted to the right side of the brain and the sensations from the right visual field of both eyes are transmitted to the left side of the brain.

optimal foraging model The basis for analyzing behavior as a compromise between feeding costs and feeding benefits.

oral cavity The mouth of an animal.

orbital The three-dimensional space where an electron is found 90% of the time.

order In classification, the taxonomic category above the level of family.

organ A specialized center of body function composed of several different types of tissues.

organ identity gene A plant homeotic gene that uses positional information to determine which emerging leaves develop into which types of floral organs.

organ of Corti The actual hearing organ of the vertebrate ear, located in the floor of the cochlear duct in the inner ear; contains the receptor cells (hair cells) of the ear.

organ system A group of organs that work together in performing vital body functions.

organelle (ōr-guh-nel′) Any of several membrane-enclosed structures with specialized functions, suspended in the cytosol of eukaryotic cells.

organic chemistry The study of carbon compounds (organic compounds).

organismal ecology The branch of ecology concerned with the morphological, physiological, and behavioral ways in which individual organisms meet the challenges posed by their biotic and abiotic environments.

organogenesis (ōr-gan′-ō-jen′-uh-sis) The process in which organ rudiments develop from the three germ layers after gastrulation.

orgasm Rhythmic, involuntary contractions of certain reproductive structures in both sexes during the human sexual response cycle.

origin of replication Site where the replication of a DNA molecule begins, consisting of a specific sequence of nucleotides.

orthologous genes Homologous genes that are found in different species because of speciation.

osculum (os′-kyuh-lum) A large opening in a sponge that connects the spongocoel to the environment.

osmoconformer An animal that is isoosmotic with its environment.

osmolarity (oz′-mō-lār′-uh-tē) Solute concentration expressed as molarity.

osmoregulation Regulation of solute concentrations and water balance by a cell or organism.

osmoregulator An animal that controls its internal osmolarity independent of the external environment.

osmosis (oz-mō′-sis) The diffusion of water across a selectively permeable membrane.

osmotic potential A component of water potential that is proportional to the osmolarity of a solution and that measures the effect of solutes on the direction of water movement; also called solute potential, it can be either zero or negative.

osteichthyan (os′-tē-ik′-thē-an) Member of a vertebrate subgroup with jaws and mostly bony skeletons.

outer ear One of three main regions of the ear in reptiles (including birds) and mammals; made up of the auditory canal and, in many birds and mammals, the pinna.

outgroup A species or group of species from an evolutionary lineage that is known to have diverged before the lineage that contains the group of species being studied. An outgroup is selected so that its members are closely related to the group of species being studied, but not as closely related as any study-group members are to each other.

oval window In the vertebrate ear, a membrane-covered gap in the skull bone, through which sound waves pass from the middle ear to the inner ear.

ovarian cycle (ō-vār′-ē-un) The cyclic recurrence of the follicular phase, ovulation, and the luteal phase in the mammalian ovary, regulated by hormones.

ovary (ō′-vuh-rē) (1) In flowers, the portion of a carpel in which the egg-containing ovules develop. (2) In animals, the structure that produces female gametes and reproductive hormones.

overnourishment The consumption of more calories than the body needs for normal metabolism.

oviduct (ō′-vuh-duct) A tube passing from the ovary to the vagina in invertebrates or to the uterus in vertebrates, where it is also known as a fallopian tube.

oviparous (ō-vip′-uh-rus) Referring to a type of development in which young hatch from eggs laid outside the mother's body.

ovoviviparous (ō′-vō-vī-vip′-uh-rus) Referring to a type of development in which young hatch from eggs that are retained in the mother's uterus.

ovulation The release of an egg from an ovary. In humans, an ovarian follicle releases an egg during each uterine (menstrual) cycle.

ovule (o′-vyūl) A structure that develops within the ovary of a seed plant and contains the female gametophyte.

oxidation The loss of electrons from a substance involved in a redox reaction.

oxidative phosphorylation (fos′-fōr-uh-lā′-shun) The production of ATP using energy derived from the redox reactions of an electron transport chain; the third major stage of cellular respiration.

oxidizing agent The electron acceptor in a redox reaction.

oxytocin (ok′-si-tō′-sen) A hormone produced by the hypothalamus and released from the posterior pituitary. It induces contractions of the uterine muscles during labor and causes the mammary glands to eject milk during nursing.

P generation The parent individuals from which offspring are derived in studies of inheritance; P stands for "parental."

P site One of a ribosome's three binding sites for tRNA during translation. The P site holds the tRNA carrying the growing polypeptide chain. (P stands for peptidyl tRNA.)

***p53* gene** A tumor-suppressor gene that codes for a specific transcription factor that promotes the synthesis of cell cycle–inhibiting proteins.

paedomorphosis (pē′-duh-mōr′-fuh-sis) The retention in an adult organism of the juvenile features of its evolutionary ancestors.

pain receptor A sensory receptor that responds to noxious or painful stimuli; also called a nociceptor.

paleoanthropology The study of human origins and evolution.

paleontology (pā′-lē-un-tol′-ō-jē) The scientific study of fossils.

pancreas (pan′-krē-us) A gland with the following dual functions: The nonendocrine portion functions in digestion, secreting enzymes and an alkaline solution into the small intestine via a duct; the ductless endocrine portion functions in homeostasis, secreting the hormones insulin and glucagon into the blood.

pandemic A global epidemic.

Pangaea (pan-jē′-uh) The supercontinent that formed near the end of the Paleozoic era, when plate movements brought all the landmasses of Earth together.

parabasalid A protist, such as a trichomonad, with modified mitochondria.

paracrine Referring to a secreted molecule that acts on a neighboring cell.

paralogous genes Homologous genes that are found in the same genome as a result of gene duplication.

paraphyletic (pār′-uh-fī-let′-ik) Pertaining to a group of taxa that consists of a common ancestor and some, but not all, of its descendants.

parareptile First major group of reptiles to emerge, consisting mostly of large, stocky quadrupedal herbivores; died out in the late Triassic period.

parasite (pār′-uh-sīt) An organism that feeds on the cell contents, tissues, or body fluids of another species (the host) while in or on the host organism. Parasites harm but usually do not kill their host.

parasitism (pār′-uh-sit-izm) A symbiotic relationship in which one organism, the parasite, benefits at the expense of another, the host, by living either within or on the host.

parasympathetic division One of three divisions of the autonomic nervous system; generally enhances body activities that gain and conserve energy, such as digestion and reduced heart rate.

parathyroid gland Any of four small endocrine glands, embedded in the surface of the thyroid gland, that secrete parathyroid hormone.

parathyroid hormone (PTH) A hormone secreted by the parathyroid glands that raises blood calcium level by promoting calcium release from bone and calcium retention by the kidneys.

parenchyma cell (puh-ren′-ki-muh) A relatively unspecialized plant cell type that carries out most of the metabolism, synthesizes and stores organic products, and develops into a more differentiated cell type.

parental type An offspring with a phenotype that matches one of the parental phenotypes; also refers to the phenotype itself.

Parkinson's disease A progressive brain disease characterized by difficulty in initiating movements, slowness of movement, and rigidity.

parthenogenesis (par'-thuh-nō'-jen'-uh-sis) Asexual reproduction in which females produce offspring from unfertilized eggs.

partial pressure The pressure exerted by a particular gas in a mixture of gases (for instance, the pressure exerted by oxygen in air).

passive immunity Short-term immunity conferred by the transfer of antibodies, as occurs in the transfer of maternal antibodies to a fetus or nursing infant.

passive transport The diffusion of a substance across a biological membrane with no expenditure of energy.

pathogen An organism or virus that causes disease.

pattern formation The development of a multicellular organism's spatial organization, the arrangement of organs and tissues in their characteristic places in three-dimensional space.

peat Extensive deposits of partially decayed organic material formed primarily from the wetland moss *Sphagnum.*

pedigree A diagram of a family tree showing the occurrence of heritable characters in parents and offspring over multiple generations.

penis The copulatory structure of male mammals.

PEP carboxylase An enzyme that adds CO_2 to phosphoenolpyruvate (PEP) to form oxaloacetate in C_4 plants. It acts prior to photosynthesis.

pepsin An enzyme present in gastric juice that begins the hydrolysis of proteins.

pepsinogen The inactive form of pepsin that is first secreted by chief cells located in gastric pits of the stomach.

peptide bond The covalent bond between the carboxyl group on one amino acid and the amino group on another, formed by a dehydration reaction.

peptidoglycan (pep'-tid-ō-glī'-kan) A type of polymer in bacterial cell walls consisting of modified sugars cross-linked by short polypeptides.

perception The interpretation of sensory system input by the brain.

perennial (puh-ren'-ē-ul) A flowering plant that lives for many years.

pericycle The outermost layer in the vascular cylinder from which lateral roots arise.

periderm (par'-uh-derm') The protective coat that replaces the epidermis in woody plants during secondary growth, formed of the cork and cork cambium.

peripheral nervous system (PNS) The sensory and motor neurons that connect to the central nervous system.

peripheral protein A protein loosely bound to the surface of a membrane or to part of an integral protein and not embedded in the lipid bilayer.

peristalsis (par'-uh-stal'-sis) (1) Alternating waves of contraction and relaxation in the smooth muscles lining the alimentary canal that push food along the canal. (2) A type of movement on land produced by rhythmic waves of muscle contractions passing from front to back, as in many annelids.

peristome A ring of interlocking, tooth-like structures on the upper part of a moss capsule (sporangium), often specialized for gradual spore discharge.

peritubular capillary One of the tiny blood vessels that form a network surrounding the proximal and distal tubules in the kidney.

permafrost A permanently frozen soil layer.

peroxisome (puh-rok'-suh-sōm') An organelle containing enzymes that transfer hydrogen (H_2) from various substrates to oxygen (O_2), producing and then degrading hydrogen peroxide (H_2O_2).

petal A modified leaf of a flowering plant. Petals are the often colorful parts of a flower that advertise it to insects and other pollinators.

petiole (pet'-ē-ōl) The stalk of a leaf, which joins the leaf to a node of the stem.

pH A measure of hydrogen ion concentration equal to $-\log [H^+]$ and ranging in value from 0 to 14.

phage (fāj) A virus that infects bacteria; also called a bacteriophage.

phagocytosis (fag'-ō-sī-tō'-sis) A type of endocytosis in which large particulate substances are taken up by a cell. It is carried out by some protists and by certain immune cells of animals (in mammals, mainly macrophages, neutrophils, and dendritic cells).

pharyngeal cleft (fuh-rin'-jē-ul) In chordate embryos, one of the grooves that separate a series of pouches along the sides of the pharynx and may develop into a pharyngeal slit.

pharyngeal slit (fuh-rin'-jē-ul) In chordate embryos, one of the slits that form from the pharyngeal clefts and communicate to the outside, later developing into gill slits in many vertebrates.

pharynx (far'-inks) (1) An area in the vertebrate throat where air and food passages cross. (2) In flatworms, the muscular tube that protrudes from the ventral side of the worm and ends in the mouth.

phase change A shift from one developmental phase to another.

phenotype (fē'-nō-tīp) The physical and physiological traits of an organism, which are determined by its genetic makeup.

pheromone (far'-uh-mōn) In animals and fungi, a small molecule released into the environment that functions in communication between members of the same species. In animals, it acts much like a hormone in influencing physiology and behavior.

phloem (flō'-em) Vascular plant tissue consisting of living cells arranged into elongated tubes that transport sugar and other organic nutrients throughout the plant.

phloem sap The sugar-rich solution carried through sieve tubes.

phosphate group A chemical group consisting of a phosphorus atom bonded to four oxygen atoms; important in energy transfer.

phospholipid (fos'-fō-lip'-id) A lipid made up of glycerol joined to two fatty acids and a phosphate group. The hydrocarbon chains of the fatty acids act as nonpolar, hydrophobic tails, while the rest of the molecule acts as a polar, hydrophilic head. Phospholipids form bilayers that function as biological membranes.

phosphorylated Referring to a molecule that is covalently bonded to a phosphate group.

photic zone (fō'-tic) The narrow top layer of an ocean or lake, where light penetrates sufficiently for photosynthesis to occur.

photoautotroph (fō'-tō-ot'-ō-trōf) An organism that harnesses light energy to drive the synthesis of organic compounds from carbon dioxide.

photoheterotroph (fō'-tō-het'-er-ō-trōf) An organism that uses light to generate ATP but must obtain carbon in organic form.

photomorphogenesis Effects of light on plant morphology.

photon (fō'-ton) A quantum, or discrete quantity, of light energy that behaves as if it were a particle.

photoperiodism (fō'-tō-pēr'-ē-ō-dizm) A physiological response to photoperiod, the relative lengths of night and day. An example of photoperiodism is flowering.

photophosphorylation (fō'-tō-fos'-fōr-uh-lā'-shun) The process of generating ATP from ADP and phosphate by means of a proton-motive force generated across the thylakoid membrane of the chloroplast or the membrane of certain prokaryotes during the light reactions of photosynthesis.

photoreceptor An electromagnetic receptor that detects the radiation known as visible light.

photorespiration A metabolic pathway that consumes oxygen and ATP, releases carbon dioxide, and decreases photosynthetic output. Photorespiration generally occurs on hot, dry, bright days, when stomata close and the oxygen concentration in the leaf exceeds that of carbon dioxide.

photosynthesis (fō'-tō-sin'-thi-sis) The conversion of light energy to chemical energy that is stored in sugars or other organic compounds; occurs in plants, algae, and certain prokaryotes.

photosystem A light-capturing unit located in the thylakoid membrane of the chloroplast or in the membrane of some prokaryotes, consisting of a reaction-center complex surrounded by numerous light-harvesting complexes. There are two types of photosystems, I and II; they absorb light best at different wavelengths.

photosystem I (PS I) One of two light-capturing units in a chloroplast's thylakoid membrane or in the membrane of some prokaryotes; it has two molecules of P700 chlorophyll *a* at its reaction center.

photosystem II (PS II) One of two light-capturing units in a chloroplast's thylakoid membrane or in the membrane of some prokaryotes; it has two molecules of P680 chlorophyll *a* at its reaction center.

phototropism (fō'-tō-trō'-pizm) Growth of a plant shoot toward or away from light.

phragmoplast (frag'-mō-plast') An alignment of cytoskeletal elements and Golgi-derived vesicles that forms across the midline of a dividing plant cell.

phyllotaxy (fil'-uh-tak'-sē) The arrangement of leaves on the shoot of a plant.

PhyloCode System of classification of organisms based on evolutionary relationships: Only groups that include a common ancestor and all of its descendents are named.

phylogenetic bracketing An approach in which features shared by two groups of organisms are predicted (by parsimony) to be present in their common ancestor and all of its descendants.

phylogenetic species concept A definition of species as the smallest group of individuals that share a common ancestor, forming one branch on the tree of life.

phylogenetic tree A branching diagram that represents a hypothesis about the evolutionary history of a group of organisms.

phylogeny (fī-loj'-uh-nē) The evolutionary history of a species or group of related species.

phylum (fī'-lum) (plural, **phyla**) In classification, the taxonomic category above class.

physical map A genetic map in which the actual physical distances between genes or other genetic markers are expressed, usually as the number of base pairs along the DNA.

physiology The processes and functions of an organism and their study.

phytochrome (fī'-tuh-krōm) A type of light receptor in plants that mostly absorbs red light and regulates many plant responses, such as seed germination and shade avoidance.

phytoremediation An emerging nondestructive biotechnology that seeks to cheaply reclaim contaminated areas by taking advantage of some plant species' ability to extract heavy metals and other pollutants from the soil and to concentrate them in easily harvested portions of the plant.

pineal gland (pī'-nē-ul) A small gland on the dorsal surface of the vertebrate forebrain that secretes the hormone melatonin.

pinocytosis (pī'-nō-sī-tō'-sis) A type of endocytosis in which the cell ingests extracellular fluid and its dissolved solutes.

pistil A single carpel or a group of fused carpels.

pith Ground tissue that is internal to the vascular tissue in a stem; in many monocot roots, parenchyma cells that form the central core of the vascular cylinder.

pituitary gland (puh-tū'-uh-tār'-ē) An endocrine gland at the base of the hypothalamus; consists of a posterior lobe (neurohypophysis), which stores and releases two hormones produced by the hypothalamus, and an anterior lobe (adenohypophysis), which produces and secretes many hormones that regulate diverse body functions.

placenta (pluh-sen'-tuh) A structure in the pregnant uterus for nourishing a viviparous fetus with the mother's blood supply; formed from the uterine lining and embryonic membranes.

placental transfer cell A plant cell that enhances the transfer of nutrients from parent to embryo.

placoderm A member of an extinct class of fishlike vertebrates that had jaws and were enclosed in a tough outer armor.

planarian A free-living flatworm found in unpolluted ponds and streams.

Plantae (plan'-tā) The kingdom that consists of multicellular eukaryotes that carry out photosynthesis.

plasma (plaz'-muh) The liquid matrix of blood in which the cells are suspended.

plasma cell The antibody-secreting effector cell of humoral immunity; arises from antigen-stimulated B cells.

plasma membrane The membrane at the boundary of every cell that acts as a selective barrier, regulating the cell's chemical composition.

plasmid (plaz'-mid) A small, circular, double-stranded DNA molecule that carries accessory genes separate from those of a bacterial chromosome. Plasmids are also found in some eukaryotes, such as yeasts.

plasmodesma (plaz'-mō-dez'-muh) (plural, **plasmodesmata**) An open channel in the cell wall of a plant through which strands of cytosol connect from an adjacent cell.

plasmodial slime mold (plaz-mō'-dē-ul) A type of protist that has amoeboid cells, flagellated cells, and a plasmodial feeding stage in its life cycle.

plasmodium A single mass of cytoplasm containing many diploid nuclei that forms during the life cycle of some slime molds.

plasmogamy (plaz-moh'-guh-mē) The fusion of the cytoplasm of cells from two individuals; occurs as one stage of syngamy (fertilization).

plasmolysis (plaz-mol'-uh-sis) A phenomenon in walled cells in which the cytoplasm shrivels and the plasma membrane pulls away from the cell wall; occurs when the cell loses water to a hypertonic environment.

plastid One of a family of closely related organelles that includes chloroplasts, chromoplasts, and amyloplasts (leucoplasts). Plastids are found in cells of photosynthetic organisms.

platelet A pinched-off cytoplasmic fragment of a specialized bone marrow cell. Platelets circulate in the blood and are important in blood clotting.

pleiotropy (plī-o'-truh-pē) The ability of a single gene to have multiple effects.

pluripotent Describing a cell that can give rise to many, but not all, parts of an organism.

point mutation A change in a gene at a single nucleotide pair.

polar covalent bond A covalent bond between atoms that differ in electronegativity. The shared electrons are pulled closer to the more electronegative atom, making it slightly negative and the other atom slightly positive.

polar molecule A molecule (such as water) with opposite charges on different ends of the molecule.

polarity A lack of symmetry; structural differences in opposite ends of an organism or structure, such as the root end and shoot end of a plant.

pollen grain In seed plants, a structure consisting of the male gametophyte enclosed within a pollen wall.

pollen tube A tube formed after germination of the pollen grain that functions in the delivery of sperm to the ovule.

pollination (pol'-uh-nā'-shun) The transfer of pollen to the part of a seed plant containing the ovules, a process required for fertilization.

poly-A tail A sequence of 50 to 250 adenine nucleotides added onto the 3' end of a pre-mRNA molecule.

polyandry (pol'-ē-an'-drē) A polygamous mating system involving one female and many males.

polygamous Referring to a type of relationship in which an individual of one sex mates with several of the other.

polygenic inheritance (pol'-ē-jen'-ik) An additive effect of two or more genes on a single phenotypic character.

polygyny (puh-lij'-en-ē) A polygamous mating system involving one male and many females.

polymer (pol'-uh-mer) A long molecule consisting of many similar or identical monomers linked together.

polymerase chain reaction (PCR) (puh-lim'-uh-rās) A technique for amplifying DNA *in vitro* by incubating it with specific primers, a heat-resistant DNA polymerase, and nucleotides.

polynucleotide (pol'-ē-nū'-klē-ō-tīd) A polymer consisting of many nucleotide monomers in a chain; nucleotides can be those of DNA or RNA.

polyp The sessile variant of the cnidarian body plan. The alternate form is the medusa.

polypeptide (pol'-ē-pep'-tīd) A polymer (chain) of many amino acids linked together by peptide bonds.

polyphyletic (pol'-ē-fī-let'-ik) Pertaining to a group of taxa derived from two or more different ancestors.

polyploidy (pol'-ē-ploy'-dē) A chromosomal alteration in which the organism possesses more than two complete chromosome sets. It is the result of an accident of cell division.

polyribosome (polysome) (pol'-ē-rī'-bō-sōm') A group of several ribosomes attached to, and translating, the same messenger RNA molecule.

polysaccharide (pol'-ē-sak'-uh-rīd) A polymer of many monosaccharides, formed by dehydration reactions.

polytomy (puh-lit'-uh-mē) In a phylogenetic tree, a branch point from which more than two descendant taxa emerge. A polytomy indicates that the evolutionary relationships among the descendant taxa are not yet clear.

pons Portion of the brain that participates in certain automatic, homeostatic functions, such as regulating the breathing centers in the medulla.

population A localized group of individuals of the same species that can interbreed, producing fertile offspring.

population dynamics The study of how complex interactions between biotic and abiotic factors influence variations in population size.

population ecology The study of populations in relation to their environment, including environmental influences on population density and distribution, age structure, and variations in population size.

positional information Molecular cues that control pattern formation in an animal or plant embryonic structure by indicating a cell's location relative to the organism's body axes. These cues elicit a response by genes that regulate development.

positive feedback A physiological control mechanism in which a change in a variable triggers mechanisms that amplify the change.

positive pressure breathing A breathing system in which air is forced into the lungs.

posterior Pertaining to the rear, or tail end, of a bilaterally symmetrical animal.

posterior pituitary Also called the neurohypophysis; an extension of the hypothalamus composed of nervous tissue that secretes oxytocin and antidiuretic hormone made in the hypothalamus; a temporary storage site for these hormones.

postsynaptic cell The target cell at a synapse.

postzygotic barrier (pōst′-zī-got′-ik) A reproductive barrier that prevent hybrid zygotes produced by two different species from developing into viable, fertile adults.

potential energy The energy that matter possesses as a result of its location or spatial arrangement (structure).

predation An interaction between species in which one species, the predator, eats the other, the prey.

pregnancy The condition of carrying one or more embryos in the uterus.

preprophase band Microtubules in the cortex (outer cytoplasm) of a cell that are concentrated into a ring.

prepuce (prē′-pyūs) A fold of skin covering the head of the clitoris or penis.

pressure potential (Ψ_P) A component of water potential that consists of the physical pressure on a solution, which can be positive, zero, or negative.

presynaptic cell The transmitting cell at a synapse.

prezygotic barrier (prē′-zī-got′-ik) A reproductive barrier that impedes mating between species or hinders fertilization if interspecific mating is attempted.

primary cell wall In plants, a relatively thin and flexible layer first secreted by a young cell.

primary consumer An herbivore; an organism that eats plants or other autotrophs.

primary electron acceptor In the thylakoid membrane of a chloroplast or in the membrane of some prokaryotes, a specialized molecule that shares the reaction-center complex with a pair of chlorophyll *a* molecules and that accepts an electron from them.

primary growth Growth produced by apical meristems, lengthening stems and roots.

primary immune response The initial acquired immune response to an antigen, which appears after a lag of about 10 to 17 days.

primary oocyte (ō′-uh-sīt) An oocyte prior to completion of meiosis I.

primary plant body The tissues produced by apical meristems, which lengthen stems and roots.

primary producer An autotroph, usually a photosynthetic organism. Collectively, autotrophs make up the trophic level of an ecosystem that ultimately supports all other levels.

primary production The amount of light energy converted to chemical energy (organic compounds) by autotrophs in an ecosystem during a given time period.

primary structure The level of protein structure referring to the specific sequence of amino acids.

primary succession A type of ecological succession that occurs in an area where there were originally no organisms present and where soil has not yet formed.

primary transcript An initial RNA transcript; also called pre-mRNA when transcribed from a protein-coding gene.

primary visual cortex The destination in the occipital lobe of the cerebrum for most of the axons from the lateral geniculate nuclei.

primase An enzyme that joins RNA nucleotides to make the primer using the parental DNA strand as a template.

primer A short stretch of RNA with a free 3′ end, bound by complementary base pairing to the template strand, that is elongated with DNA nucleotides during DNA replication.

primitive streak A thickening along the future anterior-posterior axis on the surface of an early avian or mammalian embryo, caused by a piling up of cells as they congregate at the midline before moving into the embryo.

prion An infectious agent that is a misfolded version of a normal cellular protein. Prions appear to increase in number by converting correctly folded versions of the protein to more prions.

problem solving The cognitive activity of devising a method to proceed from one state to another in the face of real or apparent obstacles.

producer An organism that produces organic compounds from CO_2 by harnessing light energy (in photosynthesis) or by oxidizing inorganic chemicals (in chemosynthetic reactions carried out by some prokaryotes).

product A material resulting from a chemical reaction.

production efficiency The percentage of energy stored in food that is not used for respiration or eliminated as waste.

progesterone A steroid hormone that prepares the uterus for pregnancy; the major progestin in mammals.

progestin Any steroid hormone with progesterone-like activity.

progymnosperm (prō′-jim′-nō-sperm) An extinct seedless vascular plant that may be ancestral to seed plants.

prokaryotic cell (prō′-kār′-ē-ot′-ik) A type of cell lacking a membrane-enclosed nucleus and membrane-enclosed organelles. Organisms with prokaryotic cells (bacteria and archaea) are called prokaryotes.

prolactin (PRL) A hormone produced and secreted by the anterior pituitary with a great diversity of effects in different vertebrate species. In mammals, it stimulates growth of and milk production by the mammary glands.

proliferative phase That portion of the uterine (menstrual) cycle when the endometrium regenerates and thickens.

prometaphase The second stage of mitosis, in which discrete chromosomes consisting of identical sister chromatids appear, the nuclear envelope fragments, and the spindle microtubules attach to the kinetochores of the chromosomes.

promiscuous Referring to a type of relationship in which mating occurs with no strong pair-bonds or lasting relationships.

promoter A specific nucleotide sequence in DNA that binds RNA polymerase, positioning it to start transcribing RNA at the appropriate place.

prophage (prō′-fāj) A phage genome that has been inserted into a specific site on a bacterial chromosome.

prophase The first stage of mitosis, in which the chromatin condenses, the mitotic spindle begins to form, and the nucleolus disappears, but the nucleus remains intact.

prostaglandin (PG) (pros′-tuh-glan′-din) One of a group of modified fatty acids secreted by virtually all tissues and performing a wide variety of functions as local regulators.

prostate gland (pros′-tāt) A gland in human males that secretes an acid-neutralizing component of semen.

protease An enzyme that digests proteins by hydrolysis.

proteasome A giant protein complex that recognizes and destroys proteins tagged for elimination by the small protein ubiquitin.

protein (prō′-tēn) A functional biological molecule consisting of one or more polypeptides folded and coiled into a specific three-dimensional structure.

protein kinase An enzyme that transfers phosphate groups from ATP to a protein, thus phosphorylating the protein.

protein phosphatase An enzyme that removes phosphate groups from (dephosphorylates) proteins, often functioning to reverse the effect of a protein kinase.

proteoglycan (prō′-tē-ō-glī′-kan) A glycoprotein consisting of a small core protein with many carbohydrate chains attached, found in the extracellular matrix of animal cells. A proteoglycan may consist of up to 95% carbohydrate.

proteomics (prō′-tē-ō′-miks) The systematic study of the full protein sets (proteomes) encoded by genomes.

protist An informal term applied to any eukaryote that is not a plant, animal, or fungus. Most protists are unicellular, though some are colonial or multicellular.

protobiont A collection of abiotically produced molecules surrounded by a membrane or membrane-like structure.

proton (prō′-ton) A subatomic particle with a single positive electrical charge, with a mass of about 1.7×10^{-24} g, found in the nucleus of an atom.

proton pump An active transport protein in a cell membrane that uses ATP to transport hydrogen ions out of a cell against their concentration gradient, generating a membrane potential in the process.

protonema (plural, **protonemata**) A mass of green, branched, one-cell-thick filaments produced by germinating moss spores.

protonephridia (prō′-tō-nuh-frid′-ē-uh) (singular, **protonephridium**) An excretory system, such as the flame bulb system of flatworms, consisting of a network of tubules lacking internal openings.

proton-motive force The potential energy stored in the form of an electrochemical gradient, generated by the pumping of hydrogen ions across a biological membrane during chemiosmosis.

proto-oncogene (prō′-tō-on′-kō-jēn) A normal cellular gene that has the potential to become an oncogene.

protoplast fusion The fusing of two protoplasts from different plant species that would otherwise be reproductively incompatible.

protostome development In animals, a developmental mode distinguished by the development of the mouth from the blastopore; often also characterized by spiral cleavage and by the body cavity forming when solid masses of mesoderm split.

provirus A viral genome that is permanently inserted into a host genome.

proximal tubule In the vertebrate kidney, the portion of a nephron immediately downstream from Bowman's capsule that conveys and helps refine filtrate.

proximate causation The mechanistic explanation of "how" a behavior (or other aspect of an organism's biology) occurs or is modified; that is, how a stimulus elicits a behavior, what physiological mechanisms mediate the response, and how experience influences the response.

pseudocoelomate (sū′-dō-sē′-lō-māt) An animal whose body cavity is lined by tissue derived from mesoderm and endoderm.

pseudogene (sū′-dō-jēn) A DNA segment very similar to a real gene but which does not yield a functional product; a DNA segment that formerly functioned as a gene but has become inactivated in a particular species because of mutation.

pseudopodium (sū′-dō-pō′-dē-um) (plural, **pseudopodia**) A cellular extension of amoeboid cells used in moving and feeding.

pterophyte (ter′-uh-fīt) An informal name for a member of the phylum Pterophyta, which includes ferns, horsetails, and whisk ferns and their relatives.

pterosaur Winged reptile that lived during the Mesozoic era.

pulmocutaneous circuit A branch of the circulatory system in many amphibians that supplies the lungs and skin.

pulmonary circuit The branch of the circulatory system that supplies the lungs.

pulse The rhythmic bulging of the artery walls with each heartbeat.

punctuated equilibria In the fossil record, long periods of apparent stasis, in which a species undergoes little or no morphological change, interrupted by relatively brief periods of sudden change.

Punnett square A diagram used in the study of inheritance to show the predicted results of random fertilization in genetic crosses.

pupil The opening in the iris, which admits light into the interior of the vertebrate eye. Muscles in the iris regulate its size.

purine (pyū′-rēn) One of two types of nitrogenous bases found in nucleotides, characterized by a six-membered ring fused to a five-membered ring. Adenine (A) and guanine (G) are purines.

pyrimidine (puh-rim′-uh-dēn) One of two types of nitrogenous bases found in nucleotides, characterized by a six-membered ring. Cytosine (C), thymine (T), and uracil (U) are pyrimidines.

quantitative character A heritable feature that varies continuously over a range rather than in an either-or fashion.

quaternary structure (kwot′-er-nār-ē) The particular shape of a complex, aggregate protein, defined by the characteristic three-dimensional arrangement of its constituent subunits, each a polypeptide.

R plasmid A bacterial plasmid carrying genes that confer resistance to certain antibiotics.

radial cleavage A type of embryonic development in deuterostomes in which the planes of cell division that transform the zygote into a ball of cells are either parallel or perpendicular to the vertical axis of the embryo, thereby aligning tiers of cells one above the other.

radial glia In an embryo, supporting cells that form tracks along which newly formed neurons migrate from the neural tube; can also act as stem cells that give rise to other glia and neurons.

radial symmetry Symmetry in which the body is shaped like a pie or barrel (lacking a left side and a right side) and can be divided into mirror-image halves by any plane through its central axis.

radiation The emission of electromagnetic waves by all objects warmer than absolute zero.

radicle An embryonic root of a plant.

radioactive isotope An isotope (an atomic form of a chemical element) that is unstable;

the nucleus decays spontaneously, giving off detectable particles and energy.

radiolarian A protist, usually marine, with a shell generally made of silica and pseudopodia that radiate from the central body.

radiometric dating A method for determining the absolute ages of rocks and fossils, based on the half-life of radioactive isotopes.

radula A straplike rasping organ used by many molluscs during feeding.

***ras* gene** A gene that codes for Ras, a G protein that relays a growth signal from a growth factor receptor on the plasma membrane to a cascade of protein kinases, ultimately resulting in stimulation of the cell cycle.

ratite (rat′-īt) Member of the group of flightless birds.

ray-finned fish Member of the class Actinopterygii, aquatic osteichthyans with fins supported by long, flexible rays, including tuna, bass, and herring.

reabsorption In excretory systems, the recovery of solutes and water from filtrate.

reactant A starting material in a chemical reaction.

reaction-center complex A complex of proteins associated with a special pair of chlorophyll *a* molecules and a primary electron acceptor. Located centrally in a photosystem, this complex triggers the light reactions of photosynthesis. Excited by light energy, the pair of chlorophylls donates an electron to the primary electron acceptor, which passes an electron to an electron transport chain.

reading frame On an mRNA, the triplet grouping of ribonucleotides used by the translation machinery during polypeptide synthesis.

receptacle The base of a flower; the part of the stem that is the site of attachment of the floral organs.

receptor potential An initial response of a receptor cell to a stimulus, consisting of a change in voltage across the receptor membrane proportional to the stimulus strength. The intensity of the receptor potential determines the frequency of action potentials traveling to the nervous system.

receptor tyrosine kinase A receptor protein in the plasma membrane, the cytoplasmic (intracellular) part of which can catalyze the transfer of a phosphate group from ATP to a tyrosine on another protein. Receptor tyrosine kinases often respond to the binding of a signaling molecule by dimerizing and then phosphorylating a tyrosine on the cytoplasmic portion of the other receptor in the dimer. The phosphorylated tyrosines on the receptors then activate other signal transduction proteins within the cell.

receptor-mediated endocytosis (en′-dō-sī-tō′-sis) The movement of specific molecules into a cell by the inward budding of membranous vesicles containing proteins with receptor sites specific to the molecules being taken in; enables a cell to acquire bulk quantities of specific substances.

recessive allele An allele whose phenotypic effect is not observed in a heterozygote.

reciprocal altruism Altruistic behavior between unrelated individuals, whereby the altruistic individual benefits in the future when the beneficiary reciprocates.

recombinant chromosome A chromosome created when crossing over combines the DNA from two parents into a single chromosome.

recombinant DNA A DNA molecule made *in vitro* with segments from different sources.

recombinant type (recombinant) An offspring whose phenotype differs from that of the parents; also refers to the phenotype itself.

recruitment The process of progressively increasing the tension of a muscle by activating more and more of the motor neurons controlling the muscle.

rectum The terminal portion of the large intestine where the feces are stored until they are eliminated.

red alga A photosynthetic protist, named for its color, which results from a red pigment that masks the green of chlorophyll. Most red algae are multicellular and marine.

redox reaction (rē'-doks) A chemical reaction involving the complete or partial transfer of one or more electrons from one reactant to another; short for oxidation-reduction reaction.

reducing agent The electron donor in a redox reaction.

reduction The addition of electrons to a substance involved in a redox reaction.

reflex An automatic reaction to a stimulus, mediated by the spinal cord or lower brain.

refractory period (rē-frakt'-ōr-ē) The short time immediately after an action potential in which the neuron cannot respond to another stimulus, owing to the inactivation of voltage-gated sodium channels.

regulator An animal for which mechanisms of homeostasis moderate internal changes in the face of external fluctuations.

regulatory gene A gene that codes for a protein, such as a repressor, that controls the transcription of another gene or group of genes.

reinforcement A process in which natural selection strengthens prezygotic barriers to reproduction, thus reducing the chances of hybrid formation. Such a process is likely to occur only if hybrid offspring are less fit than members of the parent species.

relative abundance The proportional abundance of different species in a community.

relative fitness The contribution an individual makes to the gene pool of the next generation, relative to the contributions of other individuals in the population.

renal artery The blood vessel bringing blood to the kidney.

renal cortex The outer portion of the vertebrate kidney.

renal medulla The inner portion of the vertebrate kidney, beneath the renal cortex.

renal pelvis The funnel-shaped chamber that receives processed filtrate from the vertebrate kidney's collecting ducts and is drained by the ureter.

renal vein The blood vessel that carries blood away from the kidney.

renin-angiotensin-aldosterone system (RAAS) A hormone cascade pathway that helps regulate blood pressure and blood volume.

repeated reproduction Reproduction in which adults produce offspring over many years; also known as iteroparity.

repetitive DNA Nucleotide sequences, usually noncoding, that are present in many copies in a eukaryotic genome. The repeated units may be short and arranged tandemly (in series) or long and dispersed in the genome.

replication fork A Y-shaped region on a replicating DNA molecule where the parental strands are being unwound and new strands are growing.

repressor A protein that inhibits gene transcription. In prokaryotes, repressors bind to the DNA in or near the promoter. In eukaryotes, repressors may bind to control elements within enhancers, to activators, or to other proteins in a way that blocks activators from binding to DNA.

reproductive isolation The existence of biological factors (barriers) that impede members of two species from producing viable, fertile offspring.

reproductive table An age-specific summary of the reproductive rates in a population.

reptile Member of the clade of amniotes that includes tuataras, lizards, snakes, turtles, crocodilians, and birds.

residual volume The amount of air that remains in the lungs after forceful exhalation.

resource partitioning The division of environmental resources by coexisting species such that the niche of each species differs by one or more significant factors from the niches of all coexisting species.

respiratory pigment A protein that transports oxygen in blood or hemolymph.

response (1) In cellular communication, the change in a specific cellular activity brought about by a transduced signal from outside the cell. (2) In homeostasis, a physiological activity that helps return a variable to a set point.

resting potential The membrane potential characteristic of a nonconducting excitable cell, with the inside of the cell more negative than the outside.

restoration ecology Applying ecological principles in an effort to return ecosystems that have been disturbed by human activity to a condition as similar as possible to their natural state.

restriction enzyme An endonuclease (type of enzyme) that recognizes and cuts DNA molecules foreign to a bacterium (such as phage genomes). The enzyme cuts at specific nucleotide sequences (restriction sites).

restriction fragment A DNA segment that results from the cutting of DNA by a restriction enzyme.

restriction fragment length polymorphism (RFLP) A single nucleotide polymorphism (SNP) that exists in the restriction site for a particular enzyme, thus making the site unrecognizable by that enzyme and changing the lengths of the restriction fragments formed by digestion with that enzyme. A RFLP can be in coding or noncoding DNA.

restriction site A specific sequence on a DNA strand that is recognized and cut by a restriction enzyme.

reticular formation (re-tik'-yū-ler) A diffuse network of neurons in the core of the brainstem that filters information traveling to the cerebral cortex.

retina (ret'-i-nuh) The innermost layer of the vertebrate eye, containing photoreceptor cells (rods and cones) and neurons; transmits images formed by the lens to the brain via the optic nerve.

retinal The light-absorbing pigment in rods and cones of the vertebrate eye.

retrotransposon (re'-trō-trans-pō'-zon) A transposable element that moves within a genome by means of an RNA intermediate, a transcript of the retrotransposon DNA.

retrovirus (re'-trō-vī'-rus) An RNA virus that reproduces by transcribing its RNA into DNA and then inserting the DNA into a cellular chromosome; an important class of cancer-causing viruses.

reverse transcriptase (tran-skrip'-tās) An enzyme encoded by certain viruses (retroviruses) that uses RNA as a template for DNA synthesis.

reverse transcriptase–polymerase chain reaction (RT-PCR) A technique for determining expression of a particular gene. It uses reverse transcriptase and DNA polymerase to synthesize cDNA from all the mRNA in a sample and then subjects the cDNA to PCR amplification using primers specific for the gene of interest.

Rhizaria (rī-za'-rē-uh) One of five supergroups of eukaryotes proposed in a current hypothesis of the evolutionary history of eukaryotes; a morphologically diverse protist clade that is defined by DNA similarities. *See also* Excavata, Chromalveolata, Archaeplastida, and Unikonta.

rhizobacterium A soil bacterium whose population size is much enhanced in the rhizosphere, the soil region close to a plant's roots.

rhizoid (rī'-zoyd) A long, tubular single cell or filament of cells that anchors bryophytes to the ground. Unlike roots, rhizoids are not composed of tissues, lack specialized conducting cells, and do not play a primary role in water and mineral absorption.

rhizosphere The soil region close to plant roots and characterized by a high level of microbiological activity.

rhodopsin (rō-dop'-sin) A visual pigment consisting of retinal and opsin. When rhodopsin absorbs light, the retinal changes shape and dissociates from the opsin, after which it is converted back to its original form.

rhythm method A form of contraception that relies on refraining from sexual intercourse when conception is most likely to occur; also called natural family planning.

ribonucleic acid (RNA) (rī´-bō-nū-klā´-ik) A type of nucleic acid consisting of nucleotide monomers with a ribose sugar and the nitrogenous bases adenine (A), cytosine (C), guanine (G), and uracil (U); usually single-stranded; functions in protein synthesis, gene regulation, and as the genome of some viruses.

ribose The sugar component of RNA nucleotides.

ribosomal RNA (rRNA) (rī´-buh-sō´-mul) The most abundant type of RNA, which together with proteins makes up ribosomes.

ribosome (rī´-buh-sōm´) A complex of rRNA and protein molecules that functions as a site of protein synthesis in the cytoplasm; consists of a large and a small subunit. In eukaryotic cells, each subunit is assembled in the nucleolus. *See also* nucleolus.

ribozyme (rī´-bō-zīm) An RNA molecule that functions as an enzyme, catalyzing reactions during RNA splicing.

RNA interference (RNAi) A technique used to silence the expression of selected genes. RNAi uses synthetic double-stranded RNA molecules that match the sequence of a particular gene to trigger the breakdown of the gene's messenger RNA.

RNA polymerase An enzyme that links ribonucleotides into a growing RNA chain during transcription.

RNA processing Modification of RNA transcripts, including splicing out of introns, joining together of exons, and alteration of the 5′ and 3′ ends.

RNA splicing After synthesis of a eukaryotic primary RNA transcript, the removal of portions (introns) of the transcript that will not be included in the mRNA.

rod A rodlike cell in the retina of the vertebrate eye, sensitive to low light intensity.

root An organ in vascular plants that anchors the plant and enables it to absorb water and minerals from the soil.

root cap A cone of cells at the tip of a plant root that protects the apical meristem.

root hair A tiny extension of a root epidermal cell, growing just behind the root tip and increasing surface area for absorption of water and minerals.

root pressure The upward push of xylem sap in the vascular tissue of roots.

root system All of a plant's roots, which anchor it in the soil, absorb and transport minerals and water, and store food.

rooted Describing a phylogenetic tree that contains a branch point (typically, the one farthest to the left) representing the last common ancestor of all taxa in the tree.

rough ER That portion of the endoplasmic reticulum studded with ribosomes.

round window In the mammalian ear, the point of contact between the stapes and the cochlea, where vibrations of the stapes create a traveling series of pressure waves in the fluid of the cochlea.

r-selection Selection for life history traits that maximize reproductive success in uncrowded environments; also called density-independent selection.

rubisco (rū-bis´-kō) Ribulose bisphosphate (RuBP) carboxylase, the enzyme that catalyzes the first step of the Calvin cycle (the addition of CO_2 to RuBP).

ruminant (rū´-muh-nent) An animal, such as a cow or a sheep, with an elaborate, multicompartmentalized stomach specialized for an herbivorous diet.

S phase The synthesis phase of the cell cycle; the portion of interphase during which DNA is replicated.

sac fungus *See* ascomycete.

saccule In the vertebrate ear, a chamber in the vestibule behind the oval window that participates in the sense of balance.

salicylic acid (sal´-i-sil´-ik) A signaling molecule in plants that may be partially responsible for activating systemic acquired resistance to pathogens.

salivary gland A gland associated with the oral cavity that secretes substances to lubricate food and begin the process of chemical digestion.

salt A compound resulting from the formation of an ionic bond; also called an ionic compound.

saltatory conduction (sol´-tuh-tōr´-ē) Rapid transmission of a nerve impulse along an axon, resulting from the action potential jumping from one node of Ranvier to another, skipping the myelin-sheathed regions of membrane.

sarcomere (sar´-kō-mēr) The fundamental, repeating unit of striated muscle, delimited by the Z lines.

sarcoplasmic reticulum (SR) (sar´-kō-plaz´-mik ruh-tik´-yū-lum) A specialized endoplasmic reticulum that regulates the calcium concentration in the cytosol of muscle cells.

saturated fatty acid A fatty acid in which all carbons in the hydrocarbon tail are connected by single bonds, thus maximizing the number of hydrogen atoms that are attached to the carbon skeleton.

savanna A tropical grassland biome with scattered individual trees and large herbivores and maintained by occasional fires and drought.

scaffolding protein A type of large relay protein to which several other relay proteins are simultaneously attached, increasing the efficiency of signal transduction.

scanning electron microscope (SEM) A microscope that uses an electron beam to scan the surface of a sample to study details of its topography.

schizophrenia (skit´-suh-frē´-nē-uh) Severe mental disturbance characterized by psychotic episodes in which patients lose the ability to distinguish reality from hallucination.

Schwann cell A type of glial cell that forms insulating myelin sheaths around the axons of neurons in the peripheral nervous system.

scion (sī´-un) The twig grafted onto the stock when making a graft.

sclera (sklār´-uh) A tough, white outer layer of connective tissue that forms the globe of the vertebrate eye.

sclereid (sklār´-ē-id) A short, irregular sclerenchyma cell in nutshells and seed coats. Sclereids are scattered throughout the parenchyma of some plants.

sclerenchyma cell (skluh-ren´-kim-uh) A rigid, supportive plant cell type usually lacking a protoplast and possessing thick secondary walls strengthened by lignin at maturity.

scrotum A pouch of skin outside the abdomen that houses the testes; functions in maintaining the testes at the lower temperature required for spermatogenesis.

second law of thermodynamics The principle stating that every energy transfer or transformation increases the entropy of the universe. Ordered forms of energy are at least partly converted to heat.

second messenger A small, nonprotein, water-soluble molecule or ion, such as a calcium ion (Ca^{2+}) or cyclic AMP, that relays a signal to a cell's interior in response to a signaling molecule bound by a signal receptor protein.

secondary cell wall In plants, a strong and durable matrix often deposited in several laminated layers for cell protection and support.

secondary consumer A carnivore that eats herbivores.

secondary endosymbiosis A process in eukaryotic evolution in which a heterotrophic eukaryotic cell engulfed a photosynthetic eukaryotic cell, which survived in a symbiotic relationship inside the heterotrophic cell.

secondary growth Growth produced by lateral meristems, thickening the roots and shoots of woody plants.

secondary immune response The acquired immune response elicited on second or subsequent exposures to a particular antigen. The secondary immune response is more rapid, of greater magnitude, and of longer duration than the primary immune response.

secondary oocyte (ō´-uh-sīt) An oocyte that has completed the first of the two meiotic divisions.

secondary plant body The tissues produced by the vascular cambium and cork cambium, which thicken the stems and roots of woody plants.

secondary production The amount of chemical energy in consumers' food that is converted to their own new biomass during a given time period.

secondary structure The localized, repetitive coiling or folding of the polypeptide backbone of a protein due to hydrogen bond formation between constituents of the backbone.

secondary succession A type of succession that occurs where an existing community has been cleared by some disturbance that leaves the soil or substrate intact.

secretion (1) The discharge of molecules synthesized by a cell. (2) The discharge of wastes from the body fluid into the filtrate.

secretory phase That portion of the uterine (menstrual) cycle when the endometrium continues to thicken, becomes more vascularized, and develops glands that secrete a fluid rich in glycogen.

seed An adaptation of some terrestrial plants consisting of an embryo packaged along with a store of food within a protective coat.

seed coat A tough outer covering of a seed, formed from the outer coat of an ovule. In a flowering plant, the seed coat encloses and protects the embryo and endosperm.

seedless vascular plant An informal name for a plant that has vascular tissue but lacks seeds. Seedless vascular plants form a paraphyletic group that includes the phyla Lycophyta (club mosses and their relatives) and Pterophyta (ferns and their relatives).

selective permeability A property of biological membranes that allows them to regulate the passage of substances.

self-incompatibility The ability of a seed plant to reject its own pollen and sometimes the pollen of closely related individuals.

semelparity Reproduction in which an organism produces all of its offspring in a single event; also known as big-bang reproduction.

semen (sē´-mun) The fluid that is ejaculated by the male during orgasm; contains sperm and secretions from several glands of the male reproductive tract.

semicircular canals A three-part chamber of the inner ear that functions in maintaining equilibrium.

semiconservative model Type of DNA replication in which the replicated double helix consists of one old strand, derived from the old molecule, and one newly made strand.

semilunar valve A valve located at each exit of the heart, where the aorta leaves the left ventricle and the pulmonary artery leaves the right ventricle.

seminal vesicle (sem´-i-nul ves´-i-kul) A gland in males that secretes a fluid component of semen that lubricates and nourishes sperm.

seminiferous tubule (sem´-i-nif´-er-us) A highly coiled tube in the testis in which sperm are produced.

senescence (se-nes´-ens) The growth phase in a plant or plant part (as a leaf) from full maturity to death.

sensitive period A limited phase in an individual animal's development when learning of particular behaviors can take place; also called a critical period.

sensor In homeostasis, a receptor that detects a stimulus.

sensory adaptation The tendency of sensory neurons to become less sensitive when they are stimulated repeatedly.

sensory neuron A nerve cell that receives information from the internal or external environment and transmits signals to the central nervous system.

sensory reception The detection of the energy of a stimulus by sensory cells.

sensory receptor An organ, cell, or structure within a cell that responds to specific stimuli from an organism's external or internal environment.

sensory transduction The conversion of stimulus energy to a change in the membrane potential of a sensory receptor cell.

sepal (sē´-pul) A modified leaf in angiosperms that helps enclose and protect a flower bud before it opens.

septum (plural, **septa**) One of the cross-walls that divide a fungal hypha into cells. Septa generally have pores large enough to allow ribosomes, mitochondria, and even nuclei to flow from cell to cell.

serial endosymbiosis A hypothesis for the origin of eukaryotes consisting of a sequence of endosymbiotic events in which mitochondria, chloroplasts, and perhaps other cellular structures were derived from small prokaryotes that had been engulfed by larger cells.

serotonin (ser´-uh-tō´-nin) A neurotransmitter, synthesized from the amino acid tryptophan, that functions in the central nervous system.

set point In animal bodies, a value maintained for a particular variable, such as body temperature or solute concentration, to achieve homeostasis.

seta (sē´-tuh) (plural, **setae**) The elongated stalk of a bryophyte sporophyte.

sex chromosome A chromosome responsible for determining the sex of an individual.

sex pilus (plural, **sex pili**) (pī´-lus, pī´-lī) In bacteria, a structure that links one cell to another at the start of conjugation; also known as a conjugation pilus.

sex-linked gene A gene located on a sex chromosome (usually the X chromosome), resulting in a distinctive pattern of inheritance.

sexual dimorphism (dī-mōr´-fizm) Marked differences between the secondary sex characteristics of males and females.

sexual reproduction A type of reproduction in which two parents give rise to offspring that have unique combinations of genes inherited from the gametes of the parents.

sexual selection A form of natural selection in which individuals with certain inherited characteristics are more likely than other individuals to obtain mates.

Shannon diversity An index of community diversity symbolized by H and represented by the equation $H = [(p_A \ln p_A) + (p_B \ln p_B) + (p_C \ln p_C) + . . .]$, where A, B, C . . . are the species in the community, p is the relative abundance of each species, and ln is the natural logarithm.

shared ancestral character A character, shared by members of a particular clade, that originated in an ancestor that is not a member of that clade.

shared derived character An evolutionary novelty that is unique to a particular clade.

shoot system The aerial portion of a plant body, consisting of stems, leaves, and (in angiosperms) flowers.

short tandem repeat (STR) Simple sequence DNA containing multiple tandemly repeated units of two to five nucleotides. Variations in STRs act as genetic markers in STR analysis, used to prepare genetic profiles.

short-day plant A plant that flowers (usually in late summer, fall, or winter) only when the light period is shorter than a critical length.

short-term memory The ability to hold information, anticipations, or goals for a time and then release them if they become irrelevant.

sickle-cell disease A human genetic disease caused by a recessive allele that results in the substitution of a single amino acid in a globin polypeptide that is part of the hemoglobin protein; characterized by deformed red blood cells (due to protein aggregation) that can lead to numerous symptoms.

sieve plate An end wall in a sieve-tube element, which facilitates the flow of phloem sap in angiosperm sieve tubes.

sieve-tube element A living cell that conducts sugars and other organic nutrients in the phloem of angiosperms; also called a sieve-tube member. Connected end to end, they form sieve tubes.

sign stimulus An external sensory cue that triggers a fixed action pattern by an animal.

signal In animal behavior, transmission of a stimulus from one animal to another. The term is also used in the context of communication in other kinds of organisms and in cell-to-cell communication in all multicellular organisms.

signal peptide A sequence of about 20 amino acids at or near the leading (amino) end of a polypeptide that targets it to the endoplasmic reticulum or other organelles in a eukaryotic cell.

signal transduction The linkage of a mechanical, chemical, or electromagnetic stimulus to a specific cellular response.

signal transduction pathway A series of steps linking a mechanical or chemical stimulus to a specific cellular response.

signal-recognition particle (SRP) A protein-RNA complex that recognizes a signal peptide as it emerges from a ribosome and helps direct the ribosome to the endoplasmic reticulum (ER) by binding to a receptor protein on the ER.

simple fruit A fruit derived from a single carpel or several fused carpels.

simple sequence DNA A DNA sequence that contains many copies of tandemly repeated short sequences.

single bond A single covalent bond; the sharing of a pair of valence electrons by two atoms.

single circulation A circulatory system consisting of a single pump and circuit, in which blood passes from the sites of gas exchange to the rest of the body before returning to the heart.

single nucleotide polymorphism (SNP) A single base-pair site in a genome where nucleotide variation is found in at least 1% of the population.

single-lens eye The camera-like eye found in some jellies, polychaetes, spiders, and many molluscs.

single-strand binding protein A protein that binds to the unpaired DNA strands during DNA

replication, stabilizing them and holding them apart while they serve as templates for the synthesis of complementary strands of DNA.

sinoatrial (SA) node A region in the right atrium of the heart that sets the rate and timing at which all cardiac muscle cells contract; the pacemaker.

sister chromatid Either of two copies of a duplicated chromosome attached to each other by proteins at the centromere and, sometimes, along the arms. While joined, two sister chromatids make up one chromosome; chromatids are eventually separated during mitosis or meiosis II.

sister taxa Groups of organisms that share an immediate common ancestor and hence are each other's closest relatives.

skeletal muscle Muscle that is generally responsible for the voluntary movements of the body; one type of striated muscle.

sliding-filament model The theory explaining how muscle contracts, based on change within a sarcomere, the basic unit of muscle organization. According to this model, thin (actin) filaments slide across thick (myosin) filaments, shortening the sarcomere. The shortening of all sarcomeres in a myofibril shortens the entire myofibril.

slow block to polyspermy The formation of the fertilization envelope and other changes in an egg's surface that prevent fusion of the egg with more than one sperm. The slow block begins about 1 minute after fertilization.

slow-twitch fiber A muscle fiber that can sustain long contractions.

small interfering RNA (siRNA) A small, single-stranded RNA molecule generated by cellular machinery from a long, double-stranded RNA molecule. The siRNA associates with one or more proteins in a complex that can degrade or prevent translation of an mRNA with a complementary sequence. In some cases, siRNA can also block transcription by promoting chromatin modification.

small intestine The longest section of the alimentary canal, so named because of its small diameter compared with that of the large intestine; the principal site of the enzymatic hydrolysis of food macromolecules and the absorption of nutrients.

smooth ER That portion of the endoplasmic reticulum that is free of ribosomes.

smooth muscle A type of muscle lacking the striations of skeletal and cardiac muscle because of the uniform distribution of myosin filaments in the cell; responsible for involuntary body activities.

social learning Modification of behavior through the observation of other individuals.

sociobiology The study of social behavior based on evolutionary theory.

sodium-potassium pump A transport protein in the plasma membrane of animal cells that actively transports sodium out of the cell and potassium into the cell.

soil horizon A soil layer that parallels the land surface and has physical characteristics that differ from those of the layers above and beneath.

solute (sol′-yūt) A substance that is dissolved in a solution.

solute potential (Ψ_S) A component of water potential that is proportional to the molarity of a solution and that measures the effect of solutes on the direction of water movement; also called osmotic potential, it can be either zero or negative.

solution A liquid that is a homogeneous mixture of two or more substances.

solvent The dissolving agent of a solution. Water is the most versatile solvent known.

somatic cell (sō-mat′-ik) Any cell in a multicellular organism except a sperm or egg.

somite One of a series of blocks of mesoderm that exist in pairs just lateral to the notochord in a vertebrate embryo.

soredium (plural, **soredia**) In lichens, a small cluster of fungal hyphae with embedded algae.

sorus (plural, **sori**) A cluster of sporangia on a fern sporophyll. Sori may be arranged in various patterns, such as parallel lines or dots, which are useful in fern identification.

Southern blotting A technique that enables specific nucleotide sequences to be detected in a sample of DNA. It involves gel electrophoresis of DNA molecules and their transfer to a membrane (blotting), followed by nucleic acid hybridization with a labeled probe.

spatial learning The establishment of a memory that reflects the environment's spatial structure.

spatial summation A phenomenon of neural integration in which the membrane potential of the postsynaptic cell is determined by the combined effect of EPSPs or IPSPs produced nearly simultaneously by different synapses.

speciation (spē′-sē-ā′-shun) An evolutionary process in which one species splits into two or more species.

species (spē′-sēz) A population or group of populations whose members have the potential to interbreed in nature and produce viable, fertile offspring, but do not produce viable, fertile offspring with members of other such groups.

species diversity The number and relative abundance of species in a biological community.

species richness The number of species in a biological community.

species-area curve The biodiversity pattern, first noted by Alexander von Humboldt, that shows that the larger the geographic area of a community is, the more species it has.

specific heat The amount of heat that must be absorbed or lost for 1 g of a substance to change its temperature by 1°C.

spectrophotometer An instrument that measures the proportions of light of different wavelengths absorbed and transmitted by a pigment solution.

sperm The male gamete.

spermatheca (sper′-muh-thē′-kuh) in many insects, a sac in the female reproductive system where sperm are stored.

spermatogenesis The continuous and prolific production of mature sperm cells in the testis.

spermatogonium A cell that divides mitotically to form spermatocytes.

sphincter (sfink′-ter) A ringlike valve, consisting of modified muscles in a muscular tube, that regulates passage between some compartments of the alimentary canal.

spinal nerve In the vertebrate peripheral nervous system, a nerve that carries signals to or from the spinal cord.

spiral cleavage A type of embryonic development in protostomes in which the planes of cell division that transform the zygote into a ball of cells are diagonal to the vertical axis of the embryo. As a result, the cells of each tier sit in the grooves between cells of adjacent tiers.

spliceosome (splī′-se-ō-sōm) A large complex made up of proteins and RNA molecules that splices RNA by interacting with the ends of an RNA intron, releasing the intron and joining the two adjacent exons.

spongocoel (spon′-jō-sēl) The central cavity of a sponge.

sporangium (spōr-an′-jē-um) (plural, **sporangia**) A multicellular organ in fungi and plants in which meiosis occurs and haploid cells develop.

spore (1) In the life cycle of a plant or alga undergoing alternation of generations, a haploid cell produced in the sporophyte by meiosis. A spore can divide by mitosis to develop into a multicellular haploid individual, the gametophyte, without fusing with another cell. (2) In fungi, a haploid cell, produced either sexually or asexually, that produces a mycelium after germination.

sporocyte A diploid cell, also known as a spore mother cell, that undergoes meiosis and generates haploid spores.

sporophyll (spō′-ruh-fil) A modified leaf that bears sporangia and hence is specialized for reproduction.

sporophyte (spō-ruh-fīt′) In organisms (plants and some algae) that have alternation of generations, the multicellular diploid form that results from the union of gametes. The sporophyte produces haploid spores by meiosis that develop into gametophytes.

sporopollenin (spōr-uh-pol′-eh-nin) A durable polymer that covers exposed zygotes of charophyte algae and forms the walls of plant spores, preventing them from drying out.

stabilizing selection Natural selection in which intermediate phenotypes survive or reproduce more successfully than do extreme phenotypes.

stamen (stā′-men) The pollen-producing reproductive organ of a flower, consisting of an anther and a filament.

standard metabolic rate (SMR) The metabolic rate of a resting, fasting, and nonstressed ectotherm at a particular temperature.

stapes The third of three bones in the middle ear of mammals; also called the stirrup.

starch A storage polysaccharide in plants, consisting entirely of glucose monomers joined by α glycosidic linkages.

statocyst (stat'-uh-sist') A type of mechanoreceptor that functions in equilibrium in invertebrates by use of statoliths, which stimulate hair cells in relation to gravity.

statolith (stat'-uh-lith') (1) In plants, a specialized plastid that contains dense starch grains and may play a role in detecting gravity. (2) In invertebrates, a grain or other dense granule that settles in response to gravity and is found in sensory organs that function in equilibrium.

stele (stēl)The vascular tissue of a stem or root.

stem A vascular plant organ consisting of an alternating system of nodes and internodes that support the leaves and reproductive structures.

stem cell Any relatively unspecialized cell that can produce, during a single division, one identical daughter cell and one more specialized daughter cell that can undergo further differentiation.

stenohaline (sten'-ō-hā'-līn) Referring to organisms that cannot tolerate substantial changes in external osmolarity.

steroid A type of lipid characterized by a carbon skeleton consisting of four rings with various chemical groups attached.

sticky end A single-stranded end of a double-stranded restriction fragment.

stigma (plural, **stigmata**) The sticky part of a flower's carpel, which traps pollen grains.

stimulus In homeostasis, a fluctuation in a variable that triggers a return to a set point.

stipe A stemlike structure of a seaweed.

stock The plant that provides the root system when making a graft.

stoma (stō'-muh) (plural, **stomata**) A microscopic pore surrounded by guard cells in the epidermis of leaves and stems that allows gas exchange between the environment and the interior of the plant.

stomach An organ of the digestive system that stores food and performs preliminary steps of digestion.

stramenopile A protist in which a "hairy" flagellum (one covered with fine, hairlike projections) is paired with a shorter, smooth flagellum.

stratum (strah'-tum) (plural, **strata**) A rock layer formed when new layers of sediment cover older ones and compress them.

striated muscle Muscle in which the regular arrangement of filaments creates a pattern of light and dark bands.

strobilus (strō-bī'-lus) (plural, **strobili**) The technical term for a cluster of sporophylls known commonly as a cone, found in most gymnosperms and some seedless vascular plants.

stroke The death of nervous tissue in the brain, usually resulting from rupture or blockage of arteries in the head.

stroke volume The volume of blood pumped by a heart ventricle in a single contraction.

stroma (strō'-muh) Within the chloroplast, the dense fluid of the chloroplast surrounding the thylakoid membrane; involved in the synthesis of organic molecules from carbon dioxide and water.

stromatolite Layered rock that results from the activities of prokaryotes that bind thin films of sediment together.

structural formula A type of molecular notation in which the constituent atoms are joined by lines representing covalent bonds.

structural isomer One of several compounds that have the same molecular formula but differ in the covalent arrangements of their atoms.

style The stalk of a flower's carpel, with the ovary at the base and the stigma at the top.

substance P A neuropeptide that is a key excitatory neurotransmitter that mediates the perception of pain.

substrate The reactant on which an enzyme works.

substrate feeder An animal that lives in or on its food source, eating its way through the food.

substrate-level phosphorylation The formation of ATP by an enzyme directly transferring a phosphate group to ADP from an intermediate substrate in catabolism.

sugar sink A plant organ that is a net consumer or storer of sugar. Growing roots, shoot tips, stems, and fruits are sugar sinks supplied by phloem.

sugar source A plant organ in which sugar is being produced by either photosynthesis or the breakdown of starch. Mature leaves are the primary sugar sources of plants.

sulfhydryl group A chemical group consisting of a sulfur atom bonded to a hydrogen atom.

suprachiasmatic nucleus (SCN) A group of neurons in the hypothalamus of mammals that functions as a biological clock.

surface tension A measure of how difficult it is to stretch or break the surface of a liquid. Water has a high surface tension because of the hydrogen bonding of surface molecules.

surfactant A substance secreted by alveoli that decreases surface tension in the fluid that coats the alveoli.

survivorship curve A plot of the number of members of a cohort that are still alive at each age; one way to represent age-specific mortality.

suspension feeder An aquatic animal, such as a sponge, clam, or baleen whale, that feeds by sifting small food particles from the water.

sustainable agriculture Long-term productive farming methods that are environmentally safe.

sustainable development Development that meets the needs of people today without limiting the ability of future generations to meet their needs.

swim bladder In aquatic osteichthyans, an air sac that enables the animal to control its buoyancy in the water.

symbiont (sim'-bē-ont) The smaller participant in a symbiotic relationship, living in or on the host.

symbiosis An ecological relationship between organisms of two different species that live together in direct and intimate contact.

sympathetic division One of three divisions of the autonomic nervous system of vertebrates; generally increases energy expenditure and prepares the body for action.

sympatric speciation (sim-pat'-rik) The formation of new species in populations that live in the same geographic area.

symplast In plants, the continuum of cytoplasm connected by plasmodesmata between cells.

synapse (sin'-aps) The junction where one neuron communicates with another cell across a narrow gap. Neurotransmitter molecules released by the neuron diffuse across the synapse, relaying messages to the other cell.

synapsid Member of an amniote clade distinguished by a single hole on each side of the skull. Synapsids include the mammals.

synapsis (si-nap'-sis) The pairing and physical connection of replicated homologous chromosomes during prophase I of meiosis.

synaptic cleft (sin-ap'-tik) A narrow gap separating the synaptic terminal of a transmitting neuron from a receiving neuron or an effector cell.

synaptic terminal A bulb at the end of an axon in which neurotransmitter molecules are stored and from which they are released.

synaptic vesicle Membranous sac containing neurotransmitter molecules at the tip of an axon.

systematics A scientific discipline focused on classifying organisms and determining their evolutionary relationships.

systemic Occurring throughout the body and affecting many or all body systems or organs.

systemic acquired resistance A defensive response in infected plants that helps protect healthy tissue from pathogenic invasion.

systemic circuit The branch of the circulatory system that supplies all body organs except those involved in gas exchange.

systems biology An approach to studying biology that aims to model the dynamic behavior of whole biological systems.

systole (sis'-tō-lē) The stage of the cardiac cycle in which a heart chamber contracts and pumps blood.

systolic pressure Blood pressure in the arteries during contraction of the ventricles.

T cell receptor The antigen receptor on T cells; a membrane-bound molecule consisting of one α chain and one β chain linked by a disulfide bridge and containing one antigen-binding site.

T cells The class of lymphocytes that mature in the thymus and that includes both effector cells for the cell-mediated immune response and helper cells required for both branches of adaptive immunity.

taproot A main vertical root that develops from an embryonic root and gives rise to lateral (branch) roots.

tastant Any chemical that stimulates the sensory receptors in a taste bud.

taste bud A collection of modified epithelial cells on the tongue or in the mouth that are receptors for taste in mammals.

TATA box A DNA sequence in eukaryotic promoters crucial in forming the transcription initiation complex.

taxis (tak′-sis) An oriented movement toward or away from a stimulus.

taxon (plural, **taxa**) A named taxonomic unit at any given level of classification.

taxonomy (tak-son′-uh-mē) A scientific discipline concerned with naming and classifying the diverse forms of life.

Tay-Sachs disease A human genetic disease caused by a recessive allele for a dysfunctional enzyme, leading to accumulation of certain lipids in the brain. Seizures, blindness, and degeneration of motor and mental performance usually become manifest a few months after birth, followed by death within a few years.

technology The application of scientific knowledge for a specific purpose, often involving industry or commerce but also including uses in basic research.

telomerase An enzyme that catalyzes the lengthening of telomeres in eukaryotic germ cells.

telomere (tel′-uh-mēr) The tandemly repetitive DNA at the end of a eukaryotic chromosome's DNA molecule that protects the organism's genes from being eroded during successive rounds of replication. *See also* repetitive DNA.

telophase The fifth and final stage of mitosis, in which daughter nuclei are forming and cytokinesis has typically begun.

temperate broadleaf forest A biome located throughout midlatitude regions where there is sufficient moisture to support the growth of large, broadleaf deciduous trees.

temperate grassland A terrestrial biome dominated by grasses and forbs.

temperate phage A phage that is capable of reproducing by either a lytic or lysogenic cycle.

temperature A measure of the intensity of heat in degrees, reflecting the average kinetic energy of the molecules.

template strand The DNA strand that provides the pattern, or template, for ordering the sequence of nucleotides in an RNA transcript.

temporal summation A phenomenon of neural integration in which the membrane potential of the postsynaptic cell in a chemical synapse is determined by the combined effect of EPSPs or IPSPs produced in rapid succession.

tendon A fibrous connective tissue that attaches muscle to bone.

terminator In bacteria, a sequence of nucleotides in DNA that marks the end of a gene and signals RNA polymerase to release the newly made RNA molecule and detach from the DNA.

territoriality A behavior in which an animal defends a bounded physical space against encroachment by other individuals, usually of its own species.

tertiary consumer (ter′-shē-ār′-ē) A carnivore that eats other carnivores.

tertiary structure Irregular contortions of a protein molecule due to interactions of side chains involved in hydrophobic interactions, ionic bonds, hydrogen bonds, and disulfide bridges.

testcross Breeding an organism of unknown genotype with a homozygous recessive individual to determine the unknown genotype. The ratio of phenotypes in the offspring reveals the unknown genotype.

testis (plural, **testes**) The male reproductive organ, or gonad, in which sperm and reproductive hormones are produced.

testosterone A steroid hormone required for development of the male reproductive system, spermatogenesis, and male secondary sex characteristics; the major androgen in mammals.

tetanus (tet′-uh-nus) The maximal, sustained contraction of a skeletal muscle, caused by a very high frequency of action potentials elicited by continual stimulation.

tetrapod A vertebrate with two pairs of limbs. Tetrapods include mammals, amphibians, and birds and other reptiles.

thalamus (thal′-uh-mus) One of two integrating centers of the vertebrate forebrain. Neurons with cell bodies in the thalamus relay neural input to specific areas in the cerebral cortex and regulate what information goes to the cerebral cortex.

thallus (plural, **thalli**) A seaweed body that is plantlike, consisting of a holdfast, stipe, and blades, yet lacks true roots, stems, and leaves.

theory An explanation that is broad in scope, generates new hypotheses, and is supported by a large body of evidence.

thermal energy *See* heat.

thermocline A narrow stratum of rapid temperature change in the ocean and in many temperate-zone lakes.

thermodynamics (ther′-mō-dī-nam′-iks) The study of energy transformations that occur in a collection of matter. *See* first law of thermodynamics; second law of thermodynamics.

thermoreceptor A receptor stimulated by either heat or cold.

thermoregulation The maintenance of internal body temperature within a tolerable range.

theropod Member of an ancient group of dinosaurs that were bipedal carnivores.

thick filament A filament composed of staggered arrays of myosin molecules; a component of myofibrils in muscle fibers.

thigmomorphogenesis A response in plants to chronic mechanical stimulation, resulting from increased ethylene production. An example is thickening stems in response to strong winds.

thigmotropism (thig-mo′-truh-pizm) A directional growth of a plant in response to touch.

thin filament A filament consisting of two strands of actin and two strands of regulatory protein coiled around one another; a component of myofibrils in muscle fibers.

threatened species A species that is considered likely to become endangered in the foreseeable future.

threshold The potential that an excitable cell membrane must reach for an action potential to be initiated.

thrombus A fibrin-containing clot that forms in a blood vessel and blocks the flow of blood.

thylakoid (thī′-luh-koyd) A flattened membranous sac inside a chloroplast. Thylakoids exist in an interconnected system in the chloroplast and contain the molecular "machinery" used to convert light energy to chemical energy.

thymus (thī′-mus) A small organ in the thoracic cavity of vertebrates where maturation of T cells is completed.

thyroid gland An endocrine gland, located on the ventral surface of the trachea, that secretes two iodine-containing hormones, triiodothyronine (T_3) and thyroxine (T_4), as well as calcitonin.

thyroxine (T_4) One of two iodine-containing hormones that are secreted by the thyroid gland and that help regulate metabolism, development, and maturation in vertebrates.

Ti plasmid A plasmid of a tumor-inducing bacterium (the plant pathogen *Agrobacterium*) that integrates a segment of its DNA (T DNA) into a chromosome of a host plant. The Ti plasmid is frequently used as a vector for genetic engineering in plants.

tidal volume The volume of air a mammal inhales and exhales with each breath.

tight junction A type of intercellular junction in animal cells that prevents the leakage of material between cells.

tissue An integrated group of cells with a common function, structure, or both.

tissue system One or more tissues organized into a functional unit connecting the organs of a plant.

TLR Toll-like receptor. A membrane receptor on a phagocytic white blood cell that recognizes fragments of molecules common to a set of pathogens.

tonicity The ability of a solution surrounding a cell to cause that cell to gain or lose water.

top-down model A model of community organization in which predation influences community organization by controlling herbivore numbers, which in turn control plant or phytoplankton numbers, which in turn control nutrient levels; also called the trophic cascade model.

topoisomerase A protein that breaks, swivels, and rejoins DNA strands. During DNA replication, topoisomerase helps to relieve strain in the double helix ahead of the replication fork.

topsoil A mixture of particles derived from rock, living organisms, and decaying organic material (humus).

torpor A physiological state in which activity is low and metabolism decreases.

torsion In gastropods, a developmental process in which the visceral mass rotates up to 180°, causing the animal's anus and mantle cavity to be positioned above its head.

totipotent (tō´-tuh-pōt´-ent) Describing a cell that can give rise to all parts of the embryo and adult, as well as extraembryonic membranes in species that have them.

trace element An element indispensable for life but required in extremely minute amounts.

trachea (trā´-kē-uh) The portion of the respiratory tract that passes from the larynx to the bronchi; also called the windpipe.

tracheal system In insects, a system of branched, air-filled tubes that extends throughout the body and carries oxygen directly to cells.

tracheid (trā´-kē-id) A long, tapered water-conducting cell found in the xylem of nearly all vascular plants. Functioning tracheids are no longer living.

trait Any detectable variant in a genetic character.

trans fat An unsaturated fat containing one or more *trans* double bonds.

transcription The synthesis of RNA using a DNA template.

transcription factor A regulatory protein that binds to DNA and affects transcription of specific genes.

transcription initiation complex The completed assembly of transcription factors and RNA polymerase bound to a promoter.

transcription unit A region of DNA that is transcribed into an RNA molecule.

transduction (1) A type of horizontal gene transfer in which phages (viruses) carry bacterial DNA from one host cell to another. (2) In cellular communication, the conversion of a signal from outside the cell to a form that can bring about a specific cellular response.

transfer cell In a plant, a companion cell with numerous ingrowths of its wall, which increase the cell's surface area and enhance the transfer of solutes between apoplast and symplast.

transfer RNA (tRNA) An RNA molecule that functions as an interpreter between nucleic acid and protein language by picking up specific amino acids and recognizing the appropriate codons in the mRNA.

transformation (1) The conversion of a normal animal cell to a cancerous cell. (2) A change in genotype and phenotype due to the assimilation of external DNA by a cell.

transgenic Pertaining to an organism whose genome contains a gene introduced from another organism of the same or a different species.

translation The synthesis of a polypeptide using the genetic information encoded in an mRNA molecule. There is a change of "language" from nucleotides to amino acids.

translocation (1) An aberration in chromosome structure resulting from attachment of a chromosomal fragment to a nonhomologous chromosome. (2) During protein synthesis, the third stage in the elongation cycle when the RNA carrying the growing polypeptide moves from the A site to the P site on the ribosome. (3) The transport of organic nutrients in the phloem of vascular plants.

transmission The passage of a nerve impulse along axons.

transmission electron microscope (TEM) A microscope that passes an electron beam through very thin sections and is primarily used to study the internal ultrastructure of cells.

transpiration The evaporative loss of water from a plant.

transport epithelium One or more layers of specialized epithelial cells that regulate solute movements.

transport protein A transmembrane protein that helps a certain substance or class of closely related substances to cross the membrane.

transport vesicle A tiny membranous sac in a cell's cytoplasm carrying molecules produced by the cell.

transposable element A segment of DNA that can move within the genome of a cell by means of a DNA or RNA intermediate; also called a transposable genetic element.

transposon A transposable element that moves within a genome by means of a DNA intermediate.

transverse (T) tubule An infolding of the plasma membrane of skeletal muscle cells.

triacylglycerol (trī-as´-ul-glis´-uh-rol) Three fatty acids linked to one glycerol molecule; also called a fat or a triglyceride.

triiodothyronine (T₃) (trī´-ī-ō´-dō-thī´-rō-nēn) One of two iodine-containing hormones that are secreted by the thyroid gland and that help regulate metabolism, development, and maturation in vertebrates.

trimester In human development, one of three 3-month-long periods of pregnancy.

triple response A plant growth maneuver in response to mechanical stress, involving slowing of stem elongation, a thickening of the stem, and a curvature that causes the stem to start growing horizontally.

triplet code A set of three-nucleotide-long words that specify the amino acids for polypeptide chains.

triploblastic Possessing three germ layers: the endoderm, mesoderm, and ectoderm. Most eumetazoans are triploblastic.

trisomic Referring to a diploid cell that has three copies of a particular chromosome instead of the normal two.

trochophore larva (trō´-kuh-fōr) Distinctive larval stage observed in some lophotrochozoan animals, including some annelids and molluscs.

trophic efficiency The percentage of production transferred from one trophic level to the next.

trophic structure The different feeding relationships in an ecosystem, which determine the route of energy flow and the pattern of chemical cycling.

trophoblast The outer epithelium of a mammalian blastocyst. It forms the fetal part of the placenta, supporting embryonic development but not forming part of the embryo proper.

tropic hormone A hormone that has another endocrine gland as a target.

tropical rain forest A terrestrial biome characterized by high levels of precipitation and high temperatures year-round.

tropics Latitudes between 23.5° north and south.

tropism A growth response that results in the curvature of whole plant organs toward or away from stimuli due to differential rates of cell elongation.

tropomyosin The regulatory protein that blocks the myosin-binding sites on actin molecules.

troponin complex The regulatory proteins that control the position of tropomyosin on the thin filament.

true-breeding Referring to plants that produce offspring of the same variety when they self-pollinate.

tubal ligation A means of sterilization in which a woman's two oviducts (fallopian tubes) are tied closed to prevent eggs from reaching the uterus. A segment of each oviduct is removed.

tube foot One of numerous extensions of an echinoderm's water vascular system. Tube feet function in locomotion, feeding, and gas exchange.

tumor-suppressor gene A gene whose protein product inhibits cell division, thereby preventing the uncontrolled cell growth that contributes to cancer.

tundra A terrestrial biome at the extreme limits of plant growth. At the northernmost limits, it is called arctic tundra, and at high altitudes, where plant forms are limited to low shrubby or matlike vegetation, it is called alpine tundra.

tunicate Member of the subphylum Urochordata, sessile marine chordates that lack a backbone.

turgid (ter´-jid) Swollen or distended, as in plant cells. (A walled cell becomes turgid if it has a greater solute concentration than its surroundings, resulting in entry of water.)

turgor pressure The force directed against a plant cell wall after the influx of water and swelling of the cell due to osmosis.

turnover The mixing of waters as a result of changing water-temperature profiles in a lake.

turnover time The time required to replace the standing crop of a population or group of populations (for example, of phytoplankton), calculated as the ratio of standing crop to production.

twin study A behavioral study in which researchers compare the behavior of identical twins raised apart with that of identical twins raised in the same household.

tympanic membrane Another name for the eardrum, the membrane between the outer and middle ear.

ultimate causation The evolutionary explanation of "why" a behavior (or other aspect of an organism's biology) occurs, that is, the benefit to survival and reproduction or the evolutionary significance of the behavioral act.

undernourishment A condition that results from a diet that consistently supplies less chemical energy than the body requires.

uniformitarianism The principle stating that mechanisms of change are constant over time. *See* catastrophism.

Unikonta (yū′-ni-kon′-tuh) One of five super-groups of eukaryotes proposed in a current hypothesis of the evolutionary history of eukaryotes. This clade, which is supported by studies of myosin proteins and DNA, consists of amoebozoans and opisthokonts. *See also* Excavata, Chromalveolata, Rhizaria, and Archaeplastida.

unsaturated fatty acid A fatty acid possessing one or more double bonds between the carbons in the hydrocarbon tail. Such bonding reduces the number of hydrogen atoms attached to the carbon skeleton.

urea A soluble nitrogenous waste produced in the liver by a metabolic cycle that combines ammonia with carbon dioxide.

ureter (yū-rē′-ter) A duct leading from the kidney to the urinary bladder.

urethra (yū-rē′-thruh) A tube that releases urine from the mammalian body near the vagina in females and through the penis in males; also serves in males as the exit tube for the reproductive system.

uric acid A product of protein and purine metabolism and the major nitrogenous waste product of insects, land snails, and many reptiles. Uric acid is relatively nontoxic and largely insoluble.

urinary bladder The pouch where urine is stored prior to elimination.

uterine cycle The changes that occur in the uterus during the reproductive cycle of the human female; also called the menstrual cycle.

uterus A female organ where eggs are fertilized and/or development of the young occurs.

utricle In the vertebrate ear, a chamber in the vestibule behind the oval window that opens into the three semicircular canals.

vaccination *See* immunization.

vaccine A harmless variant or derivative of a pathogen that stimulates a host's immune system to mount defenses against the pathogen.

vacuole (vak′-yū-ōl′) A membrane-bounded vesicle whose function varies in different kinds of cells.

vagina Part of the female reproductive system between the uterus and the outside opening; the birth canal in mammals. During copulation, the vagina accommodates the male's penis and receives sperm.

valence The bonding capacity of a given atom; usually equals the number of unpaired electrons required to complete the atom's outermost (valence) shell.

valence electron An electron in the outermost electron shell.

valence shell The outermost energy shell of an atom, containing the valence electrons involved in the chemical reactions of that atom.

van der Waals interactions Weak attractions between molecules or parts of molecules that result from localized charge fluctuations.

variation Differences between members of the same species.

vas deferens In mammals, the tube in the male reproductive system in which sperm travel from the epididymis to the urethra.

vasa recta The capillary system in the kidney that serves the loop of Henle.

vascular cambium A cylinder of meristematic tissue in woody plants that adds layers of secondary vascular tissue called secondary xylem (wood) and secondary phloem.

vascular plant A plant with vascular tissue. Vascular plants include all living plant species except mosses, liverworts, and hornworts.

vascular tissue Plant tissue consisting of cells joined into tubes that transport water and nutrients throughout the plant body.

vascular tissue system A transport system formed by xylem and phloem throughout a vascular plant. Xylem transports water and minerals; phloem transports sugars, the products of photosynthesis.

vasectomy The cutting and sealing of each vas deferens to prevent sperm from entering the urethra.

vasocongestion The filling of a tissue with blood, caused by increased blood flow through the arteries of that tissue.

vasoconstriction A decrease in the diameter of blood vessels caused by contraction of smooth muscles in the vessel walls.

vasodilation An increase in the diameter of blood vessels caused by relaxation of smooth muscles in the vessel walls.

vector An organism that transmits pathogens from one host to another.

vegetal pole The point at the end of an egg in the hemisphere where most yolk is concentrated; opposite of animal pole.

vegetative reproduction Cloning of plants by asexual means.

vein (1) In animals, a vessel that carries blood toward the heart. (2) In plants, a vascular bundle in a leaf.

ventilation The flow of air or water over a respiratory surface.

ventral Pertaining to the underside, or bottom, of an animal with bilateral symmetry.

ventricle (ven′-tri-kul) (1) A heart chamber that pumps blood out of the heart. (2) A space in the vertebrate brain, filled with cerebrospinal fluid.

venule (ven′-yūl) A vessel that conveys blood between a capillary bed and a vein.

vernalization The use of cold treatment to induce a plant to flower.

vertebrate A chordate animal with a backbone: the mammals, reptiles (including birds), amphibians, sharks and rays, ray-finned fishes, and lobe-fins.

vesicle (ves′-i-kul) A sac made of membrane in the cytoplasm.

vessel A continuous water-conducting micropipe found in most angiosperms and a few nonflowering vascular plants.

vessel element A short, wide water-conducting cell found in the xylem of most angiosperms and a few nonflowering vascular plants. Dead at maturity, vessel elements are aligned end to end to form micropipes called vessels.

vestigial structure A structure of marginal, if any, importance to an organism. Vestigial structures are historical remnants of structures that had important functions in ancestors.

villus (plural, **villi**) (1) A finger-like projection of the inner surface of the small intestine. (2) A finger-like projection of the chorion of the mammalian placenta. Large numbers of villi increase the surface areas of these organs.

viral envelope A membrane that cloaks the capsid that in turn encloses a viral genome.

viroid (vī′-royd) A plant pathogen consisting of a molecule of naked, circular RNA a few hundred nucleotides long.

virulent Describing a pathogen against which an organism has little specific defense.

virulent phage A phage that reproduces only by a lytic cycle.

visceral mass One of the three main parts of a mollusc; the part containing most of the internal organs. *See also* foot, mantle.

visible light That portion of the electromagnetic spectrum that can be detected as various colors by the human eye, ranging in wavelength from about 380 nm to about 750 nm.

vital capacity The maximum volume of air that a mammal can inhale and exhale with each breath.

vitamin An organic molecule required in the diet in very small amounts. Vitamins serve primarily as coenzymes or as parts of coenzymes.

vitreous humor The jellylike material that fills the posterior cavity of the vertebrate eye.

viviparous (vī-vip′-uh-rus) Referring to a type of development in which the young are born alive after having been nourished in the uterus by blood from the placenta.

vocal cord One of a pair of bands of elastic tissue in the larynx. Air rushing past the tensed vocal cords makes them vibrate, producing sounds.

voltage-gated ion channel A specialized ion channel that opens or closes in response to changes in membrane potential.

vulva Collective term for the female external genitalia.

water potential (Ψ) The physical property predicting the direction in which water will flow, governed by solute concentration and applied pressure.

water vascular system A network of hydraulic canals unique to echinoderms that branches into extensions called tube feet, which function in locomotion, feeding, and gas exchange.

wavelength The distance between crests of waves, such as those of the electromagnetic spectrum.

wetland A habitat that is inundated by water at least some of the time and that supports plants adapted to water-saturated soil.

white matter Tracts of axons within the CNS.

wild type An individual with the phenotype most commonly observed in natural populations; also refers to the phenotype itself.

wilting The drooping of leaves and stems as a result of plant cells becoming flaccid.

wobble Flexibility in the base-pairing rules in which the nucleotide at the 5′ end of a tRNA anticodon can form hydrogen bonds with more than one kind of base in the third position (3′ end) of a codon.

xerophyte A plant adapted to an arid climate.

X-ray crystallography A technique that depends on the diffraction of an X-ray beam by the individual atoms of a crystallized molecule to study the three-dimensional structure of the molecule.

xylem (zī′-lum) Vascular plant tissue consisting mainly of tubular dead cells that conduct most of the water and minerals upward from the roots to the rest of the plant.

xylem sap The dilute solution of water and dissolved minerals carried through vessels and tracheids.

yeast Single-celled fungus that reproduces asexually by binary fission or by the pinching of small buds off a parent cell; some species exhibit cell fusion between different mating types.

yeast artificial chromosome (YAC) A cloning vector that combines the essentials of a eukaryotic chromosome—an origin for DNA replication, a centromere, and two telomeres—with foreign DNA.

yolk Nutrients stored in an egg.

yolk plug A group of large, nutrient-laden endodermal cells surrounded by the completed blastopore in an amphibian gastrula. These cells will be covered by ectoderm and end up inside the embryo.

yolk sac One of four extraembryonic membranes. It encloses the yolk in reptiles and is the first site of blood cell and circulatory system function.

zero population growth (ZPG) A period of stability in population size, when the per capita birth rate and death rate are equal.

zona pellucida The extracellular matrix surrounding a mammalian egg.

zone of polarizing activity (ZPA) A block of mesoderm located just under the ectoderm where the posterior side of a limb bud is attached to the body; required for proper pattern formation along the anterior-posterior axis of the limb.

zoned reserve An extensive region that includes areas relatively undisturbed by humans surrounded by areas that have been changed by human activity and are used for economic gain.

zoonotic pathogen A disease-causing agent that is transmitted to humans from other animals.

zoospore Flagellated spore found in chytrid fungi and some protists.

zygomycete (zī′-guh-mī′-sēt) Member of the fungal phylum Zygomycota, characterized by the formation of a sturdy structure called a zygosporangium during sexual reproduction.

zygosporangium (zī′-guh-spōr-an′-jē-um) In zygomycete fungi, a sturdy multinucleate structure in which karyogamy and meiosis occur.

zygote (zī′-gōt) The diploid product of the union of haploid gametes during fertilization; a fertilized egg.

Index

sustainable, 787–89
vegetative propagation of plants and, 814–15
water molds and crops, 588–89
Agrobacterium tumefaciens, 403, 421, 568*f*, 572, 736
α helix, **82***f*, 211*f*
A horizon, soil, 786*f*
AIDS (acquired immunodeficiency syndrome), **388, 950**
    HIV viral infection causing, 388–90, 391, 951 (*see also* HIV (human immunodeficiency virus))
Air circulation, climate and global, 1157*f*
Air roots, 740*f*
Air sacs, 922
α-lactalbumin, 440
Alanine, 79*f*
Alarm calls, social learning of, 1141–42
Albatross, 954, 958, 959*f*
Albinism, 277, 325
Albumin, 361*f*, 910
Albuterol, 63*f*
Alcohol fermentation, **178**
Alcohols, 64*f*
Aldehydes, **64***f*
Aldolase, 168*f*
Aldoses, 64*f*, **70***f*
Aldosterone, **971**–72, 993
Algae
    brown, 586, 587*f*
    as earliest multicellular eukaryotes, 517–18
    fossils, 511*f*
    fungi and, as lichens, 645, 649
    golden, 586
    green, 591–92, 600–606
    marine, 585–89
    as photoautotroph, 186*f*
    preventing blooms of, 1226
    red, 590–91
    sexual life cycle of, 252*f*
Algin, 586
Alimentary canal, **676, 883**
    in carnivore, vs. in herbivore, 891*f*
    human, 884*f*
    rotifer, 676
    variation in, 883*f*
Alkalinity, semen, 1013
Alkaptonuria, 325–26
Allantois, 715*f*, **1033**
Allee, W. C., 1184
Allee effect, 1184
Allele(s), **265**–66
    alteration in frequencies of, in populations, 475–79
    as alternative versions of genes, 265*f*
    assortment of, into gametes, 268*f*
    correlating, with behavior of chromosome pairs, 288–89
    dominant (*see* Dominant alleles)
    frequencies of, in populations, 472–75
    homologs and, 253
    multiple, 273
    multiple, of ABO blood groups, 273*f*
    recessive, 277–78
    segregation of, as chance, 270*f*
Allergens, 818, 948
Allergies, 948–49
Alligators, 717*f*, 718
Allolactose, 354
Allopatric speciation, **492**–94
    continental drift and, 520
    evidence of, 493–94
    in hybrid zones, 498–501

process of, 493
    reproductive isolation and, 495*f*
    sympatric speciation vs., 493*f*
Allopolyploids, **496**
Allosteric regulation, **157**–59
    activation and inhibition of enzymes by, 157–58
    of caspase enzymes, 158*f*
    feedback inhibition as, 159
    identification of, 158
Allosteric sites, 157
Almonds, 633
Alpha (α) carbon atom, 78
Alpha cells, 982
Alpha proteobacteria subgroup, 568*f*
Alpine woodsorrel, 813*f*
Alternate phyllotaxy, 766
Alternation of generations, **252, 587, 602**
    in plants, 602*f*
    in protists (brown algae), 587*f*
Alternative RNA splicing, **336, 362,** 363*f*, 433
Altman, Sidney, 509
Altruism, **1138**–39
    inclusive fitness and, 1139–40
    reciprocal, 1140
    social learning and, 1140–42
Alu elements, 436, 443
Aluminum, modifying plants for resistance to, 792
Alvarez, Luis, 522
Alvarez, Walter, 522
Alveolates, **582**–85
    apicomplexans, 583–84
    ciliates, 584–85
    dinoflagellates, 582–83
Alveoli, 582*f*, **920**
Alzheimer's disease, **1082**–83
Amacrine cells, **1104**
Amazon rain forest, 1255*f*
Amborella trichopoda, 630*f*
Amebic dysentery, 596
American alligator, 717*f*
American beech, 1159
American black bear, 12*f*
Amines, **65***f*
    solubility of, 977*f*
Amino acid(s), **78**. *See also* Protein(s)
    activation of, in eukaryotic cells, 348*f*
    amino group and, **65***f*
    as essential nutrients, 876
    genetic code and, 328–31
    monomers of, 78–80
    as neurotransmitters, 1059*t*, 1060
    organic compounds and, in early Earth atmosphere, 508
    polymers of, 80
    sequence of, in human globin proteins, 440*t*
    sickle-cell disease and, 84*f*
    solubility of, 977*f*
    specified by triplets of nucleotides, 329*f*, 330, 337
    twenty, in proteins, 79*f*
Aminoacyl-tRNA synthetases, **338**–39
    joining specific amino acids to tRNA, 338*f*
Amino end, polypeptide. *See* N-terminus
Amino group, **65***f*. *See also* Amino acid(s)
Amitochondriate protists, 576
Ammonia, 41*f*, 59*f*, 954, **959,** 965
Ammonification, 1233*f*
Ammonifying bacteria, 793
Ammonites, 511*f*, **680**
Amniocentesis, **280,** 281*f*
Amnion, 715*f*, **1033**
Amniotes, **713**–20, **1033**
    derived characters of, 713–15

developmental adaptations of, 1033
    early, 715
    evolution of, 657
    mammals as, 720–28
    phylogeny, 714*f*
    reptiles as, 715–20
Amniotic egg, **713,** 715*f*
Amoebas, 579*f*, **589,** 853*f*
Amoebocytes, **670**
Amoeboid movement, 117*f*
Amoebozoans, **594**–96
    entamoebas, 596
    gymnamoebas, 596
    slime molds, 594–96
AMP (adenosine monophosphate), 181, 338*f*
Amphetamine, 1081
Amphibia class, 711–13
Amphibians, **711**–13
    body axes in, 1026*f*
    breathing in, 920
    double circulatory system of, 902
    embryo development fate in, 1041–42
    evolution of, 657
    kidney adaptations in, 968
    reproduction in, 1000*f*
Amphipathic molecule, **125**
Ampicillin resistance, 399–400
Amplification, **1089**
    of cell signals, 221
    of sensory stimuli, 1089
amp^R gene, 399–400
Ampulla, sea star, 693*f*
Amygdala, **1078**
Amygdalin, 633
Amylase, **884**
Amylopectin, 71*f*
Amylose, 71*f*
Anabolic pathways, **143,** 180–81. *See also* Protein synthesis
Anaerobic respiration, 163, 177–79, **564**
Analogous structures, **465**
Analogy, **540**
    homology vs., 540–41
Anaphase, **231,** 233*f*, 236*f*, 256*f*
Anaphase I, 254*f*, 256*f*, 257*f*
Anaphase II, 255*f*
Anaphylactic shock, 948
Anatomy, **852.** *See also* Animal form and function; Morphology; Plant structure
Ancestral character, shared, **543**
Anchorage, roots and, 765–67
Anchorage dependence, **242**
Anchoring junctions, 121*f*
Androgens, **993,** 1007
Aneuploidy, **297,** 299
Angiosperms, **606,** 801–20
    agriculture and, 814–15
    asexual reproduction in, 812–15
    biotechnology and modification of crop, 815–19
    bulk flow by positive pressure in translocation in, 780
    characteristics of, 625–28
    diversity of, 630–31
    double fertilization in, 806–7
    evolution of, 628–30
    flowers of, 625–26, 801–5 (*see also* Flower(s))
    fruit of, 626, 809–10, 811*f* (*see also* Fruit)
    gametophyte development in, 803*f*
    gametophyte-sporophyte relationships, 619*f*
    life cycle of, 627*f*, 628
    links between animals and, 630–32
    mechanisms preventing self-fertilization in, 813

Australia
- continental drift and species in, 521
- distribution of red kangaroos in, 1151*f*
- evolution of birds in, 450–51
- gene flow in, 489*f*

Australian scaly-foot lizard, 536
Australian thorny devil lizard, 717*f*
Australopithecus anamensis, 728
Australopiths, 727–30
Autocrine, **976**
- signaling, 976*f*

Autoimmune diseases, **949**
- diabetes mellitus, 983–84

Autonomic nervous system, **1068**
- parasympathetic division of, 1068, 1069*f*
- sympathetic division of, 1068, 1069*f*

Autophagy, lysosomes and, 107*f*, 108
Autopolyploids, 495–96
Autosomes, **250**
Autotrophs, **185**, **564***t*
Auxin, 826, **827***t*, 828–29
- apical dominance and, 830*f*
- cell elongation and, 828, 829*f*
- greening and, 824
- as herbicide, 829
- polar movement of, 828*f*
- root formation and, 828

Average heterozygosity, **469**
Average kinetic energy, 48
Avery, Oswald, 306
Avian flu, 392, 451, 950, 1218–19
Avirulent pathogens, **846**, 847*f*
Avogadro's number, 52
Axel, Richard, 1098–99
Axial polarity, 758*f*
Axillary bud, **740**
Axis establishment in early development, 371–73
Axolotl, 898
Axon hillock, **1048**
Axons, 859*f*
- action potentials as signals conducted by, 1052–56
- nerves formed from bundles of, 1065

Ayre, Brian, 841
Azidothymidine (AZT), 391

B

Bacillus thuringiensis, 816
Bacteria, 306. *See also* Bacteria domain; Prokaryotes
- antibiotic resistance in, 563–64
- binary fission in, 236, 237*f*
- biofilms of, 207
- bioremediation and, 1261
- cell structure of rod-shaped, 98*f*
- chromosomes of, vs. eurkaryotic chromosomes, 320–23
- communication among, 207*f*
- conjugation in, 562–64
- cyclic electron flow in, 195–96
- designing synthetic, 573
- as DNA experimental organism, 305
- DNA replication in, 317*f*
- DNA transformation of genetic material in, 306
- evolution of mitosis in, 237*f*
- expression systems of cloned, 403
- genome sequencing of, 428–29
- Gram staining of, 557*f*
- mutualistic, and digestion, 892–93
- nitrogen-fixing, 793–94
- as pathogens, 571–72

as photoautotrophs, 186*f*
plasmids of (*see* Plasmids)
proteins involved in DNA replication in, 317*t*
regulation of transcription in, 351–56
in soils, and plant nutrition, 793–95
transcription and translation in, 329*f*, 346, 347*f*
transfer of genetic traits between strains of, 306*f*
using RFLP analysis to determine diversity of, 1205*f*
viruses in (*see* Bacteriophages (phages))

Bacteria domain, **13**, 551–51. *See also* Bacteria; Prokaryotes
- compared with Archaea and Eukarya, 567*t*
- gene expression in, compared with other life domains, 346–47
- genome size in, 432, 433*t*
- phylogeny of, 567–70

Bacterial artificial chromosome (BAC), **401**
- genome sequencing and, 427
- library of, 400*f*

Bacteriophages (phages), **307**, **383**
- determining genetic material of T2, 307*f*
- DNA evidence in, 306–8
- libraries of, 400*f*
- Phage λ (lambda), 386
- reproductive cycles of, 385–87
- T4 (*see* T4 phage)
- transduction and role of, 561–62

Bacteriorhodopsin, 556
Bacteroides thetaiotaomicron, 571
Bacteroids, **794**
Baker, C. S., 539*f*
Baker's yeast, 651
Balance, locomotion and, 1115
Balancing selection, **483**–84
Ball-and-socket joints, 1114*f*
Ball-and-stick models
- molecular shape and, 41*f*
- organic molecules, 60*f*

β-amyloid, 1082–83
Banded iron formations, 516, 516*f*
Bandicoot, 722*f*
Barbs, 626*f*
Bark, **754**
Barley, 631*f*, 831*f*
Barnacles, 692, 1200*f*
Barn swallows, 719*f*
Barr body, **291**
Barrier defenses, 931*f*, 933
Barrier methods, **1016**–17
Barrier reef, 1165*f*
Basal angiosperms, **630**
Basal animals, sponges as, 662
Basal apparatus, 558*f*
Basal body, 115*f*, **116**
Basal lamina, 856*f*
Basal metabolic rate (BMR), **869**–70
Basal nuclei, 1073
Basal surface, 856*f*
Base(s), 52, **53**
- nitrogenous (*see* Nitrogenous bases)
- in nucleotides (*see* Nucleotide(s))

Base pairing, DNA, 310, 310*f*
- DNA replication and, 311–12

Base-pair substitutions, **344**–45
Basidiocarps, **646**
Basidiomycetes, 642*f*, **646**–47
Basidiospores, 647
Basidium, **646**
Basin wetlands, 1162*f*
Bates, Henry, 20

Batesian mimicry, **1201**
Bats, 16*f*, 969
- flower pollination by, 805*f*
- sensory and motor mechanisms of, 1087

β-catenin, gastrulation control and, 658
B cell(s), 913*f*, **936**, 944–46
- activation of, in humoral immune response, 944–46
- antibodies and, 945–46
- antigen receptors of, 937–38
- clonal selection of, 941*f*

B cell receptor, **937**–38
Bdelloidea, 677
Beadle, George, 326, 327*f*
Beagle, H.M.S., Charles Darwin's voyage on, 455–56
Beaks, of finches, 23, 468
Beans
- seed germination, 809*f*
- seed structure, 808*f*
- vegetarian diet and, 876*f*

Bears, 12*f*
- population conservation of, 1253, 1258*f*

Bees
- communication signals among, 1124*f*
- flower pollination by, 804*f*

Beetles
- evolution and, 452
- magnolia trees and, 1
- natural selection and, 16*f*

Behavior, **1120**–45
- agonistic, 1136–37
- altruistic, and concept of inclusive fitness, 1138–42
- animal signals and communication, 1123–25
- chimpanzee, 18*f*
- cognition and problem solving, 1128
- courtship and mating, 1123*f*, 1134–38
- evolution, human culture, sociobiology and, 1142
- experience and, 1129–30
- fixed action patterns, 1121
- foraging, 1133–34
- genetic component of, 1130–32
- habitat selection and species distribution/ dispersal, 1153
- imprinting, 1126
- innate, 1125
- learning and, 1125–29, 1140–42
- natural selection of, 1133–38
- oriented movement, 1122
- proximate and ultimate causes of, 1121
- regulatory genes and, 1130–31
- review, 1142–43
- rhythms of, 1122–23
- selection for survival and reproductive success as explanations of, 1133–38
- sensory inputs as stimulus for, 1120–25
- social learning, 1140–42
- thermoregulation and, 866
- variations in genetically based, 1131–32

Behavioral ecology, **1121**
- altruistic behavior and, 1138–42
- genetics and, 1130–31
- genetic and environmental influences on behavior, 1129–33
- natural selection and, 1133–38
- proximate and ultimate causes of behavior and, 1121

Behavioral isolation, 490*f*

Behavioral variation in natural populations, 1131–32
    in migratory patterns, 1131
    in prey selection, 1131–32
Beijerinck, Martinus, 382
Belding's ground squirrel, 872*f*
    kin selection and altruism in, 1140*f*
    life table, 1177*t*
    reproductive table, 1178, 1179*t*
    survivorship curves, 1178*f*
Benign tumor, 243
Bennettitales plants, 629
Bent grass, 478, 479*f*
Benthic zone, **1161**
Benthos, **1161**
Berries, 626*f*
Berthold, Peter, 1131
Bertness, Mark, 1209
Berzelius, Jöns Jakob, 58
Beta-carotene, 879
Beta cells, 982
Beta oxidation, **180**
Beta proteobacteria subgroup, 568*f*
β-galactosidase, 354, 399–400
β-globin gene, 399, 406*f*
B horizon, soil, 786*f*
Bicoid gene, **372**–73
Biennials, **746**
Big-bang reproduction, **1179**
Bilateral symmetry
    animal phylogeny and, 662
    body plans and, **659**
    flower shape and pollination rate, 632
Bilateria, **662**
    chordates and, 698
    evolutionary relationships of, 662–64
Bile, **888**
Bile salts, 889*f*
Binary fission, **236**, 237*f*
    prokaryotes and, 559–61
Binding, ligand, 210
Binding sites, ribosome, 339*f*
Binomial nomenclature, **537**
Biochemical level, phenotype, 272
Biochemical pathways
    feedback mechanisms in, 11*f*
    gene specification of enzymes functioning in, 327*f*
Biochemistry, 97
Biodiesel, 421
Biodiversity, 12–14
    biogeographical factors affecting community, 1214–17
    S. Carroll on, 534–35
    effects of mass extinctions on, 521*f*, 522–23
    evolutionary developmental biology and (*see* Evolutionary developmental biology (evo-devo))
    hot spots, **1257***f*, 1258
    levels of (genetic, species, ecosystem), 1246–47
    phylogeny and (*see* Phylogeny)
    of species in communities (*see* Species diversity)
    structure of landscape and, 1255–60
    threats to, 1248–50
Bioenergetics, **143**, **868**–72
    energy budgets, 871
    energy costs of foraging behavior, 1134*f*
    influences on metabolic rate, 870–71
    of locomotion, 1116–17
    osmoregulation, 957–58
    overview of animal, 869*f*

oxygen consumption in pronghorn, 869*f*
    quantifying energy use, 869
    thermoregulation and minimum metabolic rate, 869–70
    torpor and energy conservation, 871–72
Bioethanol, 420–21
Biofilms, 207, **565**
Biofuels, 420–21, **817**
Biogenic amines, **1060**
    depression and, 1082
    as neurotransmitters, 1059*t*, 1060
Biogeochemical cycles, **1231**, 1232–33*f*
    effects of human activities on, 1236–42
Biogeography, **465**, 1151
    community diversity affected by, 1214–17
    as evidence for evolution, 465
Bioinformatics, **11**, 86, **426**
Biological augmentation, **1261**
Biological carbon pump, 585–87
Biological clock, 994, **1072**, 1112. *See also* Circadian rhythms
    plants and, 838–39
    regulation of, by hypothalamus, 1072–73
Biological diversity. *See* Biodiversity
Biological Dynamics of Forest Fragments Project, 1255–56
Biological magnification, **1238**
Biological molecule(s), 68–91
    carbohydrates, 69–74
    chemical groups as key to functioning of, 63–66
    lipids, 74–77
    macromolecules, 68–69
    nucleic acids, 86–89
    proteins, 77–86
    review, 90–91
    theme of emergent properties, 89
Biological order and disorder, 145
Biological organization, 3–6
    emergent properties and, 3
    levels of, 4–5*f*
    reductionism and study of, 3
    systems and, 6*f*
Biological species concept, 487–92. *See also* Species
    alternatives to, 492
    defined, **488**
    limitations of, 492
    reproductive isolation and, 488–89, 490–91*f*
Biology, **1**–27
    cells (*see* Cell(s))
    chemical connection to, 30–31 (*see also* Chemistry)
    conservation (*see* Conservation biology)
    evolution as core theme of, 12–18 (*see also* Evolution)
    forms of science and inquiry in, 18–24
    genetics (*see* Genetics)
    D. Gordon on research in, 28–29
    importance of viruses to molecular, 381
    as information science, 10*f*
    review, 25–26
    as scientific inquiry about life, 1–2 (*see also* Life)
    systems, 6, 9–11
    themes connecting concepts of, 3–11
Bioluminescence, 142*f*, 571*f*, 672*f*
Biomanipulation, **1210**
Biomass, **1206**
    fuel, 817
    pyramid, 1229

Biome(s), **1159**
    aquatic, 1159–66
    terrestrial, 1166–71
Biophilia, 1247, 1265
Bioremediation, **572**–73, **1260**–61
Biorhythms, melatonin and, 994. *See also* Biological clock; Circadian rhythms
Biosafety Protocol, 422
Biosphere, **1149***f*. *See also* Earth
    biophilia and future of, 1265
    ecological role of prokaryotes in, 570–71
    importance of photosynthesis in, 185
    as level of biological organization, 4*f*
Biosphere-2, 55*f*
Biosynthesis, 143, 180–81
Biotechnology, **396**. *See also* DNA technology
    applied to crop plants, 816–19
    phytoremediation, 789
Biotic factors, **1151**
    species distribution/dispersal and, 1153–54
Biotic stresses, **843**
Bipedalism, 730
Bipolar cells, **1103**
Bipolar disorder, **1081**
Bird(s), 452, 958*f*
    adaptive radiation of finches, 17*f*
    alimentary canal, 883*f*
    breathing by, 921
    cognition regions in brain of, 1074*f*
    derived characters of, 718
    diseases of, 451
    dispersal of cattle egret in Americas, 1152*f*
    double circulation in, 902–3
    earliest, 719*f*
    effects of toxin biological magnification on, 1238*f*, 1239
    energy costs of flight, 1116*f*
    evolution of, 450–51, 657–58
    extraembryonic membranes in, 1033*f*
    flower pollination by, 805*f*
    form and function in wings and feathers of, 7*f*, 719*f*
    gastrulation in embryo of, 1030*f*
    greater prairie chicken, 477–78, 1251, 1252*f*
    imprinted behavior in, 1126*f*
    kidney adaptations in, 968
    living, 719, 720*f*
    migration by, 1122, 1126*f*
    nitrogenous wastes, 959*f*
    organogenesis in embryo of, 1032*f*
    origin of, 718–19
    phylogenetic tree of, 547*f*
    red-cockaded woodpecker, 1254–55
    as reptiles, 716 (*see also* Reptiles)
    salt excretion in seabirds, 958, 959*f*
    species-area curve for North American, 1216*f*
    wing development in, 1042*f*
Birth control, human, 1016–18
Birth control pills, **1017**
Births
    dietary deficiencies linked to human birth defects, 880*f*
    human, 1015–16
    human birth rate, 1186*f*, 1192
    population dynamics and, 1175*f*
Bivalves, 679–80
Bivalvia, 678*t*
β-keratin, bird feathers and, 718
Black bear, 12*f*
Black bread mold, 643–44
Blackcap warbler, 1131

photosynthesis in (*see* Photosynthesis)

plant, 101*f* (*see also* Plant cell(s))

plant cell expansion, 756, 757*f*

producing clones of, to carry recombinant plasmids, 399–400

programmed death in (*see* Apoptosis)

prokaryotic, 557–59 (*see also* Prokaryotic cell(s))

protein folding in, 85–86

recognition, 129*f*, 130

reproduction (*see* Cell cycle; Cell division)

respiration in (*see* Cellular respiration)

review, 122–24

sequential regulation of gene expression during differentiation of, 368–69

signal induction of directional growth in, 220*f*

size range of, 95*f*

stem (*see* Stem cells)

surface-to-volume ratio of, 99*f*

systems biology and, 9–11

systems map of protein interactions in, 10*f*

transcription specific to type of, 361*f*

ultrastructure, 96

Cell adhesion molecules (CAMs), **1036**

animal morphogenesis and, 1036–38

Cell body, **1048**

Cell-cell communication. *See* Cell signaling

Cell-cell recognition

membrane protein, 129*f*

role of membrane carbohydrates in, 130

Cell cycle, **228**–45. *See also* Cell division

alternation of mitotic phase and interphase in, 230–38

cancer and abnormal, 242–43

cell division by binary fission and, 236, 237*f*

cytokinesis in, 234–36

formation of daughter cells during cell division, 229–30

genetic changes affecting, and cancer development, 373–77

molecular control system in eukaryotic, 238–43

P. Nurse on, 92–93

phases of, 231*f*

review, 244–45

roles of cell division in, 228–29

Cell-cycle control system, 238–43, **239**

anchorage dependence, 242*f*

cancer as failure of, 242–43

cell cycle clock, 239–41

checkpoints in, 239*f*, 240*f*, 241–42

cytoplasmic signals and, 238

density-dependent inhibition, 242*f*

mechanical analogy for, 239*f*

stop and go (internal and external signals) at checkpoints, 241–42

Cell cycle-inhibiting pathway, 375*f*

Cell cycle-stimulating pathway, 375*f*

Cell differentiation, 366–67, **1021**

cytokinins and, 829

Cell division, **228**, **230**. *See also* Cell cycle

binary fission as bacterial, 236, 237*f*

cancer as uncontrolled, 242–43

cell cycle and, 230–43

cellular organization of genetic material and, 229

chromosomes distribution during, 229–30

cytokinesis and, 234–36

cytokinins and, 829

daughter cells produced by, 229–30

embryonic development and, 366

key roles of, 228–29

meiosis and (*see* Meiosis)

mitosis and, 230, 231, 232–33*f*, 234, 235*f*, 236*f*, 237

plane and symmetry of, and plant morphogenesis, 755, 756*f*

P. Nurse on, 92–93

signaling pathways that regulate, 375*f*

Cell fate in animal development, 1038–44

cellular asymmetries in, 1040–41

determination of, and pattern formation by inductive signals, 1041–44

establishing cellular asymmetries, 1040–41

mapping, 1038–40

Cell fate in plant development, 759–60

Cell fractionation, **97***f*

Cell junctions, 208*f*

Cell-mediated immune response, 931*f*, **942**

cytotoxic T cell function against pathogens in, 943

helper T cells and, 943

overview of, 942*f*

Cell motility, 112–18

animal morphogenesis and, 1035–36

Cell plate, 235*f*, **236**

Cell signaling, 206–27, 221*f*

cancer and interference with normal, 374–76

conversion of external signals into cell responses, 206–10

cytoplasmic, 238

in endocrine and nervous systems, 859*f*

endocrine system and, 981–84

evolution of, 206–7

hormones and, 975–80

integration of, in apoptosis, 223–25

local and distance, 208–9

local regulators and, 976, 980–81

neurotransmitters and neurohormones, and, 976–77

in plants (*see* Plant responses)

reception of signals, 209, 210–14

responses to, 210, 218–23

review, 225–27

signal transduction pathways in, 207

specificity of, and coordinated response, 221–22

three stages of, 209–10

transduction and relay of signals to target cells, 209–10, 214–18

P. Zambryski on, 736–37

Cell-type specific transcription, 361*f*

Cellular innate immune defenses, 933–34

Cellular respiration, 162–84

ATP production, 176–77

ATP yield at each stage of, 176*f*

biosynthesis (anabolic pathways) and, 180–81

as catabolic pathway, 143, 162–67

chemiosmosis in, 173–76

citric acid cycle of, 170–72, 180–82

control of, 181*f*

defined, **163**

electron transport chain in, 172–73, 175*f*

energy flow in ecosystems and, 162*f*

feedback mechanisms in regulation of, 181–82

fermentation and aerobic respiration forms of, 177–79

formula, 163

free energy and, 148*f*

glycolysis in, 167–69, 179, 180–82

measuring, 869*f*

metabolism and, 142

mitochondria as site of, 109, 110*f*, 162, 166*f*, 174*f*, 175*f*

origin of, 516

oxidative phosphorylation in, 172–77

redox reactions in, 163–66

review, 182–83

stages of, 166–67

versatility of catabolism, 180–81

Cellular skeleton, 94*f*

Cellular slime mold, **595**–96, 595*f*

Cellulose, **72**

digesting of, by prokaryotes, 74*f*

in plant cell walls, 73*f*

role of microtubules in orienting deposition of, in plant cell walls, 119*f*

structure of, 73*f*

Cell wall(s), 654

cellulose in plant, 72, 73*f*

plant, 101*f*, **118**, 119*f*

prokaryotic, 98*f*, 557–58

role of microtubules in orienting cellulose deposition in plant, 119*f*

Celsius scale, **48**

Cenozoic era, 514, 515*t*

animal evolution in, 658

Center for Plant Conservation, 1246

Centimorgan map unit, 295, 296*f*

Centipedes, 687–88

Central canal, **1067**

Central disk, sea star, 693*f*

Central dogma, DNA, 328

Central nervous system (CNS), **1048**, 1065–68

brain and (*see* Brain)

plasticity of, 1079

stem cell-based therapy and, 1083

vertebrate, 1066*f*

Central vacuoles, **108**

plant cell, 101*f*

Centrifugation, differential, **97***f*

Centrioles, **114**

Centromere, **229**, 230*f*

Centromeric DNA, 436

Centrosomes, **114**, **231**

animal cell, 100*f*

Cephalization, **659**, 1065

Cephalochordates, 698, 700–701

Cephalopods (Cephalopoda), 678*t*, 680

Cerebellum, **1072**

Cerebral cortex, **1070**, 1075–78

body part representation in, 1076*f*

consciousness and, 1078

emotions and, 1077–78

information processing in, 1075–76

language and speech and, 1076–77

lateralization of cortical function in, 1077

limbic system and, 1077*f*

lobes of human, 1075*f*

Cerebral ganglia

earthworm, 681*f*

insect, 688*f*

Cerebral hemispheres, **1073**

Cerebrospinal fluid, **1067**

Cerebrum, 1074–74. *See also* Cerebral cortex

Cervix, **1004**, 1016*f*

Cestoidea class, 674*t*, 676

Cetaceans, 725*f*

evolution of, 462*f*

Cetartiodactyla, 725*f*

CFCs (chlorofluorocarbons), 1241–42

Chaetae, 681

Chagas' disease, 581

Chambered nautilus, 680*f*

Chance. *See* Probability, Mendelian inheritance governed by laws of

Index

Index

Index

between populations, 470
within populations, 469
preservation of, by diploid and balanced
polymorphism, 483–84
in prokaryotes, 561–64
sexual reproduction as source of, 471
sexual selection, 481–83
Gene trees, 489*f*
Gene variability, 469–70
Genome(s), **9, 229,** 426–49, 548–49. *See also*
Gene(s)
bioinformatics for analysis of, 426, 429–32
comparing, of different species, 442–47
complete, 571, 646, 755*f*, 835
complete sequences, 426, 432
DNA changes in, leading to evolution of,
438–42
estimated number of genes in, 432, 433*t*
eukaryotic, 434–38 (*see also* Eukaryotic
genome)
evolution of, 549
gene density and noncoding DNA in,
433–34
human (*see* Human genome)
Phanerochaete chrysosporium, 652
prokaryotic, 559 (*see* Prokaryotic genome)
sequencing, 427–29 (*see also* Genome
sequencing)
size of, 432, 433*t*
study of (genomics), 426
viral, 382
Genome sequences
comparing, 442–47
resources used in analysis of, 429
Genome sequencing, 427–29
bioinformatics as tool in, 429–32
entire genome of bacterium *Haemophilus
influenzae*, 396
three-stage approach to, 427–28
whole-genome shotgun approach to,
428*f*, 429
Genomic equivalence, 412*f*
Genomic imprinting, **300,** 301*f*, **358**
Genomic libraries, **400**–401, 400*f*
S. Edwards on, 451
Genomics, **426.** *See also* Genome(s)
Genotype, **267**
ABO blood group, 273*f*
determining, with testcross, 267*f*
heterozygote advantage and, 483
phenotype vs., 267*f*, 275
relative fitness of, 479–80
Genus (genera), 12*f*, **537**
Geographical barriers, speciation with and
without, 492–98
Geographical hybrid zones, speciation and,
498–501
Geographic ranges, snake mimicry and,
21–22
Geographic variability, **470**
Geologic record, **514,** 515*t*
Geometric isomers, **62,** 62*f*
Germ cells, 251
Germination
gibberellins and, 831, 831*f*
phytochromes and, 836–37, 836*f*
seed, 809, 809*f*
Germ layers, **1028**
adult derivatives of three embryonic, 1032*f*
Gestation, **1013**
Ghost crabs, 692*f*

Ghrelin, 894*f*
Giant panda, 162*f*
Giardia intestinalis, 578*f*, 580
Gibberellins, 827*t*, **830**–31
fruit growth and, 831
germination and, 831
stem elongation and, 830–31
Gibbons, 727*f*
Gibbs, J. Willard, 146
Gibbs free energy, 146
Gill filaments, 917*f*
Gills, 916*f*, 917–18, 917*f*
arthropod, 685
mollusc, 679
Gill slits, 700, 702–3
Ginkgo biloba, 622*f*
Ginkgophyta, 622*f*
GLABRA-2 gene, 758, 759*f*
Glacial retreat, succession following, 1213–14,
1213*f*, 1214*f*
Glans, **1004**
Glanville fritillary, 1190, 1190*f*
Gleason, H. A., 1211
Glia, **858,** 859*f*, **1048,** 1067–68, 1067*f*
Global ecology, **1149***f*
Global warming, 1239–41
coal and, 615
coral reefs and, 673
dendrochronology and, 753*f*
habitat loss and, 1248
Globin genes and proteins
evolution of human, 439, 440*f*
human, 437*f*, 439–40, 440*t*
human, as gene family, 437*f*
Globular proteins, 81
Glomeromycetes, 642*f*, **644**
Glomerulus, **964**
Glottis, 885
Glucagon, 893, 893*f*, **982**
control of blood glucose and, 982–84
steroid hormones and, 993
Glucocorticoids, **993**
Glucose, 70, 71*f*, 151*f*
α and β ring structures, 73*f*
Calvin cycle, and conversion of carbon dioxide into, 198, 199*f*
cellular respiration and metabolism of, 164,
167–77
homeostasis of blood levels of, 982,
983*f*, 984
homeostatic regulation and, 893*f*
linear and ring forms of, 71*f*
as monosaccharide, 70*f*
steroid hormones and, 993
Glutamate, **1060**
schizophrenia and, 1081
Glutamic acid, 79*f*, 84*f*
Glutamine, 79*f*
Glyceraldehyde, 70*f*
Glyceraldehyde-3-phosphate (G3P), 198–99
Glycerol, fats and, 75*f*
Glycerol phosphate, 65*f*
Glycine, **65***f*, 79*f*
Glycogen, **72,** 893*f*
animal cells storage of, 72*f*
breakdown of, 209
Glycogen phosphorylase, 209, 219*f*
Glycolipids, **130**
Glycolysis, **166,** 167–69
ATP yield, 176*f*
cellular respiration and, 166*f*

citric acid cycle and, 170*f*
connection of, to other metabolic pathways,
180–82
energy input and output of, 167*f*
energy investment phase in, 168*f*
energy payoff phase of, 169*f*
evolutionary significance of, 179
pyruvate as key juncture in catabolism, 179*f*
Glycolytic fibers, 1111
Glycoproteins, **105, 130**
viruses and, 383*f*, 388*f*
Glycosidic linkage, **70**–71*f*
Glyoxysomes, 111
Gnathostomes, **705**–10
chondrichthyans (sharks, rays), 706–8
derived characters of, 705–6
fossil, 706, 706*f*
ray-finned, and lobe-finned fishes, 708–10
tetrapods, 710–13
Gnetophyta, 622*f*, 628
Gnetum, 622*f*
Goatsbeard plants, 496
Goiter, 32*f*
Golden algae, **586,** 586*f*
Golden rice, 572, 817, 817*f*, 879, 880
Golgi apparatus, **105**–7
animal cell, 100*f*
endomembrane system and, 109*f*
plant cell, 101*f*
structure, 106*f*
Gonadotropin-releasing hormone (GRH)
human female cycles and, 1010–11
mammalian reproduction and, 1007
Gonadotropins, 989, 1007
Gonads, **1001**
germ cells and, 251
meiosis and, 230
Gondwana, 520*f*
Gonzales, Carlos Rivera, 1265*f*
Goodall, Jane, 18, 18*f*
Goodwin, William, 732*f*
Gordon, Deborah M.
on chemical communication in ants,
28–29
devil's gardens and, 30–31
Gorillas, 727*f*
Gorter, E., 126
Gould, Stephen Jay, 502, 534
Gout, 960
G protein, **211***f*
G protein-coupled receptor (GPCR), **211***f*, 979,
1098
cyclic AMP as second messenger in pathway
of, 216–17, 216*f*
M. Yanagisawa on, 850
Graded potentials, 1052
action potentials and, 1053*f*
Grades (taxonomy)
clades vs., 659, 660
plant, **605**–6
Gradients, solute, 966
Grafting of plants, 814
Graft vs. host reaction, 948
Gram, 52
Gram, Hans Christian, 557
Gram-negative bacteria, **557**–58, 557*f*
Gram-positive bacteria, **557**–58, 557*f*, 569*f*
Gram staining, **557**–58, 557*f*
Grana, 187
Grant, Peter and Rosemary, 23, 468
Granum, **110,** 111*f*

derived characters of, 728
diseases and disorders of (*see* Diseases and disorders)
disturbances in communities as environmental impact of, 1214
diversity within the species, 488*f*
earliest hominins, 728, 729*f*
early *Homo* genus, 731
effects of activities of, on ecosystem chemical cycles, 1235–42
effects of genetically modified organisms on health of, 818
embryo of, 1034*f* (*see also* Embryonic development)
evolution of culture in, 1142
family tree of, 536*f*
flatworm as parasites in, 675, 675*f*
gene flow and evolution of, 478*f*
gene therapy for, 417–18
genetic disorders (*see* Genetic disorders)
Homo sapiens, 732–22
importance of seed plants to, 632–34
life cycle, 251*f*
Mendelian inheritance patterns in, 276–81
mutualism and, 571
Neanderthals, 731–32
nutrition (*see* Human nutrition)
organs and organ systems of, 5*f*
reducing hunger and malnutrition in, using transgenic crops, 816–17
sex chromosomes, 289*f*
sex determination in, 289, 290*f*
tapeworms as parasites in, 676
tool use in, 730
windpipe cell cilia in, 14*f*
Human body, 963*f*
body part representation in cerebral cortex, 1076*f*
brain (*see* Human brain)
colon, **890**, 890*f*
differential growth rates in, 525*f*
digestive system, 884–90, 884*f*, 887*f*
diseases and disorders of (*see* Diseases and disorders)
ear, and hearing, 1093*f*, 1094*f*, 1095*f*
endocrine glands in, 981*f*, 987*t*
endocrine system (*see* Endocrine system)
energy budget for female, 871*f*
excretory system, 963–72, 963*f* (*see also* Excretory systems)
eye, 529, 529*f*
fat cells, 893*f*
lymphatic system, 934*f*
maintaining energy balance in, 893–96
naturally occurring elements in, 32*t*
nervous system, 1065, 1066*f*, 1067–69
olfaction (smelling sense) in, 1097, 1098, 1099*f*
overnourishment, obesity, and, 894–96
PET scans and, 34*f*
sensory receptors in skin of, 1090*f*
skull, 525*f*
thermoregulation in, 868, 868*f*
tongue, and tasting, 1097*f*
two-solute model of kidney function, 967*f*
water balance in, 957*f*
water-soluble proteins, 51*f*
white blood cell apoptosis, 223*f*
Human brain, 1070–78
cerebral cortex of, 1075–78, 1075*f*
cognition and, 1074*f*

consciousness and, 1078
development of, 1070*f*
endocrine glands in, 985*f*
hypothalamus, 868*f*
mapping activity in, 1064, 1064*f*
memory, learning, and synaptic connections in, 1078–80
reward system, 1082, 1082*f*
view from rear, 1073*f*
Human chorionic gonadotropin (HCG), 946, **1013**
Human genome, 871*f*. *See also* Genome(s)
α-globin and β-globin gene family, 437*f*
α-globin and β-globin gene family and evolution of, 439–40, 440*t*
compared with other species, 442–44, 443*f*, 444*f*
complete sequence for, 426
function of *FOXP2* gene in, 444*f*
globin genes, 439, 440*f*
microarray chips containing, 432, 432*f*
mouse genome compared with, 438, 438*f*
reverse pharmacology and, 851
size of, 433, 433*t*
types of DNA sequences in, 434*f*
Human Genome Project, 10*f*, **427**–29, 427*f*
alternative RNA splicing and, 336
Human growth hormone (HGH), 397*f*, 418
Human immunodeficiency virus. *See* HIV (human immunodeficiency virus)
Human nutrition
birth defects and, 880
dietary deficiencies in, 879
essential nutrients needed by, 876–79
mineral requirements for, 878–79, 878*t*
vitamin requirements for, 877–78, 877*t*
Human population, 1190–95
characteristics of global, 1190–93
global carrying capacity for, 1193–95
Human reproduction
detecting disorders of, during pregnancy, 1018
female reproductive anatomy, 1003–5, 1004*f*
female reproductive cycles, 1010–12, 1011*f*
fetal development, 1014*f*, 1015*f*
gametogenesis, 1008–9*f*
life cycle, 251*f*
male reproductive anatomy, 1005–6, 1005*f*
pregnancy and childbirth in, 1012–16
prevention of, by contraception and abortion, 1016–18
sexual response, 1006
treating infertility, 1018
Humboldt, Alexander von, 1215
Hummingbird, 2*f*, 805*f*
gene cloning of, 399–400, 399*f*
Humoral immune response, 931*f*, **942**, **943**
antibodies and, 945–46
B cell activation in, 944*f*, 945
helper T cells and, 943, 943*f*
overview of, 942*f*
Humpback whale, 881*f*
Humus, **786**
Hunger, biotechnology and, 816–17, 817*f*
Hunt, R. Timothy, 92, 93
Huntington's disease, 279, 415–16
Hutchison, Victor, 866–67
Hutton, James, 454
Hybrid breakdown, 491*f*
Hybridization, **264**, 816
of orbitals, 41*f*
transgenic, 818
Hybrid-orbital model, molecular shape and, 41*f*

Hybrids, **488**
reproductive barriers and, 491*f*
sterility of, 491*f*, 504
Hybrid zones, speciation and, **498**–501
formation of, and possible outcomes, 499*f*
over time, 499–501
patterns within, 498–99
sunflowers and, 503*f*
toads in Europe, 498*f*
Hydra, 249*f*
cnidocyte, 671*f*
digestion in, 882*f*
exchange with environment of, 853*f*
Hydration shell, 50*f*, **51**
Hydrocarbon tail, chlorophyll, 192*f*
Hydrocarbons, **61**
in fats, 62*f*
Hydrochloric acid (HCl), 886
Hydroelectric systems, 148*f*
Hydrogen, 32, 38*f*, 39*f*, 59*f*, 61*f*
carbon compounds and, 58
saturated fatty acids and, 76
Hydrogen bonds, **40**, 41*f*, 46, 47*f*
acidic and basic conditions and, 52–54
of ice, 50*f*
proteins and, 83*f*
of water molecules, 46–47
Hydrogen ion, **52**
Hydrogenosomes, 580
Hydrolysis, **68**–69
ATP, 149–50, 150*f*
Hydrolytic enzymes, fungi and, 636–37
Hydronium ion, **52**
Hydrophilic heads, phospholipid, 76*f*
Hydrophilic regions, cell, 99*f*
Hydrophilic substances, **51**
Hydrophobic interaction, **83***f*
Hydrophobic regions, cell, 99*f*
Hydrophobic substances, **51**
Hydrophobic tails, phospholipid, 76*f*
Hydroponic culture, **790**, 790*f*
Hydrostatic skeleton, **1112**–13
Hydrothermal vents, 508*f*, 893
extreme thermophiles and, 566–67
Hydroxide ion, **52**
Hydroxyl group, **64***f*
Hydrozoans, 672, 672*f*, 672*t*, 673*f*
Hymen, **1004**
Hymenoptera, 690*f*
Hyperosmotic solutions, 955, 955*f*, 968
Hyperpolarization, **1052**, 1052*f*
Hypersensitive response in plants, **846**, 847*f*
Hypertension, **915**
Hypertonic solution, **133**, 955
animal and plant cells, 133*f*
Hyphae, fungal, **637**
fossil, 640*f*
specialized, 638*f*
structure of, 637*f*
Hypoblast, 1030, 1034
Hypocotyl, **808**
Hypodermis, mammalian, 864*f*
Hypoosmotic solutions, 955, 955*f*
Hypothalamus, 868, 969, **984**–86, 985*f*, **1072**
mammalian reproduction and, 1007
regulation of biological clock by, 1072–73
thermoregulatory function of, 868*f*
Hypothesis, **19**
theory vs., 23
Hypothesis-based science, 19–20
discovery science vs., 18
example, 19*f*

high oxygen consumption rates in mammals, 926f

histone phosphorylation in meiotic chromosome behavior, 322f

innate immune response from antimicrobial peptide, 932f

internal rod rotation in ATP synthase, and ATP synthesis, 174f

intracellular recording for measuring membrane potentials, 1052f

kinetochore microtubule shortening during mitosis, 235f

location of melanocyte-stimulating hormone, 978f

Mendel's genetics research, 264f

models of DNA replication, 312f

most effective light wavelengths for photosynthesis, 191f

movement of membrane proteins, 128f

nutrient limitations on phytoplankton production, 1227f

ob and *db* genes and regulation of appetite, 895f

polar movement of auxin, 828f

prokaryotic evolution, 560f

protein kinase effects on cell cycle, 240f

protein receptor for opiates in mammalian brain, 1061f

relationship between Neanderthals and *Homo sapiens*, 731f

relationship of species richness to area, 1217f

results of cross between wild-type and mutant fruit flies, 289f

role of β-catenin in control of gastrulation, 658

role of GABA gradients in plant reproduction, 806f

role of microtubules in cellulose deposition, 119f

role of sex hormones in sex determination, 993f

role of zone of polarizing activity in limb pattern formation in vertebrates, 1043f

seabird excretion of excess salt, 958f

seed germination and effects of red light illumination, 836f

sexual selection, 482f

sexual selection as reproductive barrier, 497f

shape and function of RNA polymerase, 86f

signal induction of directional cell growth, 220f

signal transduction in phototropism, 825f, 826f

sister chromatids during meiosis, 257f

snake mimicry and predation, 22f

species identity of whales sold as meat, 539f

sugar content of phloem sap, 781f

suprachiasmatic nucleus and control of mammalian circadian rhythms, 1073f

symplastic communication and plant development, 782f

transfer of genetic traits in bacterial strains, 306f

Insect(s), 686t, 688–89, 845f, 917f, 1002f. *See also names of specific insects*

anatomy, 688f

ants, 28–29, 30–31

chemoreceptors in, 1090f

communication signals among, 1123f, 1124f

diversity, 690–91f

ear, and sensing sound, 1092f

flower pollination by, 804f, 805f

hormonal regulation of development in, 985f

Hox genes in, 446f

Malpighian tubules, 962f

metamorphosis of butterflies, 689f

neurohormone function, 984, 985f

origin of body plan in, 527f

plant response to herbivory of, 845

reproduction in, 1002

reproductive anatomy of, 1002f

thermogenesis in, 867, 867f

tracheal systems and gas exchange in, 918, 918f

transgenic crops and pests, 816

use of landmarks by, 1127f

Insertions (point mutation), 345–46, 345f

In situ hybridization, 409–10, 410f

Instability, free energy and, 146

Insulation

ice as, 49–50

thermoregulation and animal body, 864

Insulin, 78t, 80, 893, 893f, 894f, **982**

amino acid sequence for, 409

control of blood glucose and, 982–84

manufacturing, 418

solubility of, 977f

Insulin-like growth factors (IGFs), 300–301, 301f, 989

Integral proteins, **129**

Integrins, **120**

extracellular matrix and, 120f

Integument, **620**, 803

Integumentary system, **864**

mammalian, 864f

Interaction, as biological theme, 6–7

Intercalary meristems, 749

Intercalated disks, **1111**

Intercellular junctions, 120–22

animal cell, 121f

membrane protein, 129f

plasmodesmata in plant cells, 120f, 121

tight junctions, desmosomes, and gap junctions in animal tissues, 121f

Interferons, **934**

Intermediate disturbance hypothesis, **1211**–12

Intermediate filaments, **118**

cytoskeleton, 113t

plant cell, 101f

properties, 113f

Internal defenses, 931f, 933–34

Internal environment, animal exchange with, 854f

Internal fertilization, **1000**

International Biological Program (IBP), 1146

International Union for Conservation of Nature and Natural Resources (IUCN), 1246

Internet resources, genome sequences, 429, 430f

Interneurons, **1048**, 1049f

knee-jerk reflex and, 1066f

Internodes, **740**

Interphase, **231**, 232f

Intersexual selection, **482**, 482f, 1136

Interspecific competition, **1199**–1200

species' niche affected by, 1200f

Interspecific interactions, **1198**–1204

competition, 1199–1200

herbivory, 1202

predation, 1201–2

symbiosis, 1202–3

Interstitial fluid, 910f

Intertidal zones, **1164f**

Interviews, list of, xi

Sean B. Carroll, 534–35

Scott V. Edwards, 450–51

Deborah M. Gordon, 28–29

Paul Nurse, 92–3

Terry L. Orr-Weaver, 246–47

Diana H. Wall, 1146–47

Masashi Yanagisawa, 850–51

Patricia Zambryski, 736–37

Intestinal bacteria, 571

Intestine. *See* Large intestine; Small intestine

Intracellular digestion, **882**

Intracellular receptors, 210–14, 213f

Intracytoplasmic sperm injection (ICSI), **1018**

Intrasexual selection, **482**, 1136

Intrinsic (physiological) factors, density-dependent population regulation due to, 1187

Introduced species, **1249**–50

Introns, **335**

functional and evolutionary importance of, 336

gene density and, 433–34

in human genome, 434f

Invagination, **1028**

Invasive species, **1207**

Inversion, **298**, 298f

Invertebrates, **666**–97

animal phylogeny and, 666f

arthropods, 684–92

chemoreceptors in, 1090f

chordates as, 695

cnidarians, 671–73

coordination of endocrine and nervous systems in, 984

deuterostomes, 669f, 693–95

diversity of, 667–69f

ecdysozoans, 668–69f, 683–92

echinoderms, 693–95

innate immunity in, 931–33

lophotrochozoans, 667–68f, 674–82

nervous systems of, 1065f

parental care among, 1001f

sensing gravity and sound in, 1092

simple sensory pathway in, 1088f

sponges, 667f, 670–71

statocysts in, 1092f

vision in, 1099–1100

In vitro DNA amplification, 403–5

In vitro fertilization (IVF), 807, **1018**

cloning with, 814–15

In vitro mutagenesis, **411**

Involution, **1030**

Iodine

deficiency, 32f

human requirements for, 878

thyroid gland and, 990–91, 990f

Ion(s), 39f, **40**

as second messengers, 215–18

Ion-channel receptors, 213f

Ion channels, **135**, **1050**

ligand-gated, 213f

maintaining neuron resting potential, 1050–52

production of action potentials, 1052–56

Ionic bonds, 39, **40**

electron transfer and, 39f

proteins and, 83f

Ionic compounds, **40**

Ion pumps

maintaining neuron resting potential, 1050–52

membrane potential maintained by, 136–37

Iridium, 522

Iris, **1100**

Iron, human requirements for, 878

Irrigation, 787–88

Island equilibrium model, 1216–17, 1216f

Island species, 465

Islets of Langerhans, **982**

Isolated system, 144, 148f

Index

Metabolism, **142**–61
    anabolic pathways in, 143 (*see also* Protein synthesis)
    ATP in, 149–51 (*see also* ATP (adenosine triphosphate))
    catabolic pathways in, 143 (*see also* Cellular respiration)
    cooperative prokaryotic, 565, 565*f*
    crassulacean acid (CAM), 201, 202*f*
    energy transformation laws (thermodynamics), 144–45
    enzymes, catalysis of metabolic reactions by, 151–56
    forms of energy and, 143–44
    free energy and, 146–49
    metabolic pathways of, 142–43
    nitrogen in prokaryotic, 565
    organelles and structural order in, 159*f*
    osmoregulation and, 957–58
    oxygen in prokaryotic, 564
    photosynthetic (*see* Photosynthesis)
    protobiont, 509*f*
    regulation of enzyme activity, and controls on, 157–59
    review, 160–61
    thyroid hormone and control of, 990–91
    transformation of matter and energy in, 142–45
    urea production, 960
Metamorphosis, **655**
    butterfly, 689*f*
    frog, 712*f*
    hormones and, 975, 975*f*
    hormones and frog, 980*f*
    insect, 689
Metanephridia, **962**, 962*f*
    earthworm, 681*f*
Metaphase, **231**, 233*f*, 234*f*, 236*f*, 256*f*, 321*f*
Metaphase I, 254*f*, 256*f*
Metaphase II, 255*f*
Metaphase plate, **231**–34
Metapopulations, **1190**
Metastasis, **243**, 243*f*
Metazoa clade, 662
Meteorites, 508–9
Methane, 38*f*, 41*f*, 59*f*, 60*f*, 164*f*
Methanogens, **567**
Methionine, 79*f*, 330, 330*f*
Methylated compounds, **65***f*
Methylation, 301
    DNA, 358
    histone, 358
Methyl group, **65***f*
Methylsalicylic acid, 847
Metric system table, C-1
Mexico, demographic transition in, 1191*f*
MHC. *See* Major histocompatibility complex (MHC)
Microarray chips, human genome, 432, 432*f*
Microbial diversity, 1205*f*
Microclimate, **1155**, 1158–59
Microevolution, **468**–86, **487**
    gene flow as cause of, 478–79
    genetic drift as cause of, 475–78
    genetic variation and, 468–70, 483–84
    mutations as cause of, 470–71
    natural selection as cause of, 475, 479–85
    review, 485–86
    sexual reproduction and, 471, 481–83
    speciation and, 487
    using Hardy-Weinberg equation to test, 472–75

Microfibrils, cell division orientation and, 757*f*
Microfilaments, **116**–18
    actin filaments as, 116
    cell motility and, 117*f*
    cytoskeleton, 112*f*, 113*t*
    plant cell, 101*f*
    properties, 113*t*
    structural role of, 117*f*
Micronutrients, **790**
    plant, 790, 791*t*
Microphylls, **612**, 613*f*
Micropyle, **628**, 803
MicroRNAs (miRNAs), **365**
    effects of, on mRNAs, 365–66
    generation and function of, 365*f*
Microscopy, 94–97
    electron, 95, 96*f*, 97, D-1
    light, 95, 96*f*, D-1
Microspores, **613**, **803**
Microsporidia
    eukaryotic cell infected by, 641*f*
    relationship of, to fungi, 641
Microsporocyte, 803
Microtubule-organizing center, 231
Microtubules, **113**–16
    cilia and, 115*f*
    cytoskeleton, 112*f*, 113*t*
    kinetochore, 235*f*
    plant cell, 101*f*
    plant growth and, 757
    properties of, 113*t*
    role of, in orienting cellulose deposition in plant cell walls, 119*f*
Microvilli, **889**
    animal cell, 100*f*
    microfilaments and, 117*f*
Midbrain, **1070**
Middle ear, **1093***f*
Middle lamella, **119**
Mifepristone (RU486), 1018
Migration, **1122**
    gray whales, 1148, 1148*f*
    imprinting and whooping crane, 1126, 1126*f*
    imprinting of, 1126*f*
    as oriented movement behavior, 1122
    variations in genetically-based, 1131
Milkweed, 626*f*
Miller, Carlos O., 829
Miller, Stanley, 59, 508
Millipedes, 687, 687*f*
Mimicry, case study of, in snakes, 20–22
Mimics, molecular, 42*f*
Mimivirus, evolution of viruses and, 390
Mineralization, teeth and, 704–5
Mineralocorticoids, **993**
Minerals, **878**
    deficiency of, in plants, 790–92, 791*f*
    as essential nutrient, 878*t*, 879
    vascular plant acquisition of, 766–67, 772
    vascular plant transport of, 767–82, 772–76
Minimum viable population (MVP), **1251**
Minke whales, 539–40, 539*f*
Minnows, 1125*f*
Minorsky, Peter, v
Mismatch pair, **317**
Missense mutations, **344**–45, 345*f*
Mistletoe, 798*f*
Mitchell, Peter, 176
Mitochondria, **109**–11
    animal cell, 100*f*
    in bird flight muscles, 7*f*

chemical energy conversion by, 109–10
comparison of chemiosmosis in chloroplasts and, 196–98
as endosymbionts, 516–17, 517*f*
inheritance and, 300–301
metabolism and, 159*f*
mitochondrial myopathy, 301
plant cell, 101*f*
protists with, 576–77
as site of cellular respiration, 162, 166*f*, 174*f*, 175*f*
Mitochondrial matrix, **110**
Mitosis, **230**–38
    comparison of meiosis and, in diploid cells, 256*f*, 257–58
    cytokinesis and, 233*f*, 234–36
    evolution of, 237, 237*f*
    human life cycle, 251f
    kinetochore microtubule shortening during anaphase of, 235*f*
    mitotic spindle and, 231, 234*f*
    as phase of cell cycle, 231
    in plant cells, 236*f*
    stages of, 231, 232–33*f*
Mitosomes, 580
Mitotic (M) phase, cell cycle, **231**
Mitotic spindle, **231**–34, 234*f*
Mixotrophs, **576**, 581
Mobile genetic elements, evolution of viruses and, 390
Model organism, 1021*f*, **1022**
Models
    of biological membranes, 126
    helium atom, 33*f*
    molecular-shape, 41*f*
    scientific, **23**
Modified leaves, 742*f*
Modified roots, 740*f*
Modified stems, 741*f*
Molarity, **52**
Molar mass, 52
Molds, **639**–40, 642*f*
    life cycle, 643–44, 643*f*
    pathogenic, 651
    slime, 594–96
Mole (mol), **52**
Molecular basis of inheritance, 305–24
    chromosome structure, 320–23
    DNA as genetic material, evidence for, 305–8
    DNA replication and repair, proteins and, 311–19
    DNA structural model, process of building, 308–10
    evolution of gene concept from, 347
    review, 323–24
Molecular biology, importance of viruses to, 381
Molecular clocks, **549**–51
    application of, to origin of HIV, 550–51, 551*f*
    difficulties with, 550
    fungal lineages determined by, 640–41
    for mammals, 550*f*
    neutral theory and, 550
Molecular fingerprints, 24*f*
Molecular formula, **38**
Molecular genealogy, 89
Molecular genetics, 651–52
Molecular homologies, 540–42
    evaluating, 541–42
Molecular level, phenotype, 272
Molecular mass, **51**–52
Molecular mimics, 42*f*
Molecular-shape models, 41*f*

Index

Mycosis, **651**
Myelin sheath, **1055**–56, 1056*f*
Myeloid stem cells, 913*f*
Myoblasts, 368, 369*f*
Myocardial infarction, 914–15
MyoD protein, 368–69, 369*f*
Myofibrils, **1106**
Myoglobin, **926**, **1111**
Myosin, 78*t*, **117**
    cell motility and, 117*f*
    cytokinesis and, 234
    muscle fiber contraction and, 1107*f*, 1108*f*
    M. Yanagisawa on, 850
Myotonia, **1006**
Myriapods, **686**, 686*t*, 687
Myrmelachista schumanni, 31
Myxobacteria (slime bacteria), 207*f*, 568*f*

N

NAD$^+$ (nicotinamide adenine dinucleotide), **164**
    as electron shuttle, 165*f*
    energy harvest in cellular respiration via, 164, 165*f*, 166
    fermentation and, 178*f*
NADH
    citric acid cycle and, 170*f*, 171*f*
    fermentation and, 177, 178*f*
    glycolysis and, 167*f*, 169*f*
    as source of electrons for electron transport chain, 164, 165*f*, 166*f*, 172, 173*f*
NADP$^+$ (nicotinamide adenine dinucleotide phosphate), photosynthetic light reactions and role of, **188**–89, 189*f*, 194, 195*f*
NADPH
    Calvin cycle and conversion of carbon dioxide to sugar using, 198–99
    photosynthetic light reactions and, 188, 189*f*, 194, 195*f*
Naked mole rats, 1138, 1138*f*
Nanoarchaeota clade, 567
Nanotechnology, 174
Narcolepsy, in mice, 851
Nasal glands, seabird, 958, 958*f*, 959*f*
National Cancer Institute, 431
National Center for Biotechnology Information (NCBI), 429, 430*f*
National Institutes of Health (NIH), 429, 431
National Library of Medicine, 429
Natural edges, 1255*f*
Natural family planning, **1016**
Natural history, 1148
Natural killer (NK) cells, **935**
Natural plastics, 572, 572*f*
Natural range expansion, 1152
Natural selection, **456**, 479–85
    alteration of population allele frequencies due to, 475
    beetles and, 16*f*
    C. Darwin and theory of, 14–16
    C. Darwin's observations and inferences on, 458–59
    directional, disruptive, and stabilizing modes of, 480–81, 480*f*
    earliest, at molecular level, 509–10
    effect of predation on, 460*f*
    evolution of developmental genes and, 526*f*
    gene flow and, 479*f*
    key role of, in adaptive evolution, 481
    limitations of, for creating perfect organisms, 484
    relative fitness and, 479–80
    species selection as, 531

summary of, 459
    of survival and reproductive behaviors, 1133–38
Nature, describing, vs. explaining, 18
Nature and nurture applied to environment and genetics, 274–75
Nature reserves, philosophy of, 1258
Neanderthals, 731–32
    relationship to *Homo sapiens*, 732*f*
Near vision, 1101*f*
Nectarine, 626*f*
Negative feedback, **11**, **861**, 861*f*, **982**
    in biological systems, 11*f*
    in endocrine system function, 981–84
Negative gene repression in bacteria, 353–55
Negative pressure breathing, **920**, 921*f*
Nematocysts, **671**–72
Nematoda, 669*f*
Nematodes, 683–84, 683*f*
    controls on Antarctic, 1210*f*
    D. Wall on ecology of, 1146–47
Nemertea, 668*f*
Neocortex, 1074
Neon, 37*f*
Neoproterozoic era, animal origins and, 656–57
Nephridium, 678*f*
Nephron, **964**
    blood vessels associated with, 964
    mammalian types of, 963*f*
    processing of filtrate to urine by, 965–66, 965*f*
Neritic zone, **1165***f*
Nerve cells, 655
Nernst equation, 1051
Nerve cord
    dorsal and hollow, 699*f*, 700
    insect, 688*f*
Nerve net, **1065**
Nerves, **1065**
    cranial, 1068
    spinal, 1068
Nervous system, **975**, 1064–86
    action potentials in (*see* Action potentials)
    brain, 1064, 1064*f*, 1070–78
    cell signaling in, 859*f*
    central nervous system, 1065, 1066*f*, 1067–68
    coordination of endocrine system with, 984–90
    disorders of, 1080–84
    glia of, 1067–68
    human brain (*see* Human brain)
    invertebrate, 1065*f*
    long-distance signaling and, 209
    neuron organization in, 1047–48
    neurons and nerves of, 1064–65 (*see also* Neuron(s))
    patterning of, 1078
    peripheral nervous system, 1068–69
    review, 1084–85
    squid, 1048*f*
    synaptic connections underlying learning and memory, 1078–80
    vertebrate, 1065–68, 1066*f*
Nervous tissue, **858**, 859*f*
Net primary production (NPP), **1225**–26
    global, in year 2002, 1226*f*
    relationship of actual evapotranspiration to, 1228*f*
Neural crest, **702**, 702*f*
Neural crest cells, **1031**
Neural development, 880, 1078
Neural pathways, for vision, 1105*f*
Neural plasticity, **1079**, 1079*f*
Neural plate, 1030, 1031*f*
Neural progenitor cells, 1079

Neural tube, **1030**, 1031*f*
Neural tube defects, 880
Neuraminidase, 392
Neuroendocrine signaling, 976*f*
Neurohormones, **977**
    as cell signaling molecule, 976–77
    insect development and, 984, 985*f*
    simple pathway, 986*f*
Neurohypophysis, 985
Neuron(s), **858**, 859*f*, **1047**–63
    action potentials of, 1052–56
    circuits of, and nerve formation, 1064–65
    information processing and, 1048
    ion pumps/ion channels and maintenance of resting potential in, 1050–52
    knee-jerk reflex and, 1066*f*
    membrane potential of, 1050–52
    motor, 1048, 1049*f*
    organization and structure of, 1047–48, 1049*f*
    resting potential of, 1050–52
    review, 1062–63
    sensory, 1048, 1049*f*
    synapses and communication between cells and, 1056–61
Neuropeptides, **1060**
    M. Yanagisawa on, 851
    as neurotransmitters, 1059*t*, 1060–61
Neurospora crassa (bread mold), 645–46, 645*f*
    gene-enzyme relationships in, 326, 327*f*
Neurotransmitters, **976**, **1048**, 1059–61
    acetylcholine, 1060
    amino acids, 1060
    biogenic amines, 1060
    as cell signaling molecule, 976–77
    gases, 1061
    major, 1059*t*
    neuropeptides, 1060–61
Neutralization, 946, 946*f*
Neutral theory, **550**
Neutral variation, **484**
Neutrons, **33**
Neutrophils, **933**
Newborns, screening of, for genetic disorders, 280–81
Newt lung cells, 7*f*
Niches. See Ecological niche(s)
Nicolson, G., 126
Night, flowering and critical length of, 839–40
Nile crocodile, 2*f*
Nirenberg, Marshall, 330
Nitric oxide (NO), 210, 908, **981**, 1006
    as neurotransmitter, 1061
Nitrification, 793, 1233*f*
Nitrifying bacteria, 793
Nitrogen, 32, 61*f*
    bryophytes and leaching of soil, 609*f*
    carbon compounds and, 58
    deficiency, 32*f*
    soil fertilization and, 788
Nitrogen cycle, **793**
    bacteria in, 793
    terrestrial ecosystem, 1233*f*
    terrestrial ecosystem, and effects of agriculture on, 1236, 1237*f*
Nitrogen fixation, **794**, 1233*f*
    cyanobacteria and, 569*f*
    prokaryotic metabolism and role of, **565**
Nitrogen-fixing bacteria, 793
Nitrogenous bases
    DNA, 308
    pairing of, and DNA structure, 309, 310*f*, 311–12

Index

Index

Index

Poliovirus, 391
Pollen
    monocot vs. eudicot, 631*f*
    sperm production and, in seed plants, 620
Pollen cones, 625
Pollen grain, **620**, 627–28, **803**, 803*f*
Pollen sacs, 803
Pollen tube, **803**, 806, 806*f*
Pollination, **620**, 801, 801*f*, **805**
    asexual reproduction vs., 812
    flower shape and, 632, 632*f*
    insects and, 689
    mechanisms of flower, 804–5*f*
Pollinator choice, reproductive isolation and,
        503–4, 504*f*
Pollution
    biomanipulation and, 1210
    coral reefs and, 673
    nitrogen, 1237*f*
    prokaryotes and bioremediation of,
        572–73
Polyandry, **1134**, 1135*f*
Poly-A tail, **334**, 334*f*, 401
Polychaeta, 680*t*
Polychaetes, 682, 682*f*
Polyclonal antibodies, 945
Polydactyly, 273
Polygamous relationships, **1134**
Polygenic inheritance, **274**
    skin color model, 274*f*
Polygyny, **1134**, 1135*f*
Polymer(s), **68**
    diversity of, 69
    nucleotide, 88
    synthesis and breakdown of, 68–69
Polymerase chain reaction (PCR), **403**–5, 404*f*,
        409*f*, 419–20, 1205*f*, 1248
    diagnosing diseases with, 416–17
    gene cloning vs., 404
    genetic prospecting with, 566
Polymerases, viruses and, 384
Polymorphism, 1137*f*
Polynucleotides, **87**–88
    as nucleic acids, 87*f* (*see also* Nucleic acid(s))
Polyp, 376
Polypeptides, **78**–80
    amino acid monomers, 78–80
    amino acid polymers, 80
    one gene–directed production of one, 326
        (*see also* Protein synthesis)
    point mutations affecting structure/function
        of, 344–46
    proteins as, 78, 80–81
    quaternary structure of, 83*f*
    solubility of, 977*f*
    stages of synthesis of, 340–42
    targeting, to specific locations, 343–44
    translation and construction of, 340–42
    translation as synthesis of, 328
Polyphyletic clades, 542*f*, 543
Polyplacophora, 678*t*
Polyploidy, **297**, 438, **495**–96, 495*f*, 496*f*
Polyps, **671**, 671*f*, 673
Polyribosomes (polysomes), **342**, 342*f*
Polysaccharides, **71**–74
    storage, 71–72
    structural, 72–74
Polyspermy, 807
    fast block to, 1022
    slow block to, 1023
Polysyndactyly, 1044*f*
Polytomy, **539**

Pons, **1070**
    breathing control centers, 922
Poplar, 817
Poppy, 631*f*
Population(s), **472**, 1149*f*, **1174**
    carrying capacity of, 1183
    conservation of (*see* Population conservation)
    ecology of (*see* Population ecology)
    evolution in, 459
    evolution of (*see* Microevolution; Population
        genetics)
    gene flow between widely separated, 489*f*
    genetic variation between, and within,
        469–70
    human (*see* Human population)
    as level of biological organization, 4*f*
    metapopulations, 1190
    region patterns of change in human, 1191–92
    variations in, 458*f*
Population conservation
    declining-population approach, 1253–55
    small-population approach, 1251–53
    weighing conflicting demands in, 1255
Population cycles, 1189–90
Population dynamics, 1175*f*, 1176, **1188**–90
    cycles of populations, 1189–90
    immigration, emigration, and metapopula-
        tions, 1190
    stability and fluctuation in, 1188–89
Population ecology, **1149***f*, **1174**–97
    density-dependent factors in population
        growth, 1186–90
    exponential model of population growth,
        1181–83
    human population growth and, 1190–95
    life history traits produced by natural selec-
        tion and, 1179–81
    logistic model of population growth and,
        1183–86
    population density, dispersion, and demo-
        graphics, 1174–79
    review, 1195–96
Population genetics. *See also* Microevolution
    evolutionary significance of genetic variation
        and, 260
    gene flow and, 478–79
    gene pools and allele frequencies in, 472
    genetic drift and, 475–78
    genetic variation due to sexual reproduction
        and recombination in, 471
    genetic variation within and between popula-
        tions and, 469–70
    Hardy-Weinberg theorem and equilibrium in,
        472–75
    mutations affecting, 470–71
    natural selection and, 475
Population growth
    density-dependent factors regulating, 1186,
        1187–90
    exponential model of, 1181–83
    human, 1190, 1191*f*
    logistical model of, 1183–86
Population size
    determining, using mark-recapture
        method, 1175*f*
    effective, 1252
    limits on human, 1193–95
    minimum viable, 1251
Populus trichocarpa, genome of, 835
Pore complex, 102, 103*f*
Pore formation, 946*f*
Porifera, 518, 518*f*

Poro flower, 805*f*
Porphyrin ring, chlorophyll, 192*f*
Portal vein, 890, 901
Positional information, **369**, **757**, **1042**
    in plants, 757–58
Positive feedback, **11**, **862**, **986**
    in biological systems, 11*f*
    posterior pituitary hormones and, 986
Positive gene regulation in bacteria, 355–56
Positive pressure breathing, **920**
Positron-emission tomography (PET), brain
        imaging, 1076–77, 1077*f*
Possum, 722*f*
Posterior pituitary gland, **985**, 985*f*
    hormones of, 986, 986*f*, 987*t*
Posterior sides, **659**
Postsynaptic cell, **1048**, 1049*f*, 1057*f*
Postsynaptic potentials, 1058–59
    excitatory, 1058
    inhibitory, 1058
    summation of, 1058–59, 1058*f*
Post-transcriptional regulation, 357*f*, 362–64
Post-translational modifications, 342–43
Postzygotic barriers, **488**–89, 491*f*
Potassium
    human requirements for, 878
    soil fertilization and, 788
    stomatal opening and closing and, 777*f*
Potassium-40, 512
Potato blight, 579*f*, 588–89
Potatoes, 822, 822*f*
Potential energy, **35**, **143**
    transformations, 143*f*
Potential evapotranspiration, 1215
Potential range, 1153
Poymorphisms, 417
Prairie chickens, 477–78
Prairies, 1170*f*
Prairie voles, 1132*f*
Precapillary sphincters, 910
Precipitation
    acid, 54–56, 55*f*, 1237–38
    climate and global patterns of, 1157*f*
    forest response to altered, 1150*f*
    mountains and, 1158*f*
Predation, **1201**–2
    density-dependent population regulation
        through, 1187
    effect of, on natural selection for color pat-
        terns in guppies, 460–61, 460*f*
Predators
    keystone species as, 1208*f*
    mass extinctions and, 523
    variations in genetically-based behaviors
        of, 1131*f*
Preformation, 1021
Pregnancy, **1013**–16
    conception and, 1013
    detecting disorders during, 1018
    ectopic, 1012
    first trimester of, 1014–15
    prevention of, 1016–18
    second and third trimesters of, 1015–16
Pre-mRNA, 328
    splicing, 335*f*
Preprophase band, **756**, 756*f*
Prepuce, **1004**
Pressure
    bulk flow by negative, 773–76
    bulk flow by positive, 780
    effect of, on water potential, 769
Pressure flow, 780, 780*f*, 781*f*

Index

Index

texture of, 786
topsoil composition, 786–87
Soil bacteria, 568*f*, 570*f*, 1205*f*
Soil compaction, preventing, 789
Soil conservation, 787–89, 787*f*
Soil erosion, controlling, 788–89, 788*f*
Soil horizons, **786**, 786*f*
Soil worm (*Caenorhabditis elegans*), 223–24, 224*f*
    cell lineage in, 1039*f*
    complete genome sequence for, 426
    DNA microarray assays on, 411
    as nematode, 683
Solute potential, **769**
Solutes, 50, **768**
    concentration of, in aqueous solution, 51–52
    diffusion and active transport of, in vascular
        plants, 767–68, 768*f*
    effects of, on water potential, 769
    osmoregulation, water balance, and concen-
        tration of, 954, 955*f*
    two-solute model of water conservation,
        966–68
Solution, **50**
Solvent, water as, 50–52
Somatic cells, **229, 250**
Somatosensory receptors, 1075–76, 1076*f*
Somites, 701, **1031**, 1031*f*
Songbirds, evolution of, 451
Songs, green lacewing, 1130–31, 1130*f*
Sonic hedgehog growth factor, 1043
Soredia, **650**
Sori, **612**
Sound, sensing, in invertebrates, 1092. *See also*
        Hearing
Southern, Edwin, 406
Southern blotting, 405–6, **406**, 407*f*
Space-filling model
    covalent bonding, 38*f*
    DNA double-helix structure, 309*f*
    molecular shape and, 41*f*
    organic molecules, 60*f*
    phospholipid, 76*f*
    protein structure, 81*f*
Spacek, Sissy, 248*f*
Spanish flu, 392, 392*f*
Spatial heterogeneity, 1154
Spatial learning, **1126–27**
Spatial summation, **1058**, 1058*f*
Spawning, 1000
Speciation, **487–506**
    allopatric, 492–95*f*, 497–98
    biological species concept, 487–92
    C. Darwin on, 457–59
    flower shape linked to seed plant, 632*f*
    genetics of, 503–4
    hybrid zones and, 498–501
    macroevolution and, 487, 504
    morphological, ecological, and phylogenetic
        concepts of, 492
    reproductive isolation and, 488–89, 490–91*f*,
        495*f*, 497*f*, 498–501
    review, 505–6
    sexual selection and, 451
    sympatric, 493*f*, 495–98
    tempo and rate of, two models, 501–3,
        502*f*, 503*f*
Species, **488**, 1151–59
    abiotic factors affecting, 1154–55
    behavior and habitat selection of, 1153
    biological concept of, 487–92
    biological organization and, 4*f*

biotic factors affecting, 1153–54
C. Darwin on origin of, 457–59
climate affecting, 1155–59
in communities (*see* Community ecology;
        Community(ies))
comparing genomes of closely related,
        442–45
comparing genomes of distantly related, 442
comparing genomes within, 445
determining number of genes in, 432, 433*t*
dispersal and distribution of, 1151*f*, 1152–53
diversity and number of, 12
diversity and similarity within, 488*f*
diversity of (*see* Biodiversity; Species
        diversity)
dominant, 1207
early classification schemes for, 453
ecological concept of, 492
ecological niche of, and resource partitioning,
        1199–1200
endangered and threatened, 1246
endemic, 465
extinctions of (*see* Extinction of species; Mass
        extinctions)
foundation, 1207–9
geographic distribution of, 465
identifying whale, 539*f*
introduced, 1249–50
keystone, 1208
morphological concept of, 492
origin of (*see* Speciation)
phylogenetic concept of, 492
S. Edwards on, 451
transplants of, 1153
Species-area curve, **1215**, 1216*f*
Species diversity, **1204**, 1246–47. *See also*
        Biodiversity
    benefits of, 1248
    biogeographic factors affecting, 1214–17
    influence of disturbances on, 1211–14
    using molecular tools to determine, 1205*f*
Species richness, **1204**
    relationship of geographical area to, 1217*f*
Species selection, 531
Specific heat, 48–49
Specificity, PCR, 404
Specific transcription factors, 359, 824
Spectrophotometer, **190**, 191*f*
Speech
    brain function and, 1076–77
    FOXP2 gene and, 443–44, 444*f*
Spemann, Hans, 1040*f*, 1041, 1041–42, 1041*f*
Spemann's organizer, 1042, 1042*f*
Sperm, **997**, 1021*f*
    acrosomal reaction in, 1022, 1023*f*
    biased usage of, in female flies, 1003*f*
    pollen and, in seed plants, 620
    structure of flagellated, **601**
Spermatheca, **1002**
Spermatocytes, 1008*f*
Spermatogenesis, **1007**
    in humans, 1008*f*
Spermatogonia, **1008***f*
Sphagnum moss, 610, 610*f*
S (synthesis) phase of cell cycle, **231**
Spherical prokaryotes, 557*f*
Sphincters, **884**
Sphygmomanometer, 909*f*
Spices, 633
Spiders, 82*f*, 686*f*, 687*f*
    anatomy, 687*f*

Spike mosses, 613, 614*f*
Spinal nerves, **1068**
Spines, 742*f*
    sea star, 693*f*
Spiral cleavage, **660**
Spiral phyllotaxy, 766
Spiral prokaryotes, 557*f*
Spiral valve, 707
Spirochetes, 569*f*
Spirochetes clade, 569*f*
Spliceosome, **335**, 335*f*
Sponges, 667*f*, 670–71
    anatomy, 670*f*
    as basal animals, 662
Spongocoel, **670**
Spongy mesophyll, 750
Spontaneous change, free energy and, 147*f*
Spontaneous mutations, 346
Spontaneous processes, 145
Sporangia, **603***f*
    pine cones and, 625
    walled plant spores produced in, 603*f*
Spores, **252**, **602***f*
    fungal, 638–40, 640*f*
    seeds vs., 620–21
    variations of, in seedless vascular plants,
        612–13
Sporocytes, **603***f*
Sporophylls, **612**
    in seedless vascular plants, 612–13
Sporophyte, **252**, **602***f*
    in bryophytes, 609
    gametophytes vs., 619*f*
    pine trees as, 625
    in seedless vascular plants, 610–12, 611*f*
Sporopollenin, **601**
Sporozoites, 583
Spotted skunks, 490*f*
Squamous epithelium, 856, 856*f*
Squids, 680*f*
    nervous system, 1048*f*
Stability, 1211
Stability, hybrid zones and, 499*f*, 500
Stability, relationship of free energy to, 146, 147*f*
Stability of populations, 1188–89
Stabilizing selection, 480*f*, **481**
Staghorn coral, 1218
Staghorn fern, 798*f*
Stahl, Franklin, 312*f*
Staining microscopy, 96*f*
Stalk-eyed flies, 1136*f*
Stamens, 625–26, **802**
Staminate flowers, 813
Standard metabolic rate (SMR), **870**
Standing crop, 1225, 1229*f*
Stanley, Steven, 531
Stanley, Wendell, 382
Stapes, **1093***f*
Star anise, 630*f*
Starch, **71**
    plant storage of, 71–72
    structure, 73*f*
Start codons, 330, 330*f*
Statins, 915
Statocyst, **1092**
Statolith hypothesis, 841*f*, 842
Statoliths, **842**, **1092**
Stearic acid, 75*f*
Stechmann, Alexandra, 593–94, 593*f*
Steinbeck, John, 785
Steinhardt, Rick, 1024*f*

nervous, 858, 859f
plant (see Tissue systems, plant)
proteins specific to, 368
Tissue plasminogen activator (TPA), 418, 441, 441f
Tissue systems, plant, **742**–43
dermal, 742f
ground, 742f, 743
leaves, 750
meristems, 746–47
vascular, 742f, 743
Toads, hybrid zones and, 498–99, 498f
Tobacco mosaic virus (TMV), 381–82, 382f, 383f, 393
Toll-like receptor (TLR), **933**, 933f
Tollund man, 610f
Tomato, 626f
Tongue, taste and, 1097f
Tonicity, **133**
Tool use in early humans, 730
Top-down model, **1209**, 1210f
Topoisomerase, **314**, 314f, 315t
Topsoil, **786**
inorganic components of, 786–87
organic components of, 787
Torpor, **871**–72
Torsion, **679**, 679f
Tortoiseshell cats, 292f
Total kinetic energy, 48
Totipotent cells, **1040**
restricting, in animal morphogenesis, 1040–41
Totipotent plants, **412**
Touch, plant response to, 842–43
Toxic waste cleanup, DNA cloning and, 397f
Toxic wastes, density-dependent population regulation through, 1187
Toxins, human release of, into environment, 1238–39
Trace elements, **32**
Tracers, radioactive, 34f
Trachea, 885, **919**
Tracheal systems, **918**
Tracheal tubes, insect, 688f
Tracheids, **612**, **745**f
Tracheoles, 918f
Traits, genetic, **263**. See also Character, genetic
dominant, 266, 271–73, 276f, 278–79
inheritance of, 458–59
life history (see Life history)
pedigrees for tracing, 276–77
recessive, 266, 276f, 277–78, 291f
transfer of, between bacterial strains, 306f
Tranport function, membrane protein, 129f
Tranposition, 441–42
Transacetylase, 354f
Transcription, **328**, 331–34
in bacterial cells, 329f, 347f
cell type-specific, 361f
in eukaryotic cells, 329f, 333f, 334–36, 348f
molecular components of, 331–32
overview, 328
post-transcriptional gene regulation, 824
post-transcription modification of RNA, 334–36
regulation of bacterial, 351–56
regulation of eukaryotic gene expression at, 824
regulation of gene expression following, 362–64
regulation of initiation in eukaryotic, 358–62
silencing of, by siRNAs, 366

stages of, 332f
synthesis of RNA transcript during, 332–34
template for, 329f, 330
termination of, 333–34
triplet code and, 329f
Transcription activators, 360–61, 361f
Transcription factor genes, vertebrate, 704
Transcription factors, 213, 219f, **333**, 333f, 359–61
control of gene activation and, 361
enhancers and specific, 359–61
general, 359
Transcription initiation complex, **333**, 333f, 359
Transcription unit, **332**
Trans double bonds, fatty acids and, 76
Transduction (signal-transduction pathway), 209, 214–18, **561**. See also Signal transduction
overview, 209f
in plants, 822–23
in prokaryotes, 561–62, 562f
protein phosphorylation and dephosphorylation in, 214, 215f
signal-transduction pathways in, 214
small molecules and ions as second messengers in, 215–18
Trans face, Golgi apparatus, 106–7, 106f
Trans fats, **76**, 915
Transfer cells, **780**
Transfer RNA (tRNA), **337**
ribosomal binding sites for, 340
ribosome model with, 339f
role of, in translation, 337–39
structure, 338f
structure and function of, 337–39
Transformation, **243**, **306**, **561**
in prokaryotes, 561–62
Transfusions, blood, 947–48
Transgene, escape of, 818–19
Transgenic animals, **419**, 421
Transgenic crops
debate over, 817–19
reducing fossil fuel dependency by using, 817
reducing hunger and malnutrition by using, 816–17
Transgenic organisms, **814**. See also Genetically modified organisms (GMOs)
agricultural, 816–19
Transgenic plants, 421–22, 421f
Trans isomers, 62
Transition state, 152
Translation, **328**, 337–44
in bacterial cells, 347f
basic concept of, 337f
building polypeptides in, 340–42
completing and targeting functional proteins in, 342–44
elongation cycles of, 341f
in eukaryotic and bacterial cells, 329f
in eukaryotic cells, 348f
initiation of, 340f
molecular components of, 337–40
overview, 328
regulation of gene expression at initiation of, 363
termination of, 341, 342f
Translation initiation complex, 340, 340f
Translocation, **298**, 298f, 341f, **779**
bulk flow by positive pressure in angiosperms as, 780
cancers and, 300, 300f
chromosomal, 298f, 300f
movement of sugars in plants by, 779–80

Transmembrane proteins, 129
structure of, 129f
Transmembrane route, 773f
Transmission, **1088**
of action potentials to central nervous system, 1088–89
Transmission electron microscope (TEM), **96**, 96f
Transpiration, **773**, 776–79
adaptations for reducing water loss, 778–79
bulk flow, negative pressure, and, 773
effects of, on plant wilting and leaf temperature, 778
stomata opening and closing as control on, 776–78, 776f, 777f
Transpirational pull on xylem sap, 774–75, 774f, 775f
Transpiration-cohesion-tension mechanism, 774–76
Transplants, immune system rejection of, 948
Transport across membranes, 132–39
active, 135–38
bulk, 138, 139f
passive, 132–35
review of active and passive, 136f
Transport epithelia, **958**
nephron function and, 965f, 966
osmoregulation and role of, 958–59
Transport in animals. See Circulatory system
Transport in vascular plants, 612, 764–84. See also Plant nutrition
bulk flow and, 771–72, 773–76
cell compartments and routes for short-distance, 771f
diffusion and active transport of solutes, 767–68
diffusion of water (osmosis), 768–71
dynamic nature of symplast, 781–82
phloem and, 779, 782
resource acquisition and, 764–67 (see also Resource acquisition in land plants)
review, 783–84
roots to shoots transport, 772–76
sugar-conducting cells in phloem, 745f
of sugars, 779–81
three major pathways of, 771
transpiration, stomata, and, 776–79
water, 47f
water-conducting cells in xylem, 745f
xylem and, 772, 773f, 774–76
Transport proteins, 78t, **131**, 767–68
aquaporins, 771
channel proteins (see Channel proteins)
facilitated diffusion aided by, 134–35, 135f
Transport vesicles, **105**, 105f
endomembrane system and, 109f
Golgi apparatus, 106f
Transport work, 149
ATP (adenosine triphosphate) and, 151f
Transposable elements, 434, **435**–36
DNA sequences related to, 436
genome evolution and role of, 441–42
movement of eukaryotic, 435f
Transposition, 435
Transposons, **435**, 435f
evolution of viruses and, 390
Transverse (T) tubules, **1108**
Tree frogs, 482f
Tree of life, 16–17, 536, 551–53. See also Biodiversity; Phylogeny
C. Darwin's evolutionary tree, 457f, 464, 464f
review, 554–55
as ring, 553, 553f

summary, for all life, 552–53, 553f
from two kingdoms to three domains in, 551–52
Tree rings, studying Earth's climate using, 753, 753f
Trees
climate change and range of American beech, 1159f
devil's gardens and *Duroia hirsuta,* 30–31
magnolia, 1, 1f
Tree trunk anatomy, 754f
Trehalose, 957
Trematodes, 674t, 675–76, 675f
Trends, evolutionary, 530–31
Triacylglycerol, **75**
synthesis and structure of, 75f
Trichinosis, 683, 683f
Trichomes, 742–43, 778f
Trichomonas vaginalis, 580
Trichoptera, 691f
Triglycerides, 75, 889f
Triiodothyronine (T₃), **990**
Trilobites, 684f
evolution of, 462f
Trimesters, **1014**
Triose phosphate dehydrogenase, 169f
Trioses, 70f
Triple response in plants, **832**, 833f
Triplet code, **329**, 329f
Triploblastic animals, **659**, 660f
Triploidy, 297
Trisomic zygote, **297**
Trisomy 21, 299
Trisomy X, 299
Triticale grain, 816
tRNA. *See* Transfer RNA (tRNA)
Trochophore larva, 674
Trophic cascade model, 1209
Trophic efficiency, **1229**
ecological pyramids and, 1229f
Trophic levels in ecosystems, 1223–24
energy transfer between, 1228–30
Trophic structure, **1205–7**
bottom-up and top-down controls affecting, 1209–10
food webs, 1205–6
limits on food chain length, 1206–7
Trophoblast, **1014**, **1034**
Tropical dry forest, **1168f**
in Costa Rica, 1262f
Tropical forest(s), ant behavior in, 31f
Tropical rain forest, **1168f**
Tropic hormones, **988–89**
regulation of mammalian reproduction by, 1007–12
Tropics, **1156f**
Tropism, **825**. *See also specific type, e.g.,* Phototropism
Tropomyosin, **1108**
Troponin complex, **1108**
Troponin T, 363f
TRP channel proteins, 1091, 1098
Trp operon, 352–53, 353f
Trp repressor, **353**
Truckee River, 1262f
True-breeding, **264**
Trumpeter swans, 1135f
Trypanosoma, 580–81, 581f
Trypsin, 888
Tryptophan, 79f, 330, 352, 352f, 353f
Tuataras, 716–17, 717f
Tubal ligation, **1017–18**

Tube cells, angiosperm, 627, 803
Tube feet, **693**
sea star, 693f
Tuberculosis, 558, 569f, 571, 936
Tubers, 741f
Tubeworms, 893
Tubulidentata, 725f
Tubulin, 113–16, 231
properties, 113t
Tucker, Vance, 1116
Tumbleweeds, 811f
Tumors
cancer, 243 (*see also* Cancer)
P. Zambryski on plant, 736
Tumor-suppressor genes, **374**
cancer and, 376–77, 376f
Tumor viruses, 373–74
Tuna, 709f
Tundra, **1171f**
Tunicates, **701**, 701f
cell fate mapping for, 1039f
Turbellarians, 674–75, 674t
Turgeon, Robert, 841
Turgid cells, 133f, **134**, **770**
Turgor movements in plants, 843, 843f
Turgor pressure, **769**, 777
Turner syndrome, 299
Turnover, **1161**
seasonal, in lakes, 1161f
Turnover time, **1230**
Turtles, 717f, 718
Twins, human, 1014
Twin studies, 1081, **1130**
Tympanic membrane, **1093f**
Type 1 diabetes mellitus, 949, 983
Type 2 diabetes mellitus, 983–84
Typhoid, 572
Tyrosine, 79f

U

Ubiquitin, 364f
Ubx gene, 526f, 527, 527f
Ulcers, 887
Ultimate causation, **1121**
Ultracentrifuges, 97
Ultrasound technique, 280
Ultraviolet (UV) radiation, 1100
atmospheric ozone depletion and, 1242
mutations and, 346
sensitivity to, 821–22
Undernourishment, **879**
Undershoot, 1054, 1054f
Unicellular organisms, first, 514–17
Unicellular protist, as photoautotroph, 186f
Unicellular protists, evolution of mitosis in, 237f
Uniform dispersion, 1176, 1176f
Uniformitarianism, **454**
Unikonta (unikonts), 579f, **593–96**
amoebozoans, 594–96
opisthokonts, 596
relationship of, to fungi and animals, 593
United States, age-structure pyramid for, 1192f
Unity of life, 14
Unity within species, 492
Unsaturated fats, 75–76, 75f
Unsaturated fatty acid, **76**
Uracil, 87f, 328, 329f
Uranium, bioremediation and, 1261f
Uranium-238, 512
Urea, 62, **960**
Ureter, **963**

Urethra, **963**, **1005**
Urey, Harold, 508
Uric acid, **960**
Urinary bladder, **963**
Urine
concentration of, 967f
nephron processing of blood filtrate to, 965–66
Urochordata, 701
Urochordates, 698, 701, 701f
Urodeles, 711–12
Urry, Lisa, iv, 29f
Ursus americanus (American black bear), 12f
Use and disuse principle, Lamarck's, 454
Uterine cycle, **1010**, 1011–12, 1011f
Uterus, **1004**
mammalian, 723
Utricle, **1094**, 1095f

V

Vaccination, **391**, **947**
DNA technology to produce, 418
Vacuoles, 108
osmoregulation and, 134f
plant cell, 108f
Vagina, **1004**
Valence, **39**
Valence electrons, **36**
Valences, organic molecule elements and, 61f
Valence shell, **36**
Valine, 79f, 84f
Vampire bat, 969, 969f
Van Alphen, Jacques, 497f
Van der Waals interactions, 40, **41**
DNA double-helix structure and, 309f
hydrophobic interactions and, 83f
Van Leeuwenhoek, Antoni, 95, 575, 1193
Van Niel, C. B., 188
Vaporization, heat of, **49**
Variable (V) region, 938
Variation, genetic, 248. *See also* Genetic variation
Variegated leaves, 300f
Vasa recta, **964**, 967
Vascular bundles, 743, 750f
Vascular cambium, **746**
secondary plant growth and, 751–54, 753f
Vascular cylinder, 743
Vascular plants, **604**
origin and traits of, 610–12
overview of resource acquisition and transport in, 765f
phylogeny, 605t
resource acquisition in, 764–67, 772
seedless, 605, 610–15
transport in (*see* Transport in vascular plants)
Vascular rays, 753
Vascular tissue, **604**. *See also* Phloem; Xylem
resource acquisition and, 765
Vascular tissue system, plant, 742f, **743**
phloem, 743, 745f
xylem, 743, 745f
Vas deferens, **1005**
Vasectomy, **1018**
Vasocongestion, **1006**
Vasoconstriction, 864, **907–8**, 908f
Vasodilation, 864, **907–8**
Vasopressin, 969–71
posterior pituitary and, 986
Vector, **1218**
Vegetal plate, 1028
Vegetal pole, **1026**

Vegetarian diet, 876*f*
Vegetative reproduction, **812**
   agriculture and, 814–15
Veins, **741**, 750, **901**
   blood flow in, 909*f*
Veldts, 1170*f*
Velvet monkeys, 1141, 1141*f*
Vena cavae, 903
Venter, Craig, 428–29, 428*f*, 573
Ventilation, **917**
Ventral nerve cords
   earthworm, 681*f*
   planarian, 675*f*
Ventral sides, **659**
Ventral tegmental area, 1082
Ventricles, heart, **901**
Ventricles, brain, **1067**, 1067*f*
Venules, **901**
Venus flytrap, 2*f*, 782, 798*f*, 843
Vernalization, **840**
Vertebrates, **698**–735
   acquired immunity in, 936–48
   adult derivates of embryonic germ layers
      in, 1032*f*
   amniotes and development of land-adapted
      egg in, 713–20
   amphibians, 711–13
   anatomical similarities in embryos of, 463*f*
   bones and teeth in, origins of, 705
   cellular organization of retina, 1104*f*
   chondrichthyans (sharks, rays), 706–8
   as chordates, 698–702
   circulatory system, 900–903
   coordination of endocrine and nervous
      systems in, 984–86
   as craniates, 702–4
   derived characters of, 704
   developmental gene expression in, 702*f*
   development in (*see* Animal development)
   digestive systems, evolutionary adaptations
      of, 891–93
   disparity of, 698
   emergence of, 657
   evolution of cognition in, 1074
   first, 698*f*
   formation of limbs in, 1042–44, 1042*f*, 1043*f*
   fossils of early, 704–5
   gnathostomes and development of jaws in,
      705–10
   hearing and equilibrium in, 1094–96
   Hox genes and origin of, 526–27, 526*f*
   humans as, 728–33 (*see also* Human(s))
   innate immunity in, 933–35
   kidney adaptations in, 968–69
   mammals as, 720–28 (*see also* Mammal(s))
   nervous system organization, 1065–69, 1066*f*
   ray-finned and lobe-finned fishes, 708–10
   reproduction in (*see* Animal reproduction)
   reptiles, 715–20
   review, 734–35
   structure of eye, 1101*f*
   tetrapods and development of limbs and feet
      in, 710–13
   vision system, 1099–1105
Vertical transmission, 393
Vesicles, **104**
   motor proteins and, 112*f*
   pinocytosis, 139*f*
   transport, 105, 105*f*, 106*f*, 109*f*
Vessel elements, **745***f*
Vessels, **745***f*

Vestigial structures, **463**
Viagra, 206, 206*f*, 217
Villi, **888**, 889*f*
Vinegar, Allen, 866–67
Viral envelope, **383**
   animal diseases and, 387, 388*f*
Viral movement proteins, 781
Viral neutralization, 946*f*
Virchow, Rudolf, 228
Virginia, Ross, 1210, 1210*f*
Viroids, **393**
Virulent pathogens, **846**
Virulent phage, **385**
Viruses, 381–95
   avian flu and West Nile, 451
   in bacteria, 306–8 (*see also* Bacteriophages
      (phages))
   capsids and envelopes of, 383
   cellular RNAi pathway and, 365–66
   classes of animal, 387*t*
   discovery of, 381–82
   as DNA experimental organism, 305
   emerging, 391–92
   evolution of, 390
   host range of, 384
   latency, 950
   mutations and, 471
   as pathogens, 382*f*, 383*f*, 390–94
   P. Zambryski on plant, 736–37
   reproduction of, general features, 384–85
   reproductive cycle of animal, 387–90
   reproductive cycle of phages, 385–87
   review, 394–95
   structure of, 382–84, 383*f*
Visceral mass, **677**, 678*f*
Visible light, **190**
Vision, 1099–1105. *See also* Eye
   in invertebrates, 1099–1100
   neural pathways for, 1105*f*
   vertebrate system of, 1100–1105
Visual communication, 1123
Vitalism, 58–59
Vitamin A deficiency, 817, 817*f*
Vitamins, **878**
   D, blood calcium levels and, 991
   as essential nutrient, 877*t*, 878
   pathway for D, 979
Vitelline layer, 1022
Vitellogenin, 979, 979*f*
Vitreous humor, **1101**
Viviparous species, **708**
Vocal cords, **919**
Volcanic springs, extreme thermophiles and,
   566, 567*f*
Voltage, 1054
Voltage-gated ion channels, 212*f*, **1052**
   at chemical synapse, 1057*f*
   production of action potential and role of,
      1052–53, 1054*f*
Volume, 1094
Vulva, **1004**

W

Wagler's pit viper, 717*f*
Walking motion, 116*f*
Wall, Diana H., 1146–47*f*, 1210, 1210*f*
Wallace, Alfred Russel, 456–57
Walrus, 863*f*
Walters, Jeffrey, 1255
Warren, Robin, 887

Wasps, 801, 801*f*, 845, 845*f*
Wasserman, Steven, v, 851*f*
Wastes. *See* Nitrogenous wastes
Watanabe, Yoshinori, 257–58, 257*f*
Water, 38*f*, 39*f*, 41*f*, 46–57, 968*f*
   albatross drinking of salt, 954, 954*f*
   cohesion and adhesion of, 47–48
   conduction of, in plant cells, 745*f*
   effects of, on climate, 1155, 1158*f*
   emergent properties of, 47–52
   fruit and seed dispersal by, 811*f*
   hydrogen bonding and polarity of, 46–47
   hydrolysis and, 69
   imbibition, 809
   insulation of, by floating ice, 49, 50*f*
   molecular changes in, and acid/base
      conditions, 52–54
   osmoregulation in animals living in
      temporary, 956–57
   phospholipids and, 77*f*
   plant adaptations for reducing loss of,
      778–79, 778*f*
   plant response to flooding, 844, 844*f*
   review, 56–57
   as solvent for living organisms, 50–52
   species distribution/dispersal and, 1154
   splitting of, in photosynthesis, 188
   as support for all life, 46
   temperature moderation by, 48–49
   threats to quality of Earth's, 54–56
   transpiration and plant loss of, 776–79
   vascular plant acquisition of, 766–67, 772
   vascular plant transport of, 768–71, 772–76
Water balance
   of cells without walls, 133–34
   of cells with walls, 134
   kidney function, blood pressure and, 969–72
   osmolarity and, 954–59
Water buffalo, 1203*f*
Water bugs, 1001*f*
Water conservation
   bird adaptation for, 968, 968*f*
   kidney role in, 966–68
Water cycle, 1232*f*
Water fleas, 999, 1185*f*
Water lily, 630*f*
Watermelon snow, 591*f*
Water molds, 588–89, 588*f*
Water potential, **768**–71
   aquaporins and, 771
   effects of solutes and pressure on, 769
   measuring, 769–70, 769*f*
Water potential equation, 769
Water-soluble hormones, 977*f*
   pathway for, 978–79
   receptors for, 977–78, 978*f*
Water-soluble vitamins, 877*t*
Water spiders, 686
Water vascular system, **693**
Watkinson, Andrew, 1186
Watson, James, 3, 24, 88, 305, 305*f*
   base pairing model, 311–12
   discover of double-helix structure of DNA,
      308–10
Wavelengths of light, **190**
   photosynthesis and, 191*f*
Wavelike motion, 116*f*
Weak chemical bonds, 40–41
Weddell seals, 926–27
Weight, 31
Welch, Allison, 482*f*

Index